PHYSICS OF SEMICONDUCTORS

To learn more about AIP Conference Proceedings,
including the Conference Proceedings Series, please visit the webpage
http://proceedings.aip.org/proceedings

PHYSICS OF SEMICONDUCTORS

28th International Conference on the Physics of Semiconductors

ICPS 2006

Vienna, Austria   24 – 28 July 2006

PART B

EDITORS
Wolfgang Jantsch
Friedrich Schäffler
Johannes Kepler University
Linz, Austria

All papers have been peer-reviewed

SPONSORING ORGANIZATIONS
Austrian Research Centers (ARCS)
Infineon
BMBMWK: Austrian Federal Ministry of Education, Science and Culture
FFG
Austrian Nano Initiative
Vienna Convention Bureau
ICPS 27
Marabun Research
Raith
International Union of Pure and Applied Physics (IUPAP C8 Commission)
MNA Networking, Austria
GMe, Austrian Society for Micro- and Nanoelectronics, Austria
Austrian Airlines
Institute of Physics (IOP)
Austriamicrosystems
Agilent Technologies
NIST
LOT-ORIEL
Panasonic
ONR Office of Naval Research
Volkswagen
European Office of Aerospace Research and Development, Air Force Office
    of Scientific Research, United States Air Force Research Laboratory
Darpa

AMERICAN INSTITUTE OF PHYSICS

Melville, New York, 2007
AIP CONFERENCE PROCEEDINGS ■ **VOLUME 893**

PHYS

Editors:

Wolfgang Jantsch
Friedrich Schäffler

Institute of Semiconductor and Solid State Physics
Johannes Kepler University
Altenbergerstrasse 69
A-4045 Linz
Austria

E-mail: Wolfgang.Jantsch@jku.at

L.C. Catalog Card No. 2007921371
ISBN 978-0-7354-0397-0
ISSN 0094-243X
CD-ROM Available: ISBN: 978-0-7354-0398-7

Printed in the United States of America

CONTENTS

PART A

1. GROWTH, SURFACES, AND INTERFACES

1.1. Atomic and Electron Structure

1.2. Bulk Growth and Structural Characterization

1.3. Growth and Structural Characterization of Nanostructures, Wires, and Dots

1.4. Interfaces

2. BULK: SURFACES and DYNAMICS

2.1. Bulk

2.2. Group IV: Surfaces and Bulk

2.3. Carrier and Lattice Dynamics

3. DEFECTS AND IMPURITIES

4. WIDE-BAND-GAP SEMICONDUCTORS

5. MOLECULAR SYSTEMS AND ORGANIC SEMICONDUCTORS

6. HETEROSTRUCTURES, QUANTUM WELLS, SUPERLATTICES; 2D NANOSTRUCTURES (INCLUDING GRAPHENE)

6.1. Electronic Structure

6.2. Interband Transitions, Excitons, and Exciton Condensation

6.3. Nonlinear Optical Studies

6.6. Terahertz and Quantum Cascade Structures

6.7. Transport, Tunneling, High-Frequency Transport

6.8. Phonons, Plasmons

6.9. Hybrid Structures

7. PHYSICS IN THE QHE REGIME

PART B

8. NANOSTRUCTURES: ONE- AND ZERO-DIMENSIONAL SYSTEMS

8.1. Electronic Properties, Transport: Wires

8.2. Electronic Properties, Transport: Dots and Coupled Dots

8.5. Ultrafast, Coherent, and Non-Linear Optical Studies

8.7. Nanotubes

8.8. Nanocrystals

9. SEMICONDUCTOR QUANTUM ELECTRODYNAMICS, STRONG COUPLING

10. QUANTUM INFORMATION AND PROCESSING

11. MICROCAVITIES AND PHOTONIC CRYSTAL STRUCTURES

12. SEMICONDUCTOR SPINTRONICS

12.1. Magnetic and Semimagnetics Semiconductors

12.2. Spin Injection and Spin Transport

12.3. Optical Studies and Spin Dynamics, Relaxation

13. APPLICATIONS AND DEVICES

13.1. Electronic Devices

13.4. Novel Device Concepts

14. NEW MATERIALS, CONCEPTS, AND TECHNIQUES

CHAPTER 8

NANOSTRUCTURES: ONE- AND ZERO-DIMENSIONAL SYSTEMS

Conductance Quantisation In An Induced Hole Quantum Wire

O. Klochan[1], W.R. Clarke[1], R. Danneau[1], A.P. Micolich[1], L.H. Ho[1],
A.R. Hamilton[1], K. Muraki[2] and Y. Hirayama[2]

[1]School of Physics, University of New South Wales, Sydney NSW 2052, Australia.
[2]NTT Basic Research Laboratory, NTT Corporation, 3-1 Morinosato Wakamiya, Atsugi,
Kanagawa 243-0198, Japan

Abstract. We have fabricated and studied a ballistic one-dimensional p-type quantum wire using an undoped AlGaAs/GaAs structure. The absence of modulation doping eliminates long-range disorder potential scattering and allows high carrier mobilities to be achieved over a wide range of hole densities, and in particular, at very low densities where carrier-carrier interactions are strongest. The device exhibits clear quantised conductance plateaus with highly stable gate characteristics.

Keywords: holes, quantum wire, undoped heterostructure.
PACS: 71.70.Ej, 73.21.Hb, 73.23.Ad

One dimensional (1D) electron systems have been studied for about 20 years. However, 1D hole systems are considered to be difficult to work with, particularly because of gate instabilities in doped 1D hole systems [1-4]. These instabilities might be due to the modulation doping layer, in which ionized dopants act as carrier traps with long recombination times [5].

Here we report the development of a 1D hole quantum wire fabricated using an AlGaAs/GaAs SISFET structure without modulation doping. Our device shows clear quantised conductance plateaus at milli-Kelvin temperatures, including the 0.7-structure. We also present source-drain bias measurements, which gives the energy separation between 1D subbands.

The SISFET heterostructure has an undoped (311)A GaAs substrate with consequently grown epitaxial layers of 1.5 μm GaAs buffer, 175 nm AlGaAs barrier, 25 nm GaAs spacer and 75 nm degenerately doped p^+-cap (see ref. [6]). In order to induce a two dimensional hole system (2DHS), the cap layer is negatively biased to a voltage below the threshold (typically ~ -0.1 V). The 2DHS is induced directly beneath the top gate, reproducing the shape of the gate. We have used electron beam lithography and wet etching to pattern and etch the p^+-GaAs cap into three separate, independently biasable gates - two side gates (SG) and a top gate (TG) (shown schematically in the Fig. 1(a)). When the TG is negatively biased a 1DHS (400 by 400 nm) connected to two 2D reservoirs (used to measure the hole density p) is induced. The TG for this device operates over a bias range from V_{TG} = -0.16 V to V_{TG} = -0.41 V, corresponding to the 2D hole density between 3.29×10^{10} cm^{-2} and 1.39×10^{11} cm^{-2}.

Electrical measurements were performed using standard low-frequency lock-in techniques in a constant-voltage two-terminal configuration with an applied bias of 200 μV (most of this is dropped across the ohmic contacts, with ≈20 μV dropped across the 1D channel). The sample was mounted in a dilution refrigerator with a base temperature of T = 17 mK.

Figure 1(b) shows the trace of conductance g_{raw} vs SG voltage at V_{TG} = -0.36 V (corresponding to 2D hole density p = 1.18×10^{11} cm^{-2}). Applying a positive bias V_{SG} to the side gates causes the 1D channel to narrow, reducing the conductance. The 1D channel ultimately pinches off at V_{SG} ~ 1.3 V. Conductance plateaus are evident in the raw data in Fig. 1(b). Note that at V_{SG} = 0 V, the conductance is ~ 10 μS, much less than $2e^2/h$ (77 μS). This low conductance is due to the high resistance R_C (~ 100 kΩ) of the ohmic contacts in series with the quantised resistance of the quantum wire. DC I-V characteristics show that the ohmic contacts are slightly non-linear and asymmetric with a maximal change in R_C of 3.5 % per nA.

In the inset to Fig 1(b), we plot the conductance g after the subtraction of R_C. This contact-corrected

CP893, *Physics of Semiconductors, 28th International Conference*
edited by W. Jantsch and F. Schäffler
© 2007 American Institute of Physics 978-0-7354-0397-0/07/$23.00

conductance data shows plateaus well quantised in units of $2e^2/h$, confirming that the device operates as a 1D ballistic hole system. Most significantly and in contrast to previous studies [1-4], the lower plateaus are clear and well defined, and we observe a strong and reproducible plateau at $g = 0.7 \times 2e^2/h$.

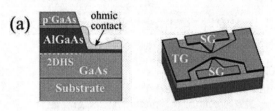

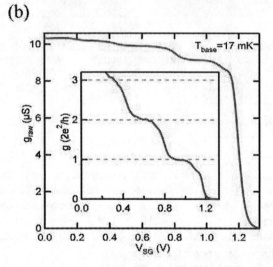

FIGURE 1. (a) Schematic diagram of the SISFET structure used in this study and schematic of the 1D wire; (b) conductance g_{raw} of the 1D wire vs side gate voltage V_{SG}. The inset shows contact-corrected conductance g vs V_{SG}.

In order to measure the spacings of the 1D subbands we performed standard DC source-drain bias spectroscopy. The measured conductance at various DC voltages is converted by subtracting R_C, and then numerically differentiating the data to produce the transconductance (dg/dV_{SG}) plotted vs V_{SG} and V_{SD}. Because of the asymmetry of the ohmics contacts, the conductance was symmetrized with respect to the DC bias (Fig. 2).

The half plateaus are clearly present on the greyscale map (labeled 1/2, 3/2, 5/2 in Fig. 2). The subband spacing is determined from V_{SD} at the half plateaus, 2 mV for both 3/2 and 5/2. Because of a large R_C, only a fraction of V_{SD} is dropped across the wire. We calculate the subband spacing to be $\Delta E_{1,2} = 0.35$ mV and $\Delta E_{2,3} = 0.21$ mV. These results are comparable with previous measurements of modulation doped 1D hole systems [7]. However, Danneau et al. found the spacing to be approximately

constant for the lower subbands, suggesting that the confinement potential is different for induced and doped 1D systems.

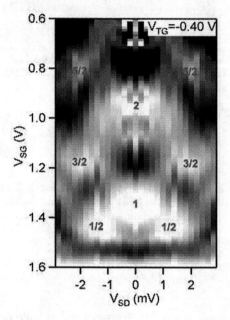

FIGURE 2. Greyscale map of transconductance (dg/dV_{SG}) vs side gate voltage and SD bias voltage. White areas correspond to the plateaus in conductance and black areas correspond to the risers between the plateaus.

In conclusion, we present results obtained from a 1D quantum wire fabricated using an AlGaAs/GaAs SISFET structure without modulation doping. Our 1D hole device exhibits very stable, clear conductance quantisation, including the 0.7-structure. This device stability will enable studies at very low densities where strong interactions ($r_s > 10$) and high mobility can be achieved simultaneously, and thereby provide new opportunities for studying the effects of spin-orbit coupling and strong carrier-carrier interactions in mesoscopic hole systems.

This work was funded by Australian Research Council (ARC). O.K. acknowledges support from the UNSW IPRS scheme. A.P.M. acknowledges an ARC Postdoctoral Fellowship.

REFERENCES

1. I. Zailer et al., Phys. Rev. B **49**, 5101 (1994).
2. A.J. Daneshvar et al., Phys. Rev. B **55**, R13409 (1997).
3. L.P. Rokhinson et al., Superlatt. & Microstruct. **32**, 99 (2002).
4. L.N. Pfeiffer et al., Appl. Phys. Lett. **87**, 073111 (2005).
5. R.H. Harrell et al., Appl. Phys. Lett. **74**, 2328 (1999).
6. W.R. Clarke et al., J. Appl. Phys. **99**, 023707 (2006).
7. R. Danneau et al., Appl. Phys. Lett. **88**, 012107 (2006).

Oscillatory persistent currents in nano-volcanoes

N.A.J.M. Kleemans [1], I.M.A. Bominaar-Silkens [2], V.M. Fomin[1,3], V.N. Gladilin [3],
D. Granados [4], A.G. Taboada[4], J.M. García [4], P. Offermans [1], U. Zeitler [2],
P.C.M. Christianen[2], J.C. Maan [2], J.T. Devreese[1,3], J.H. Wolter [1], P.M. Koenraad [1]

[1] COBRA, Eindhoven University of Technology, Den Dolech 2, 5612 AZ Eindhoven, The Netherlands
[2] HFML, Radboud University Nijmegen, Toernooiveld 7, Nijmegen, The Netherlands
[3] TFVS, Universiteit Antwerpen, Universiteitsplein 1, Antwerpen, Belgium
[4] CSIS, Instituto de Microelectrónica de Madrid Isaac Newton 8, Tres Cantos, Spain

Abstract. Using an ultra sensitive torque magnetometer we performed magnetic moment measurements on a sample containing 29 layers of self-assembled InAs/GaAs quantum rings. These strongly non-ideal rings, in fact they more resembling nano-volcanoes, show a surprisingly high magnetic moment signal corresponding to a single electron persistent current of about 0.2 μA. The predictions of our theoretical model, based solely on X-STM measurements, is in good agreement with our experiments.

Keywords: Persistent current, self-assembled quantum rings, nano-volcano, magnetic moment.
PACS: 73.21.La, 73.23.Ra, 74.78.-w

INTRODUCTION

In the past, rings of mesoscopic dimensions attracted a lot of attention since they are very interesting from a quantum mechanical point of view, because such rings can trap magnetic flux quanta. The trapping is linked to the occurrence of persistent currents in the ring which are a direct consequence of the Aharonov-Bohm effect. Recently ring-shaped self-assembled InAs/GaAs nanostructures have become available [1]. Several reports such as [2] have already appeared on the quantum character of self-assembled quantum rings, which are formed by reshaping of InAs/GaAs dots. However, the existence of persistent currents in these rings has not been demonstrated yet. The observation of these persistent currents would be the ultimate proof of the specific quantum character of the electrons in these rings. Moreover these nanostructures allow for operation in the true quantum limit of a single electron per ring in contrast to the mesoscopic rings.

EXPERIMENTAL SETUP

In order to observe the oscillating persistent current we measured the magnetic moment on a sample consisting of 29 layers of quantum rings, designed such that each quantum ring confines one or two electrons. We performed the magnetic moment measurements at low-temperature using an ultrasensitive torsion magnetometer in magnetic fields up to 15T.

THEORETICAL MODEL

X-STM measurements have shown that these self-assembled InAs/GaAs quantum rings have a depression rather than an opening at their centre and that they can be strongly asymmetric [3]. The rings under investigation in fact more resemble like nanovolcanoes. We model the self-assembled quantum rings using the structural information from our X-STM measurements. From this we calculate the in-plane potential. Additionally we included strain and piezoelectric effects and predicted the presence of Aharonov-Bohm oscillations in the magnetic moment of these non-ideal quantum rings. Figure 1a shows the oscillations for fields up to 50T for different temperatures and for a size distribution of the rings of 5%. Our model thus predicts that the occurrence of a persistent current is surprisingly robust against such deviations from a perfect ring.

CP893, *Physics of Semiconductors, 28th International Conference*
edited by W. Jantsch and F. Schäffler
© 2007 American Institute of Physics 978-0-7354-0397-0/07/$23.00

EXPERIMENTAL RESULTS

The observed magnetic moment of a single electron in a nano-volcano is shown in Figure 1b. Both the shape and the field (B≈14T) at which the Aharonov-Bohm oscillation occurs are in good agreement with our theoretical model. Our experiments show that InAs/GaAs self-assembled non-ideal quantum rings have an amplitude of the renormalized magnetic moment signal Δm, which is as large as about 60-70% of the magnetic moment of an electron in an ideal ring.

The experimental value for the oscillation amplitude of the magnetic moment per electron, $\Delta m \sim 17$ μB, lies in between the value for the ideal ring geometry, ~26 μB, and the value ~4 μB calculated for the model of the nano-volcano. A possible explanation for a discrepancy between the experimental and calculated values of the oscillation amplitude of the magnetic moment with the model may be the fact that theaverage ring shape deviates less from the perfect ring as compared to what we expected from the X-STM measurements. From the value of the magnetic moment signal the single electron persistent current in a nano-volcano is estimated to be as high as 0.2 μA.

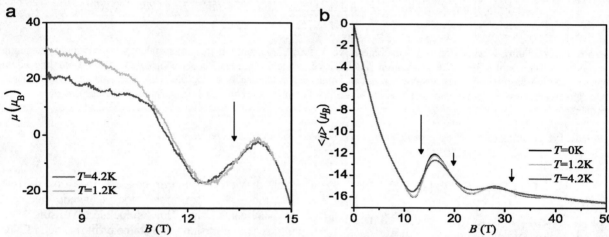

FIGURE 1. a Measured magnetic moment normalized for a single electron in a ring. There is a clear similarity with the theoretical curve (see b). Both the shape and the position (long arrow) of the oscillation are in good agreement. **b** Calculated magnetic moment <μ> for a size distribution of 5% and three different temperatures. From the calculations one expect that one flux quant is trapped at a field of 18T and a second flux quant is trapped around 30T (indicated with short arrows). The first jump in the magnetic moment is expected at a field of about 14T (long arrow).

CONCLUSIONS

In conclusion we have demonstrated that it is possible to design and fabricate non-magnetic semiconductors with magnetic properties. Such properties come associated with the presence of persistent currents in semiconductor self-assembled nanostructures with nontrivial geometries. Through advanced growth capabilities, experimental characterization and theoretical modeling we have pointed out the existence of an oscillatory persistent current (~0.2μA) due to electrons in self-assembled nano-volcanoes. Even though the nano-structures under investigation deviate from ideal rings, they still show magnetization behaviour peculiar to ideal-ring geometry that allows the observation of interference patterns revealing the quantum nature of electrons.

ACKNOWLEDGMENTS

This work was supported by the GOA BOF UA 2000, IUAP and FWO-V projects, the WOG (Belgium), the NANOSELF II and NANIC project (Spain) and the EC SANDiE Network of Excellence.

REFERENCES

1. D. Granados & J.M. García, *Appl. Phys. Lett.* **82,** 2401-2403 (2003).
2. R. J. Warburton, C. Schäfleln, D. Haft, F. Bickel, A. Lorke, K. Karrai, J.M. García, W. Schoenfeld and P.M. Petroff, *Nature* **405**, 926-929, (2000)
3. P. Offermans, P.M. Koenraad, J.H. Wolter, D. Granados, J.M. García, V.M. Fomin, V.N. Gladilin and J.T.Devreese, *Appl. Phys. Lett.* **87**, 131902 (2005).

High-Performance Thermoelectrics Based on Heterostructure Nanowires

Heiner Linke[a], Tammy E. Humphrey[b], and Mark O'Dwyer [c]

[a] Materials Science Institute and Physics Department, University of Oregon, Eugene, OR 97403-1274, U.S.A.
[b] Département de Physique Théorique, University of Geneva, CH – 1211, Geneva, Switzerland
[c] School of Engineering Physics and Institute for Superconducting and Electronic Materials, University of Wollongong, Wollongong NSW 2522, Australia

Abstract. There is great scientific, economic and environmental interest in the development of thermoelectric materials capable of direct thermal-to-electric energy conversion with high efficiency. We predict that in materials with a fine-tuned electronic density of states, electrons can be placed in energy-specific equilibrium, and the efficiency of thermoelectric power generation can approach the fundamental Carnot limit. To prove this concept experimentally, we propose to use heterostructured, group III/V nanowires with a built-in double-barrier resonance, which will allow electron energy filtering via 1D-0D-1D resonant tunneling. We present a concept study on the expected thermoelectric performance of realistic nanowires, and discuss the potential for applications of nanowires in future thermoelectrics.

Keywords: Nanowires, thermoelectrics, efficiency, energy-specifc equilibrium.

PACS: 72.20.Pa, 05.70.–a, 73.63.Kv, 85.35.Be

INTRODUCTION

Thermoelectric devices exploit a temperature gradient to create electrical power, or they can use electricity to refrigerate. Their advantages over other energy converters include high reliability, long life, lack of moving parts, low maintenance requirements, scalability, possible miniaturization and absence of emissions [1,2]. Potential applications of low-cost, high-efficiency thermoelectric energy converters would include microprocessor cooling, household refrigeration, and the partial recovery of waste heat from car engine. We recently predicted that the use of low-dimensional conductors, such as superlattices or nanowires, in which mobile electrons are restricted to a very narrow energy range can achieve electronic energy-conversion efficiencies approaching the Carnot limit [3,4]. Here we discuss the underlying theory and its experimental test in heterostructure nanowires.

BASIC PRINCIPLE

The idea behind thermoelectric power generation is that electrons in a warm reservoir are excited to higher energies than those in a cold reservoir. If the two reservoirs are connected electrically, hot electrons and/or holes flow to occupy empty states in the cold reservoir. Materials or devices with an appropriate bandstructure can selectively filter either electrons or holes, and a thermally driven net current is obtained. Since the current can flow against a bias voltage, electric power can be extracted from the heat gradient. To achieve high efficiency one must ensure that heat is used mainly to drive charge carrier flow, while heat leaks through the lattice and through the thermal conductivity of electrons must be minimized. Thermal-to-electric energy conversion with an efficiency near the Carnot limit thus would require negligible lattice heat conduction, and *reversible* electron transport between the hot and cold reservoirs, that is, current flow without entropy production. We recently showed that the latter conditions can indeed be achieved in principle if the only electrons that can travel between the heat reservoirs are those that have a specific energy given by [3]

$$E_0 = \frac{\mu_C T_H - \mu_H T_C}{T_H - T_C}$$

(1)

CP893, *Physics of Semiconductors, 28th International Conference*
edited by W. Jantsch and F. Schäffler
© 2007 American Institute of Physics 978-0-7354-0397-0/07/$23.00

where μ_H and μ_C are the hot and cold reservoir electrochemical potentials. Electrons at this energy are said to be in 'energy-specific equilibrium' [4] because they can move reversibly between the two reservoirs. If electrons are transmitted between hot and cold at an energy infinitesimally close to E_0, the efficiency of energy conversion will approach the Carnot value.

NANOWIRE-BASED CONCEPT

To implement the above condition, consider a one-dimensional nanowire with an embedded a double-barrier resonant tunneling structure [5,6] that restricts electron flow to an energy range of width ΔE, around a specific energy E_{res}. One end of the wire has a higher electronic temperature than the other end, and the length (barrier widths b plus barrier separation w) of this "energy filter" is chosen to be much shorter than the electron mean free path for inelastic scattering, The net flow of electrons will be from the reservoir with the higher occupation of states at E_{res}. When the two electron reservoirs have different temperatures and electrochemical potentials, E_0 is the energy at which the occupation of states cross. Net current will flow against the bias voltage from hot to cold when $E_{res} > E_0$ (power generation), and from cold to hot when $E_{res} < E_0$ (refrigeration). In an ideal device, the highest power generation and refrigeration efficiencies will be obtained when E_{res} is just higher than or just lower than E_0, respectively [3].

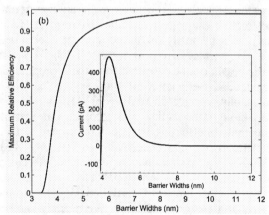

Figure 2. Calculated efficiency of power conversion of a single nanowire operating between cold and warm reservoirs held a 1 K and 10K respectively. Device efficiency is shown relative to the Carnot value $\eta_c = (1-1K/10K) = 90\,\%$ versus barrier width b for a double-barrier separation of $w = 7$ nm. For each value of b, μ_C and V_{bias} have been tuned to find the maximum efficiency value. (Inset) Device current (sampled at -1 mV) versus b.

The objective of ongoing experiments (in collaboration with the group of Lars Samuelson at Lund University) is to demonstrate the possibility of near-Carnot efficient thermoelectric power conversion in principle. Specifically, we work with single nanowires at very low temperatures (less than 10K) where electron-phonon coupling is weak, and where phonon heat leaks between the hot and cold electron reservoirs are expected to be small. Fig. 1 show details on the expected performance of a InP/InAs heterostructure nanowire under these conditions [7]. We find that electronic power conversion efficiencies of up to about 90% of the Carnot value may be achievable if the resonant tunneling structure is tuned such that the energy levels are well separated (several kT) and their width is less than about one kT. For a more extensive concept study, see Ref. [7].

ACKNOWLEDGMENTS

This work was supported by the Office of Naval Research (ONR) and ONR Global, by the Australian Research Council (M.O'D.) and by a Marie Curie Incoming International fellowship from the European Commission (T.E.H.).

REFERENCES

[1] G. D. Mahan, J. Appl. Phys. **70,** 4551-4554 (1991).
[2] G. D. Mahan, J. Appl. Phys. **76,** 4362-4366 (1994).
[3] T. E. Humphrey, R. Newbury, R. P. Taylor, and H. Linke, Phys. Rev. Lett. **89,** 116801-1-4 (2002).
[4] T. E. Humphrey and H. Linke, Phys. Rev. Lett. **94,** 096601-1-4 (2005).
[5] M. T. Björk, B. J. Ohlsson, T. Saas, A. I. Persson, C. Thelander, M. H. Magnusson, K. Deppert, L. R. Wallenberg, and L. Samuelson, Nano Lett. **2,** 87-89 (2002).
[6] M. T. Björk, B. J. Ohlsson, T. Sass, A. I. Persson, C. Thelander, M. H. Magnusson, K. Deppert, L. R. Wallenberg, and L. Samuelson, Appl. Phys. Lett. **80,** 1058-1060 (2002).
[7] M. O'Dwyer, T.E. Humphrey, H. Linke, Nanotechn. **17,** S338 – S343 (2006)

Electrical properties of atomically controlled Si:P nanowires created by scanning probe microscopy

F. J. Rueß,[1,2] K. E. J. Goh,[1,2] Bent Weber[2], A. R. Hamilton[2] and M. Y. Simmons[1,2]

[1] Australian Research Council Centre of Excellence for Quantum Computer Technology,
[2] School of Physics, University of New South Wales, Sydney, NSW 2052, Australia

Abstract. We report on the electrical properties of highly phosphorus-doped, planar nanowires with widths of 90, 50 and 27 nm. I-V measurements at 4 K show that all wires are highly ohmic with resistivities as low as 1×10^{-8} Ωcm. Magnetotransport measurements are consistent with 2D weak localization theory and demonstrate an increasing contribution to conductance as the electron phase coherence length approaches the wire width.

Keywords: silicon, scanning probe microscopy, nanoelectronics, transport measurements, dephasing mechanisms

PACS: 68.37Ef, 68.47Fg, 68.65La, 73.63Nm, 91.16.Nd, 81.07-b, 73.63Rt

INTRODUCTION

Silicon nanowires (SiNWs) have received considerable attention in recent years due to their potential as building blocks and interconnects in future generations of nanoelectronics. Recently another advance has allowed the fabrication of P-doped SiNWs using the atomic-scale resolution capability of a scanning tunneling microscope (STM)[1,2] allowing for the first time to comprehensively study the fundamental limits of conduction at the atomic-scale.

In this paper, we show that we can obtain ohmic characteristics of such STM-defined wires with widths of 90, 50 and 27 nm. Magnetotransport measurements performed on these wires at 4 K are consistent with 2D weak localization theory[3] in the highly diffusive regime. We also show that the weak localization contribution increases as we decrease the wire width.

FABRICATION METHOD

The fabrication scheme[1,4] consists of 7 steps: (1) Fabrication of etched registration markers on P-doped (1-10 Ωcm) Si(100) 1×1 cm² sized substrates defined by conventional optical lithography and wet chemical etching using TMAH.[9] (2) Standard sample annealing to ~1200 °C to obtain the Si(2×1) surface reconstruction followed by exposure to atomic hydrogen to form a monolayer of hydrogen (H) on the surface acting as a lithographic resist. (3) STM litho-

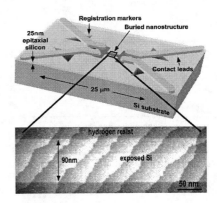

FIGURE 1. *above:* A schematic diagram of an STM-patterned 90 nm wide wire pattern is shown (in grey). The wire is patterned between two STM-patterned contact regions (2.5 × 2.5 μm²) which allow connection of the wire to four surface Al leads created by optical lithography. *below:* A filled state STM image of the lithographic pattern; imaging conditions: V = -2.3V, I – 0.2 nA.

graphy to define the wire pattern into the H- resist. (4) Exposure to phosphine molecules which we use as the dopant source. (5) Thermal incorporation of the P atoms into the Si surface at T = 350 °C. (6) Low temperature encapsulation with epitaxial Si. (7) Formation of four Al metal contacts to the buried wire to perform electrical measurements.

Fig. 1 shows a schematic of the final device structure and an STM image of a 90 nm wide wire patterned into the H:Si(100) surface. Note that the exposed Si

CP893, *Physics of Semiconductors, 28th International Conference*
edited by W. Jantsch and F. Schäffler
© 2007 American Institute of Physics 978-0-7354-0397-0/07/$23.00

surface appears bright due to the additional tunneling current attributed to the silicon surface states.

TRANSPORT MEASUREMENTS

Fig. 2 shows the four terminal DC I-V characteristics at 4 K for three SiNWs fabricated with this technique: a 90 nm × 900 nm wire (triangles), a 50 nm × 310 nm wire (stars) and a 27 nm × 320 nm wire (circles). All wires clearly demonstrate ohmic behavior over the entire voltage range and up to currents of several hundred nanoampere. The corresponding current densities are quite high, in excess of 1250 kA/cm^2 for the 27 nm wire. This high current density corresponds to a power of several nanowatts. The four terminal resistances[4] emerging from Fig. 2 show a resistance increase from 10 kΩ for the 90 nm wire, to 34 kΩ for the 50 nm wire and up to 50 kΩ for the 27 nm wire with corresponding resistivities of 1, 3 and 3 × 10^{-8} Ωcm respectively.

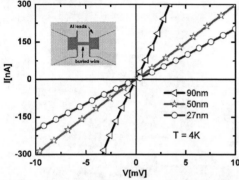

FIGURE 2. Four terminal I-V characteristics of a 90 nm × 900 nm wire (triangles), a 50 nm × 310 nm wire (stars) and a 27 nm × 320 nm wire (circles) at 4 K. *inset:* Schematic showing the buried wire pattern aligned to the four terminal leads.

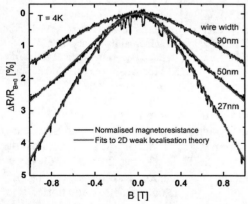

FIGURE 3. Normalized magnetoresistance (black traces) taken at 4 K and corresponding fits to 2D weak localization (red traces) of a 90 nm × 900 nm wire, a 50 nm × 310 nm wire and a 27 nm × 320 nm wire.

Fig. 3 shows the normalized magnetoresistance and corresponding fits to 2D weak localization theory[3] for

all wires at 4 K. Some random telegraph noise is seen which is most likely related to charging/discharging of traps near the wires. The electron phase coherence length l_φ, determined from the fits, decreases from 32 nm over 30 nm to 24 nm as the wire width is reduced from 90 nm to 50 and 27 nm respectively. We see that the resistance correction due to weak localization increases as the electron phase coherence length approaches the width of the wire. It is interesting to note, that as l_φ increases as the temperature is lowered into the mK regime, a crossover to 1D weak localization behavior is expected for the 27 nm wide wire.

CONCLUSION

In summary, we have demonstrated ohmic conductance of STM-fabricated SiNWs down to widths of ~25 nm exhibiting low resistivities compared to other SiNWs.[2] The magnitude of the resistance correction at 4 K increases with decreasing wire width. Comparing the electron phase coherence length with the wire width, 1D weak localization is expected to be observed for both, narrower wire as well as for the ~25 nm wire at lower temperatures. As such, STM-defined nanowires represent an excellent test bed to study the mechanisms which ultimately limit conduction at the atomic scale.

ACKNOWLEDGMENTS

MYS acknowledges an Australian Government Federation Fellowship. This work was supported by the Australian Research Council, the Australian Government, the US Advanced Research and Development Activity, National Security Agency, Army Research Office under contract DAAD19-01-1-0653, and the Semiconductor Research Corporation.

REFERENCES

1. Rueß, F. J. *et al.*, Toward atomic-scale device fabrication in silicon using scanning probe microscopy. *Nano Letters* **4**(10), 1969–1973 (2004) and references therein.
2. Shen, T.-C. *et al.*, Nanoscale electronics based on two-dimensional dopant patterns in silicon. *J. Vac. Sci. Technol. B* **22**(6), 3182–3185 (2004).
3. Hikami, S., Larkin, A. I. and Nagaoka, Y, Spin-orbit interaction and magnetoresistance in 2-dimensional systems. *Prog. Theor. Phys.* **63**, 707 (1980).
4. Rueß, F. J. *et al.*, The use of etched registration markers to make four-terminal electrical contacts to STM-patterned nanostructures. *Nanotechnology* **16**, 2446 (2005).

Magneto-resistance studies on evenly curved Hall bars in InGaAs/GaAs-microtubes

O. Schumacher, M. Stampe, Ch. Heyn and W. Hansen

Institute of Applied Physics, University of Hamburg, Jungiusstrasse 11, 20355 Hamburg, Germany

Abstract. We present transport measurements on evenly curved two-dimensional electron systems in InGaAs/GaAs-microtubes. The method of self-rolling strained semiconductor double layers enables us to build tubes with tuneable radii. With an optimized epitaxial layer design we fabricate InGaAs/GaAs-microtubes containing a high-mobility two-dimensional electron system. A special lithographic procedure enables us to roll up Hall bars with four voltage probes. In a magnetic field the component perpendicular to the 2-DES plane is strongly modulated. We discuss measurements on rolled up Hall bars with current direction parallel to the axis of the microtube, i.e. the modulation direction of the perpendicular magnetic field component is transversal to the Hall bar. By rotating the tube we are able to adjust this modulation between the voltage probes on opposite sides of the Hall bar. We find that the Hall resistance is given by the average perpendicular magnetic field component and shows a sinusoidal dependency for different rotation angles.

Non-planar 2-dimensional electron systems (2-DES) have been subject of many theoretical [1, 2] and experimental [3, 4] works, in recent years. Furthermore, the effect of a non-uniform perpendicular magnetic field component caused by e.g. a ferro-magnetic stripe on top of a Hall bar has been studied [5, 6]. Today, the method of self-rolling strained semiconductor double layers [7] enables us to build tubes with tuneable radii. Beside optical [8, 9] and mechanical [10] applications it is now possible to roll up special MBE-grown layer sequences to obtain curved high-mobility 2-DES [11]. Since the 2-DES is only sensitive to the perpendicular field component, the effective magnetic field in the 2-DES plane is modulated sinusoidally. Investigation of 2-DES in microtubes avoids ambiguities arising from influences due to strain or changes in the crystal structure present in other systems realized for transport studies in strongly modulated magnetic fields.

Evenly curved Hall bars (ECBH) can be arranged perpendicular [11] and parallel to the axis of the microtube. In this contribution we will focus on the case where the modulation direction is transversal to the Hall bar, i. e. the ECHB is aligned with the tube axis. By rotating the microtube in an external magnetic field we adjust the Hall bar with respect to the line at which the perpendicular component of the magnetic field vanishes. If this line runs within the ECHB the magnetic field component has opposite signs at the edges of the bar and new electron trajectories like snake orbits are predicted [1]. In recent experiments done on flat Hall bars with modulated magnetic field caused by a magnetic stripe on top [5, 6] signatures related to such orbits were reported.

Our samples were grown in a solid-source Riber 32P molecular-beam epitaxy system. On the GaAs-substrate we grew a 400 nm lattice matched AlAs sacrificial layer. The next layer, 20 nm $In_{20}Ga_{80}As$, contains the pseudomorphical strain arising from the lattice mismatch of about one percent. It is followed by a 95 nm $GaAs/Al_{33}Ga_{67}As$-layer system containing a modulation doped quantum well. After removing the AlAs-layer by selective etching the strained layer system bends and rolls up into a tube. The radius is given by the layer thicknesses and the amount of strain, i.e. the indium content. Details of the MBE-layer sequence and the preparation of our rolled up Hall bars using the template-scroll technique are given in Ref. [11]. Figure 1 shows a tube with

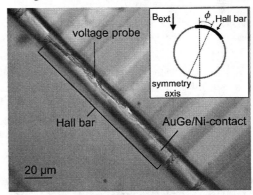

FIGURE 1. ECHB along the tube axis with alloyed AuGe/Ni-contacts. The tube diameter is about d=20 μm. The inset shows a sketch defining the rotation angle ϕ of the Hall bar with respect to the magnetic field.

a rolled up 12 μm wide Hall bar and alloyed AuGe/Ni-contacts. The tube diameter is about d=20 μm. The inset sketches a cross section of the tube on which the circular arc occupied by the Hall bar is marked. Figure 2 shows the magneto-resistance of a ECHB aligned

CP893, *Physics of Semiconductors, 28th International Conference*
edited by W. Jantsch and F. Schäffler
© 2007 American Institute of Physics 978-0-7354-0397-0/07/$23.00

with the tube axis for two rotation angles ϕ (see inset in Fig. 1). The measurements were performed with standard Lock-In technique at T=4.2 K with a relatively small source-drain current of I=10 nA to avoid thermal effects. If the maximum perpendicular field component ($B_{\perp,max}$) is right between the Hall voltage contacts ($\phi=0°$), the slope of the Hall resistance is maximal and the longitudinal resistance shows pronounced Shubnikov-de Haas-oscillations (SdH). The SdH-oscillations are periodic in $\frac{1}{B}$ as long as $B_{\perp,max}$ is located on the Hall bar. If $B_{\perp,max}$ leaves the Hall bar the SdH-oscillations are shifting to higher fields and a slight damping is visible. If the zero line of the perpendicular magnetic field ($B_{\perp,0}$) is aligned in the middle of the bar the Hall resistance vanishes. The longitudinal resistance shows a positive magneto-resistance. We tentatively address this to magnetic barrier effects in the voltage probes. Since one might expect that the predicted snake orbits show a lowered resistance related to the current direction we also performed DC-measurements. In Fig.3(a) the DC Hall resistance at

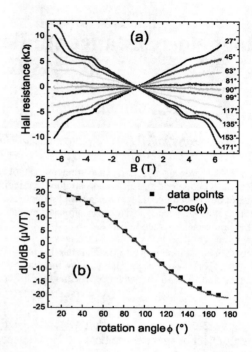

FIGURE 3. (a) DC-measurements of the magneto-resistance in Hall geometry and (b) corresponding slopes for different rotation angles ϕ.

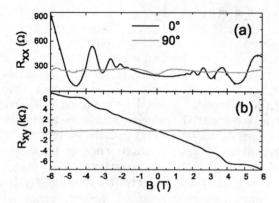

FIGURE 2. (a) AC-measurements of the magneto-resistance in Hall geometry and (b) corresponding longitudinal resistance for $\phi=0°$ and $\phi=90°$.

T=4.2 K with an injected current of I=15 nA is plotted. We have carefully compared AC- and DC-measurements and did not resolve any differences in the corresponding magneto-resistances. Figure 3(b) shows the slopes for different rotation angles. It is clearly seen that the gradients are showing a sinusoidal dependency on the average perpendicular magnetic field. So far, no signature in the magneto-resistance has been found in our measurements that could be addressed to snake orbits. We ascribe this to the still relatively small magnetic field gradient in our ECHB that we estimate to $\frac{dB}{dR}=0.7\frac{T}{\mu m}$ for a tube with a radius R=10 μm and a maximum external magnetic field of B=7 T. Nogaret et al. reported signatures both in the longitudinal [5] and in the Hall resistance [6] which depend on the magnetization of the used materials, i.e. the magnetic field gradient ($\frac{dB}{dx} \approx$2-7$\frac{T}{\mu m}$).

In summary, we study magneto-resistance of evenly curved Hall bars arranged parallel to the axis of the microtube. The Hall resistance is determined by the average perpendicular magnetic field component. By rotating the tube in an external magnetic field we have tuned the magnetic field modulation cutout such that there is a zero-crossing on the Hall bar. So far, no clear signature of snake orbits is observed.

The authors would like to thank the Deutsche Forschungsgemeinschaft (DFG) for financial support via Sonderforschungsbereich 508 "quantum materials".

REFERENCES

1. J. Müller, *Phys. Rev. Lett.* **68**, 385 (1992).
2. M. V. Entin, and L. I. Magarill, *Phys. Rev. B* **64**, 85330 (2001).
3. M. Leadbeater, *Phys. Rev. B* **52**, R8629 (1995).
4. S. Löhr, *Phys. Rev. B* **67**, 45309 (2003).
5. A. Nogaret, *Phys. Rev. Lett.* **84**, 2231 (2000).
6. A. Nogaret, *Phys. Rev. B* **67**, 165317 (2003).
7. V. Prinz, *Proc. 24th ICPS, Israel* (1998).
8. S. Mendach, *Appl. Phys. Lett.* **88**, 111120 (2006).
9. T. Kipp, *Phys. Rev. Lett.* **96**, 077403 (2006).
10. O. Schumacher, *Appl. Phys. Lett.* **86**, 143109 (2005).
11. S. Mendach, *Appl. Phys. Lett.* **88**, 212113 (2006).

Acoustic charge transport in a *n-i-n* three terminal device

Giorgio De Simoni*, Marco Cecchini*, Vincenzo Piazza*, Fabio Beltram*,
H. E. Beere[†] and D. A. Ritchie[†]

NEST-CNR-INFM and Scuola Normale Superiore, I-56126 Pisa, Italy
[†]*Cavendish Laboratory, University of Cambridge, Cambridge CB3 0HE, United Kingdom*

Abstract. We present a novel scheme for acoustic-charge-transport devices based on a *n-i-n* lateral junction as electron injector and show that surface acoustic waves are able to pick up electrons from a current flowing through the junction and drive them towards an Ohmic output contact. The main advantage of this geometry is the possibility to drive the *n-i-n* injector by means of both voltage or current signals. The device also includes a pair of lateral gates to allow further control on the collector current. We show device performance in both voltage- and current-driven regimes, discuss output contact current dependence from SAW power and temperature and the possibility to modulate charge transfer to the output contact by properly biasing the lateral gates.

Keywords: Surface acoustic waves, Acoustic charge transport, *n-i-n* lateral juction
PACS: 85.50.-n

Acoustic-charge-transport (ACT) devices [1] allow digital programmability to be applied in analog-signal-processing devices. These systems are based on charge transport due to the electric field produced by a surface acoustic wave (SAW) travelling in a piezoelectric mean [2, 3]. Electrons are bunched in packets by a SAW travelling along a depleted channel connecting an input Ohmic contact (IC) to an output one (OC). The charge amount in each packet depends on the signal applied to the IC from which electrons are extracted and can be easily manipulated by means of gates located along the channel. The number of electrons in each packet extracted from the OC constitutes the output signal.

In this work we demonstrate a novel ACT scheme in which electrons are injected by means of an unconventional input region. Our device consists of an *n-i-n* lateral junction as electron injector separated from a conventional Ohmic OC by an intrinsic channel. We shall show that SAWs travelling along the *i*-channal extract electrons from a current flowing through the *n-i-n* junction and drive them to the OC. The main advantage of such an approach is the possibility to process both voltage and current signals. The device incorporates a couple control gates in the *i*-part of the device between the injection region and the OC.

The proposed device is based on a *n*-type $Al_{0.3}Ga_{0.7}As$/GaAs modulation-doped heterostructure containing a 30-nm-thick quantum well (QW) embedded 90 nm below the surface. The two sides of the *n-i-n* junction ("source" and "drain") are separated by a thin shallow-wet-etched spacer defined by e-beam lithography. In the same processing step a 70 μm-long intrinsic channel and the lateral split-gate were fabricated. The intrinsic region separates the junction

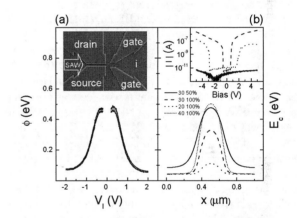

FIGURE 1. (a): Height of the potential barrier $\phi(V_I)$ in the spacer region measured by thermoionic emission. The gray areas represent the uncertainty in the measurement procedure. Inset: scanning electron microscope image of the *n-i-n* region. The SAW propagation direction coincides with the $(0\bar{1}\bar{1})$ crystal direction. (b): Calculated conduction-band energy profile within the QW in the spacer region. Labels report the depth of the etching (in nm) and the percentage of the active donors with respect to the nominal value. The spacer width was 250 nm. Inset: Measured source-drain (dashed line), source-collector (solid line) and source-gate (dotted line) current-voltage characteristics at 5 K.

from a third *n*-type region called "collector" where the Ohmic OC was located. For further fabrication details see [4]. A scanning electron microscope image of the *n-i-n* injection region is reported in the inset of Fig. 1(a). The vertical and lateral dimensions of the spacer (30 nm deep, 250 nm wide) were chosen by means of

CP893, *Physics of Semiconductors, 28th International Conference*
edited by W. Jantsch and F. Schäffler
© 2007 American Institute of Physics 978-0-7354-0397-0/07/$23.00

self-consistent Poisson simulations of the device in order to obtain a barrier height of ~ 0.5 eV having a width as small as possible to limit the conduction threshold of the *n-i-n* to a few Volts. Figure 1(b) displays the calculated data for the potential-barrier height for different sizes of the spacer and donor concentration and the measured barrier height vs. source-drain bias. The source-collector, source-gate and source-drain *I-V* characteristics at $T = 5$ K show [see inset of Fig. 1(b)] that biasing the junction between -3 V and 2 V it is possible to induce a current between source and drain with negligible leaks towards the other leads. The observed asymmetry of the *I-V*s probably originates from inhomogenieties of the etching process and does not affect the device operation.

SAWs are excited along the $(0\bar{1}\bar{1})$ crystal direction by means of an interdigital transducer (IDT) with a periodicity of 1 μm fabricated at a distance of 500 μm from the injection region. The measured IDT resonance frequency was ~ 2.93 GHz at 5 K.

We monitored the collector current I_C as a function of the frequency f_{RF} of the IDT excitation signal while imposing a constant voltage/current (from now on V_I and I_I respectively) between source and drain. Unless otherwise specified, the gates were left floating. We observed a pronounced current peak at the SAW excitation frequency. This effect corresponds to electrons being picked up in the spacer and pushed along the intrinsic channel towards the collector by the SAW. I_C at resonance was observed to increase with increasing I_I or V_I. At $V_I=0$ or $I_I=0$ no current was observed at the OC. Figure 2 shows I_C as a function of f_{RF} at 5 K for different V_I and I_I. V_I and I_I must be negative in order to observe ACT: the opposite case, while maintaining the drain grounded, corresponds to lowering the conduction-band bottom in spacer region with respect to the channel. In this regime the SAW potential is not able to drive electrons from the barrier to the channel.

The electron-extraction efficiency was studied by measuring I_C as function of f_{RF} with fixed V_I or I_I for different SAW power levels P_{RF}. We observed ACT for $P_{RF} \geq 0$ dBm. The efficiency increases with P_{RF} and reaches the limiting value of 32% of the injected electrons at $P_{RF} = 10$ dBm.

Finally we demonstrated the modulation effect of the lateral gates on the ACT. I_C was observed to decrease as V_G became more negative [see inset of Fig. 2(a)]. The current peak was reduced by 82% for $V_G \sim -1$. For $V_G \leq -1$ current leakages appear, but a further optimization of the geometry will allow operation over a wider voltage range.

The performance of the device was explored up to room temperature: we observed that its behaviour was mainly determined by the changes of the injection threshold. ACT was clearly observed up to ~ 120 K. For higher temperature the threshold became too large (~ 20 V).

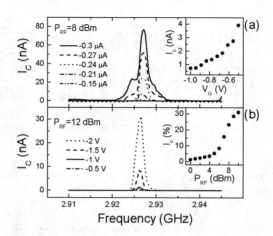

FIGURE 2. Collector current as a function of the frequency of the signal applied to the IDT (f_{RF}) for several values of the source-drain current [Panel (a)] or voltage [Panel (b)] at T = 5 K. Inset of Panel (a): Collector current as a function of the gate voltage at T = 5 K, for $f_{RF} = 2.9305$ GHz and a power level (P_{RF}) of 12 dBm. The injection bias was -2 V. Inset of Panel b: Electron extraction efficiency as a function of P_{RF} at $f_{RF} = 2.927$ GHz and a junction current of -0.25 μA.

In conclusion we demonstrated ACT in an original device in which a *n-i-n* lateral junction is used as injector in an intrinsic channel. We showed that SAWs can extract electrons from a current flowing in an intrinsic region of a semiconductor and steer them for a macroscopic distance towards an Ohmic OC. ACT was characterized as a function of the injection voltage and current at different SAW power levels. We also showed that by means of a lateral split-gate it is possible to modulate the charge transfer from the source to the collector.

REFERENCES

1. M. J. Hoskins, H. Morkoç and B. J. Hunsinger, *Appl. Phys. Lett.*, **41** 332 (1982).
2. F. Guediri, R. L. Martin, B. J. Hunsinger and F. M. Fliegel, *Proc. IEEE Ultrasonic Symp.*, 11 (1987).
3. R. M. Miller, C. E. Nothnick, D. S. Bailey, *Acoustic Charge Transport: Device Technology and Applications*, Artech House (1992)
4. M. Cecchini, G. De Simoni, V. Piazza, F. Beltram, H. E. Beere and D. A. Ritchie, *Appl. Phys. Letters* **88**, 212101 (2006).

Spin Interference In Silicon One-Dimensional Rings

N.T. Bagraev[a], N.G. Galkin[a], W. Gehlhoff[b], L.E. Klyachkin[a], A.M. Malyarenko[a] and I.A. Shelykh[a]

[a]Ioffe Physico-Technical Institute, 194021, St.Petersburg, Russia
[b]Technische Universitaet Berlin, D-10623, Berlin, Germany

Abstract. We present the first findings of the spin transistor effect in the Rashba gate-controlled ring embedded in the p-type self-assembled silicon quantum well that is prepared on the n-type Si (100) surface. The coherence and phase sensitivity of the spin-dependent transport of holes are studied by varying the value of the external magnetic field and the bias voltage that are applied perpendicularly to the plane of the double-slit ring and revealed by the Aharonov-Bohm (AB) and Aharonov-Casher (AC) conductance oscillations, respectively. Firstly, the amplitude and phase sensitivity of the *"0.7·(2e²/h)"* feature of the hole quantum conductance staircase revealed by the quantum point contact inserted in the one of the arms of the double-slit ring are found to result from the interplay of the spontaneous spin polarization and the Rashba spin-orbit interaction (SOI). Secondly, the values of the AC oscillations caused by the Rashba SOI are found to take in the fractional form with both the plateuas and steps as a function of the bias voltage.

Keywords: Spin interference, silicon quantum well, Spin-orbit interaction, Aharonov-Bohm double-slit ring.
PACS: 71.70.Ej; 75.20.Hr; 73.20.Dx

INTRODUCTION

The spin-correlated transport in low-dimensional systems was in focus of both theoretical and experimental activity in the last decade [1]. The studies of the Rashba spin-orbit interaction (SOI) that results from the structure inversion asymmetry in mesoscopic nanostructures have specifically attracted much of the efforts [2, 3]. For instance, the spin-interference device shown schematically in Fig. 1 represents the Aharonov-Bohm (AB) ring covered by the top gate electrode, which in addition to the geometrical Berry phase provides the phase shift between the transmission amplitudes for the particles moving in the clockwise and anticlockwise direction [3, 4]. Here we study the effects of the Rashba SOI tuning by the top gate voltage on the amplitude and the phase sensitivity of the *"0.7·(2e²/h)"* feature in the quantum conductance staircase that is revealed by the quantum point contact (QPC), which is inserted within one of the arms of the AB ring (Fig. 1).

METHODS

The device is based on the ultra-narrow, 2 nm, p-type high-mobility silicon quantum well (Si-QW) confined by the δ - barriers heavily doped with boron on the n-type Si (100) surface [5]. The one-dimensional ring, R=2500 nm, which has been embedded electrostatically in the Si-QW using the nanolithography technique, contains the source and the drain constrictions that represent QPCs as well as the QPC inserted in its arm by the split-gate method. The top gate is used to control the sheet density of holes.

The initial value of the sheet density of 2D holes defined by the Hall measurements, $4 \cdot 10^9$ cm^{-2}, was

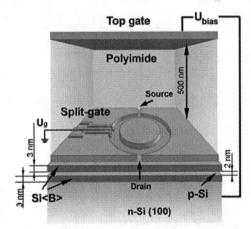

FIGURE 1. Schematic diagram of the device that demonstrates a perspective view of the p-type silicon quantum well on the n-type Si (100) surface and the depletion regions, which indicate the double-slit ring with QPC inserted in one of its arms.

CP893, *Physics of Semiconductors, 28th International Conference*
edited by W. Jantsch and F. Schäffler

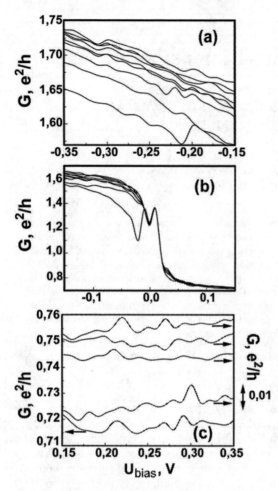

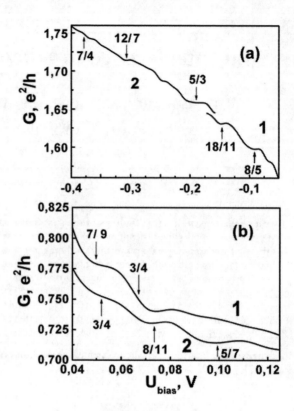

FIGURE 2. The AC conductance oscillations (a, c) that attend the changes in the amplitude of the *"0.7·(2e²/h)"* feature (b) in the double-slit ring with QPC inserted in one of its arms. The external magnetic field value was changed from 0.05 mT (bottom) to 0.5 mT (top) in 0.05 mT step.

changed controllably over one order of magnitude, between $5 \cdot 10^8$ cm^{-2} and $9 \cdot 10^9$ cm^{-2}, by biasing the top gate, which fulfils the application of the p$^+$-n bias junction. The variations in the mobility measured at 3.8 K that corresponded to this range of the p_{2D} values appeared to occur between $8 \cdot 10^5$ and $4.2 \cdot 10^6$ cm^2/vs.

RESULTS

The quantum conductance staircase caused by the QPC inserted within one of the arms of the AB ring was controlled by varying the split-gate voltage. The first quantum step of this staircase is found to reveal the *"0.7·(2e²/h)"* feature that is caused by the spin interference in the QPC. Then, the amplitude of the *"0.7·(2e²/h)"* feature fixed by the split-gate voltage is shown to exhibit the Aharonov-Casher (AC) conductance oscillations by varying the top gate voltage of both signs, which are due to the Rashba SOI

FIGURE 3. The fractional values of the conductance that revealed by varying the value of the Rashba SOI controlled by the top gate voltage. (a): 1-B=0.157 mT; 2-B=0.253 mT; (b): 1-B=0.0025 mT; 2-B=0.0080 mT.

(Figs. 2a and 2c). The values of the AC oscillations are found to take in the fractional form with both plateaus and steps as a function of the gate voltage (Figs. 3a and 3b). At low positive gate voltage, the large decrease of the amplitude of the *"0.7·(2e²/h)"* feature is found, which appears to result from the spontaneous spin polarization of heavy holes in the SQW that is created by decreasing of their concentration (Fig. 2b).

SUMMARY

The spin interference in the three-terminal AB ring has been found by the measurements of the AC conduction oscillations by varying the Rashba SOI value, which demonstrated the fractional values of the plateaus and steps.

REFERENCES

1. S. A. Wolf et al, *Science* **294** 1488-1498 (2001).
2. E. I. Rashba, *Phys. Rev. B* **62** R16267-R16270 (2000).
3. A. G. Aronov and Y. B. Lyanda-Geller, *Phys. Rev. Lett.* **70** 343-346 (1993).
4. I. A. Shelykh et al, *Phys. Rev. B* **71** 113311-4 (2005).
5. N. T. Bagraev et al, *Phys. Rev. B* **70** 155315-24 (2004).

Magnetic-Field Control Of Tunnel-Coupling In Strongly Confined One-Dimensional Electron Systems

S.F. Fischer*, G. Apetrii*, U. Kunze*, D. Schuh[†,**] and G. Abstreiter[†]

*Werkstoffe und Nanoelektronik, Ruhr-Universität Bochum, D-44780 Bochum
[†]Walter Schottky Institut, Technische Universität München, D-85748 Garching, Germany
**Angewandte und Experimentelle Physik, Universität Regensburg, D-93040 Regensburg, Germany

Abstract. One-dimensional (1D) ballistic electron transport is studied through stacked 1D quantum conductors separated by a thin tunneling barrier. The 1D electron systems of large 1D subband spacings (more than 10 meV) allow single mode operation. Degeneracies of 1D subbands of equal lateral mode index are lifted by the formation of symmetric and antisymmetric states and are depicted by anti-crossings of transconductance maxima. We observe a mode-dependent turnover from level anti-crossings to crossings in longitudinal magnetic fields.

Keywords: one-dimensional transport, tunnel-coupled quantum wires, quantized conductance, wavefunction hybridization, GaAs/AlGaAs
PACS: 73.63.Nm,73.23.Ad,72.20.My,73.21.Hb

In tunnel-coupled one-dimensional (1D) quantum conductors wave function hybridization [1] is of fundamental interest and manifests itself by splitting of degenerate 1D-subband edges. Here, we explore the transport in one-dimensional electron systems (1DES) with large 1D-subband spacings (> 10 meV) for which we demonstrated the direct high-resolution energy spectroscopy of each 1D subband structure as-well as the splitting of mode-coupled subbands [2]. The control of mode coupling becomes feasible in the single mode limit which is a prerequisite for future quantum logic devices as bi-directional couplers [3, 4, 5], quantum waveguide inverters [6] and quantum waveguide networks [7].

Hitherto, vertically-stacked tunnel-coupled 1DES were defined electrostatically by split-gate structures [8, 9, 10] leading to 1D subband separations of a few meV. Here, we provide a stronger lateral 1D confinement using local barriers induced by etched nanogrooves [11], as shown in the inset of Fig 1 (a).

Closely spaced vertically-stacked 1DES were prepared on a GaAs/AlGaAs heterostructure comprising two 14.5 nm-wide GaAs quantum wells (QWs) separated by a 1 nm-wide $Al_{0.32}Ga_{0.68}$ As barrier [11]. Delta-doping is provided by top and bottom supply layers. The upper bound of the top QW is situated 60 nm below the heterostructure surface. A sheet electron density of 4.3×10^{11} cm^{-2} and a mobility of 2.4×10^{5} cm^{2}V^{-1}s^{-1} were measured in the dark at 4.2 K for the ungated structure. The sample fabrication is detailed in Refs. [2, 11]. Two-terminal differential conductance $g_d = I_d/V_d$ and transconductance $g_m \propto \partial g_d/\partial V_{tg}$ measurements were performed by means of standard lock-in technique at 4.2 K. I_d and V_d denote the drain current and voltage, respectively, and V_{tg} the topgate voltage.

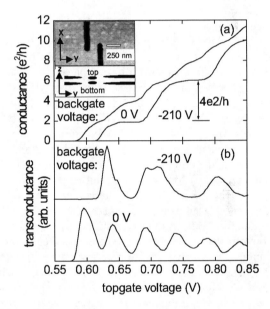

FIGURE 1. Transport measurements of two tunnel-coupled 1DES within a 130 nm-wide lateral constriction formed by 60-65 nm deep nanogrooves at 4.2 K. The lateral modes are coupled at the backgate voltage of 0 V and decoupled at -210 V.(a) Quantized conductance corrected for series resistances of 1.1 kΩ and 2.1 kΩ. Inset: Atomic force microscopy image of constriction topography (top) and schematic cross-sectional view of the vertically stacked electron systems in dark (bottom). (b) Transconductance.

The symmetric-antisymmetric energy gap of the tunnel-coupled electron layers amounts to about 4 meV [11]. Resonantly coupled 1D states exhibit splitting energies up to 5 meV [2] and show a quantized conductance in steps of $2e^2/h$ as a function of topgate

CP893, *Physics of Semiconductors, 28th International Conference*
edited by W. Jantsch and F. Schäffler

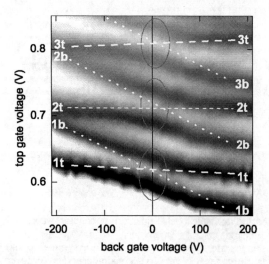

FIGURE 2. Grey-scale plots of the transconductance maxima versus top gate and back gate voltage at 4.2 K for the tunnel-coupled 1DES of Fig. 1.

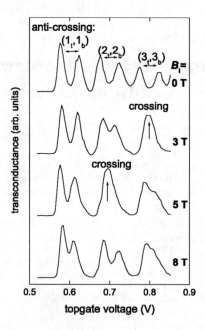

FIGURE 3. Transconductance vs. topgate voltage (zero back gate voltage) at different longitudinal magnetic fields at 2 K for the tunnel-coupled 1DES of Figs. 1 and 2.

voltage. Degenerate 1D subbands of different lateral mode index lead instead to an increase of $4e^2/h$ in the conductance as shown in Fig. 1. Grey-scale plots of the transconductance versus top- and back-gate voltage allow the distinction of the two subladders, see Fig. 2.

The lateral confinement of each 1DES can be approximated by a saddle-point potential [12] $V(x,y) = V_0 - \frac{1}{2}m\omega_x^2x^2 + \frac{1}{2}m\omega_y^2y^2$, where x is the direction of free electron movement and y that of the 1D lateral confinement. At the the saddle point the harmonic oscillator (HO) potential $V(x=0,y)$ forms 1D-subband edges $E_n = (n+1/2)\hbar\omega_y$, where $n = 1,2,3...$ is the lateral mode index. Subsequent 1D-subbands are separated by $\Delta E = \hbar\omega_y$. Additionally, the lateral modes n in the top (t) and m in the bottom (b) 1DES interact with each other through the tunnel barrier in z-direction expressed by the non-zero matrix element [8, 13] $M = <\Psi_{nt}|V(z)|\Psi_{mb}>$ with the total wavefunctions $\Psi_j(x,y,z) = e^{-ik_xx}\phi_j(y)\chi_j(z)$ and $j = nt$ or mb. The orthogonal HO stationary eigenstates for $n \neq m$ turn M to zero for a separable confining potential. For equal mode index ($n = m$) symmetric and antisymmetric coupled wavefunctions are formed and the degenerate 1D-subband edges split up as shown by the encircled anti-crossings in Fig. 2 at about zero backgate voltage.

In longitudinal magnetic fields we observe a clear cross-over from splitting of 1D subband edges to a degeneracy and vice versa. In Fig. 3 this can be seen in the shifts of the transconductance maxima for the second and third lateral modes, indicating an oscillatory mode-dependent variation of the energy splittings with the magnetic field. Semiclassically, this finding may be understood as follows: Electrons may experience an orbital motion in y- and z-direction while passing the tunnel-coupled constrictions. Wavefunction hybridization may be suppressed by the loss of phase coherence due to a phase change in the electron's wavefunction while completing the orbit including the magnetic flux Φ.

ACKNOWLEDGMENTS

We are thankful for the financial support of the DFG - GRK 384 (GA), the Dr. Isolde Dietrich Stiftung (GA) and the BMBF grant no. 01BM920.

REFERENCES

1. e.g. C. Cohen-Tannoudji, B. Diu, F. Lalo e, *Quantum Mechanics Vol. 1* (John Wiley & Sons, 2005) pp. 406.
2. S.F. Fischer, *et al.*, Nature Physics. **2**, 91 (2006).
3. N. Tsukuda, *et al.*, Appl. Phys. Lett. **56**, 2527 (1990).
4. C.C. Eugster, *et al.*, Appl. Phys. Lett. **64**, 3157 (1994).
5. J. Harris, *et al.*, Appl. Phys. Lett. **79**, 2214 (2001).
6. M.J. Gilbert,*et al.*, Appl. Phys. Lett. **81**, 4284 (2002).
7. A. Bertoni, *et al.*, Phys. Rev. Lett. B **84**, 5912 (2001).
8. K.J. Thomas, *et al.*, Phys. Rev. B **59**, 12252 (1999).
9. M. A. Blount, *et al.*, Physica E **6**, 689 (2000).
10. K.J. Friedland, *et al.*, Physica E **11**, 144 (2001).
11. G. Apetrii, *et al.*, EPDS-16 (2005), Physica E, in press.
12. M. Büttiker, Phys. Rev. B **41**, 7906 (1990).
13. N. Mori, *et al.*, Phys. Rev. B, **51**, 1735 (1995).
14. H.A. Fertig, Phys. Rev. B **38**, 996 (1988).

Single-Electron Backscattering Resonances In a Small Quantum Ring Interferometer

Ze.D.Kvon*, E.A.Galaktionov[†], V.A.Sablikov**, A.K.Savchenko[†], D.V.Scheglov*
and A.V.Latyshev*

*Institute of Semiconductor Physics, Novosibirsk, 630090, Russia
[†]School of Physics, University of Exeter, Stocker Road, Exeter EX4 4QL, UK
**Institute of Radioengineering and Electronics, Fryazino, Moscow region, 141190, Russia

Abstract. Large conductance oscillations, quasi-periodic in the gate voltage, are observed in the open state of a small-size quantum interferometer (of effective radius 100 nm) based on a high-mobility 2D electron gas in a AlGaAs/GaAs heterojunction. These oscillations presumably come from multi-particle effects that occur in the interferometer arms. These effects produce strong backscattering and result in conductance peaks whose period corresponds to a single-electron change in the number of electrons in the arms.

Keywords: Interference, mesoscopics, interaction, backscattering, Coulomb blockade
PACS: 73.23.-b, 73.63.Kv, 73.63.Nm

Although ring interferometers have been studied for more than 20 years, it has been difficult to observe the predicted Mach-Zehnder and Fabry-Perot effects. In experiments the amplitude of the interference-caused conductance oscillations with changing gate voltage did not exceed 10% [1, 2]. Attempts were made to explain this by suggesting that the experimentally realized confinement potential was insufficiently sharp. A technique of local oxidation of the sample's surface by the tip of an atomic force microscope has made it possible to fabricate ring interferometers with the size of the confinement potential comparable to the electron wavelength. In this method a heterostructure with a 2D electron gas lying close to its surface (within 30 nm) is used. Experiments with such interferometers should resolve the aforementioned problem.

In this paper, we present the results obtained on such a structure. The experimental sample is a small quantum ring with effective radius $90-100$ nm (found from Aharonov-Bohm oscillations). It is fabricated on the basis of an AlGaAs/GaAs structure with a high-mobility two-dimensional electron gas (2DEG). The 2DEG is formed at 25 nm below the surface where the gate is placed. The details of the fabrication and measurements of Aharonov-Bohm oscillations in similar structures are given in [3, 4]. Experiments have been carried out at temperatures $0.24-5$ K and magnetic fields up to 2 T.

We have observed large conductance oscillations with varying gate voltage in this structure. The dependence $G(V_g)$ of the sample can be divided into three regions of V_g (Fig. 1): *first* – at highest V_g, with peak values of about $2e^2/h$ and an average period of about 15 mV; *second* – with peak values of about $0.5e^2/h$ and an

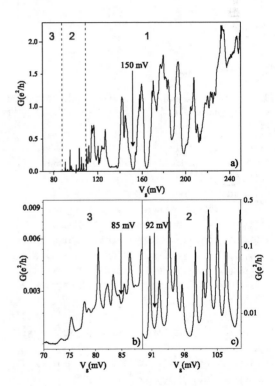

FIGURE 1. (a) Conductance as a function of the gate voltage. Zoomed in regions: (b) $90\,\mathrm{mV} < V_g < 115\,\mathrm{mV}$ and (c) $70\,\mathrm{mV} < V_g < 90\,\mathrm{mV}$.

average period of about 2 mV; *third* – the Coulomb blockade regime with peak values less than $0.05e^2/h$ and an average period of about 1.5 mV. In region 1, the oscillatory behaviour of the conductance is caused by backscattering of electrons due to the interference of electron waves propagating in the arms of the ring and waves scattered from triangular quantum dots in the input and output of the ring [5, 6].

Let us consider the second region in more detail. At first glance, its pattern differs little from that of $G(V_g)$ dependences usually observed for the Coulomb blockade in semiconductor quantum dots (region 3). The quasi-period of conductance oscillations in region 2 is close to that of the Coulomb blockade peaks in the third region (see Figs. 1b and 1c). These oscillations are similar to those observed in small quantum dots with strong coupling to the leads [7]. However the temperature de-

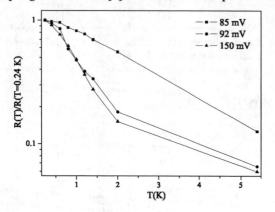

FIGURE 2. Temperature dependence of the resistance in different regions of $G(V_g)$. The V_g points are shown in Fig.1 by the arrows.

pendence of the conductance minima in region 2 is very different from that in region 3 and is close to $R(T)$ in region 1 (Fig. 2). For instance the activation energy for these minima is 0.5 K, i.e. more than 10 times less than the Coulomb charging energy for our structure. The similarity between regions 1 and 2 is also seen in the giant negative magnetoresistance observed in both regions (Fig. 3). Also it is necessary to note that such a big effect of small magnetic fields (less than 1T) is not usually observed in Coulomb blockade-like structure. The described properties of the ring in region 2 show that we deal with very large single electron oscillations in an open structure caused by the same backscattering as in region 1.

We want to stress, however, that the features in $G(V_g)$ in regions 1 and 2 are caused by fundamentally different mechanisms of backscattering. The former is due to ordinary coherent scattering which is entirely described in the framework of noninteracting electrons [5, 6]. In this case the phase change leading to backscattering is due to an altered electron wavelength and requires a large change of the gate voltage. On the other hand, we believe that the latter phenomenon can be due to an electron-electron interaction effect. Phase changes here can be caused by Friedel oscillation screening, appearing as the

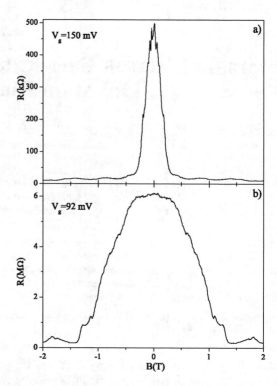

FIGURE 3. Dependence of the resistance on magnetic field for two different V_g: (a) $V_g = 150$ mV (region 1) and (b) $V_g = 92$ mv (region 2).

result of wave scattering by small quantum dots placed in the input and output of the ring. To change the phase radically in this case it is enough to add or remove just one electron from an arm of the ring. This results in more frequent conductance oscillations seen in the second region of $G(V_g)$.

REFERENCES

1. C. J. B. Ford, A. B. Fowler, J. M. Hong, et al., Surf. Sci. 229, 307 (1990).
2. Z. D. Kvon, L. V. Litvin, V. A. Tkachenko, and A. L. Aseev, Usp. Fiz. Nauk 169, 471 (1999) [Phys. Usp. 42, 402 (1999)].
3. V.A.Tkachenko, Z.D.Kvon, D.V.Sheglov, A.V.Latyshev, A.I.Toropov, O.A.Tkachenko, D.G.Baksheyev, and A.L.Aseev, JETP Lett. 79, 136 (2004).
4. E.B.Olshanetsky, Z.D.Kvon, D.V.Scheglov, A.V.Latyshev, A.I.Toropov, J.C.Portal, JETP Lett. 81, 625 (2005).
5. A. A. Bykov, D. V. Nomokonov, A. K. Bakarov, et al., Pis'ma Zh. Eksp. Teor. Fiz. 78, 36 (2003) [JETP Lett. 78, 30 (2003)].
6. O. A. Tkachenko, V. A. Tkachenko, D. G. Baksheyev,et al., Pis'ma Zh. Eksp. Teor. Fiz. 79, 351 (2004) [JETP Lett. 79, 293 (2004)].
7. A. Vidan, M. Stopa, R. M. Westervelt, M. Hanson, and A.C. Gossard PRL, 96, 156802 (2006).

Anisotropic Zeeman Splitting In Ballistic One-Dimensional Hole Systems

R. Danneau*, O. Klochan*, W. R. Clarke*, L. H. Ho*, A. P. Micolich*, M. Y. Simmons*, A. R. Hamilton*, M. Pepper[†], D. A. Ritchie[†] and U. Zülicke**

*School of Physics, University of New South Wales, Sydney, New South Wales, 2052, Australia.
[†]Cavendish Laboratory, Madingley Road, Cambridge, CB3 OHE, United Kingdom.
**Institute of Fundamental Sciences and MacDiarmid Institute for Advanced Materials and Nanotechnology, Massey University, Palmerston North, New Zealand.

Abstract.
We have studied the effect of an in-plane magnetic field B on a one-dimensional hole system in the ballistic regime created by surface gate confinement. We observed clearly the lifting of the spin degeneracy due to the Zeeman effect on the one dimensional subbands for B applied parallel to the channel. In contrast, no Zeeman splitting is detected for B applied perpendicular to the channel, revealing an extreme anisotropy of the effective Landé g-factor g^*. We demonstrate that this anisotropy is a direct consequence of the one-dimensional confinement on a system with strong spin-orbit coupling.

Keywords: 1D hole systems, quantized conductance, Zeeman effect
PACS: 71.70.Ej, 73.21.Hb, 73.23.Ad

It has been proposed to exploit the intrinsic coupling between the spin and orbital motion of quantum particles to control spin-splitting with an electric field [1], offering new opportunities to implement a spintronic paradigm [2]. The ability to control the spin-splitting with an external electric field has led to proposals for a spin-field-effect transistors [3] which could be used to perform new kinds of logic operations.

Electric-field-tuneable spin-orbit (SO) interactions for electrons arise through the coupling between conduction and valence band that is induced by structural inversion asymmetry. Consequently, such SO effects are larger in narrow-gap materials such as InGaAs and InAs. However, the small band gap makes it difficult to use conventional metal surface gate technique, due to the absence of a Schottky barrier, to create nanostructures for electrical field control of spin studies. An alternative is to use holes rather than electrons in a wider gap material. In a tight binding view, as valence-band states are predominantly p-like (unlike conduction-band states which are s-like), SO effects are particularly important in low-dimensional hole systems such as p-type GaAs, making this material system interesting for spin-controlled devices.

In bulk, zinc-blende compounds such as GaAs, SO coupling causes splitting of the top-most valence band in four fold degenerate heavy and light hole state (with total angular momentum $J = 3/2$) and the two fold degenerate split off state (with total angular momentum $J = 1/2$). However, two dimensional (2D) confinement lifts the heavy hole (HH)-light hole (LH) degeneracy at $k = 0$. As a result the carrier transport is predominantly through the HH subband. In addition, the confinement gives rise to mixing ($k \neq 0$) and non-parabolicity of the HH and LH subbands (for a complete review see [4]).

We have studied how confining holes in a 1D channel affects their spin properties. We used the intrinsic conductance quantization properties of ballistic one-dimensional (1D) systems to probe the 1D subband edges and studied the effect of an in-plane magnetic field B. We have performed Zeeman splitting measurements in a ballistic 1D hole system aligned along the $[\overline{2}33]$ direction and formed in a GaAs (311)A quantum well by surface gate confinement (see [5] for description of the device). Application of an in-plane magnetic field parallel ($B_\parallel$) to the wire lifts the spin degeneracy and eventually causes the 1D subbands edges to cross. Figure 1 clearly shows the splitting of the subband edges (white regions) in the transconductance grayscale plot (dG/dV_{SG} as a function of side gate voltage V_{SG} and B; the derivative has been numerically calculated from the differential conductance G corrected for a series resistance). After thermal cycling and sample re-orientation, we have studied the effect of an in-plane magnetic field perpendicular to the wire $B_\perp$. In contrast, the transconductance grayscale (Fig. 1(b)) shows that the degenerate 1D subbands are not affected by $B_\perp$ up to 8.8 T, i.e. no Zeeman splitting is seen when the magnetic field is aligned perpendicular to the channel.

Combining Zeeman effect measurements and source-drain bias spectroscopy, and knowing that the spin-splitting is linear in B (see [7]), one can extract the effective Landé g-factor g^* using the basic relation $\Delta E_N =$

CP893, *Physics of Semiconductors, 28th International Conference*
edited by W. Jantsch and F. Schäffler
© 2007 American Institute of Physics 978-0-7354-0397-0/07/$23.00

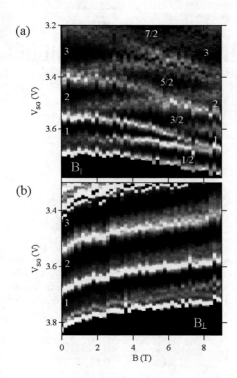

FIGURE 1. Zeeman effect in a 1D hole system: (a) Transconductance grayscale as a function of V_{SG} and $B_\parallel$; black regions correspond to low transconductance (*i.e.* conductance plateaus, labelled in units of $2e^2/h$), white regions correspond to high transconductance (subband edges): splitting of the 1D subbands is clearly observed. (b) Transconductance grayscale as a function of V_{SG} and $B_\perp$: no Zeeman splitting is seen. Data are taken with a back gate and mid-line gate voltage of 2.5 and -0.225 V respectively (see [5] for description of the device).

$g_N^* \mu_B B$ [6]. The g^* ratio $g_\parallel^*/g_\perp^*$ (*i.e.* for $B_\parallel$ and $B_\perp$) can be estimated *at least* to be 4.5 [7], significantly larger than the anisotropy calculated [8] and measured [9] in 2D hole systems. One can explain this strong anisotropy by the following arguments. As mentioned above, only HH participate in the carrier transport in a 2D hole system. It has been demonstrated that Zeeman splitting is suppressed for a magnetic field applied parallel to a 2D hole quantum well, in which the total angular momentum axis J is aligned along the growth axis [10, 4]. Only a magnetic field applied along J generates the energy splitting due to the Zeeman effect for both HH and LH bands. *This is a result of strong SO coupling in the valence band.* In our system, the 1D confinement forces J to lie along the 1D constriction: this explains why no Zeeman splitting is measured for B applied perpendicular to the channel (see Fig. 2), though B applied parallel to the channel lifts the spin degeneracy of the 1D subbands.

In conclusion, we have measured a strong anisotropy of the Zeeman splitting in a 1D hole system with respect

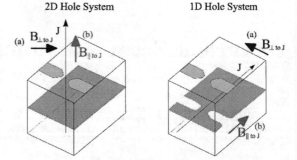

(a) Suppression of HH Zeeman splitting if B is applied perpendicular to J
(b) HH Zeeman splitting if B is applied parallel to J

FIGURE 2. Sketch of the effect of a magnetic field perpendicular (a) and parallel (b) to the quantization axis for total angular momentum $\hat{J}$, on a 2D hole (as in [10]) and 1D hole system created by two side gates [7].

to an in-plane magnetic field B oriented along or parallel to the channel. Our results show that confining holes to a 1D system fundamentally alters their spin properties, and that it is possible to tune the g^* anisotropy (as well as the absolute value of the effective Landé g-factor [7]), by electrostatically changing the width of the 1D system.

We acknowledge support from the Australian Research Council, the EPSRC and the Marsden Fund of the Royal Society of New Zealand. R. D. acknowledges an Australian Research Council Postdoctoral Fellowship and M. Y. S. acknowledges an Australian Research Council Fedaration Fellowship.

REFERENCES

1. Yu. A. Bychkov and E. I. Rashba, J. Phys. C: Solid State Phys., **17**, 6039 (1984).
2. I. Žutić , J. Fabian and S. Das Sarma , Rev. Mod. Phys. **76**, 323 (2004).
3. S. Datta and B. Das, Appl. Phys. Lett. **56**(7), 665 (1990).
4. R. Winkler, *Spin-Orbit Coupling Effects in Two-Dimensional Electron and Hole Systems* (Springer, Berlin, 2003).
5. R. Danneau, W. R. Clarke, O. Klochan, A. P. Micolich, A. R. Hamilton, M. Y. Simmons, M. Pepper, and D. A. Ritchie, Appl. Phys. Lett. **88**, 012107 (2006).
6. F. F. Fang, and P. J. Stiles Phys. Rev. **174**, 823 (1968).
7. R. Danneau , O. Klochan, W. R. Clarke, L.H. Ho, A. P. Micolich, A. R. Hamilton, M. Y. Simmons, M. Pepper, D. A. Ritchie, and U. Zülicke, Phys. Rev. Lett. **97**, 026403 (2006).
8. R. Winkler, S. J. Papadakis, E. P. De Poortere, and M. Shayegan, Phys. Rev. Lett. **85**, 4574 (2000).
9. S. J. Papadakis, E. P. De Poortere, M. Shayegan, and R. Winkler, Phys. Rev. Lett. **84**, 5592 (2000).
10. H. W. van Kesteren, E. C. Cosman, W. A. J. A. van der Poel, and C. T. Foxon, Phys. Rev. B **41**, 5283 (1990).

Anomalous field-effect characteristics in double-wall carbon nanotubes due to proximity effect

X. R. Wang[1], J. Lu[1], L. M. Peng[2]

[1]*Physics Department, The Hong Kong University of Science and Technology, Clear Water Bay, Hong Kong, China*
[2]*Department of Electronics, Peking University, Beijing 100871, China*

Abstract. The anomalous field-effect characteristic (FEC) in so-called semiconductor-metal (S-M) double-wall carbon nanotubes (DWCNTs) is explained by proximity effect. By using a two-band tight-binding model on a ladder of two legs, it is demonstrated that the proximity effect can convert a semiconducting shell into a weak metal. The gate voltage dependence of the metallicity corresponds to the anomalous FEC.

Keywords: Nanotubes, wires, transport, proximity.
PACS: 73.63.Fg, 73.63.-b, 73.20.At

INTRODUCTION

Field-effect characteristic (FEC) of double-wall carbon nanotubes (DWCNTs) has been measured recently [1]. The DWCNT devices can experimentally be classified into three groups: metal-metal (M-M) or metal-semiconductor (M-S), semiconductor-semiconductor (S-S), and semiconductor-metal (S-M) combinations of two shells of DWCNTs (the first symbol is for the outer shell and the second for the inner one). The S-S and M-M (or M-S) DWCNTs exhibit similar FEC as those of semiconducting and metallic single-wall carbon nanotubes (SWCNTs)[1], respectively. However, S-M DWCNT devices show FEC with distinct features. 1) In the negative gate voltage V_G region, on-off source-drain current ratio (I_{on}/I_{off}) is of the order of 10^1 or even 10^2, in contrast with no obvious switching characteristic for metallic tubes and 10^5 of on-off ratio for semiconducting ones. 2) The gate-voltage dependence of source-drain current I_{sd} is not exponential in the on-off transition region which is much wider than that in a usual semiconductor device.

In this report, we provide an explanation to the anomalous FEC. We show that the anomaly can be attributed to the proximity effect of metallic phase. The penetration of electron wavefunctions in the inner metallic shell into the outer semiconducting shell generates density of states in the energy gap so that the outer shell becomes weakly conducting. The anomalous FEC is nothing but the manifestation of the gate voltage dependence of the proximity effect.

MODEL

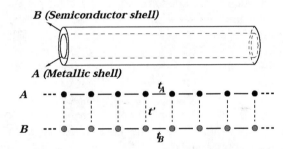

FIGURE 1. An S-M DWCNT (top) is modeled by a two-leg ladder (bottom) on which a tight-binding model is defined. t_A, t_B, and t' are the hopping coefficients in legs A and B and between the legs.

An S-M DWCNT is modeled by a two-leg ladder as shown in Fig. 1. Legs A and B are for the inner metallic and outer semiconducting shells, respectively. Following the experiment [1], it is assumed that the semiconducting shell is p-doped so that its Fermi level is near the top of the valence band. A tight-binding model is defined on the ladder with t_A, t_B and t' being the hopping coefficients on legs A, B, and between the legs. The Hamiltonian is

$$H = \sum_{\alpha,i}\left(\varepsilon_\alpha c^+_{\alpha,i}c_{\alpha,i} + t_\alpha c^+_{\alpha,i}c_{\alpha,i+1}\right) + \sum_i t'c^+_{A,i}c_{B,i} + h.c., \quad (1)$$

where α labels the legs, ε_α is the on-site energy. $c^\dagger_{\alpha,i}$

and $c_{\alpha,i}$ are the creation and annihilation operators at site i of leg α, respectively. Both ε_A and ε_B depend on V_G, but ε_A is less sensitive to V_G because of Fermi level pining at large DOS. Therefore, the gate voltage applies mainly on the outer shell, and it is reasonable to assume a constant ε_A and $\varepsilon_B = U_0 - e\beta V_G$, where U_0 is the initial on-site energy and $\beta = C_1/(C_1+C_2)$ relates to the mutual capacitance C_1 between the substrate and the DWCNT and the self-capacitance C_2 of DWCNT. Without losing generality, the Fermi level of the source lead is set to zero. Model parameters are chosen so that $E = 0$ is inside the energy band of leg A but outside that of leg B at $V_G = 0$.

The important quantity is the DOS in leg B:

$$g_B(E) \equiv \frac{1}{2\pi} \sum_{\lambda=\pm,k} \left|\frac{\partial E_{\lambda,k}}{\partial k}\right|^{-1} P_{\lambda,k,B}\delta(E_{\lambda,k} - E), \qquad (2)$$

where $P_{\lambda,k,B} = \Sigma_{i(B)}|\psi_{\lambda,k}[i(B)]|^2$ is the probability of finding an electron in leg B when it is in eigenstate $\psi_{\lambda,k}(x)$.

RESULTS AND DISCUSSIONS

The local DOS $g_B(E)$ near the Fermi level reveals how conducting the outer shell is. Fig. 2 is the $g_B(E_F)$ as a function of V_G for the following set of typical parameters for carbon nanotubes (CNTs) [3]: $t_A=0.65eV$, $t_B=0.35eV$, $t'=0.3eV$, $U_0=-0.75eV$, $\varepsilon_A=0eV$ and $\beta=1$. For large V_G, the Fermi level is deep inside the energy gap, and the value of $g_B(E_F)$ is of the order of $10^{-3}(eV{\cdot}site)^{-1}$. Near $V_G = -0.12V$, the DOS is of the order of $10^{-1}(eV{\cdot}site)^{-1}$, an order of 10^2 change in $g_B(E_F)$ which is, in turn, the same order of change in electronic conduction.

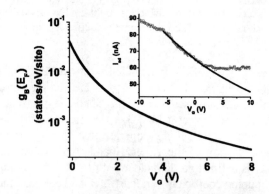

FIGURE 2. The logarithm of $g_B(E_F)$ vs. V_G when $\varepsilon_B = U_0 - eV_G$ is used. Inset: Fitting between the analytical form (solid line) of the local DOS at Fermi level and the experimental data (Ref. 1) at 290K. The saturated I_{sd} (around 60nA) is interpreted as the leakage current.

Under a small source-drain bias, we can assume that the current is proportional to the local DOS on the outer shell at the Fermi level. The inset of Fig.2 is the fitting curve of experimental FEC at temperature 290K [1] by $\eta g_B(E_F)$ for $V_G > -5V$, where proximity effect dominates the electron transport process. The fitting parameters are $t_A=0.95eV$, $t_B=0.44eV$, $t'=0.42eV$, $\varepsilon_A=0.11eV$, $U_0=-1.05eV$, $\eta=3.1\mu A{\cdot}eV$ and $\beta=0.025$. The fitting is not bad for $I_{sd} \gtrsim 60nA$. The deviation for $I_{sd} < 60nA$ can be attributed to the leakage current or the gate-voltage dependence of β due to screening effect. It is not difficult to understand the deviation because the proximity effect does not take into account the leakage current and the screening effect. The leakage current is very sensitive to the temperature, and I_{on}/I_{off} decreases with the increase of the temperature, exactly as what was found in experiment [1]. It should be emphasized that the anomalous FEC observed in S-M DWCNTs is not due to the change of hole (electron) concentration under a gate voltage as that of usual semiconductor devices. Rather, it is due to the change of DOS originated from the proximity effect. Although the detail atomic and energy-band structures of DWCNT are neglected, the essential physics of the anomalous FEC of S-M DWCNTs is universal. It should be pointed out that the terminology of hybridization and proximity are synonymous. Hybridization is often used when electronic structure is the concern while proximity is more proper to refer to phases of systems.

SUMMARY

The anomalous FEC in so-called S-M DWCNTs is attributed to the proximity effect. The proximity effect is stronger and stronger when the Fermi level approaches the top of the valence band of the outer p-doped tube. As a result, the semiconducting outer tube becomes more and more metallic.

ACKNOWLEDGMENTS

This work was supported by RGC of HKSAR, China.

REFERENCES

1. S. Wang, X. L. Liang, Q. Chen, Z. Y. Zhang, and L. M. Peng, *J. Phys. Chem. B* **109**, 17361 (2005).
2. S. J. Tans, M. H. Devoret, H. J. Dai, A. Thess, R. E. Smalley, L. J. Geerligs, and C. Dekker, *Nature* **386**, 474 (1997); Z. Yao, H. W. C. Postma, L. Balents, and C. Dekker, *Nature* **402**, 273 (1999).
3. M. S. Dresselhaus, G. Dresselhaus, R. Saito, and A. Jorio, *Phys. Reports* **409**, 47 (2005).

Helical nanostructures and Aharonov-Bohm quantum rings in a transverse electric field

M.E. Portnoi[*,†], O.V. Kibis[**,†], V.L. Campo Jr[†], M. Rosenau da Costa[†], L. Huggett[*] and S.V. Malevannyy[**]

[*]*School of Physics, University of Exeter, Stocker Road, Exeter EX4 4QL, United Kingdom*
[†]*International Center for Condensed Matter Physics, University of Brasilia, 70904-970 Brasilia DF, Brazil*
[**]*Dept. of Applied and Theoretical Physics, Novosibirsk State Technical University, Novosibirsk 630092, Russia*

Abstract. We show a striking similarity between the electronic energy spectrum of a helical nanostructure in a transverse electric field and the spectrum of a quantum ring pierced by a magnetic flux in the presence of an in-plane electric field. Optimal parameters of quantum rings are found, for which electric field can be used for the observation of Aharonov-Bohm oscillations.

Keywords: quantum rings, Aharonov-Bohm effect, nanostructures
PACS: 73.21.-b

The widespread fascination with helical nanostructures probably stems from the miracle of the DNA, the majestic double-helix underlying the life on Earth. It has recently become possible to fabricate artificial nanohelices in different material systems, including In-GaAs/GaAs [1], Si/SiGe [2], ZnO [3] and pure carbon [4]. Soon after the discovery of carbon nanotubes (CNTs), it was realized that a chiral CNT can be viewed as a helical motif [5], which becomes a single helix containing all elementary cells of the rolled graphene sheet in a special case of a $(n,1)$ CNT [6].

We show that a quasi-one-dimensional helical nanostructure in the presence of an electric field normal to the helix axis behaves as a superlattice with parameters controlled by the applied field. This behavior includes Bragg scattering of electrons on a periodic potential created in a helix by the field, which results in the energy gap opening at the edge of the superlattice Brillouin zone. The gap is proportional to the helix radius and the strength of the applied electric field, $\Delta \varepsilon = eER$. In Fig.1, the three lowest energy subbands for an electron confined to an ideal helix of radius R and pitch d in a transverse electric field E are plotted as a function of dimensionless parameter k/g, where k is the electron wave number along the helical line, $g = 2\pi/l_0$ and $l_0 = \sqrt{4\pi^2 R^2 + d^2}$ is the length of one coil of the helix. Only the first Brillouin zone of the superlattice is shown.

The energy spectrum of an electron, confined in an infinitely-narrow ring pierced by a magnetic field flux (Aharonov-Bohm quantum ring) and subjected to an in-plane electric field, is exactly the same as the energy spectrum of an electron in a helix in a transverse electric field. Here the magnetic flux $\Phi = \pi R^2 B$ through the ring of radius R plays the same role as the electron momen-

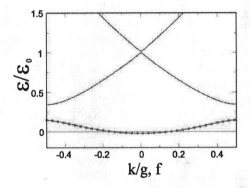

FIGURE 1. The energy spectrum of an electron confined to an ideal helix in a transverse electric field and the spectrum of an electron in the infinitely narrow Aharonov-Bohm ring in an electric in the plane of the ring. For the helix $\varepsilon_0 = \hbar^2 g^2/2M$ and for the ring $\varepsilon_0 = \hbar^2/2MR^2$, where M is the electron effective mass. In both cases $eER = 0.2\varepsilon_0$. Red dots show the results obtained from a simple analytic formula.

tum along the helical line. The spectrum shown in Fig.1 is applicable to the ring if the dimensionless parameter $f = \Phi/\Phi_0$, where $\Phi_0 = h/e$, is used instead of k/g. The spectrum is periodic in f and only one period is shown in the figure. The linear in electric field splitting in the energy spectrum of the ring occurs when Φ is equal to an odd number of $\Phi_0/2$. This splitting takes place when the electric field mixes two states with the values of the angular momentum m differing by one, which are degenerate when $f = (2m+1)/2$ in the absence of electric field. The two resulting states, which are separated by the gap $\Delta\varepsilon = eER$, have the same absolute value but the opposite sign of the electric dipole moment. At zero temperature, the discussed effect results in the periodic in

CP893, *Physics of Semiconductors, 28th International Conference*
edited by W. Jantsch and F. Schäffler

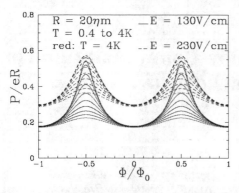

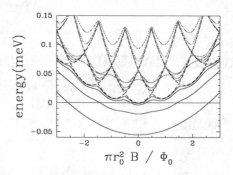

FIGURE 2. Magnetic flux oscillations of the electric dipole moment P of a quantum ring of radius $R=20$ nm, pierced by a magnetic flux Φ and subjected to an in-plane electric field $E = 130$ V/cm or $E = 230$ V/cm at T from 0.4 to 4K.

FIGURE 3. A finite-width ring in a magnetic field for different values of in-plane electric field strength: $E = 1, 2, 5$ and 10 V/cm. The ring radius is $r_0 = 100$ nm and its width is 20 nm.

magnetic flux increase of the dipole moment P up to its maximum value of eR in the arbitrary weak electric field. With increasing temperature these oscillations become suppressed, since the population of the two states with opposite dipole moments becomes effectively the same, unless $eER > k_BT$. However, to observe pronounced oscillations the field should not be too large, so that it does not mix the states with different angular momenta for $\Phi = 0$, which requires $eER \ll \hbar^2/2MR^2$. At higher electric fields all traces of the Aharonov-Bohm effect are completely eliminated from the ground state spectrum [7]. The latter condition shows that the effect of magnetic flux oscillations of the dipole moment becomes stronger with decreasing the ring radius R. The smallest nanoring radius achievable by existing growth techniques [8, 9] is about 10nm. In fact, the further reduction of the ring size will make it difficult to achieve a flux through the ring of the order of the flux quantum at experimentally attainable magnetic fields of several Tesla. Our analysis shows that pronounced oscillations of the dipole moment can be observed in the nanorings with radius between 10 and 20 nm in relatively weak electric fields in the range of 100–200 V/cm and temperatures below 4K. Figure 2 shows the magnetic flux dependence of the dipole moment of the 20nm ring for two values of the in-plane field E and several temperatures. As discussed above the oscillations are more pronounced in weaker electric fields and their amplitude is strongly temperature-dependent.

It is important to emphasize that the discussed effect is not an artifact of the infinitely-narrow ring model, but it persists in finite-width rings in a uniform magnetic field. Indeed, the essential feature required for this effect is the degeneracy of the states with the angular momenta differing by one at certain magnetic field values. This degeneracy is well-known to take place for finite-width rings. In Fig. 3 we show the energy spectrum of a finite-width ring in a uniform magnetic field normal to the

plane of the ring for several values of in-plane electric fields. In our calculations we adopted the 'soft-edge' ring model of Ref.[10], which allows for analytical solutions in the absence of electric field. Not-too-large electric fields open the gaps linear in field, whereas large fields destroy the oscillations completely.

The discussed mixing of two states, which are degenerate in the absence of electric field, is completely controlled by the direction of the in-plane field with respect to a fixed axis. This brings the potential possibility for creating nanoring-based qubits, which do not require weak spin-orbit coupling between the electric field and electron spin. Arrays of the Aharonov-Bohm rings can also be used for polarization sensitive single-photon detection.

This work was supported by the EU Foundation IN-TAS (Grants 03-50-4409 and 05-1000008-7801), the Russian Foundation for Basic Research (Grants 06-02-16005 and 06-02-81012), the Russian Ministry for Education and Science (Grant RNP.2.1.1.1604), UK EPSRC, MCT and FINEP (Brazil). MEP and OVK are grateful to the ICCMP staff for hospitality.

REFERENCES

1. V. Ya. Prinz *et al.*, *Physica E* **6**, 828–831 (2000).
2. V. Ya. Prinz *et al.*,*Nanotechnology* **12**, 399–402 (2001).
3. P. X. Gao *et al.*, *Science* **309**, 1700–1704 (2005).
4. G. Zhang, X. Jiang, and E. Wang, *Appl. Phys. Lett.* **84**, 2646–2648 (2004).
5. C. T. White, D. H. Robertson, and J. W. Mintmire, *Phys. Rev. B* **47**, 5485–5488 (1993).
6. O. V. Kibis, D. G. W. Parfitt, and M. E. Portnoi, *Phys. Rev. B* **71**, 035411 (2005).
7. Z. Barticevic, G. Fuster, and M. Pacheco, *Phys. Rev. B* **65**, 193307 (2002).
8. A. Lorke *et al.*, *Phys. Rev. Lett.* **84**, 2223–2226 (2000).
9. T. Mano *et al.*, *Nano Lett.* **5**, 425–428 (2005).
10. W.-C. Tan and J.C. Inkson, *Phys. Rev. B* **60**, 5626–5635 (1999).

The metallic-like temperature dependence of the conductivity in two-dimensions

A. V. Germanenko*, G. M. Minkov†, O. E. Rut*, A. A. Sherstobitov†, L. E. Golub** and B. N. Zvonkov‡

*Institute of Physics and Applied Mathematics, Ural State University, 620083 Ekaterinburg, Russia
†Institute of Metal Physics RAS, 620219 Ekaterinburg, Russia
**A.F. Ioffe Physico-Technical Institute, Russian Academy of Sciences, 194021 St. Petersburg, Russia
‡Physical-Technical Research Institute, University of Nizhni Novgorod, 603600 Nizhni Novgorod, Russia

Abstract. The temperature and magnetic field dependences of the conductivity of the heterostructures with asymmetric $In_xGa_{1-x}As$ quantum well are studied. It is shown that the metallic-like temperature dependence of the conductivity observed in the structures investigated is understandable quantitatively within the whole temperature range. It is caused by the interference quantum correction at fast spin relaxation for 0.4 K$< T < 1.5$ K. At higher temperatures, $1.5 < T < 4$ K, it is due to the interaction quantum correction. Finally, at $T > 4 - 6$ K, the metallic-like behavior is determined by the phonon scattering.

Keywords: electron-electron interaction, weak localization and antilocalization
PACS: 73.20.Fz, 73.61.Ey

Transport properties of two dimensional (2D) systems reveal the intriguing features. One of them is a metallic-like temperature dependence of the conductivity, σ, at low temperature $d\sigma/dT < 0$. As a rule such a behavior is observed in the structures with strong hole-hole (h-h) or electron-electron (e-e) interaction characterized by large value of the gas parameter $r_s = \sqrt{2}/(a_B k_F) > 1$. That is why the interaction quantum correction is often considered as the main reason for the metallic-like T-dependence of σ [1].

On the other hand, there is a physically transparent mechanism, which should result in the metallic-like behavior in the system of weakly interacting electrons (holes), $r_s < 1$ [2, 3]. It is the interference quantum correction to the conductivity. Theoretically, the sign of $d\sigma/dT$ for this mechanism depends on the relation between the spin and phase relaxation rates, $1/\tau_s$ and $1/\tau_\phi$, respectively. The sign of $d\sigma/dT$ is negative at $\tau_s < \tau_\phi$. This phenomenon is known as the weak *anti*localization in contrast to the weak localization characterized by the positive sign of $d\sigma/dT$.

In this paper we experimentally study the transport in the hole single quantum well with the asymmetric doping. Such a doping manner results in the relatively large value of the spin-orbit splitting of the energy spectrum due to the Bychkov-Rashba mechanism and, as consequence, in the fast spin relaxation. The heterostructures were grown by MOVPE on semi-insulator GaAs substrate. The structures consist of a $0.2~\mu$m-thick undoped GaAs buffer layer, a 7 nm $In_{0.2}Ga_{0.8}As$ well, a 6-7 nm spacer of undoped GaAs, a C δ-layer and

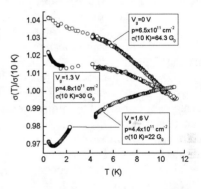

FIGURE 1. The temperature dependence of the conductivity for sample 4153-2g measured at different gate voltages.

200 nm cap layer of undoped GaAs. The samples were mesa etched into standard Hall bars. An Al gate electrode was deposited onto the cap layer. The parameters of the samples are $p = (4.0 - 7.5) \times 10^{11}$ cm^{-2}, $\mu = (4000 - 8000)$ cm^2/V s.

The temperature dependences of the conductivity at $B = 0$ measured for one of the structure at different gate voltages are presented in Fig. 1. It is seen that they are metallic-like at high hole density and insulating at lower one. The magnetoconductivity curves $\Delta\sigma(B) = \rho_{xx}^{-1}(B) - \rho_{xx}^{-1}(0)$ reveal a characteristic antilocalization maximum at $B = 0$ [Fig. 2(a)]. As shown in [4], the Dyakonov-Perel mechanism is the main mechanism of spin relaxation in such a type systems. It has been also shown that in p-type GaAs/$In_xGa_{1-x}As$/GaAs quantum wells the Bychkov-Rashba mechanism is responsible for

CP893, *Physics of Semiconductors, 28th International Conference*
edited by W. Jantsch and F. Schäffler
© 2007 American Institute of Physics 978-0-7354-0397-0/07/$23.00

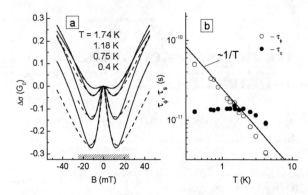

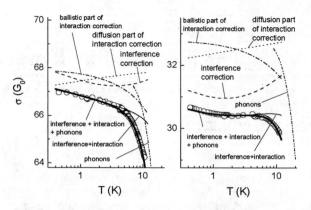

FIGURE 2. (a) – The $\Delta\sigma$-vs-B dependence for $V_g = 1.3$ V. The conductivity is measured in units of $G_0 = e^2/2\pi^2\hbar$. Solid lines are experimental data. Dashed lines are the results of the fitting procedure performed at low magnetic fields, $B < 0.2B_{tr}$ (shown by hatch). (b) – The T-dependence of τ_ϕ and τ_s obtained from the fit of the magnetoconductivity curves.

FIGURE 3. The T-dependence of σ for $V_g = 0$ V (left panel) and 1.3 V (right panel). Symbols are the experimental results. Lines are the results of calculation with the τ_ϕ, τ_s, and F_0^σ found experimentally.

the spin-orbit splitting of the energy spectrum, and this splitting is cubic in quasimomentum. In this case the spin relaxation rate can be found from the fit of the magnetoconductivity curve by the Hikami-Larkin-Nagaoka expression [5]. The results of such a data treatment are shown in Fig. 2(b). One can see that at low temperatures, $T < 1.5 - 2$ K, the spin relaxation time is really shorter that the dephasing time. As sequence the temperature dependence of σ caused by this mechanism is metallic-like only at low temperatures (see dashed lines in Fig. 3 which are calculated according to [5] with the use of experimental values of τ_ϕ and τ_s).

A different mechanism which can contribute to the temperature dependence of the conductivity is the h-h interaction. The value and the temperature dependence of the interaction quantum correction is controlled by the Fermi-liquid interaction constant, F_0^σ. This correction in analogous 2D systems was thoroughly studied in our previous paper [6], where the value of F_0^σ was experimentally obtained for different hole densities. Dotted and dash-dotted curves in Fig. 3 are the diffusion and ballistics parts of the interaction correction calculated with F_0^σ from [6]. Thin solid lines in this figure are drawn with taking into account both the interaction and interference quantum corrections. It is seen that the consideration of both quantum corrections allows us to describe the experimental data in wider temperature range. A good agreement is evident up to $T \simeq 4-6$ K.

At last, our analysis shows that starting from $T \simeq 4$ K the phonon scattering becomes important. The bold lines in Fig. 3 are calculated with taking into account all three effects: the interference correction, the interaction correction with τ_s, τ_ϕ and F_0^σ found experimentally and with phonon scattering calculated according to [7]. It is clearly seen that the calculation results are in excellent

agreement with the experimental results.

Thus, there is not one universal mechanism which is responsible for the metallic-like temperature dependence of the conductivity in the whole temperature range for the structures investigated. There are three different mechanisms: the weak antilocalization, the hole-hole interaction, and the phonon scattering. Each of them is the main within the corresponding temperature range. The first one dominates at 0.4 K$< T <$ 1.5 K. At higher temperatures, $1.5 < T < 4$ K, the interaction quantum correction becomes essential. Finally, the phonon scattering is important at $T > 4 - 6$ K.

This work was supported in part by the RFBR (Grant Nos. 04-02-16626, 05-02-16413, and 06-02-16292), and by a Grand from the President of Russian Federation for Young Scientists MK-1778.2205.2.

REFERENCES

1. V. M. Pudalov, M. E. Gershenson, and H. Kojima, "On the Electron-Electron Interactions in Two Dimensions," in *Fundamental Problems of Mesoscopic Physics.*, edited by I.V.Lerner, B.L.Altshuler, and Y.Gefen, Kluwer Academic Publishers, Dordrecht, 2004, pp. 309–327.

2. I. V. Gornyi, A. P. Dmitriev, and V. Yu. Kachorovskii, *Pis'ma ZhETF* **68**, 314–319 (1998) [*JETP Lett* **68**, 338–343 (1998)].

3. L. E. Golub and S. Pedersen, *Phys. Rev. B* **65**, 245311 (2002).

4. G. M. Minkov, A. A. Sherstobitov, A. V. Germanenko, O. E. Rut, V. A. Larionova, and B. N. Zvonkov, *Phys. Rev. B* **71**, 165312 (2005).

5. S. Hikami, A. I. Larkin, and Y. Nagaoka, *Prog. Theor. Phys.* 63, 707–710 (1980).

6. G. M. Minkov, A A. Sherstobitov, A. V. Germanenko, O. E. Rut, V. A. Larionova, B. N. Zvonkov, *Phys. Rev. B* **72**, 165325 (2005).

7. V. Carpus, *Semicond. Sci. Technol.* **5**, 691–694 (1990).

Pseudo-intersubband transitions in lateral superlattices with fluctuating period

Hiroshi Tsukahara and Tsuneya Ando

Department of Physics, Tokyo Institute of Technology, 2-12-1 Ookayama, Meguro-ku, Tokyo 152-8551, Japan

Abstract. The dynamical conductivity of a quantum-wire array with small fluctuations in the period, height, and direction is calculated in the self-consistent Born approximation. The presence of a pseudo-band-structure manifests itself in interband optical transitions as long as the disorder is sufficiently small, although the intensity is reduced considerably. With the increase in the disorder, this band structure is smeared out completely.

Keywords: lateral superlattice, anisotropic scattering, periodic corrugation, Bragg scattering, period fluctuation, interband transition
PACS: 73.21.-b, 73.21.Hb, 72.10.-d

A GaAs/AlAs superlattice grown on a (775)B GaAs substrate has a periodic interface corrugation of a zigzag shape illustrated in Fig. 1 and can be regarded as a high density quantum-wire array [1]. In transport experiments a huge anisotropic mobility was observed [2, 3]. In such systems, the zigzag structure has a certain amount of fluctuations in its period, modulation height, etc. In this case, the resulting effective potential becomes flat to the lowest order because of averaging and therefore the band structure is destroyed completely. Intuitively, however, electrons are expected to possess a band structure locally as long as the disorder remains small. In this paper, we explore how this pseudo-band-structure formation is restored in disordered quantum-wire arrays through calculations of the dynamical conductivity.

The key ingredient lies in the presence of strong diffuse Bragg scattering in the vicinity of the zone boundary because of a broadened Bragg peak present in the correlation function of the corrugation. It has been shown that this diffuse Bragg scattering constitutes the major origin of the large anisotropic mobility observed experimentally [4, 5]. As long as the disorder remains small, however, a pseudo-band-gap has been shown to exist and manifest itself in the density of states, the spectral function, and the static conductivity [6, 7].

An interface corrugation $\Delta(\mathbf{r})$ causes an effective potential

$$V_{\text{eff}}(\mathbf{r}) = F_{\text{eff}}\Delta(\mathbf{r}), \qquad (1)$$

where F_{eff} is the effective field at the interface. The validity of this approximation was demonstrated by self-consistent calculations [8]. The strength of periodic potential is characterized by the gap at the first zone boundary ε_G as illustrated in Fig. 1. In the following we shall assume $\varepsilon_G/\varepsilon_0 = 0.2$ where $\varepsilon_0 = (\hbar^2/2m^*)(\pi/a)^2$ is the energy at the boundary with a being the corrugation period and m^* being the effective mass.

In the presence of fluctuations in the period, height, and direction of the quantum-wire array, the sample average $\langle\Delta(\mathbf{r})\rangle$ vanishes and therefore the corrugation is characterized by the correlation function

$$D(\mathbf{r} - \mathbf{r}') = \langle\Delta(\mathbf{r})\Delta(\mathbf{r}')\rangle. \qquad (2)$$

The correlation function was calculated previously and its approximate but analytic expression was obtained [4]. It is characterized by four parameters, (i) α characterizing fluctuations of the corrugation period, (ii) $\nabla\xi$ fluctuations of the local quantum-wire direction, (iii) Δ_0 fluctuations of the height of the corrugation averaged locally, and (iv) λ correlation length of fluctuations of the height of the corrugation in the quantum-wire direction.

In addition to this disorder, we shall assume impurities with a model short-range potential

$$V_{\text{imp}}(\mathbf{r}) = \sum u_i\delta(\mathbf{r} - \mathbf{R}_i). \qquad (3)$$

The strength of impurities is characterized by the mean free path $l = v_0\tau_0$ with the velocity at zone boundary $v_0 = \pi\hbar/m^*a$ and relaxation time τ_0 given by $\hbar/2\tau_0 = \langle n_i u_i^2\rangle m^*/2\hbar^2$, where n_i is the impurity concentration.

We use Green's function technique to calculate the retarded and advanced Green's function in a self-consistent

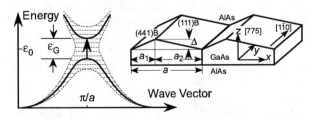

FIGURE 1. Schematic illustration of the corrugated quantum well (right) and the pseudo-band-structure (left).

CP893, *Physics of Semiconductors, 28th International Conference*
edited by W. Jantsch and F. Schäffler

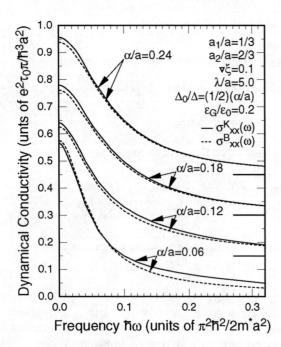

FIGURE 2. Calculated Kubo conductivity $\sigma_{xx}^K(\omega)$ and Boltzmann conductivity $\sigma_{xx}^B(\omega)$ in the direction perpendicular to quantum wires. The disorder in the periodic corrugation becomes larger as α/a increases. The origin of the vertical axis is shifted by 0.15 for different values of α/a.

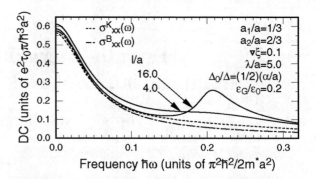

FIGURE 3. The interband conductivity calculated for an ideal superlattice with short-range scatterers added to the Boltzmann conductivity (solid lines) for $\alpha/a = 0.06$. The dotted line represents result of the Kubo conductivity and the dot-dashed line the Boltzmann conductivity in the superlattice with the disorder in the corrugation.

Born approximation. We calculate the dynamical conductivity using the Kubo formula and taking into account vertex corrections in the ladder approximation consistent with the self-consistent Born approximation. Because of the strong anisotropy in the diffuse Bragg scattering, the self-consistency equation for the Green's function and the self-energy can be solved only numerically and the same is applicable to the Bethe-Salpeter equation for the vertex part. We solve also the Boltzmann transport equation exactly to calculate the dynamical conductivity. Through the comparison between the Boltzmann conductivity without interband transitions and the Kubo conductivity, we can extract the contribution due to interband optical transitions.

Figure 2 shows some examples of calculated Kubo conductivity $\sigma_{xx}^K(\omega)$ perpendicular to the quantum-wire direction and the Boltzmann conductivity $\sigma_{xx}^B(\omega)$. The Fermi energy is chosen at $\varepsilon_F = \varepsilon_0$. For $\alpha/a = 0.06$ for which the disorder in the periodic corrugation is small, $\sigma_{xx}^K(\omega)$ exhibits a broad peak structure at about $\hbar\omega/\varepsilon_0 = 0.2$ corresponding to the band gap and therefore is larger than $\sigma_{xx}^B(\omega)$. This feature decreases and vanishes with the increase of the disorder in the corrugation.

In Fig. 3 the results for $\alpha/a = 0.06$ are compared also with $\sigma_{xx}^B(\omega)$ added by the interband conductivity of an ideal superlattice with short-range scatterers character-ized by $l/a = 16$ and 4. This result shows that the intensity of interband transitions is reduced considerably in the superlattice with disorder in corrugation, corresponding to the destruction of the band structure.

In summary, the dynamical conductivity of a quantum-wire array with small fluctuations in the period, height, and direction has been calculated in the self-consistent Born approximation. The presence of a pseudo-band-structure manifests itself in interband optical transitions as long as the disorder is sufficiently small, although the intensity is reduced considerably. With the increase in the disorder, this band structure is smeared out completely.

ACKNOWLEDGMENTS

This work was supported in part by a 21st Century COE Program at Tokyo Tech "Nanometer-Scale Quantum Physics" from the Ministry of Education, Culture, Sports, Science and Technology, Japan.

REFERENCES

1. M. Higashiwaki, M. Yamamoto, T. Higuchi, S. Shimomura, A. Adachi, Y.Okamoto, N. Sano, and S. Hiyamizu, Jpn. J. Appl. Phys. **35**, L606 (1996).
2. Y. Ohno, T. Kitada, S. Shimomura, and S. Hiyamizu, Jpn. J. Appl. Phys. **40**, L1058 (2001).
3. Y. Iye, A. Endo, S. Katsumoto, Y. Ohno, S. Shimomura, and S. Hiyamizu, Physica E **12**, 200 (2002).
4. Y. Zheng and T. Ando, J. Phys. Soc. Jpn. **72**, 2568 (2003).
5. T. Ando and Y. Zheng, Physica E **22**, 294 (2004).
6. H. Tsukahara and T. Ando, Physica E **29**, 614 (2005).
7. H. Tsukahara and T. Ando, J. Phys. Soc. Jpn. **74**, 3035 (2005).
8. Y. Zheng and T. Ando, Phys. Rev. B **66**, 085328 (2002).

Magnetic field symmetry and phase rigidity of the nonlinear conductance in a ring

R. Leturcq*, R. Bianchetti*, G. Götz*, T. Ihn*, K. Ensslin*, D. C. Driscoll† and A. C. Gossard†

*Solid State Physis Laboratory, ETH Zurich, 8093 Zurich, Switzerland
†Materials Department, University of California, Santa Barbara, CA 93106, USA

Abstract. We have performed nonlinear transport in a two-terminal ring showing the Aharonov-Bohm effect. We show experimentally that the nonlinear conductance is not symmetric in magnetic field, in contrast to the linear conductance. In addition, the asymmetry can be tuned by changing the potential of an electrostatic gate, showing that it is related to the phase accumulated by the electrons along the arms of the ring.

Keywords: mesoscopic transport; Aharonov-Bohm effect; nonlinear transport
PACS: 73.23.-b, 73.50.Fq, 73.63.-b

The equilibrium properties of mesoscopic conductors have been widely studied in semiconductor and metallic nanostructures. Recently, the problem of non-equilibrium transport has attracted many studies, both theoretically [1, 2, 3, 4, 5] and experimentally [6, 7, 8, 9, 10, 11]. The main characteristic pointed out is the prediction and observation that the nonlinear conductance of a two-terminal system is not symmetric in magnetic field, in contrast to the linear conductance [12]. While the behavior observed in carbon nanotubes and quantum dots can be understood in terms of electron-electron interactions [1, 2, 4, 7, 8, 10], the origin of the effect observed in quantum rings is still unclear [9, 11]. In order to further investigate the origin of the nonlinear conductance and its asymmetry in magnetic field, we study here a sample similar to the one of Ref. [9], but with a more symmetric geometry, and a better tunability of the electronic properties.

The sample was fabricated from a two-dimensional electron gas (2DEG), using an atomic force microscope to locally oxidize the surface of the GaAs/AlGaAs heterostructure [13]. The resulting oxide lines deplete locally the 2DEG, forming the ring structure shown in the inset of Fig. 1. The ring, of diameter 460 nm, is connected to two reservoirs S and D, the gates QPC1 and QPC2 controlling the coupling of the ring to the reservoirs, and the lateral gates LG and RG controlling the phase accumulated by the electrons along each path of the ring.

In order to study the nonlinear transport, a dc bias is applied between contacts S and D, with $V_S = V_{bias}/2$ and $V_D = -V_{bias}/2$, and the dc current is measured. The resulting $I - V$ characteristics is fitted with the Taylor

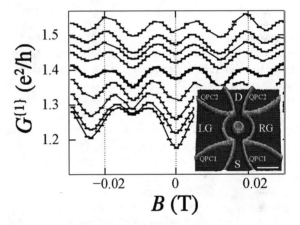

FIGURE 1. Linear conductance $G^{\{1\}}$ as a function of the magnetic field for several voltages applied on RG, varying from -30 (bottom curve) to -110 mV (upper curve), with a step of 10 mV. The curves are shifted by steps of 0.05 e^2/h for clarity. The voltages applied on the other gates QPC1, QPC2 and LG are rescpetively -75, -25 and 0 mV. Inset: AFM micrograph of the sample, taken just after the lithography. The white line represents a 500 nm scale.

series:

$$I(V) = \sum_{i=1}^{7} G^{\{i\}}(V - V_0)^i, \qquad (1)$$

where V_0 is an offset voltage coming from the amplifier and the rectification of ac noise. A magnetic field is applied perpendicular to the plane of the structure, and the the conductance parameters $G^{\{i\}}$ of the fit are determined for each value of the magnetic field.

The linear conductance $G^{\{1\}}$ shows Aharonov-Bohm oscillations as a function of the magnetic field, with two periods of respectively 25 and 12.5 mT, corresponding to

CP893, *Physics of Semiconductors, 28th International Conference*
edited by W. Jantsch and F. Schäffler

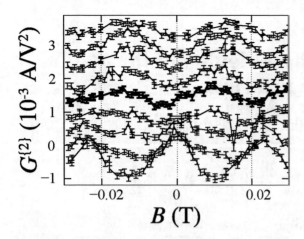

FIGURE 2. Quadratic conductance $G^{\{2\}}$ as a function of the magnetic field for several voltages applied on RG, varying from -30 (bottom curve) to -110 mV (upper curve), with a step of 10 mV. The curves are shifted by steps of 0.5×10^{-3} A/V^2 for clarity.

electron paths enclosing one (h/e oscillations) and two ($h/2e$ oscillations) flux quanta through the ring. Figure 1 shows that the relative magnitude of both h/e and $h/2e$ oscillations is tuned by changing the potential on gate RG. This behavior is related to a change in the phase accumulated in the left arm of the ring, $\delta_l = k_{F,l} L_l$, by changing either the Fermi wave vector $k_{F,l}$ or the length L_l of this arm [14, 15, 16, 17, 18]. In addition, the phase of the oscillation is always restricted to 0 or π. This result is compatible with the Onsager-Casimir relations for equilibrium transport, and is characteristic for transport through a two-terminal system [19, 18].

The second order conductance $G^{\{2\}}$ shows a very different behavior, as shown in Fig. 2. While AB oscillations are still observed, only one period corresponding to h/e is observed. In addition, the oscillations are not symmetric in magnetic field, as emphasized by the bold curve in Fig. 2. A nonlinear conductance is expected for a mesoscopic system asymmetrically coupled to the leads, as it is probably the case in our system. The magnetic field asymmetry for the quadratic term is also compatible with recent theories for mesoscopic transport out-of-equilibrium [1, 2]. We have also shown that the symmetry relations are not limited to $G^{\{1\}}$ and $G^{\{2\}}$, and higher order terms follow a general rule: while odd terms are symmetric in magnetic field, even terms are not symmetric in magnetic field [9]. Finally, the phase of the oscillations observed in $G^{\{2\}}$ varies when the voltage on gate RG is changed. This points out the importance of the electronic phase for the observed magnetic field asymmetry.

In conclusion, we have observed magnetic field asymmetries in the nonlinear conductance of a two-terminal

ring, which are compatible with recent theories for mesoscopic transport out-of-equilibrium. However, the origin of the asymmetry, as well as the different periods observed for the linear and quadratic conductances, are still not clearly understood.

ACKNOWLEDGMENTS

We thank M. Büttiker, M. Polianski and D. Sánchez for useful discussions. We acknowledge support from the Swiss Science Foundation (Schweizerischer Nationalfonds) via NCCR Nanoscience, the EU Human Potential Program via the Bundesministerium für Bildung und Wissenschaft.

REFERENCES

1. D. Sánchez, and M. Büttiker, *Phys. Rev. Lett.* **93**, 106802 (2004).
2. B. Spivak, and A. Zyuzin, *Phys. Rev. Lett.* **93**, 226801 (2004).
3. M. Büttiker, and D. Sánchez, *Int. J. Quantum Chem.* **105**, 906 (2005).
4. D. Sánchez, and M. Büttiker, *Phys. Rev. B* **72**, 201308(R) (2005).
5. M. L. Polianski, and M. Buttiker, *Phys. Rev. Lett.* **96**, 156804 (2006).
6. A. Löfgren, C. A. Marlow, I. Shorubalko, R. P. Taylor, P. Omling, L. Samuelson, and H. Linke, *Phys. Rev. Lett.* **92**, 046803 (2004).
7. J. Wei, M. Shimogawa, Z. Wang, I. Radu, R. Dormaier, and D. H. Cobden, *Phys. Rev. Lett.* **95**, 256601 (2005).
8. C. A. Marlow, R. P. Taylor, M. Fairbanks, I. Shorubalko, and H. Linke, *Phys. Rev. Lett.* **96**, 116801 (2006).
9. R. Leturcq, D. Sánchez, G. Götz, T. Ihn, K. Ensslin, D. C. Driscoll, and A. C. Gossard, *Phys. Rev. Lett.* **96**, 126801 (2006).
10. D. M. Zumbühl, C. M. Marcus, M. P. Hanson, and A. C. Gossard, *Phys. Rev. Lett.* **96**, 206802 (2006).
11. L. Angers, E. Zakka-Bajjani, R. Deblock, S. Gueron, A. Cavanna, U. Gennser, cond-mat/0603303.
12. M. Büttiker, *Phys. Rev. Lett.* **57**, 1761–1764 (1986).
13. R. Held, T. Heinzel, P. Studerus, K. Ensslin, and M. Holland, *Appl. Phys. Lett.* **71**, 2689–2691 (1997).
14. P. G. N. de Vegvar, G. Timp, P. M. Mankiewich, R. Behringer, and J. Cunningham, *Phys. Rev. B* **40**, 3491–3494 (1989).
15. G. Cernicchiaro, T. Martin, K. Hasselbach, D. Mailly, and A. Benoit, *Phys. Rev. Lett.* **79**, 273–276 (1997).
16. S. Pedersen, A. E. Hansen, A. Kristensen, C. B. Sørensen, and P. E. Lindelof, *Phys. Rev. B* **61**, 5457–5460 (2000).
17. A. Yacoby, M. Heiblum, V. Umansky, H. Shtrikman, and D. Mahalu, *Phys. Rev. Lett.* **73**, 3149–3152 (1994).
18. A. Yacoby, R. Schuster, and M. Heiblum, *Phys. Rev. B* **53**, 9583–9586 (1996).
19. A. Yacoby, M. Heiblum, D. Mahalu, and H. Shtrikman, *Phys. Rev. Lett.* **74**, 4047–4050 (1995).

A Study of Alloyed Nanowires from Two Perspectives: Approximate Dispersion and Transmission

Gerhard Klimeck[1,2], Timothy B. Boykin[3], Mathieu Luisier[4],
Neerav Kharche[1], Andreas Schenk[4]

[1] Network for Computational Nanotechnology, Purdue University, West Lafayette, IN 47906, USA
[2] Jet Propulsion Laboratory, California Institute of Technology, Pasadena, CA 91109, USA
[3] Department of Electrical and Computer Engineering, University of Alabama, Huntsville, AL 35899, USA
[4] Integrated Systems Laboratory, ETH Zürich, 8092 Zürich, Switzerland

Abstract. Local atomic arrangement in heterostructures or disorder due to alloying, surface roughness and impurities strongly influence the bandstructure and charge transport. With decreasing diameters down to nanometer scales, disorder can no longer be treated in an average manner using the virtual crystal approximation (VCA) and the need for atomistic simulations arises. This work looks at the nanoscale devices from two different perspectives. The materials science perspective in which average bandstructure of the whole nanowire is computed using the nanoelectronic modeling tool (NEMO-3D) and the zone-unfolding algorithm. The device physics perspective, where the transmission coefficient is calculated with an atomistic non-equilibrium Green's function (NEGF) approach. Both approaches use 20 band $sp^3d^5s^*$ empirical tight-binding model with spin orbit coupling. The connection between dispersions and transmission coefficients of AlGaAs random alloy nanowires is highlighted. Both, transmission coefficients and average bandstructures show reduced bandgaps and noisy behavior. Their complimentary and mutually supporting nature provides a significant insight into the physics of charge transport through disordered systems.

Keywords: nanowire, tight binding, transmission, transport, NEGF, disorder, alloy
PACS: 71.20.-b, 71.23.-k, 73.21.Cd

INTRODUCTION AND APPROACH

Theoretical approaches to study transport through semiconductor nanostructures can be classified into two broad classes: bandstructure and transport. Most often effective-mass or **k.p** models are used [1], however, more complete, multi-band calculations based on methods such as pseudopotentials[2] tight-binding[3], or the bond-orbital model[4] have appeared recently. Disorder is known to influence electronic structure at the nano-scale[5]. To study the effects of alloy-disorder in nanowires we perform atomistic random-alloy calculations of approximate bandstructures as well as the transport characteristics of $Al_{0.15}Ga_{0.85}As$ nanowires.

In this work, we calculate approximate bandstructure in freestanding [100] directed $Al_{0.15}Ga_{0.85}As$ nanowires and compare them to transmission coefficient calculations. All calculations have been done in 20-band $sp^3d^5s^*$ tight-binding model with spin-orbit coupling [6]. The nanowire geometry is specified in terms of zincblende conventional unit cubes (lattice parameter a_0=0.565 nm) $n_x \times n_y \times n_z$, where n_i is the number of cubes in i-direction. Eigenspectrum (eigenvalues and wavefunctions) of $40 \times 6 \times 6$ $Al_{0.15}Ga_{0.85}As$ nanowire supercell is computed using NEMO_3D [5]. The supercell is periodic in the transport (x-direction) and the wire mantle surfaces are passivated [7]. Small cell bandstructure for a $1 \times 6 \times 6$ cell is then projected out of the supercell eigenspectrum using our zone-unfolding method [8].

Transmission coefficients through the same nanowire are computed using a hybrid method combining a recursive NEGF method and a wavefunction calculation [9]. In these calculations the semi-infinite emitter (collector) region is identical to the first (last) slab of the nanowire.

RESULTS

Figure 1(a) shows bandstructures of an $Al_{0.15}Ga_{0.85}As$ random alloy nanowire calculated using conventional VCA method and unfolding $40 \times 6 \times 6$ supercell eigenspectrum. The random alloy calculation

CP893, *Physics of Semiconductors, 28th International Conference*
edited by W. Jantsch and F. Schäffler

results in significantly lower conduction band minima than VCA calculation. Transmission coefficients through the same nanowire supercell are shown in figure 1(b). The VCA transmission shows an ideal step like behavior, however, the transmission coefficient from random alloy calculations shows a noisy behavior as a consequence of random placement of Al atoms in AlGaAs nanowire. Features in transmission are related to the approximate bandstructure and vice versa. Each band corresponds to two transmission channels for up and down spins. The lowest approximate band at $k=0$ produces a transmission turn on near 1.92 eV. More channels turn on at about 1.97 eV due to approximate bands near π/a_0.

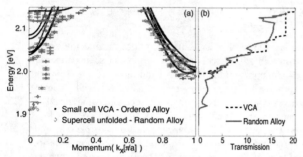

FIGURE 1. (a) Conduction bands of the 40×6×6 $Al_{0.15}Ga_{0.85}As$ nanowire as calculated with the VCA (small solid symbols) and as projected out of random-alloy supercell eigenstates (large, open symbols with error bars). Note in particular that the randomalloy calculation gives a significantly lower minimum at $k = 0$. (b) Transmission characteristics. Dotted line: VCA nanowire; this nanowire is effectively a pure nanowire made of a pseudo-material, and shows step-like transmission. Solid line: random-alloy supercell wire.

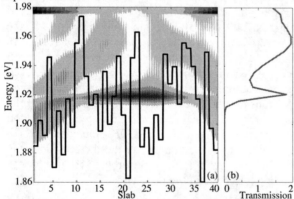

FIGURE 2. (a) Logarithm of the DOS (shaded region) neglecting spin, for the random-alloy nanowire superimposed over the wire conduction-band edge profile (thick line). (b) Transmission coefficient. The injected state is spin-up. The concentration of the DOS corresponds to the resonance peak in the transmission coefficient.

Figure 2(a) shows the local conduction band minima for each slab (1×6×6 cell) and a density of states of the same 40×6×6 AlGaAs nanowire. The transmission spike at about 1.92 eV in figure 2(b) corresponds to a localised density of states seen in figure 2(a).

In summary, we have found that approximate bandstructures from random alloy supercell calculations and atomistic NEGF transport calculations are complimentary and mutually supporting. Both methods provide better insight into the disordered nanowire device physics.

ACKNOWLEDGMENTS

The work at Purdue was supported by the National Science Foundation, Grant No. EEC-0228390 and ONR. nanoHUB.org computational resources were used in this work. The work at UAH was supported by Jet Propulsion Laboratory, California Institute of Technology and ONR.

REFERENCES

1. L. C. Lew Yan Voon, B. Lassen, R. Melnik, and S. Willatzen, J. Appl. Phys. vol. 96, no. 8, pp. 4660, 2004; L. C. Lew Yan Voon, and S. Willatzen, J. Appl. Phys., vol. 93, no. 12, pp. 9997, 2003; S. Jaziri and R. Ferreira, J. Appl. Phys., vol. 84, no. 2, pp. 893-900, 1998; M. Tsetseri and G. P. Tribera, Phys. Rev. B vol. 69, no. 7, art. 075313, 2004; H. T. Johnson, L. B. Freund, C. D. Akyüz, and A. Zaslavsky, J. Appl. Phys., vol. 84, no. 7, pp. 3714, 1998.
2. A. Francheschetti and A. Zunger, Phys. Rev. B, vol. 52, no. 20, pp. 14 664-14 670, 1995.
3. S. Pescetelli, A. Di Carlo, and P. Lugli, Phys. Rev. B, vol. 56, no. 4, pp. R1668-R1671, 1997; A. Di Carlo, S. Pescetelli, A. Kavokin, M. Vladimirva, and P. Lugli, Phys. Rev. B, vol. 57, no. 16, pp. 9770- 9779, 1998; M. P. Persson and H. Q. Xu, Phys. Rev. B, vol. 70, no. 16, art. 161310(R), 2004; Y.-J. Ko, M. Shin, S. Lee, and K. W. Park, J. Appl. Phys., vol. 89, no. 1, pp. 374, 2001.
4. L.-X. Li and Y.-C. Chang, J. Appl. Phys., vol. 84, no.11, pp.6162, 1998; L.-X. Li, S. Sun, and Y.-C. Chang, J. Appl. Phys, vol 89, no. 4, pp. 2251-2260, 2001.
5. G. Klimeck, F. Oyafuso, T. B. Boykin, R. C. Bowen, and P. von Allmen, *Computer Modeling in Engineering and Science*, **3**, 601-642 (2002).
6. Jean-Marc Jancu, Reinhold Scholz, Fabio Beltram, and Franco Bassani, Phys. Rev. B vol. 57, pp. 6493, 1998.
7. S. Lee, F. Oyafuso, P. von Allmen, and G. Klimeck, Phys. Rev. B vol. 69, pp. art. 045316, 2004.
8. T.B. Boykin and G Klimeck, Phys. Rev. B vol. 70, no. 11, pp. art. 115215, 2005; T.B. Boykin, N. Kharche, G. Klimeck, and M. Korkusinski (subm. IEEE Nano).
9. M Luisier, et al., (accepted in Phys. Rev. B).

Novel many-body state in quantum wires near pinch-off

T. Morimoto[1], M. Hemmi, R. Naito, K. Tsubaki[1], N. Aoki[1], J. P. Bird[2]
and Y. Ochiai[1]

[1]*Department of Electronics and Mechanical Engineering, Chiba University, 1-33 Yayoi-cho, Inage-ku
Chiba 263-8522, Japan*
[2]*Department of Electrical Engineering, University at Buffalo, Buffalo, NY 14216*

Abstract. We observe novel behavior in the non-linear conductance of semiconductor quantum wires near pinch-off. In this regime, their low-temperature (<1K) differential conductance increases dramatically from zero to a value above $2e^2/h$. This enhancement depends strongly on temperature, in-plane magnetic field, and wire length. Our results suggest that this resonance is related to the formation of a novel many-body state in the quantum wires near pinch-off.

Keywords: Quantum Wire, Quantum Point Contact, differential conductance,
PACS: 73.21.Hb, 73.63.-b, 72.90.+y

INTRODUCTION

Interest in the many-body aspects of quasi one-dimensional (1D) transport in quantum wires (QWs) has been growing for more than a decade now. In these studies, non-equilibrium measurements are frequently performed by applying a source-drain bias voltage that can exceed the subband spacing of the QW [1,2]. This method provides a powerful tool to probe the intrinsic structure of QWs and a Kondo effect related to the 0.7 feature has been reported using such methods [3]. When combined with studies of linear transport, these measurements therefore provide a powerful probe of 1D systems. In this report, we discuss the observation of novel resonances in the differential conductance of QWs near pinch off. The resonances have a strong dependence on temperature, in-plane magnetic field and QW length, and suggest that a novel many-body spin state is formed in the QWs near pinch-off.

SAMPLE & MEASUREMENT DETAILS

QWs were formed in the same two-dimensional electron gas (2DEG) layer of GaAs/AlGaAs hetero-structure, with a carrier density of 2.5×10^{11} cm^{-2} and a mobility of 1.1×10^6 cm^2/Vs. The 2DEG was located 75 nm below the top surface and QWs of different length (150-, 450- and 600-nm) were realized using surface gates with a rectangular shape (Fig 1, inset). Transport properties were studied by making two types of conductance measurement: (i) linear conductance using small AC excitation, and (ii) differential conduc-

tance with a variable DC voltage (V_{sd}) + small fixed AC bias. The 2DEG carrier density was decreased down to 1.9×10^{11} cm^{-2} by use of a back gate. The sample was mounted in the mixture of a dilution refrigerator for measurement between 0.2- and 13-K.

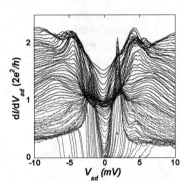

FIGURE 1. The differential conductance of the 450-nm QW at 0.2 K.

EXPERIMENTAL RESULTS

The QWs show fairly typical behavior of their linear conductance. The observation of well-quantized plateaus in integer units of $2e^2/h$ indicates that transport in this regime occurs via non-interacting spin-degenerate subbands.

In the usual single-particle description of QW transport, a bunching of the differential conductance is expected near zero bias in the regions close to the integer-quantized steps [4,5]. The bunched regions reflect the number of spin-degenerate 1D subbands that are

CP893, *Physics of Semiconductors, 28th International Conference*
edited by W. Jantsch and F. Schäffler
© 2007 American Institute of Physics 978-0-7354-0397-0/07/$23.00

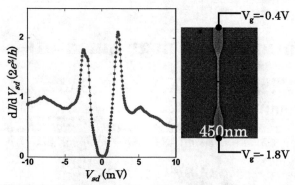

FIGURE 2. Left panel: The differential conductance with asymmetric measurement. Right panel: The SEM image of 450nm wire and measurement voltage configuration.

populated by the two reservoirs. For non-zero V_{sd}, the bunching occurs near "half-plateaus", reflecting a difference in the number of subbands populated by the reservoirs. In our experiment, however, the non-linear differential conductance shows a very different response at low temperatures (< 1 K, Fig. 1). In the curves for which the linear conductance is pinched off, in particular, the differential conductance quickly rises up to exceed $2e^2/h$, before dropping back to the e^2/h half plateau. This *isolated* resonance is strongly sensitivity to temperature, in-plane magnetic field and QW length [6,7]. On the resonance is robust, however, to asymmetric gate biasing and variation of the 2DEG density. These results are inconsistent with the resonance arising from simple tunneling via an impurity site, or from the occupation of a higher 2DEG subband.

The differential conductance is intrinsically related to the form of the *I-V* characteristic. In Fig. 3, we show the form of the *I-V* curve that gives rise to the resonance in differential conductance. The zero current

region corresponds to pinch-off, while the slope in the nearly-saturated region corresponds to the half plateau in the differential conductance. We can clearly see from Fig. 3 that the steep rise in the *I-V* curve near ±2 mV gives rise to the associated resonance in the differential conductance. This sudden change is unexpected from a simple non-interacting picture of transport and we believe that it indicates a strong modification in the form of the electron distribution function near pinch off that is probably caused by a many-body effect.

CONCLUSION

We have presented the results of experimental studies of non-equilibrium transport in QWs of various length. We have found a sudden enhancement of the differential conductance, to a value that exceeds $2e^2/h$, in the pinch-off region and at low temperatures. The enhancement is strongly dependent on temperature, in-plane magnetic field and QW length [6]. It is difficult to explain these results within the usual framework of non-interacting 1D transport in QWs. We believe instead that our observations point to an interpretation involving a novel many-body state that forms *dynamically* in the transition from pinch-off to finite conductance. While our conclusions on this matter remain tentative at present, further research on this striking phenomenon should clarify it origins and further enhance our understanding of transport in quasi-1D systems.

ACKNOWLEDGEMENT

This work was supported in part by Grant-in-Aids for Scientific research of Japan Society for the Promotion of Science (JPSJ) No.14750005, 13450006, and JSPS Research Fellows, and also supported in part by Chiba University 21COE "Frontiers of Super-Functionality Organic Devices". JPB acknowledges support from NSF, DoE and NYSTAR.

REFERENCES

1. N. K. Patel et al., J. Phys. Condense. Matter **2**, 7247, (1990).
2. D. J. Reilly et al., Phys. Rev. Lett. **89**, 246801 (2002).
3. S. M. Cronenwett et al., Phys. Rev. Lett. **88**, 226805 (2002).
4. L. I. Glazman and A. V. Khaetskii, Europhys. Lett. **9**, 263 (1989).
5. N. K. Patel et al., Phys. Rev. B **44**, 13549 (1991).
6. T. Morimoto et al., Journal of Physics: Conference Series. **38**, 83 (2006).
7. T.Morimoto et al., Phys. Rev. Lett. **97**, 096801, (2006).

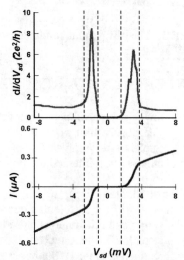

FIGURE 3. Upper panel: resonant enhancement of differential conductance in the 600-nm QW at 0.2 K. Lower panel: corresponding *I-V* curve.

Scanning Gate Imaging of Transport within an InGaAs QPC

N. Aoki[*,†], C. R. da Cunha[†,¶], T. Morimoto[*], R. Akis[†], D. K. Ferry[†], and Y. Ochiai[*]

[*]Department of Electronics and Mechanical Engineering, Chiba University, 1-33 Yayoi-cho, Inage-ku, Chiba 263-8522, Japan
[†]Department of Electrical Engineering and Center for Solid State Electronics Research, Arizona State University, Tempe, AZ 85287-5706, USA
[¶]McGill University, 3600 rue University, Montreal, QC H3A 2T8, Canada

Abstract. Quantum transport in a quantum point contact of InGaAs has been successfully visualized using a low temperature scanning gate microcopy. The images involves three kinds of features: (i) conductance fluctuations due to quantum interference, (ii) characteristic peaks corresponding to the propagating mode, (iii) a static-peak pattern observed just before the pinch-off condition. Furthermore, the fluctuations in the image reveal that the area distribution has a peak at around 2.5×10^4 nm^2 and follows Gaussian unitary ensemble. It is consistent with a distribution of frequency components of the magnetoconductance fluctuations of the quantum point contact.

Keywords: Scanning gate microscopy, quantum point contact, quantum interference
PACS: 68.65.-k, 07.79.Lh

INTRODUCTION

Low-temperature scanning gate microscopy (SGM) has been investigated for a spatial visualization of a transport in semiconductor quantum structures such as quantum point contact (QPC) and quantum dot (QD). In SGM, a negatively biased tip is brought into the constriction and modulates the local potential, and then a change of the conduction depending on the tip position is stored and visualized as an image. Using this method, a current flow from a QPC[1] and Coulomb blockade in a QD[2] have been visualized so far. Recently, we have successfully visualized quantum transport inside a QPC of InGaAs[3]. In this paper, we demonstrate a typical SGM image of a disordered QPC and discuss the interpretation of features in the image. Especially, interference patterns observed around the constricted region show that the size distribution of the pattern is consistent with the interference area obtained from the Fast Fourier Transform (FFT) analysis of the magnetoconductance fluctuations.

EXPERIMENTAL

The QPC was fabricated in an InAlAs/InGaAs/ InAlAs quantum well whose two-dimensional electron gas (2DEG) located 45 nm below the surface. The structure was designed using 100 nm deep trenches defined via wet etching, which allowed us to scan the entire surface area. The QPC had an opening of 0.6 μm and a radius of 0.8 μm as indicated by the broken lines in Fig. 1. The 2DEG had occupations of two subbands with carrier concentrations of 7.2 and 2.4×10^{11} /cm^2. The mobility found from the total carrier concentration was 7.4×10^4 cm^2/Vs, and the calculated mean free path was 1.2 μm, which indicates a certain level of disorder in this material. The SGM was performed at 300 mK with a piezolever whose tip is coated by 15 nm of PtIr, and by lifting it up 50 nm above the surface

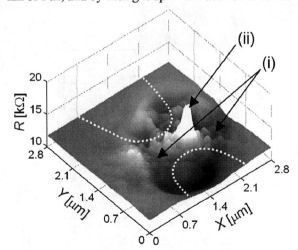

FIGURE 1. A typical SGM image obtained at around 1G₀. The Z-axis shows the resistance across the QPC. The broken lines show the outer edge of the trench defining the QPC.

CP893, *Physics of Semiconductors, 28th International Conference*
edited by W. Jantsch and F. Schäffler
© 2007 American Institute of Physics 978-0-7354-0397-0/07/$23.00

with applying a small negative voltage.

RESULTS AND DISCUSSION

The role of the tip in perturbing the transport is a modulation of the background potential, since the tip slightly depletes the 2DEG underneath and the small protrusion of the tip induced potential is brought into the constriction during the scan. Figure 1 shows a typical SGM image of the QPC taken around the base conductance of $1G_0$ ($G_0 = 2e^2/h$) at zero magnetic field. The image involves some kinds of features. One is the conductance fluctuations due to quantum interference inside the channel, indicated by (i) in Fig. 1. Because this sample has a certain level of disorder in the background potential, the QPC shows conductance fluctuations in nature even without the tip[3]. However, when the tip is brought into the channel, the tip-induced potential modifies the interference condition. Consequently, the change of the conductance could be visualized as the fluctuations in the SGM image. The amplitude of the fluctuations is smaller than $0.1G_0$ and decays as the tip moves outwards along the direction of the channel. The fluctuated patterns are not fixed and vary depending on the side gate voltage, and they

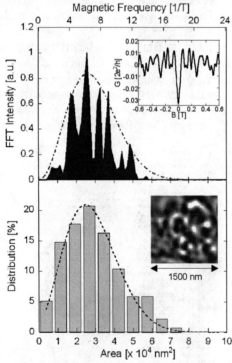

FIGURE 2. The upper figure shows a FFT result of the magnetofluctuations, shown in the inset, across the QPC. This follows also lower horizontal axis. The lower one (bar graph) shows a result of a grain analysis of the fluctuations in the SGM image taken at 1.5×1.5 μm^2 region, shown in the inset, around the center of the QPC. Both distributions show similar peak position and are fit well by GUE.

disappear at high temperature (> 4 K)[3].

Another is characteristic peak(s) corresponding to perturbing the eigenmodes of the channel[5], indicated by (ii) in Fig. 1. The conductance variations at the peaks are significantly higher than the conductance fluctuations. One peak is clearly observed at around $1G_0$ in Fig. 1 however two peaks appear at around $2G_0$. Moreover, the disordered background potential it self observed just before the pinch-off condition (not shown here)[3].

As mentioned before, the fluctuations given by the dark and light regions in the image, shown in the lower par of Fig. 2, are related to variations in conductance that arise from interference within the QPC. The area distribution obtained from a grain analysis has a peak at around 2.5×10^4 nm^2 as shown in the lower part of Fig. 2. We reveal the distribution show a good agreement with the interference area estimated from the FFT-peak distribution of the magneto-fluctuations shown in the upper part of Fig. 2. Moreover, both distributions are well fit by the Gaussian unitary ensemble (GUE), a distribution that applies when a system is chaotic[6]. Given that the electrons in the channel encounter scattering from a background potential determined by the random placement of impurities and the alloy potential, the confining walls and also from the tip-induced potential, it is reasonable that the system could show chaotic behavior. However, this match indicates a direct correspondence between the two experimental results.

SUMMARY

Quantum transport in an InGaAs QPC has been visualized by low temperature SGM. The image shows that quantum fluctuations are dominant in the transport of the channel due to the disorder of background potential. The area of the fluctuations in the image shows a quite similar distribution to the interference area obtained from the magnetofluctuations.

ACKNOWLEDGMENTS

This work was supported by the Office of Naval Research; N. Aoki was supported by the JSPS Post Doctoral Fellowships for Research Abroad 2004.

REFERENCES

1. M. A. Topinka *et al.*, Science **289**, 2323 (2000).
2. A. Pioda *et al.*, Phys. Rev. Lett. **93**, 216801 (2004).
3. N. Aoki *et al.*, Appl. Phys. Lett. **87**, 223501 (2005).
4. J. A. Nicson *et al.*, Phys. Rev. B **43**, 12638 (1991).
5. G.-P. He *et al.*, Phys. Rev. B **65**, 205321 (2002).
6. N. E. Hurt, Quantum Chaos and Mesoscopic Systems (Kluwer Academic Publishers, Netherlands 1997).

Ballistic rectification in four-terminal fork-shaped Si/SiGe junctions

Egmont Fritz[1], Ulrich Wieser[1], Ulrich Kunze[1], and Thomas Hackbarth[2]

[1]*Werkstoffe und Nanoelektronik, Ruhr-Universität Bochum, D-44780 Bochum, Germany*
[2]*DaimlerChrysler Forschungszentrum Ulm, D-89081 Ulm, Germany*

Abstract. We present a new type of a ballistic rectifier where electrons are injected under zero injection angle into a straight central voltage stem of a four-terminal Si/SiGe junction. For small input current a sign reversal of the rectified output signal is found which depends reversibly on the voltage applied to two side gate electrodes.

Keywords: ballistic rectification; ballistic transport; Si/SiGe; electron waveguides
PACS: 73.23.Ad, 73.63.Nm, 73.40.Lq

Ballistic electron transport in mesoscopic systems attracts increasing attention due to the possibility to design novel devices with nonlinear transport characteristics. One example is ballistic full-wave rectification observed in mesoscopic T- and Y-junctions [1, 2, 3], which can be explained in a picture of mainly mode-controlled nonlinearity. In this work, we study a four-terminal ballistic Si/SiGe rectifier which enables to separate the mode-controlled from an inertial-ballistic signal [4]. Recent work on Ψ-shaped GaAs/AlGaAs-junctions shows that the efficiency of inertial-ballistic rectification systematically depends on the injection angle Φ between the injectors and a central stem [5]. With decreasing Φ the amplitude of the inertial-ballistic signal increases at constant driving voltage. Consequently, we realize a device-geometry where electrons are injected under zero injection angle (Fig. 1a). Three parallel 250 nm wide electron waveguides (1, 3, 4) merge into a 1 µm wide straight central voltage stem (2) and form a trident-fork-shaped junction. Contacts (1) and (3) act as injectors, (2) and (4) as two independent voltage probes. A pair of in-plane side-gate electrodes (G) is placed near the orifices of the outer waveguides (1) and (3).

If an input bias $V_{13} = V_1 - V_3$ is applied in push-pull fashion ($V_1 = -V_3$) between the injection leads (1) and (3) a current flows and a rectified negative output voltage develops at the stem (V_2) as well as at the central voltage probe (V_4). The voltage V_4 is identified as the mode-controlled signal which is explained by a bias-induced position-dependent variation of the local resistance along the current path. Independent from the input bias current polarity the momentum component of the injected electrons is directed towards the lower part of the stem. The resulting accumulation of negative charge carriers leads to a superimposed inertial-ballistic and mode-controlled signal. The geometrical configuration enables to separate the rectified inertial-ballistic signal $V_{24} = V_2 - V_4$ from the mode-controlled signal V_4.

The ballistic rectifiers are prepared from a high-mobility modulation-doped Si/Si$_{0.7}$Ge$_{0.3}$ heterostructure by combining high-resolution electron-beam lithography, conventional photolithography, and low-damage plasma etching. For details of the device preparation see [6].

DC transport measurements are performed at a temperature of $T = 4.2$ K using an Agilent Precision Semiconductor Parameter Analyzer 4156B.

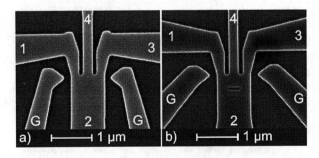

FIGURE 1. a) Scanning electron micrograph of the rectifier. Contacts (1, 3) represent the 250 nm wide current injectors, (2, 4) a lower and upper voltage probe, and (G) a pair of in-plane side-gate electrodes. b) Rectifier with embedded artificial scatterer.

CP893, *Physics of Semiconductors, 28th International Conference*
edited by W. Jantsch and F. Schäffler

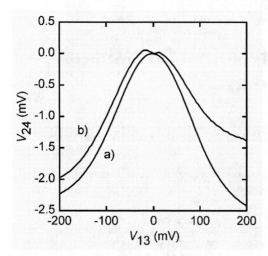

FIGURE 2. Transfer characteristic V_{24} vs. V_{13} a) before and b) after applying a large negative gate voltage.

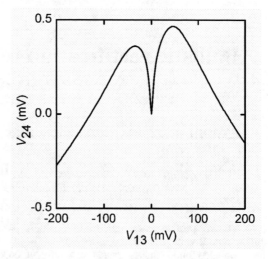

FIGURE 3. Transfer characteristic V_{24} vs. V_{13} of a device with embedded artificial scatterer.

The transfer characteristic V_{24} versus V_{13} (Fig. 2) shows a nearly parabolic dependency for low input bias. A rectified output voltage $V_{24} < 0$ is observed due to negative charge accumulation in lead 2. As $|V_{13}|$ increases a linear dependency of V_{24} on V_{13} is found. At $|V_{13}| > 120$ mV both carrier heating and an increased resistance in the positively biased injector lead to a saturation of V_{24}. Due to the small energy separation between one-dimensional (1D) subbands a large number of 1D modes contribute to the electron transport in the electron waveguides (multi-mode regime). Under this condition it is not possible to resolve quantum-mechanical collimation effects in the transfer characteristics. Defining a rectification efficiency $\eta = |V_{24}/V_{13}|$, we obtain $\eta_{max} \approx 1.5\%$ for $V_{13} \approx \pm 120$ mV.

Two side-gate electrodes enable to influence the number of occupied modes in the injectors. Unfortunately gate leakage currents make it impossible to pinch-off injectors 1 and 3, i.e. even at negative gate voltages the device is operated in the multi-mode regime. After applying a large negative gate voltage ($V_G < -2.5$ V) we found that for $V_G \approx 0$ the polarity of the rectified inertial-ballistic signal V_{24} is inverted for small V_{13} (Fig. 2), while the mode-controlled signal V_4 is nearly unchanged. At higher input bias V_{13} the voltage V_{24} becomes negative and qualitatively follows the characteristic described above. The effect holds up, until a high positive gate voltage ($V_G > 2$ V) is applied. This reversible characteristic is attributed to recharging of trap states in the SiGe buffer layer by gate leakage currents. The resulting space charge forms a repulsive potential in the voltage stem, at which low-energy electrons are reflected. Thus the electron flow is directed upwards and V_{24} becomes positive.

Since the kinetic energy increases with $|V_{13}|$ a change of sign is observed in V_{24} if the energy is sufficient to pass the barrier.

To confirm this interpretation a second device is prepared where an artificial scatterer (width: 350nm, length: 75nm) is embedded in the central voltage stem orthogonal to the injection leads (Fig. 1b). A 60-nm-deep etch transfer of the scatterer leads to a local depletion of the 2DEG in this region causing a repulsive potential. Due to the wide angular distribution of injected electrons at small $|V_{13}|$ most electrons are reflected at the scatterer (Fig. 3). The positive sign of V_{24} indicates a charge accumulation in contact 4, i.e. the momentum component of the reflected electrons is directed upwards. With increasing V_{13} electron collimation enables more and more electrons to pass the scatterer at both sides. This results in an electron accumulation in the lower part of the stem and a sign reversal of V_{24}. The characteristic holds up even upon applying a high positive gate-voltage $V_G > 2.5$ V.

E.F. acknowledges financial support by the Deutsche Forschungsgemeinschaft via Graduiertenkolleg 384.

REFERENCES

1. I. Shorubalko *et al.*, *Appl. Phys. Letters* **79**, 1384 (2001).
2. K. Hieke *et al.*, *Phys. Rev. B* **62**, 16727 (2000).
3. L. Worschech *et al.*, *Appl. Phys. Letters* **79**, 3287 (2001).
4. M. Knop *et al.*, *Physica E* **32**, 536 (2006).
5. M. Knop *et al.*, *Appl. Phys. Letters* **88**, 082110 (2006).
6. S.A. Poenariu *et al.*, *Physica E* **32**, 539 (2006).

Enhanced Rectification Efficiency In Cascaded Ballistic GaAs/AlGaAs Rectifiers

U. Wieser*, M. Knop*, P. Koop*, U. Kunze*, D. Reuter[†], and A.D. Wieck[†]

*Werkstoffe und Nanoelektronik, Ruhr-Universität Bochum, D-44780 Bochum, Germany
[†]Angewandte Festkörperphysik, Ruhr-Universität Bochum, D-44780 Bochum, Germany

Abstract. We report on an enhanced efficiency of inertial-ballistic rectification in a cascade of rectifier stages. Each rectifier stage is composed of a pair of current injecting branches which oppositely merge into a central voltage stem. The voltages obtained at both ends of the stem enable to separate inertial-ballistic and mode-controlled rectification. In a cascade composed of two rectifier stages the total inertial-ballistic signal is enhanced compared to the single contributions while the mode-controlled signal is almost unaffected.

Keywords: ballistic rectification; ballistic transport; quantum wires; GaAs/AlGaAs.
PACS: 73.23.Ad; 73.63.Nm; 73.40.Kp

Instantaneous onset of rectification without threshold voltage and low in-plane capacitance are preferable properties of rectifiers required to detect ultra-small signals at very high frequencies. One type of devices which could satisfy these requirements is the ballistic rectifier [1-8]. The present work deals with a cascade of ballistic rectifier stages where each stage is designed as non-centrosymmetric junction. It will be shown that in a cascade the rectification efficiency of the inertial-ballistic signal is enhanced compared to single rectifier stages.

The device is prepared from a GaAs/AlGaAs heterostructure embedding a high-mobility two-dimensional electron gas 55 nm below the sample surface. At $T = 4.2$ K an electron mean-free path of about 8 μm is calculated from the mobility $\mu = 8 \times 10^5$ cm^{2}V^{-1}s^{-1} and sheet density $n_S = 3.6 \times 10^{11}$ cm^{-2}. Generally, the cascaded rectifier is composed of n laterally staggered pairs of current injecting branches. Each pair oppositely merges under an injection angle $\varphi < 90°$ into a central voltage stem. The upper (U) and lower (L) endings of the stem act as voltage probes from which we detect V_U and V_L. Here, we refer to a six-terminal cascade composed of two rectifier stages (i.e. $n = 2$). Fig. 1a shows a scanning electron micrograph of the central part of the cascade. The width of the branches (stem) amounts to 500 nm (1 μm). The injection angle is $\varphi = 30°$. Details of the device preparation are to be found in [9].

DC transport measurements are performed at $T = 4.2$ K. Fig. 1b shows the current-voltage (I-V)

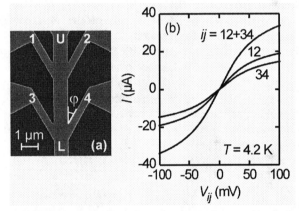

FIGURE 1. (a) Scanning electron micrograph of the cascaded rectifier. (b) Current-voltage characteristics of the injector pairs. The input bias V_{ij} is applied to single (V_{12} or V_{34}) and both (V_{12+34}) injector pairs.

characteristics of the injector pairs. The input bias $V_{ij} = V_i - V_j$ ($V_j = -V_i$) is applied between single (V_{12} or V_{34}) and both (V_{12+34}) injector pairs. For small input bias I linearly depends on V_{ij}. At higher V_{ij} the current saturates due to carrier heating and an increased resistance in the positively biased branches [4]. If the bias is applied to both injector pairs the enhanced total current is given by the parallel connection of both current paths. The slightly different I-V characteristic of the injector pairs is attributed to a non-perfect geometry and non-uniform contact resistances.

Independent from the bias current polarity the non-centrosymmetric design of the injector branches causes

CP893, *Physics of Semiconductors, 28th International Conference*
edited by W. Jantsch and F. Schäffler
© 2007 American Institute of Physics 978-0-7354-0397-0/07/$23.00

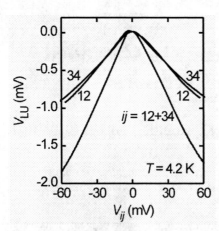

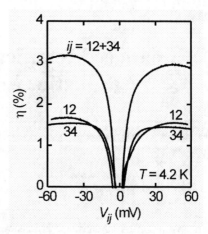

FIGURE 2. Transfer characteristics of the inertial-ballistic signal V_{LU}. The input bias V_{ij} is applied to single (V_{12} or V_{34}) and both (V_{12+34}) injector pairs.

FIGURE 3. Voltage rectification efficiency of the inertial-ballistic signal. The input bias V_{ij} is applied to single (V_{12} or V_{34}) and both (V_{12+34}) injector pairs.

an electron momentum component which is directed towards the lower end of the stem. Consequently, ballistic electrons induce a negative electrostatic potential in contact (L) [4]. Since mode-controlled rectification develops at both ends of the stem the geometry enables to separate the mode-controlled signal V_U from the inertial-ballistic signal $V_{LU} = V_L - V_U$ [10]. Fig. 2 shows the transfer characteristics of V_{LU}. Again, the input bias V_{ij} ($V_j = -V_i$) is applied to single (V_{12} or V_{34}) and both (V_{12+34}) rectifiers stages. In order to avoid equalizing currents between different injector pairs in the test circuit external resistors ($R_0 = 1\ M\Omega$) are connected in series with all injectors. Since R_0 by far exceeds the resistance of the device we record I and extract the voltage drop V_{ij} across the device from the I-V_{ij} characteristics of Fig. 1. As shown in Fig. 2 an almost identical signal V_{LU} is found for both rectifier stages. If both injector pairs are connected simultaneously V_{LU} is enhanced. The analysis of the signal amplitude reveals a nearly additive increase of V_{LU} with respect to the contributions of the single rectifier stages. In contrast to V_{LU} the mode-controlled signal V_U solely depends on the voltage drop across the injector pairs. Therefore, in a cascaded device V_U is independent of the number of injector pairs. Measurements of the cascaded device (without external series resistors) confirm that V_U is given by an average value of the contributions of the single rectifier stages.

In order to demonstrate the scalability of the inertial-ballistic signal the voltage rectification efficiency $\eta = -V_{LU}/|V_{ij}|$ is calculated (Fig. 3). In accordance with the roughly parabolic increase of V_{LU} a linear characteristics of η is found at small $|V_{ij}|$. If V_{ij}

is applied to a single injector pair a maximum efficiency $\eta_{max} < 1.7\%$ develops at $V_{ij} \approx \pm 40$ mV. If both injector pairs are connected the efficiency is enhanced and a maximum efficiency $\eta_{max} = 3.1\%$ is found for $V_{12+34} = -45$ mV. The shift of the maximum along the V_{ij}-axis is mainly caused by the contact resistance of the injectors.

Part of this work was supported by the Bundesministerium für Bildung und Forschung under grant no. 01BM454.

REFERENCES

1. K. Hieke and M. Ulfward, *Phys. Rev. B* **62**, 16727 (2000).
2. L. Worschech, H.Q. Xu, A. Forchel, and L. Samuelson, *Appl. Phys. Letters* **79**, 3287-3289 (2001).
3. I. Shorubalko, H.Q. Xu, I. Maximov, P. Omling, L. Samuelson, and W. Seifert, *Appl. Phys. Letters* **79**, 1384-1386 (2001).
4. M. Knop, U. Wieser, U. Kunze, D. Reuter, and A.D. Wieck, *Appl. Phys. Letters* **88**, 082110 (2006).
5. A.M. Song, A. Lorke, A. Kriele, and J.P. Kotthaus, *Phys. Rev. Lett.* **80**, 3831-3834 (1998).
6. A. Löfgren, I. Shorubalko, P. Omling, and A.M. Song, *Phys. Rev. B* **67**, 195309 (2003).
7. S. de Haan, A. Lorke, J.P. Kotthaus, W. Wegscheider, and M. Bichler, *Phys. Rev. Lett.* **92**, 056806 (2004).
8. B. Hackens, L. Gence, C. Gustin, X. Wallart, S. Bollaert, A. Cappy, and V. Bayot, *Appl. Phys. Letters* **85**, 4508-4510 (2004).
9. M. Knop, M. Richter, R. Maßmann, U. Wieser, U. Kunze, D. Reuter, C. Riedesel, and A.D. Wieck, *Semicond. Sci. Technol.* **20**, 814-818 (2005).
10. M. Knop, U. Wieser, U. Kunze, D. Reuter, and A.D. Wieck, *Physica E* **32**, 536-538 (2006).

Graphene-based quantum wires

J. Milton Pereira Jr.*, V. Mlinar*, F. M. Peeters* and P. Vasilopoulos[†]

*Department of Physics, University of Antwerp, Groenenborgerlaan 171, B-2020 Antwerpen
[†]Department of Physics, Concordia University, Montreal, Quebec, Canada H3G 1M8

Abstract. We investigate the properties of carriers in graphene-based quantum wires created by potential barriers, by means of analytical and numerical calculations. We obtain expressions for the energy spectrum as a function of barrier height, well width and linear momentum along the wire. The results demonstrate a direction-dependent resonant transmission across the potential well.

Keywords: Graphene, Quantum Wire
PACS: 71.10.Pm, 73.21.-b, 81.05.Uw

INTRODUCTION AND FORMALISM

Recent studies have demonstrated the production of stable, ultrapure, two-dimensional carbon crystals (graphene) with unusual properties, such as unconventional quantum Hall effect [1, 2] and a strong electric-field effect [3]. In this work we investigate the nature of electron states in graphene quantum wires (QW) and their quantized spectrum. The low-energy band structure of graphene is gapless, and the carrier dynamics is equivalent to that of a 2D gas of massless charged fermions. Their behavior is governed by the 2D Dirac equation

$$[v_F(\vec{\sigma} \cdot \hat{\mathbf{p}}) + mv_F^2 \sigma_z]\Psi = (E - U)\Psi. \quad (1)$$

where the pseudospin matrix $\vec{\sigma}$ has components given by Pauli's matrices, $\hat{\mathbf{p}} = (p_x, p_y)$ is the momentum operator, v_F the Fermi velocity $v_F \approx 1 \times 10^6$ m/s, U is an external potential and mv_F^2 represents a non-zero effective mass-like term and may arise from spin-orbit interaction. Equation (1) acts on the states represented by the two-component spinors $\Psi = [\psi_A, \psi_B]^T$, where ψ_A and ψ_B represent the envelope functions associated with the probability amplitudes at two sublattice sites of the graphene structure. For a circularly symmetric potential with $m = 0$, the solutions inside the potential well match free-particle solutions outside, therefore ruling out bound states. This can be understood as a manifestation of a relativistic tunnelling effect first discussed by Klein [4]. However, it was recently demonstrated [5] that, for a 1D potential, a finite value of the momentum parallel to the potential barrier can suppress this tunnelling and thus allow the confinement of electrons. Let us consider the 1D square-well potential $U(x) = U_0 \theta(|x| - L/2)$, $U_0 > 0$. We look for solutions in the form $\psi_C(x,y) = \phi_C(x)e^{ik_y y}$, C=A, B, and obtain for ϕ_A,

$$\frac{d^2\phi_A}{d\xi^2} + \frac{u'}{(\varepsilon - u + \Delta)}\frac{d\phi_A}{d\xi}$$
$$- \left[\beta^2 + \beta\frac{u'}{(\varepsilon - u + \Delta)} - (\varepsilon - u)^2 + \Delta^2\right]\phi_A = 0 \quad (2)$$

where $\xi = x/L$, $\beta = k_y L$, $\varepsilon = EL/\hbar v_F$, $u = U(x)L/\hbar v_F$, $\Delta = mv_F L/\hbar$ (for graphene $\hbar v_F = 0.539$ eV nm) and u' is the derivative of the potential. The character of the solutions depends on the value of β, which determines the sign of the last term on the left side of Eq. (2). The solutions are of three types: (i) traveling waves, (ii) standing waves, which for massless fermions arise only from finite values of β above an energy-dependent cut-off and decay exponentially in the barrier regions; (iii) tunneling waves, which are oscillatory outside the well whereas inside it they are combinations of exponentials with real exponents.

RESULTS

In this work we focus on type (ii) solutions which describe electron states confined across the well and propagating along it. Their energies are in the region delimited by the curves $E = (\hbar v_F k_y^2 + m^2 v_F^4)^{1/2} + U_0$ and $E = (\hbar v_F k_y^2 + m^2 v_F^4)^{1/2}$. At smaller wavevectors, tunneling across the barriers introduces a cut-off in the spectrum for $E < -(\hbar v_F k_y^2 + m^2 v_F^4)^{1/2} + U_0$. For confined-states, the spinor components decay exponentially in the region $\xi < -1/2$. Requiring the continuity of ϕ_A and ϕ_B at $\xi = -1/2$ and $\xi = 1/2$ we obtain the spectrum as a solution of a transcendental equation. Numerical results are shown in Fig. 1 for $U_0 = 50$ meV, $L = 200$ nm, and $\Delta = 0$. The dashed lines delimit the continuum region, which corresponds to free-electrons ($E \geq \hbar k_y + U_0$) with energies greater than the barrier height, and free-

CP893, *Physics of Semiconductors, 28th International Conference*
edited by W. Jantsch and F. Schäffler
© 2007 American Institute of Physics 978-0-7354-0397-0/07/$23.00

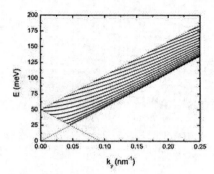

FIGURE 1. Spectrum of confined states in a graphene QW with $L = 200$ nm, $mv_F^2 = 0$ and $U_0 = 50$ meV.

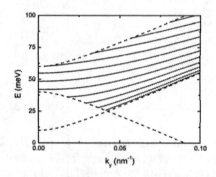

FIGURE 2. Spectrum of confined states in a graphene QW with $L = 200$ nm, $mv_F^2 = 10$ meV and $U_0 = 50$ meV.

holes ($E \leq -\hbar v_F k_y + U_0$) The cut-off at low wavevectors thus arises due to the conversion of confined electrons to free holes. For large values of k_y the dispersion branches are given approximately by $E = \hbar v_F[(n\pi/L)^2 + k_y^2]^{1/2}$, where n is an integer. Figure 2 shows the effect of the mass, with $mv_F^2 = 10$ meV. The dashed lines again represent the limits of the free-particle continua. In this case, confined states are allowed, for $k_y = 0$, in the range $u_0 - \Delta < \varepsilon < u_0 + \Delta$. This energy range broadens as k_y increases and remains constant for $k_y > (u_0^2/4 - \Delta^2)^{1/2}$.

We also calculated the transmission coefficient of electrons incident on a square well, which is found to depend on the direction of propagation and displays an oscillatory behavior. For a significant range of incident angles T is always equal to 1. This includes the case of nearly normal incidence, $k_y \approx 0$, and is in sharp contrast with the non-relativistic case in which T exhibits periodic maxima equal to 1 as a function of k_x. A similar direction-dependent transmission through graphene barriers was reported recently [6]. Figure 3 shows T plotted versus the angle of incidence $\theta = \arctan(k_y/k_x)$, for different

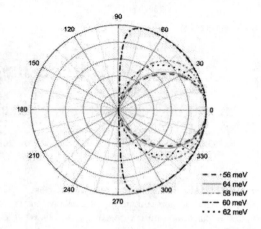

56 meV
64 meV
58 meV
60 meV
62 meV

FIGURE 3. Transmission probability for electrons incident on a graphene QW, with $L = 200$ nm and $U_0 = 50$ meV.

electron energies as indicated. The QW parameters are $L = 200$ and $U_0 = 50$ meV. For $\theta \approx 0$, we have $T \approx 1$. As seen, T oscillates with the energy due to the resonance effect caused by the confined states.

In summary, we showed that it is possible to confine massless carriers by means of electrostatic potentials, due to the wavevector-dependent suppression of the electron-hole conversion at the potential barriers. We obtained the spectrum of confined electrons in graphene quantum wires (QW) as a function of the y component of the wavevector. The results show a dependence of the eigenvalues on k_y with a cut-off at low wavevectors. There is also a wavevector dependence of the number of confined states due to the electron-hole conversion at the continuum edges. This is further demonstrated by the directional dependence of the transmission shown in Figs. 2 and 3.

This work was supported by the Brazilian Council for Research (CNPq), the Flemish Science Foundation (FWO-Vl), the Belgian Science Policy (IUAP) and the Candian NSERC Grant No. OGP0121756.

REFERENCES

1. K. S. Novoselov *et al.*, Nature **438**, 197 (2005).
2. Y. Zheng and T. Ando, Phys. Rev. B **65**, 245420 (2002).
3. Y. Zhang, J. P. Small, M. E. S. Amori and P. Kim, Phys. Rev. Lett. **94**, 176803 (2005).
4. O. Klein, Z. Phys. **53**, 157 (1929).
5. J. Milton Pereira Jr., V. Mlinar, F. M. Peeters and P. Vasilopoulos, Phys. Rev. B (unpublished).
6. M. I. Kattsnelson *et al.*, (cond-mat/0604323); V. V. Cheianov and V. Falko (cond-mat/0603624).

Momentum effects on focusing in one-dimensional systems

K. Kishen, A. C. Graham, M. Pepper, I. Farrer, D. A. Ritchie and G. A. C. Jones

Cavendish Laboratory, University of Cambridge, J. J. Thomson Avenue, Cambridge, CB3 0HE, UK

Abstract. We present a study of the effect of a dc source-drain bias on the transverse electron focusing spectrum of two parallel quantum wires (QWs) at conductances less than $2e^2/h$. Focusing spectra exhibit peaks periodic in field. Application of a source-drain bias lifts momentum degeneracy in the 1D channel and reveals additional features at low conductances. We observe a change in the position of focusing peaks as the emitter conductance is increased through the high bias features. It is demonstrated that there is a shift in electron momentum direction directly caused by population of the 1D subband responsible for the low conductance feature in the emitter.

Keywords: semiconductors, electron transport, electron focusing, 1D quantization
PACS: 73.23.Ad

INTRODUCTION

In transverse electron focusing (TEF), current is passed through the emitter QW and voltage measured across the collector QW. Peaks in the spectrum as a function of perpendicular magnetic field $B_\perp$ have been well understood in terms of the classical electron cyclotron orbits [1]. The nth peak is at nB_f where $E_{foc} = (er_cB_f)^2/2m^*$ (Fig. 1(a). E_{foc} is the electron energy and r_c the cyclotron radius. The effect of applying a dc bias V_{dc} across the emitter has been studied [2]. Here we study the effect of observed low conductance structure [3] on TEF spectra. We see a shift in peak position which we attribute to a change in the quantized electron momentum direction.

SAMPLE AND MEASUREMENT

The device was fabricated on a GaAs/AlGaAs heterostructure with the 2DEG 100nm below the surface. Carrier density and mobility were assessed as 1.2×10^{11} cm^{-2} and 1.4×10^6 cm^{2}V^{-1}s^{-1} at 1.5 K. Non-magnetic AuGe Ohmic contacts were used. TiAu gates were defined using electron-beam lithography. The schematic device layout is shown in Fig. 1(b). The lithographic width of the QWs was 0.3μm and the separation between their centres L was 2.3μm. Dc bias spectroscopy [3] gave a subband spacing of ~ 2meV. The spacing between the large top gate and those defining the QWs was 0.15μm.

Measurements were performed using standard lock-in techniques (see ref. [2] for details). A bias V_{dc} was applied across the emitter in addition to the small ac voltage for measurement. The ac source-drain current I_{SD} was measured concurrently with V_{AB} across the collector. Negative V_{dc} were used to focus hot electrons from emitter into collector.

For better comparison of different TEF spectra, I_{SD}

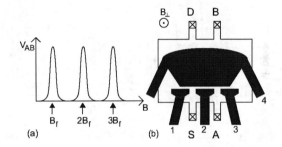

FIGURE 1. (a) Example of a TEF spectrum. (b) Schematic diagram of the device. Ohmic contacts are S and D for source and drain of emitter, A and B across collector. Gates are labelled 1 - 4 as shown. V_i is voltage applied to gate i.

was adjusted to be the same for all measurements. The gate voltages V_2, V_3 and V_4 were fixed at -0.8V, -0.59V and +0.1V respectively whilst V_1 was varied to change the conductance setting of the emitter. V_3 set the conductance of the collector to $2e^2/h$ and V_4 gave a good contrast between peaks from electron paths under gate 4 and those not. All basic data characteristics were reproducible after thermal cycling.

RESULTS AND DISCUSSION

Evolution of the low conductance feature with V_{dc} is shown in Fig. 2(a). The "dc structure" has G_{1-2} less than the expected half-plateau conductance of $0.5(2e^2/h)$ and is not well understood. Recent studies suggest it is due to spontaneous spin polarization of the lowest subband in a high dc bias [4]. We have studied the effect of this feature on the TEF spectra. Fig. 2(b) shows the TEF peak position moving to higher B with increasing G at high V_{dc}, with the majority of the shift taking place on or below the dc structure. For constant carrier density, this

CP893, *Physics of Semiconductors, 28th International Conference*
edited by W. Jantsch and F. Schäffler
© 2007 American Institute of Physics 978-0-7354-0397-0/07/$23.00

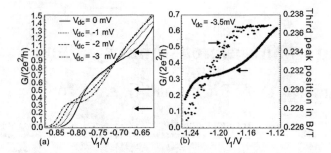

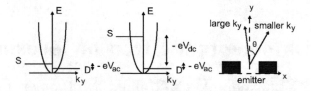

FIGURE 2. (a) Conductance of the emitter QW G_{1-2} as a function of dc source-drain bias at low conductances (arrows indicate values of G_{1-2} used for TEF in Fig. 3, (b) B of third TEF peak and G_{1-2} as a function of V_1 at high dc bias.

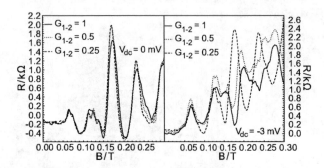

FIGURE 3. TEF spectra for three different conductance settings of the emitter, $V_{dc} = 0$ mV (left) and $V_{dc} = -3$ mV (right), G_{1-2} in units of $2e^2/h$.

shift must be caused by a change either in electron energy or momentum direction on exiting the emitter QW.

The rising background seen in the -3 mV spectra of Fig. 3 is not significant as this is eliminated by performing a three-terminal current measurement. We can again see the shift in peak position above and below the dc structure. We also observe a clear difference in the smaller features of the peaks. We attribute these extra features and the suppression of the first two peaks to scattering from electrons when under gate 4. The feature shapes then can only change when the electron path through the 2DEG is altered. Interestingly, there is little change in the $0.25(2e^2/h)$ spectra with dc bias compared to the dramatic alteration at higher G.

From this evidence we attribute the shift in peak position of Fig. 2(b) to a change in momentum direction of electrons from the emitter with increasing G. Electrons at the source chemical potential μ_S (See Fig. 4) are collected. At high V_{dc}, their forward momentum k_y is large and so we see this shift. Below the dc structure we expect little change with increasing bias as at all times the bottom of the 1D subband is just at μ_S. In a quantized ballistic system [5] the total momentum is fixed and as k_y increases, the QW ejection angle parallel to the QW,

FIGURE 4. TEF is of electrons at μ_S - in a high dc bias exiting electrons have a greater k_y, therefore smaller θ.

TABLE 1. Variation in θ with V_{dc} from r_c, accounting for bias drop across S - note increase in $\theta_{0.25} - \theta_1$ with bias.

V_{dc}/ mV	$\theta_1/°$	$\theta_{0.5}/°$	$\theta_{0.25}/°$	$(\theta_{0.25} - \theta_1)/°$
0	11.6	16.8	17.9	6.3
-1	11.1	19.4	21.2	10.1
-2	10.5	17.4	25.7	15.2
-3	0.0	14.7	27.4	27.4

θ, becomes smaller. Using the method in [2], E_{foc} is calculated for each V_{dc}. We then approximate the angular variation by calculating r_c for each B_f (see Table 1).

CONCLUSIONS

Investigation of TEF in dc bias has shown a change in peak position and characteristics which can be attributed to a change in k_y due to momentum quantization in the 1D subband. We estimate a variation in the angle of less than 28° at the highest dc bias measured.

ACKNOWLEDGMENTS

The authors acknowledge assistance from David Anderson in device fabrication. Funding was provided by EPSRC. ACG acknowledges financial support from Emmanuel College, Cambridge.

REFERENCES

1. H. van Houten, C. W. J. Beenakker, J. G. Williamson, M. E. I. Broekaart, P. H. M. van Loosdrecht, B. J. van Wees, J. E. Mooji, C. T. Foxon, and J. J. Harris, *Phys. Rev. B* **39**, 8556 (1989).
2. J. G. Williamson, H. van Houten, C. W. J. Beenakker, M. E. I. Broekaart, L. I. A. Spendler, B. J. van Wees, and C. T. Foxon, *Surf. Sci.* **229**, 303 (1990).
3. N. K. Patel, J. T. Nicholls, L. Martín-Moreno, M. Pepper, J. E. F. Frost, D. A. Ritchie, and G. A. C. Jones, *Phys. Rev. B* **44**, 13549 (1991).
4. A. C. Graham, M. Pepper, M. Y. Simmons, and D. A. Ritchie, New interaction effects in quantum point contacts at high magnetic fields (to be published in Physica E).
5. T. Ueta, *J. Phys. Soc. Jpn.* **64**, 4813 (1995).

Transport Spectroscopy Of In-Plane Dual Electron Waveguides

Jean-Laurent Deborde*, Saskia F. Fischer*, Ulrich Kunze*, Dirk Reuter† and
Andreas D. Wieck†

*Werkstoffe und Nanoelektronik, Ruhr-Universität Bochum, D-44780 Bochum, Germany
†Angewandte Festkörperphysik, Ruhr-Universität Bochum, D-44780 Bochum, Germany

Abstract. Lateral tunneling spectroscopy between two one-dimensional (1D) electron waveguides (EWGs) in a GaAs/AlGaAs heterostructure is accomplished by preparing a thin barrier using atomic force microscope lithography. The barrier transmission and the 1D mode occupation in the EWGs are controlled by a top-gate. Both 1D wires exhibits quantized conductance at 4.2K. At top-gate voltages larger than the tunneling onset, the tunneling conductance as a function of the tunneling bias shows oscillations reflecting the density of states of the dual EWGs.

Keywords: electron waveguide, tunnel coupling, GaAs/AlGaAs heterostructure, atomic force microscope lithography
PACS: 73.21.Hb, 73.23.-b, 73.40.Gk, 73.6.Ey

Tunnel coupling between low-dimensional electron systems is of great interest for implementation of functional nanoelectronic devices such as directional couplers [1]. Considerable effort has been spent on tunneling transport between vertically stacked one-dimensional (1D) electron waveguides (EWGs) [2, 3]. In the present work we study *laterally* coupled dual EWGs.

Gate-voltage controlled in-plane tunneling structures can be prepared by means of atomic force microscope (AFM) lithography [4, 5]. Here we apply the same lithography technique to separate the in-plane dual EWGs by a tunnel barrier. The sample was processed on a GaAs/Al$_{0.35}$Ga$_{0.65}$As heterostructure containing a 2DEG buried 55 nm underneath the surface. At 4.2 K, the electron density and mobility in the dark are 4.1×10^{11} cm^{-2} and 1.1×10^6 cm^2/Vs respectively. A mesa structure and remote side gates are defined by means of electron beam lithography and wet etching [7]. Using the vibrating tip of an AFM, a furrow is dynamically ploughed into a 7 nm thick polymer resist layer previously deposited on the surface of the sample [6]. Wet etching transfers the line pattern resulting in a nanoscale groove ($\approx$ 25 nm deep, 88 nm wide on top) which creates a narrow potential barrier between the two adjacent 400 nm long EWGs. As shown by Fig. 1 the two EWGs have different widths of 65 nm (left wire) and 95 nm (right wire) which lead to different lateral confinements. Finally, alloyed Au-Ge-Ni ohmic contacts are formed and a 35 nm thick Au-Schottky gate is deposited on top of the device in order to control the transmission through the barrier as well as the 1D mode occupation in both quantum wires.

Using the standard lock-in technique, the two-terminal differential drain conductance $g_D = dI_D/dV_D$ of each

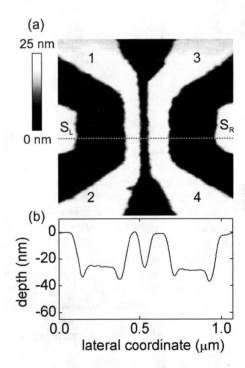

FIGURE 1. (a) Atomic force micrograph of the inner part of the 1D-1D tunneling device. Dark areas represent etched regions where the electron gas underneath is depleted. The numbers 1 to 4 denote the ohmic contacts for the left (1-2) and the right (3-4) wires, S_L and S_R refer to the left and right side gates respectively. (b) Cross section of the structure along the grey dashed line in (a).

waveguide (contacts 1-2 and 3-4) is measured as a function of the top-gate voltage V_G at a 433 Hz ac drain voltage of $\tilde{V}_D = 0.1$mV, as well as the tunnel conduc-

CP893, *Physics of Semiconductors, 28th International Conference*
edited by W. Jantsch and F. Schäffler
© 2007 American Institute of Physics 978-0-7354-0397-0/07/$23.00

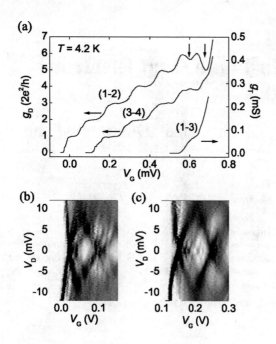

(a)

(b)   (c)

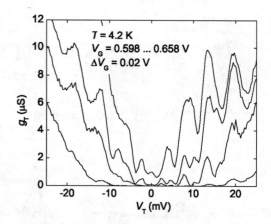

FIGURE 3. Tunneling conductance g_T vs. bias voltage V_T for different gate voltages $V_G \geq 0.55$V.

FIGURE 2. (a) Differential conductance of the two 1D waveguides (contacts 1-2 and 3-4) and through the barrier (1-3). A series resistance of about 800Ω was corrected. (b)-(c) Grey scale plots of the transconductance of the left (b) and the right (c) 1D waveguides.

tance $g_T = dI_T/dV_T$ (contacts 1-3) across the potential barrier (Fig. 2 (a)). Both EWGs exhibit a conductance quantized in units of $2e^2/h$. Each conductance step corresponds to the opening of a new 1D propagation mode in a waveguide. As expected a larger threshold voltage is observed for the narrower wire because of its stronger confining potential. The measured tunneling conductance g_T reflects the transmission through the potential barrier. The tunnel transmission increases while tuning V_G more positively. Additionally the 1D mode occupation in the EWGs is simultaneously changed. The opening of the tunnel barrier from $V_G = 0.55$V coincides with significant losses in the conductance of the wider wire (vertical arrows on Fig. 2 (a)) which might reflect the effect of the tunnel leakage.

The transconductance of each EWG is measured under applied dc source-drain voltage $dg_D = d(dI_D/dV_D)/dV_G$, and thus the energy separation between the lowest 1D subbands is determined. Subband spacings of $\Delta E_{1,2} = 8 \pm 0.5$meV for the wide wire (Fig. 2 (b)) and $\Delta E_{1,2} = 10 \pm 0.5$meV for the narrow wire (Fig. 2 (c)) are found.

The tunneling spectroscopy is performed by measuring g_T at 4.2K with a modulation voltage $\tilde{V}_T = 0.7$mV imposed upon V_T. Figure 3 shows a series of tunneling

spectra for different V_G. Conductance oscillations appear for top-gate voltages larger than the transmission threshold $V_G \geq 0.55$V. They correspond to electrons tunneling between the EWGs and map the density of states of the coupled 1D electron systems. At positive V_T, the electrons tunnel through the potential barrier from the narrow wire into empty 1D energy states above the Fermi level of the wide wire, and oppositely when the polarity is changed. Furthermore the oscillation period measured for large top-gate bias, $V_G \geq 0.658$V, corresponds to an energy interval of $\Delta E = 5.5 \pm 0.5$meV which is the same order of magnitude than the subband energy separations found in each EWG.

The amplitude of the oscillations increases with increasing V_G because the effective tunneling barrier height is decreased. Additionally, the periodicity of the tunneling oscillations also depends on the top-gate voltage and might reflect 1D mode coupling effects between the two electron waveguides. Further experimental efforts are expected in order to answer in detail this issue.

This work was supported by the Bundesministerium für Bildung und Forschung (BMBF) under Grant No 01BM454.

REFERENCES

1. J. A. del Alamo, C. C. Eugster *et al.*, Appl. Phys. Lett. **56**, 78 (1989).
2. S. F. Fischer *et al.*, Nature Physics **2**, 91-96 (2006).
3. E.Bielejec *et al.*, Appl. Phys. Lett. **86**, 0831011 (2005).
4. J.-L. Deborde *et al.*, AIP **772** (Part A), 437 (2005).
5. J.-L. Deborde *et al.*, Physica E in press 2006.
6. U. Kunze, Superlatt. Microstruct. **31**, 3 (2002).
7. M. Knop *et al.*, Semicond. Sci. Technol. 20, 814 (2005).

First-principles Theory of Inelastic Transport and Local Heating in Atomic Gold Wires

Thomas Frederiksen, Magnus Paulsson, Mads Brandbyge and Antti-Pekka Jauho

*MIC – Department of Micro and Nanotechnology, NanoDTU, Technical University of Denmark,
Ørsteds Plads, Bldg. 345E, DK-2800 Lyngby, Denmark*

Abstract. We present theoretical calculations of the inelastic transport properties in atomic gold wires. Our method is based on a combination of density functional theory and non-equilibrium Green's functions. The vibrational spectra for extensive series of wire geometries have been calculated using SIESTA, and the corresponding effects in the conductance are analyzed. In particular, we focus on the heating of the active vibrational modes. By a detailed comparison with experiments we are able to estimate an order of magnitude for the external damping of the active vibrations.

Keywords: Inelastic scattering, atomic wires, local heating, density functional theory, non-equilibrium Green's functions
PACS: 63.22.+m, 71.15.-m, 73.21.Hb, 73.23.-b.

Inelastic effects in electron transport through nano-sized devices are currently under intense investigation [1, 2]. This research area is partly fueled by the potential of molecular electronics—where a detailed understanding of energy dissipation and device stability will be crucial—but attracts also much attention because fundamental quantum phenomena can be explored.

Accordingly we have developed methods which combine density-functional theory (DFT) and non-equilibrium Green's functions (NEGF) to model the conductance of atomic-scale junctions. This scheme involves the calculation of (i) relaxed geometries, (ii) vibrational frequencies, (iii) electron-phonon couplings, and (iv) the inelastic current-voltage characteristics [3].

To benchmark our methods we have applied the procedure to model the inelastic effects in atomic gold wires for which high quality experimental data are available for comparison [4]. We have studied comprehensive series of wire geometries containing 3 to 7 atoms under various electrode separations, hereby extending our previously reported results [5]. Here we will focus on the physical signatures of the heating of the wire as an electronic current is passing through the wire.

To determine the detailed geometries we consider periodic supercell representations of the wires, as shown in Fig. 1, and use the SIESTA DFT package [6] to relax the wire, the contacts, and the first surface layers. The calculation of the vibrations is performed by diagonalization of the dynamical matrix extracted from finite differences. As the active atoms we consider the wire and the pyramidal bases. The corresponding vibrational frequencies are plotted in Fig. 2. They lie in a range up to around 20 meV and—in agreement with the experiments—exhibit a mode softening upon elongation (related to bond weakening with increased interatomic distance).

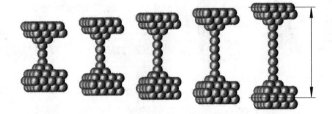

FIGURE 1. (Color online) Geometry setup for the modeling of 3- to 7-atom long gold wires. The electrode separation L is measured between the second-topmost Au(100) surface layers.

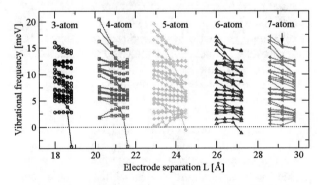

FIGURE 2. (Color online) Vibrational frequencies calculated for the different wires under varying electrode separation. Negative values represent imaginary frequencies implying the breaking of an unstable wire.

The transport calculation uses infinite electrodes according to the TRANSIESTA scheme [7], and the inelastic conductance is calculated to lowest order in the electron-phonon couplings as described in Ref. [3, 8]. The heating of the vibrational modes as a result of interaction with the electronic current is addressed with a rate equation for

CP893, *Physics of Semiconductors, 28th International Conference*
edited by W. Jantsch and F. Schäffler
© 2007 American Institute of Physics 978-0-7354-0397-0/07/$23.00

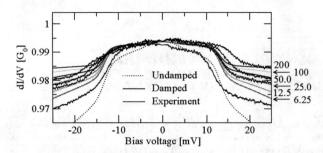

FIGURE 3. (Color online) Inelastic differential conductance dI/dV versus bias voltage. The black noisy curves are the experimental data from Ref. [4] measured on a wire (about seven atoms long) under different states of strain. The colored smooth curves are our theoretical calculations for a 7-atom long wire with different settings for the external damping γ_{damp} (the values are indicated to the right of the graph in units of μeV/$\hbar$). The dotted curve corresponds to no external damping. The temperature in both experiment and theory is $T = 4.2$ K.

the average population $\langle n_\lambda \rangle$ of mode λ. Under steady-state conditions we thus seek the solution to

$$\langle \dot{n}_\lambda \rangle = \frac{p_\lambda}{\hbar \omega_\lambda} + \gamma_{\mathrm{damp}}^\lambda [n_B(\hbar \omega_\lambda) - \langle n_\lambda \rangle] = 0, \quad (1)$$

where p_λ is the net power delivered by scattering electrons to the vibrational mode λ with frequency ω_λ (including both emission and absorption processes). The parameter $\gamma_{\mathrm{damp}}^\lambda$ represents the damping of the vibration, e.g., by coupling to bulk phonons. n_B is the usual Bose-Einstein distribution for the equilibrium population.

As a representative example of the calculated inelastic conductances we show in Fig. 3 our results for a 7-atom wire which has been stretched close to the point of breaking. This wire has a slight zig-zag shape. The corresponding frequencies are indicated with an arrow in Fig. 2. The experimental data obtained by Agraït et al. [4] with a cryogenic scanning tunneling microscope are also shown for direct comparison (due to a small uncertainty in the absolute value of the measured conductance we have scaled their data by less than 1% to align them with our theoretical curves). The zero-bias conductance is close to the conductance quantum $G_0 = 2e^2/h$ as expected for an atomic gold wire which has a single completely open conductance channel. At finite bias voltages a symmetric drop in the conductance of the order 1% is observed. At low temperatures this decrease is associated with the onset of vibrational excitation, and the main contribution is due to an alternating bond length mode of the wire [4, 5]. The fact that a single mode dominates can effectively be understood from momentum conservation under inelastic transitions in a one-dimensional band structure. At bias voltages beyond the vibrational onset the conductance decrease is effectively proportional to the average mode excitation $\langle n_\lambda \rangle$; the slope in the experimental conductance may thus be interpreted as voltage-induced excess mode population which in turn increases the scattering events via stimulated emission and absorption. This is the signature of the local heating of the wire.

The different theoretical curves in Fig. 3 correspond to different values of the external damping γ_{damp}. The dotted curve is the result in the *externally undamped* limit, i.e., $\gamma_{\mathrm{damp}} = 0$, where the heating is maximal. From Eq. (1) this implies that $p_\lambda = 0$ and thus that the mode population is determined by a balance between emission and absorption processes. Compared to the experimental curves, this calculation clearly overestimates the slope beyond the vibrational threshold voltage. The colored theoretical curves with a finite external damping have a closer resemblance with the experimental ones. In fact, with a damping of the order $\gamma_{\mathrm{damp}} \approx 10 - 50$ μeV/$\hbar$, the agreement with the experimental slope is very reasonable. In terms of a quality factor this corresponds to $Q = \omega_\lambda / \gamma_{\mathrm{damp}} \approx 200 - 1000$, i.e., the active vibrational mode oscillates hundreds of times before being damped out. This result is rather surprising since the vibrations localized in the wire region are resonant with the phonon modes in the bulk electrodes. However, it can be understood by realizing that the active mode is essentially localized within the wire itself (pyramids and contact atoms are hardly moving) and hence cannot couple well to the electrodes.

In summary, we have applied our first-principles methods for modeling the inelastic conductance in nanoscale junctions to the case of atomic gold wires. We presented the strain dependence of the frequency spectra of wires containing different number of atoms. As a representative example of the inelastic conductance calculations we showed the results for a 7-atom wire under various damping conditions. From a direct comparison with experimental measurements we were able to determine the order of magnitude of the vibrational damping, and hence to characterize the local heating of the wire.

The authors acknowledge many fruitful discussions with N. Agraït and N. Lorente. Computational resources were provided by the Danish Center for Scientific Computing (DCSC).

REFERENCES

1. G. Cuniberti, G. Fagas, and K. Richter, *Introducing Molecular Electronics*, Springer, 2005.
2. N. Agraït et al., *Phys. Rep.* **377**, 81–279 (2003).
3. T. Frederiksen et al., unpublished.
4. N. Agraït et al., *Phys. Rev. Lett.* **88**, 216803 (2002).
5. T. Frederiksen et al., *Phys. Rev. Lett.* **93**, 256601 (2004).
6. J. M. Soler et al., *J. Phys.: Cond. Mat.* **14**, 2745 (2002).
7. M. Brandbyge et al., *Phys. Rev. B* **65**, 165401 (2002).
8. M. Paulsson et al., *Phys. Rev. B* **72**, 201101 (2005).

One-Dimensional Conductance in Surface Gated InSb/AlInSb Quantum Well Heterostructures

J.M.S.Orr[1,2], P.D.Buckle[1], M.Fearn[1], C.J.Bartlett[1], L.Buckle[1], and T.Ashley[1]

1. QinetiQ. St Andrews Road, Malvern. Worcestershire. UK. WR143PS
2. Department of Electrical and Electronic Engineering,
University of Manchester, Sackville Street. Manchester. M60 1QD.

Abstract. Low temperature quantised conductance effects in InSb/AlInSb heterostructures are reported. The one-dimensional confinement is provided by metal Schottky split-gate structures patterned directly onto the material surface. Extremely low Schottky barrier leakage is demonstrated for these devices, in part due to the air bridge gate arrangement implemented. Up to seven quantised energy subbands are discerned in the conductance of the devices as a function of increasingly negative gate bias

Keywords: Conductance quantisation, InSb/AlInSb, QW, 2DEG.

PACS: 73.23.Ad

INTRODUCTION

InSb/AlInSb quantum well (QW) heterostructures, although challenging to grow due to significant lattice mismatch, are emerging as promising materials for uncooled, low power dissipation high speed transistors [1], for quantum devices [2], and even for novel surface acoustic wave single electron devices [3]. This material system offers the smallest electron effective mass (m*~0.014) and highest intrinsic mobility of all III-V semiconductors, as well as the largest g-factor (-51), that promises effective spin manipulation and control in future spintronic and quantum information processing devices.

The lateral confinement of a two-dimensional electron gas (2DEG) over length scales below the ballistic transport length can create a system in which charge transport takes place in only one dimension. Such a system is known as a quantum wire, or point contact, the characteristics of which were first demonstrated independently by van Wees et al [4] and Wharam et al. [5] twenty years ago in GaAs/AlGaAs structures at very low temperatures (<1K). Variable lateral confinement across a 2DEG can be achieved by defining Schottky gates onto the surface of the 2DEG material (creating so-called "soft" confinement), so that regions either side of a small conducting n-channel can be depleted by the application of a negative voltage. This method of defining conducting

regions offers considerable advantages over the use of etching and in-plane gates, such as simpler fabrication and the opportunity to create systems with a larger number of Schottky gates in complex geometries for more generic quantum transport devices [6]. Such devices can be designed to generate single or double quantum dots for example by affecting the potential so that small regions of charge in the 2DEG can be isolated from external contacts via potential barriers.

DISCUSSION

InSb/AlInSb QW material was grown by solid-source molecular beam epitaxy (MBE) on a semi-insulating GaAs substrate. In growth order, the structure consists of an accommodation layer, a 3μm $Al_xIn_{1-x}Sb$ buffer (x=0.15), a 15nm InSb quantum well, followed by a 50nm $Al_xIn_{1-x}Sb$ (x=0.20) cap with Te δ-doping (~$1x10^{12}cm^{-2}$) located 5nm above the quantum well. This forms a type I heterostructure alignment, providing confinement for both electrons and holes in the quantum well channel. Hall measurements for the material reported here have determined the mobility to be 27,500$cm^2V^{-1}s^{-1}$ (RT)/50,000$cm^2V^{-1}s^{-1}$ (77K) with a carrier concentration of 6.5x$10^{11}cm^{-2}$ (RT)/ 4.6x$10^{11}cm^{-2}$ (77K).

Quantum well split-gate devices were fabricated using optical lithography to define source and drain contacts. Electron-beam lithography was used to

CP893, *Physics of Semiconductors, 28th International Conference*
edited by W. Jantsch and F. Schäffler
© 2007 American Institute of Physics 978-0-7354-0397-0/07/$23.00

define Ti/Au Schottky split-gate structures with gate lengths of ~200nm. These devices were then isolated by wet chemical etching into mesas of widths 3-12μm. The gates are airbridge arrangements from the lead out pads to the mesa surface. The gate metal is fed in from either side of the mesa and terminates in a small gap of around 250nm in the centre of the mesa. The air-bridge strongly minimises leakage current due to material or surface conduction, by minimising surface contact to the active region. A scanning electron micrograph (fig. 1, inset) illustrates the layout of these devices. Samples were measured using a triaxial screened system using a HP4146b source-measurement unit, and immersed in a liquid helium bath cryostat. The devices created by this process are intentionally depletion mode, and consequently are designed to operate under negative gate biases. Low gate leakage (no more than a few nA) has been demonstrated in a number of devices over a significant range of gate voltages. Fig. 1 shows the gate leakage current as a function of gate bias in the range -0.8V to +0.8V at 1.6K, where the current does not exceed 1nA. This is essential for observation of quantum effects. Gate leakage for these small devices is believed to be associated with defects in the cap material and analysis is the subject of ongoing work [7]

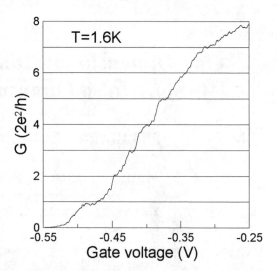

FIGURE 2. Quantised conductance in InSb/AlInSb split-gate devices at 1.6K. 100μV was applied between the source and drain contacts. Conductance was extracted from the measurement of Id. Noise observed is due to instrumentation.

Features are clearly observable at values of $2ne^2/h$ for n between 1 and 7. A small gate leakage current of the order of a few nA was detected and removed and a series resistance of 2.5kΩ has been accounted for in the production of this data.

ACKNOWLEDGMENTS

This work was supported by the UK MoD, under output 4 of E.S domain.

REFERENCES

1. T. Ashley, et al. Proc. 7th Int. Conf. Solid State and Integrated Circuit Tech. 2253. (2004)
2. Goel, N., Graham, J., Keay, J. C., Suzuki, K., Miyashita, S., Santos, M. B., Hirayama, Y. Physica E. 26 pp.455-459 (2005)
3. Smith, S.J., Nash, G.R., Bartlett, C.J., Buckle, L., Emeny, M.T., Ashley, T. Accepted in App Phys Lett.
4. Van Wees, B. J., van Houten, H., Beenakker, C. W. J., Williamson, J. G., Kouwenhoven, L. P.,van der Marel, D. Phys. Rev. Lett. 60 9 (1988)
5. Wharam D. A., Thornton, T. J., Newbury, R., Pepper, M., Ahmed, H., Frost, J. E. F., Hasko, D.G., Peacock, D. C., Ritchie, D. A., Jones, G. A. C. J. Phys. C: Solid State Phys. 21 (1988)
6. R. Hanson, L. H. Willems van Beveren, I. T. Vink, J. M. Elzerman, W. J. M. Naber, F. H. L. Koppens, L. P. Kouwenhoven, L. M. K. Vandersypen. Phys. Rev. Lett. 94, 196802 (2005)
7. J.M.S.Orr, P.D.Buckle, M.Fearn, P.J.Wilding, C.J.Bartlett, M.T.Emeny, L.Buckle, T.Ashley. Accepted for publication in Semi Sci Tech.

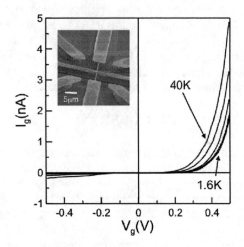

FIGURE 1. Gate leakage current (<1nA) over a significant range of gate voltages (-0.8V to +0.8V) for a split-gate Schottky contact on InSb/AlInSb 2DEG material at 1.6K. Inset: SEM image of a typical split-gate device.

Fig. 2 shows the conductance of an InSb/AlInSb split-gate quantum device as a function of gate bias, driven towards pinch off. A constant voltage of 100μV was applied between the source and drain contacts, while the gate bias was swept from -0.2V to -0.6V at 1.6K in the absence of a magnetic field.

LOW-FREQUENCY NOISE PROPERTIES OF GaN NANOWIRES

L. C. Li*, K. H. Huang*, Y. W. Suen[1]*, W. H. Hsieh†, C. D. Chen†, M. W. Lee* and C. C. Chen**

*Department of Physics, National Chung Hsing University, Taichung, Taiwan, R.O.C.
†Institute of Physics, Academia Sinica, Nankang, Taipei, Taiwan, R.O.C.
**Department of Chemistry, National Taiwan Normal University, Taipei, Taiwan, R.O.C.

Abstract. We report the temperature (T) dependance (77K to 300K) of the low-frequency electric noise of GaN nanowires. Our results show that these GaN nanowires exhibit the $1/f$-like excess noise. A Lorentzian-like feature is observed embedded in the $1/f$ noise when the applied bias current is large enough. Our four-wire measurement results reveal that the characteristic time τ_L of the Lorentzian-like noise of the nanowire decreases with T.

Keywords: nanowire, $1/f$ noise, Lorentzian noise, GaN
PACS: 72.70.+m,73.23.-b

According to the Hooge's phenomenological equation,[1] the excess $1/f$ noise follows $S_V = AV^2/f^\alpha$, where A is the noise amplitude, and α is a constant. The $1/f$ excess noise of the carbon nanotubes has been observed and investigated at room temperature. For single-wall carbon nanotubes, $\alpha = 1 \sim 1.1$ and $A = 1.0 \times 10^{-11}R^{0.99}$.[2] For multi-wall nanotubes, $\alpha = 0.96 \sim 1.14$ for individual multiwalled carbon nanotnbes and $\alpha = 1.49 \sim 1.63$ for two crossing multi-walled carbon nanotubes.[3] In this work, we found that the GaN nanowires also exhibit the $1/f$-like excess noise besides the thermal noise, and the corner frequency f_c (the cross-over frequency of $1/f$ noise and white thermal noise) of our samples is more than one order of magnitude lower than those of the carbon nanotubes of similar resistance at the same bias current. Furthermore, a Lorentzian-like noise spectrum, which emerged from the $1/f$ noise background at reduced temperatures, can also be observed at room temperature (RT) if the applied bias current is large enough.

The GaN nanowires are grown by the Vapor-Liquid-Solid (VLS) method.[4] The diameter of the nanowires is ranging from several 50nm to 150nm. Several 300-400 nm-wide Al electrodes to the nanowires are defined by the e-beam lithography. The typical two-wire resistance of the samples ranges from few kΩ to hundreds of kΩ.

We use a balanced circuit to measure the noise of a GaN nanowire. A battery bank provides the biasing voltage source and connects to a pair of resistors in series with the sample. The loading effect of the series resis-

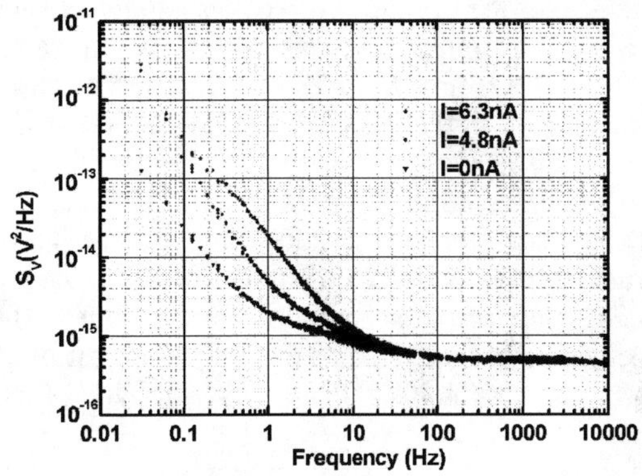

FIGURE 1. The 2-wire power spectrum density of GaN nanowire with different bias current I at room temperature. The sample shows a clear Lorentzian-like excess noise at I=6nA. The characteristic time τ_L is 0.13s.

tors to the spectrum is carefully calibrated. In a direct fast Fourier-transform Spectrum(FFT) measurement, the amplified signal from the sample is fed into the FFT dynamic signal analyzer, SR780.[5] We measure the two-wire and four-wire power spectral density (PSD) of the nanowires from 0.01Hz to 10kHz. The sample is in a vacuum-loaded open-cycle cryogenic system with a temperature controlling system. Linearity of all contacts is carefully checked.

From our data collected from different samples and I, $\alpha = 1.04 \pm 0.07$ in average, and A is ranging from 8×10^{-8} to 2×10^{-6}. We also notice that A keeps at about the same value for each individual sample at different I.

---

[1] corresponding auther:ysuen@phys.nchu.edu.tw

CP893, *Physics of Semiconductors, 28th International Conference*
edited by W. Jantsch and F. Schäffler

The corner frequency f_c roughly increases linearly with I^2.

Figure 1 shows the two-wire PSD of the sample with a 2-wire resistance 23kΩ at RT. Clearly a Lorentzian-like noise appears for I=6nA. Usually, the PSD of a Lorentzian-like noise can be written as $S_v(f) = S_v(0)/[1 + (f/f_0)^2]$, where the magnitude $S_v(0)$ is related to the number of carriers or specific type of defects and $f_0 = 1/2\pi\tau_L$.[6] In this case, the characteristic time τ_L is 0.13s, and f_0=1.25Hz at RT. When T is below 288K, the Lorentzian-like feature disappears. As T is lower than 200K, the Lorentzian-like noise is observed again. From 200K to 140K, τ_L becomes smaller as T decreases. At 140K, τ_L=0.0067s, which is much smaller than the RT value. Most samples exhibit similar behavior in two-wire PSD measurement in this T range. For T decreasing further below 130K, conversely τ_L becomes larger as T decreases. At 77 K, τ_L roughly has the same values as that at 273 K. Apparently, there are different types of noise source yielding different T-dependence.

The Lorentzian-like noise appears in the four-wire measurement as well, indicating that the GaN nanowire itself generates the Lorentzian-like noise. Figure 2 shows the PSD of a four-wire measurement for a sample with R_{4W}=230Ω, and R_{2W}=1.2kΩ. The resistances of the two voltage probes are 3.1kΩ and 14.1kΩ respectively. The insets are the extracted Lorentzian-like noise and fitting lines after subtracting the $1/f$ and thermal noise background. At 230K, the Lorentzian-like spectrum f_0=1.6Hz (τ_L=0.067s). At 303K, f_0=2.37Hz (τ_L=0.102s). τ_L of the nanowire decreases with T. This T-dependence strongly indicates that the origin of this Lorentzian excess noise is from a specific type of electron traps.

The tendency of $S_v(0)$ shows a very strong resistance (in either 2 or 4-wire configuration) dependence. As the resistance of the sample decreases with T, $S_v(0)$ decreases with T. The value of $S_v(0)$ is from 8×10^{-14} to 9×10^{-16} V^2/Hz.

We investigate both the $1/f$ and the Lorentzian-like excess noise of GaN nanowires in two-wire and four-wire measurements. In the two-wire measurement, the contact of the nanowires plays an essential role in contributing the Lorentzian-like noise. The characteristic time usually increases with the temperature at high T. We believe that the impact-ionization like mechanism dominates in the contact region. From the results of the four-wire measurement, the GaN nanowire does exhibit excess Lorentzian-like noise when the bias current is large enough. The T-dependence of τ_L shows that the Lorentzian-like noise of the nanowires is from a thermal-emission process of electrons in a specific type of energy traps. The Lorentzian-like noise from the contact region between the metal electrode and the nanowire is much more complicated and further investigation is needed.

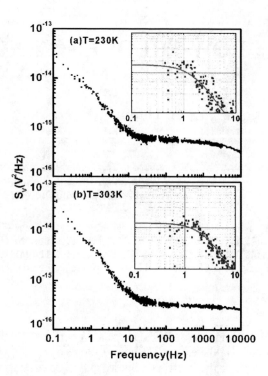

FIGURE 2. The sample exhibits the Lorentzian-like noise in the four-wire measurement. (a)$f_0 = 1.6$Hz at 230K.(b)$f_0 = 2.37$Hz at 303K. The insets are the Lorentzian-like noise and the fitting lines after subtracting the $1/f$ and thermal noise background

ACKNOWLEDGMENTS

This work is supported by the National Science Council of the Republic of China under Contract No.NSC 94-2112-M-005-011.

REFERENCES

1. P. Dutta and P. M. Horn, *Rev. Mod. Phys.*, **53**, 497–516, (1981).
2. P. G. Collins, M. S. Fuhrer, and A. Zettl, *Appl. Phys. Lett.*, **76**, 894–896, (2000).
3. H. Ouacha, M. Willander, H. Y. Yu, Y. W. Park, M. S. Kabir, S. H. Magnus Persson, L. B. Kish, and A. Ouacha, *Appl. Phys. Lett.*, **80**, 1055–1057, (2002).
4. C.C.Chen, C.C.Yeh, C.H.Chen, M.Y.Yu, H.L.Liu, J.J.Wu, K.H.Chen, J.Y.Peng, and Y.F.Chen, *J. Am. Chem. Soc.*, **123**, 2791-2905, (2001).
5. Stanford Research Systems Inc., 1290-D Reamwood Avenue, Sunnyvale, CA 94089, U.S.A.
6. Sh. Kogan,*Electronic noise and fluctuations in solids*, Cambridge university press, Cambridge, 1996.

Quantized Conductance without the Reservoir Picture

Bart Sorée* and Wim Magnus[†]

*IMEC, Kapeldreef 75, B-3001 Leuven, Belgium
[†]IMEC, Kapeldreef 75, B-3001 Leuven, Belgium
Universiteit Antwerpen, Groenenborgerlaan 171, B-2020 Antwerpen, Belgium

Abstract. We derive a set of quantum kinetic equations based on quantum mechanical balance equations. The quantum kinetic equations are solved self-consistently together with Poisson's equation. We show that these kinetic equations can be used to rederive the Landauer formula for the conductance of a quantum point contact, without any reference to reservoirs at different chemical potentials. Instead, energy dissipation is taken into account explicitly through the electron-phonon interaction. We find that both elastic and inelastic scattering are necessary to obtain the Landauer conductance.

Keywords: Landauer Formula, Quantum Transport
PACS: 72.10.d-, 72.10.Bg

INTRODUCTION

The classic derivation of the Landauer-Büttiker formula for conductance is based upon dissipationless (coherent) transmission of electrons from left to right reservoir where it is assumed that both reservoirs are at different chemical potentials. Moreover it is assumed that all the energy dissipation takes place deep in the reservoirs. This classic derivation thus excludes any energy dissipation (phonon scattering) in the wire connected to the leads. A consistent derivation based upon a set of quantum kinetic equations that include all relevant (dissipative) interactions in the channel and the reservoirs also yields the Landauer formula for the conductance of a one-channel quantum point contact. Finally, a connection is made between our approach and the method of M.P. Das and F. Green [4].

NONEQUILIBRIUM STATISTICAL OPERATOR

The expectation value of an arbitrary Hermitian operator $\hat{X}$ at time t for a quantum statistical ensemble in non-equilibrium is given by $\langle \hat{X} \rangle(t) = \text{Tr}\left[\hat{\rho}(t)\hat{X}\right]$ where $\hat{\rho}(t)$ is the non-equilibrium statistical operator (NSO). According to Zubarev the NSO has the form [1] :

$$\hat{\rho}(t) = \frac{1}{Z(t)}\exp\left[-\sum_m \int_{-\infty}^t dt'\, \varepsilon e^{\varepsilon(t'-t)} F_m(t')\hat{P}_m(t'-t)\right] \quad (1)$$

where the F_m are intensive variabels thermodynamically conjugate to the operators $\hat{P}_m$ which correspond to observable macrovariables. The NSO satisfies the conditions $\langle \hat{P}_m \rangle(t) = \text{Tr}\langle \hat{\rho}(t)\hat{P}_m \rangle = \text{Tr}\langle \hat{\rho}_l(t)\hat{P}_m \rangle = \langle \hat{P}_m \rangle_l^t$ where

$\hat{\rho}_l(t)$ is the local-equilibrium statistical operator. Within the framework of Zubarev's approach we propose the following form for the quasi-equilibrium statistical operator :

$$\hat{\rho}_l^B(t) = \frac{1}{Z(t)}\exp\left[-\beta_e(t)(\hat{H}_e^B - \mu(t)\hat{N}) - \beta(t)\hat{H}_p\right] \quad (2)$$

where the "boosted" Hamiltonian $\hat{H}_e^B$ is given by :

$$\hat{H}_e^B = \hat{H}_{e0} + \tau(t)\int_\Omega d\mathbf{r}\,\hat{\mathbf{J}} \cdot \mathbf{E} \quad (3)$$

where $\hat{H}_{e0}$ and $\hat{\mathbf{J}}$ denote the Hamiltonian and current density operator of the unperturbed electron system and $\hat{H}_P$ refers to the free phonon bath. Eq. (2) represents a current-carrying quasi-equilibrium statistical operator due to the presence of the time-reversal breaking term in (3). It is possible to show that the generalized statistical operator can also be derived from the principle of maximum entropy under the constraint that it yields the correct total current $\langle \hat{I} \rangle$. In the steady-state regime where the quasi-equilibrium statistical operator becomes time-independent the integral containing the dot product of $\hat{\mathbf{J}}$ and $\mathbf{E}$ can be disentangled [7] and we obtain $\hat{H}_B = \tau \hat{I} V_\varepsilon$ where V_ε is the applied electromotive force. This corresponds to the following choice of the thermodynamic parameters $F_m = \{\beta_e, \beta_e \tau V_\varepsilon, -\beta_e \mu, \beta\}$ with corresponding operators $\hat{P}_m = \{\hat{H}_{e0}, \hat{I}, \hat{N}, \hat{H}_P\}$. The parameters $\beta_e = 1/k_B T_e$ and $\beta = 1/k_B T$, where T_e and T respectively denote the electron and lattice temperature, whereas τ represents a scattering time and μ is the chemical potential. The time-reversal breaking term $\hat{H}_B(t)$ is a measure of the average energy increase of the electron ensemble at time t due to the power supplied by the non-conservative electric field $\mathbf{E}$.

CP893, *Physics of Semiconductors, 28th International Conference*
edited by W. Jantsch and F. Schäffler
© 2007 American Institute of Physics 978-0-7354-0397-0/07/$23.00

SELF-CONSISTENT SOLUTION

We consider a system with total Hamiltonian $\hat{H} = \hat{H}_e + \hat{H}_\Phi + \hat{H}_{ep} + \hat{H}_{imp} + \hat{H}_p$ where $\hat{H}_e$ represents the total electron energy, while $\hat{H}_\Phi$ represents the interaction energy of the electrons with the electrostatic potential Φ, and $\hat{H}_{ep}$ and $\hat{H}_p$ represent the electron-phonon interaction energy and phonon bath energy respectively, while $\hat{H}_{imp}$ is the Hamiltonian of the electron-impurity interaction. In the steady-state the parameters β_e, μ and τ are obtained from a set of balance equations for energy and momentum [2] which are derived from the Heisenberg equations of motion for the field operators $\hat{\Psi}$:

$$IV_\varepsilon = \frac{i}{h}\langle[\hat{H}_e, \hat{H}_{ep}]\rangle \qquad (4)$$

$$\int d\tau\, \rho_e \mathbf{E} = \frac{i}{h}\langle[\hat{\mathbf{P}}, \hat{H}_{ep}]\rangle + \frac{i}{h}\langle[\hat{H}_e, \hat{H}_{imp}]\rangle \qquad (5)$$

which need to be solved self-consistently with Poisson's equation

$$\nabla^2\Phi = \frac{e}{\varepsilon}\left[n(\mathbf{r}) - n_0\right] \qquad (6)$$

and the conservation of particle number $N_e = \langle\hat{N}\rangle$. Due to the presence of the electron-phonon interaction Hamiltonian $\hat{H}_{ep}$ in the balance equations (4)-(5) energy dissipation is explicitly included. The expectation values in Eqs. (4)-(6) are calculated by making use of the NSO of Zubarev [1].

QUANTIZED CONDUCTANCE

The Schrödinger equation for the free electron wavefunctions in the 2DEG without elastic scattering barrier in the channel is solved by making the following ansatz :

$$\Psi(x,y) = \xi(x)\begin{cases} \sin\left(\frac{n\pi y}{W(x)}\right) & n \text{ even} \\ \cos\left(\frac{n\pi y}{W(x)}\right) & n \text{ odd} \end{cases} \qquad (7)$$

We obtain an effective one-dimensional Schrödinger equation in the WKB approximation where an effective potential $V_n(x) = \frac{\hbar^2\pi^2 n^2}{2mW^2(x)}$ is present. Next, we assume that the minimum width of the QPC is sufficiently small such that only one channel must be taken into account, i.e. all states $n > 1$ are completely reflected by the effective potential $V_n(x)$, while the $n = 1$ state is completely transmitted. In the case of a one-channel QPC at low temperature in the linear response regime charge neutrality in the asymptotic regions of the QPC requires that $n(x \rightarrow \pm\infty) = n_0$ where

$$n(x) = 2\sum_k F(E_k + \tau V_\varepsilon I_k - e\Phi(x))\rho_k(x) \qquad (8)$$

Eq. (8) for the electron density is calculated with the NSO including the effect of the electrostatic potential Φ in the Thomas-Fermi approximation with the electron probability density $\rho_k(x)$ calculated with the wavefunctions obtained in the WKB approximation, while n_0 is considered as a uniform background density (jellium). In the linear-response and low-temperature region the condition $n(x \rightarrow \pm\infty) = n_0$ yields $\tau = L/2v_F$, where L is the operational length of the QPC and the connecting wires, while v_F is the Fermi-velocity. Calculating the current I with this value for τ, we obtain for a one-channel QPC that $I \approx 2e^2V_\varepsilon/h$ where $I_k = -e\hbar k/mL$ is the one-particle current. As a result we have rederived the Landauer conductance through a self-consistent calculation without referring to the reservoir picture. For the particular case of the QPC the value of the corresponding total relaxation time $\tau = L/2v_F$ was also obtained by Das and Green [4] from the Kubo-Greenwood formula for the conductance. In their treatment the assumption that $\tau_{in} = \tau_{el} = L/v_F$ was crucial to extract the Landauer conductance [5, 6] from the Drude-Lorenz expression for the conductance of a one-dimensional system $G = ne^2\tau/mL = 2e^2/h$ where $n = 2k_F/\pi$ is the linear electron density at $T = 0$, while the total relaxation time τ was obtained from Matthiessen's rule $\tau^{-1} = \tau_{in}^{-1} + \tau_{el}^{-1} = 2v_F/L$. The corresponding total scattering length $\lambda = v_F\tau = L/2$ is thus half the length L of the QPC and reflects the presence of inelastic (phonons) and elastic scattering. The appearance of both elastic and inelastic scattering can be understood if one considers the interface regions between the QPC and the connecting wires. These regions exhibit enhanced elastic and inelastic scattering due to the presence of the effective scattering potential $V_n(x)$ originating from the presence of the constriction. Indeed, in ref. [3] we have shown that the presence of an elastic scatterer enhances the bare electron-phonon interaction and therefore increases local dissipative processes.

REFERENCES

1. D. N. Zubarev , *Nonequilibrium Statistical Thermodynamics*, Consultant bureau N.Y., 1974
2. Bart Sorée, Wim Magnus, Wim Schoenmaker, Phys.Rev.**B66** (2002) 035318
3. Bart Sorée, Wim Magnus, Wim Schoenmaker, Phys.Lett.**A310** (2003) 322-328
4. M.P. Das and F. Green, J.Phys. : Condens. Matter **12** (2003) L687-693
5. R. Landauer, IBM Journ. Res. Development **1** (1957) 223 and Philos. Mag. **21** (1970) 863
6. M. Büttiker and Y. Imry and R. Landauer and S. Pinhas , Phys.Rev. **B31** (1985) 6207
7. W. Magnus and W. Schoenmaker, J. Math. Phys.,**39** (1998) 6715

Conductance of Disordered Wires with Symplectic Symmetry :Random-matrix Approach and Numerical Simulation

Hiroshi Sakai, Katsunori Wakabayashi and Yositake Takane

Department of Quantum Matter, Graduate School of Advanced Sciences of Matter, Hiroshima University,
Higashi-Hiroshima 739-8530, Japan

Abstract. The properties of quantum electron transport in disordered wires with symplectic symmetry is studied by a random-matrix approach and a numerical simulation. It has been shown that the behavior of the conductance crucially depends on whether the number of conducting channels is even or odd. We focus on the long-wire regime where the wire length is much longer than the conductance decay length, and evaluate the averaged conductance for the even- and odd-channel cases. From the random-matrix theory, we find that the dimensionless conductance in the even-channel case decays exponentially as $\langle g_{\text{even}} \rangle \to 0$ with increasing system length, while $\langle g_{\text{odd}} \rangle \to 1$ in the odd-channel case. It is also shown that the decay of g_{odd} is much faster than g_{even}. We examine this even- odd difference by a numerical simulation based on the tight-binding model. The numerical results are in good agreement with the random-matrix results.

Keywords: disorderd quantum wire, symplectic class, random-matrix theory, numerical simulation, conductance
PACS: 71.23.An, 72.10.-d, 72.80.Ng, 72.15.Rn, 73.21.Hb

Statistical properties of conductance in disordered quantum wires are characterized by the three universality classes, i.e. orthogonal, unitary and symplectic, according to the time-reversal and spin-rotation symmetries [1]. These classes, so-called standard three, have been believed to inevitably cause the Anderson localization. However, on the basis of the random matrix theory [1], we show that this widely accepted understanding does not apply to the symplectic class with an odd number of channels (symplectic-odd class), where one perfectly conducting channel without backward scattering exists even in the limit where the wire length $L \to \infty$ [2-8]. The existence of a perfectly conducting channel indicates the absence of the Anderson localization. Since the symplectic-even class is free from such an anomalous behavior, we have to separate the sympletic class into two subclasses depending on the even-odd of the channel number. Here, we consider the disordered quantum wires with N_α (α = even or odd) conducting channels. The dimensionless conductance g_α is given by

$$g_\alpha = \text{tr}(t^\dagger t), \qquad (1)$$

where t is transmission matrix. Hermitian matrix $t^\dagger t$ has a set of eigenvalues $T_1, T_2, ..., T_m$ in the even-channel case of $N_{\text{even}} = 2m$. Each eigenvalue is two-fold degenerate due to Kramers degeneracy. In the odd-channel case of $N_{\text{odd}} = 2m + 1$, there arises one additional eigenvalue which corresponds to the perfectly conducting channel. Since the dimensionless conductance is equal to the sum of all the transmission eigenvalues, we can write the dimensionless conductance as $g_{\text{odd}} = 1 + 2\sum_{a=1}^m T_a$, $g_{\text{even}} = 2\sum_{a=1}^m T_a$. Our purpose is to make a comparison between the even- and odd-channel cases in the symplectic class. Particulary, we focus on the transport properties in the long-wire regime, where the even- odd difference clearly appears

Adopting the random-matrix approach, we derive the Dorokhov-Mello-Pereya-Kumar (DMPK) equation which is the evolution equation for the probability distribution of transmission eigenvalues $\{T_a\}$ and evaluate the ensemble average of g_α. In terms of $\Gamma_\alpha = \sum_{a=1}^m T_a$ (α = even or odd), the dimensionless conductance g_α is given by $g_\alpha = \delta_{\alpha,\text{odd}} + 2\Gamma_\alpha$. In the long-wire limit, Γ_α is approximated as $\Gamma_\alpha \cong 4e^{-2x_1}$, where x_1 is related to the maximum transmission eigenvalue T_1 by $T_1 = 1/\cosh^2 x_1$. The distribution for x_1 is obtained by solving the DMPK equation as [5, 7]

$$p_\alpha(x_1; s) = \left(\frac{\gamma_\alpha}{2\pi s} \right)^{\frac{1}{2}} e^{-\frac{\gamma_\alpha}{2s} \left(x_1 - \frac{l}{\xi_{\alpha,1}} s \right)^2}, \qquad (2)$$

where $\xi_{\alpha,1} = \gamma_\alpha l/(1 + 2\delta_{\alpha,\text{odd}})$, $\gamma_\alpha = 2(N_\alpha - 1)$, $s = L/l$ and l is the mean free path. Using the above distribution, we obtain the ensemble average $\langle x_1 \rangle$ as

$$\langle x_1 \rangle = \frac{(1 + 2\delta_{\alpha,\text{odd}})L}{\gamma_\alpha l}. \qquad (3)$$

From eq. (3), we can estimate the decay length ξ_α of the conductance by identifying $\exp[\langle \ln \Gamma_\alpha \rangle] \sim \exp[-2\langle x_1 \rangle] \equiv \exp[-2L/\xi_\alpha]$. We find that $\xi_{\text{odd}} = 4ml/3$ and $\xi_{\text{even}} = 2(2m - 1)l$. Note that $\xi_{\text{odd}} < \xi_{\text{even}}$ for any positive integer m. This result indicates that g_{odd} decays much faster than g_{even} with increasing L. Since the random matrix approach is based on the assumption of

CP893, *Physics of Semiconductors, 28th International Conference*
edited by W. Jantsch and F. Schäffler
© 2007 American Institute of Physics 978-0-7354-0397-0/07/$23.00

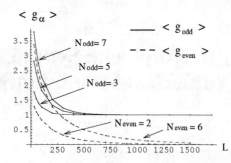

FIGURE 1. The dimensionless conductance $\langle g_{odd} \rangle$ for $N_{odd} = 3,5,7$ with solid line and $\langle g_{even} \rangle$ for $N_{even} = 2,6$ with dashed line as a function of system length L.

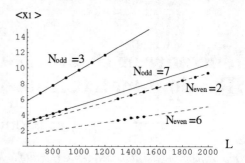

FIGURE 2. The ensemble-average $\langle x_1 \rangle$ for $N_{odd} = 3$ and 7 with solid line and for $N_{even} = 2$ and 6 with dashed line as a function of system length L.

equivalent scattering channels, we have to examine the valitity of the random-matrix results by comparing them with results of a numerical simulation.

To numerically calculate the conductance, we adopt the tight-binding Hamiltonian given by

$$H = \sum_{j,l} \sum_{\sigma,\sigma'} \Big[\{|j,l+1,\sigma\rangle \hat{V}_x(\sigma,\sigma')\langle j,l,\sigma'| + h.c.\}$$
$$+ \{|j,l+1,\sigma\rangle \hat{V}_y(\sigma,\sigma')\langle j,l,\sigma'| + h.c.\}$$
$$+ \{|j,l,\sigma\rangle V_{imp}(j,l)\langle j,l,\sigma'|\} \Big] \quad (4)$$

with $\hat{V}_x = -it_x\sigma_x$ and $\hat{V}_y = it_y\sigma_y$, where σ_x and σ_y are pauli matrices. Here, $V_{imp}(j,l)$ denotes the impurity potential at the (j,l)th site, and t_y and t_x are the longitudinal and transverse hopping integrals. We assume that $V_{imp}(j,l) \neq 0$ only in a sample region of length L. The left and right regions with $V_{imp}(j,l) \equiv 0$ are regarded as ideal leads. Although $\hat{V}_x$ and $\hat{V}_y$ break the spin-rotation invariance, H has the time-reversal symmetry. Thus, our Hamiltonian belongs to the symplectic class [8]. If the potential range of scatteres is much larger than the lattice constant, the number N_α of conducting channels becomes odd (even) when the number M of lattice sites in transverse direction is odd (even). Thus, we can consider not only the odd-channel case but also the even-channel case. Using a recursive Green's function method [9], we can numerically obtain the elements of transmission matrix t of eq. (1). Fig. 1 shows the numerical results of the ensemble-averaged dimensionless conductance $\langle g_\alpha \rangle$ (α = even or odd) as a function of L. The ensemble average is taken over 10000 samples for all the cases. We observe that $\langle g_{odd} \rangle$ decreases towards unity with increasing L. This result is in agreement with the random-matrix theory which predicts the conductance quantization (i.e., $g_{odd} \to 1$) in the long-L limit.

Fig. 2 shows the wire length dependence of $\langle x_1 \rangle$, where the ensemble average is taken over 3000 samples for all cases. It is clearly recognized that $\langle x_1 \rangle$ linearly depends on L, i.e. consistent with eq. (3). The standard de-

viation of x_1 is very much smaller than $\langle x_1 \rangle$ in the long-L regime. The slope of $\langle x_1 \rangle$ gives the decay length. Note that the slope of $\langle x_1 \rangle$ with N_{odd} is steeper than that of $\langle x_1 \rangle$ with N_{even}. This tendency also agrees with the random matrix theory.

From eq. (2), the distribution of x_1 is a Gaussian with the width $\Delta = \sqrt{8s/\gamma_\alpha}$ and the hight $h = \sqrt{\gamma_\alpha/2\pi s}$. The even-odd difference appears in both Δ and h. We numerically obtain the distribution for the odd-channel case of $N_{odd} = 3$ with $M = 11$ and $L = 1000$ and that for the even-channel case of $N_{odd} = 2$ with $M = 10$ and $L = 2000$. Here the 100000 samples are taken in each numerical simulation. The resulting distributions are well fitted by a Gaussian, and the obtained values of Δ and h for both the even- and odd-channel cases have a good agreement with the random-matrix theory.

In summury, we have studied the conductance in the symplectic class for the even- and odd-channel cases based on the random-matrix theory and the numerical simulation. We found that the perfectly conducting channel induces the clear even-odd difference in the long-wire regime.

This work was supported in part by a Grant-in-Aid for Scientific Research (C) from the Japan Society for the Promotion of Science.

REFERENCES

1. C. W. J. Beenakker: Rev. Mod. Phys. **69** (1997) 731.
2. T. Ando and H. Suzuura: J. Phys. Soc. Jpn. **71** (2002) 2753.
3. T. Ando and T. Nakanishi: J. Phys. Soc. Jpn. **67** (1998) 1704.
4. Y. Takane and K. Wakabayashi: J. Phys. Soc. Jpn. **72** (2003) 2710.
5. Y. Takane: J. Phys. Soc. Jpn. **73** (2004) 9.
6. H. Sakai, Y. Takane: J. Phys. Soc. Jpn. **74** (2005) 1521.
7. H. Sakai, Y. Takane: J. Phys. Soc. Jpn. **75** (2006) 54711.
8. Y. Takane: J. Phys. Soc. Jpn. **73** (2004) 2366.
9. T. Ando: Phys. Rev. B **44** (1989) 5325.

Comparison of Device Performance and Scaling Properties of Cylindrical-Nanowire (CNW) and Carbon-Nanotube (CNT) Transistors

E. Gnani, A. Marchi, S. Reggiani, M. Rudan and G. Baccarani

ARCES and DEIS, University of Bologna
Viale Risorgimento 2, 40136 Bologna, Italy
Phone: +39 051 209 3773, Fax: +39 051 209 3779, E-mail: egnani@arces.unibo.it

Abstract. In this work we investigate the performance of cylindrical nanowire (CNW) and carbon-nanotube (CNT) FETs at their extreme miniaturization limits. The model self-consistently solves Poisson's and the quantum transport equations using the formalism of the Quantum Transmitting Boundary Method (QTBM). The performance comparison between CNW- and CNT-FETs with the same diameter demonstrates that the CNW-FET provides a better scaling trend at very low sizes.

Keywords: Silicon nanowires, Carbon nanotubes, Electronic Structures, Ballistic transport.
PACS: 73.22.-f, 73.23.Ad, 73.40.Gk, 73.63.Nm

INTRODUCTION

According to the provisions of the ITRS 2005 [1], sub-10-nm channel-length FETs will be manufactured in year 2016 for the HP22 technology node, and 5-nm channel lengths will be required for the HP14 node in year 2020. At these extreme limits, thin-body silicon-on-insulator transistors have been shown to suffer severe short-channel effects (SCE) [2]. More specifically, they show an increased subthreshold slope (SS), which leads to a high leakage current, and high drain-induced barrier lowering (DIBL), which leads to a strong change of the threshold voltage with the drain bias [3]. Therefore, new device architectures with multi-gate configuration are being investigated in order to exploit the ultimate potential of the CMOS technology. This leads to the consideration of silicon-based cylindrical nanowire (CNW) FETs [4] and to carbon-nanotube (CNT) FETs [5].

DEVICE SIMULATION

A full-quantum transport simulator is used to provide some insight on the upper-limit performance of the devices investigated in this work, whose schematic structures are shown in fig. 1. Due to the cylindrical symmetry in CNTs and to the structural quantum confinement in the radial and angular directions in the CNWs, the conduction band is split into energy subbands along the transport direction for both devices.

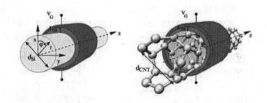

FIGURE 1. The analyzed structures: CNW-FET (left); CNT-FET (right).

In the transport direction the Schrödinger equation is solved using the QTBM method where the starting point is the discretized Hamiltonian, which is augmented with traveling waves at the boundary points of the simulation region in order to obtain open boundary conditions [6]. Moreover, in order to take into account narrow resonances at some energies for the calculation of the electron charge density, an adaptive procedure based on the Simpson quadrature during the scanning of the energy interval has been implemented to achieve the desired accuracy. The Schrödinger equation is solved within the effective-mass m^* approach because the analysis of the m^* change with diameter is beyond the scope of this work and is not addressed here. Moreover, for the CNT-FET the mass value has been chosen so as to obtain the same equilibrium inversion charge as that given by the

CP893, *Physics of Semiconductors, 28th International Conference*
edited by W. Jantsch and F. Schäffler
© 2007 American Institute of Physics 978-0-7354-0397-0/07/$23.00

TABLE 1. Main technological parameters for the simulated devices.

	CNW	CNT	CNT	CNT
Diameter (nm)	1, 2, 5	1	2	5
Lg (nm)	1, 2, 5	1, 2, 5	1, 2, 5	2, 5
EOT (nm)	0.5	0.5	0.5	0.5
E_G (eV)	1.12	0.720	0.360	0.144

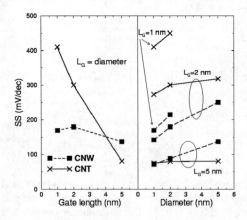

FIGURE 2. Left: SS vs L_g for CNW- and CNT-FETs. In this plot, the device diameter is kept equal to the gate length. Right: SS vs diameter for different gate lengths. The CNW-FET provides a better scaling trend at the extreme miniaturization limits.

universal density of states of [7]. Consequently, the material properties are fully accounted for. Finally, the Schrödinger solution is self-consistently coupled with the Poisson equation using a Newton-Raphson scheme. The Jacobian matrix is computed at each iteration by numerically differentiating the space charge.

RESULTS AND DISCUSSION

The numerical analysis is carried out on devices with geometrical and electrical requirements that follow those provided by the ITRS 2005 [1]. We examine devices with channel lengths and diameters varying from 1 to 5 nm. An intrinsic material is assumed within the channel; heavily-doped source and drain regions are used with ohmic contacts at the ends. Abrupt junctions are taken into account in both devices to provide a clear definition of the channel length. The metal work function is chosen so that I_{off} = 108 nA/μm as indicated by the ITRS. The most important parameters of the investigated devices are reported in Table I along with some key material properties. We assume V_{DD} = 0.8 V and fix the oxide thickness at 0.5 nm.

To provide a first comparison between CNW- and CNT-FETs, we plot the SS in fig. 2 and the DIBL in fig. 3. Both of them are degraded by the reduction in the gate length. Also, the CNW-FET provides a better

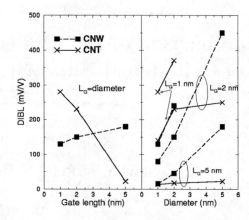

FIGURE 3. Left: DIBL vs L_g for CNW- and CNT-FETs with the gate length equal to the device diameter. Right: DIBL vs. diameter for different gate lengths. The CNW-FET provides a better DIBL at the extreme miniaturization limits.

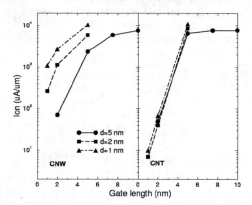

FIGURE 4. I_{on} current for the CNW- (left) and CNT- (right). For small gate lengths the CNT-FET provides low on-currents because the high SS prevents the device from turning on. A similar trend is obtained for all diameters.

scaling trend at the extreme miniaturization limits. Fig. 4 shows the on-current vs gate length L_g for the two devices: for small gate lengths the CNT-FET provides lower on-currents because the poor SS prevents the device from turning on.

REFERENCES

1. Int. Technology Roadmap for Semiconductors 2005 Edition, http://public.itrs.net.
2. B. Doris et al., IEDM 2002, p.267.
3. J.-T. Park et al., IEEE TED, v. 49, 2002, p.2222.
4. F. Yang et al., IEDM 2002, p. 255.
5. P. Avouris et al., Proc. IEEE, vol. 91, 2003, p. 1772.
6. C. S. Lent et al., K. Appl. Phys., 67, 1990, p. 6353.
7. K. Uchida et al., IEDM 2002, p. 47.

Properties of Silicon Nanowhiskers Grown by Molecular-Beam Epitaxy

Olga V. Naumova[*], Yuri V. Nastaushev[*], Svetlana N. Svitasheva[*], Leonid V. Sokolov[*,†], Peter Werner[†], Nikolay D. Zakharov[†], Tatyana A. Gavrilova[*], Fedor N. Dultsev[*], and Alexander L. Aseev[*]

[*]Institute of Semiconductor Physics, SB RAS, 630090 Novosibirsk, Russia
[†]Max-Planck-Institut Für Mikrostrukturphysik, D-06120 Halle (Saale), Germany

Abstract. Silicon nanowhiskers (NW) in the diameter range of 70 to 200 nm and the length range of 580 to 890 nm were grown on silicon <111> wafers by molecular beam epitaxy. Small clusters of gold on the silicon surface were used as seeds to initiate the growth of NW. Current-voltage and current-temperature dependencies for the NW structures revealed Schottky barrier effect and the presence of the centers which are nonhomogeneously distributed along the length of NWs. Recharging of these centers provides the conductivity of NWs at temperatures below 280 K.

Keywords: Nanowhiskers, Electrical properties, Recharging centers
PACS: 68.70.+w, 61.82.Fk, 68.37.Hk, 73.63.-b

INTRODUCTION

Silicon whiskers (also called nanopillars, nanowires) are a topic of significant research due to their physical properties, as well as due to their potential for new nanodevices of nanophotonics, ULSI silicon microelectronics, nanoelectronics [1-3]. Remarkable progress has been achieved during the recent years in the ways of preparing the whiskers with definite radius, position, and length [3].

The aim of this work was to investigate electrical properties of silicon nanowhiskers (NW) grown by molecular-beam epitaxy (MBE).

EXPERIMENTAL

Silicon NWs were fabricated on silicon <111> wafers with a resistivity of 5 Ωcm in the MBE system (UHV chamber RIBER SIVA 45). Clusters of gold on Si surface were used as seeds to initiate the growth of NWs. As a result, hemispherical Au/Si droplets were found on the top of NWs after their fabrication. The details of structure manufacturing process were described in [3]. The length of NWs was within the range 580-890 nm. An average distance between them varied within the range 720 - 850 nm. The diameter of NWs was within the range 70 - 200 nm.

Current-voltage (I-V) and current-temperature (I-T) dependencies were used for electrical characterization of NW structures. For this purpose, the wafers with NWs were covered with a layer of PMMA 800 nm or 500 nm thick. After that, the aluminum layer was evaporated to provide the contact to NWs. Thus, two types of structures were prepared for electrical measurements: structures A with a contact to the highest (800-890 nm long) NWs, and structures B with contacts to the whole array of NWs.

RESULTS

Fig.1 shows the I-V characteristics of the NW structure. The I-V curves for the structure without NWs (epitaxial Si layer/ Si substrate) are also shown for comparison. One can see that the I-V characteristics of the NW structure have a rectifying behavior with the ratio $I_F/I_R \sim 10^2$ for 5 V. The structures without NWs (epitaxial Si layer/substrate) have unessential rectifying. This allows us to conclude that the rectifying property of NW structures is caused by Schottky barrier formed between the metal contact and NWs (but not by the barrier between the epitaxial Si layer and the substrate).

Fig.2 shows temperature dependencies of current for structures B, measured with different reverse bias V_g. One can see that the temperature behavior of

CP893, *Physics of Semiconductors, 28th International Conference*
edited by W. Jantsch and F. Schäffler
© 2007 American Institute of Physics 978-0-7354-0397-0/07/$23.00

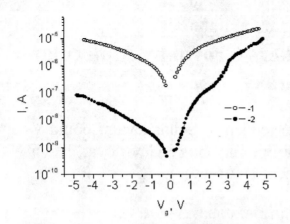

FIGURE 1. Current-voltage characteristics of the structures: epitaxial Si/ substrate (1) and NW (2). The positive bias applied to the NWs (or epitaxial Si layer) is in the forward direction and the negative bias is in the reverse direction.

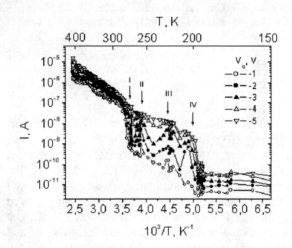

FIGURE 2. The dependencies of current on temperature for structures B, measured at different reverse bias

current depends on the bias voltage applied to the structure within the temperature range 280-200 K. The current 1) abruptly decreases at T_I=280 K, but only at the reverse bias V_g=(1-3) V, 2) decreases non-monotonically (with maxima at T_{II}=257 K and T_{III}=224 K) within the temperature range 280-200 K at the reverse bias 2 V and 3 V, and 3) abruptly decreases again at T_{IV}~200 K and V_g=(2-4) V.

In contrast to structures B, I-T characteristics for structures A did not depend on the bias voltage applied to the structure. The current exponentially decreased with temperature within the range 480-280 K, sharply (to 4 orders) changed (decreased) at T_I=280 K and did not depend on temperature below 280 K.

These results allow us to conclude that NWs contain different recharging centers, which are non-homogeneously distributed along the whiskers.

TABLE 1. Maximally possible region of localization for centers I-IV in nanowhiskers and the position of the Fermi level for the center recharging temperatures

Center	L_{max}-L_{min}, nm	E_c-E_F, eV
I	890-264	0.15
II	528-264	0.14
III	528-264	0.11
IV	below 528	0.10

The position of centers I-IV along the length of NWs, defined by using the expression for the depletion region of Schottky barriers, is shown in Table 1 [4]. The position of Fermi level with respect to the Si conduction band for temperatures I-IV is also given in Table 1. We suggest that the position of Fermi level corresponds to the position of the recharging center level E_i. It is interesting to note that the electrical level of oxygen-related thermal donor in the forbidden band of silicon is E_c-0.15 eV [5].

CONCLUSIONS

We can conclude that the rectifying property of NW structures originates from Schottky barrier formed between the metal contact and silicon NWs.

The I-T dependencies revealed the presence of at least four different recharging centers, which are non-homogeneously distributed along a whisker (so, the upper part of the highest NWs (within the range 500-890 nm) has the centers of only one type, which is supposedly caused by the oxygen-related thermal donor). Recharging of these centers provides the conductivity of NWs at temperatures below 280 K.

ACKNOWLEDGMENTS

This work was partly supported by the Russian Foundation for Basic Research (04-02-16541, 04-02-16747).

REFERENCES

1. D.M. Pooley, H.Ahmed, H.Mizuta, K.Nakazato, *Appl. Phys. Lett.*,**74**, 2191-2193 (1999).
2. D.V. Scheible, R.H.Blick. *Appl. Phys. Lett.* **84**, 4632-4636 (2004).
3. L. Schubert, P. Werner, N.D. Zakharov, G. Gerth, F.M. Kolb, L. Long, and U. Gösele, *Appl. Phys. Lett.* **84**, 4968-4970 (2004).
4. S.M. Szi, *Physics of Semiconductor devices*, N.Y.,1981, p.261.
5. F.Bridgest, G.Devies, J.Robertson, and A.Stoneham, *J. Phys. Cond. Mat*, **2**, 2875-2928 (1990)

Conductance fluctuations in a quantum wire with a non-uniform scattering potential

D. W. Horsell*, E. A. Galaktionov*, A. K. Savchenko*, A. V. Kretinin*, A. Ghosh†,
H. E. Beere† and D. A. Ritchie†

*School of Physics, University of Exeter, Stocker Road, Exeter, EX4 4QL, U.K.
†Cavendish Laboratory, University of Cambridge, Cambridge, CB3 0HE, UK

Abstract. We study fluctuations in the conductance of a narrow GaAs/AlGaAs quantum wire. In strong magnetic fields we show that these fluctuations originate from a complex mixture of transport processes. Here back-scattering of electrons is determined by the position in energy of the bulk Landau level. We experimentally resolve a diffusion–tunnelling transition as the Fermi level is moved between integer filling factors.

Keywords: Conductance fluctuations, scattering potential, quantum wire, quantum Hall effect
PACS: 72.20.My, 73.23.-b, 72.60.+g, 73.63.Nm

Fluctuations of the conductance of sub-micron structures have been studied for over two decades. Those in diffusive systems result from electron interference and have been shown to have a universal character. However, as devices have become smaller and of higher mobility, purely diffusive transport is no longer realised and the picture of universal conductance fluctuations (UCF) breaks down [1]. There has also been a great deal of recent interest in the origin of mesoscopic fluctuations observed at high magnetic fields, e.g. [2]. At these fields the nature of electron transport is substantially altered by the quantisation of the energy spectrum into Landau levels and the formation of edge-states. Many issues, both qualitative and quantitative, remain unclear. In particular, it is not understood how resonant tunnelling, interference, and interaction combine to produce the fluctuations observed in these systems: it is our aim here to address this.

We study a δ-doped GaAs/AlGaAs wire formed in the centre of a wide, wet-etched Hall bar mesa. A $2.5 \times 10^{12} \, \text{cm}^{-2}$ silicon-doped layer is separated from the electron gas at the heterojunction by a 40 nm spacer. The wire has an etched width $W_{\text{etch}} = 2 \, \mu\text{m}$ and length $L = 20 \, \mu\text{m}$. The four-terminal resistance of this wire was measured in the temperature range $0.03 \leq T \leq 3 \, \text{K}$ and magnetic fields (perpendicular to the wire) up to 15 T, at a fixed ac current of 0.3 nA at 11 Hz.

At low magnetic fields ($\omega_c \tau < 1$) we previously observed fluctuations of the conductance that depended strongly on diffusive scattering at the boundaries [3]. When a magnetic field was applied such that the electrons (that travelled ballistically at zero field) were driven into the boundaries by the Lorentz force, the fluctuations were strongly enhanced. At high magnetic fields we show here that the character of electron scattering can also be changed by similar tuning of the field strength.

In the field range where individual Landau levels are not well resolved the fluctuations are inextricably mixed with the Shubnikov–de Haas oscillations. With the "period" and magnitude of the two effects comparable the results of previous studies (and our own results in this field range) are open to question. Methods of separation of the two effects by temperature dependence [4], non-local resistance measurement [5], asymmetries in the field dependence [6] and second harmonic generation [7] fail to eliminate the Shubnikov–de Haas oscillations completely (indeed the effective correlation field of these oscillations $\Delta B_c = (e/8hn)B^2$ can fit the published data rather well).

At high fields the period of the Shubnikov–de Haas oscillations is much larger than that of the fluctuations making their extraction possible. In the centre of a Landau level, where extended states in the bulk of the sample allow diffusive backscattering across it, fluctuations should correspondingly be diffusive (UCF-like) in origin [1]. Away from the centre, the bulk Landau level no longer connects the edge states and backscattering can only occur via tunnelling through states in the tail of the level [8]. The spin-resolved Landau levels in the range $\nu = 2 \rightarrow 4$ are shown in Fig. 1. The temperature independent centre of the resistance peak between $\nu = 2$ and $\nu = 3$ is shown in the inset. In the region of this centre the fluctuations are of a different nature to those in the flanks: the variance and "period" are observed to be significantly smaller.

This different nature is highlighted in the Fourier spectra of the fluctuations in the centre and in the flanks, Fig. 2(a,b). For UCF (centre) one would expect an exponential decay of the Fourier spectrum [9] and for resonant tunnelling (flanks) a peak associated with the Aharanov–Bohm-type oscillations [8]. This difference is

CP893, *Physics of Semiconductors, 28th International Conference*
edited by W. Jantsch and F. Schäffler

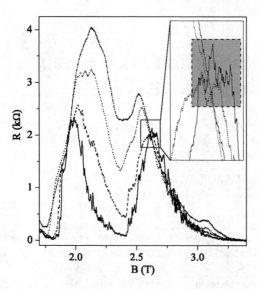

FIGURE 1. Resistance in the range $\nu = 2 - 4$ at 0.03 (bottom), 0.2, 0.4, and 0.8 K (top). A magnified region is shown in the inset where the dashed grey box defines the range of the centre of the Landau level considered in the analysis.

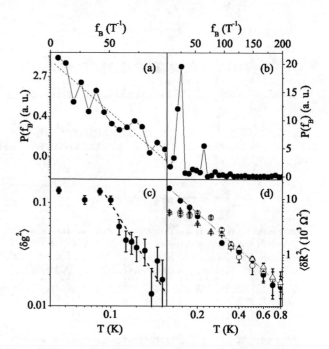

FIGURE 2. The power spectrum of the fluctuations in the centre (a) and flank (b) of the $\nu = 3 \rightarrow 2$ Landau level. (c,d) The variance in the regions of (a) and (b), respectively. The variance for several regions of the flanks are shown by different symbols in (d). Fits are shown by the dashed lines.

clearly seen in the experiment. To add weight to this, the variance in the two regions as a function of temperature is shown in Fig. 2(c,d). In the centre $\langle \delta g^2 \rangle = (h/e^2)^2 \langle \delta R^2 \rangle / \langle R \rangle^4 \propto T^{-1.4(\pm 0.2)}$ (where $\langle R \rangle = 2\,\mathrm{k}\Omega$) agreeing well with the expected $T^{-3/2}$ dependence of UCF (where $L_\phi \approx L_T$ [10]). The maximum variance $\langle \delta g^2 \rangle = 0.12\,(\pm 0.02)$ is comparable to the value $1/15$ predicted in [1] (a numerical difference was also seen in [9]). In the flanks the temperature dependence is $T^{-2.1(\pm 0.1)}$, which agrees with the T^{-2} dependence expected for fluctuations caused by resonant tunnelling.

Following [11] we estimate the typical size of the potential hills causing the tunnelling resonances from $\Delta B_c = (h/e)(\pi r^2 + h^2 n_{2\mathrm{D}} r / em^* F_r(\mu))^{-1}$, where $F_r(\mu)$ is the radial electric field at the Fermi level μ. Using $F_r(\mu) = 10^5\,\mathrm{Vm}^{-1}$ [11], $n_{2\mathrm{D}} = 1.5 \times 10^{11}\,\mathrm{cm}^{-2}$ (found from Shubnikov–de Haas oscillations in the wide contact regions), and $\Delta B_c = 40\,\mathrm{mT}$ from Fig. 2(b) we find $r \approx 160\,\mathrm{nm}$, which accords with our independent estimations of the scale of the potential from the quantum lifetime.

In conclusion, by tuning the magnetic field in a quantum wire we have shown a transition from diffusive to tunnelling-type backscattering. This manifests itself as a change in the nature of the conductance fluctuations. In the centre of a Landau level diffusive scattering dominates and the fluctuations behave in a similar way to UCF, whereas in the tails of the level tunnelling prevails and the fluctuations have a periodic character due to Aharanov–Bohm-type interference.

REFERENCES

1. S. Xiong, N. Read, and A. D. Stone, *Phys. Rev. B* **56**, 3982 (1997).
2. E. Peled, Y. Chen, E. Diez, D. C. Tsui, D. Shahar, D. L. Sivco, and A. Y. Cho, *Phys. Rev. B* **69**, 241305 (2004).
3. D. W. Horsell, A. K. Savchenko, A. Kretinin, A. Ghosh, H. Beere, and D. Ritchie, *Physica E* (2006), in press (published online 16th April 2006).
4. J. P. Bird, K. Ishibashi, Y. Ochiai, M. Lakrimi, A. D. C. Grassie, K. M. Hutchings, Y. Aoyagi, and T. Sugano, *Phys. Rev. B* **52**, 1793 (1995).
5. A. Geim, P. C. Main, P. H. Beton, L. Eaves, S. P. Beaumont, and C. D. W. Wilkinson, *Phys. Rev. Lett.* **69**, 1248 (1992).
6. A. Morgan, D. H. Cobden, M. Pepper, G. Jin, Y. S. Tang, and C. D. W. Wilkinson, *Phys. Rev. B* **50**, 12187 (1994).
7. D. W. Horsell, Ph.D. thesis, University of Exeter, Exeter, U.K. (2004).
8. J. K. Jain, and S. A. Kivelson, *Phys. Rev. Lett.* **60**, 1542 (1988).
9. F. Hohls, U. Zeitler, and R. J. Haug, *Phys. Rev. B* **66**, 073304 (2002).
10. D. G. Polyakov, and K. V. Samokhin, *Phys. Rev. Lett.* **80**, 1509 (1998).
11. J. A. Simmons, S. W. Hwang, D. C. Tsui, H. P. Wei, L. W. Engel, and M. Shayegan, *Phys. Rev. B* **44**, 12933 (1991).

Resistance Switching Induced by an Electric Field in ZnO:Li, Fe Nanowires

Gennady. N. Panin[*,#], Andrey. N. Baranov[¶], Oleg. V. Kononenko[#], Sergey. V. Dubonos[#] and Tae Won Kang[*],

[*]Quantum-functional Semiconductor Research Center, Department of Physics, Dongguk University, 26 3-ga Pildong, Chung-gu, Seoul, 100-715 Korea
[#]Institute of Microelectronics Technology, RAS, 142432 Chernogolovka, Moscow Region, Russia
[¶]Moscow State University, Chemistry Department, 119992, Moscow, Russia

Abstract. We report on a stable hysteresis in the current-voltage curve of an individual ZnO nanowire doped by Li and Fe impurities and a persisting reproducible resistance modulation by a dc voltage at room temperature. I-V curves corresponding to resistive switching are explained by a nonuniform distribution of trapped charges and their electric polarization when the voltage is varied.

Keywords: Resistive Switching, ZnO Nanowires, nonvolatile memory.
PACS: 73.63.-b

INTRODUCTION

The electric-field controlled resistive switching has been shown in many different materials such as oxides [1-5], organic materials [5, 6] and semiconductors [7-10].This effect is of a great interest for future nonvolatile memories. Resistive information storage has the higher potential compared to charge based storage due to faster programming, smaller bit cell size and lower power consumption [11]. Several mechanisms have been proposed to explain the resistive switching such as (i) trapping/detrapping effects and charge transfer processes via donor and acceptor levels [12], (ii) a Mott metal-insulator transition [13], (iii) formation of local current domains [14], and (iv) conductivity changes due to a reversal of a local spontaneous polarization [15] and the depletion zone width of a ferroelectric Shottky-like interface [7]. Polarization changes might not be stringently of ferroelectric nature, but might also be due to defect dipoles, e.g., formed by acceptor/oxygen vacancy defect associates [16]. In the present work, we investigate the charge carrier transport in ZnO nanowires doped by 2% Fe and 2% Li. A stable hysteresis in the current-voltage curve of the individual nanowire has been found at room temperature.

EXPERIMENT

ZnO nanowires with diameters from 40 to 150 nm and 1-3 μm in length were grown from NaCl–Li$_2$CO$_3$ salt mixture with a solution-processed Zn-containing precursor at 700°C as described previously [17]. Individual ZnO NWs were configured as two terminal device with the electrode-ZnO:Li,Fe-electrode structure on a silicon substrate capped with a SiO$_2$ layer. E-beam lithography was used to pattern aluminum electrodes contacting individual nanowires (Fig. 1, insert). Electrical transport properties of the nanowires were studied by applying to the electrodes quasi-dc voltage $0 \rightarrow V_{max} \rightarrow -V_{max} \rightarrow 0$ with a constant sweep velocity.

RESULTS AND DISCUSSION

In Figure 1 the current-voltage (I-V) characteristics are shown for a dc voltage loop ranging from $0 \rightarrow 3 \rightarrow -3 \rightarrow 0$ V on a Al electrode. The I-V curve exhibits a rectifying behaviour and displays stable hysteresis. The hysteresis at negative voltages is more pronounced than at positive voltages. The nanowire starts in the low resistive state when sweeping the voltage from zero to positive voltages

CP893, *Physics of Semiconductors, 28th International Conference*
edited by W. Jantsch and F. Schäffler
© 2007 American Institute of Physics 978-0-7354-0397-0/07/$23.00

(1). In the subsequent voltage sweep from positive to negative (2, 3) the nanowire shows an increased resistance. At negative voltage the wire resistance switches back from a high to a low resistance. The virgin nanowire shows a higher resistance than obtained in the subsequent cycles with a carrier injection.

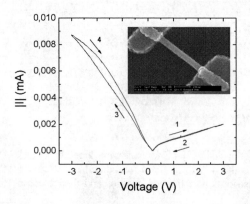

FIGURE 1. I-V characteristics of a ZnO nanowire for a voltage sweep from 0→3→-3→0 V. The insert shows a SEM image of the nanowire with deposited Al contacts patterned by e-beam lithography.

In contrast to abrupt resistance changes, a smooth resistance change is observed. It is likely, that electric-field domains [18] are built and attenuated resulting in

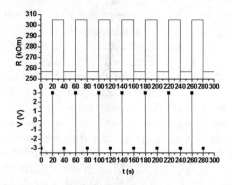

FIGURE 2. Two state resistive switching of the ZnO nanowire device at RT. Applied voltage vs time (lower curve); readout resistance vs time (upper curve).

the observable switching effect. Moreover one has to take a nonuniform distribution of trapped charges and the surface band bending [19] into account, which can be altered by applying voltage in forward or reverse directions.

Figure 2 shows two state resistive switching at RT. Emploing a positive voltage of +3V switches the nanowire device into a high impedance state. After applying negative voltage of -3 V the low impedance state is recovered. Between these write and erase voltages the state is readout with 1.5V

CONCLUSIONS

Two-level resistive switching of ZnO:Li,Fe nanowires at room temperature are demonstrated. Electrical measurements show a weak but stable hysteretic behavior in the current-voltage mode. I-V curves corresponding to the resistive switching are explained by a nonuniform distribution of trapped charges and their electric polarization.

ACKNOWLEDGMENTS

The authors gratefully acknowledge supports from the Korean Science and Engineering Foundation through the Quantum-Functional Semiconductor Research Center at Dongguk University and the "Rosnauka" from the project "IN- 12.5/002".

REFERENCES

1. W. R. Hiatt and T. W. Hickmott, Appl. Phys. Lett. **6**, 106-108 (1965).
2. K. Szot, W. Speier, and W. Eberhardt, Appl. Phys. Lett. **60**, 1190 -1192 (1991).
3. Y. Watanabe, Appl. Phys. Lett. **66**, 28-30 (1995).
4. D. C. Kim, S. Seo, S. E. Ahn, D. –S. Suh, M. J. Lee et al, Appl. Phys. Lett. **88**, 202102 (2006).
5. R. Oligschlaeger, R. Waser, R. Meyer, S. Karthauser, and R. Dittmann, Appl. Phys. Lett. **88**, 042901 (2006).
5. R. S. Potember, T. O. Poehler, and D. O. Cowan, Appl. Phys. Lett. **34**, 405 (1979).
6. T. Oyamada, H. Tanaka, K. Matsushige, H. Sasabe, and C. Adachi, Appl. Phys. Lett. **83**, 1252 (2003).
7. P. W. M. Blom, R. M. Wolf, J. F. M. Cillessen, and M. P. C. M. Krijn, Phys. Rev. Lett. **73**, 2107 (1994).
8. P. van der Sluis, Appl. Phys. Lett. **82**, 4089 (2003).
9. Fu, J. C. Lee, S. W. Choi, C. S. Park, G. N. Panin, and T. W. Kang, X. J. Fan, Appl. Phys. Lett., **83**, 2214-2216 (2003).
10. M. Joseph, H. Tabata, and T. Kawai, Appl. Phys. Lett. **74**, 2534-2536 (1999).
11 R. Waser, *Nanoelectronics and Information Technology* (Wiley,Weinheim, 2003).
12. A. Beck, J. G. Bednorz, Ch. Gerber, C. Rossel, and D. Widmer, Appl. Phys. Lett. **77**, 139 (2000).
13. M. J. Rozenberg, Phys. Rev. Lett. **92**, 178302-1 (2004).
14. C. Rossel, G. I. Meijer, D. Brémaud, and D. Widmer, J. Appl. Phys. **90**, 2892 (2001).
15. R. Meyer, J. R. Contreras, A. Petraru, and H. Kohlstedt, Integr. Ferroelectr. **64**, 77 (2004).
16. G. Arlt, Ferroelectrics **87**, 109 (1988).
17. A.N. Baranov, G.N. Panin T.W. Kang and Y.-J. Oh, Nanotechnology **16**, 1918 (2005).
18. X.R. Wang and Q. Niu, Phys. Rev. B **59**, R12755 (1999).
19. G.N. Panin, T.W. Kang, A. N. Aleshin, A. N. Baranov, Y.-J. Oh, I. A. Khotina, Appl. Phys. Lett. **86**, 113114 (2005).

Spontaneous spin polarization in quantum point contacts

L. P. Rokhinson*, L. N. Pfeiffer† and K. W. West†

*Department of Physics, Purdue University, West Lafayette, IN 47907 USA
†Bell Laboratories, Lucent Technologies, Murray Hill, New Jersey 07974 USA

Abstract. We investigate ballistic transport in quantum point contacts fabricated from high mobility two-dimensional hole gas. At low temperatures conductance quantization in units of $2e^2/h$ is observed. Incorporation of point contacts into a magnetic focusing device allows us to measure relative population of the spin subbands. While both subbands are found to be equally populated at the $2e^2/h$ plateau, there is a finite polarization when conductance is $< 2e^2/h$. Polarization is stronger in samples with well defined "0.7 structure".

Keywords: quantum wires, spin detection, spin polarization
PACS: 72.25.-b, 73.23.Ad, 71.70.Ej, 85.75.-d

Quantization of the ballistic conductance G in integer multiples of $g_0 = 2e^2/h$ is a fundamental property of 1D systems [1, 2], which originates from the exact cancellation of velocity and the 1D density of state. Each energy level below the Fermi energy inside a 1D channel contributes $0.5g_0$ to the total conductance, an extra factor of two accounts for the spin degeneracy. Strong magnetic fields can lift the degeneracy; in this case quantization in multiples of $0.5g_0$ is observed. Thus, observation of a quantized plateau at $0.7g_0$ in the absence of magnetic field first in n-GaAs [3] and, later, in p-Si, n-GaN and p-GaAs quantum point contacts (QPCs) pose a serious challenge to our understanding of 1D conductors.

Phenomenologically, the observed structure can be explained if one assumes the existence of *static* spin polarization at zero magnetic field and confinement-dependent spin splitting of the spin subbands. However, the well-known Lieb–Mattis theorem forbids polarization in 1D systems [4]. Some theories suggest possible deviation from this theorem in a realistic channel with finite width. Recently, it has been pointed out that temperature and bias dependence of differential conductance around the $0.7g_0$ plateau are similar to the Kondo phenomena, thus suggesting *dynamic* spin polarization. Alternative theories assume *no polarization* and attribute the phenomena to electron-phonon interactions or formation of a Wigner crystal. None of the above theories describe the variety of the observed phenomena in a unified and consistent fashion. Thus, direct measurement of spin polarization becomes of a paramount importance.

Magnetic focusing devices are fabricated from a two-dimensional hole gas (2DHG) using an atomic force microscopy local anodic oxidation technique (AFM LAO). AFM micrograph of one of the devices is shown in Fig. 1a. Light lines are oxide which separates the 2DHG underneath by forming ~ 200 mV potential barriers. Devices consist of two QPCs separated by a central gate.

The potential inside the point contacts can be controlled separately by the two side gates G_{inj} and G_{det}, or by the central gate G_c. Several specially designed heterostructures are grown by MBE on [113]A GaAs[5]. Despite very close proximity to the surface (350Å), the 2DHG has exceptionally high mobility $\sim 0.5 \cdot 10^6$ V·s/cm^2. Devices are fabricated from two wafers with hole densities $p = 1.47 \cdot 10^{11}$ cm^{-2} (wafer A) and $p = 0.9 \cdot 10^{11}$ cm^{-2} (wafer B). For quantitative analysis we use data collected during a single cooldown for each device, the qualitative features are reproducible upon several thermal cyclings.

Conductance of the injector point contact is plotted in Fig. 1c as a function of voltage on gate G_{inj}. At zero field (left-most curve) plateaus with conductance quantized at g_0 and $2g_0$ are clearly observed. In addition, an extra plateau can be seen at $G \sim 0.7g_0$. When an in-plane magnetic field $B_{||}$ is applied, the $0.7g_0$ plateau gradually shift toward $0.5g_0$, saturating for $B_{||} > 4$ T. This gradual decrease is different from the abrupt appearance of half-integer plateaus for higher energy levels. In that case plateaus become more prominent as Zeeman splitting increases, but conductance values of the plateaus do not change with $B_{||}$, consistent with the single-particle picture.

Another signature of "0.7 structure" is the anomalous nonlinear differential conductance $g = dI/dV$. A distinct peak in g vs dc bias V_{bias} has been reported in electron QPCs [6]. Nonlinear conductance in our hole device is analyzed in Fig. 1b,d. Indeed, there is a well developed zero-bias peak at the base temperature $T = 25$ mK and $B_{||} = 0$. The peak is suppressed if T or $B_{||}$ are increased. A zero-bias peak and its suppression by T and $B_{||}$ is a hallmark of Kondo phenomena. Landé factor $g^* \approx 0.3$ in the point contact is too small to result in a measurable Zeeman splitting of the zero-bias anomaly in our samples.

Experimentally, polarization of carriers emerging

CP893, *Physics of Semiconductors, 28th International Conference*
edited by W. Jantsch and F. Schäffler

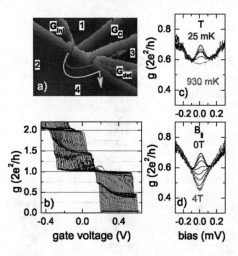

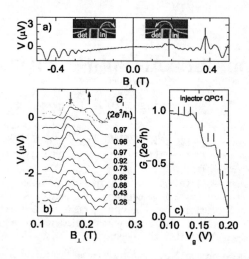

FIGURE 1. a) AFM micrograph of a magnetic focusing device. b) differential conductance $g = dI/dV$ of the injector QPC as a function of gate voltage for different in-plane magnetic fields from $B_{||} = 0$ (left) to $B_{||} = 8$ Tesla (right). c,d) g is measured as a function of dc bias voltage with the gate fixed in the middle of the $0.7 \times 2e^2/h$ plateau at the lowest T and $B_{||} = V_{bias} = 0$ at different c) temperatures and d) magnetic fields.

FIGURE 2. a) magnetoresistance as a function of the orbital magnetic field $B_\perp$. Positions of the first two magnetic focusing peaks are marked with vertical lines. b) The first focusing peak is measured at different injector conductances with detector tuned into the middle of the $2e^2/h$ plateau. The curves are vertically offset by -0.4 μV relative to the top one. The $G = 0.66g_0$ curve is also plotted without an offset (red dashed line). c) Gate voltage characteristic of QPC1, vertical lines mark positions where curves in b) are taken.

from the QPC can be measured in a ballistic magnetic focusing device with strong spin-orbit interaction, where carriers with opposite spins have different cyclotron orbits in small external magnetic field, as shown schematically in Fig. 1a by arrows. Thus, carriers injected from a QPC with opposite spins can be selectively focused into the detector QPC at different orbital magnetic fields $B_\perp^{\uparrow\downarrow}$ and measured separately [7, 8].

Magneto-focusing data are plotted in Fig. 2a. At $|B_\perp| > 0.25$ T Subnikov de-Haas oscillations in the adjacent 2D hole gas are observed. At $B_\perp > 0$ extra peaks due to magnetic focusing are superimposed on Shubnikov de-Haas oscillations and the first two peaks are clearly observed. Positions of the peaks are close to the expected values for QPC1-QPC2 separation $L = 0.8$ μm and scale with 2D hole density. The two peaks within the first focusing peak correspond to the focusing conditions for the two orthogonal spin states in the 2DHG and are adiabatically related to the pure spin states inside the point contacts.

The two peaks within the first focusing peak are plotted in Fig. 2b for different gate voltages. Strength of the peaks is a direct measure of the corresponding spin subband population and their ratio reflects carrier polarization. The peaks have equal height (no polarization) on the g_0 plateau. Polarization is almost 40% when g approaches $0.7g_0$. Moderate polarization of 10-15% is measured in QPCs with no "0.7 anomaly" at $g < g_0$.

ACKNOWLEDGMENTS

This work was supported by NSF grant ECS-0348289.

REFERENCES

1. B. J. van Wees, H. van Houten, C. W. J. Beenakker, J. G. Williamson, L. P. Kouwenhoven, D. van der Marel, and C. T. Foxon, *Phys. Rev. Lett.* **60**, 848 (1988).
2. D. A. Wharam, T. J. Thornton, R. Newbury, M. Pepper, H. Ahmed, J. E. F. Frost, D. G. Hasko, D. C. Peacock, D. A. Ritchie, and G. A. C. Jones, *J. Phys. C* **21**, L209–214 (1988).
3. K. J. Thomas, J. T. Nicholls, M. Y. Simmons, M. Pepper, D. R. Mace, and D. A. Ritchie, *Phys. Rev. Lett.* **77**, 135–138 (1996).
4. E. Lieb, and D. Mattis, *Phys. Rev.* **125**, 164–172 (1962).
5. L. P. Rokhinson, D. C. Tsui, L. N. Pfeiffer, and K. W. West, *Superlattices Microstruct.* **32**, 99–102 (2002).
6. S. M. Cronenwett, H. J. Lynch, D. Goldhaber-Gordon, L. P. Kouwenhoven, C. M. Marcus, K. Hirose, N. S. Wingreen, and V. Umansky, *Phys. Rev. Lett.* **88**, 226805 (2002).
7. L. P. Rokhinson, V. Larkina, Y. B. Lyanda-Geller, L. N. Pfeiffer, and K. W. West, *Phys. Rev. Lett.* **93**, 146601 (2004).
8. L. Rokhinson, L. Pfeiffer, and K. West, *Phys. Rev. Lett.* **96**, 156602 (2006).

Rectified Coulomb Drag Induced by Wigner Crystallization in Quantum Wires

Michihisa Yamamoto[1,2], Hiroyuki Takagi[1], Michael Stopa[3] and Seigo Tarucha[1,4]

[1]Department of Applied Physics, University of Tokyo, Bunkyo-ku, Tokyo 113-8656, Japan,
[2]SORST Interacting Carrier Electronics, Kawaguchi-shi, Saitama 331-0012, Japan,
[3]Center for Nanoscale Systems, Harvard University, Cambridge MA 02138,
[4]ICORP Quantum Spin Information Project, Atsugi-shi, Kanagawa 243-0198, Japan

Abstract. We measure Coulomb drag between parallel quantum wires which have the same length but are slightly displaced from each other along the wire direction. We observe a rectified Coulomb drag in which sign of the drag voltage is the same, independent on the current direction in the drive-wire, under the conditions of strong correlation, i.e., low electron density, high magnetic field and low temperature. From this experiment, we conclude the formation of Wigner crystal and discuss the non-linear motion of Wigner crystal in the drag-wire induced by an electrostatic potential from the adjacent drive-wire.

Keywords: Quantum wire, Winger crystal, Coulomb drag.
PACS: 73.20.Qt, 73.21.Hb, 73.23.-b

Coulomb drag occurs for adjacent current-carrying systems, which exchange momentum and energy via Coulomb interaction [1]. Because Coulomb drag is induced by charge fluctuations and the resulting Coulomb scattering in the electronic systems, it can be used to investigate charge density inhomogeneity in electronic systems. In particular, electron correlation, which leads to spontaneous inhomogeneity, is highly suitable for investigation via drag.

In previous work [2], we employed symmetric coupled quantum wires and observed negative Coulomb drag in the low electron density, high magnetic field, and low temperature regime. Negative drag in 1D cannot be explained by standard theories of Coulomb drag via momentum transfer and has different features from negative drag between 2D layers [3]. We proposed a model in which a Wigner crystal is formed in the drag-wire and attracted by screening holes in the drag-wire leads induced by particle-like electrons in the drive-wire. In this study, we employ coupled quantum wires, which have the same length but are slightly displaced from each other along the wire direction (See Fig. 1). In this geometry, only one of the leads is adjacent to the wire and we can more clearly verify the effect of the lead connected to the drag-wire. Our results agree with the model of sliding Wigner crystal which we proposed in the previous paper.

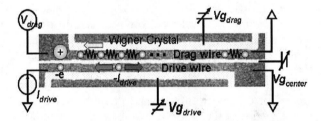

FIGURE 1. SEM image of a coupled wire device and the measurement circuit. Wire length is 8 μm and two wires are displaced by 1 μm. Tunneling current between the two wires is suppressed by applying negative bias to Vg_{center}. Electron density in the two wires is controlled by Vg_{drive} and Vg_{drag}. Quantized conductance plateaus can be observed though they are not perfect in a low magnetic field. Rectified hydrodynamic drag is also schematically depicted. Screening hole is induced in the drag wire lead by an electron in the drive wire. Since the Wigner crystal in the drag wire is rigid, it has small dielectric response and the screening charge (circle with plus sign) is confined to the drag-wire lead.

Before describing the experiments, we first discuss the expected behavior of the Coulomb drag in our device based on the model proposed in the previous paper. We have two components of the overall drag. One results from standard momentum transfer between electrons in different wires. This produces positive drag, in which electrons in the drag-wire are dragged in the same direction as the electron flow in the drive-wire. However, when a Wigner crystal is formed in the

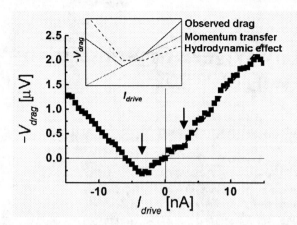

FIGURE 2. Measured I_{drive}-V_{drag} for Vg_{center} = −1.300 V, Vg_{drive} = −1.680 V and Vg_{drag} = −1.488 V, and the fitting to the model described in text. Inset is schematic I_{drive}-V_{drag} characteristics. Lines corresponds to the drag contribution from momentum transfer (red dash), hydrodynamic effect (black dash), and the sum (solid black).

drag-wire and electron density is inhomogeneous in the drive-wire, we expect a second contribution, which is basically hydrodynamic, to the drag. Electrons in the drive-wire are screened in the drag-wire lead, but not in the drag-wire since the Wigner crystal is incompressible. In this device configuration, the drive-wire interior is adjacent to the drag-wire lead on only one side (to the left in Fig. 1). Thus, *irrespective of the direction of I_{drive}*, the positive image kicks the Wigner crystal to the left (in Fig. 1). This occurs every time a single drive-wire electron passes through the region near the edge of the drag-wire. In the experiments, we observe both contributions of momentum transfer and hydrodynamic effect. The latter shows the properties of the rectification described above.

An n-AlGaAs/GaAs heterostructure is used to fabricate displaced coupled wires in a 2D electron gas using a split-gate technique (Fig. 1). The length of the two wires is 4 and 8 μm, separated by a narrow center gate whose width is about 80 nm. The width of the wires is 0.35 μm at the surface and the confinement potential is about 2 meV. Here we only show the results obtained with an 8 μm long coupled quantum wire but the results are similar in both samples.

In the Coulomb drag measurement, we inject a current I_{drive} into the drive-wire and measure the voltage drop V_{drag} along the drag-wire. We perform DC measurements with a dilution refrigerator in a perpendicular magnetic field. We measure the drag effect in the regime where I_{drive} is small enough to suppress intersubband coupling of electrons propagating in the drive-wire.

Fig. 2 shows the typical measured I_{drive}-V_{drag} characteristic under the conditions for strong correlation. The electron density in the drive wire is

sufficiently low that it has a charge density inhomogeneity. The electron density in the drag-wire is set in such a way that the conductance is slightly below the first quantization plateau, where the correlation within the drag-wire becomes maximal [2]. A perpendicular magnetic field of 5T is also applied to quench the kinetic energy and the temperature of the mixing chamber is 40 mK. We find that the sign of the drag resistance defined as $R_D \equiv -dV_{drag}/dI_{drive}$ reverses at $I_{drive} \approx$ −3 nA and R_D rapidly increases at $I_{drive} \approx$ +3 nA (arrow). This drag is interpreted as the summation of the linear contribution from momentum transfer and a presumed non-linear contribution from hydrodynamic drag.

The I_{drive}-V_{drag} characteristics of these contributions are illustrated in Fig. 2 inset. It is natural to assume that V_{drag} of the momentum transfer term is linear with I_{drive}. By contrast, the hydrodynamic term is not proportional to I_{drive} and disappears for small I_{drive}. This property is analyzed by considering the non-linear motion of a Wigner crystal [2]. Since the Wigner crystal is weakly pinned in the drag-wire and since its motion induces damped currents in the leads, a small discontinuous driving force might be insufficient to initiate sliding. In that case, the Wigner crystal only oscillates around its equilibrium position for small I_{drive}. On the other hand, when I_{drive} becomes sufficiently large, Wigner crystal motion can be excited into its sliding modes with finite probability, producing a rectified drag. We can see this non-linear rectified drag property by subtracting the linear contribution of momentum transfer from the experimental data. Detailed I_{drive}-V_{drag} characteristics will be discussed elsewhere.

In conclusion, we measure Coulomb drag between displaced coupled quantum wires. We observe both linear drag by momentum transfer and non-linear rectified drag by hydrodynamic electronic motion between Wigner crystal and the drag wire lead.

We acknowledge financial supports from the DARPA grant no. DAAD19-01-1-0659 of the QuIST program, the Grant-in-Aid for Scientific Research A (No. 40302799) and Focused Research and Development Project for the Realization of the World's Most Advanced IT Nation, IT Program, MEXT. We acknowledge the National Nanotechnology Infrastructure Network Computation Project for support.

REFERENCES

1. T.J. Gramila *et. al.*, *Phys. Rev. Lett.* **66**, 1216 (1991).
2. M. Yamamoto, M. Stopa, Y. Tokura, Y. Hirayama, S. Tarucha, Science **313**, 204 (2006).
3. J.G.S. Lok *et. al.*, *Phys. Rev. B* **63**, 41305(R) (2001); K. Muraki *et. al.*, *Phys. Rev. Lett.* **92**, 246801 (2004).

Conductance Quantization in Schottky-gated Si/SiGe Quantum Point Contacts

G. Scappucci,[1,*] L. Di Gaspare,[1] E. Giovine,[2] A. Notargiacomo,[2] R. Leoni,[2] and F. Evangelisti[1,2]

[1]Dipartimento di Fisica "E. Amaldi", Università Roma TRE, V. Vasca Navale 84, 00146 Roma, Italy.
[2]Istituto di Fotonica e Nanotecnologie, IFN-CNR, Via Cineto Romano 42, 00156 Roma, Italy.

Abstract. We report on the fabrication and electronic transport characterisation of Schottky-gated strongly confined Si/SiGe quantum point contacts (QPC). At zero magnetic field and T=450mK the QPC conductance as a function of gate voltage shows a quantization in units of e^2/h, indicative of transport through 1D modes which appear to lack both spin and valley degeneracy.

Keywords: silicon-germanium, conductance quantization, quantum point contact, 1DEG, 2DEG
PACS: 73.23.-b ; 73.23.Ad.

INTRODUCTION

Despite the high quality reached in the last decade for the Si/SiGe two-dimensional electron gas (2DEG), only recently significant progress has been achieved in obtaining high confinement of charge carriers and effective gating action on Si/SiGe quantum devices.[1, 2]
This allows also for the Si electron gas conductance investigations that have previously been restricted to GaAs systems. In this paper we report on the fabrication of highly confined Si/SiGe etched quantum point contact efficiently controlled by Schottky gates and discuss the presence of a surprising e^2/h conductance quantization.

EXPERIMENTAL

We fabricated Schottky-gated QPCs on high mobility Si/SiGe 2DEG. The Si/SiGe 2DEG heterostructure was grown by chemical vapour deposition on Si(001) substrates. At T=300mK, the value of the 2DEG carrier density, estimated from low-field Hall measurements on mesa-etched Hall bars, was 9.8×10^{11}cm^{-2} and the electron mobility 4.1×10^4cm^2/Vs. From these values we estimate a mean-free path of the 2D unconstrained carriers of the order of 500 nm. [2] The QPCs were obtained by confining the 2DEG in a double-bend like geometry by electron-beam lithography (EBL) and reactive ion etching. In Fig. 1 we report a scanning electron micrograph of a complete device.

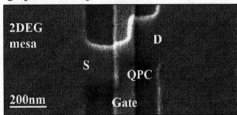

FIGURE 1. Scanning electron micrograph of a Si/SiGe etched quantum point contact controlled by a Schottky top-gate.

The QPC is formed by the narrow conducting channel (lithographic width $w \sim 170$ nm, effective width much smaller due to lateral depletion) that originates at the 2DEG mesa protrusions labeled S and D in Fig. 1. By EBL and lift-off we patterned a 5/30-nm-thick Ti/Au 100nm-wide finger gate crossing the central constriction and folding along the etched surfaces of the constriction; the electric field imposed by the gate on the lateral walls is screened by the surface states so that in this configuration the gate varies the carrier concentration without changing the width of the QPC.[3] At T=450mK the leakage from the Schottky gate (active area less than $0.1\times0.16\mu m^2$) to the 2DEG was negligible (leakage current $I_{GATE}<0.2$ pA) in the -2V to +1V gate voltage range. This large available working range enabled a full control of electronic transport through the QPC from conduction to depletion.

CP893, *Physics of Semiconductors, 28th International Conference*
edited by W. Jantsch and F. Schäffler
© 2007 American Institute of Physics 978-0-7354-0397-0/07/$23.00

RESULTS AND DISCUSSION

Electronic transport characterisation of the QPC devices was performed at T = 450 mK in a ³He refrigerator at zero magnetic field using standard ac low frequency lock-in techniques. The linear conductance G versus the gate voltage V_G is reported in Fig. 2(a). The curve was corrected to take in account for a series resistance R_S= 19.4 kΩ, originating from both the outer 2DEG mesa structure as well as the source and drain contacts. The conductance shows clearly a staircase with plateau-like structures close to multiple integers of e^2/h, suggesting transport through 1D modes in with both spin and valley degeneracy appear removed at zero magnetic field. The data were highly reproducible upon sweeping the gate from positive to negative voltages or cycling the temperature from 450 mK to room temperature.

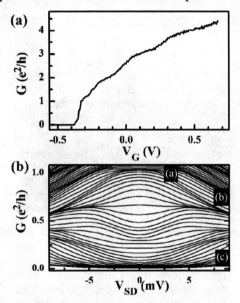

FIGURE 2. Electronic transport characterisation of the Si/SiGe QPC at T = 450 mK. (a) Conductance vs. gate voltage exhibiting e^2/h quantization. (b) Finite source-drain bias spectroscopy showing the presence of a integer plateau that at finite V_{SD} evolves in a half e^2/h plateau.

To gain insight into the e^2/h quantization, finite source-drain bias spectroscopy was performed by measuring the non-linear conductance G versus source-drain bias V_{DS} at different V_G. In Fig. 2(b) we report the curves measured by changing the gate voltage in the range where the linear conductance in Fig. 2(a) develops the e^2/h feature. The data were corrected to take in account the presence of an electrostatic self-gating effect and, again, of a series resistance. The G-V_{SD} curves show an evolution with the gate voltage as expected for the e^2/h quantization. Several curves bundle at $V_{SD} \sim 0$ mV at the

conductance value e^2/h in the gate voltage range where the G-Vg curve developed the e^2/h plateau [$V_G \sim$ -0.3125 V, label (a)]; this integer plateau evolves into a half-integer plateau (G $\sim$ 0.5 e^2/h) as the source-drain bias is increased to a finite value [V_{SD}~4mV, label (b)]. From the V_{SD} position of the half-integer plateau we estimate the energy spacing between the first two 1D subband ΔE $\sim$ 4 meV, indicating that significant quantum confinement is achieved in the device. At large negative gate values [label (c)], there is no conduction at $V_{SD} \sim$ 0 mV meaning that the Fermi level is below the onset of the first 1D band.

The behaviour of the linear and non-linear conductance upon changing the gate bias can be explained considering adiabatic transmission through 1D modes with complete removal of valley and spin degeneracies. In a Si 1D electron gas the conductance quantization was previously found in units of $4e^2/h$, as expected in a valley and spin degenerate electron gas.[4] In our devices the removal of the valley degeneracy is likely to be the result of the strong confining potential; more unexpected is the presence of the e^2/h plateau at zero magnetic field and evidence for the e^2/h quantization. Recently an unexpected e^2/h quantization was reported also in carbon nanotubes.[5] These findings might be closely related to the "0.7 anomaly", a spin-related phenomenon observed at zero magnetic field in clean 1D GaAs systems which is assumed to signal the occurrence of non negligible correlation effects. [6]

ACKNOWLEDGMENTS

This work was partially supported by the FIRB project RBNE01FSWY "Nanoelettronica" and the FISR project "Nanotecnologie per dispositivi di memoria ad altissima densità".

REFERENCES

* Present address: School of Physics, University of New South Wales, Sydney NSW 2052, Australia.
1. G. Scappucci, L. Di Gaspare, F. Evangelisti, E. Giovine, A. Notargiacomo, R. Leoni, V. Piazza, P. Pingue, and F. Beltram, *Phys. Rev. B* **71**, 245311 (2005).
2. G. Scappucci, L. Di Gaspare, E. Giovine, A. Notargiacomo, R. Leoni , and F. Evangelisti, *Phys. Rev. B*, in press (2006).
3. G. Curatola and G. Iannaccone, *J. Appl. Phys.* **95**, 1251 (2004).
4. D. Tobben, D. A. Wharam, G. Abstreiter, J. P. Kolthaus, and F. Schaffler, *Semicond. Sci. Technol.* 10, 711 (1995).
5. M. J. Biercuk, N. Mason, J. Martin, A. Yacoby, and C. M. Marcus, *Phys. Rev. Lett.* **94**, 026801 (2005).
6. K. J. Thomas, J. T. Nicholls, M. Y. Simmons, M. Pepper, D. R. Mace, and D. A. Ritchie, *Phys. Rev. Lett.* **77**, 135 (1996).

Counting statistics of single electron transport in a quantum dot

S. Gustavsson*, R. Leturcq*, B. Simovič*, R. Schleser*, T. Ihn*,
P. Studerus*, K. Ensslin*, D. C. Driscoll† and A. C. Gossard†

*Solid State Physics Laboratory, ETH Zürich, CH-8093 Zürich, Switzerland
†Materials Departement, University of California, Santa Barbara, CA-93106, USA

Abstract. We present measurements of counting statistics for electron transport in a quantum dot. By counting the electrons one by one using a quantum point contact as a charge detector, we are able to generate the distribution function of the current fluctuations. From the distribution function, higher order noise correlations can be determined. We measure a reduction of both the second moment (variance, related to shot noise) and the third moment (asymmetry) of the current distribution compared to a Poisson distribution. The reduction of noise can be explained by the increase in electron correlation due to Coulomb blockade.

PACS: 2.70.+m, 73.23.Hk, 73.63.Kv

Temporal current fluctuations in conductors have been intensely investigated due to the additional information they provide compared to the average current, in particular for interacting systems [1]. In semiconductor quantum dots it has been proposed that shot noise measurements might provide a way to demonstrate entanglement of electrons [2, 3]. However, for these systems conventional noise measurements are difficult to perform due to the very low current levels. Here, we present measurements of the current fluctuations in a quantum dot (QD), which were performed by detecting the electrons using a quantum point contact (QPC) as a charge detector [4]. By counting the electrons one by one, we get direct access to the full distribution of the current fluctuations, known as the full counting statistics.

The sample consists of a QD [dotted circle Fig. 1(a)] with a nearby quantum point contact (QPC) used for reading out the charge state of the QD [4]. The structure was fabricated using scanning probe lithography [5] on a GaAs/Al$_{0.3}$Ga$_{0.7}$As heterostructure with a two-dimensional electron gas 34 nm below the surface. The gates G_1 and G_2 are used to tune the tunnel coupling between the dot and the source and drain leads. The P-gate is used to keep the conductance through the QPC in a regime where the sensitivity to changes in its electrostatic potential is maximal. The measurements were performed in a dilution refrigerator with a base temperature of 60 mK.

In the low-bias, weak coupling Coulomb blockade regime, the dot can hold only one excess electron. Because of the electrostatic coupling between the QD and the QPC, the conductance of the QPC will change whenever an electron enters or leaves the dot. By performing time-resolved measurements of the QPC current, tun-

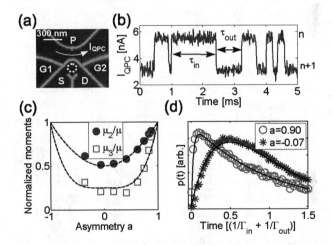

FIGURE 1. (a) Quantum dot with integrated charge read-out used in the experiment. (b) Typical time trace of the QPC conductance. The tunneling rates extracted from this trace are $\Gamma_{in} = 1.44$ kHz and $\Gamma_{out} = 1.34$ kHz. (c) Normalized moments versus asymmetry of the tunnel coupling, $a = (\Gamma_{in} - \Gamma_{out})/(\Gamma_{in} + \Gamma_{out})$. The dashed lines are the theoretical predictions for a two-state model, giving $\mu_2/\mu = (1 + a^2)/2$ and $\mu_3/\mu = (1 + 3a^4)/4$. (d) Distribution of times needed for one electron to pass through the QD, measured with both symmetric and asymmetric tunnel couplings. To make qualitative comparisons of the two distributions easier, the two curves are plotted with different vertical axes. The time scale is normalized to the average time needed for one electron to pass the dot.

neling of single electrons can be detected in real-time [6, 7, 8]. To ensure that the charge detector is measuring transport through the dot and not tunneling due to thermal fluctuations, we perform all measurements in a bias regime where the electrochemical potential of the dot is

CP893, *Physics of Semiconductors, 28th International Conference*
edited by W. Jantsch and F. Schäffler
© 2007 American Institute of Physics 978-0-7354-0397-0/07/$23.00

far away from the thermal broadening of the leads [9].

The transport in this regime is governed by one rate for electrons entering the QD from the source lead and another rate for electrons leaving the QD to the drain. Assuming that the tunneling events are independent, the probability distribution for the times needed for an electron to tunnel into or out of the QD will follow the exponential law [7]

$$p_{\text{in/out}}(t) = \Gamma_{\text{in/out}} \exp(-\Gamma_{\text{in/out}} t). \tag{1}$$

Here, $\Gamma_{\text{in/out}} = 1/\langle \tau_{\text{in/out}} \rangle$, with $\tau_{\text{in/out}}$ being the distribution of tunneling times for the two barriers.

Figure 1(b) shows a typical measurement of the QPC current. The low level corresponds to a situation where the dot holds one excess electron. The labels τ_{in} and τ_{out} mark tunneling times for electrons entering and leaving the dot, respectively. By analyzing the distribution of tunneling times, one can use Eq. (1) to extract the tunnel coupling strengths Γ_{in} and Γ_{out}. To obtain correct results, it is important to take the bandwidth of the detector into account [10]. For the data presented here, we measured traces of length $T = 0.5$ s with a bandwidth of 30 kHz. To minimize statistical errors, the extracted quantities were averaged over ~ 30 similar traces.

To calculate the noise of the current flowing through the QD, we start by forming the distribution function $p_{t_0}(N)$. The distribution describes the probability for N electrons to travel through the QD within a time t_0. The mean (μ) of the distribution gives the current through the dot, while the variance (μ_2) is equal to the shot noise. Higher order moments $\mu_i = \langle (N - \langle N \rangle)^i \rangle$ can also be calculated easily. In Fig. 1(c), we show measurements of the normalized moments μ_2/μ (the Fano factor) and μ_3/μ as a function of asymmetry of the tunneling barrier, $a = (\Gamma_{\text{in}} - \Gamma_{\text{out}})/(\Gamma_{\text{in}} + \Gamma_{\text{out}})$. The dashed lines are theoretical results calculated using a two-state model [11, 12].

The figure shows a reduction of the noise for a symmetrically coupled QD compared to the values $\mu_2/\mu = \mu_3/\mu = 1$ expected for a single barrier. This is due to the Coulomb blockade; a second electron cannot enter the dot before the first one leaves. The effect increases the correlations between tunneling electrons and thereby reduces the noise. As the tunnel couplings of the barriers grow more asymmetric, the transport is essentially governed by the weakly transparent barrier and the noise approaches the single barrier value.

A complementary way of investigating the correlations is to look at the time statistics of electron transport. Instead of evaluating the probability distribution for the number of electrons that are transferred within a fixed time t_0, we examine the continuous distribution $p_N(t)$ describing the time needed for a fixed number of N electrons to pass through the QD. With the rates for tunneling

into and out of the QD given by Eq. (1), we find for $N = 1$

$$
\begin{aligned}
p_{\text{N}=1}(t) &= \int_0^t p_{\text{in}}(t') p_{\text{out}}(t - t') dt' = \\
&= \frac{\exp(-\Gamma_{\text{in}} t) - \exp(-\Gamma_{\text{out}} t)}{1/\Gamma_{\text{in}} - 1/\Gamma_{\text{out}}}.
\end{aligned} \tag{2}
$$

In Fig. 1(d), we show the experimentally determined distribution $p_{N=1}(t)$ for two different values of the asymmetry together with the results of Eq. (2). For the symmetric case [$a = -0.07$ in Fig. 1(d)], there is a clear suppression of transfer probability for short timescales. Again, this is due to the Coulomb blockade. We measure anti-bunching of electrons and sub-Poisson noise levels. For the more asymmetric case [$a = 0.9$ in Fig. 1(d)], the anti-bunching is less prominent and the probability distribution approaches the exponential behavior expected for a single tunnel barrier.

In conclusion, we have measured current fluctuations in a semiconductor QD using a QPC to detect single electron traveling through the QD. For a symmetrically coupled QD, we measure anti-bunching of electrons, giving a reduction of the second and third moments of the distribution compared to a single tunneling barrier. The anti-bunching of the electrons is due to the Coulomb blockade effect. We like to note that measurement method is general and can be extended to detect even higher moments [13] as well as to investigate super-Poissonian noise [14].

REFERENCES

1. Y. M. Blanter, and M. Büttiker, *Physics Reports* **336**, 1 (2000).
2. D. Loss, and E. V. Sukhorukov, *Phys. Rev. Lett.* **84**, 1035 (2000).
3. D. S. Saraga, and D. Loss, *Phys. Rev. Lett.* **90**, 166803 (2003).
4. M. Field *et al.*, *Phys. Rev. Lett.* **70**, 1311 (1993).
5. A. Fuhrer *et al.*, *Superl. and Microstruc.* **31**, 19–42 (2002).
6. T. Fujisawa *et al.*, *Appl. Phys. Lett.* **84**, 2343 (2004).
7. R. Schleser *et al.*, *Appl. Phys. Lett.* **85**, 2005 (2004).
8. L. M. K. Vandersypen *et al.*, *Appl. Phys. Lett.* **85**, 4394 (2004).
9. S. Gustavsson *et al.*, *Phys. Rev. Lett.* **96**, 076605 (2006).
10. O. Naaman, and J. Aumentado, *Phys. Rev. Lett.* **96**, 100201 (2006).
11. J. H. Davies *et al.*, *Phys. Rev. B* **46**, 9620 (1992).
12. D. A. Bagrets, and Y. V. Nazarov, *Phys. Rev. B* **67**, 085316 (2003).
13. S. Gustavsson *et al.*, cond-mat/0607192 (2006).
14. S. Gustavsson *et al.*, cond-mat/0605365 (2006).

Higher-order moment of single-electron current noise in a double quantum dot

T. Fujisawa[1,2], T. Hayashi[1], and Y. Hirayama[1,3,4]

[1]*NTT Basic Research Laboratories, NTT Corporation,*
3-1 Morinosato-Wakamiya, Atsugi, 243-0198, Japan
[2]*Tokyo Institute of Technology, 2-12-1 Ookayama, Meguro-ku, Tokyo, 152-8551, Japan*
[3]*SORST-JST, 4-1-8 Honmachi, Kawaguchi, 331-0012, Japan*
[4]*Department of Physics, Tohoku University, Sendai, Miyagi, 980-8578, Japan*

Charge detection measurement on a double quantum dot allows bidirectional counting of single-electrons for extremely small current. We discuss higher-order moment of current noise in single-electron transport through a double quantum dot, and find that the third order moment is insensitive to the thermal noise. The counting statistics provides useful technique for studying correlated transport.

Counting statistics of electron transport provides various information about interactions and correlations in mesoscopic systems[1, 2]. However, conventional current noise measurements cannot be applied to a small current in a weak tunneling regime, because existing current meters require millions of electrons to flow. In contrast, individual tunneling events through a quantum dot can be detected with a charge detector like a quantum point contact (QPC) [3–6]. Moreover, charge detection on a double quantum dot (DQD) allows bidirectional counting, in which forward and reverse tunneling events can be separately detected [7]. This bidirectional counting gives various statistical analyses on correlated transport. Here, we focus on analyses with higher-order moment of the current to investigate correlated transport.

The single-electron counting is based on charge detection for a DQD in the Coulomb blockade regime. Figure 1(a) shows a measurement setup with a scanning electron micrograph (SEM) of the device fabricated in an Al-GaAs/GaAs heterostructure. The upper electrical channel involving a DQD provides single-electron transport, and the charge state of the DQD is measured with a QPC formed in the lower channel. The QPC is adjusted in the tunneling regime with a typical average current $\langle I_{QPC} \rangle \sim$ 12 nA at an excitation voltage $V_Q = 0.8$ mV. The current changes by a few percent depending on the charge state of the DQD. The charge state (n, m), in which n and m excess electrons occupy the left and the right dot respectively, can be controlled by gate voltages V_L and V_R, and the transport through the DQD is allowed only when the electrochemical potentials for (n, m), $(n+1, m)$ and $(n, m+1)$ are energetically degenerated within the applied bias voltage, eV_S. The transport involves three tunneling processes between these charge states. We adjusted these tunneling rates within the bandwidth (about 10 kHz) of the current amplifier used to measure I_{PC} so that individual tunneling events are clearly visible in the time domain, as shown in Fig. 1(b). The observed three-level fluctuation corresponds to tunneling between

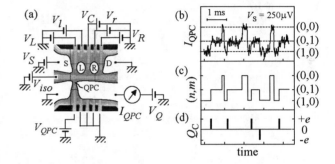

FIG. 1: (a) Schematic diagram of the measurement system with a colored scanning electron micrograph of the device. A DQD (L and R) is formed in the upper electrical channel, and QPC in the lower channel measures the charge state of the DQD. (b) Typical fluctuation of the QPC current. (c) Digitized data from (b), (d) Pulsed current across the central barrier. Positive and negative pulses represent forward and reverse electron flow, respectively.

$(0, 0)$, $(0, 1)$, and $(1, 0)$ charge state. Note that n and m are *excess* electron number, while the actual electron number is about 10. The fluctuation can be digitized with appropriate filtering as shown in Fig. 1(c), which substantially removes the current noise in I_{QPC}. The temporal changes in the electron numbers (n, m) can be converted into a pulsed current, for example, through a central barrier by considering transition between $(1, 0)$ and $(0, 1)$, as shown in Fig. 1(d). Each current pulse represents transport of elementary charge e.

Basically, analyses on all tunneling events gives complete information about the electron transport in a DQD. Here, we focus on the current fluctuation in the pulsed current, which is sufficient to understand the correlated transport of the system. Moreover, since the current is conserved in an electrical circuit, the analyses can be ap-

CP893, *Physics of Semiconductors, 28th International Conference*
edited by W. Jantsch and F. Schäffler
© 2007 American Institute of Physics 978-0-7354-0397-0/07/$23.00

plied to investigate a current from other devices.

First, we discuss distribution of net electron number, N, transferred through the DQD during the averaging period T_{avr}. Figure 2(a) shows a typical distribution taken under a large bias voltage $eV_S = 300$ μV. In order to restrict the analyses in the low-frequency limit, $T_{avr} = 4$ ms which is sufficiently long as compared to the correlation time of 0.3 ms (data not shown) is chosen. The distribution can be characterized by n-th moment, $\langle N^n \rangle$. The first moment (average) gives the average current, $I = e\langle N \rangle/T_{avr}$. We obtained $I = 5.9 \times 10^{-17}$ A for Fig. 2(a). The second moment is related to the noise of the current, $S = e^2 \langle \delta N^2 \rangle/T_{avr}$, through the second central moment $\langle \delta N^2 \rangle = \langle N^2 \rangle - \langle N \rangle^2$, where $\delta N = N - \langle N \rangle$ is the deviation from the central value. For the case of Fig. 2(a), we obtained S = 8.5×10^{-36} A^2/Hz and corresponding Fano factor S/eI = 0.88. The Fano factor less than unity indicates antibanching correlation in the transport. However, since the second noise also involves thermal noise and other extrinsic noise, for example, in the measurement system, the simple analysis overestimates the Fano factor unless current or temperature dependence is discussed.

The third-order moment of the distribution, which is called skewness, is of particular interest for its insensitivity to the thermal distribution[8–10]. The slight asymmetric distribution seen in Fig. 2(a) indicates the presence of skewness and corresponding third-order noise $C = e^3 \langle \delta N^3 \rangle/T_{avr}$ is 2.7×10^{-55} A^3/Hz^2. The relative value to the full shot noise, $C/e^2 I$, measures the correlation of the transport [8, 11]. The ratio of 0.17 for Fig. 2(a) indicates antibanching correlation (< 1), consistent with calculation ($\sim$0.2) based on Ref. [12]. In order to test how closely the measurement can be performed in the equilibrium condition at zero bias, the second- and third-order noise are plotted as a function of the bias voltage in Figs. 2(b) and (c). Here, we have chosen the linear conductance region, where the current is restricted by one of the barriers (equivalent to the single barrier case for the noise). In this case, the second- and third-order noise should coincide with full shot noise eI and $e^2 I$, respectively, if other noise does not contribute. The second-order noise is significantly higher than eI at small voltage $V_S \lesssim 100$ μV, where the thermal noise is dominant ($k_B T_e = 15$ μeV). In contrast, the third-order noise follows $e^2 I$ in the whole range, and no additional noise is observed. This demonstrated insensitivity to thermal noise is desirable for measuring meaningful non-Gaussian noise even at high temperature.

In summary, higher-order moment of current noise is investigated with bidirectional counting scheme. We have shown that the third-order noise is insensitive to the thermal noise, which is useful for studying correlated transport in nearly equilibrium condition.

This work was supported by the SCOPE from the Ministry of Internal Affairs and Communications of Japan, and by a Grant-in-Aid for Scientific Research from the JSPS.

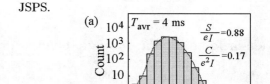

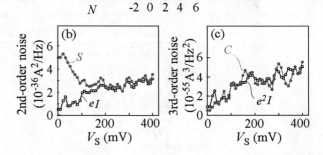

FIG. 2: (a) Electron number distribution of net current through the central barrier. (b) Bias voltage dependence of the second order noise. Significant thermal noise appears at zero bias. (c) Bias voltage dependence of the third order noise.

REFERENCES

[1] Quantum Noise in Mesoscopic Physics, Yu. V. Nazarov Ed. (NATO Science Series II Vol. 97, Kluwer, Dordrecht, The Netherlands, 2003).

[2] Ya. M. Blanter, M. Büttiker, Phys. Reports 336, 1 (2000).

[3] T. Fujisawa, T. Hayashi, Y. Hirayama, H. D. Cheong, Y. H. Jeong, Appl. Phys. Lett. 84, 2343 (2004).

[4] W. Lu, Z. Ji, L. Pfeiffer, K. W. West, A. J. Rimberg, Nature 423, 422 (2003).

[5] J. Bylander, T. Duty, P. Delsing, Nature 434, 361 (2005).

[6] S. Gustavsson, R. Leturcq, B. Simovič, R. Schleser, T. Ihn, P. Studerus, K. Ensslin D. C. Driscoll, A. C. Gossard, Phys. Rev. Lett. 96, 076605 (2006).

[7] T. Fujisawa, T. Hayashi, R. Tomita, and Y. Hirayama, Science 312, 1634 (2006).

[8] L. S. Levitov, M. Reznikov, Phys. Rev. B 70, 115305 (2004).

[9] B. Reulet, J. Senzier, D. E. Prober, Phys. Rev. Lett. 91, 196601 (2003).

[10] Yu. Bomze, G. Gershon, D. Shovkun, L. S. Levitov, M. Reznikov, Phys. Rev. Lett. 95, 176601 (2005).

[11] G. Kießlich, P. Samuelsson, A. Wacker, E. Schöll, Phys. Rev. B 73, 033312 (2006).

[12] D. A. Bagrets, Yu. V. Nazarov, Phys. Rev. B 67, 085316 (2003).

Interaction of a 2-level system with 2D phonons

W.J.M. Naber[*,†], T. Fujisawa[†,**], H.W. Liu[†,‡] and W.G. van der Wiel[*,§]

[*]SRO NanoElectronics, MESA+ Institute for NanoTechnology, University of Twente,
PO Box 217, 7500 AE Enschede, The Netherlands
[†]NTT Basic Research Labs., NTT Corporation, 3-1 Morinosato-Wakamiya, Atsugi, Kanagawa 243-0198, Japan
[**]Tokyo Institute of Technology, 2-12-1 Okayama, Meguro-ku, Tokyo 152-8551, Japan
[‡]SORST-JST, 4-1-8 Honmachi, Kawaguchi, Saitama 331-0012, Japan; National Laboratory of Superhard
Materials, Institute of Atomic and Molecular Physics, Jilin University, Changchun 130012, China
[§]PRESTO-JST, 7-3-1, University of Tokyo, Hongo, Bunkyo-ku, Tokyo 113-8656, Japan

Abstract.
We report on the non-adiabatic interaction between 2D acoustic phonons and an artificial 2-level system in a GaAs/AlGaAs heterostructure. The 2-level system is formed by two discrete energy levels inside a double quantum dot, and monochromatic surface acoustic waves (~2 GHz) are generated by an on-chip interdigital transducer (IDT). An IDT for better performance is proposed.

Keywords: 2-level system, quantum dots, surface acoustic waves
PACS: 73.23.Hk,63.20.Kr,77.65.Dq

INTRODUCTION

A double quantum dot (DQD) [1] forms a tunable device for studying the coupling of a two-level quantum system to a dissipative environment. The dephasing of such systems [2] is of particular interest in the light of quantum computation and information, where two-level quantum systems are the basic building blocks. Inelastic transi-

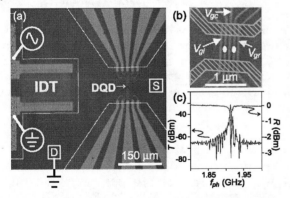

FIGURE 1. (a) Picture of the device. The IDT, DQD, source (S) and drain (D) are indicated. The IDT has a 1.4 μm periodicity. (b) Scanning electron micrograph of the DQD. The distance between the dots is 220 nm. (c) Transmission (T) and reflection (R) of a similar IDT at room temperature.

tions between discrete energy levels, in which energy is exchanged with the environment in the form of bosons, are often undesirable. In Ref. [3] the inelastic transition rates in a DQD were described in term of the Einstein coefficients, relating absorption and stimulated emission to spontaneous emission. It was found that piezoelectric coupling to acoustic phonons is the dominant mechanism for relaxation, as confirmed by theory [4]. The experimental results of Ref. [3], nor the the theory of Ref. [4], however, are decisive about the nature (2D or 3D) of the acoustic phonons.

Here, we present experimental results on phonon induced electron transport through a lithographically defined DQD with an on-chip generator of monochromatic (1.94 GHz) surface acoustic waves (SAWs). The DQD acts as a sensitive detector for the tunable phonon environment, giving a direct measure for the amplitude of the local piezoelectric potential oscillations.

EXPERIMENTS

Our device is shown in Fig. 1(a), where the interdigital transducer (IDT) for generating the SAWs and the DQD are indicated [5]. Figure 1(b) is a scanning electron micrograph of the DQD, showing the Ti/Au gate pattern and the shallow etch region (hashed). The IDT design is characterized at room temperature using a different GaAs/AlGaAs heterostructure with two identical IDTs facing each other, allowing for a two-channel microwave measurement. The transmission and reflection spectra in Fig. 1(c) show a clear resonance at 1.92 GHz, as expected from the IDT design. The reflection dip is more than 3 dB, indicating that more than half of the incident power is absorbed in the IDT. The transmission reaches a maximum of -30 dB at resonance, implying additional loss in the device. Possible mechanisms for power loss are impedance mismatch, electromechanical

CP893, *Physics of Semiconductors, 28th International Conference*
edited by W. Jantsch and F. Schäffler
© 2007 American Institute of Physics 978-0-7354-0397-0/07/$23.00

conversion loss and Bragg reflection within the IDT. We found that the reflection and transmission spectra do not change when a DQD device is fabricated in the middle between the IDTs. By assuming identical characteristics for both IDTs, acoustic power at the site of the DQD is 15 dB less than the incident microwave power, P.

Figure 2(a) shows the single-electron tunneling current through the DQD versus gate voltages V_{gl} and V_{gr} with a large bias voltage of 500 μV with no microwave power ($P = 0$) applied to the IDT ($T = 50$ mK). The triangular conduction regions correspond to electron-like and hole-like transport through the DQD [1]. Resonant tunneling through the ground states (GG), as well as through the left dot ground state and the first and second excited states of the right dot are indicated (GE1 and GE2) We now simultaneously sweep V_{gl} and V_{gr} along the white arrow, so that the energy difference $\Delta E = E_1 - E_2$ between the ground state energies of the left dot (E_1) and the right dot (E_2) is varied.

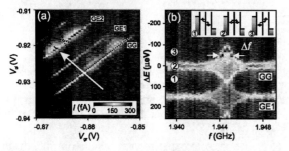

FIGURE 2. (a) Grayscale plot of the DQD current vs. gate voltages V_{gl} and V_{gr} at source drain voltage $V_{SD} = 500$ μV without SAWs. Resonant tunnelings lines are visible within the triangles. (b) Grayscale plot of the DQD current vs. ground state level spacing ΔE and microwave frequency f ($P = -40$ dBm). The schematics in the inset illustrate emission (1), elastic transport (2), and absorption (3).

Figure 2(b) shows the GG resonance when microwaves are applied to the IDT. Significant broadening and splitting of the resonant tunneling peaks only at the IDT resonant frequency, $f_{SAW} = 1.9446$ GHz. Photon assisted tunneling [6] is ruled out, since there is no reason why there should be an electromagnetic resonance coinciding with the IDT resonance frequency. We also exclude resonant heating, since the energy levels are well separated from the Fermi levels of the leads. Note that no broadening is observed at off-resonant frequencies, also indicating that heating and spurious electromagnetic coupling are negligible.

The traveling SAW causes a time-dependent potential $V_{ac} \cos(2\pi f_{SAW} t)$ between the two quantum dots, due to the piezoelectric coupling. We have found [5] that our data reveal clear quantum behavior, and that transport can be described in terms of the nonadiabatic theory of resonant tunneling via two discrete states with a time-dependent energy difference [7]. One can say that the

DQD is exposed to surface acoustic phonons with energy $hf_{SAW} = 8$ μeV. As the FWHM of the elastic current resonance is 14 μeV in our experiment, we have not succeeded in measuring clearly resolved satellites as in former DQD experiments [1]. IDTs with a higher resonance frequency, such as the 6 GHz IDT ($hf = 25$ μeV) in Fig. 3(a) would allow us to do so. The depicted IDT is double-fingered, i.e. it has 4 fingers per period instead of 2. In single-fingered IDTs, constructive interference occurs between propagating SAWs and reflected SAWs, thereby reducing the output of the IDT. In the double-finger geometry this problem is reduced by turning the internal interference into a negative one (see Fig. 3(b)).

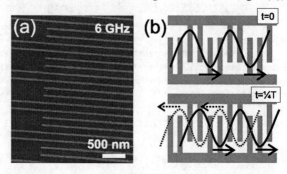

FIGURE 3. (a) Scanning electron micrograph of a double-fingered 6GHz IDT. (b) Schematics illustrating the destructive interference between right-moving SAWs and reflected (left-moving) SAWs in a double-fingered IDT.

ACKNOWLEDGMENTS

We thank S. Tarucha, P.V. Santos, R. Aguado, L.P. Kouwenhoven and Y. Hirayama for fruitful discussions and help. We acknowledge financial support from DARPA grant number DAAD19-01-1-0659 of the QuIST program, and SCOPE from the Ministry of Internal Affairs and Communications of Japan.

REFERENCES

1. W.G. van der Wiel *et al.*, Rev. Mod. Phys. **75**, 1 (2003).
2. A.J. Leggett *et al.*, Rev. Mod. Phys. **59**, 1 (1987).
3. T. Fujisawa *et al.*, Science **282**, 932 (1998); T. Fujisawa, W.G. van der Wiel and L.P. Kouwenhoven, Physica E **7**, 413 (2000).
4. T. Brandes and B. Kramer, Phys. Rev. Lett. **83**, 3021 (1999).
5. W.J.M. Naber *et al.*, Phys. Rev. Lett. **96**, 136807 (2006).
6. W.G. van der Wiel *et al.*, Photon Assisted Tunneling in Quantum Dots in Strongly Correlated Fermions and Bosons in Low-Dimensional Disordered Systems, eds. I.V. Lerner *et al.*, pp. 43-68, Kluwer (2002).
7. T.H. Stoof and Yu.V. Nazarov, Phys. Rev. B **53**, 1050 (1996).

Magnetotunneling through stacked InAs/InGaAs/InP self-assembled quantum dots

A.G. Silva[1], P.S.S. Guimarães[1], S.M. Landi[2], M.P. Pires[3], P.L. Souza[2], G.S. Vieira[4].

[1]*Departamento de Física, Universidade Federal de Minas Gerais, Belo Horizonte MG, Brazil*
[2]*LabSem, CETUC, Pontifícia Universidade Católica do Rio de Janeiro, Rio de Janeiro RJ, Brazil*
[3]*Instituto de Física, Universidade Federal do Rio de Janeiro, Rio de Janeiro RJ, Brazil*
[4]*Instituto de Estudos Avançados, CTA, São José dos Campos SP, Brazil*

Abstract. We report an investigation of magnetotransport in stacked self-assembled quantum dot multi-layers, with applied magnetic fields up to 12 T parallel to the tunneling current. We observe tunneling between quantum dot states in adjacent layers and we show evidence of tunneling through Zeeman-split quasi-zero dimensional states.

Keywords: Self-assembled quantum dots, magnetotunneling, Zeeman-split.
PACS: 73.40.Gk, 73.63.Kv, 85.60.Gz.

INTRODUCTION

The application of magnetic fields has been intensively used to investigate self-assembled quantum dots (SAQDs). Nevertheless, the majority of the experimental investigations of magnetic field effects on the electronic states of SAQDs employ optical techniques and therefore the states observed are in reality exciton states, making it difficult to separate the electron and hole contributions. Transport experiments in suitably designed structures allow one to probe separately the electrons and holes states. In this respect, magnetotunneling measurements[1] have been used to study the electronic states of single quantum dots. Investigation of tunneling through double layers of stacked InAs SAQDs has also been reported[2]. However, so far there has been no study of electronic transport at low temperatures through quantum dot multi-layers. We describe here an investigation of magnetotunneling on stacked InAs SAQDs layers.

EXPERIMENTS AND RESULTS

The samples were grown by metalo-organic vapor phase epitaxy on semi-insulating (100) InP substrate and consist of 10 layers of InAs quantum dots (QDs) each one grown on a 12 nm thick InGaAs layer lattice-matched with InP and capped by 16 nm of InP. This structure was sandwiched between 0.4 μm InP contact layers doped with Si to 10^{18} cm^{-3}. A control sample exactly like the first one, but without the InAs dots

was also grown. Apart from the ohmic contacts, the sample was not intentionally doped. For the transport measurements, mesas with (150 x 260) μm^2 area were fabricated. Transmission Electron Microscopy (TEM) characterization of the structures shows that InAs dots in adjacent layers are well aligned. Both the TEM images and an atomic force microscopy study of uncapped dots in similar structures with different numbers of stacked layers[3] show a gradual increase in size of the InAs dots as the number of layers increases.

Measurements of the tunneling current across the multi-layer structures were performed at low temperature, with magnetic fields (B) applied parallel to the tunneling current. Positive voltage means that the top of the sample is positive relative to the substrate. The current voltage (I-V) characteristic for the control sample shows the sequence of current steps and plateaus that is a trademark of sequential resonant tunneling, as expected for this sample, which is in reality a weakly coupled InGaAs/InP superlattice. For the sample with QDs, the steps and plateaus in the tunneling current are much less pronounced, in an indication that different electronic conduction mechanisms are present. More interestingly, at low voltages (~ 100 to 400 mV, Fig. 1) clear oscillations are seen in the I-V characteristics with magnetic field. These local maxima in the current at low bias are seen only in the sample with the stacked dot structure; no similar oscillations are seen for the control sample.

In Fig. 2, the voltage at which the current maxima are observed is plotted as a function of B, at 4 K and

CP893, *Physics of Semiconductors, 28th International Conference*
edited by W. Jantsch and F. Schäffler

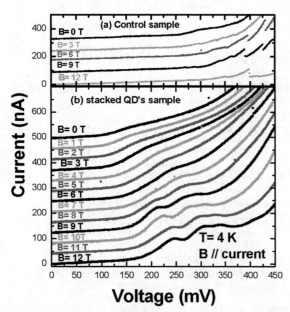

FIGURE 1. *I-V* characteristics for (a) the control sample, and (b) for the multi-layer QD structure, for B = 0 up to 12 T. The curves are displaced vertically for clarity. The current scale is valid for the curve at 12 T.

27 K. At 4 K and low magnetic field, only one oscillation is clearly seen in the *I-V* curve. For higher magnetic fields this oscillation splits into two peaks. At the highest magnetic fields another current peak can be seen. At 27 K the same general behavior is observed, but more oscillations appear, indicating that more states are involved in the tunneling process.

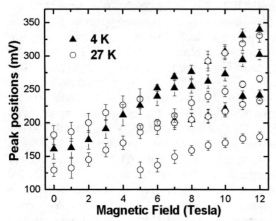

FIGURE 2. Peak positions of the maxima in the *I-V* curves in the low voltage region, as a function of the magnetic field.

We attribute these oscillations in the *I-V* curves at low bias to tunneling between QD states in adjacent layers. Photocurrent measurements[4] performed in the multi-layer QD sample showed that only the ground state of the dots is occupied at zero bias. We estimate that at low temperatures there is one electron per dot approximately, due to charge transfer from the contacts. Therefore, the tunneling processes at low voltages and low temperatures should involve only the quantum dot states. The origin of the current oscillations is shown schematically in Fig. 3. At zero magnetic field, as the voltage is increased, a maximum is observed in the tunneling current when the ground state of a dot in one layer comes into resonance with the first excited state of the dot in the adjacent layer (Fig. 3a). At 27 K, with the increase in occupation of higher energy states, other tunneling resonances are observed. In the presence of a magnetic field the Zeeman splitting of the energy levels allows one to observe tunneling between states with same spin polarization, as shown schematically in Figs 3b,c.

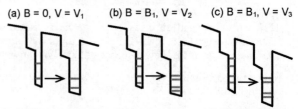

FIGURE 3. Model for the origin of the current oscillations.

Note that if the Zeeman splitting were identical for all QDs then just one oscillation would be seen at all magnetic fields. The fact that the current maxima at B = 0 splits into two peaks indicates that the Zeeman splitting is not the same for adjacent dots. This is due to the dependence of the *g*-factor on the amount of confinement. Since the quantum dots gradually increase in size as one moves from the bottom to the top of the dot stack, a difference in the *g*-factor of dots in adjacent layers is expected. Since we see a splitting into only two peaks this means that tunneling with spin flip is not observed. We estimate an average Landé *g*-factor for the QDs of $0.8 \leq g \leq 1.5$. The main uncertainty here is the percentage of voltage actually dropped across the QD layers.

CONCLUSION

We observe resonances at low temperatures and low bias in stacked InAs/InGaAs/InP self-assembled quantum dots that we associate to resonant tunneling via zero-dimensional states. At high magnetic fields evidence is seen of spin-split tunneling.

ACKNOWLEDGEMENTS

Financial support from FAPEMIG, CNPq, FAPERJ, FINEP (CT- Aeronáutica) is acknowledged.

REFERENCES

1. A. Patanè et al., *Phys. Rev. B* **65**, 165308 (2002).
2. M. H. Son et al., *Appl. Phys. Letters* **82**, 1230 (2003).
3. S.M. Landi et al., *Physica Stat. Solid C* **2**, 3171 (2005).
4. T. Gebhard et al., this conference.

Sharp Electroluminescence Lines Excited by Tunneling Injection Into a Large Ensemble of Quantum Dots

A. Baumgartner, L. Turyanska, A. Chaggar, A. Patanè, L. Eaves and M. Henini

School of Physics and Astronomy, University of Nottingham, Nottingham NG7 2RD, UK

Abstract. We observe a strong bias-dependence of the electroluminescence spectra of an ensemble of self-assembled InAs quantum dots (QDs) excited by tunnelling injection of carriers from the *n*- and *p*-doped GaAs layers of a *p-i-n* diode. We show that the dot emission evolves from a broad band above flat-band condition to a series of sharp emission lines below a characteristic bias voltage. Also, we present a study of the electroluminescence under resonant bias excitation of the dots and demonstrate up-conversion luminescence.

Keywords: Electroluminescence excitation, self-assembled InAs quantum dots, tunnelling injection
PACS: 73.21.La, 73.40.Kp, 73.43.Jn

INTRODUCTION

Self-assembled InAs quantum dots (QDs) are artificial nanostructures with discrete and narrow electronic energy levels [1]. High-resolution spatially-resolved optical techniques, such as near-field scanning optical microscopy and micro-photoluminescence, have been extensively used to study individual dots. Selective emission from a small number of dots within a large ensemble has also been achieved by incorporating the dots in lithographically patterned small area diodes [1-4], microcavities pillars [5] and nanowires [6]. Such studies have provided information about the electronic properties of the dots and are crucial for novel applications in spintronics [7] and quantum information processing [8]. In this work, we report sharp electroluminescence (EL) lines and up-conversion luminescence (UCL) from individual QDs excited by resonant tunnelling injection of carriers from the *n*- and *p*-doped GaAs layers of a *p-i-n* diode.

EXPERIMENTAL DETAILS

Our *p-i-n* diode was grown by Molecular Beam Epitaxy and incorporates a single layer of self-assembled InAs QDs in the intrinsic (*i*) GaAs region. The spacer layers between the dots and the contact layers are 100 nm and 60 nm wide on the *n*- and *p*-side of the diode, respectively. The density of QDs is $\sim 10^{11}$ cm^{-2}. The QDs have mean diameter of ~ 20 nm and mean height of ~ 2 nm [9]. The *p-i-n* structure was processed into a circular mesa of 400 μm diameter and contains an ensemble of $\sim 10^8$ QDs. A ring-shaped electrical contact was fabricated on top of the mesa to permit optical access to the sample for measurements of EL and current-voltage (*I-V*) characteristics at 4.2K.

RESULTS

Figure 1(a) shows a series of EL spectra at various applied voltages, *V*. At *V*=1.56 V, well above the flat band condition at $\sim$1.50V, the QD EL spectrum has approximately Gaussian shape. With decreasing *V*, the EL intensity decreases and the QD EL band evolves into a series of sharp lines as *V* is decreased below a characteristic voltage $V^* \approx 1.40$ V. At the lowest voltages ($V \sim 1.2$ V), we observe sharp EL lines with line widths limited by the resolution of our spectrometer. At these low voltages, the applied bias provides a means of tuning the electron and hole injection into a small number of QDs within the large ensemble [9]. As shown schematically in Fig. 2, the electrons and holes can enter the QDs either directly by tunnelling from the *p*- and *n*- doped contacts (through the potential barriers due to the intrinsic GaAs layers) into the respective ground states, or else via the states of the InAs wetting layer (WL) subband. This also leads to a well defined resonant feature in the normalised differential conductance $(dI/dV)I^{-1}$ at $V \approx 1.2$ V (see Figure 1(b)). These bias conditions correspond to an enhancement of the current flow due to tunnelling of electrons and holes into the dots.

CP893, *Physics of Semiconductors, 28th International Conference*
edited by W. Jantsch and F. Schäffler
© 2007 American Institute of Physics 978-0-7354-0397-0/07/$23.00

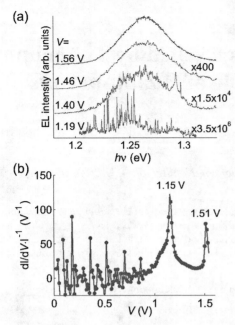

Figure 1. (a) Normalised EL spectra for a series of bias voltages, V. (b) Normalised differential conductance $(\mathrm{d}I/\mathrm{d}V)I^{-1}$ as a function of V (T=4.2 K).

We now consider the series of EL lines corresponding to resonant excitation of the QD ground states, see Figure 1(a). We have observed up-conversion luminescence (UCL), i.e. emission from the dots at energies higher than the excitation energy provided by the applied bias. Up-conversion luminescence in InAs self-assembled QDs has already been observed under resonant excitation of the dots by photons [10-11]. However, to our knowledge it was never observed in a p-i-n diode incorporating QDs. In previous works [10-11], the UCL was tentatively attributed to a two-photon absorption process. In our samples, electrons and holes are injected electrically into the dots and other mechanisms should therefore be responsible for the UCL. Auger-like mechanisms involving the ground and excited states of the QDs could explain this unusual UCL (Fig. 2d) and require further investigation.

CONCLUSIONS

We reported sharp electroluminescence lines from a small number of InAs self-assembled QDs excited by resonant tunnelling injection of carriers from the n- and p-doped layers of p-i-n diodes. Bias-tunable tunnelling of carriers provides us with a means of controlling injection and light emission without resorting to small area lithography. We also observed up-conversion electroluminescence from the dots.

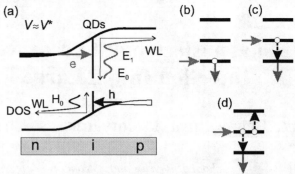

Figure 2. (a) Schematic of electron and hole injection into the dot from the n and p-side of the diode. (b) Resonant electron injection into the ground state of a QD followed by electron-hole recombination; (c) injection of an electron into an excited QD state followed by relaxation to the ground state; (d) Auger-like process and up-conversion luminescence.

ACKNOWLEDGMENTS

This work is supported by the EPSRC (UK) and the European SANDiE Network of Excellence.

REFERENCES

[1] D.J. Mowbray and M.S. Skolnick, J. Phys. D- Appl. Phys. 38, 2059 (2005).

[2] I. E. Itskevich, S. I. Rybchenko, I. I. Tartakovskii, S.T. Stoddart, A. Levin, P. C. Main, L. Eaves, M. Henini, and S. Parnell, Appl. Phys. Lett. 76, 3932 (2000).

[3] Z. Yuan, B.E. Kardynal, R.M. Stevenson, A.J. Shields, C. J. Lobo, K. Cooper, N. S. Beattie, D. A. Ritchie, and M. Pepper, Science 295, 102 (2002).

[4] X.L. Xu, D.A. Williams, and J.R.A. Cleaver, Appl. Phys. Lett. 85, 3238 (2004).

[5] P. Michler, A. Kiraz, C. Becher, W.V. Schoenfeld, P.M. Petroff, L.D. Zhang, E. Hu, and A. Imamoglu, Science 290, 2282 (2000).

[6] M.T. Borgstrom, V. Zwiller, E. Muller, and A. Imamoglu, Nano Lett. 5, 1439 (2005).

[7] M. Kroutvar, Y. Ducommun, D. Heiss, M. Bichler, D. Schuh, G. Abstreiter, and J.J. Finley, Nature 432, 81 (2004).

[8] S. Stufler, P. Ester, A. Zrenner, and M. Bichler, Phys. Rev. Lett. 96, 037402 (2006).

[9] L. Turyanska, A. Baumgartner, A. Chaggar, A. Patanè, L. Eaves and M. Henini, submitted to Appl. Phys. Lett.

[10] P.P. Paskov, P.O. Holtz, B. Monemar, J.M. Garcia, W.W. Schoenfeld, P.M. Petroff, Appl. Phys. Lett. 77, 812 (2000).

[11] C. Kammerer, G. Cassabois, C. Voisin, C. Delalande, P. Roussignol, and J.M. Gerard, Phys. Rev. Lett. 87, 207401 (2001).

Comparable Homogeneous and Inhomogeneous Quantum Dot Luminescence Linewidths at Room Temperature

M. Benyoucef, A. Rastelli, and O.G. Schmidt

Max-Planck-Institut für Festkörperforschung
Heisenbergstr. 1, D-70569 Stuttgart, Germany

Abstract. We report on the experimental observation of bright and narrow emission at room temperature from single unstrained GaAs quantum dots (QDs). Remarkably, the width of a single-QD emission (~ 8.5 meV) is comparable to the ensemble inhomogeneous broadening of about 12.4 meV and is three times smaller compared to the thermal broadening (25.85 meV).

Keywords: 42.50.Ar, 78.55.Cr, 78.67.Hc.

INTRODUCTION

During the last decade, much attention has been paid to the fabrication of semiconductor quantum dots (QDs) and to their optical properties. Single dot spectroscopy is a direct experimental technique to investigate the optical and electronic properties of QDs. Recently, a novel growth technique was used to fabricate self-assembled GaAs/AlGaAs QDs [1]. These systems offer several advantages compared to Stranski-Krastanow (SK) grown QDs: The grown material is ideally unstrained with sharp interfaces and emits light in the visible range.

The variation of the emission energy and the full width at half maximum (FWHM) of SK-grown QDs with increasing temperature have been extensively studied [see e.g., 2-4]. Because of the small lateral confinement in such QDs it is not possible to study their emission at high temperatures. In this work, we report on the observation of a bright and narrow (about 8.5 meV) PL emission at room temperature from a single unstrained GaAs QD and compared to PL emission from ensemble GaAs QDs.

Experimental Procedure

The investigated samples were grown on GaAs (001) substrate by a solid-source molecular beam epitaxy system equipped with an $AsBr_3$ etching unit. The GaAs QDs are obtained by overgrowing a GaAs surface containing self-assembled nanoholes [5] with 7 nm $Al_{0.45}Ga_{0.55}As$, 2 nm GaAs, 100 nm $Al_{0.35}Ga_{0.65}As$, 20 nm $Al_{0.45}Ga_{0.55}As$ and 20 nm GaAs (see Ref. [1] for details). The 2-nm-thick GaAs layer fills up the nanoholes in the underlying AlGaAs barrier leading to the formation of inverted GaAs QDs below a thin GaAs quantum well. For single-QD and ensemble investigations, the QD density is chosen as 1.10^8 cm^{-2} and 4.10^9 cm^{-2}, respectively. The studied samples were placed in a cold-finger helium flow cryostat which allows to vary the temperature between 5 K and 300 K. For optical measurements, a standard micro-photoluminescence (PL) setup was used. The samples were excited by a continuous wave laser emitting at 532 nm.

Results and Discussions

The single GaAs QD PL spectra taken at excitation powers of ~1.6 Wcm^{-2} and ~95 Wcm^{-2} are shown in Figure 1(a). At very low powers only one sharp PL line is visible, which is attributed to an exciton (X) line. The top spectrum in Figure 1 (a) consists of resolution-limited well separated sharp excitonic lines with almost no background. The X line saturates at a power of ~95 Wcm^{-2} with intensity of ~9.10^4 counts/s.

The PL peak energy shows a redshift of about 97 meV as the temperature increases from 5 K to 295 K due to the bandgap shrinkage. Figure 1(b) compares the room temperature PL emission from an unstrained single GaAs QD located at 1.545 eV and a PL spectrum from ensemble GaAs QDs peaked at

CP893, *Physics of Semiconductors, 28th International Conference*
edited by W. Jantsch and F. Schäffler

1.528 eV from a different sample with high QD-density taken at excitation power of ~ 480 Wcm^{-2} with integration times of 1 s. The ground state PL linewidth of the single GaAs QD at room temperature is ~8.5 meV, which is comparable to the inhomogeneous linewidth of the ensemble GaAs QDs ~12.4 meV. This is a surprising result, since it is commonly assumed that the FWHM of a QD ensemble is mainly determined by the size/composition fluctuations of the QDs. While this remains true at low temperature, Figure. 1(b) shows that the room temperature emission-linewidth of our QDs is dominated by the homogeneous broadening of the single QD emission. Such a result, which is attributed to the good size homogeneity of our QDs, suggests the possibility of using these QDs with large surface density as efficient active region (e.g., in a microcavity laser).

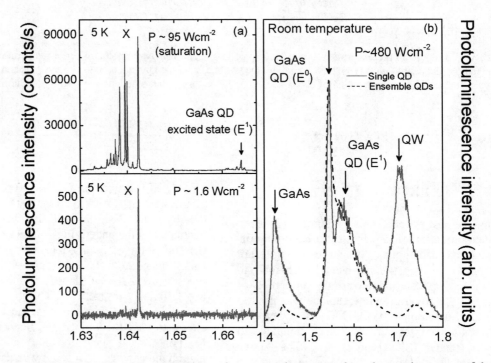

FIGURE 1 (a) PL spectra of a single GaAs QD at 5 K taken at low power (bottom graph) and saturation power of the exciton line (top graph) (b) PL spectra measured at room temperature from a single GaAs QD (solid line) and from an ensemble of GaAs QDs (dashed line). The ensemble spectrum was shifted to higher energy by 17~meV for comparison because this sample is characterized by slightly larger QDs.

ACKNOWLEDGMENTS

The authors would like to thank K. v. Klitzing for his interest and support. This work was financially supported by the BMBF (01BM459) and DFG (Research group: *Positioning of single nanostructures-single quantum devices*).

REFERENCES

1. A. Rastelli, S. Stufler, A. Schliwa, R. Songmuang, C. Manzano, G. Costantini, K. Kern, A. Zrenner, D. Bimberg, and O. G. Schmidt, Phys. Rev. Lett. **92**, 166104 (2004).

2. K. Matsuda, K. Ikeda, T. Saiki, H. Tsuchiya, H. Saito and K. Nishi, Phys. Rev. B **63**, 121304(R) (2001).

3. M. Bayer and A. Forchel, Phys. Rev. B **65**, 041308(R) (2002).

4. E.C. Le Ru, J. Fack, and R. Murray Phys. Rev. B **67**, 245318 (2003).

5. S. Kiravittaya, R. Songmuang, N.Y.~Jin-Phillipp, S. Panyakeow, O.G. Schmidt, J. Cryst. Growth **251**, 258 (2003).

Tunnelling Transient Spectroscopy on self-assembled InAs Quantum Dots

A. Schramm*, S. Schulz*, J. Schaefer*, Ch. Heyn* and W. Hansen*

**Institute of Applied Physics, University of Hamburg, Jungiusstrasse 11, 20355 Hamburg, Germany*

Abstract. We study electron tunnelling from self-assembled InAs quantum dots with time-resolved capacitance measurements at low temperature ($T = 10$ K). Within a simple WKB model the electric field dependence of the tunnelling rate is analyzed. The data reveal that tunnelling emission from s- and p-like quantum dot states can clearly be resolved. The binding energies obtained from a triangular-well model are in good agreement with values obtained with DLTS experiments.

Deep Level Transient Spectroscopy (DLTS) is a powerful tool to probe electronic levels in self-assembled quantum dots (QDs)[1, 2, 3, 4, 5]. However, it has been pointed out that as a consequence of multiple emission paths in multi-level QDs the conventional analysis of thermal DLTS data may be too simple[2, 6, 7].

Here we report tunnelling transient spectroscopy (TTS) that avoids ambiguities arising, e. g., from temperature dependent effective capture cross sections or emission via excited levels[7, 8]. Similar to conventional DLTS the electron occupation of QDs is probed with time-resolved capacitance measurements. However, in contrast to conventional DLTS, where the escape rates are probed as function of temperature, here we probe the electric field dependence of the emission at such a low temperature that escape takes place by tunnelling alone. Different thermal emission paths and cross-talk between thermal and tunnelling emission can thus be neglected[4]. The electric field dependence of the escape rates are analyzed with a simple WKB model.

The self-assembled InAs QDs are embedded in slightly Si-doped ($N_D = 4 \times 10^{15}$ cm^{-3}) Schottky diodes grown with solid-source MBE on (001) GaAs. The dots were grown at 485°C depositing 2.1 ML InAs with 0.01 ML/s growth rate. They are located 750 nm below the surface. AFM maps of a reference dot layer grown on the surface with same growth parameters as for embedded dots yield a dot density of $N_{QD} = 4 \times 10^9$ cm^{-2}. For Schottky contacts, 50 nm chromium was evaporated with 1 mm diameter.

During a filling voltage pulse V_p with a duration $t_p = 1$ ms electrons are injected into dots. The capacitance transient of the diode is recorded after the voltage has been reduced from the filling pulse value to the reverse voltage V_r. At V_r the dot layer is located within the depletion zone. Its depth depends on the QD occupation.

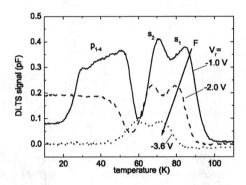

FIGURE 1. DLTS spectra of a Schottky diode containing InAs QDs. Dashed, dashed dotted and full lines mark data recorded at effective electric fields of 1, 2, and 3.3×10^6 V/m, respectively.

The transients thus reflect the time evolution of the dot occupation.

First, we show conventional DLTS-spectra obtained on a typical sample in Fig. 1. The two peaks denoted with s_1 and s_2 reflect the emission from singly and doubly occupied dots[5]. The broad peak at temperatures between 25 K and 55 K evolves with increasing QD occupation. We assign it to emission from the p-level which is further confirmed by measurements in magnetic fields normal to the dot layer[5]. The electric field at the dots is controlled by the reverse bias. Both s-peaks decrease in temperature with increasing field. Below a temperature that decreases with increasing electric field we observe a temperature independent signal which is attributed to tunnelling processes[2, 4]. E. g., the signal becomes temperature independent below 20 K and 40 K at $V_r = -1.0$ V and $V_r = -2.0$ V, respectively.

CP893, *Physics of Semiconductors, 28th International Conference*
edited by W. Jantsch and F. Schäffler

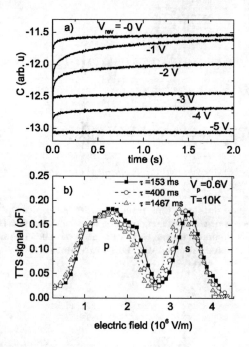

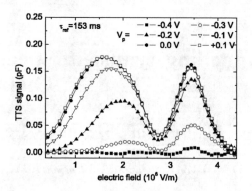

FIGURE 3. TTS spectra recorded with different filling pulse voltages (as labeled in figure) at a reference time of $\tau_{ref} = 77$ ms and $T = 10$ K. The pulse length was $t_p = 1$ ms.

FIGURE 2. a) Capacitance transients of a Schottky diode with embedded SAQDs recorded at $T = 10$ K. The transients are offset for clarity. b) TTS spectra showing the capacitance change associated to tunnel emission from the QDs.

Note that the height of the signal arising from tunnelling processes strongly depends on the applied reverse voltage. In the following, we will focus on this field dependence at low T. In Fig. 2 (a) capacitance transients recorded at $T = 10$ K and different V_r are depicted. The time evolution of the dot occupation is strongly dependent on the reverse voltage and thus on the electric field in the dot layer. The electric field is calculated from the equilibrium value of the diode capacitance at V_r, i.e. assuming no charge in the dot layer.

In contrast to Ref. [8] we apply a double box car filter in order to define a rate window $\tau_{ref} = (t_2 - t_1)/ln(t_2 - t_1)$[7]. In Fig. 2 (b) we depict $\Delta C = C(t_2) - C(t_1)$ versus the electric field F for three different rate windows. We clearly observe two pronounced maxima which are associated to the s- and p-states[7]. Furthermore, with increasing τ_{ref} the TTS maxima shift to lower electric fields. Assuming that the electric field dependence of the tunnelling rates can be described by a simple triangular barrier model [9] we derive binding energies with an Arrhenius-like analysis [7]. We determine electron binding energies of $E_i^s = 159 \pm 10$ meV for dots with 1 or 2 electrons and $E_i^p = 89 \pm 6$ meV for dots with 3 to 6 electrons. The error intervals indicate the variation of the results if in the calculation of the field the dot occupation

with up to 6 electrons is taken into account.

The data in Fig. 3 demonstrate the dependence of the TTS spectra on the pulse heights. In CV measurements performed at $T = 100$ K s-state occupation sets in at $V_p = -0.8$ V [5]. This is much lower than the voltage at which s-state occupation becomes noticeable in Fig. 3. Obviously, at the voltages at which the barrier is sufficiently reduced for charging both the s- and p-states can be occupied. This explains why in the sample discussed here the peaks associated to tunneling from s- and p-states arise almost simultaneously in the TTS spectra. We find that in Schottky diodes with higher doping level pulse-height control of the dot charge becomes easier.

In conclusion, we use the tunnelling transient spectroscopy to derive the binding energies of self-assembled InAs QDs. The obtained values are in very good agreement to previous DLTS-data[4, 5].

REFERENCES

1. Anand, S., Carlsson, N., Pistol, M.-E., Samuelson, L., and Seifert, W., *Appl. Phys. Lett.*, **67**, 3016 (1995).
2. Kapteyn, C. M. A., Heinrichsdorff, F., Stier, O., Heitz, R., Grundmann, M., Zakharov, N. D., Werner, P., and Bimberg, D., *Phys. Rev. B*, **60**, 14265 (1999).
3. Engström, O., Malmkvist, M., Fu, Y., Olafson, H. O., and Sveinbjörnsson, E. O., *Appl. Phys. Lett.*, **83**, 3578 (2003).
4. Schulz, S., Schnüll, S., Heyn, C., and Hansen, W., *Phys. Rev. B*, **69**, 195317 (2004).
5. Schramm, A., Schulz, S., Schaefer, J., Zander, T., Heyn, C., and Hansen, W., *Appl. Phys. Lett.*, **88**, 213107 (2006).
6. Engström, O., and Landsberg, P. T., *Phys. Rev. B*, **72**, 75360–75367 (2005).
7. Schulz, S., Schramm, A., Heyn, C., and Hansen, W., *Phys. Rev. B*, **in Press** (2006).
8. Geller, M., Stock, E., Kapteyn, C., Sellin, R. L., and Bimberg, D., *Phys. Rev. B*, **73**, 205331 (2006).
9. Korol, E. N., *Sov. Phys. Solid State*, **8**, 1327 (1977).

Pseudo-spin Kondo effect in Aharonov-Bohm interferometer containing laterally coupled double quantum dots

Toshihiro Kubo[1], Yasuhiro Tokura[1,2], and Seigo Tarucha[1,3]

[1]Quantum Spin Information Project, ICORP, JST, Atsugi-shi, Kanagawa 243-0198, Japan
[2]NTT Basic Research Laboratories, NTT Corporation, Atsugi-shi, Kanagawa 243-0198, Japan
[3]Department of Applied Physics, University of Tokyo, Hongo, Bunkyo-ku, Tokyo 113-8656, Japan

Abstract. We investigate pseudo-spin Kondo effect in an Aharonov-Bohm (AB) interferometer having laterally coupled two quantum dots in the two interferometer arms with strong inter-dot Coulomb interaction in terms of the slave-boson mean-field theory. We introduce an indirect coupling parameter α, which provides the exotic pseudo-spin Kondo effect, showing AB oscillations and asymmetric Kondo resonant peaks with respect to the Fermi energy.

Keywords: pseudo-spin Kondo effect, laterally coupled double quantum dots, slave-boson mean-field theory
PACS: 72.15.Qm, 73.23.-b, 73.40.Gk

INTRODUCTION

Recently the pseudo-spin Kondo effect in laterally coupled double quantum dots (DQDs) has been investigated both theoretically and experimentally [1-3]. In a DQD with a finite inter-dot tunnel coupling, the symmetric (pseudo-spin up), and anti-symmetric (pseudo-spin down) state correspond to the spin-up, and spin-down state in $S=1/2$ Kondo system, respectively. That is, the inter-dot tunnel coupling, and the inter-dot Coulomb interaction in a pseudo-spin Kondo system correspond to the Zeeman energy and the on-site Coulomb interaction in $S=1/2$ Kondo system, respectively. Since both QDs couple to the two reservoirs (Fig. 1), the DQD pseudo-spin is screened by the higher order tunneling processes between the reservoirs and the DQD, leading to the pseudo-spin Kondo effect.

In this article, we discuss the pseudo-spin Kondo effect for an AB interferometer containing a laterally coupled DQD, using the slave-boson mean-field theory (SBMFT). In particular, we consider the effects of the indirect coupling parameter α, which characterizes the strength of the coupling between the two QDs via the reservoirs [4,5]. When we consider the indirect couping between two QDs via the reservoirs, we take into account the propagation of electrons in the reservoirs. In Fig. 1, s_{12} indicates the propagation length. This propagation process leads to

the indirect coupling parameter in the linewidth function. For $0<|\alpha|<1$, we have the pseudo-spin dependent linewidth functions, which indicates the exotic pseudo-spin Kondo effect.

MODEL AND FORMULATION

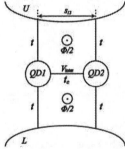

FIGURE 1. Schematic diagrams of an AB interferometer with laterally coupled DQDs.

Figure 1 schematically shows an AB interferometer having DQDs considered in this work. We assume just a single level of the same energy ε_0 for each QD and ignore the spin degree of freedom. Consequently, each QD can accommodate one electron at most because of Pauli exclusion principle. We take into account the indirect coupling parameter α, and then we have the following pseudo-spin dependent linewidth function Γ in a basis of the pseudo-spin state [5]

$$\Gamma = \gamma \begin{pmatrix} 1 + \alpha \cos(\pi\Phi/\Phi_0) & 0 \\ 0 & 1 - \alpha \cos(\pi\Phi/\Phi_0) \end{pmatrix}, \quad (1)$$

where γ is the averaged linewidth function [5].

The energy levels of the DQD split to form a symmetric state and an anti-symmetric state because of the inter-dot tunnel coupling t_c. We assume that the inter-dot Coulomb interaction V_{inter} is infinite, which prevents the occupation of both the symmetric and anti-symmetric states. To describe this situation, we adopt the SBMFT [6], using the non-equilibrium Green's function method.

NUMERICAL RESULTS

Here we consider only the Kondo regime $\varepsilon_0/\hbar\gamma = -3$ (we measure the energy from the Fermi level). We first set the AB flux to be zero, namely $\Phi = 0$ to make clear the effect of α parameter on the Kondo effect. Figure 2 shows the density of states (DOS) calculated for $\alpha = 0$ and $\alpha = 0.5$. The DOS has a single peak at the Fermi level ($\varepsilon = 0$) when $t_c = 0$ (Fig. 2(a)). The symmetric peak splitting for $t_c \neq 0$ is due to the inter-dot tunnel coupling since the linewidth function is independent of the pseudo-spin for $\alpha = 0$. In contrast, the peak splitting is asymmetric in Fig. 2(b) because the linewidth function depends on the pseudo-spin for $\alpha \neq 0$. The full-width-at-half-maximums of the two Kondo resonance peaks shown in Fig. 2(b) are proportional to $1 + \alpha$ and $1 - \alpha$.

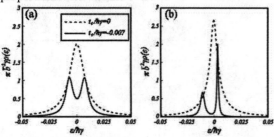

FIGURE 2. DOS $\rho(\varepsilon)$ in the Kondo regime for (a) $\alpha = 0$ (a) and $\alpha = 0.5$ (b). The Fermi level is taken as $\varepsilon = 0$. $\bar{b}$ is one of the variational parameters of SBMFT.

In Fig. 3, we plot the differential conductance dI/dV_{SD} calculated for the DOS as shown in Fig. 2. When $t_c = 0$ (dashed line), we find a zero bias peak at the Fermi level. Due the inter-dot tunnel coupling, the zero bias peak splits and the linear conductance (dI/dV_{SD} at zero bias) is suppressed. When $\alpha = 0.5$, for a finite inter-dot tunnel coupling (solid line), there appears an additional structure in each split peak as shown in Fig. 3 (b). The subpeak at the smaller (larger) $|V_{SD}|$ in the additional structure arises from the sharp

peak at lower energy (broad peak at higher energy) in the asymmetric DOS shown in Fig. 2(b).

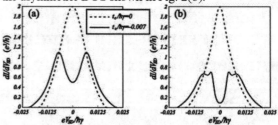

FIGURE 3. Differential conductance in the Kondo regime. (a) $\alpha = 0$. (b) $\alpha = 0.5$.

The AB oscillations of the linear conductance are shown in Fig. 4. The conductance oscillates with the period $\Phi_0 = h/e$ for $t_c = 0$ (solid line). For a finite t_c, the AB oscillation period becomes $2\Phi_0$. As the inter-dot tunnel coupling increases, the linear conductance becomes smaller and its maximum at zero flux transforms to the minimum[7].

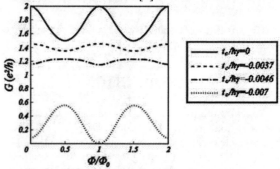

FIGURE 4. AB oscillations of the linear conductance for $\alpha = 0.5$.

ACKNOWLEDGMENTS

We thank T. Aono, W. Izumida, S. Amaha, Y.-S. Shin, and M. Pioro-Ladrière for useful discussions. ST acknowledges financial supports from the DARPA grant no. DAAD19-01-1-0659 of the QuIST program, the Grant-in-Aid for Scientific Research A (No. 40302799), SORST-JST and IT Program, MEXT.

REFERENCES

1. T. Pohjola *et al.*, Europhys. Lett. **54**, 241 (2001).
2. U. Wilhelm *et al.*, Physica E **14**, 385 (2002).
3. A. W. Holleitner *et al.*, Phys. Rev. B **70**, 075204 (2004).
4. T. V. Shahbazyan *et al.*, Phys. Rev. B **49**, 17123 (1994).
5. T. Kubo *et al.*, cond-mat/0602539.
6. N. Read *et al.*, J. Phys. C **16**, L1055 (1983).
7. B. Kubala *et al.*, Phys. Rev. B **65**, 245301 (2002).

Quantum-current transport through an array of coupled quantum-dots accounting for k·p electronic bandstructure

M. Willatzen* and B. Lassen[†]

*Mads Clausen Institute, University of Southern Denmark, Grundtvigs Alle 150, DK-6400 Sonderborg, Denmark
[†]Department of Physics, Lund University, Box 118, 22100 Lund, Sweden

Abstract. Due to advances in fabrication methods of nanowires it is now possible to grow high quality modulated nanowire structures [1]. As these structures are promising candidates for new and improved devices, there is a need to understand the electronic transport properties of such structures. We here propose a method of constructing dot localized states for non-periodic structures based on modified Wannier functions. These states can be used to express the Hamiltonian of the system in second quantization, which is normally the starting point of quantum transport models, thereby bridging the gap between electronic band structure calculations and transport. We furthermore present I-V curves found using nonequilibrium Greens function theory [2]. Although we here only study modulated nanowires, the theory is applicable to general 3D arrays of quantum dots [3].

Keywords: Localized states, modified Wannier states, $k \cdot p$ theory, electronic transport, modulated nanowires.
PACS: 72.10.Bg, 72.80.Ey, 72.80.Tm

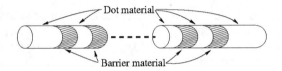

FIGURE 1. System under consideration.

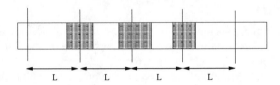

FIGURE 2. Periodic set of intervals.

THEORY

The system studied here is a modulated nanowire structure as shown in Fig. 1.

We want to derive a Hamiltonian in second quantization using dot localized states. Our starting point for doing so is a one-particle Hamiltonian:

$$H = H^{(0)} + H^{(1)}, \tag{1}$$

where the first part ($H^{(0)}$) will be used to construct the dot localized basis set and the second part ($H^{(1)}$) includes all additional one-particle contributions, e.g., interactions due to an applied electric field.

The dot localized states are found using the following procedure. First, the domain is split into a periodic set of intervals, see Fig. 2. Second, a set of periodic Hamiltonians are defined (one for each interval). Let z_i denote the center of the i'th interval. The periodic Hamiltonian associated with the i'th interval is then defined by

$$(H_{z_i}^{(0)}\psi)(\mathbf{r},t) = \left(T_{z_j-z_i}^{-1} H^{(0)} T_{z_j-z_i}\psi\right)(\mathbf{r},t), \text{ for } \mathbf{r} \text{ in interval } j, \tag{2}$$

where

$$T_v: \mathbf{r} \mapsto \mathbf{r} + v\hat{z} \tag{3}$$

and $\hat{z} = (0,0,1)$. Third, eigenstates and eigenvalues for the set of periodic Hamiltonians are found. For each $H_{z_i}^{(0)}$ we find solutions to:

$$H_{z_i}^{(0)}\phi_n(\mathbf{r},z_i) = E_n(z_i)\phi_n(\mathbf{r},z_i), \tag{4}$$

that satisfy $\phi_n(\mathbf{r} + (z_j - z_i)\hat{z}, z_i) = \phi_n(\mathbf{r}, z_i)$ for all z_j, i.e., the functions $\phi_n(\mathbf{r}, z_i)$ are periodic zone-center solutions of $H_{z_i}^{(0)}$. Finally, modified Wannier states are constructed according to:

$$w_n(\mathbf{r}, z_i) = \delta_B(\mathbf{r} - z_i\hat{z})\phi_n(\mathbf{r}, z_i), \tag{5}$$

where

$$\delta_B(\mathbf{r}) = \frac{L}{2\pi}\int_{-\pi/L}^{\pi/L} e^{ik\hat{z}\cdot\mathbf{r}}dk. \tag{6}$$

The function δ_B modulates the periodic solutions so that the w's are primarily localized inside the respective intervals.

Based on the complete orthonormal basis set $\{w_n(\mathbf{r}, z_i)\}$ found above we can now derive the Hamiltonian in second quantization and we arrive at:

$$H = \sum_{nn'z_iz_j} H_{nn'z_iz_j} a_{n'z_j}^\dagger a_{nz_i}, \tag{7}$$

CP893, *Physics of Semiconductors, 28th International Conference*
edited by W. Jantsch and F. Schäffler

where

$$H_{nn'z_iz_j} = \int w_{n'}(\mathbf{r},z_j)^* H w_n(\mathbf{r},z_i) d^3r, \qquad (8)$$

and $a_{nz_i}^\dagger$ and a_{nz_i} are creation and annihilation operators associated with the state $w_n(\mathbf{r},z_i)$.

Example - One-Band Model

In the one-band model the Hamiltonian is given by:

$$H^0\psi(\mathbf{r}) = \left[-\nabla\frac{\hbar^2}{2m_c(\mathbf{r})}\nabla + V(\mathbf{r})\right]\psi(\mathbf{r}) = E\psi(\mathbf{r}), \quad (9)$$

where $\hbar$ is Planck's constant divided by 2π, m_c is the conduction-band effective mass, V is the potential resulting from the heterostructure, and $\psi(\mathbf{r})$ is the envelope part of the wavefunction. The effective mass and the potential are constant in each material making up the modulated nanowire.

The above described procedure can now be applied resulting in a complete orthonormal basis set for the specific Hamiltonian given here, see [3] for a detailed derivation. Assuming that only the groundstate of each dot is involved in transport and that only dots next to each other interact we find:

$$H_d \approx \sum_{i=1}^{N} H_{diag,i} a_i^\dagger a_i + \sum_{i=1}^{N-1}\{H_{ii+1}a_i^\dagger a_{i+1} + H.c.\}, \quad (10)$$

where $H.c$ denotes the hermitian conjugate of the previous expression, $a_i^\dagger$ (a_i) is the creation (annihilation) operator of the ground-state basis element of dot i,

$$H_{diag,i} = H_{11z_iz_i}, \qquad (11)$$

and

$$H_{ii+1} = H_{11z_{i+1}z_i}. \qquad (12)$$

Assuming non-interacting contacts and that the contacts only interact with the dot next to them, the contacts can be modelled by:

$$H_c = \sum_{k,\alpha\in L,R} \varepsilon_{k\alpha}c_{k\alpha}^\dagger c_{k\alpha}, \qquad (13)$$

and the Hamiltonian responsible for the coupling between the contacts and the modulated nanowire structure will be given by:

$$H_{d-c} = \sum_k\{(V_L c_{kL}^\dagger a_1 + H.c) + (V_R c_{kR}^\dagger a_N + H.c)\}, \quad (14)$$

where $c_{k\alpha}^\dagger$ $(c_{k\alpha})$ is the creation (annihilation) operator for the electrons in contact $\alpha = L,R$ (L=Left and R=Right), the sum over k runs over all the states in the contacts that are coupled with the neighboring dots, and $\varepsilon_{k\alpha}$, V_L and V_R are input parameters to the model. The Hamiltonian of the whole system is then given by:

$$H_{sys} = H_d + H_c + H_{d-c}. \qquad (15)$$

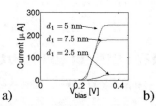 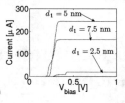

FIGURE 3. I-V curves for three dot structures where the length of a) the first dot d_1, b) the second dot d_2 is varied.

Results

In this section we present I-V curves calculated using the expression for the current derived by Shangguan et al. [2] based on nonequilibrium Greens function theory. We study GaAs/AlAs modulated nanowires at 1 K and we have chosen to use flat bands with the coupling to the contacts given to by $\Gamma_l = 2\pi V_l^2 \rho_0 = 0.05$ eV, where ρ_0 is the constant density of states (flat band approximation). In the figures the chemical potential of the right contact is kept fixed and the chemical potential of the left contact is varied.

In Fig. 3 we show I-V curves for three dot structures where the length of the first (left plot) or the second (right plot) dot is varied and the length of the other two dots is equal to 5 nm.

CONCLUSION

We have presented a method to construct dot localized states for non-periodic structures based on modified Wannier states and how to express the Hamiltonian of the system in second quantization based on the dot localized states. In addition, we have shown I-V curves calculated using nonequilibrium Greens function theory.

REFERENCES

1. M. S. Gudiksen, L. J. Lauhon, J. Wang, D. C. Smith, and C. M. Lieber. *Nature*, 415:617, 2002.
2. W. Z. Shangguan, T. C. Au Yeung, Y. B. Yu, and C. H. Kam. *Phys. Rev. B*, 63:235323, 2001.
3. B. Lassen and M. Willatzen. *Phys. Rev. B*, 2006. Accepted for publication.

768

Ferromagnetic Lead Effects on Inelastic Cotunneling Current and Shot Noise of an Interacting Quantum Dot

Bing Dong*, X. L. Lei* and Norman J. M. Horing†

*Department of Physics, Shanghai Jiaotong University, 1954 Huashan Road, Shanghai 200030, China
†Department of Physics and Engineering Physics, Stevens Institute of Technology, Hoboken, New Jersey 07030, USA

Abstract. We analyze inelastic cotunneling through a strongly Coulomb-blockaded quantum dot attached to two ferromagnetic leads in the weak coupling limit using a quantum Langevin equation approach, from which we derive a fully microscopic quantum based Bloch-type equation to describe the cotunneling-induced spin relaxation dynamics. Based on this, we then obtain explicit analytical expressions for the local magnetization, cotunneling current, and its fluctuations.

Keywords: Inelastic cotunneling, ferromagnetic lead, spin-polarized tunneling, shot noise
PACS: 72.25.Dc, 73.63.Kv, 72.10.Fk, 72.70.+m

Spin-dependent tunneling in nanoscale semiconductor devices has become a focal point of intensive research activity recently[1, 2, 3]. In this paper, we study lowest-order cotunneling through a strongly Coulomb-blockaded quantum dot (QD) attached to two ferromagnetic leads in the weak tunneling regime at temperatures above the Kondo temperature. Explicit expressions for QD magnetization, cotunneling current, and its current noise are obtained employing a quantum Langevin equation approach.

Cotunneling through a single-level interacting QD connected to two ferromagnetic leads is modeled by the two-lead Kondo Hamiltonian:[4, 5]

$$H = H_0 + H_I, \tag{1}$$

$$H_0 = \sum_{\eta k \sigma} (\varepsilon_k - \mu_\eta) c_{\eta k \sigma}^\dagger c_{\eta k \sigma} - \Delta S^z,$$

$$H_I = \sum_{\eta,\eta',k,k'} J_{\eta\eta'} [(c_{\eta k \uparrow}^\dagger c_{\eta' k' \uparrow} - c_{\eta k \downarrow}^\dagger c_{\eta' k' \downarrow}) S^z$$

$$+ c_{\eta k \uparrow}^\dagger c_{\eta' k' \downarrow} S^- + c_{\eta k \downarrow}^\dagger c_{\eta' k' \uparrow} S^+] + H_{\text{dir}},$$

$$H_{\text{dir}} = J_0 \sum_\sigma (c_{Lk\sigma}^\dagger + c_{Rk\sigma}^\dagger)(c_{Lk\sigma} + c_{Rk\sigma}),$$

where $c_{\eta k \sigma}^\dagger$ ($c_{\eta k \sigma}$) creates (annihilates) an electron in lead η ($= L, R$) with energy ε_k and spin σ, and $J_{\eta\eta'}$ is the Kondo exchange coupling constant between these electrons and the localized QD spin-1/2, $\mathbf{S} = (S^x, S^y, S^z)$, $S^\pm = S^x \pm iS^y$. Δ is the effective spin splitting. H_{dir} is the potential scattering term, $2J_0 = J_{\eta\eta'}$, which is decoupled from the electron spin due to the number of electrons in the dot level being one. As a result, this term has no influence on the dynamic evolution of the electron spin and behaves only as a direct bridge to connect the left and right leads, and consequently it contributes a current independent of the dynamics of the QD. The

ferromagnetism of the leads is represented in terms of a spin-dependent, flat density of states, $\rho_{\eta\sigma}$: $\rho_{L\uparrow} = \rho_{R\uparrow} = (1+p)\rho_0$; $\rho_{L\downarrow} = \rho_{R\downarrow} = (1-p)\rho_0$ for the P configuration, and $\rho_{L\uparrow} = \rho_{R\downarrow} = (1+p)\rho_0$; $\rho_{L\downarrow} = \rho_{R\uparrow} = (1-p)\rho_0$ for the AP configuration, with the degree of spin polarization p ($|p| \le 1$) for both leads.

We employ a generic Langevin equation approach to analyze this system in the weak cotunneling limit[5]. In our derivation, operators of the QD spin and the reservoirs are first expressed formally by integration of their Heisenberg equations of motion (EOM), exactly to all orders of $J_{\eta\eta'}$. Next, under the assumption that the time scale of decay processes is much slower than that of free evolution, we replace the time-dependent operators involved in the integrals of these EOM's approximately in terms of their free evolutions. Thirdly, these EOM's are expanded in powers of $J_{\eta\eta'}$ up to second order. To this end, a Bloch-type dynamical equation is established to describe the time evolution of the QD spin variable as,

$$\dot{S}^z = -4C_{\text{P(AP)}}(\Delta) S^z + 2R_{\text{P(AP)}}(\Delta), \tag{2}$$

in which

$$C_{\text{P}}(\omega) = \frac{\pi}{2}(g_{LL} + g_{RR})(1-p^2)T\varphi\left(\frac{\omega}{T}\right)$$
$$+ \frac{\pi}{2}g_{LR}(1-p^2)T\left[\varphi\left(\frac{\omega+V}{T}\right) + \varphi\left(\frac{\omega-V}{T}\right)\right] \tag{3}$$

$$R_{\text{P}}(\omega) = \frac{\pi}{2}(g_{LL} + g_{RR} + 2g_{LR})(1-p^2)\omega, \tag{4}$$

for the P configuration, and

$$C_{\text{AP}}(\omega) = \frac{\pi}{2}(g_{LL} + g_{RR})(1-p^2)T\varphi\left(\frac{\omega}{T}\right) + \frac{\pi}{2}g_{LR}T$$
$$\times \left[(1+p)^2\varphi\left(\frac{\omega+V}{T}\right) + (1-p)^2\varphi\left(\frac{\omega-V}{T}\right)\right] \tag{5}$$

CP893, *Physics of Semiconductors, 28th International Conference*
edited by W. Jantsch and F. Schäffler
© 2007 American Institute of Physics 978-0-7354-0397-0/07/$23.00

$$R_{AP}(\omega) = \frac{\pi}{2}(g_{LL}+g_{RR})(1-p^2)\omega$$
$$+\pi g_{LR}(1+p^2)\omega + 2\pi g_{LR}pV, \qquad (6)$$

for the AP configuration, with $g_{\eta\eta'} \equiv J_{\eta\eta'}^2\rho_0^2$ and $\varphi(x) \equiv x\coth(x/2)$. V is a symmetrically applied bias-voltage; T is temperature. We use units with $\bar{h} = k_B = e = 1$. The nonequilibrium local magnetization, $S_{P(AP)}^{z\infty}$, of the QD in P(AP) configuration is readily obtained using the steady-state solution of Eq. (2).

The current operator is based on the equation of motion for the charge density $N_\eta = \sum_{k\sigma} c_{\eta k\sigma}^\dagger c_{\eta k\sigma}$ in lead η: $J_\eta = \dot{N}_\eta$. Using linear-response theory we obtain

$$I = \langle J_\eta(t)\rangle = -i\int_{-\infty}^{t} dt' \langle [J_\eta(t), H_I(t')]_-\rangle_0, \qquad (7)$$

where the statistical average $\langle\cdots\rangle$ is performed with respect to the two decoupled subsystems, QD and reservoirs. Another observable of interest is the current noise, whose spectrum is defined as the Fourier transform of the symmetric current-current correlation function. Here, we only consider the frequency-independent shot noise. Based on the linear-response theory, we have

$$S_{LL} = \int_{-\infty}^{\infty} d\tau \langle [J_L(\tau), J_L(0)]_+\rangle_0. \qquad (8)$$

Considering that the interaction Hamiltonian H_I in Eq. (1) contains two components, the direct tunneling term H_{dir} (the direct tunneling channel) and the cotunneling term (the indirect tunneling channel), we can divide the current and shot noise into three contributions,

$$I = I^0 + I^d + I^{in}, \qquad (9)$$
$$S_{LL} = S_{LL}^0 + S_{LL}^d + S_{LL}^{in}, \qquad (10)$$

due to the indirect channel, direct channel, and the interference effect between the two channels, respectively. After lengthy but straightforward calculations, we obtained explicit expressions for steady-state current and frequency-independent noise via the indirect channel:

$$I_P^0/\pi g_{LR} = (1+p^2)V + 2(1-p^2)V + 2TS_P^{z\infty}$$
$$\times (1-p^2)\left[\varphi\left(\frac{V-\Delta}{T}\right) - \varphi\left(\frac{V+\Delta}{T}\right)\right], \qquad (11)$$

$$S_{LL}^{P,0}(0)/\pi g_{LR} = (1+p^2)T\varphi\left(\frac{V}{T}\right) + (1-p^2)T$$
$$\times \left[\varphi\left(\frac{V-\Delta}{T}\right) + \varphi\left(\frac{V+\Delta}{T}\right)\right] - 4S_P^{z\infty}(1-p^2)\Delta, \qquad (12)$$

for the P configuration, and

$$I_{AP}^0/\pi g_{LR} = (1-p^2)V + [(1-p)^2(V-\Delta)$$
$$+(1+p)^2(V+\Delta)] + 2TS_{AP}^{z\infty}$$
$$\times \left[(1-p)^2\varphi\left(\frac{V-\Delta}{T}\right) - (1+p)^2\varphi\left(\frac{V+\Delta}{T}\right)\right], \qquad (13)$$

$$S_{LL}^{AP,0}(0)/\pi g_{LR} = (1-p^2)T\varphi\left(\frac{V}{T}\right)$$

$$+T\left[(1-p)^2\varphi\left(\frac{V-\Delta}{T}\right) + (1+p)^2\varphi\left(\frac{V+\Delta}{T}\right)\right]$$
$$+2S_{AP}^{z\infty}[(1-p)^2(V-\Delta) - (1+p)^2(V+\Delta)], \qquad (14)$$

for the AP configuration. The direct tunneling yields:

$$I_P^d/\pi g_{LR} = 4\frac{g_0}{g_{LR}}(1+p^2)V, \qquad (15)$$

$$S_{LL}^{P,d}(0)/\pi g_{LR} = 4\frac{g_0}{g_{LR}}(1+p^2)T\varphi\left(\frac{V}{T}\right), \qquad (16)$$

for the P configuration, and

$$I_{AP}^d/\pi g_{LR} = 4\frac{g_0}{g_{LR}}(1-p^2)V, \qquad (17)$$

$$S_{LL}^{AP,d}(0)/\pi g_{LR} = 4\frac{g_0}{g_{LR}}(1-p^2)T\varphi\left(\frac{V}{T}\right), \qquad (18)$$

for the AP configuration with $g_0 = J_0^2\rho_0^2 = g_{LR}/4$. Because direct tunneling is a spin-conserving process, it only interferes with the non-spin-flip cotunneling processes. This interference effect thus contributes to the current and shot noise only for the P configuration:

$$I_P^{in}/\pi g_{LR} = 16\sqrt{\frac{g_0}{g_{LR}}} pS_P^{z\infty}V, \qquad (19)$$

$$S_{LL}^{P,in}(0)/\pi g_{LR} = 16\sqrt{\frac{g_0}{g_{LR}}} pS_P^{z\infty}T\varphi\left(\frac{V}{T}\right). \qquad (20)$$

ACKNOWLEDGMENTS

This work is supported by Projects of the National Science Foundation of China and the Shanghai Municipal Commission of Science and Technology. NJMH is supported by the DURINT Program administered by the US Army Research Office, DAAD Grant No.19-01-1-0592.

REFERENCES

1. G.A. Prinz, Science **282**, 1660 (1998).
2. J. Martinek, Y. Utsumi, H. Imamura, J. Barnaś, S. Maekawa, J. König, and G. Schön, Phys. Rev. Lett. **91**, 127203 (2003); B. Dong, H.L. Cui, S.Y. Liu, and X.L. Lei, J. Phys.: Condens. Matter **15**, 8435 (2003); J. Martinek, M. Sindel, L. Borda, J. Barnaś, J. König, G. Schön, and J. von Delft, Phys. Rev. Lett. **91**, 247202 (2003); M.S. Choi, D. Sánchez, R. López, Phys. Rev. Lett. **92**, 56601 (2004).
3. A.N. Pasupathy, R.C. Bialczak, J. Martinek, J.E. Grose, L.A.K. Donev, P.L. McEuen, and D.C. Ralph, Science **306**, 86 (2004); J. Nygård, W.F. Kochl, N. Mason, L. DiCarlo, and C.M. Marcus, cond-mat/0410467.
4. K.A. Matveev, Zh. Eksp. Teor. Fiz. **99**, 1598 (1991) [Sov. Phys. JETP **72**, 892 (1991)]; A. Furusaki and K.A. Matveev, Phys. Rev. B **52**, 16676 (1995).
5. B. Dong, N.J.M. Horing, and H.L. Cui, Phys. Rev. B **72**, 165326 (2005).

Geometrical and impurities effects on the energy spectrum in quantum rings

G. A. Farias*, J. A. K. Freire*, M. H. Degani* and R. Ferreira†

*Departamento de Física, Universidade Federal do Ceará, Caixa Postal 6030, Campus do Pici, 60455-900
Fortaleza, Ceará, Brazil
†Laboratoire Pierre Aigrain, Ecole Normale Superieure, 24 Rue Lhomond, F75005 Paris, France

Abstract. The energy spectrum in semiconductor quantum rings (QR's) is calculated considering an external magnetic field applied perpendicular to those structures. The existence of positive hydrogenic impurities is also investigated, showing that, depending on their signal and localization, they can destroy AB oscillations. The effects on the energy spectrum due to an arbitrary deformation in the QR are considered and we observed that, in some cases the AB oscillations can also be suppressed.

Keywords: Impurities, Quantum Rings
PACS: 73.21-b, 73.20.Hb

INTRODUCTION

Recent progress in nanofabrication techniques allows us the construction of a new confined structure called QR's. The QR is modelled by a cylindrical quantum dot with an internal axially symmetric cavity. [1] In the presence of an axially directed magnetic field, persistent current and oscillations of the electron energy as a function of the magnetic flux (Aharonov-Bohm effect) (ABE) were found to occur.[2]

Dias da Silva et al. [3] analyze the effects of impurities in QR's on the AB oscillations and their consequence on the photoluminescence (PL) emission. Monozon and Schmelcher [4] consider an analytical approach to the problem of an impurity in a QR, but their results are valid only in some magnetic field regimes. Recently, Bruno-Alfonso and Latgé [5] analyzed the effects of eccentricity in QR's. This effect can suppress the AB oscillations. In all of these calculations we observe restrictions due to the perturbation method or to the fact that the carriers are confined by infinite barriers outside the ring.

In the present paper we study the energy spectrum of an electron in semiconductor quantum rings considering an external magnetic field applied perpendicularly to those structures, taking into account a realistic model consisting of rings with finite size and barrier potential.

HAMILTONIAN MODEL

We consider a QR formed by the revolution of a rectangle around the z axis with internal (external) radius $|\vec{\rho}| = a(b)$. The ring thickness in the growth direction (z) will be taken much smaller than the QR average radius, in this way, it is possible to separate the electron motion along the z-direction and x,y plane. Consequently, without loss of generality, we can consider our system as a two-dimensional one, with the electron confined at the plane $z = 0$. We also consider an external uniform magnetic field B parallel to the z axis and hydrogenic impurities located at $\vec{\rho} = \vec{\rho}_{imp}$ and at a distance $z = z_i$ to the QR plane. The confining potential is given by $V_e(\vec{\rho}) = 0$ if $a \leq |\vec{\rho}| \leq b$, and $V_e(\vec{\rho}) = V_0$, otherwise.

The QR is embedded in a (GaAl) As matrix with the barrier height $V_0 = 190$ meV, corresponding to an Al concentration of $x = 0.25$. Considering for the free electron and the impurity states a parabolic conduction band, and assuming no effective-mass discontinuities at the interfaces, the Hamiltonian can be written as:

$$H = -\frac{1}{2m^*}(\vec{p} + \frac{e}{c}\vec{A})^2 + V_e + \sum_{i=1}^{N} V_{imp}^i, \quad (1)$$

where m^* is the electron effective mass ($m^* = 0.067m^0$ where m^0 is the free electron mass), the vector potential is chosen in the symmetric gauge $\vec{A} = \frac{1}{2}\vec{B} \times \vec{\rho}$, the potential due to each impurity is $V_{imp}^i = \frac{Z_i e}{4\pi\varepsilon}/(\rho_{imp}^2 + z_i^2)$, with Z_i as the impurity charge and N is the number of impurities and the dielectric constant of the GaAs is taken as $\varepsilon = 12.5$.

The evolution method used to obtain the energy levels is based on the solution of the time dependent Schrödinger equation. [6]. See Ref. [6] for a detailed description of the method.

ENERGY LEVELS

To analyze the effects of hydrogenic impurities, we consider a ring with size $a = 140.0$ Å and $b = 240.0$ Å and one single impurity charge located at the position $\vec{\rho}_{imp}$

CP893, *Physics of Semiconductors, 28th International Conference*
edited by W. Jantsch and F. Schäffler
© 2007 American Institute of Physics 978-0-7354-0397-0/07/$23.00

= (190.0 Å, z_i) with two different distances to the ring plane ($z = 0.0$), that is, $z_1 = 10.0$ Å and $z_2 = 30.0$ Å, respectively.

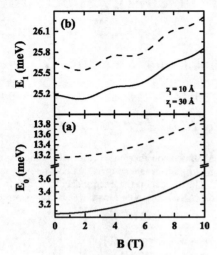

FIGURE 1. Ground (a) and first excited state (b) energy, as a function of the magnetic field, for a positive impurity at two different distances z_i to the ring plane ($z = 0.0$ Å): $z_1 = 10.0$ Å (solid line) and $z_1 = 30.0$ Å (dashed line).

Taking an impurity with positive charge, in Fig. 1 we present the energy of the ground state and first excited state, as a function of the external magnetic field, respectively. As we can see, the effects on the electronic structure due to a single hydrogenic impurity is similar to a presence of an external electric field applied in the ring plane, representing a break of symmetry due to the field acting on the confined electron. As can be seen in Fig. 1 (a), the AB oscillations were suppressed for the ground state at all positions of the impurity. The hydrogenic potential breaks down the cylindrical symmetry and in the ground state the electron confinement will be strongly related with the impurity charge. The electron tend to be bounded and consequently confined close to the impurity charge. Considering the first excited state (Fig. 1 (b)) we observe small energy oscillations due to the state delocalization, showing that the external magnetic field now starts to play an important role.

To analyze geometrical effects on the AB oscillations, we consider elliptical QRs composed of concentric ellipses. To compare our results we will consider systems which present different eccentricities, but with the same area in order to have an equal magnetic flux through the rings, without the presence of impurities. The rings have eccentricities $\xi = a/b$, with minor(major)-axis $a_j = R_j \sqrt{\xi}$ ($b_j = R_j/\sqrt{\xi}$), being $j = I$ for the internal ellipse and $j = E$ for the external ellipse, respectively. Starting with a cylindrical ring ($\xi = 0.95$) with $R_I = 140.0$ Å and $R_E = 240.0$ Å, in Fig.2 we present the energy of the ground and first excited state as a function of the mag-

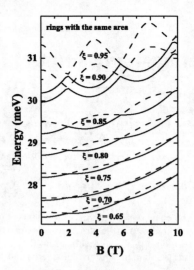

FIGURE 2. Energy of the ground state and the first excited state, as a function of the external magnetic field, with different values of eccentricity.

netic field, for different values of the eccentricity. We observe that AB oscillations are suppressed when ξ decreases. In fact, when ξ decreases the two states tend to become degenerate and the densities of charge are localized in the regions of the ellipse of large curvature.

In this paper we used a effective potential model with no fitting parameters to calculate the energy spectrum of an electron in semiconductor quantum rings, considering an external magnetic field applied, in the presence of one positive hydrogenic impurity and the effects of an arbitrary deformation on the energy spectrum. Contrary to previous theoretical studies, we apply a non-perturbative method, that can be used independently of the magnetic field intensity, locations of the impurities and ring shape. The existence of positive hydrogenic impurities and the existence of an arbitrary deformation, such as lack of symmetry on the QR geometry, can destroy the AB oscillations.

G. A. Farias, M. H. Degani and J. A. K. Freire were supported by CNPq, CAPES and FUNCAP.

REFERENCES

1. B. Szafran, and F. M. Peeters, *Europhys. Lett.* **12**, 271 (2005).
2. Y. Aharonov, and D. Bohm, *Phys. Rev.* **115**, 485 (1959).
3. L. G. G. Dias da Silva, S. E. Ulhoa, and A. O. Govorov, *Phys. Rev. B* **70**, 155318 (2004).
4. B. S. Monozon and P. Schmelcher, *Phys. Rev. B* **67**, 045203 (2003).
5. A. Bruno-Alfonso and A. Latgé, *Phys. Rev. B* **71**, 125312 (2005).
6. M. H. Degani, *Phys. Rev. B* **66**, 233306 (2002).

Removing spin blockade in a double quantum dot: role of spontaneous emission of phonons

J. Iñarrea*, G. Platero† and Allan H.MacDonald**

*Escuela Politécnica Superior, Universidad Carlos III, Leganes, Madrid, 28911, Spain and Instituto de Ciencia de Materiales, CSIC, Cantoblanco, Madrid, 28049, Spain
†Instituto de Ciencia de Materiales, CSIC, Cantoblanco, Madrid, 28049, Spain
**Department of Physics, University of Texas at Austin.Austin, Texas 78712

Abstract. The electron and nuclei spin dynamics and their interplay due to the Hyperfine interaction are self-consistently analyzed within the framework of the density matrix formalism. Our results indicate that the current leakage experimentally observed in the spin-blockade region of the current-voltage curve, occurs due to spin-flip processes induced by hyperfine interaction. We show as well how a magnetic field applied parallel to the current allows excited states to participate in the electronic current and removes spin blockade. Our model includes also a self-consistent description of inelastic transitions where the energy is exchanged through interactions with acoustic phonons in the environment.

Keywords: Spin blockade, double quantum dots, phonon emission
PACS: 73.40Hm, 73.20Dx

INTRODUCTION

Recent transport experiments in vertical double quantum dots (DQD's) show that Pauli exclusion principle plays an important role[1] in current rectification. In particular, spin blockade (SB) is observed at certain regions of dc voltages, and the interplay between Coulomb and SB can be used to block the current in one direction of bias while allowing it to flow in the opposite one. In order to explain their results, we consider simultaneously hyperfine (HF) interaction to be responsible for the leakage current in the SB region, and the emission of phonons to be also responsible of the observed features in the experimental current/voltage (I/V_{DC}) curve. According to our calculations, phonon-assisted tunneling plays a key role and it needs to be included to have a full understanding of the physics behind the experimental results.

MODEL

The theoretical model presented in this paper has been carried out in the frame of the density matrix (DM) formalism and consists in time-evolution equations for electronic charge occupations and nuclei polarizations which are coupled and which we solve self-consistently. Our theoretical results reproduce the I/V_{DC} observed plateau due to SB and also the main current peaks. HF interaction is proposed as the candidate to lift SB, producing spin-flip (sf) of electrons and nuclei. Phonon-assisted tunneling is proposed, in parallel with the direct tunneling, to sustain the total current through the device. We

have made use of the density matrix (DM) formalism starting from a basis which contains 20 states. The states mainly involved are:

$|1\rangle = |0, \uparrow\rangle; |2\rangle = |0, \downarrow\rangle; |3\rangle = |\uparrow, \uparrow\rangle; |4\rangle = |\downarrow, \downarrow\rangle;$
$|5\rangle = |\uparrow, \downarrow\rangle; |6\rangle = |\downarrow, \uparrow\rangle; |7\rangle = |0, \uparrow \uparrow^*\rangle; |8\rangle = |0, \downarrow \downarrow^*\rangle;$
$|9\rangle = |0, \uparrow\downarrow\rangle.$

Those states marked with (*) correspond to the excited state in the right QD. Following density matrix one arrives at the time evolution equations for the DM elements [2, 3, 4]. From here we calculate the diagonal (occupations$\equiv \rho_i$) DM elements: $\dot\rho(t)_{ss} = \sum_{m\neq s} W_{sm}\rho_{mm} - \sum_{k\neq s} W_{ks}\rho_{ss}$ where ρ_{ss} is the s-diagonal element of the reduced DM. It represents the probability to find the electron in the s-state. $W_{i,j}$ is the transition rate, i.e., the probability per unit time that the electrons make a transition from the j- state to the i-state. For elastic tunneling we calculate $W_{i,j}$ by using the Fermi Golden Rule, i.e., first order in perturbation theory [5, 6, 7]. For inelastic transitions, energy is exchanged with phonons in the environment. In other words, at $T \approx 0$ (we have considered zero temperature in our calculations) the inelastic tunneling between the two dots is assisted by the emission of acoustic phonons, yielding a significant contribution to the current (I). This contribution has been experimentally measured by Fujisawa et al.,[8] and theoretically analyzed by Brandes et al.,[9]. In order to calculate the inelastic transition rate $W_{1,2}^{ph}$ due to the emission of phonons, we have considered the theory developed by Brandes et al.,[9]. The electronic spin-flip scattering rate $W_{i,j}^{sf}$ is phenomenologically introduced through $\tau_{sf}(\tau_{sf} \approx \mu s)$, being $W_{i,j}^{sf} \propto 1/\tau_{sf}$. The system of time evolution equations for the electronic states occupations

CP893, *Physics of Semiconductors, 28th International Conference*
edited by W. Jantsch and F. Schäffler
© 2007 American Institute of Physics 978-0-7354-0397-0/07/$23.00

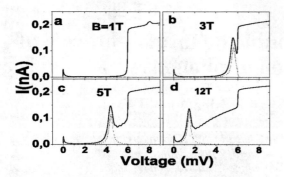

FIGURE 1. Stationary I/V_{DC} curve for different B (1a to 1d). We observe an additional peak at finite B which moves to lower V_{DC} as B increases: for different values of B the resonance condition through the triplet states in the right QD occurs at different values of V_{DC}. A shoulder at the right side of the resonance is also observed. Single line corresponds to both elastic (direct tunneling) and inelastic (phonon-assisted) contributions. The dotted line considers only elastic transitions: in this case it can be observed that the shoulder to the right of the resonances and the large main peak at $V_{DC} \approx 6$ meV collapses. The resonant current peak through the triplet state of the right QD moves to lower V_{DC} as B increases.

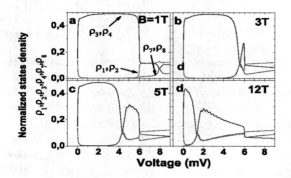

FIGURE 2. Stationary charge occupation of different electronic states for the same cases of B as in Fig. 1.

ρ_i is self-consistently solved and from that we calculate I through the system .

RESULTS

In Fig. 1 we present the stationary I/V_{DC} curve calculated for different B (Figs. 1a to 1d). We observe an additional peak at finite B which moves to lower V_{DC} as B increases, as in the experiments by Ono[1]: for different values of B, the resonance condition: $|3\rangle = |\uparrow,\uparrow\rangle \Rightarrow |7\rangle = |0,\uparrow\uparrow^*\rangle$ and $|4\rangle = |\downarrow,\downarrow\rangle \Rightarrow |8\rangle = |0,\downarrow\downarrow^*\rangle$, occurs at different values of V_{DC}. The calculated results presented are also

very similar to the experimental ones presented by Ono et al., including the shoulder at the right side of the B-dependent peak. In Fig. 1, the single line corresponds to the situation where both elastic (direct tunneling) and inelastic (phonon-assisted) contributions are considered and the dotted line means that only elastic inter-dot transitions are taken into account. According to these results, inelastic transitions play a crucial role to sustain the current not only in the large right peak, but also in the right shoulder of the moving central peak where elastic inter-dot transitions do not contribute because the corresponding levels in each dot are out of resonance. Fig. 2 shows the charge occupation for different states and for the same values of B as in Fig. 1. For small B (Figs. 2a and 2b), the electrons occupy mainly the inter-dot triplet states ($|\uparrow,\uparrow\rangle$ and $|\downarrow,\downarrow\rangle$) in the SB region with a probability of almost 0.5 for each one. However at larger B, (see Figs. 2c and 2d), the resonant condition is fulfilled inside the SB region giving rise to a lifting of the blockade. The opening of this new current channel corresponds to a decrease in the occupation of $|3\rangle$ and $|4\rangle$ and to an increase in the occupation of $|7\rangle$ and $|8\rangle$. The shoulder at the right side of the resonant peak produces a removal of SB too and is due to inelastic tunneling through the inner barrier assisted with the emission of acoustic phonons. Therefore we can state that, apart from the leakage current due to HF interaction, SB removal is due to a combination of both elastic tunneling due to excited triplet states coming into the transport window by the magnetic field, and additional inelastic contributions corresponding to phonon emission.

In conclusion we reproduce experimental features by Ono et al.[1], and show how, inelastic transitions with the corresponding emission of phonons play a crucial role in sustaining the current through the device.

ACKNOWLEDGMENTS

This work was supported by the MCYT (Spain) grant MAT2005-06444, the "Ramon y Cajal" program (J.I.). and the EU Human Potential Programme HPRN-CT-2000-00144.

REFERENCES

1. K. Ono et al., Science **297** 1313 2002.
2. K. Blum. *Density Matrix Theory and Applications.* (New York:Plenum) 1981
3. G. Mahler et al.,*Quantum Networks: Dynamics of Open Nanostructures.* (Berlin:Springer) 1995
4. H-A Engel et al., Phys. Rev. B **65**, 195321 (2002)
5. B. Dong et al., Cond-mat 0205278 2002.
6. W.G. van der Wiel et al., Rev. Mod. Physics **75** 1 (2003).
7. S.A. Gurtvitz et al., Phys.Rev. B **53** 15932 (1996).
8. T.Fujisawaetal.,Science,282,932,(1998).
9. T.Brandesetal.,Phys.Rev.Lett.,83,3021,(1999).

Charge correlation and spin coupling in double quantum dots

Hyuga Masu, Jun Nakamura, Akiko Natori

Department of Electronic-Engineering, The University of Electro-Communications, 1-5-1 Chofu, Tokyo 182-8585, Japan

Abstract.
We study both the spin and the charge correlations between two electrons in vertically coupled quantum dots with a finite well width, using a diffusion quantum Monte Carlo method. We clarify the mechanism of their dependence on both a barrier thickness and a magnetic field. When the barrier thickness increases, two-electron occupation probability in the same dot is suppressed drastically by enhanced charge correlation relative to the electron transfer effect and a magnitude of the antiferromagnetic spin coupling decreases in two stages, from a strong coupling to a weak coupling. As the magnetic field increases, both the antiferromagnetic spin coupling constant and the two-electron occupation probability in the same dot are suppressed. In the case of weak lateral confinement, transitions of the ground state can be also induced by a magnetic field and they accompany changes of the spin coupling between antiferromagnetic and ferromagnetic couplings.

Keywords: vertically coupled quantum dots, Diffusion Quantum Monte Calro method, spin coupling, charge correlation
PACS: 73.21.La, 75.75.+a, 73.21.-b

INTRODUCTION

Semiconductor quantum dots (QD's), in which electrons are confined in all three space-dimensions, are considered as artificial atoms. Accordingly, electrons in the two-coupled QD's can form an artificial molecule. Recently, the antiferromagnetic spin coupling between two electrons in a vertically coupled QD's was observed experimentally [1, 2]. In this report, we explore the mechanism of the spin coupling using a diffusion quantum Monte Carlo method [3]. Furthermore, we study the effects of external magnetic fields to consider a possibility of controlling the spin coupling in the vertically coupled QD's.

MODEL AND FORMULATION

We consider a vertically coupled QD's in which electrons are confined by a parabolic potential in the $x - y$ plane and by a symmetric double quantum well potential with a finite well width in the axial z direction. According to the experimental situation [1, 2], the depth of each well was assumed to be 270 meV and the width of each well was assumed to be 4 nm and the barrier thickness b between the two wells was varied between 3 nm and 10 nm. As for the parabolic confining potential with the strength ω_0, the oscillator length $l = 1 \sqrt{\omega_0}$ was assumed to be 7 nm ($\hbar\omega_0 = 24\ 4$meV, a solid line 'a' in Fig.1). This value of l corresponds to strong lateral confinement. We also studied the case of weak lateral confinement of $l = 14$nm ($\hbar\omega_0 = 6\ 1$meV, B and C points in Fig.1) in

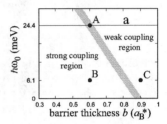

FIGURE 1. The schematic diagram of electron coupling between two electrons in vertically coupled QD's.

calculation under magnetic field. We used the effective atomic unit in the following; the effective Hartree Ha* $= 2$Ry* ≈ 12meV and the effective Bohr radius $a_B^* \approx 9\ 8$nm for GaAs. We calculate the two energies E_s and E_t of the spin-singlet ground states and the spin-triplet ground states to evaluate the spin coupling constant $J = E_s - E_t$, using a diffusion quantum Monte Carlo method.

NUMERICAL RESULTS

We study the barrier thickness dependence of the spin coupling along the line 'a' in Fig.1. When the barrier thickness increases, the magnitude of the antiferromagnetic spin coupling decreases exponentially in two stages, from a strong coupling region to a weak coupling region as seen in Fig.2. To study the charge correlation effects in coupled QD's, we calculate the normalized projected distribution function $P(z_1\ z_2) = \int |\Psi(r_1\ r_2)|^2 dx_1 dy_1 dx_2 dy_2$ in $z_1 - z_2$ plane using the

CP893, *Physics of Semiconductors, 28th International Conference*
edited by W. Jantsch and F. Schäffler

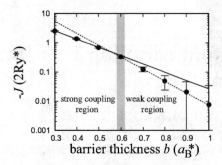

FIGURE 2. Barrier thickness b dependence of the spin coupling constant J with the standard deviation.

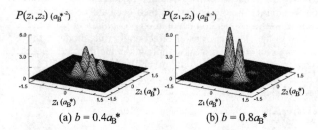

(a) $b = 0.4a_B^*$ (b) $b = 0.8a_B^*$

FIGURE 3. The projected distribution function $P(z_1\ z_2)$ for the spin singlet two-electron ground state.

two-electron wavefunction Ψ. In Fig.3, $P(z_1\ z_2)$ is shown at $b = 0\ 4a_B^*$ in a strong coupling region and at $b = 0\ 8a_B^*$ in a weak coupling region for the spin singlet ground state. We define the double occupation ratio $P = [\int_0^\infty dz_1 \int_0^\infty dz_2 + \int_{-\infty}^0 dz_1 \int_{-\infty}^0 dz_2]P(z_1\ z_2)$ as a measure of two-electron configuration in the same dot. The double occupation ratio P for the spin singlet ground state is plotted in Fig.4 as a function of the barrier thickness b. It is seen that P is suppressed significantly in a weak coupling region.

As a magnetic field is applied, the ground state holds to be the spin singlet state with the angular momentum quantum number $m = 0$ in $\omega_c\ \omega_0 < 10$, for point A in

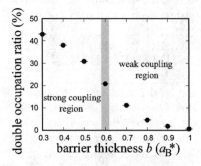

FIGURE 4. The double occupation ratio P with the standard deviation for the spin singlet ground state, as a function of the barrier thickness b.

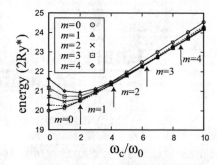

FIGURE 5. Magnetic field dependence of the two-electron state energies with the angular momentum quantum number of $m = 0\ 1\ 2\ 3\ 4$ at $b = 0\ 6a_B^*$, in the case of weak lateral confinement of $\hbar\omega_0 = 6\ 1$meV.

Fig.1. Here, ω_c is the cyclotron frequency. The magnitude of the spin coupling constant $|J|$ and the double occupation ratio P decreases slowly by increasing magnetic field. For point B in Fig.1, on the other hand, the ground state exhibits many transitions to the state with higher angular momentum $m = 0\ 1\ 2\ 3\ 4$ as the magnetic field increases, as seen in Fig.5. Hence, the spin coupling of the ground state changes alternatively between antiferromagnetic for the even m state and ferromagnetic for the odd m state by the Pauli principle. However, the double occupation ratio of the ground states is not so suppressed near the critical field and the charge distribution is delocalized over two dots.

We address also a possibility of magnetic field control of the spin coupling between two electrons localized in individual dots. For point C in Fig.1, the double occupation ratio P is suppressed and the ground states transition occurs at $\omega_c\ \omega_0 \approx 4$.

The calculated dependences of $|J|$ and P on both the barrier thickness and the magnetic field can be explained semi-quantitatively by the Hubbard model.

CONCLUSION

We studied both the spin correlation and the charge correlation for the two-electron ground state in vertically coupled QD's with a finite well width and clarified the mechanism of the spin coupling.

REFERENCES

1. A. Takeuchi, T. Kuroda, R. Sasou, T. Nakata, and N. Yokoyama, *Physica B* **314**, 25 (2002).
2. A. Takeuchi, et al., *Jpn. J. Appl. Phys* **42**, 4278 (2003).
3. H. Masu, T. Yamada, J. Nakamura, and A. Natori, *Phys. Rev. B* **74**, (2006) in press.

Hole transport in p-type GaAs quantum dots and point contacts

B. Grbić*, R. Leturcq*, T. Ihn*, K. Ensslin*, D. Reuter† and A. D. Wieck†

*Solid State Physics Laboratory, ETH Zurich, 8093 Zurich, Switzerland
†Angewandte Festkörperphysik, Ruhr-Universität Bochum, 44780 Bochum, Germany

Abstract. Strong spin-orbit interaction characteristic for p-type GaAs systems, makes such systems promising for the realization of spintronic devices. Here we report on transport measurements in nanostructures fabricated on p-type, C-doped GaAs heterostructures by scanning probe oxidation lithography. We observe conductance quantization in a quantum point contact, as well as pronounced Coulomb resonances in two quantum dots with different geometries. Charging energies for both dots, extracted from Coulomb diamond measurements are in agreement with the lithographic dimensions of the dots. The absence of excited states in Coulomb diamond measurements indicates that the dots are in the multi-level transport regime.

Keywords: p-type GaAs, spin-orbit interaction, AFM oxidation lithography, quantum dot, Coulomd blockade
PACS: 73.21.La, 73.23.Hk, 73.63.Kv

The interest in low dimensional hole-doped GaAs systems arises primarily from the fact that spin-orbit [1] as well as carrier-carrier Coulomb interaction effects are more pronounced in such systems compared to the more established electron doped systems, due to the fact that holes have approximately 6 times larger effective mass than electrons [2]. However, the investigation of electronic transport in low-dimensional p-type GaAs systems was mainly limited to two-dimensional bulk samples, due to difficulties to fabricate stable p-type nanodevices with conventional split-gate technique. The main problems we encountered in measurements on split-gate devices tested on several different p-type heterostructures are strong hysteresis effects in gate sweeps, as well as significant gate instabilities and charge fluctuations.

In order to overcome these problems with metallic gates, we employ a different lithography technique, namely, Atomic Force Microscope (AFM) oxidation lithography [3, 4] to define nanostructures on two-dimensional hole gases (2DHG). We demonstrate that for a 2DHG 45 nm below the sample surface the AFM written oxide lines with a height of 15-18 nm completely deplete the 2DHG beneath at low temperatures [5]. Density and mobility of the unpatented sample at 4.2 K are: $p = 4 \times 10^{11}$ cm^{-2}, μ=120'000 cm^2/Vs.

We fabricated a quantum point contact (QPC) with a lithographic width of 165 nm and tested its electronical functionality by measuring its conductance at low temperatures (Fig. 1). At the temperature of 500 mK quantized conductance plateaus are observed corresponding to transmission of one and two modes through the QPC. In addition, a plateau-like structure is observed at ~ $0.8 \times 2e^2/h$. As the temperature is reduced to ~ 70 mK, this plateau-like feature evolves into a dip-like structure

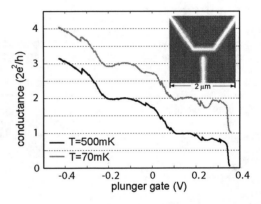

FIGURE 1. Two-terminal QPC conductance measurement at T=500 mK (black curve) and T=70 mK (gray curve). The trace corresponding to T=70 mK is shifted upwards by one conductance unit for clarity. A bias of 10 μV is applied symmetrically across the QPC. Inset: AFM micrograph of the QPC

below the first plateau (Fig. 1). In differential conductance vs. bias measurements we observe a pronounced zero-bias peak for a QPC conductance ~ $0.8 \times 2e^2/h$, which weakens as the conductance increases to $2e^2/h$, and completely disappears above the first plateau. This behavior might indicate that the structure below the first plateau is related to Kondo-like effect [6]. Besides, at T= 70 mK another plateau-like structure at ~ $1.7 \times 2e^2/h$ appears. All features observed in this sample were stable and reproducible in several different cool-downs.

Hole transport in p-type GaAs quantum dots is also explored. Two quantum dots were fabricated with AFM lithography - one rectangular (Fig. 2(b)) with lithographic dimensions 430×170 nm^2, and the other circular (Fig. 2(d)) with lithographic radius ~ 320 nm. The trans-

CP893, *Physics of Semiconductors, 28th International Conference*
edited by W. Jantsch and F. Schäffler

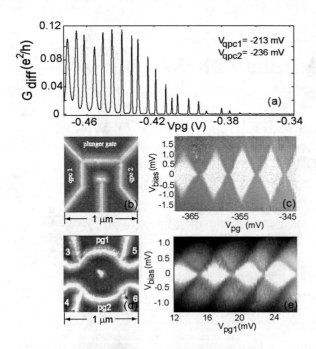

FIGURE 2. (a) Differential conductance of the rectangular dot (b) in the configuration V_{qpc1} = -213 mV, V_{qpc2} = -236 mV as a function of plunger gate voltage. (b) AFM micrograph of the rectangular quantum dot with designations of the gates. (c) Coulomb diamonds in differential conductance for the rectangular dot in the configuration V_{qpc1} = -225 mV, V_{qpc2} = -235 mV, represented in a logarithmic gray scale plot (white regions represent low conductance). (d) AFM micrograph of the circular quantum dot. (e) Coulomb diamonds in differential conductance for the circular dot in the configuration: V_{pg2} = -32 mV, V_3 = 72 mV, V_4 = 120 mV, V_5 = 310 mV, V_6 = 200 mV represented in a logarithmic gray scale plot.

port measurements in both dots have been performed in a dilution refrigerator at a base temperature of ∼ 70 mK. We have measured the two-terminal conductance of the dots by applying either a small dc or ac bias voltage V_{bias} between source and drain, and measuring the current through the dot with a resolution better than 50 fA.

The QPC gates are tuned to configurations where the dots are symmetrically coupled to the leads. Pronounced Coulomb resonances are observed in both dots (Fig. 2(a) shows Coulomb peaks from the rectangular dot). It is important to note that the dots close when the value of the plunger-gate voltage increases − this is a clear indication that we measure hole transport. Coulomb resonances are fitted both with an expression for a thermally broadened Coulomb blockade peak in the multi-level transport regime and a coupling broadened Lorentzian peak. In all cases the thermally broadened resonance fits better to the data than a coupling broadened resonance, indicating that the dots are in the weak coupling regime. The electronic temperature extracted from the fitting is ∼ 130 mK.

Coulomb diamond measurements are performed in the weak coupling regime for both dots, and the results are shown in Fig. 2. The uniform size of the diamonds indicates that all confined holes reside in one single potential minimum rather than occupying several disconnected or tunnel-coupled potential minima. From the extent of the diamonds in bias direction we estimate a charging energy of the rectangular dot to be $E_{C,rect} \approx 1.5$ meV, while the lever-arm of the plunger gate is $\alpha_{rect} \approx 0.26$. In case of the circular dot we obtain $E_{C,circle} \approx 0.5$ meV and $\alpha_{circle} \approx 0.14$. Assuming a disk-like shape of the dots allows us to estimate electronic radius of the dots from the values of their charging energies. The obtained value for the rectangular dot is $r_{rect} \approx 115$ nm, and for the circular $r_{circle} \approx 340$ nm, which is consistent with the lithographic dimensions of the dots and indicates that the dots are really formed in the regions encircled by the oxide lines.

Due to the large effective mass of holes, the single-particle level spacing in case of hole quantum dots is significantly smaller compared to electron quantum dots with similar size. The estimated mean single-particle level spacing in the rectangular dot is $\triangle_{rect} \leq 15$ μeV, and in the circular dot is $\triangle_{circle} \leq 2$ μeV. Therefore we were not able to resolve excited states in Coulomb diamond measurements in neither of the two dots. This fact, together with the observed temperature dependence of Coulomb peak heights [5] indicates that both dots are in the multi-level transport regime. In order to be able to investigate the single-particle level spectrum in hole quantum dots, one has to significantly reduce the lateral dimensions of the dot as well as the hole temperature.

In conclusion, we fabricated tunable nanodevices on p-type GaAs heterostructures by AFM oxidation lithography. By using this fabrication technique we were able to overcome the problems with large hysteresis effects present in gate sweeps in conventional split-gate defined nanostructures on p-type GaAs, and the stability of the structures improved as well. Electronic functionality of these structures was demonstrated by observing conductance quantization in a QPC, and Coulomb blockade in two quantum dots with different geometries. Further reduction in size of the p-type quantum dots is necessary in order to explore the influence of spin-orbit and carrier-carrier interactions on single-particle level spectra.

Financial support from the Swiss National Science Foundation is gratefully acknowledged.

REFERENCES

1. R. Winkler, Springer Tracts in Modern Physics, Volume **191**, Springer-Verlag (2003)
2. B. Grbić et al., Appl. Phys. Lett. **85**, 2277 (2004)
3. R. Held et al., Appl. Phys. Lett. **73**, 262 (1998).
4. L. P. Rokhinson et al., Superl. and Microstr. **32**, 99 (2002).
5. B. Grbić et al., Appl. Phys. Lett. **87**, 232108 (2005)
6. S. Cronenwett et al., Phys. Rev. Lett. **88**, 226805 (2002)

Theory and experiment of InAs/InP quantum dots: from calculations to laser emission

C. Cornet[1], M. Hayne[2,3], A. Schliwa[4], F. Doré[1], C. Labbé[1], H. Folliot[1], J. Even[1], D. Bimberg[4], V. V. Moshchalkov[2] and S. Loualiche[1]

[1] LENS – UMR FOTON 6082 au CNRS, INSA de Rennes, 20, avenue des buttes de Coesmes, 35043 Rennes cedex, France
[2] INPAC Pulsed Fields Group, Katholieke Universiteit Leuven, Celestijnenlaan 200D, B-3001 Leuven, Belgium
[3] present address: Department of Physics, Lancaster University, Lancaster LA1 4YB, United Kingdom
[4] Institut für Festkörperphysik, Technische Universität Berlin, Hardenbergstrasse 36, 10623 Berlin, Germany
charles.cornet@ens.insa-rennes.fr

Abstract. We report a brief overview of recent research developments on InAs/InP quantum dots (QDs). Eight-band k•p calculations are performed on single InAs/InP QDs, and the impact of substrate orientation ((311)B or (100)) on electronic and optical properties is studied. It is then demonstrated that high QDs density can be reached on such a system, leading to lateral coupling between dots in a InGaAsP quaternary alloy matrix. Calculations and (magnetophoto-) (photo-) (electro-) luminescence experiments are used to demonstrate that the lateral coupling leads to miniband effects, and to a better charge carrier redistribution between QDs for laser applications..

Keywords: Quantum dots, lateral coupling, eight-band kp, magneto-photoluminescence

PACS: 73.21.La; 71.15.-m; 71.70.Gm ; 78.67.Hc ; 78.65.Cr

INTRODUCTION

Recently there have been considerable research developments in the field of nanostructured semiconductor materials, and especially QDs.[1] InAs QDs grown on InP (311) substrate are usually considered as a good candidate for the emission at 1.55 μm wavelength used for long haul telecommunications. Here, we report a summary of recent results obtained on InAs/InP QDs. These results deal with many aspects of InAs/InP QDs, such as calculation of electronic structure, optical characterization of several kind of QDs (especially leading to understanding of growth mechanisms, and lateral coupling), and finally, laser applications.

CALCULATIONS

Eight-band k•p calculations including strain and piezoelectricity,[2,3] are performed on truncated conical InAs/InP dots of several heights, on both (311)B and (100) substrates. Corresponding optical absorption spectra for the full cone QDs are presented on fig. 1. A blue shift of first order transitions is observed on the (311)B substrate spectrum compared to the (100) substrate spectrum, mainly attributed to the difference of hydrostatic strain contributions on both substrates.

Second order transitions are also activated on (311)B substrate. This is interpreted as a consequence of the incompatibility between QD structural symmetry and the crystal symmetry.[3]

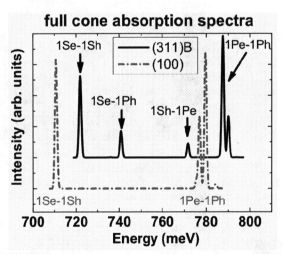

FIGURE 1. Optical absorption spectra for conical InAs/InP QDs on (100) and on (311)B substrate orientation. Cross-transitions appear when the (311)B substrate is used.

CP893, *Physics of Semiconductors, 28th International Conference*
edited by W. Jantsch and F. Schäffler
© 2007 American Institute of Physics 978-0-7354-0397-0/07/$23.00

IMPACT OF CAPPING LAYERS BY MAGNETO-PHOTOLUMINESCENCE

The impact of the capping layers on lateral confinement in InAs/InP (311)B QDs is then studied by magneto-photoluminescence. Several capping layers are considered such as InP or a GaInAsP quaternary alloy (Q1.18).[4] Exciton Bohr radii are measured to be 7.7 and 6.8 nm for InP and Q1.18 respectively. Surprisingly, the Q1.18 is found to induce a better confinement, attributed to the different shapes of the QDs in these two different systems. Confirmation is given by X-STM measurements.[5] The Q1.18 thus leads both to a better optical confinement and a better carrier confinement in InAs/InP QDs.

INTER-QD LATERAL COUPLING AND LASERS

The Q1.18 presented in the last part also allows to reach a high QD density.[6] Figure 2 presents AFM pictures for several stacked QDs layers samples.

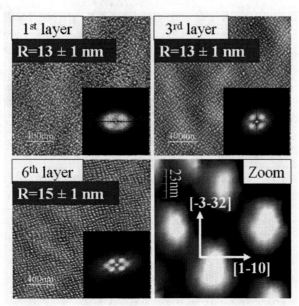

FIGURE 2. AFM pictures of the last QD layer on 1, 3 and 6 QDs stacked layers samples. Insets show the 2D-FFT of the corresponding AFM pictures. Self-organisation and anisotropy of QDs is demonstrated.

In this case, the self-organization and high QD density (QDD) raise the interesting problem of the presence of inter-QD lateral coupling.[7] Magneto-photoluminescence have been performed on samples with respectively high and low QDD. The Bohr radii are found to be unexpectedly larger for the low QDD sample than for the high QDD sample, interpreted as a consequence of a lateral expansion of the wavefunction in the high QDD sample, due to lateral coupling.[8] Electroluminescence is also performed on both high QDD and low QDD samples. The high QDD sample is found to have a lower spectral width and a lower threshold current density.[8] The lateral coupling of QDs is thus considered responsible for an improved charge carrier redistribution in QDs lasers. However, a complete study at low temperature would be helpful to solve this problem. Moreover, effects of inhomogeneous broadening, QD density should also be explored. In conclusion, the use of the Q1.18 in InAs/InP QDs lasers for the 1.55 μm wavelength seems to be the appropriate choice as it allows to reach high QD density, good optical and electronic confinement, enhanced redistribution because of the inter-QD lateral coupling, keeping the atomic-like character of the excitonic ground state transition.

ACKNOWLEDGMENTS

This work was supported by the SANDiE Network of Excellence (Contract No. NMP4-CT-2004-500101) of the sixth Framework Program of the European Commission, and the EuroMagNET project.

REFERENCES

[1] D. Bimberg, M. Grundmann and N. N. Ledentsov, Quantum dot Heterostructure, (Wiley, Chichester, 1999).

[2] O. Stier, M. Grundmann and D. Bimberg, Phys. Rev. B **59**, 5688 (1999).

[3] C. Cornet, A. Schliwa, J. Even, F. Doré, C. Celebi, A. Létoublon, E. Macé, C. Paranthoën, A. Simon, P. M. Koenraad, N. Bertru, D. Bimberg and S. Loualiche, Phys. Rev. B., in press (July 2006).

[4] C. Cornet, C. Levallois, P. Caroff, H. Folliot, C. Labbé, J. Even, A. Le Corre, S. Loualiche, M. Hayne and V. V. Moshchalkov, Appl. Phys. Lett. **87**, 233111 (2005).

[5] C. Celebi, J. M. Ulloa, P. M. Koenraad, A. Simon, A. Létoublon and N. Bertru, Appl. Phys. Lett., in press (2006).

[6] P. Caroff, N. Bertru, A. Le Corre, T. Rohel, I. Alghoraibi, H. Folliot and S. Loualiche, Jpn. J. Appl. Phys. **44**, L1069 (2005).

[7] C. Cornet, C. Platz, P. Caroff, J. Even, C. Labbé, H. Folliot, A. Le Corre and S. Loualiche, Phys. Rev. B **72**, 035342 (2005).

[8] C. Cornet, M. Hayne, P. Caroff, C. Levallois, L. Joulaud, E. Homeyer, C. Paranthoën, J. Even, C. Labbé, H. Folliot, V. V. Moshchalkov and S. Loualiche, submitted to Phys. Rev. B, (2006).

Andreev tunneling through an interacting quantum dot: Numerical renormalization group approach

Yoichi Tanaka*, Norio Kawakami* and Akira Oguri†

*Department of Applied Physics, Osaka University, Suita, Osaka 565-0871, Japan
†Department of Material Science, Osaka City University, Sumiyoshi-ku, Osaka 558-8585, Japan

Abstract. We theoretically study the Andreev tunneling through a quantum dot (QD) coupled to normal and superconducting leads by means of the numerical renormalization group (NRG) method. As the coupling between the QD and the normal lead gets smaller, we find that the peak structure is developed in the conductance, which clearly features crossover behavior between two distinct regions of spin-singlet ground states, i.e. the superconducting singlet state and the Kondo singlet state. We discuss the characteristic transport properties of the Andreev tunneling in the light of local electron correlations in the QD.

Keywords: Quantum dot, Andreev tunneling, Kondo effect, Numerical renormalization group.
PACS: 73.63.Kv, 74.45.+c, 72.15.Qm, 73.23.-b

INTRODUCTION

Recent rapid progress in nanotechnology has stimulated extensive investigations on transport properties of a mesoscopic system with hybrid normal(metal)-superconductor junction, in which the Andreev reflection plays a key role in controlling characteristic transport properties. In particular, the Andreev tunneling through a QD embedded in the normal-superconductor junction (N-QD-S) has attracted much attention. For such systems we can expect intriguing phenomena coming from the interplay between the Andreev reflection and local electron correlations such as the Kondo effect. In order to address this problem, theoretical analyses [1-8] as well as experimental investigations [9] have been done intensively.

In this paper, we theoretically study this problem with the use of the NRG method, which has been applied successfully to a Josephson current through a QD [10, 11]. We calculate the conductance through a N-QD-S junction at zero temperature and discuss some characteristic features which were not examined in the previous studies.

MODEL AND FORMULATION

The Hamiltonian of a QD coupled to normal and superconducting leads is given by

$$H = H_d + H_N + H_S + H_{dN}^T + H_{dS}^T, \qquad (1)$$

where $H_d = (\varepsilon_d + U/2)(n_d - 1) + U/2(n_d - 1)^2$, $H_N = \sum_{k,\sigma} \varepsilon_k c_{k\sigma}^\dagger c_{k\sigma}$ and $H_S = \sum_{q,\sigma} \varepsilon_q s_{q\sigma}^\dagger s_{q\sigma} + \sum_q (\Delta s_{q\uparrow}^\dagger s_{-q\downarrow}^\dagger + \text{H.c.})$ are the Hamiltonians of the QD, the normal lead and the superconducting lead (Δ is the superconducting gap), respectively. $H_{dN}^T = V_N \sum_{k,\sigma} (c_{k\sigma}^\dagger d_\sigma + \text{H.c.})/\sqrt{N}$

and $H_{dS}^T = V_S \sum_{q,\sigma} (s_{q\sigma}^\dagger d_\sigma + \text{H.c.})/\sqrt{N}$ denote the tunneling parts between the QD and the leads. In this work, we assume that the amplitude of the superconducting gap $|\Delta|$ is sufficiently large ($|\Delta| \to \infty$). The essential physics of the Andreev reflection, which occurs inside the superconducting gap, is still captured in this limit. This assumption enables us to reduce the Hamiltonian (1) to an effective single-channel model, in which the QD is coupled only to the normal lead and the role of the superconducting lead is replaced simply by an extra onsite superconducting gap in the QD, $H_d^{SC} = \Delta_d d_\uparrow^\dagger d_\downarrow^\dagger + \text{H.c.}$ [11]. Here, $\Delta_d \equiv \Gamma_S$, and $\Gamma_{S(N)}$ is the resonance width between the QD and the superconducting (normal) lead. The low-energy properties of this system can be described by a generalized version of the local Fermi liquid theory [12]. Furthermore in the limit of $|\Delta| \to \infty$, the linear conductance $G_{V=0} = dI/dV|_{V=0}$ at zero temperature is determined by the renormalized parameters, $\widetilde{E}_d$ and $\widetilde{\Gamma}_N$, for quasiparticles,

$$G_{V=0} = \frac{4e^2}{h} 4 \frac{\Gamma_S^2}{E_d^2} \frac{(\widetilde{E}_d/\widetilde{\Gamma}_N)^2}{\{1 + (\widetilde{E}_d/\widetilde{\Gamma}_N)^2\}^2}, \qquad (2)$$

where $E_d = \sqrt{(\varepsilon_d + U/2)^2 + \Gamma_S^2}$. We calculate these two renormalized parameters from the fixed-point eigenvalues of NRG [13].

NUMERICAL RESULTS

In this work, we concentrate on electron-hole symmetric case ($\varepsilon_d + U/2 = 0$) with particular emphasis on the competition between the role of the Coulomb interaction U and that of the superconducting correlation through

CP893, *Physics of Semiconductors, 28th International Conference*
edited by W. Jantsch and F. Schäffler
© 2007 American Institute of Physics 978-0-7354-0397-0/07/$23.00

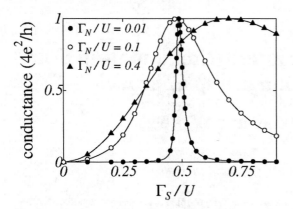

FIGURE 1. Conductance as a function of Γ_S/U for several values of Γ_N/U in the electron-hole symmetric case ($\varepsilon_d + U/2 = 0$).

Γ_S. We have carried out NRG calculations by exploiting the value of $U/D = 2.0 \times 10^{-2}$ with D being the half-width of the conduction band.

The result of the conductance is plotted in Fig. 1 as a function of the ratio Γ_S/U for several values of Γ_N/U. Note that the maximum value of the conductance is $4e^2/h$ in the presence of the Andreev reflection. As Γ_N/U gets smaller, the conductance peak becomes sharper and the peak position approaches $\Gamma_S/U = 0.5$. What happens physically at the point of $\Gamma_S/U = 0.5$ can be inferred from that in the case of $\Gamma_N \to 0$, where the QD is disconnected from the normal lead. In this case the ground state is a nonmagnetic singlet or a magnetic doublet depending on the value of Γ_S/U. Specifically in the limit of $|\Delta| \to \infty$, the ground state is a super-conducting spin-singlet state for $\Gamma_S/U > 0.5$, while it is the spin-doublet state for $\Gamma_S/U < 0.5$. For finite Γ_N, the conduction electrons from the lead screen the free spin moment to form the Kondo singlet state in the region of $\Gamma_S/U < 0.5$. For this reason, the ground state of the N-QD-S junction is always a singlet. There are, however, two distinct singlets, namely one of which for $\Gamma_S/U > 0.5$ has the superconducting-singlet character, while the other for $\Gamma_S/U < 0.5$ has the Kondo-singlet character.

Taking this into account, we consider the behavior of the conductance in Fig. 1. In the region of $\Gamma_S/U < 0.5$ where the Kondo resonance is well developed, the super-conducting lead is almost decoupled from the QD, which results in the suppression of the Andreev reflection at the QD-S interface. This explains why the conductance in this region is suppressed. On the other hand, in the region of $\Gamma_S/U > 0.5$, the Andreev reflection at the QD-S interface effectively drives the Kondo resonance away from the Fermi level, reducing the Andreev tunneling currents around the Fermi energy. Thus, the conductance

in this region is also suppressed. The special condition $\Gamma_S/U \simeq 0.5$ can avoid these suppressions of the conductance. Therefore, the conductance peak in Fig. 1 appears in the crossover region between these two different spin-singlet states.

Finally, we would like to briefly comment on the conductance for the asymmetric case, $\varepsilon_d + U/2 \neq 0$. In this case, the onset of the singlet-doublet transition of the ground state at $\Gamma_N = 0$ is given by $\Gamma_S = \sqrt{(U/2)^2 - (\varepsilon_d + U/2)^2}$, which is reduced to $\Gamma_S = U/2$ in the symmetric case. Therefore, away from the symmetric case the conductance peak that emerges in a similar plot as in Fig. 1 [12] changes its position to a smaller Γ_S. This means that charge fluctuations, which are enhanced away from the symmetric case, make the region of the ground state with the Kondo-singlet character small.

ACKNOWLEDGMENTS

We would like to thank Y. Nisikawa for valuable discussions. This work was partly supported by a Grant-in-Aid from the Ministry of Education, Culture, Sports, Science and Technology of Japan. Y. Tanaka is supported by JSPS Research Fellowships for Young Scientists. A. Oguri is supported by JSPS.

REFERENCES

1. R. Fazio and R. Raimondi, Phys. Rev. Lett. **80**, 2913 (1998); **82**, 4950(E) (1999).
2. P. Schwab and R. Raimondi, Phys. Rev. B **59**, 1637 (1999).
3. A. A. Clerk, V. Ambegaokar, and S. Hershfield, Phys. Rev. B **61**, 3555 (2000).
4. Q. -f. Sun, H. Guo, and T. -h. Lin, Phys. Rev. Lett. **87**, 176601 (2001).
5. J. C. Cuevas, A. L. Yeyati, and A. Martin-Rodero, Phys. Rev. B **63**, 094515 (2001).
6. Y. Avishai, A. Golub, and A. D. Zaikin, Phys. Rev. B **63**, 134515 (2001); Europhys. Lett. **55**, 397 (2001).
7. T. Aono, A. Golub, and Y. Avishai, Phys. Rev. B **68**, 045312 (2003).
8. M. Krawiec and K. I. Wysokiński, Supercond. Sci. Technol. **17**, 103 (2004).
9. M. R. Gräber, T. Nussbaumer, W. Belzig, and C. Scönenberger, Nanotechnology **15**, S479 (2004).
10. M. -S. Choi, M. Lee, K. Kang, and W. Belzig, Phys. Rev. B **70**, 020502 (2004).
11. A. Oguri, Y. Tanaka, and A. C. Hewson, J. Phys. Soc. Jpn. **73**, 2494 (2004).
12. Yoichi Tanaka, N. Kawakami, A. Oguri, unpublished.
13. A. C. Hewson, A. Oguri, and D. Meyer, Eur. Phys. J. B **40**, 177 (2004).

Excitation spectra of two correlated electrons in a quantum dot

T. Ihn*, C. Ellenberger*, K. Ensslin*, C. Yannouleas†, U. Landman†, D.C. Driscoll** and A.C. Gossard**

*Solid State Physics Laboratory, ETH Zurich, CH-8093 Zurich, Switzerland
†School of Physics, Georgia Institute of Technology, Atlanta, Georgia 30332-0430
**Materials Department, University of California, Santa Barbara, CA 93106

Abstract. Measurements and a theoretical interpretation of the excitation spectrum of a two-electron quantum dot fabricated on a parabolic Ga[Al]As quantum well are reported. Experimentally, excited states are found beyond the well-known lowest singlet- and triplet states. These states can be reproduced in an exact diagonalization calculation of a parabolic dot with moderate in-plane anisotropy. The calculated spectra are in reasonable quantitative agreement with the measurement, and suggest that correlations between the electrons play a significant role in this system. Comparison of the exact results with the restricted Hartree–Fock and the generalized Heitler–London approach shows that the latter is more appropriate for this system because it can account for the spatial correlation of the electron states.

Keywords: quantum dots, correlated electrons, Wigner-molecule
PACS: 73.23.Hk, 71.70.Ej, 73.63.Kv

Two-electron quantum dots (2eQDs) are the simplest man-made structures that allow to study the effects of electron–electron interaction including exchange and correlation. Pioneering experiments measuring the excitation spectrum of such systems with finite bias spectroscopy have been reported on vertical few-electron quantum dots [1, 2]. Measurements on lateral dots became possible [3, 4, 5] driven by the potential use of such systems for the implementation of qubits [6].

Here we present finite bias spectroscopy measurements performed on a system designed to have a g-factor close to zero and a small lateral anisotropy. We find that the magnetic field dependent excited state spectrum found experimentally can be closely reproduced by exact diagonalization calculations and is reasonably well described by a generalized Heitler–London (GHL) approach. The calculations suggest that electronic correlations are significant at low magnetic field, leading to spatially separated single-particle GHL orbitals, reminiscent of the formation of a Wigner molecule.

The dot is fabricated with electron-beam lithography defined top-gates on a 55 nm wide parabolic Ga[Al]As quantum well. The aluminium concentration varies in growth direction and was chosen such that the Zeeman-splitting of electronic levels is negligible. The particular gate geometry of the dot (see Fig. 1, inset) leads to a moderate spatial anisotropy of the confinement potential. Further details about the sample can be found in Ref. [5].

Measurements were performed in a dilution refrigerator with an electronic temperature of 300 mK as determined from the width of conductance resonances in the Coulomb blockade regime. Finite bias $I(V)$ traces were recorded using standard DC current measurement techniques. Later on the data was numerically differentiated to obtain the differential conductance dI/dV_{bias}.

The sample was tuned into the Coulomb-blockade regime in the region of the transitions between one and two, and two and three electrons on the dot. The electron number was confirmed by measurements of Coulomb-blockade diamonds [5] and by using the on-chip quantum point contact as a charge detector. In this region, the dot had a single-particle level spacing of 5 meV and a charging energy of 6.9 meV.

The magnetic field dependent excitation spectrum shown in 1 is measured employing tunneling spectroscopy with varying plunger gate voltage V_{pg} at a fixed bias voltage of 2.5 mV. We plot the derivative dI/dV_{pg}. Resonances in this quantity correspond to resonances in the differential conductance dI/dV_{bias}. Two families of resonances can be seen corresponding to transitions between electron numbers $N = 1$ and 2, and $N = 2$ and 3.

First we concentrate on the $N = 1$ and 2 region. At zero magnetic field we observe – in addition to the well-known singlet ground state S_0 and triplet excited state T_+ that can be seen in Fig. 1 – an additional triplet state T_- split from the T_+ state by the confinement anisotropy (not seen in the figure, see [5]). At finite magnetic fields we find an additional excited singlet state S_2 (see Fig. 1) which shows an avoided crossing with S_0 at a magnetic field beyond the singlet–triplet transition (at 4 T) in the ground state of the system. Another excited state $T_{+,CM}$ even higher in energy than S_2 is found and attributed to

CP893, *Physics of Semiconductors, 28th International Conference*
edited by W. Jantsch and F. Schäffler
© 2007 American Institute of Physics 978-0-7354-0397-0/07/$23.00

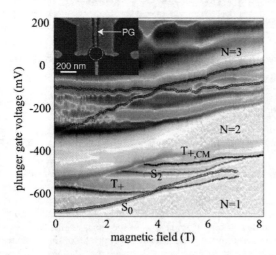

FIGURE 1. Measured excited state spectra as a function of magnetic field and plunger gate voltage. Inset: sample geometry.

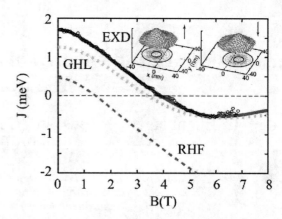

FIGURE 2. Comparison of $J(B)$ calculated with different methods and the experimental results. Inset: single-particle orbitals (modulus square) of the GHL approach.

a triplet state combining an excitation in the relative and the center of mass motion (see below). In the transition region between $N = 2$ and 3 we observe resonances that correspond to transitions between the two-electron states S_0 and T_+ and the three-electron ground state.

The experimental findings can be quantitatively interpreted by comparing to the results of exact diagonalization (EXD) calculations for two electrons in an anisotropic harmonic confinement potential. Details of the model can be found in Ref. [5]. The calculated magnetic field dependent energy splitting $J(B) = E_{T+} - E_{S0}$ between the two lowest states S_0 and T_+ is found to be in remarkable agreement with the experiment. All the additional excited states observed in the experiment can be unambiguously identified with calculated excited states of the two-electron dot [5].

The EXD calculations give strong evidence for the importance of correlation effects. Closer inspection of the total electron densities and conditional probabilities (CPDs) reveals a strongly correlated ground state at zero magnetic field, in which the electrons do not occupy the same single-particle state. Already at magnetic fields below the singlet-triplet transition, the CPDs indicate localization of the two electrons and formation of a state resembling an H_2-like Wigner molecule.

We gain further insight into the importance of correlations in the system by comparing the results for $J(B)$ calculated exactly and within different approximations. Figure 2 shows the predictions obtained from EXD calculations, restricted Hartree–Fock (RHF) calculations and

from a generalized Heitler–London (GHL) approach in comparison with the measured data. Details about the approximative calculations can be found in [7]. The RHF and GHL schemes have the advantage that they minimize the energy using single-particle orbitals. It is evident from Fig. 2 that the RHF method, which assumes that both electrons occupy the same single-particle orbital, is not able to reproduce the experimental findings. The GHL approach, which allows the two electrons to occupy two spatially separated states, appears to be a good approximation. Plotting the two single-particle orbitals resulting from this approach clearly demonstrates that the two electrons do not occupy the same spatial orbital, but rather fill single-particle states that are spatially separated significantly (inset).

ACKNOWLEDGMENTS

We thank R. Nazmitdinov for valuable discussions. Support from the Schweizerischer Nationalfonds, the US D.O.E. (Grant No. FG05-86ER45234), and the NSF (Grant No. DMR-0205328) is gratefully acknowledged.

REFERENCES

1. T. Schmidt *et al.*, Phys. Rev. B **51**, R5570 (1995).
2. L.P. Kouwenhoven *et al.*, Science **278**, 1788 (1997).
3. J. Kyriakidis *et al.*, Phys. Rev. B **66**, 035320 (2002).
4. D.M. Zumbühl *et al.*, Phys. Rev. Lett. **93**, 256801 (2004).
5. C. Ellenberger *et al.*, Phys. Rev. Lett. **96**, 126806 (2006).
6. D. Loss and D.P. DiVincenzo, Phys. Rev. A **57**, 120 (1998).
7. C. Yannouleas and U. Landman, Phys. Rev. Lett. **82**, 5325 (1999); J. Phys.: Condens. Matter **14**, L591 (2002); Int. J. Quant. Chem. **90**, 699 (2002).

Dependence of charge trapped on nanocrystals and electron transport on excess Si in silicon –rich SiO$_2$

I.V.Antonova[*], M.B.Gulyaev[*], Z.S.Yanovitskaya[*], Y.Goldstein[†], J.Jedrzejewski[†],

[*]Institute of Semiconductor Physics, 630090, Novosibirsk, Lavrentieva 13, Russia,
[†] Racah Institute of Physics, Hebrew University, 91904, Jerusalem, Israel

Abstract. The system of silicon nanocrystals embedded in SiO$_2$ was characterized by electrical measurements depending on the excess Si content in oxide ranged from 6 to 74%. Electron transport through the oxide after percolation transient demonstrates the activation character of current at T > 230 K with activation energy from 2.1 eV near percolation threshold and down to 0.1 eV for higher Si content. The variable range hopping conductivity strongly depended on the excess Si content was observed at lower temperatures.

Keywords: silicon nanocrystals, oxide matrix, conductivity, excess Si content.
PACS: 73.63.-b, 73.61.-r.

INTRODUCTION

The system of silicon nanocrystals embedded in SiO$_2$ (ncSi-SiO$_2$) are candidates for optoelectronic and photonic applications due to their intense visible emission at room temperature, high thermal and chemical stability and compatibility with CMOS technology. The research of ncSi-SiO$_2$ has attracted much attention also due to variable electrical properties that depend on the excess Si content and nanocrystal sizes and density [1]. Aim of the present report was to study charge trapping on nanocrystals and electron transport in silicon-rich oxide as a function of the excess Si content.

EXPERIMENTAL DETAILS

Structures were fabricated by deposition of oxide and silicon on silicon substrate from different sources placed at distance about of 100 mm one from other. Subsequent annealing at 1150°C for 40 min in nitrogen ambient leads to formation of silicon nanocrystals (nc-Si) in oxide. The excess Si content in SiO$_2$ layer was varied along the 140 mm sample from 6 to 74% (volume percents). Capacitance – voltage, current - voltage characteristics and their temperature dependences in the range of 77 -300 K were analyzed.

RESULTS AND DISCUSSION

Resistivity R of the nc-Si-SiO$_2$ layer along the sample extracted from I-V characteristics for voltage of -30 V is given in Fig.1 as a function of the distance, d, from the Si-poor edge of the sample. R value appears sharp reduce at d ~ 63 mm (Si content about 34%), which corresponds to percolation threshold. It was found that for Si content about 26% the charge in oxide extracted from capacitance-voltage characteristics has the maximum (insert in Fig.1). The position of maximal charge along the sample is found to correlate with maximal photoluminescence (~ 830 nm) [2]. Decrease in charge and photoluminescence intensity with further increase in the excess Si content in SiO$_2$ layer correlates with appearance of the percolation conductivity. Temperature dependences of current through the nc-Si SiO$_2$ layer for different d (d ≥ 63 mm) are presented in Fig.2. Before the percolation threshold (d < 63 mm) current drastically decreases with reduction in temperature. The current values are grown with increase in the excess silicon in oxide. Large hysteresis of current is revealed for all cases: the current is decreased after voltage sweep for both voltage polarities.

It was found that I(U) dependence in area of percolation threshold (~34% of the excess Si in SiO$_2$) is drastically changed for different sweeps of voltage.

CP893, *Physics of Semiconductors, 28th International Conference*
edited by W. Jantsch and F. Schäffler
© 2007 American Institute of Physics 978-0-7354-0397-0/07/$23.00

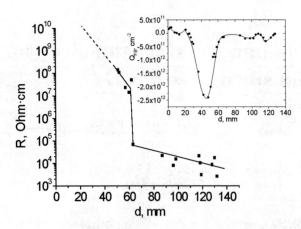

FIGURE 1. Resistivity, R, of the nc-Si-SiO$_2$ layer extracted from I-V characteristics for voltage of -30 V versus distance d from the Si poor edge of the sample. Insert presents distribution along the sample of charge in oxide extracted from C-V characteristics with use of flat band voltage.

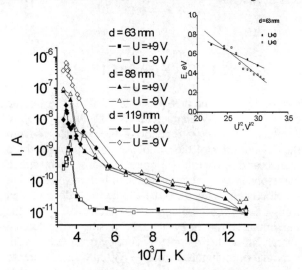

FIGURE 2. Current as a function of reverse temperature for different d and voltages of +9 V and -9 V. Insert presents activation energy extracted from linear approximation of lnI(1/T) versus U$^{1/2}$. d = 63 and 88 mm correspond to 34 and 46% of Si in SiO$_2$.

In the case of voltage decreasing the current-voltage characteristics are flattening in Frenkel-Poole coordinates for temperature T > 230 K. The temperature dependence of current obeys an activation law I ~ exp(-E$_a$/kT) in this case. Values of activation energy extracted from linear approximation of lnI(1/T) are presented in insert of Fig.2. Extrapolation of the dependence E$_a$(U$^{1/2}$) to zero allows us to calculate energies of traps E$_{ao}$, which determine the current through the structures. E$_{ao}$ values for negative and positive voltage polarity are equal to 2.1 and 1.3 eV. In the case of voltage increasing for d = 63 mm and in the case of both direction of voltage sweeps for d > 63 mm activation energies are slightly increased with increase in applied voltage. The values of activation energies for d > 63 mm becomes relatively low (0.1 – 0.2 eV). Increase in the excess silicon content up to 66 % (d = 120 mm) leads to independence of current from T for T > 230 K, which corresponds to tunnel current in nc-Si-SiO$_2$ system. Change in value of activation energy with variation of applied voltage, with a time, or voltage polarity demonstrates complicated character of electron transport in ncSi-SiO$_2$ composite.

For T < 230 K the temperature dependence of current is described by I ~ 1/T$^{1/4}$, which corresponds to the variable range hopping conductivity.

C-V characteristics were found to appear of large hysteresis at T < 230 K. Hysteresis is caused by charge trapped on nc-Si during measurements. This fact is the base for suggestion given above that recharging of nc-Si (or another traps) is partially blocking of conductivity paths in nc-Si-SiO$_2$ system. It has to be emphasized that hysteresis appears at temperatures ~230 K when mechanism of electron transport through nc-Si-SiO$_2$ have been changed.

SUMMARY

Electron transport in the system of silicon nanocrystals embedded in SiO$_2$ matrix was studied as a function of excess Si content ranged from 6 to 74%. Percolation threshold was observed at the excess Si content about of 34%. Electron transport through the oxide after percolation transient demonstrates the activation character of current at T > 230 K. At lower temperature the variable range hopping conductivity was observed.

ACKNOWLEDGMENTS

This work was supported by Russian Foundation for Basic Research, grants 05-02-16479 and 05-02-16455. Authors are thankful to Dr. O.Naumova from Institute of Semiconductor Physics, Novosibirsk for the help in measurements.

REFERENCES

1. I.Balberg, Proceed. *Int. Workshop on Semicond. Nanocristals*, Hungry, 2005, pp291-296.
2. I.V.Antonova, M.B.Gulyaev, Z.S.Yanovitskaya, V.A.Volodin, D.V.Marin, M.D.Efremov, Y.Goldstein, J.Jedrzejewski, Semicond., **40**, 1229-1235 (2006).

Coupling of quantum states in InAs/GaAs quantum dot molecule

M M Sobolev, A E Zhukov, A P Vasilev, E S Semenova, and V S Mikhrin

A F Ioffe Physico Technical Institute, 26 Polytechnicheskaya ul., 194021, St. Petersburg, Russia

Abstract. Deep level transient spectroscopy (DLTS) is used to study electron and hole emission from the states in the system of vertically correlated InAs quantum dots in the p-n InAs/GaAs heterostructures, in relation to the thickness of the GaAs spacer between two layers of InAs quantum dots and to the reverse bias voltage.

Keywords: Quantum dot molecule, coupling of electron states, localization of holes.
PACS: PACS numbers: 73.21.1Lc

INTRODUCTION

In the last few years, the effects of coupling and hybridizing of electron states semiconductor heterostructures with vertically correlated self-organized quantum dots (QDs) are extensively studied in a large number of laboratories. Due to the Coulomb interaction and quantum-mechanical tunneling, the two or more correlated semiconductor QDs can form artificial molecules. It has been theoretically shown [1] that two QDs can be in the phase of either individual atomic quantum dots or of a molecule, depending on the spacing between the QDs. All of the excited states should exhibit crossing or anticrossing with the other states, resulting in reordering of the states in high electric field. As follows from the theoretical results of [2], the bonding and antibonding states can be formed only for the electron states of the QD molecule. For holes of the valence band, the ground states and excited states should be spontaneously localized within one of the QDs. Coupling of QDs should be controlled by varying the external electric field [2].

In the present work we report the investigation by means of the DLTS of electron and hole emission from the states of vertically correlated system of InAs quantum dots in the p-n InAs/GaAs heterostructures in relation to the thickness of the GaAs spacer between two layers of InAs QDs and to reverse-bias voltage.

EXPERIMENTAL

The samples under investigation were obtained by molecular beam epitaxy using self-organization effects on n^+-GaAs substrate (100) by twofold depositing 2.0 monolayers of InAs separated by d_{GaAs} =20, 40 and 100 Å thick GaAs spacers and embedded into GaAs (p or n=$2 \cdot 10^{16}$ cm^{-3}) and covered with p^+(or n^+)- GaAs contact layer.

RESULTS AND DISCUSSION

For all samples under investigation we observed DLTS peaks. For identifying the origin of the levels responsible for these DLTS peaks, we studies how the DLTS spectra depended on the optical irradiation of the sample during the DLTS measurements. We observed an increase of the amplitudes of the DLTS spectral peaks for illuminated samples, which is due to a shift of the quasi-Fermi level for electrons to the conduction band, and attributed this effect to the emission of carriers from the quantum states in VCQDs. It is found that the positions of the maxima these DLTS peaks depends on of the reverse bias pulse voltage applied to the sample in the DLTS measurements (Figure 1). This is considered as a manifestation of the quantum confined Stark effect for VCQDs [1-4]. The DLTS spectra of structure with VCQDs embedded into n-GaAs and d_{GaAs} = 100 Å GaAs spacer exhibit two peaks that are defined by the ground state and the excited state of an individual quantum dot, with energy levels slightly shifted (by 1-2 eV), due to the Stark effect (Figure 1a). For the InAs/GaAs heterostructure with d_{GaAs} = 40 Å GaAs spacer and VCQDs embedded into n-GaAs, it is found that the quantum dots are in the molecule-type phase. Hybridization of the electron states of two closely located QDs results in the splitting of the levels into bonding and antibonding levels corresponding to the

CP893, *Physics of Semiconductors, 28th International Conference*
edited by W. Jantsch and F. Schäffler
© 2007 American Institute of Physics 978-0-7354-0397-0/07/$23.00

electron ground states and excited states. These states manifest themselves as five peaks in the DLTS spectra. For these quantum states, a large Stark shift of energy levels (10-40 meV) and crossing of the dependences of the energy on the electric field are observed (Figure 1b). The states of the structures were attributed to the corresponding states of the QD molecule: E5-1s$^+$, E4-2p$^+$, E3-1s$^-$, E2-2p$^-$ and E1-3d$^+$. Whereas DLTS peaks related to holes emission from the states of VCQD heterostructures with d$_{GaAs}$ = 20 and 40 Å GaAs spacer VCQDs and embedded into p-GaAs were attributed with states of holes are localized at one of the quantum dots due to quantum-mechanical tunneling without the formation of bonding and antibonding states. The DLTS spectra of these structures exhibit one peak that are defined by the ground state with energy level shifted (by 120 meV), due to the Stark effect (Figure 1c). For a thickness of the GaAs interlayer equal to 100 Å, it is found that the two layers of quantum dots are incompletely coupled, which results in a redistribution of the electron and hole localization between the upper and lower quantum dots as the reverse-bias voltage applied to the structure is varied.

We established that hole are localized in one of the QDs in a quantum dot molecule composed of two VSQDs in InAs/GaAs heterostructure that has a 20-Å-thick or 20-Å-thick GaAs interlayer between two layers of InAs QDs. Whereas hybridization of electron states of two QDs combined into a QD molecule results in the formation of the 1s$^+$, 1s$^-$, 2p$^+$, 2p$^-$, and 3d$^+$ bonding and antibonding states. Incomplete coupling of two QD layers was observed if the thickness of the GaAs unterlayer was 100 Å.

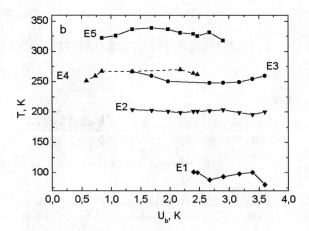

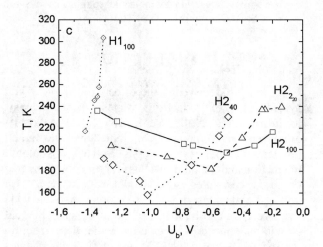

FIGURE 1. Dependence of the temperature position of the DLTS peaks on the voltage of the reverse-bias pulse U$_b$ for the structures with VCQDs embedded into n-GaAs (spacer thickness d$_{GaAs}$ = (a) 100, (b) 40 Å) and into p-GaAs (d$_{GaAs}$ = (c) 20 (H2$_{100}$), 40 (H2$_{40}$), 100 (H2$_{100}$) Å)

ACKNOWLEDGMENTS

This study was supported by the Russian Foundation for Basic Research, project no. 06-02-08088-ofi.

REFERENCES

1. B.Partoens, F.M.Peeters. *Phys. Rev. Lett.*, **84**, 4433 (2000).
2. W. Sheng, J-P. Leburton. *Appl. Phys.Lett.*, **81**, 4449 (2002).
3. M. M. Sobolev, V. M. Ustinov, A. E. Zhukov, et al.,*Semiconductors*, **36**, 1013 (2002).
4. M.M. Sobolev, G. E. Cirlin,, et al., *Semiconductors*, 39, 119 (2005).

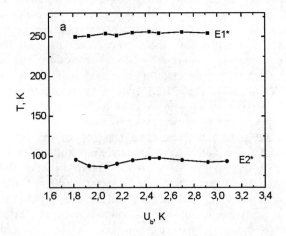

High Bias Magneto-transport Through Two Weakly Coupled Vertical Quantum Dots and Quantum Wells

D G Austing[1,2], G Yu[1], C Payette[1,2], J A Gupta[1], C Dharma-Wardana[1] and G C Aers[1]

[1]Institute for Microstructural Sciences, National Research Council of Canada, Montreal Road, Ottawa, ON K1A 0R6, Canada
[2]Department of Physics, Ernest Rutherford Physics Building, McGill University, 3600 rue University, Montréal, Quebec H3A 2T8, Canada

Abstract. We investigate high bias non-linear magneto-transport through two weakly coupled vertical quantum dots and quantum wells fabricated from the *same* triple barrier structure. We examine first the two-dimensional limit in the quantum well device. By gate tuning, we can then track continuously the crossover from the quasi-two-dimensional regime to the strong zero-dimensional limit of the lateral confinement in the quantum dot device.

Keywords: Magneto-transport, Quantum dots, Quantum wells.
PACS: 73.21.La, 73.21.Fg, 73.43.Jn.

INTRODUCTION

We investigate high bias (up to ~400mV) resonant and non-resonant tunneling in both large ungated and sub-micron gated mesas made from the *same* nominally symmetric GaAs/AlGaAs/InGaAs double quantum well triple barrier structure (DQWTBS) for which the tunnel coupling between the two quantum dots/ quantum wells is weak (<0.1meV) [1]. Such structures in the strong zero-dimensional (0D) lateral confinement limit have revealed a two-electron spin diode effect near zero-bias, and 0D-0D single electron resonant tunneling [2,3]. Here, we expand the measurement space further and observe a rich variety of phenomena especially in the presence of a magnetic field up to 8 T applied parallel to the tunneling current. High bias resonant tunneling in DQWTBS's has been investigated before [4,5], but the device mesas were either too large to be in the 0D regime, or lacked a gate and so could not be tuned through the 0D regime. Recently unusual tunneling characteristics of a large area (gate-less) DQWTBS suggesting the weakness of conservation laws were reported [6].

EXPERIMENT

We first investigate a large 50 μm diameter (ungated) mesa. In the two-dimensional (2D) limit at 0 T, referring to Fig. 1, we find non-zero conductance at zero-bias, and then in each bias direction the principal resonance (A); a secondary resonance (B); and a weaker LO-phonon-assisted-like shoulder (C). On application of a magnetic field, these features develop clear Landau level fans, and additional field-dependent current modulations are seen around zero bias. Elsewhere, to explain our observations, we will describe self-consistent calculations of resonant tunneling through independent or resonantly aligned states of the two quantum wells, together with LO-phonon mechanisms [7].

We then measure a 0.55 μm diameter gated mesa made from the *same* DQWTBS. With the gate voltage most positive (V_g=+0.5V), as shown in Fig. 2, the I-V_{sd} trace looks similar in shape to that of the large ungated mesa at 0 T, i.e. the quantum dots (QD's) are so weakly "squeezed" that they are quantum-well-like, and the measurement is in the quasi-2D regime. On making the gate voltage progressively more negative, the QD's are steadily "squeezed", the 0D-character strengthens, and eventually the strong 0D-limit is reached. During this tuning process, resonance A initially weakens, breaks up into numerous sharp resonances and steps, and ultimately 0D-0D single electron resonant tunneling (in a thin segment just below the dashed line in Fig. 3(a)) reveals the single particle spectrum of the down-stream QD as probed by the ground state of the up-stream QD [3]. Resonance B

CP893, *Physics of Semiconductors, 28th International Conference*
edited by W. Jantsch and F. Schäffler

also weakens but in the 0D regime it too evolves into numerous features. In the 0D single electron tunneling limit the amplitude of the features just to the left of the white arrows in Fig. 3 is approximately an order of magnitude greater than the amplitude just to the right.

Application of a magnetic field reveals a multitude of fan structures (see for example inside the ellipse in Fig. 3(b)), as well as changes to the resonance line-shape, through out the entire gate voltage- bias voltage (V_g-V_{sd}) plane from the quasi-2D regime to the strong 0D-limit, particularly above a threshold bias, which is equivalent to the QD's being misaligned by an energy of more than about 35 meV (to the left of the white arrows in Fig. 3). Full details of our observations will be given elsewhere [7].

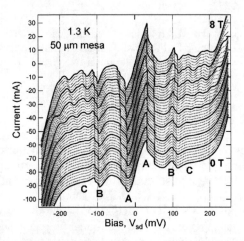

FIGURE 1. Magnetic field dependence of current-bias voltage (I-V_{sd}) characteristic, in the quantum well limit, of a 50 μm mesa.

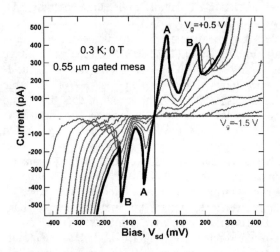

FIGURE 2. Gate voltage dependence of current-bias voltage (I-V_{sd}) characteristic of a 0.55 μm mesa at 0 T. The black bold trace, for the most positive gate voltage, corresponds to the case when the quantum dots are most quantum-well-like.

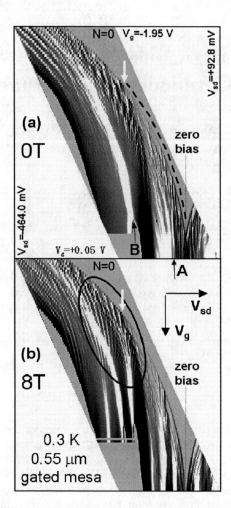

FIGURE 3. Differential conductance (dI/dV_{sd}) in the gate voltage- bias voltage (V_g-V_{sd}) plane at (a) 0 T and (b) 8 T for the 0.55 μm mesa focusing on the reverse bias portion to the left of zero bias. Black, grey, and white correspond respectively to positive, zero, and negative conductance. The zone corresponding to device "pinch-off" is marked N=0.

REFERENCES

1. D. G. Austing, T. Honda, K. Muraki, Y. Tokura and S. Tarucha, *Physica* B **249-251**, 206 (1998).
2. K. Ono, D. G. Austing, Y. Tokura and S. Tarucha, *Science* **297**, 1313 (2002).
3. K. Ono, D. G. Austing, Y. Tokura and S. Tarucha, *Physica* B **314**, 450 (2002).
4. L. D. Macks, S. A. Brown, R. G. Clark, R. P. Starrett, M. A. Reed, M. R. Deshpande, C. J. L. Fernando and W. R. Frensley, *Phys. Rev.* B **54**, 4857 (1996).
5. T. Schmidt, R. J. Haug, K. v. Klitzing, A. Förster and H. Lüth, *Phys. Rev. Lett.* **78**, 1544 (1997).
6. Y. Lin, J. Nitta, A. K. M. Newaz, W. Song and E. E. Mendez, cond-mat/0407375.
7. D. G. Austing *et al.*, (unpublished).

Thermopower due to Kondo Effect in Quantum Dot Systems with Orbitals

R. Sakano and N. Kawakami

Department of applied physics, Osaka university, Suita, Osaka 565-0871, Japan

Abstract. We study the thermopower due to the orbital Kondo effect in single quantum dot systems by exploiting the Bethe ansatz solution of the Anderson impurity model. It is elucidated how the orbital splittings induced by external fields affect the thermopower of the orbital Kondo effect.

Keywords: Quantum dot, Kondo effect, thermopower
PACS: 73.23.-b, 73.63.Kv, 71.27.+a, 75.30.Mb

INTRODUCTION

The Kondo effect is a typical electron correlation phenomenon, which has been intensively studied in dilute magnetic alloys. In the last decade, there has been renewed interest in the Kondo effect in quantum dot (QD) systems [1]. In particular, the fact that QD systems have a lot of tunable parameters has attracted much attention. It is known that high symmetry in shape of QDs gives rise to the orbital properties, which has stimulated extensive studies on the conductance due to *the orbital Kondo effect* [2-6].

The thermopower is another important transport quantity which gives complementary information to the conductance measurement: the thermopower can sensitively probe the asymmetric nature of the tunneling resonance around the Fermi level. So far, a few theoretical studies have been done on the thermopower in QD systems [7-9]. Remarkably, the thermopower of the ordinary spin Kondo effect has recently been observed in a lateral single QD system [10], which naturally motivates us to theoretically explore this transport quantity in more detail. In this paper, we discuss how orbital degrees of freedom affect the thermopower due to the Kondo effect in single QD systems. By exploiting the Bethe ansatz solution of the Anderson impurity model, we calculate the thermopower due to the orbital Kondo effect at low temperatures. It is shown how the orbital splitting enhances the thermopower.

MODEL AND CALCULATION

Let us consider a single quantum dot system with N-degenerate orbitals in equilibrium state. We assume that each energy-level splitting between the orbitals is Δ_{orb} in the presence of magnetic field and the Zeeman splitting is much smaller than it. The energy level of each orbital state is specified as

$$\varepsilon_{\sigma l} = \varepsilon + l\Delta_{orb} \tag{1}$$

where ε denotes the center of the energy levels, and we take the orbital index l from $-(N-1)/2$ to $(N-1)/2$.

We model the above quantum dot system by assuming that the Coulomb repulsion U between electrons is sufficiently strong at the quantum dot, so that we effectively put $U \to \infty$. We focus on the N-degenerate orbital states in the quantum dot, which are assumed to hybridize with the corresponding conduction channels in the leads for simplicity. Although the assumption of multiple conduction channels is nontrivial, it is known that this is legitimate for certain systems with a vertical quantum dot and a carbon nanotube quantum dot [2, 3]. In these assumptions, our system can be described by an SU(2N) multi-orbital extension of the impurity Anderson model in the strong correlation limit,

$$
\begin{aligned}
H = & \sum_{\sigma,l} \int dx\, c_{\sigma l}^{\dagger}(x) \frac{\partial}{\partial x} c_{\sigma l}(x) + \sum_{\sigma,l} \varepsilon_{\sigma l} |\sigma l\rangle\langle\sigma l| \\
& + V \sum_{\sigma,l} \int dx\, \delta(x) \left[|\sigma l\rangle\langle 0| c_{\sigma l}(x) + H.c. \right].
\end{aligned} \tag{2}
$$

Here $c_{\sigma l}^{\dagger}(x)$ ($c_{\sigma l}(x)$) creates (annihilates) a conduction electron at a position x with spin σ and orbital l.

According to the Boltzmann equation, the thermopower is given in terms of the Fermi distribution function $f(\varepsilon)$ and the local density of states $\rho_{\sigma l}(\varepsilon)$ for

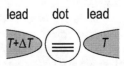

FIGURE 1. Single QD system with orbital degeneracy.

CP893, *Physics of Semiconductors, 28th International Conference*
edited by W. Jantsch and F. Schäffler

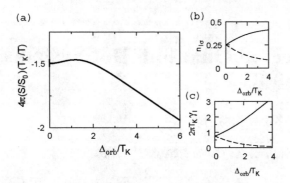

FIGURE 2. (a)Plots of the T-linear thermopower for two-orbital case as a function of the orbital splitting. Here, T_K is the SU(4) Kondo temperature of the system. (b)Number of electrons per spin in each orbital of the QD. The solid line is for orbital $l = -1/2$ and the dashed line for $l = 1/2$. (c)Similar plots of the T-linear specific heat for each orbital.

electrons in the QD,

$$ S = -\frac{1}{eT} \int \frac{\partial f(\varepsilon)}{\partial \varepsilon} \varepsilon \rho(\varepsilon) d\varepsilon \bigg/ \int \frac{\partial f(\varepsilon)}{\partial \varepsilon} \rho(\varepsilon) d\varepsilon. \quad (3) $$

Applying the local Fermi liquid relations, this is reduced to the expression at low temperatures T [11],

$$ S = -(S_0 T/2) \sum_{\sigma l} \gamma_{\sigma l} \sin(2\pi n_{\sigma l}) \bigg/ \sum_{\sigma l} \sin^2(\pi n_{\sigma l}) \quad (4) $$

where $S_0 = 2\pi^3/3e^2$, $\gamma_{\sigma l}$ is the specific heat coefficient and $n_{\sigma l}$ is the number of electrons with spin σ and orbital l in the QD. Note that all the quantities in (4) can be computed exactly [12, 13] by exploiting the Bethe-ansatz solution of the Hamiltonian (2).

RESULTS

The T-linear thermopower calculated for the two-orbital case as a function of the orbital splitting is shown in Fig. 2(a). Since, the total density of states (denominator in eq.(4)) at the Fermi level does not depend on external fields[6] for the SU(4) orbital model, we here concentrate on the numerator in eq.(4) to analyze the T-linear thermopower.

It is seen that the thermopower is enhanced as the orbital splitting becomes large since the specific-heat coefficient increases as $\gamma_{\sigma l} \sim \Delta_{orb}$ (the $l = -1/2$ curve in Fig. 2(c), which dominates the decrement due to the asymmetry factor ($\sin(2\pi n_{\sigma l})$ in the numerator). On the other hand, around $\Delta_{orb} \sim T_K$, the change in the thermopower is small since the enhancement of the specific heat is somewhat canceled by the asymmetry factor. Note here that the thermopower always has negative values, which can be confirmed by the formula (4). Since the electron

number in the QD is $0 < n_{\sigma l} < 1/2$ in our model, the negative sign naturally follows from (4). This corresponds to the fact that, for the orbital degenerate systems, the effective tunneling resonance, such as the Kondo resonance, is always located above the Fermi level.

We now observe what happens for very large orbital splittings. To this end, we first recall that the Kondo resonance for single-orbital systems, i.e. the ordinary spin Kondo resonance, is symmetric and the thermopower is zero. Therefore, it is naturally expected that the thermopower in our model tends to zero for large orbital-splittings where the system is effectively reduced to the spin Kondo model. We have indeed confirmed this tendency by the analytic Bethe-ansatz calculation. Therefore, we come to the conclusion that the thermopower is once enhanced up to intermediant orbital-splittings and then suppressed again in very large splittings. Notice, however, that the effective Kondo temperature becomes very small for such large splittings, so that even small perturbations that change the position of the Kondo resonance could possibly give rise to a large thermopower with either positive or negative sign.

SUMMARY

We have discussed how the orbital splitting affects the asymmetry of the resonance due to the orbital Kondo effect. It has been pointed out that the thermopower is enhanced in the presenc of orbital splittings, which is again suppressed in large orbital splittings. Several problems remain to be explored, e.g. the high-temperature behavior, more realistic orbital splitting including electron correlations, QD with plural electrons, etc, which are now under consideration.

We thank S. Amaha and S. Tarucha for valuable discussion. RS is supported by the Japan Society for the Promotion of Science.

REFERENCES

1. D. Goldhaber-Gordon *et al.*, *Nature (London)* **391**, 156 (1998).
2. S. Sasaki *et al.*, *Phys. Rev. Lett.* **93**, 17205 (2004).
3. P. Jarillo-Herrero *et al.*, *Nature (London)* **434**, 484 (2005).
4. M. Eto, *J. Phys. Soc. Jpn.* **74**, 95 (2004).
5. M.-S. Choi *et al.*, *Phys. Rev. Lett.* **95**, 067204 (2005).
6. R. Sakano *et al.*, *Phys. Rev. B* **73**, 155332 (2006).
7. D. Boese *et al.*, *Europhys. Lett.* **56**(4), 576 (2001).
8. B. Dong *et al.*, *J. Phys.: Condens. Matter* **14**, 11747 (2002).
9. T.-S. Kim *et al.*, *Phys. Rev. Lett.* **67**, 165313 (2003).
10. R. Scheibner *et al.*, *Phys. Rev. Lett.* **95**, 176602 (2005).
11. N. Kawakami *et al.*, *J. Phys. Soc. Jpn.* **56**, 1539 (1987).
12. P. Schlottmann, *Phys. Rev. Lett.* **50**, 1697 (1983).
13. N. Kawakami *et al.*, *J. Phys. Soc. Jpn.* **54**, 685 (1985).

Noninvasive detection of charge rearrangement in a quantum dot

C. Fricke*, M. C. Rogge*, B. Harke*, M. Reinwald†, W. Wegscheider†, F. Hohls**,* and R. J. Haug*

*Institut für Festkörperphysik, Leibniz Universität Hannover, Appelstraße 2, D-30167 Hannover, Germany
†Angewandte und Experimentelle Physik, Universität Regensburg, D-93040 Regensburg, Germany
**Cavendish Laboratory, University of Cambridge, Madingley Road, Cambridge CB20HE, U, Great Britain

Abstract. We demonstrate new results on electron redistribution on a single quantum dot caused by magnetic field. A quantum point contact is used to detect changes in the quantum dot charge. We are able to measure both the change of the quantum dot charge and also changes of the electron configuration at constant number of electrons on the quantum dot. These features are used to exploit the quantum dot in a high magnetic field where transport through the quantum dot displays the effects of Landau shells and spin blockade.

Keywords: quantum dot, quantum point contact, magnetic field, landau shells
PACS: 73.63.Kv, 73.23.Hk, 72.20.My

Recent interest in quantum dots arises from the goal to create quantum bits (qubits) in a semiconductor structure. Non-invasive methods of charge and spin detection are required to realize readout schemes for these qubits[1]. Quantum point contacts (QPC) can be used to detect individual tunneling events of electrons out of the quantum dot (QD) or between the dots of a double dot system [2, 3, 4, 5, 6].

In previous work we demonstrated that the QPC can also be used to detect changes of the electron configuration of a QD without changing the number of electrons [7]. Our interest focuses on a QD in a high magnetic field. Here we will present new result on the redistribution of charge on the QD within the Coulomb blockade regime.

Our device is based on a GaAs/AlGaAs heterostructure providing a two-dimensional electron system (2DES) 34 nm below the surface. The electron density is $n = 4.59 \cdot 10^{15}$ m^{-2}, the mobility is $\mu = 64.3$ m^2/Vs. We use an atomic force microscope (AFM) to define the QD and the QPC structure by local anodic oxidation (LAO) [8, 9, 10]. The 2DES below the oxidized surface is depleted and by this insulating areas can be written.

An AFM image of our device is presented in the inset of Fig. 1. The yellow walls depict the insulating lines written by the AFM. The QPC (green area) is separated from the QD structure (red area) by an insulating line. The QPC can be tuned using the in-plane gate G3. The QD is coupled to source and drain via two tunnelling barriers, which can be separately controlled with gates G1 and G2. These gates are also used to control the number of electrons in the QD. We use two electrically separated circuits to perform independent conductance mea-

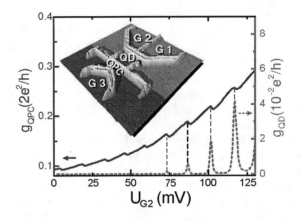

FIGURE 1. Operating principle of the device containing a QD and a QPC. Conductivity of QD (red, right axis) and QPC (green, left axis) are shown as a function of gate voltage applied to G2. The inset shows a three-dimensional AFM image of the device.

surements through the QPC and the QD at the same time. All measurements are done in a ^{3}He/^{4}He dilution refrigerator at a base temperature of 40 mK. In Fig. 1 the conductance of the QD and the QPC is shown as a function of the gate voltage applied to gate G2. The conductivity of the QD (red line) displays typical Coulomb blockade peaks: Whenever a state in the QD comes into resonance with the leads, a nonzero conductance through the QD occurs. Simultaneously a step appears in the QPC conductance as the charge of the additional electron on the QD changes. The steps are superimposed on a gradual

CP893, *Physics of Semiconductors, 28th International Conference*
edited by W. Jantsch and F. Schäffler
© 2007 American Institute of Physics 978-0-7354-0397-0/07/$23.00

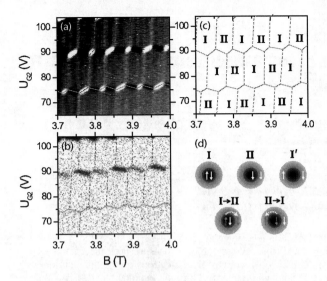

FIGURE 2. (a) dg_{QPC}/dB as a function of magnetic field and gate voltage. Between Coulomb lines additional relocation lines appear in the blockade region. (b) QD Conductance for the same parameters. The last two detectable coulomb peaks can be seen. (c) Schematic view of the QD configuration identified using the model (d) taken from [7].

rise of the conductance due to the direct influence of G2 on the QPC potential. Because of its high sensitivity the QPC is an excellent probe for charge redistributions on the QD. Not only a changing number of electrons on the QD can be detected but changes in the electron distribution for a fixed number of electrons.

This can be seen in Fig. 2(a). It shows dg_{QPC}/dB as a function of magnetic field and gate voltage applied to gate G2. White regions correspond to a decreasing charge detected by the QPC, black regions depict an increasing charge. The three horizontal Coulomb lines are divided in black and white segments due to typical zigzag pattern that occurs in high magnetic fields. In Fig. 2(b) the QD conductance is shown for the same region. Due to the high sensitivity of the QPC there are three well developed Coulomb lines in the QPC signal, while the QD conductance only shows two Coulomb lines (green line is added as a guide to the eye).

While in the QD conductance no changes can be seen in the Coulomb blockade region between two Coulomb lines, in the QPC signal additional vertical relocation lines appear. In this regions, where the total number of electrons on the QD is constant, the QPC detects small changes in the effective charge on the QD for changing magnetic field. This results from the Landau shells on the QD. For rising magnetic field electrons are redistributed from the center to the outer shell. Due to this slight change in the effective potential the QPC conductance changes whenever an electron is relocated [7, 11]. These lines are called relocation lines in the following.

In the presented results these lines are resolved for the first time in a larger region. As the red trace in Fig. 2(a,b) indicates, the full area is divided by the Coulomb lines and the relocation lines into hexagonal regions of fixed electron configuration. This is depicted in Fig. 2(c). The green lines show the position of the Coulomb blockade lines and the red lines mark the positions of the relocation lines. In this range of the magnetic field there are two different electron configuration shown in 2(c). One configuration is *I* where the electrons occupying the two highest energy states are in the same shell. For the second configuration *II* one electron occupies the inner shell and the other electron is located in the center. The relocation lines identify transitions form one configuration to the other.

Taking into account the spin blockade behavior in the QD transport (alternating conductance along the Coulomb blockade line visible in Fig. 2(b)) we can identify in detail the electron spin and charge configuration for each hexagon, using the model presented in [7].

REFERENCES

1. M. Field, C. G. Smith, M. Pepper, D. A. Ritchie, J. E. F. Frost, G. A. C. Jones, and D. G. Hasko, *Phys. Rev. Lett.* **70**, 1311 (1993).
2. J. M. Elzerman, R. Hanson, J. S. Greidanus, L. H. Willems van Beveren, S. De Franceschi, L. M. K. Vandersypen, S. Tarucha, and L. P. Kouwenhoven *Phys. Rev. B* **67**, 161308 (2003).
3. J. M. Elzerman, R. Hanson, L.H. Willems van Beveren, B. Witkamp, L. M. K. Vandersypen, and L. P. Kouwenhoven, *Nature*, **430**, 431 (2004).
4. R. Schleser, E. Ruh, T. Ihn, K. Ensslin, D. C. Driscll, and A. C. Gossard, *Appl. Phys. Lett.* **85**, 11 (2004).
5. J. R. Petta, A. C. Johnson, C. M. Marcus, M. P. Hanson, and A. C. Gossard, *Phys. Rev. Lett.* **93**, 186802 (2004).
6. L. DiCarlo, H. J. Lynch, A. C. Johnson, L. I. Childress, K. Crockett, C. M. Marcus, M. P. Hanson, and A. C. Gossard, *Phys. Rev. Lett.* **92**, 226801 (2004).
7. C. Fricke, M.C. Rogge, B. Harke, M. Reinwald, W. Wegscheider, F. Hohls, and R.J. Haug *Phys.Rev.B* **72**, 193302 (2005)
8. R. Nemutudi, M. Kataoka, C. J. B. Ford, N. J. Appleyard, M. Pepper, D. A. Ritchie , and G. A. C.Jones, *J. Appl. Phys.* **95**, 2557 (2004).
9. R. Held, T. Vancura, T. Heinzel, K. Ensslin, M. Holland, and W. Wegscheider *Appl. Phys. Lett.* **73**, 262 (1998).
10. U. F. Keyser, H. W. Schumacher, U. Zeitler, R. J. Haug, and K. Eberl *Appl. Phys. Lett.* **76**, 457 (2000).
11. P. L. McEuen, E. B. Foxman, U. Meirav, M. A. Kastner, Yigal Meir, and Ned S. Wingreen, *Phys. Rev. Lett.* **66**, 1926 (1991).

Electron confinement in nanocrystals embedded in random media: Anderson localization effects

V. A. Burdov[1], M. F. Cerqueira[2], A. M. Satanin[3], and M. I. Vasilevskiy[2]

[1]*Faculty of Physics, University of Nizhniy Novgorod, Nizhniy Novgorod, Russia*
[2]*Centro de Física, Universidade do Minho, Braga, Portugal*
[3]*Institute for Physics of Microstructures, RAS, GSP-105, Nizhniy Novgorod, Russia*

The effect of Anderson localization of electrons in nanocrystals (NC's) embedded in an amorphous matrix of the same semiconductor material is investigated. A simple condition of localization in the disorder potential produced by the amorphous matrix around a perfectly crystalline core is formulated, determined by the reflection from the inhomogeneous random barrier at the NC/matrix interface. It is found that there are confined states in the NC's, arising from an almost complete reflection of the electron wavefunction by the barrier, which can be characteristic of either strong or weak localization. The local density of states has been calculated numerically using parameters of Si NC's embedded in amorphous silicon, which contains information concerning the states confined in the NC′s. These states, with energies depending on the NC size, are resonant and have a lifetime decreasing with the increase of the energy.

Keywords: amorphous silicon, nanocrystal, localization, quantum dot
PACS: 73.23.Ad, 73.40.Gk, 73.63.Nm, 73.63.Kv

INTRODUCTION

Recently, a new class of nanostructures based on amorphous silicon (*a*-Si) films with crystalline nano-regions (i.e., nanocrystals, NC's), has been proposed and studied experimentally [1, 2]. Concerning the electronic properties of a Si NC embedded in an amorphous silicon matrix, a natural and intriguing question arises, that is, does it act as a quantum dot (QD)? The answer is not obvious, because there is no well defined barrier at the NC/matrix interface in this case. In the present work, we address this question both theoretically and experimentally.

From the quantum mechanical point of view, this question may be reformulated in the following way, could a completely random barrier confine an electron? We demonstrate that this is directly connected with the well-known problem of Anderson localization in a random potential [3]. We used the Fokker-Planck theory and direct numerical simulation to study the electron localization in an inhomogeneous disorder potential produced by

the amorphous matrix around a perfectly crystalline core (NC). The approach and results are briefly summarized below. The short answer to the question posed above is that indeed there are electronic states confined in the NC's. These states, with energies depending on the NC size, are resonant and have a lifetime decreasing with the increase of the energy.

The existence of such confined states in NC's has been indirectly confirmed in our photoluminescence (PL) excitation spectroscopy experiments performed on NC-Si/*a*-Si films grown by magnetron RF-sputtering [2]. We attempted to resonantly excite the predicted quasi-localized states in the NC's and to detect the PL signal from Er^{3+} ions located in the *a*-Si matrix, since it is known for Si/SiO_2 system that there is Förster-type energy transfer from NC's to the Er^{3+} ions [4]. We did observe a resonant enhancement of the Er^{3+} emission.

THEORY

Let us consider a perfectly crystalline spherical core surrounded by a disordered matrix producing some

CP893, *Physics of Semiconductors, 28th International Conference*
edited by W. Jantsch and F. Schäffler
© 2007 American Institute of Physics 978-0-7354-0397-0/07/$23.00

random potential. We assume that this potential has a spherical symmetry bearing in mind some averaging procedure. Then the problem can be mapped to one (radial) dimension that we denote by x. Fig. 1 shows schematically such a random potential, $V(x)$, seen by the electron, with the amplitude of the fluctuations decreasing with x because of the increasing number of atoms in the more distant shells. The dispersion of the random potential can be modeled by a function,

$$D(x) = D_0 \left(1 + x/a\right)^{-2}, \qquad (1)$$

where D_0 is a constant and a stands for the NC size. The stationary states confined in the NC are determined by the (almost) complete reflection from the inhomogeneous random barrier at the NC/matrix interface, as illustrated by the inset in Fig. 1. In other words, it is the problem of electron localization in a new class of random fields with a spatially dependent correlation function.

We obtained an explicit scaling equation describing the dependence of the reflection coefficient on the barrier width (L). It turns out that, for the random potential characterized by Eq. (1), the reflection coefficient (R) is almost independent of L, in the $L \rightarrow \infty$ limit, and $R \propto D_0/E$, where E is the kinetic energy of the electron. The confined states in the NC do arise because of the (almost complete) reflection of the electron wavefunction by the barrier. The reflection can be characteristic of either strong or weak localization. In the case of strong localization, the energies of the confined states can be calculated by the formula:

$$E_n = \pi^2 \hbar^2 (n+\eta)^2 / 2ma^2, \qquad (2)$$

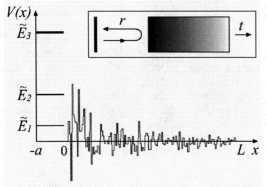

FIGURE 1. Schematics of the formation of quasi-localized levels in a spherical NC covered with random shells of the same material.

where m is the effective mass and η is a random number distributed homogeneously in the interval $(0,1)$.

NUMERICAL RESULTS

The **k·p**-method was used to derive a Schrodinger-type equation for the conduction electrons in Si, within the isotropic approximation. Some 1000 realizations of the Gaussian random potential with a spatially dependent dispersion [Eq. (1)] were generated. The eigenstates of the system containing a large number of disordered atomic shells have been found numerically. The density of states (DS) and the local DS (weighted by the integrated probability to find the particle inside the NC) have been calculated and averaged over the random potential realizations.

Fig. 2 shows the DS and the local DS for electrons with zero angular momentum. The peaks of the local DS represent the theoretically predicted quasi-localized states in the NC's, which, thus, do have the properties of QD's.

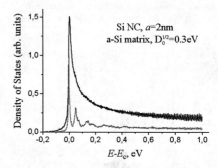

FIGURE 2. Total (black) and local (red) DS calculated for electrons moving in a potential similar to one shown in Fig. 1.

ACKNOWLEDGEMENTS

This work was supported by FCT (Portugal) through Project POCTI/CTM/39395/2001 and Russian Foundation for Basic Research (Project #04-02-16493). Travel support from the Calouste Gulbenkian Foundation is acknowledged.

REFERENCES

1. L. Pavesi et al, *Nature* **408**, 440 (2000).
2. M. Losurdo et al, *Physica E* **16**, 414 (2003).
3. P. W. Anderson, *Phys. Rev.* **109**, 1492 (1958).
4. V. Yu. Timoshenko et al, *J. Appl. Phys.* **96**, 2254 (2004).

Quantum dot with internal substructure

D. Graf*, T. Ihn*, K. Ensslin*, W. Wegscheider†, M. Bichler**, D.C. Driscoll‡ and A.C. Gossard‡

*Solid State Physics Laboratory, ETH Zurich, Switzerland
†Institut für experimentelle und angewandte Physik, Universität Regensburg, Germany
**Walter-Schottky-Institut, Technische Universität München, Germany
‡Materials Department, University of California, Santa Barbara, USA

Abstract. We report the fabrication and measurement of a finite-periode lateral superlattice within a Coulomb blockaded island, thereby creating a quantum dot with a periodic internal substructure. The potential modulation introduces an additional length scale to the quantum dot state, which can be probed with a perpendicular magnetic field.

Keywords: Local oxidation, nanostructures, coulomb-blockade, antidot lattice
PACS: -

In contrast to extended lateral superlattices [1, 2] small antidot lattices consisting of only a few periods are phase-coherent [3]. Reducing the electron density leads to a percolation-type arrangement [4], where Coulomb-blockade islands consisting of several unit cells will spontaneously form within the antidot lattice. We investigate a finite-period laterally confined superlattice weakly coupled to outer leads, where the Coulomb blockade allows the controlled addition of single electrons to the system. At intermediate magnetic field ranges we find pronounced oscillatory shifts of Coulomb-blockade resonances in gate voltage reflecting an Aharonov-Bohm(AB)-like sensitivity of the transmission through the structure to magnetic flux. This behavior is seen in the regime in which the classical cyclotron diameter is commensurate with the period of the lateral superlattice.

Local anodic oxidation [5] has been shown to be a powerful tool to design nanoscale devices based on shallow two-dimensional electron gases in Ga[Al]As heterostructures [6]. The GaAs surface is locally oxidized by applying a bias between the substrate and a conductive SFM tip in a humidity-controlled environment [Fig. 1(b)], leading to the depletion of the electron gas below the oxidized regions. In this way the plane of a 2DEG can be cut into various conductive areas, which are laterally insulated from each other. In particular, non-singly connected structures such as quantum rings and antidot lattices can be advantageously fabricated with this technique [7, 8], which would be much more difficult to realize with the split-gate method. Recently it has been shown that using a modulated voltage between tip and sample (AC oxidation) leads to an enhanced aspect ratio of the oxide lines compared to constant voltage (DC oxidation) [9]. Furthermore a better reliability and also

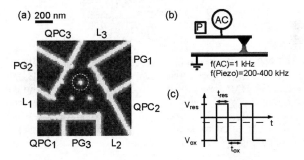

FIGURE 1. (a) SFM micrograph of the three-terminal quantum dot with a few unit cell hexagonal lattice with lattice constant of a=190nm, the bright lines/points being the oxide lines/points in the GaAs cap layer. The constrictions of the three leads L_{1-3} to the dot can be tuned through the three lateral gates QPC_{1-3}. Plunger gates PG_{1-3} change primarily the number of electrons in the dot. Not shown: Metallic top gate. For dashed circle see text. (b) Schematic drawing showing the principle of local AC oxidation with a SFM tip. A thin water film (gray) covering the sample surface serves as an electrolyte. (c) Rectangular pulse scheme used for modulating the voltage.

reproducibility of the oxidation process is found. During oxidation the SFM is operated in non-contact mode with activated feedback loop: the cantilever oscillation of typically 200-400 kHz is two orders of magnitude faster than the voltage modulation of 1kHz. In AC oxidation the tip bias consists of a square periodic signal [Fig. 1(c)]. Compared to DC oxidation, it offers more tuning parameters. Apart from the oxidation voltage V_{ox}, tip speed v and set-point, which are also controlled during the DC oxidation, we can change the modulation frequency f, the reset voltage V_{res} and the oxidation time t_{ox}. For small and dense structures requiring a lateral resolution comparable to the Fermi wavelength of typically a few tens

CP893, *Physics of Semiconductors, 28th International Conference*
edited by W. Jantsch and F. Schäffler
© 2007 American Institute of Physics 978-0-7354-0397-0/07/$23.00

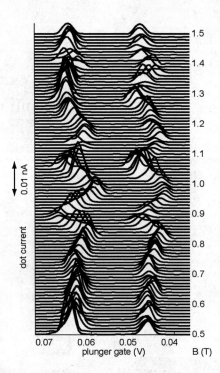

FIGURE 2. Coulomb blockade resonances as a function of perpendicular magnetic field, stepped in 10 mT intervals. All six lateral gates are swept simultaneously in order to keep the dot state maximally symmetric, but held constant in magnetic field direction. A DC bias of 10 μV is applied to lead L_1, while lead L_2 and L_3 is grounded. The plotted dot current is equal to the tunneling from Lead L_1 to the dot.

of nm the improvement of the AC oxidation becomes increasingly important.

In Fig. 1(a) the triangular shaped quantum dot with an internal hexagonal lattice is shown. The antidots along the dot edges simulate a periodic boundary condition. The quantum states can be addressed via three independent quantum point contacts (QPC). The advantage of such a multi-terminal device is twofold: 1) The individual dot-lead coupling parameters can be extracted from the full conductance matrix [10] and 2) the homogeneity as well as the symmetry of the dot state can be monitored when going to low electron densities.

In Fig. 2 two consecutive Coulomb blockade peaks are shown for increasing perpendicular magnetic field. We find a pronounced zig-zag motion of the peak position around B=1T with a periodicity corresponding to one flux quantum passing through a circular area around one antidot with a radius of r=85±5nm, see dashed circle in Fig. 1(a). It is worth noting that this magnetic field induced dot level shifting is restricted to the classical field regime defined by $2 \cdot R_C \approx a$, that is to say where the electrostatic potential modulation (a) and the classical cyclotron diameter ($2 \cdot R_C$) are commensurate. In comparison, the longitudinal resistance of quasi-infinite super-

lattices is drastically enhanced when reaching this commensurability condition [2]. In addition AB-like oscillations [3, 11] superimposed on the resistance peak were reported.

Analyzing the low-lying excitation spectrum for fixed gate voltage in perpendicular magnetic field we find a crossover of two distinct periodicities from the quantum (around B=0T) to the classical field regime (around B=1T): AB-like oscillations corresponding to a flux through one unit cell to AB-like oscillations around one antidot [12].

In summary, we presented transport measurements on a quantum dot with a hexagonal superlattice as internal substructure. Local oxidation proves to be an appropriate method to fabricate non-singly connected nanostructures. With the recently developed AC oxidation technique the aspect ratio of the oxide lines and thus the lithographic resolution could be improved. Oscillations of the Coulomb blockade peak position in a perpendicular magnetic field suggests that the periodic potential landscape dominates the properties of the quantum dot state. This happens when the classical cyclotron orbit is commensurate with the lattice constant.

Financial support from the Swiss Science Foundation (Schweizerischer Nationalfonds) is gratefully acknowledged.

REFERENCES

1. K. Ensslin and P.M. Petroff, *Phys. Rev. B* 41, 12307 (1990).
2. D. Weiss, M.L. Roukes, A. Menschig, P. Grambow, K. von Klitzung, and G. Weimann, *Phys. Rev. Lett.* **66**, 2790 (1991).
3. R. Schuster, K. Ensslin, D. Wharam, S. Kühn, J.P. Kotthaus, G. Böhm, W. Klein, G. Tränkle, and G. Weimann, *Phys. Rev. B.* **49**, 8510 (1994).
4. A. Dorn, T. Ihn, K. Ensslin, W. Wegscheider, M. Bichler, *Phys. Rev. B* **70**, 205306 (2004).
5. R. Held, T. Vancura, T. Heinzel, K. Ensslin, M. Holland, W. Wegscheider, *Appl. Phys. Lett.* **73**, 262 (1998).
6. A. Fuhrer, A. Dorn, S. Luscher, T. Heinzel, K. Ensslin, W. Wegscheider, M. Bichler, *Superl. Microstruct.*, **31** 19 (2002).
7. A. Fuhrer, S. Luescher, T. Ihn, T. Heinzel, K. Ensslin, W. Wegscheider, M. Bichler, *Nature* **413**, 822 (2001).
8. A. Dorn, M. Sigrist, A. Fuhrer, T. Ihn, T. Heinzel, K. Ensslin, W. Wegscheider, M. Bichler, *Appl. Phys. Lett.* **80**, 252 (2002).
9. D. Graf, M. Frommenwiler, P. Studerus, T. Ihn, K. Ensslin, D.C. Driscoll, A.C. Gossard, *J. Appl. Phys.* **99**, 053707 (2006).
10. R. Leturcq, D. Graf, T. Ihn, K. Ensslin, D. D. Driscoll, and A. C. Gossard, *Europhys. Lett.* **67**, 439 (2004).
11. D. Weiss, K. Richter, A. Menschig, R. Bergmann, H. Schweizer, K. von Klitzing, and G. Weimann, *Phys. Rev. Lett.* **70**, 4118 (1993).
12. D. Graf, T. Ihn, K. Ensslin, W. Wegscheider, M. Bichler, in preparation.

Electron Transport through Triple-Quantum-Dot Systems

L. Mourokh[1], A. Smirnov[1], A. Chudnovskiy[2], and D. Pfannkuche[2]

1: Physics Department, Queens College of CUNY, 65-30 Kissena Blvd., Flushing, NY 11367, USA
and Quantum Cat Analytics, 1751 67 St. #E11, Brooklyn, NY 11204, USA
2: I. Institut für Theoretische Physik, Hamburg University, Jungiusstrasse 9, 20355 Hamburg, Germany

Abstract. We analyze electron transport through the triple-quantum-dot system. The equations of motion for the electron Green's functions are derived and the expression for the electric current is obtained. We show that the current-voltage characteristics of this structure can exhibit negative differential conductance.

Keywords: Quantum Dots; Current-Voltage Characteristics; Negative Differential Conductance.
PACS: 73.63.Kv; 85.35.Be; 73.23.Hk.

INTRODUCTION

Semiconductor quantum dots which can be viewed as artificial atoms have been in the focus of research for recent years. Coupled quantum dot systems play the role of artificial molecules attracting even greater interest. Previously, the centers of attention were double-dot systems and quantum dot arrays, but due to recent progress in nanotechnology, it becomes possible to create several quantum dots with their geometry, internal properties, and coupling strengths being under the precise control.

In this work we examine quantum transport through the *triple-quantum-dot*. We analyze three different geometries: (i) three-terminal case with each of the three dots connected to their own reservoir and interconnected in the Δ-shape, (ii) two-terminal case when the double-dot system is connected in parallel to one of the reservoirs and to the third dot which is connected to the second reservoir, and (iii) two-terminal case when all three dots are connected to both reservoirs and interconnected in the Δ-shape. The first and second situations were realized experimentally in Ref. [1] and Ref. [2], respectively, and the vertical transport through the triple-dot system in the third case can be achieved using the tip of STM as one of the reservoirs and the substrate as the second one [3].

In this paper the results for the (ii) configuration are presented. We derive the equations of motion for the electron operators from the transfer Hamiltonian which includes the coupling between the dots, their coupling to reservoirs, and the inter-dot Coulomb interaction. The current-voltage characteristics are obtained and the conditions for *negative differential conductance* are determined.

FORMULATION

The Hamiltonian of the triple-dot system coupled to two leads is given by

$$H = H_{3D} + H_{Leads} + H_{tun}, \qquad (1)$$

where

$$H_{3D} = \sum_{i,j} \Delta_{ij} a_i^+ a_j + \sum_{i \ne j} a_i^+ a_j^+ U_{ij} a_i a_j, \quad (2)$$

$$H_{Leads} = \sum_k E_{Lk} c_{Lk}^+ c_{Lk} + \sum_k E_{Rk} c_{Rk}^+ c_{Rk}, \quad (3)$$

and

$$H_{tun} = \sum_k \sum_i \left(L_{ik} c_{Lk}^+ a_i + R_{ik} c_{Rk}^+ a_i + L_{ik}^* a_i^+ c_{Lk} + R_{ik}^* a_i^+ c_{Rk} \right). \quad (4)$$

We define retarded and advanced Green's functions in the triple-dot system as

$$G_{ij}^r(t, t_1) = -i \left\langle \left[a_i(t), a_j^+(t_1) \right]_+ \right\rangle \Theta(t - t_1) \quad (5)$$

and

$$G_{ij}^a(t, t_1) = i \left\langle \left[a_i(t), a_j^+(t_1) \right]_+ \right\rangle \Theta(t_1 - t), \quad (6)$$

where $\Theta(\tau)$ is the unit step function.

Using approach developed in Refs. [4,5], we obtain the expression for the electron current in terms of the Green's functions of the triple-dot system, lead-dot coupling constant, Γ, and the electron distribution functions of the leads, $f_{L,R}$, as

CP893, *Physics of Semiconductors, 28th International Conference*
edited by W. Jantsch and F. Schäffler
© 2007 American Institute of Physics 978-0-7354-0397-0/07/$23.00

$$I = e\frac{d}{dt}N_L = \frac{ie\Gamma}{2\hbar}\int\frac{d\omega}{2\pi}$$

$$\sum_{i,j}\left(L_iL_j^*f_L(\omega) - R_iR_j^*f_R(\omega)\right). \qquad (7)$$

$$\times\left(G_{ij}^r(\omega) - G_{ji}^a(\omega)\right)$$

The Green's functions and the dot populations can be obtained self-consistently from the Hamiltonian, Eq. (1), and inserted into Eq. (7).

NUMERICAL RESULTS

We present here our results obtained in the Hartree-Fock approximation for the following set of parameters: $E_1 = E_2 = E_3 = E_F + 0.01$meV, $T = 0.6$K, $L_1 = 2$, $L_2 = 0.5$, $L_3 = 0$, $R_1 = 0$, $R_2 = 0$, $R_3 = 1$, $\Delta_{12} = 0.2$meV, $\Delta_{13} = 0.01$meV, $\Delta_{23} = 0.05$meV, $U_{12} = 0.4$meV, $U_{13} = 0.02$meV, and $U_{23} = 0.1$meV, which corresponds to the experimental situation of Ref. [2], where the first and second dots are connected to the left lead and the third dot is connected to the right lead. The current-voltage characteristics for such a case is shown in Figure 1.

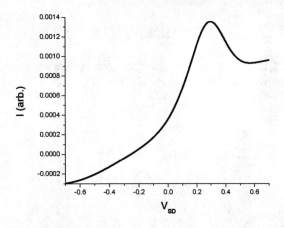

FIGURE 1. Current-voltage characteristics.

One can see that this current-voltage characteristics is asymmetric and there is region with negative differential conductance. Similar characteristics were observed in Ref. [1]. The reason for negative differential conductance is the charge redistribution between the dots (Figure 2) with source-drain voltage increasing and subsequent Coulomb blockade of the

current.

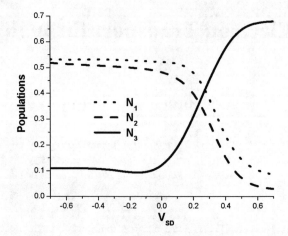

FIGURE 2. Dot populations as functions of the source-drain voltage

In conclusion, we have calculated the electron current through the triple-quantum-dot system in the configuration when two of the dots are connected to the left lead, the third dot is connected to the right lead, and all three dots are tunnel-coupled in the Δ-shape configuration. We have shown that the current-voltage characteristics exhibit the negative differential conductance due to the charge redistribution between the dots with the source-drain voltage increasing.

ACKNOWLEDGMENTS

L. M. and A. S. would like to thank S. Studenikin and A. Sachrajda for valuable discussions.

REFERENCES

1. A. Vidan, R. M. Westervelt, M. Stopa, M. Hanson, and A. C. Gossard, Appl. Phys. Lett. **85**, 3602 (2004).
2. L. Gaudreau, S. Studenikin, A. Sachrajda, P. Zawadzki, A. Kam, J. Lapointe, M. Korkusinski, and P. Hawrylak, cond-mat/0601597.
3. K. Ingersent, A. W. W. Ludwig, and I. Affleck, Phys. Rev. Lett. **95**, 257204 (2005).
4. L. G. Mourokh, N. J. M. Horing, and A. Yu. Smirnov, Phys. Rev. B **66**, 085332 (2002).
5. L. G. Mourokh and A. Yu. Smirnov, Phys. Rev. B **72**, 033310 (2005).

Thermal conductance of a weakly coupled quantum dot

Margarita Tsaousidou* and Georgios P. Triberis†

*Department of Materials Science, University of Patras, Patras 26 504, Greece
†Physics Department, University of Athens, Panepistimiopolis, 157 84, Zografos, Athens, Greece

Abstract. We calculate the heat current through a quantum dot, weakly coupled to two electron reservoirs, when small temperature and voltage differences are applied between the reservoirs. The electronic contribution to the thermal conductance, κ_e, is then readily obtained. We restrict our interest in the regime where $\Delta\varepsilon >> k_B T$, where $\Delta\varepsilon$ is the level spacing, and we show that for a dot with equidistant energy levels κ_e exhibits periodical resonance peaks as a function of the Fermi energy in the reservoirs. The periodicity of these peaks is the same as the Coulomb blockade peaks in the conductance. The resonance values of κ_e tend rapidly to zero as $exp(-\Delta\varepsilon/k_B T)(\Delta\varepsilon/k_B T)^2$. This finding underlies a clear violation of the Wiedemann-Franz law. We point out the consequence of this violation in achieving large values of the figure of merit ZT.

Keywords: thermal conductance, thermoelectric properties, zero-dimensional nanostructures, Coulomb blockade, resonant tunneling
PACS: 73.23.Hk, 73.63.Kv

We describe a theoretical model for the calculation of the electronic contribution to the thermal conductance, κ_e, of a quantum dot weakly coupled to two electron reservoirs in the Coulomb blockade regime (CB). Our analysis is based on a master equation approach [1, 2]. We consider a quantum dot with equidistant energy levels ε_p ($p = 1, 2, ...$). Each level in the dot contains 0 or 1 electrons. The charging energy $E_C = e^2/2C$, where C is the capacitance between the dot and the reservoirs, is larger than the level spacing $\Delta\varepsilon$. The tunnel rate from level p to the left (right) reservoir is denoted as Γ^L (Γ^R). Here we ignore the energy dependence of the tunnel rates. Moreover, we assume $k_B T$, $\Delta\varepsilon >> h(\Gamma^R + \Gamma^L)$ [1] and consider only sequential-tunneling processes.

Beenakker [1] and Beenakker and Staring [2] have calculated the electron current I passes through the dot when small ΔT and ΔV are applied between the two reservoirs by using a linear response theory. Here we calculate the heat current Q. Following the linearization procedure described in Refs. [1, 2] we obtain

$$Q = -\frac{\Gamma^L\Gamma^R}{\Gamma^L + \Gamma^R}\left(s_1\frac{e\Delta V}{k_B T} + s_2\frac{\Delta T}{k_B T^2}\right), \quad (1)$$

where s_m for the integers $m = 0, 1, 2$ is given by

$$s_m = \sum_{p=1}^{\infty}\sum_{N=1}^{\infty}P_{eq}(N)P_{eq}(\varepsilon_p|N)[1-f(E)](E-E_F)^m. \quad (2)$$

In Eq.(2) $f(E) = 1/\{1 + exp[\beta(E - E_F)]\}$, with $\beta = 1/k_B T$; $E = \varepsilon_p + U(N) - U(N-1)$ where $U(N) = N^2 E_C - Ne\phi_{ext}$ is the electrostatic energy for a dot with N electrons and $Ne\phi_{ext}$ in the contribution from external charges; $P_{eq}(N)$ is the probability that the dot contains N electrons in equilibrium and $P_{eq}(\varepsilon_p|N)$ is the conditional probability that in equilibrium the p state is occupied given that the dot has N electrons.

The heat current is related to ΔV and ΔT by the constitutive equation $Q = M\Delta V + K\Delta T$ [3]. Inspection of Eq. (1) shows that $M = -\frac{e}{k_B T}\frac{\Gamma^L\Gamma^R}{\Gamma^L+\Gamma^R}s_1$ and $K = -\frac{1}{k_B T^2}\frac{\Gamma^L\Gamma^R}{\Gamma^L+\Gamma^R}s_2$. The thermoelectric coefficient M is related to the thermopower, S, by the Onsager's symmetry relation $M = SGT$, where $G = \frac{e^2}{k_B T}\frac{\Gamma^L\Gamma^R}{\Gamma^L+\Gamma^R}s_0$ is the electron conductance [1]. Finally, κ_e is obtained by the standard relationship

$$\kappa_e = -K - S^2 GT. \quad (3)$$

In what follows we restrict our interest in the regime where $\beta\Delta\varepsilon >> 1$ (quantum limit). We performed numerical calculations of K as a function of E_F for a three level dot (not shown here) and we find that K shows a double peak structure with the same periodicity, $\Delta E_F = \Delta\varepsilon + (e^2/C)$, of the CB oscillations of G [1]. Most interestingly we find that $-K \approx S^2 GT$. Inspection of Eq. (3) implies that $\kappa_e \to 0$.

In order to reveal the exact way that κ_e tends to zero at low T we explore the non-zero terms. The dominant contribution to s_m in Eq.(2) is made for $N = p = N_{min}$, where N_{min} is the integer that minimizes the absolute value of $\Delta_N = E_N - E_F$ with $E_N = \varepsilon_N + U(N) - U(N-1)$ [1, 2]. In this case, $P_{eq}(N_{min}) \approx f(E_{N_{min}})$ and $P_{eq}(\varepsilon_p|N_{min}) \approx 1$. Then, $s_m \approx -k_B T f'(E_{N_{min}})(\Delta_{N_{min}})^m$, where $f'(E_{N_{min}})$ is the derivative of $f(E_{N_{min}})$ with respect to $E_{N_{min}}$. These expressions for s_m describe accurately the CB oscillations of M, K and G (not shown here) and they produce $\kappa_e = 0$ when they are substituted in Eq. (3). The non-zero terms in κ_e are due to small corrections of the order of $exp(-\beta\Delta\varepsilon)$ that are related to the energy difference between the level $p = N_{min}$ and the levels $p = N_{min} \pm 1$. By taking into account the corrections due to terms $p = N_{min} + 1$ and $p = N_{min} - 1$ we find that the electronic con-

CP893, *Physics of Semiconductors, 28th International Conference*
edited by W. Jantsch and F. Schäffler
© 2007 American Institute of Physics 978-0-7354-0397-0/07/$23.00

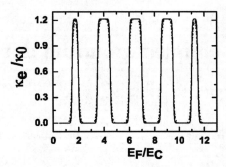

FIGURE 1. The calculated κ_e as a function of E_F in a five level quantum dot. The results for $\beta\Delta\varepsilon = 16$, 10 and 8 are shown as solid, dashed and doted lines, respectively. The three curves are hardly distinguishable. $\Delta\varepsilon = 0.5E_C$ and $\kappa_0 = L_0 T G^{max}(\beta\Delta\varepsilon)^2 e^{-\beta\Delta\varepsilon}$.

tribution to the thermal conductance is given by

$$\kappa_e = k_B \frac{\Gamma^L \Gamma^R}{\Gamma^L + \Gamma^R}(\beta\Delta\varepsilon)^2$$

$$\times \frac{(1 + e^{\beta\Delta\varepsilon})e^{\beta\Delta_{N_{min}}}}{e^{\beta\Delta\varepsilon}(e^{2\beta\Delta_{N_{min}}} + 1) + e^{\beta\Delta_{N_{min}}}(e^{2\beta\Delta\varepsilon} + 1)}. \quad (4)$$

The magnitude of the peak values of κ_e around $\Delta_{N_{min}} = 0$ ($\Delta_{N_{min}}$ becomes zero each time an electron enters the dot) is given by the simple expression

$$\kappa_e = k_B \frac{\Gamma^L \Gamma^R}{\Gamma^L + \Gamma^R}(\beta\Delta\varepsilon)^2 e^{-\beta\Delta\varepsilon}. \quad (5)$$

Equation (4) is in excellent agreement with the calculated values of κ_e obtained from Eqs.(2) and (3).

In Fig.2 we show the calculated κ_e for a five level dot with $\Delta\varepsilon = 0.5E_C$. The calculations are made for $\beta\Delta\varepsilon = 8$, 10, and 16. We see that κ_e exhibits resonance peaks with the periodicity of the CB oscillations in G. For a dot with non-equidistant energy levels the behavior of κ_e (not shown here) is different than that depicted in Fig.1.

Inspection of Eq. (5) shows that the Wiedemann-Franz (W-F) law according to which $\kappa_e/G = L_0 T$, where L_0 is the Lorentz number, fails in the quantum limit. The ratio of the peak values of κ_e and G for $\Delta_{N_{min}} = 0$ is

$$\frac{k_e^{max}}{G^{max}} = \frac{12}{\pi^2}L_0 T(\beta\Delta\varepsilon)^2 e^{-\beta\Delta\varepsilon} \quad (6)$$

where $G^{max} = (e^2/4k_B T)[\Gamma^L \Gamma^R/(\Gamma^L + \Gamma^R)]$. The violation of the W-F law leads to a significant enhancement of the figure of merit $ZT = S^2 G T/\kappa_e$ when the phononic contribution is ignored. The calculated values of ZT for a three level dot, around $\Delta_{N_{min}} = 0$, appear in Fig.2. ZT follows closely the structure of $-K$ and the magnitude of the two strong peaks increases exponentially with $\beta\Delta\varepsilon$.

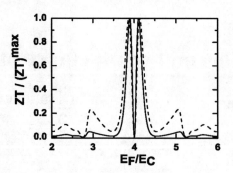

FIGURE 2. The calculated ZT in a three level quantum dot, around $\Delta_{N_{min}} = 0$, for $\beta\Delta\varepsilon = 11$ (solid line) and 9 (dashed line). $\Delta\varepsilon = 0.5E_C$ and $(ZT)^{max} = 0.44 e^{\beta\Delta\varepsilon}/(\beta\Delta\varepsilon)^2$.

Also, very recently, it has been reported that deviations from the W-F law result to large calculated values of ZT in nanocontacts made of two-capped single wall nanotubes [4]. We should remark that, the contribution of phonons could suppress ZT. However, the phonon confinement in nanostructures could decrease dramatically the phononic contribution to the thermal conductance [5]. Our findings suggest that the mutual control of the electron and phonon confinement effects in nanostructures can improve significantly their thermoelectric properties.

In conclusion, we have calculated the thermal conductance of spin-less electrons in a weakly coupled quantum dot in the quantum limit. We show that the W-F law fails in this regime. Due to this failure the calculated values of ZT are found to be significantly large when the phononic contribution to the thermal conductance is neglected.

ACKNOWLEDGMENTS

The authors wish to thank R. Fletcher for stimulating remarks and valuable suggestions. MT acknowledges X. Zianni (TEI Chalkidas, Greece) for giving the motivation through the 'Archimedes I' programme funded by the European Commission and by the Greek Ministry of Education (E.P.E.A.E.K.)

REFERENCES

1. C. W. J. Beenakker, *Phys. Rev. B* **44**, 1646 (1991).
2. C. W. J. Beenakker and A. A. M. Staring, *Phys. Rev. B* **46**, 9667 (1992).
3. P. N. Butcher *J. Phys. Condens. Matter* **2**, 4869 (1990).
4. K. Esfarjani, M. Zebarjadi and Y. Kawazoe, *Phys. Rev. B* **73**, 085406 (2006).
5. A. Ozpineci and S. Ciraci, *Phys. Rev. B* **63**, 125415 (2001).

Memory Window Improvement Effect in Boron-doped Si Nanocrystal Memory

Keein Bang, Sangsoo Kim and Koeng Su Lim

Department of Electrical Engineering and Computer Science
Korea Advanced Institute of Science and Technology (KAIST)
373-1 Guseong-dong Yuseong-gu Daejeon 305-701 Korea (ROK)

Abstract. Boron doped Si nanocrystals were found to be extremely effective to increase the memory window of nanocrystal memory for the first time. Boron-doped Si nanocrystals on thermally grown silicon have been fabricated at low temperature using the photo-chemical vapor deposition (photo-CVD) technique. Even at the low temperature, crystalline structure was successfully obtained by this method. With the reference of undoped Si nanocrystals, boron-doped Si nanocrystals were fabricated by changing the mixture ratio of SiH_4, H_2, and B_2H_6 gases. The amount of flat band voltage shifts was monitored by the capacitance-voltage measurement method, while the number density and the mean size of the undoped and the boron-doped Si nanocrystals were precisely controlled to be nearly similar, which was identified by the scanning electron microscopy (SEM) image. As a result, higher flat band voltage shifts were observed in the case of the B-doped Si nanocrystal memory, compared to the undoped Si nanocrystal memory.

Keywords: Nanocrystal memory, Photo-chemical vapor deposition, Boron doped Si nanocrystal.
PACS: 73.63.Kv

INTRODUCTION

In the practical application of Si nanocrystals in floating gate memory devices, it is significant to control the size and distribution of Si nanocrystals on the thermally oxidized Si substrate. The diameter of Si nanocrystals is theoretically expected to be in nanometer-size for room temperature operation with the Coulomb blockade effect[1]. At the same time, they should have a high number density as much as the order of 10^{12} cm^{-2} in order to guarantee a large enough memory window, and be distributed with uniformly spaced array. However, it is difficult to satisfy all of those requirements even though a lot of efforts are made. In particular, the memory window of the nanocrystal memory was too small to operate as a commercial memory. It is inevitable to improve the memory window of the nanocrystal memory.

EXPERIMENTALS AND DISCUSSION

In this paper, we suggested and demonstrated for the first time that the boron-doped Si nanocrystal memory can easily improve the memory characteristics, in particular the memory window. Boron-doped Si nanocrystals were deposited by the mercury-sensitized photo-CVD method which was shown in elsewhere[2]. A mixture of SiH_4, H_2 and B_2H_6 gases was introduced into the reaction chamber, where the gases were decomposed by ultra violet (UV) source. For the preparation of the boron-doped Si nanocrystals, the initial growth stage of the microcrystalline Si film was employed at low temperature. As a result, boron-doped Si nanocrystal arrays were fabricated on top of the 2-3 nm tunneling SiO_2 layer, in which the flow rate of B_2H_6 was varied from 0.25 sccm to 1 sccm, while those of SiH_4 and H_2 were fixed at 5 sccm and 20 sccm, respectively. In addition, a reference sample for the comparison between boron-doped and undoped Si nanocrystals was fabricated without B_2H_6 injection.

Fig. 1 shows the variation of the number density and the mean size of boron-doped Si nanocrystals depending on the flow rate of B_2H_6. The number density was precisely controlled from 7.5×10^{11}/cm^2 to 8.5×10^{11}/cm^2 and the mean size was not largely deviated from 7.5 nm as shown in figure, which could result in the accurate extraction of the influence of the boron on the Si nanocrystals.

Thereafter, about 10 nm control oxide was deposited by low temperature CVD system, followed by the Aluminum electrode formation, which resulted in the metal-oxide-semiconductor (MOS) structure of

CP893, *Physics of Semiconductors, 28th International Conference*
edited by W. Jantsch and F. Schäffler
© 2007 American Institute of Physics 978-0-7354-0397-0/07/$23.00

Al / SiO$_2$ / boron-doped Si nanocrystals / SiO$_2$ / Si substrate, as shown in Fig. 2.

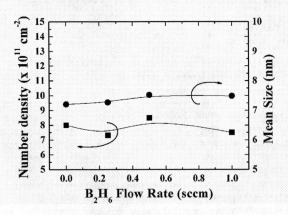

FIGURE 1. The number density and the mean size of boron-doped Si nanocrystals as a function of the flow rate of B$_2$H$_6$.

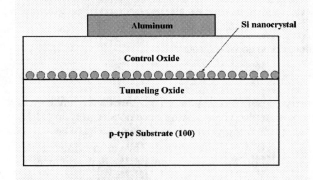

FIGURE 2. Si nanocrystals embedded MOS structure for the capacitance-voltage measurement.

For the comparison, undoped Si nanocrystals were fabricated in the same structure mentioned above. From the capacitance-voltage (CV) characteristics, the flat band voltage (V$_{FB}$) shifts were measured and evaluated in the sweep range of -3 V ~ +3 V to - 9 V ~ + 9 V. Fig. 3 shows the amount of the V$_{FB}$ shifts (ΔV$_{FB}$) from the CV measurement. The highest ΔV$_{FB}$ in the boron doped Si nanocrystal memory was about 3.8 V in the sweep range of -9V ~ +9V, where the density of nanocrystals was about 7.5x10^{11}/cm^2. On the other hand, in the undoped Si nanocrystal device, the highest value in the same sweep range was about 2.5 V, where the number density was about 8x10^{11}/cm^2. The difference of the V$_{FB}$ shifts between them was about 1.3 V, which means the memory window improvement.

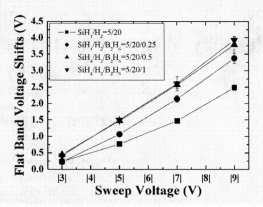

FIGURE 3. The amount of flat band voltage shifts as a function of the sweep voltage depending on the variation of B$_2$H$_6$ flow rate. X-axis means the range of the sweep voltage.

M. Fujii, *et al.* showed that the PL peak intensity decreased rapidly as boron concentration in Si nanocrystals decreases[3]. This suggested that the quenching mechanism is related to the boron atoms doped into Si nanocrystals, which resulted in the increase of the defect inside the nanocrystal. In this work, the defects induced by the boron atoms operated as charge storage sites and the memory window was increased.

CONCLUSIONS

Boron-doped Si nanocrystals were applied into the MOS structure for the first time. Compared to the undoped Si nanocrystal memory, the ΔV$_{FB}$ of the boron-doped Si nanocrystal MOS device was as high as 3.8 V. The increase of the charging sites by the boron atoms was attributed to the memory window improvement.

REFERENCES

1. K.Yano, T. Ishii, T. Hashimoto, T. Kobayashi, F. Murai and K. Seki, *IEDM* **541** (1993).
2. S. Kim, K. Bang, J. Kwak and K. S. Lim, *Jpn. J. Appl. Phys* **45**, L46 (2006).
3. M. Fujii, A. Mimura, S. Hayashi, and K. Yamamoto, *J. Appl. Phys.* **83**, 7953 (1998).

Kondo effect in quantum dots coupled to ferromagnetic leads: effect of noncollinear magnetization

Daisuke Matsubayashi* and Mikio Eto†

*Department of Physics, University of Tokyo, 7-3-1 Hongo, Bunkyo-ku, Tokyo 113-0033, Japan
†Faculty of Science and Technology, Keio University, 3-14-1 Hiyoshi, Kohoku-ku, Yokohama 223-8522, Japan

Abstract. We study the Kondo effect in a quantum dot coupled to two noncollinear ferromagnetic leads. First, we study the spin splitting $\delta\varepsilon = \varepsilon_\downarrow - \varepsilon_\uparrow$ in the quantum dot by the tunnel coupling to the ferromagnetic leads, using the Poor man's scaling method. The spin splitting takes place in an intermediate direction between magnetic moments in the two leads. $\delta\varepsilon \propto p\cos(\theta/2)$, where p is the spin polarization in the leads and θ is the angle between the magnetic moments; spin splitting is maximal in the parallel alignment of two ferromagnets ($\theta = 0$) and minimal in the antiparallel alignment ($\theta = \pi$). Second, we calculate the Kondo temperature T_K. The scaling calculation yields an analytical expression of T_K as a function of θ and p, $T_K(\theta, p)$, when $\delta\varepsilon \ll T_K$. When $\delta\varepsilon$ is relevant, we evaluate $T_K(\delta\varepsilon, \theta, p)$ using the slave-boson mean-field method. The Kondo resonance is split into two by finite $\delta\varepsilon$, which results in the suppression of Kondo effect.

Keywords: Kondo effect; Quantum dots; Noncollinear magnetism; Spin-dependent transport
PACS: 75.20.Hr, 72.15.Qm, 72.25.-b, 73.23.Hk

The Kondo effect in quantum dots (QDs) coupled to ferromagnetic leads has been studied theoretically with motives elucidating how the ferromagnetism of leads influences the fluctuation of localized spins. One of the theoretical predictions is the spin splitting $\delta\varepsilon = \varepsilon_\downarrow - \varepsilon_\uparrow$ in the QDs by the tunnel coupling to the ferromagnets, which weakens the Kondo effect [1-5]. This has been demonstrated in experiments as the suppression of zero-bias anomaly of the differential conductance [6, 7]. However, previous theoretical works have been limited to the collinear cases of two ferromagnets, parallel (P) and antiparallel (AP) alignments.

In this article, we generalize the discussion based on the scaling approach in Ref. [1] to an arbitrary alignment of ferromagnetic leads and evaluate the spin splitting $\delta\varepsilon$ and Kondo temperature. We also consider the dependence of the Kondo temperature on $\delta\varepsilon$ using the slave-boson mean-field (SBMF) approximation.

We investigate a single-level QD coupled to noncollinear ferromagnetic leads as shown in Fig. 1. The magnetic moment in the lead L (R) is tilted by $\theta/2$ ($-\theta/2$) from the z axis in the z-x plane. This system is modeled by the Anderson Hamiltonian,

$$
\begin{aligned}
H &= \sum_{k,\sigma} \varepsilon_{k\sigma} c^\dagger_{Lk,l\sigma} c_{Lk,l\sigma} + \sum_{k,\sigma} \varepsilon_{k\sigma} c^\dagger_{Rk,r\sigma} c_{Rk,r\sigma} \\
&+ \sum_\sigma \varepsilon_{z\sigma} d^\dagger_{z\sigma} d_{z\sigma} + U d^\dagger_{z\uparrow} d_{z\uparrow} d^\dagger_{z\downarrow} d_{z\downarrow} \\
&+ \sum_{k,\sigma} (V_L c^\dagger_{Lk,l\sigma} d_{l\sigma} + V_R c^\dagger_{Rk,r\sigma} d_{r\sigma} + \text{h.c.}), \quad (1)
\end{aligned}
$$

where $c_{Lk,l\sigma}$ ($c_{Rk,r\sigma}$) is a fermion operator for an electron with wavenumber k and spin $l\sigma$ ($r\sigma$) in lead L (R), and

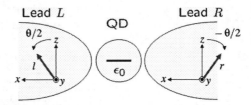

FIGURE 1. A quantum dot (QD) connected to noncollinear ferromagnetic leads, L and R. The magnetic moment in lead L (R) is tilted by $\theta/2$ ($-\theta/2$) from the z axis in the z-x plane. The spin polarization in the leads is given by p. A single level ε_0 is considered in the QD.

$d_{z\sigma}$ is that with spin $z\sigma$ in the QD level. We denote $l\uparrow / l\downarrow$ ($r\uparrow / r\downarrow$) for majority/minority spin in lead L (R) and $z\uparrow / z\downarrow$ for spin-up/down in the z direction in the QD. We assume that the two ferromagnets are identical and barriers are symmetric, $V_L = V_R \equiv V$. In this case, we can consider the z axis as a well-defined quantization axis in the QD from the symmetry of the system. In the QD, the energy level is given by $\varepsilon_{z\uparrow/z\downarrow} = \varepsilon_0 \pm E_Z/2$, considering the Zeeman effect in a magnetic field in the z direction. The Coulomb interaction, U, for double occupancy is assumed to be infinitely large in the calculations.

The density of states in the ferromagnets is constant, $\rho_\uparrow$ and $\rho_\downarrow$ for majority and minority spins, respectively ($\rho_\uparrow \geq \rho_\downarrow$), in the band of $-D_0 \leq \omega \leq D_0$. The spin polarization of the leads ($0 \leq p \leq 1$) is given by $p = (\rho_\uparrow - \rho_\downarrow)/(\rho_\uparrow + \rho_\downarrow)$.

We examine the Coulomb blockade region with one electron in the QD, $-D_0 \ll \varepsilon_0 \ll \mu - \Delta$ and $\mu + \Delta \ll \varepsilon_0 + U$, where $\mu \equiv 0$ is the Fermi energy of conduction

CP893, *Physics of Semiconductors, 28th International Conference*
edited by W. Jantsch and F. Schäffler
© 2007 American Institute of Physics 978-0-7354-0397-0/07/$23.00

electrons in the leads and $\Delta = 2\pi(\rho_\uparrow + \rho_\downarrow)|V|^2$. First, we evaluate the spin splitting in the QD, using the Poor man's scaling method [8]. By changing the energy scale D, the QD level $\varepsilon_{z\sigma}$ is renormalized by

$$\frac{d\varepsilon_{z\sigma}}{d\ln D} = -\frac{\Gamma_{\bar{\sigma}}}{\pi}, \qquad (2)$$

where $\Gamma_{\uparrow/\downarrow} = (\Delta/2)[1 \pm p\cos(\theta/2)]$ is the level broadening for spin $z\uparrow/z\downarrow$ in the QD. The spin splitting $\delta\varepsilon = \varepsilon_{z\downarrow} - \varepsilon_{z\uparrow}$ is obtained by integrating the scaling equation from D_0 to D_1, where the charge fluctuation is quenched ($D_1 \approx -\varepsilon_{z\uparrow}$) [9],

$$\delta\varepsilon = \frac{\Delta}{\pi}p\cos\frac{\theta}{2}\ln\frac{D_0}{D_1} - E_Z. \qquad (3)$$

The spin splitting arises even in the absence of magnetic field ($E_Z = 0$), which is due to the spin-dependent charge fluctuation [10]. The spin splitting decreases with increasing θ from 0 to π; $\delta\varepsilon$ is maximal in the P alignment ($\theta = 0$) and zero in the AP alignment ($\theta = \pi$). Eq. (3) is in good agreement with the experimental observation [6].

In the energy scale of $D \ll D_1$, the number of electrons in the QD is fixed to be $\langle n_d \rangle \simeq 1$. To restrict the QD states to $|z\uparrow\rangle$ or $|z\downarrow\rangle$, we apply the Schrieffer-Wolff transformation to the Anderson model with renormalized levels, $\varepsilon_{z\uparrow}$ and $\varepsilon_{z\downarrow}$. We obtain the sd Hamiltonian $H_{sd} = J_+ S^+ A_\downarrow^\dagger A_\uparrow + J_- S^- A_\uparrow^\dagger A_\downarrow + S_z(J_{z\uparrow}A_\uparrow^\dagger A_\uparrow - J_{z\downarrow}A_\downarrow^\dagger A_\downarrow)$, where operators $A_\uparrow$ and $A_\downarrow$ represent the conduction electrons which couple to the QD states $|z\uparrow\rangle$ and $|z\downarrow\rangle$, respectively [10]. $J_+ = J_- \equiv J_\perp$ and $J_{z\sigma}$ are exchange coupling constants; $J_\perp = V^2(1/|\varepsilon_{z\uparrow}| + 1/|\varepsilon_{z\downarrow}|)$ and $J_{z\sigma} = 2V^2/|\varepsilon_{z\sigma}|$. We examine the Kondo effect when $\delta\varepsilon$ is negligibly small ($\delta\varepsilon \ll T_K$), which can be realized by tuning the magnetic field [1]. In this case, $J_\perp = J_{z\uparrow} = J_{z\downarrow} \equiv J$. Using the Poor man's scaling method [8], we obtain the scaling equations as $(d/d\ln D)\tilde{k}_\perp = -(\tilde{k}_\uparrow + \tilde{k}_\downarrow)\tilde{k}_\perp$ and $(d/d\ln D)\tilde{k}_\sigma = -2\tilde{k}_\perp^2$, for $\tilde{k}_\perp = [(\rho_\uparrow + \rho_\downarrow)/2]\tilde{J}_\perp\sqrt{1 - p^2\cos^2(\theta/2)}$ and $\tilde{k}_\sigma = [(\rho_\uparrow + \rho_\downarrow)/2]\tilde{J}_{z\sigma}[1 + \sigma p\cos(\theta/2)]$. They determine the Kondo temperature [10],

$$T_K(\theta, p) = D_1\exp\left[-\frac{1}{(\rho_\uparrow + \rho_\downarrow)J}\frac{\operatorname{arctanh}\left(p\cos\frac{\theta}{2}\right)}{p\cos\frac{\theta}{2}}\right]. \qquad (4)$$

This is an extension of the result in Ref. [1] for the P alignment.

Next, to evaluate the Kondo temperature with finite $\delta\varepsilon$, we adopt the SBMF theory [11]. Here, we treat $\delta\varepsilon$ as an arbitrary parameter, which may be determined by the renormalization procedure from $D = D_0$ to D_1. In the case of $\varepsilon_{z\sigma} \ll \mu - \Delta$, where $\langle n_d \rangle \simeq 1$ (Kondo regime), we obtain the spin-split Kondo resonant levels, which are

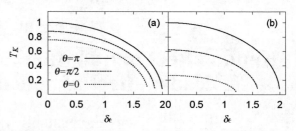

FIGURE 2. The Kondo temperature T_K as a function of the spin splitting $\delta\varepsilon$ for three different polarization angles θ. θ is the angle between the magnetic moments in the ferromagnetic leads. The polarization in the leads is (a) $p = 0.5$ and (b) 0.9. Both T_K and $\delta\varepsilon$ are normalized by the Kondo temperature at $\delta\varepsilon = 0$ and $\theta = 0$ (P alignment)

located at $\tilde{E}_{z\uparrow/z\downarrow} = \mp(\delta\varepsilon/2)[1 \pm p\cos(\theta/2)]$ below and above the Fermi level $\mu = 0$. We define the Kondo temperature as the geometric mean of the resonant widths for spins $z\uparrow$ and $z\downarrow$. It is calculated [10] as

$$T_K(\delta\varepsilon, \theta, p) = \sqrt{T_K(0, \theta, p)^2 - |\tilde{E}_{z\uparrow}\tilde{E}_{z\downarrow}|}, \qquad (5)$$

where $T_K(0, \theta, p) = D_1\exp\{-2\pi|\varepsilon_0|/\Delta - p\cos(\theta/2)\operatorname{arctanh}[p\cos(\theta/2)]\}$. $T_K(0, \theta, p)$ is a function of $p\cos(\theta/2)$, in qualitative agreement with that obtained by the scaling method, Eq. (4). In Fig. 2, $T_K(\delta\varepsilon, \theta, p)$ is plotted as a function of $\delta\varepsilon$. The Kondo temperature decreases with increasing $\delta\varepsilon$ monotonically. This is because $\delta\varepsilon$ separates the Kondo resonant levels for spins $z\uparrow$ and $z\downarrow$ and in consequence suppresses the spin fluctuation.

In conclusion, we have theoretically investigated the Kondo effect in a QD coupled to noncollinear ferromagnetic leads, using the Poor man's scaling method and the SBMF theory. A characteristic of the noncollinear ferromagnets is a factor of $p\cos(\theta/2)$ in the expression of spin splitting $\delta\varepsilon$ and Kondo temperature, in the case of symmetric barriers, $V_L = V_R$. In Ref. [10], we examine general case of asymmetric barriers, $V_L \neq V_R$.

REFERENCES

1. J. Martinek, *et al.*, Phys. Rev. Lett. **91**, 127203 (2003).
2. B. Dong, *et al.*, J. Phys.: Condens. Matter **15**, 8435 (2003).
3. J. Martinek, *et al.*, Phys. Rev. Lett. **91**, 247202 (2003).
4. M.-S. Choi, *et al.*, Phys. Rev. Lett. **92**, 056601 (2004).
5. Y. Utsumi, *et al.*, Phys. Rev. B **71**, 245116 (2005).
6. A. N. Pasupathy, *et al.*, Science **306**, 85 (2004).
7. J. Nygård, W. F. Koehl, N. Mason, L. DiCarlo, and C. M. Marcus, cond-mat/0410467.
8. P. W. Anderson, J. Phys. C **3**, 2439 (1970).
9. F. D. M. Haldane, Phys. Rev. Lett. **40**, 416 (1978).
10. D. Matsubayashi and M. Eto, to be submitted to Phys. Rev. B.
11. P. Coleman, Phys. Rev. B **29**, 3035 (1984).

Resonant tunneling through Quantum States of Enhancement Mode an In-Plane-Gate Quantum Dot Transistor

S. H. Son[1,2,4], S. W. Hwang[1,4], J. I. Lee[2], Y. J. Park[2], Y. S. Yu[3], D. Ahn[4]

[1]Dept. of Electronics & Computer Engineering, Korea University, Sungbuk, Anam, Seoul 136-075, Korea
[2]Nano Device Research Center, Korea Institute of Science and Technology,
P. O. Box 131, Cheongryang, Seoul 130-650, Korea
[3]Dept. of Information & Control Eng., Hankyong National university 67 Seokjeong, Anseong, Kyeonggi, Korea
[4]Institute of Quantum Information Processing and Systems, University of Seoul,
90 Jeonnong, Dongdaemun, Seoul 130-743, Korea

Abstract. We demonstrate electron transport in an enhancement mode in-plane-gate quantum dot transistor (IPGQDT). Deeply etched trenches allow large positive biases on the IPG with negligible leakage current. Strong negative differential resistance (NDR) peaks and single electron tunneling are observed in a wide gate bias window. The position of the NDR peaks systematically moves with the change of the gate bias, suggesting that they originate from resonant tunneling through QD quantum states.

Keywords: IPGQDT, NDR, SET
PACS: 73.21.La, 73.63.-b, 73.23.Hk

INTRODUCTION

In-Plane-Gate (IPG) field effect transistor [1-4] is an interesting electron device, in which both the channel and the gates are formed simultaneously on a 2-Dimentional Electron Gas (2DEG) heterostructure. Isolation of the gate from the channel is obtained by etching [3], focused ion beam (FIB) irradiation [1, 2], or local oxidation using an Atomic Force Microscope (AFM) [4]. This IPG transistor offers several advantages over conventional split-gate transistors [5] because they have much wider tuning of the gate bias without leakage. In this paper, we report fabrication and characterization of an enhancement mode IPG quantum dot transistor (QDT) where QD potential is controlled by trench-isolated IPGs. We investigate behaviors of negative differential resistance (NDR) originated from resonant tunneling through QD 0-dimensional states.

DEVICE FABRICATION

Figure 1 shows a schematic of the fabricated enhancement mode IPGT. A QD and tunnel barriers are defined, and two in-plane-gates (V_{CG1} and V_{CG2}) can control the potentials of the QD and the tunnel barriers. We use a modulation doped GaAs/AlGaAs 2DEG wafer grown using molecular beam epitaxy. The layer sequence from the top is as follows: 5 nm GaAs, 40 nm Si doped AlGaAs, 8 nm undoped AlGaAs, 600 nm GaAs, GaAs/AlGaAs superlattice, and semi-insulating GaAs substrate. The two-dimensional electron density is 3.1×10^{11} cm^{-2} and the mobility is 4×10^5 cm^2/Vs at 4.2 K. The device fabrication is done using electron beam lithography and subsequent wet etching (using H_2SO_4) to simultaneously form the QD, tunnel barriers, and two IPGs. The etching depth is more than 150 nm. Deeply etched trench makes the gate leakage current minimized through the undoped GaAs.

RESULT AND DISCUSSION

The fabricated IPGQDT operates in enhancement mode (It means that we apply positive IPG biases, V_{CG1} and V_{CG2} to induce electrons in the QD). Figure 2(a) and (b) show typical drain current-drain voltage (I_{DS}-V_{DS}) and differential conductance-drain voltage (dI_{DS}/dV_{DS}-V_{DS}) characteristics at different value of

CP893, *Physics of Semiconductors, 28th International Conference*
edited by W. Jantsch and F. Schäffler
© 2007 American Institute of Physics 978-0-7354-0397-0/07/$23.00

V_{CG1} and V_{CG2}. Clear NDR is observed in a wide gate bias window and it is attributed to resonant tunneling through zero-dimensional energy states of the fabricated QD. Figure 3 shows typical Coulomb oscillations as a function of V_{CG2} at several different V_{DS} values. At 4.2 K, it is extremely difficult to achieve similar quality Coulomb oscillations in other types of QDTs [5] using GaAs 2DEG wafers. Such clear Coulomb oscillations are originated from the ultra-small QD operating in the enhancement mode. The size of the QD and the energy level spacing were estimated from the contour plot (not shown here). The source capacitance and drain capacitance are 9 and 11 aF, respectively. The gate capacitance estimated from the Coulomb oscillation period is 0.8 aF. The diameter of the QD estimated from these capacitance values is about 50 nm. The diameter of the QD seen from the top is 200 nm. However, the actual size of the QD is much smaller than 200 nm due to the undercut created from the deep etching.

CONCLUSION

In conclusion, we have demonstrated electron transport in an enhancement mode IPGQDT. Deeply etched trench makes a large positive bias on the IPG with negligible leakage current possible. Strong NDR peaks originating from resonant tunneling through the quantum states are observed in a wide gate bias window. The size of the QD is also estimated from the single electron tunneling data.

ACKNOWLEDGMENTS

This work was supported by the Korea Ministry of Science and Technology through Creative Research Initiative Program. The work at KIST was supported by the nano R&D program and Nanostructure Technology Project of MOST. The work at Hankyong National University was supported by grant no. R05-2003-000-11791-0 from the Basic Research Program of the Korea Science & Engineering Foundation. The work at Korea University was supported by Brain Korea 21 Project in 2005.

REFERENCES

1. A. D. Wieck and K. Ploog, Appl. Phys. Lett. **61**, 1048 (1990).
2. T. Bever, K. v. Klitzing, A. D. Wieck and K. Ploog, Appl. Phys. Lett. **63**, 642(1993).
3. Jan-Olof J. Wesstrom, Katharina Hieke, Bjorn Stalnacke, Thomas Palm, Bjorn Stoltz, Appl. Phys. Lett. **70**, 1302 (1997).
4. R. Held, T. Vancura, K. Ensslin, M. Holland and W. Wegscheider, Appl. Phys. Lett. **73**, 262 (1998).
5. B. J. van Wees, H. van Houten, C. W. J. Beenakker, J. G. Willamson, L. P. Kouwenhoven, D. van der Marel, and C. T. Foxon, Phys. Rev. Lett. **60**, 848 (1998).

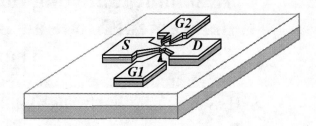

FIGURE 1 Schematic of the fabricated IPGQDT

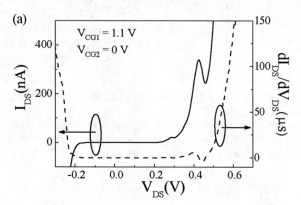

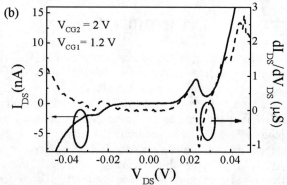

FIGURE 2 I_{DS}-V_{DS} and dI_{DS}/dV_{DS}-V_{DS} characteristics of IPGQDT.

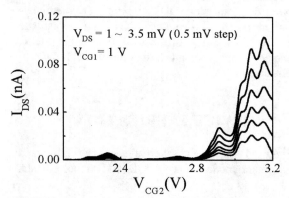

FIGURE 3 I_{DS}-V_{CG2} characteristics of IPGQDT.

Probing spin configurations in quantum dots

M. C. Rogge, C. Fühner and R. J. Haug

Institut für Festkörperphysik, Leibniz Universität Hannover, Appelstraße 2, 30167 Hannover, Germany

Abstract. We study the magnetoconductance of lateral quantum dots in high magnetic fields. We use spin blockade and Kondo effect to investigate the spin configuration and the spin filling mechanism and find a dependence on the electron number of the quantum dot.

Keywords: quantum dots, Coulomb blockade, spin blockade, Kondo effect
PACS: 73.63.Kv, 73.23.Hk, 72.15.Qm, 73.21.La

Spin blockade [1] and Kondo effect [2] in lateral quantum dots [3] have been studied intensively throughout the last years. The spin blockade induces spin dependent transport due to spin polarized edge channels in the electron reservoirs in perpendicular magnetic fields. As these channels are spatially separated the wave function overlap between the dot and the reservoirs and thus the tunneling probability depends on the spin of the tunneling electron. Spin up transport is suppressed compared to spin down transport leading to high or low conductance along Coulomb peaks. The Kondo effect enables cotunneling processes when sequential tunneling is Coulomb blocked [4, 5] and depends on the spin configuration of the dot. In a perpendicular magnetic field a periodic pattern, so called chessboard pattern, is established showing alternating low and high Kondo conductance in Coulomb valleys [6, 7].

Very recently we have shown that both effects can be combined in intermediate magnetic fields [8]. While the spin blockade reveals the spin of the tunneling electron, the Kondo effect yields information about the spin configuration in Coulomb blocked regions. Both effects combined show the full information about the spin configuration and the spin filling of dot orbitals. As both effects show the same periodicity as a function of a magnetic field only two combinations are possible. A strong peak conductance can be combined either with a strong or weak valley conductance in the next Coulomb valley at higher energy. We observed both combinations in different samples depending on the electron number. For low electron numbers we found a strong peak with a strong valley conductance reflecting an unpolarized spin configuration and a regular filling of dot orbitals [9]. The opposite combination was found in a second sample with higher electron number. Therefore a polarized spin configuration was assumed [8]. A third sample [10] revealed several regions of different combinations showing changes of the spin configuration with increasing elec-

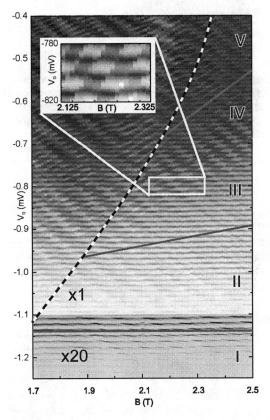

FIGURE 1. Magnetoconductance of a lateral quantum dot showing a combined pattern of spin blockade and Kondo conductance (dark for high conductance, bright for low). Five regions of different combinations are found. The transitions are marked with solid lines

tron number [11].

Here we want to focus on the transitions between the different configurations in the third sample.

Figure 1 shows the magnetoconductance of this sample with both Kondo effect and spin blockade. Right of the dashed line a regular chessboard pattern is observed

CP893, *Physics of Semiconductors, 28th International Conference*
edited by W. Jantsch and F. Schäffler
© 2007 American Institute of Physics 978-0-7354-0397-0/07/$23.00

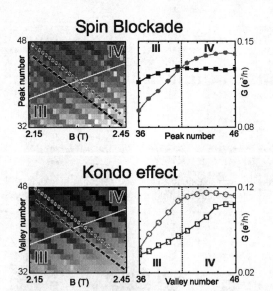

Spin Blockade

Kondo effect

FIGURE 2. At the transition from III to IV spin blockade (top) and Kondo effect (bottom) are analyzed separately by plotting either the peak conductance or the valley conductance as a function of peak (valley) number and magnetic field (left). Traces along dashed and dotted lines at the transition show a crossing of the spin blockade pattern and no change of the Kondo pattern (right).

which is shown in more detail in the inset. As a function of the magnetic field we find a periodic modulation of the peak amplitude of Coulomb peaks as well as a strong alternation of the Kondo conductance in the valleys between the peaks. The inset shows a strong Kondo conductance above a suppressed peak. The complete measurement covers five regions of different combinations. The transitions are marked with solid lines.

We now focus on the transition between regions III and IV. To investigate this transition we study spin blockade and Kondo effect separately. This is done in Fig. 2. To investigate the spin blockade we plotted the peak amplitudes as a function of the peak number and the magnetic field (left side of Fig. 2). The resulting graph is comparable with the original measurement without the Coulomb valleys. The periodicity of the peak amplitude is now visible as a pattern of lines with negative slope. Strong lines (dark) show spin down transport, weak lines (bright) show spin up transport. If we follow these lines from the lower right to the upper left we find that strong lines are changed into weak lines when crossing the transition and vice versa. Traces along two lines are shown on the right. Circles reflect the conductance along the dotted trace, squares along the dashed trace. A clear crossing is visible. Therefore the transition between regions III and IV is induced by a change of the spin blockade pattern reflecting a change in the spin filling mechanism. The same analysis was done for

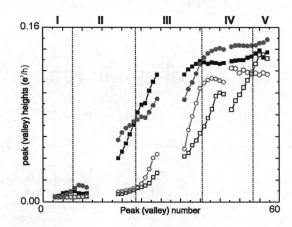

FIGURE 3. Analysis of all transitions as in Fig. 2. The first three transitions show a change of the spin blockade, the last transition a change of the Kondo conductance.

the Coulomb valleys (lower part of Fig. 2). The plot on the left can be compared with the original measurement without the Coulomb peaks. Again we find a pattern of lines with negative slopes. In contrast to the spin blockade pattern there is no change of this pattern at the transition as illustrated by the traces on the right.

This analysis was done for all transitions. The result is plotted in Fig. 3. The first three transition show a change of the spin blockade pattern and no significant change of the Kondo conductance while the last transition shows the opposite behaviour.

In conclusion we have investigated transitions of the combined Kondo-spin blockade pattern of a lateral quantum dot in high magnetic fields. We found four transitions revealing changes of the spin configuration. Detailed analysis of these transitions have shown that only one part of the pattern, either the spin blockade pattern or the Kondo pattern, is responsible for each transition.

This work has been supported by BMBF.

REFERENCES

1. M. Ciorga et al., *Phys. Rev. B* **61**, R16315 (2000).
2. J. Kondo, *Prog. Theor. Phys.* **32**, 37 (1964).
3. L. P. Kouwenhoven et al., *in Mesoscopic Electron Transport, Kluwer, Dordrecht* **345 series E**, 105–214 (1997).
4. L. I. Glazman, and M. E. Raikh, *JETP Lett.* **47**, 452 (1988).
5. T. K. Ng, and P. A. Lee, *Phys. Rev. Lett.* **61**, 1768 (1988).
6. M. Stopa et al., *Phys. Rev. Lett.* **91**, 046601 (2003).
7. M. Keller et al., *Phys. Rev. B* **64**, 033302 (2001).
8. D. Kupidura et al., *Phys. Rev. Lett.* **96**, 046802 (2006).
9. M. C. Rogge et al., *Physica Status Solidi, Quantum Dot 2006 proceeding* (to be published).
10. C. Fühner et al., *Phys. Rev. B* **66**, R161305 (2002).
11. M. C. Rogge et al., *cond-mat/0606414* (2006).

Effect Of Light Illumination On The Conductivity Of Tunnel-coupled Ge/Si Quantum Dots

N.P. Stepina[1,2], A.I. Yakimov[1], A.V. Nenashev[1], A.V. Dvurechenskii[1], A.I.Nikiforov[1], E.S. Koptev[1], Joaquim P. Leitao[2], Nikolai A. Sobolev[2], Maria Celeste do Carmo[2]

[1] Institute of Semiconductor Physics, Siberian Branch of Russian Academy of Science, 630090, Novosibirsk, Russia
[2] Research Center Rossendorf, D-01314, Dresden, Germany

Abstract. Lateral photoconductivity (PC) via dense array of Ge/Si quantum dots (QDs) has been studied at temperatures when hole hopping between dots is a dominant mechanism of charge transport. Photoconductivity with sign, depending on QDs occupancies and slow kinetics, was observed under illumination with photon energy more and less than silicon band-gap. It was found out that the photoconductivity wavelength threshold λ_{th} depends on the filling factor η of dots with holes: the greater the η, the shorter the λ_{th}. The model based on the crucial influence of hole number in dots on the photoconductivity was proposed. Using this model to analyze PC kinetics at different light intensity we restored the dependence of hopping conductivity on QDs occupancies. It was shown that the rate of hole concentration recovering depends exponentially on concentration itself.

Keywords: quantum dots, hopping conductivity, illumination, relaxation
PACS: 73.50.PZ 73.63.Kv

INTRODUCTION

It has been shown recently [1] that the interband illumination of Ge/Si quantum dots array (QDs) at low temperatures (<30K) leads to photoconductivity with sign, depending on average number of holes in dot. Kinetics of the recovery as well as the decay was extremely slow for both positive and negative PC. Two important properties of QD array can imply the conductivity variation under illumination. First, the hopping conductivity in QDs structures oscillates with charge state of dots. Thus, the change of hole concentration in excited state can lead to out-of equilibrium conductance depending on dots population. Second, the behavior of these structures can be similar to disordered systems with long-range Coulomb interaction (electron glasses): excitation from equilibrium leads to increase of the conductivity with slow decays towards initial state. To understand the mechanism of photoconductivity and sluggish response of the carriers we have analyzed the spectral and light intensity dependence of PC kinetics and proposed the model explaining experimental data.

EXPERIMENTAL TECHNIQUE

Samples were grown by molecular beam epitaxy on boron doped (001) oriented Si substrate. Ge layer with a nominal thickness of 8 ML was symmetrically embedded into 90 nm thick boron doped silicon region. To supply dots with holes, a boron δ-doping Si layer was inserted 5 nm below Ge layer. Details of sample preparation and structural characterization have been described elsewhere [2]. PC experiments have been carried out at 4.2 K using GaAs light - emitting diodes with an emission maximum at a wavelength of 0.9, 1.3 and 1.55 μm for excitation. For detail investigation of spectral dependence of the photoconductivity we used a Spex monochromator and a tungsten lamp for illumination that allows to analyze a spectral region from 0.8 to 2 μm.

RESULTS AND DISCUSSIONS

To determine the wavelength threshold λ_{th} of light initiating photoconductivity, temporal behavior of photoconductivity after consistent switch on and switch off of light was studied in the wavelength range

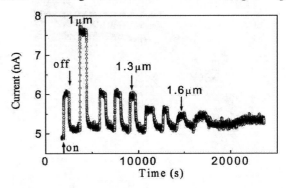

FIGURE 1. Spectral dependence of PC kinetics for the sample with 4 holes per dot. Wavelengths step is 0.1 μm.

CP893, *Physics of Semiconductors, 28th International Conference*
edited by W. Jantsch and F. Schäffler
© 2007 American Institute of Physics 978-0-7354-0397-0/07/$23.00

from 0.8 to 2 µm. The results for the wavelength step equal to 0.1µm are shown in Fig.1 for the sample with 4 holes per dot. 1.8 µm was the largest value of wavelength when photoconductivity signal was observed above the noise level. Sample with 1.5 holes per dot shows different behaviour of PC kinetics for photon energy more and less than Si band-gap (Fig.2). Moreover, photoconductivity in this sample was observed right up to ~2 µm indicating that the wavelength threshold λ_{th} depends on the filling factor η of dots with holes: the greater the η, the shorter the λ_{th}.

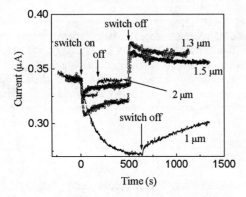

FIGURE 2. PC kinetics for the sample with $\eta = 4$.

In general, the hole concentration, changing in the QDs, can be described by the following equation:

$$\frac{dp}{dt} = -AI + f(p) \qquad (1),$$

where $J_e = AI$ – is the electron flux to the QDs, I - is light intensity, $f(p)$ – is relaxation function describing the restoration of the initial state. To find the

relaxation function we analyzed the intensity dependence of PC kinetics (Fig.3). Transforming equation (1) to conductivity G and using experimental data for different light intensity we could establish the correlation between hole concentration and conductivity:

$$\frac{-A(I_2 - I_1)}{G'(I_2) - G'(I_1)} dG = dp \qquad (2),$$

To extract $G(p)$ function and transform $G(t)$ to $p(t)$ dependence, we succeeded in finding the relaxation function (fig.4).

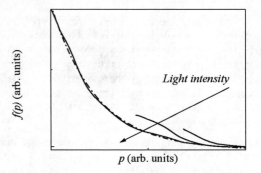

FIGURE 4. Relaxation function $f(p)$ extracted from experimental data for different light intensity.

One can see that $f(p)$ is well described by exponential law which points out the role of potential barrier in the relaxation process.

Thus, the experimental data indicates that the main factor, determining the PC, is the change of QDs occupancies. Proposed model allows to reveal the dependence of hopping conductivity on charge state of QDs, establishes the kinetics of hole concentration under illumination, determines the hole relaxation behavior.

ACKNOWLEDGMENTS

This work has been supported by Russian Foundation of Basic Research (Grant 05-02-16943), and INTAS (Grant 03-51-5015).

REFERENCES

1. N.P. Stepina, A.I. Yakimov, A.V. Dvurechenskii, A.V. Nenashev, and A.I. Nikiforov, Phys.Stat.Sol. **1**, 21 (2004).

2. A.I. Yakimov, A.V. Dvurechenskii, A.I. Nikiforov, and A.A. Bloshkin, JETP Lett. **77**, 445 (2003).

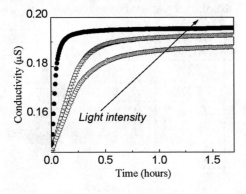

FIGURE 3. PC kinetics under illumination (λ_{th} = 0.9µm) with different light intensity, $\eta = 4$.

Investigation of the Quantum Confinement Effects in CdTe Dots by Electrical Measurements

E Płaczek-Popko[1], A Nowak[1], G Karczewski[2] T. Wojtowicz[2], M. Wiater[2]
M Guziewicz[3], Z Gumienny[1]

[1] *Institute of Physics, Wrocław University of Technology, Wybrzeże Wyspiańskiego 27, 50-370 Wrocław, Poland*
[2] *Institute of Physics, Polish Academy of Science, Al. Lotników 32/46, 02-668 Warsaw, Poland*
[3] *Institute of Electron Technology, Al. Lotników 32/46, 02-668 Warsaw, Poland*

Abstract. Hole traps in CdTe quantum dots embedded in ZnTe matrix grown by molecular beam epitaxy were investigated by deep level transient spectroscopy (DLTS) method and by admittance spectroscopy (AS). Both experiments reveal hole traps related to quantum dots. The DLTS measurement yields a hole trap of thermal activation energy equal to 0.16 eV and the AS reveals a trap of energy 0.1 eV.

Keywords: quantum dots, DLTS, admittance spectroscopy, II-VI compounds, ZnTe
PACS: 73.61.Ga, 73.21 La, 73.20 Hb

INTRODUCTION

Recently, self organized quantum dots (QDs) have attracted broad interest for their potential application in QD semiconducting devices, such as lasers, detectors of radiation or solar cells. The most important parameter determining the thermal emission of carriers from the dots is the energy level position of the quantum confined QD states relative to the band edges of the barrier material. The position can be determined by space charge capacitance techniques. Both deep level transient spectroscopy (DLTS) and admittance spectroscopy (AS) have been proved to be useful to probe the electronic properties of QD systems. In this paper the confinement depth of hole levels in CdTe QDs with respect to the valence band edge of p-type ZnTe:N has been investigated with the use of DLTS and AS methods.

RESULTS AND CONCLUSIONS

Two types of samples with the same layer structure were processed: a reference sample without quantum dots and a sample grown at the same conditions containing an assembly of quantum dots. The latter sample consists of 0.7μm thick undoped ZnTe buffer deposited on the (001) semi-insulating GaAs substrate, 4.4μm of p^+- type ZnTe:N, the layer of CdTe QDs and 0.6μm of *p*-type ZnTe:N cap. The CdTe self-assembled QDs were grown in the Stranski-Krastanow mode by deposition of 6 monolayers of CdTe. The presence of QDs was confirmed by photoluminescence measurements run at T=10K. The reference sample was identical, but without the QD layer.

To form electrical contacts a part of the sample area was etched off to open p^+ - ZnTe:N layer. The Pd/Au ohmic contacts were formed to the p^+ layer. The squared patterns for Schottky contacts were defined by *lift off* photolithography on the rest of the sample area. Indium was thermally evaporated as metallization. The capacitance – voltage (C-V) and DLTS measurements were performed on the lock-in based DLS-82E System (SEMITRAP, Hungary) and AS - with the use of the NOVOCONTROL impedance analyzer.

Good rectifying properties of the diodes were confirmed by the current-voltage (I-V) and capacitance – voltage (C-V) measurements. It was found that the ideality factor is close to 2, which means that the generation – recombination current prevails. The C-V measurements for both samples yield hole concentration of 10^{18}cm^{-3} and a barrier height of 1V.

A DLTS temperature scan performed at reverse bias equal to –3V at the so-called profile mode, with the sequence of filling pulses U1=0V and U2=-0.5V (of t$_p$=15μs width each) is shown in Fig.1. This mode of operation eliminates the influence of the electric field on the parameters of the traps. The DLTS spectrum for the reference sample is very broad, having its origin in a continuum of energy states such as dislocations (GaAs-ZnTe interface) or surface states (at the metal–ZnTe interface). The DLTS signal amplitude of the trap H1 does not show characteristic

CP893, *Physics of Semiconductors, 28th International Conference*
edited by W. Jantsch and F. Schäffler
© 2007 American Institute of Physics 978-0-7354-0397-0/07/$23.00

behaviour for dislocations: it does not grow linearly with a logarithm of t_p [1] but saturates at $t_p \sim 0.5ms$. Also the configuration of the contacts which are located far from the GaAs-ZnTe interface and the thickness of the ZnTe layer grown on the GaAs substrate [2] indicate on that rather surface states than dislocations are responsible for the broadening.

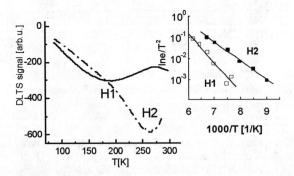

FIGURE 1. DLTS spectra taken at reverse bias $U_r=-3V$, U1=0V and U1=-0.5V: solid line – the reference sample, dash-dotted – with QDs. Lock-in frequency f=2200Hz. In the insert Arrhenius plots obtained at Ur=-3.5V are shown.

For the sample with QDs a hole trap, labeled as H2 is observed by DLTS. The low temperature shoulder of the signal indicates that there is a background broad signal, presumably also due to surface states.

Arrhenius plots associated with the traps H1 and H2 are shown in the insert of Fig. 1. The activation energy and apparent capture cross sections are equal to 0.27eV and $2.5e^{-14}cm^2$ for the trap H1 and 0.16eV and $7e^{-17}cm^2$ for the trap H2.

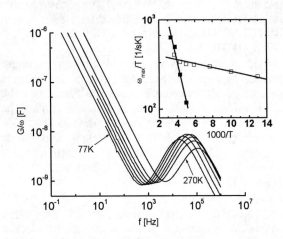

FIGURE 2. G/ω as a function of frequency at different temperatures (77K - 300K) for the reference sample. In the insert Arrhenius plots are shown: full squares – for the QDs sample, open squares – for the reference sample.

The AS measurements yield also the presence of a trap which is observed solely for the sample with QDs.

The dependence of the conductance G at $U_r=0V$ divided by frequency as a function of frequency for both samples at different temperatures are given in Fig. 2 (reference sample) and in Fig.3 (the sample with QDs). In the insert of Fig. 2 Arrhenius plots related to the maxima given in both Fig. 2 and Fig. 3 are shown.

The maximum of G/ω for the reference sample is narrow and shifts only slightly with decreasing temperature. Arrhenius plot reveals activation energy equal to 5 meV. Such a small energy can be attributed to the carrier freeze-out with decreasing temperature.

For the QDs sample the maximum of G/ω broadens and shifts considerably with decreasing temperature. The peak can be considered as a single maximum related to one trap only down to 200K. Arrhenius plot of the peak divided by temperature, ω_{max}/T, (shown in the insert of Fig. 2) results in the activation energy equal to 0.10 eV

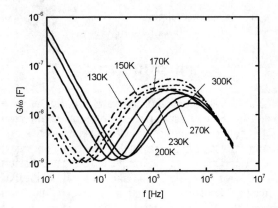

FIGURE 3. G/ω as a function of frequency at different temperatures for the QDs sample. The maxima considered for the Arrhenius plot are shown as solid lines.

In summary, DLTS and AS studies of QD related traps in our QDs structure yield one trap each, of the activation energy equal to 0.16 eV and 0.1 eV, respectively. The difference between obtained results may be due to a poor resolution in the case of both methods. It has to be pointed out that obtained results are close to the value of 0.1eV found elsewhere [3] for the valence band offset of strained ZnTe/CdTe superlattices.

REFERENCES

1. T.Wosiński, *J.Appl. Phys.* **65**, 1566-1570, (1989).
2. M. S. Jang, S.H.Oh, K.H.Lee, J.H.Bahng, J.C.Choi, K.H.Jeong, H.L.Park, D.C.Choo, D.U.Lee, T.W.Kim, *Journal of Phys. Chem. Solids* **64**, 20357-360 (2003).
3. A.Continenza, S.Massidda, *Phys. Rev. B* **50**, 11949-11954 (1994).

Super-Poissonian Shot Noise in Tunneling through Coupled Self-Assembled InAs Quantum Dots

P. Barthold*, F. Hohls*,†, N. Maire*, K. Pierz** and R. J. Haug*

**Institut für Festkörperphysik, Leibniz Universität Hannover, Appelstrasse 2, 30167 Hannover, Germany*
†*Cavendish Laboratory, University of Cambridge, Madingley Road, Cambridge CB3 OHE, UK*
***Physikalisch-Technische Bundesanstalt, Bundesallee 100, 38116 Braunschweig, Germany*

Abstract. We apply an external bias voltage to vertically coupled self-assembled InAs quantum dots. We observe pronounced peaks in the I-V characteristic due to resonant transport through a stack of coupled quantum dots. We investigate the noise properties at these peaks and we find an astonishing enhancement of the shot noise at low temperatures with a distinct double-peak structure.

Keywords: enhanced shot noise, coupled quantum dots
PACS: 73.63.Kv, 72.70.+m, 73.40.Gk

The so-called shot noise was found in 1918 by Walter Schottky in vacuum tubes [1]. The current fluctuates around its average value due to the discreteness of the charge. The average shot noise S is proportional to the average current I: $S = 2eI$, where e is the elementary charge. It has been shown that investigating the shot noise properties on tunneling devices provides more information than the DC current alone [2, 3, 4, 5].

The active part of the device consists of a GaAs-AlAs heterostructure with embedded InAs QDs (for further details of the sample see [6, 7]). The quantum dots are realized by two layers of InAs sandwiched between 5 nm AlAs barriers. Due to Stranski-Krastanov-growth the InAs quantum dots are randomly formed and vertically aligned [8]. By applying an external bias voltage V_{SD} we drive a current through the device which is amplified by a low-noise current amplifier. Parallel to the measured DC current the AC part is analyzed by a spectrum analyzer using Fast Fourier Transformation (FFT) technique. In Fig. 1 the current-voltage (I-V) characteristic for $T = 1.4$ K of the investigated sample is presented. Different well defined peaks are obvious. The inset in Fig. 1 helps to understand these peaks in the I-V characteristic. The sketch shows the energy band structure of the sample for an external bias voltage V_{SD} applied to the device. Without any external bias voltage the ground states of the QDs are above the Fermi energy E_F of the emitter and collector, therefore no current flows at $V_{SD} = 0$ mV. At a certain voltage V_{Peak}, e.g. $V_{SD} = -186.8$ mV, both energy levels in the QDs are in resonance and electrons are able to tunnel from the emitter into the QDs and into unoccupied states in the collector. Due to this sequential tunneling a peak in the I-V characteristic occurs [6, 9].

In Fig. 2 three typical current noise spectra are shown

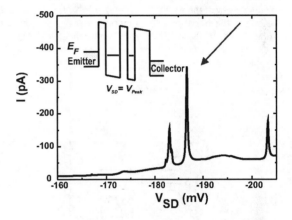

FIGURE 1. Current-Voltage characteristic of the device at $T = 1.4$ K. The marked peak at $V_{SD} = -186.8$ mV will be discussed further in this paper. The inset shows the energy band structure under a bias voltage ($V_{SD} = V_{Peak}$).

for different bias voltages in the range of the marked current peak at $T = 1.4$ K. At very low frequencies the spectra show a 1/f-behavior. We fit the function $A/f + S_0$ to the spectra to obtain information about the amplitude of the shot noise S_0. By comparing S_0 to the averaged noise spectra between 5 kHz and 12.8 kHz we find that S_0 provides reliable information. As can be seen in Fig. 2 the $1/f$ part is more than one order of magnitude smaller than the shot noise amplitude in the interesting range between 5 and 12.8 kHz.

The so-called Fano factor α compares the full-Poissonian shot noise S, that is expected for a single tunneling barrier, with the measured shot noise S_0: $\alpha := S_0/S = S_0/(2eI)$. In Fig. 3(a) a blow up of the current peak at $V_{SD} = -186.8$ mV is shown for different temperatures ($T = 1.4$ K and $T = 2.7$ K). The Fano

CP893, *Physics of Semiconductors, 28th International Conference*
edited by W. Jantsch and F. Schäffler
© 2007 American Institute of Physics 978-0-7354-0397-0/07/$23.00

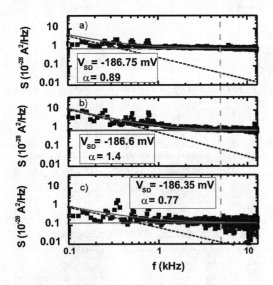

FIGURE 2. Typical noise spectra of the sample for different bias voltages at $T = 1.4$ K. The squares demonstrate the measured noise spectra, the fitting function $A/f + S_0$ is represented by the curve, the horizontal line demonstrates S_0, the dashed line shows the $1/f$, the vertical dashed line indicates 5 kHz.

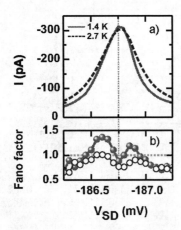

FIGURE 3. (a) Blow up of the marked current peak in Fig. 1 measured at $T = 1.4$ K and $T = 2.7$ K (dashed line). (b) The filled circles demonstrate the Fano factor α at $T = 1.4$ K and the open symbols show α at $T = 2.7$ K.

factor in this range is shown in Fig. 3(b). We observe a pronounced double-peak behavior in the Fano factor: the shot noise is enhanced on both sides of the current peak and is reduced on top of the current peak. The current changes only slightly with rising temperature whereas the shot noise shows a strong temperature dependence. Theoretical models that take only one stack of coupled quantum dots without any further coupling mechanisms into account like Ref. [10] predict a Fano factor below 1 and therefore a suppressed shot noise. Other models show that an enhanced shot noise can

be explained by coupling effects either to a nearby localized state (Ref. [4]) or by coupling between electrons and phonons (Ref. [11]). Ref. [12] explains a super-Poissonian shot noise and a double peak in the Fano factor in resonant tunneling through two vertically coupled QDs by Coulomb interaction of single-particle and doubly-occupied states at the same bias voltage. Another theoretical model describes transport through four metallic dots arranged as two parallel, only capacitively coupled stacks of two dots and shows not only an enhanced shot noise but also a double-peak behavior in the Fano factor [13]. The enhancement in this model depends on the ratio between the tunneling resistances of each parallel pair of QDs. This could be the reason for the strong temperature dependence of the shot noise power [14].

In conclusion, we have shown a reproducible double-peak behavior in the Fano factor α with values above 1, i.e. super-Poissonian shot noise, in the range of a current peak on coupled self-assembled QDs.

The authors would like to thank the BMBF for financial support.

REFERENCES

1. W. Schottky, *Annalen der Physik (Leipzig)* **57**, 541 (1918).
2. H. Birk, M. J. M. de Jong, and C. Schönenberger, *Phys. Rev. Lett.* **75**, 1610 (1995).
3. A. Nauen, I. Hapke-Wurst, F. Hohls, U. Zeitler, R. J. Haug, and K. Pierz, *Phys. Rev. B* **66**, 161303 (2002).
4. S. S. Safanov, A. K. Savchenko, D. A. Bagrets, O. N. Jouravlev, Y. V. Nazarov, E. H. Linfield, and D. A. Ritchie, *Phys. Rev. Lett.* **91**, 136801 (2003).
5. A. Nauen, F. Hohls, N. Maire, K. Pierz, and R. J. Haug, *Phys. Rev. B* **70**, 033305 (2004).
6. D. Sarkar, U. Zeitler, I. Hapke-Wurst, R. J. Haug, and K. Pierz, *Proc. 26th Int. Conf. Phys. of Semiconductors, Edinburgh, IOP Conference Series 171, (IOP, Bristol, 2003), P233* (2002).
7. I. Hapke-Wurst, U. Zeitler, U. F. Keyser, R. J. Haug, K. Pierz, and Z. Ma, *Appl. Phys. Lett.* **82**, 1209 (2003).
8. H. Eisele, O. Flebbe, T. Kalka, C. Preinesberger, F. Heinrichsdorff, A. Krost, D. Bimberg, and M. Dähne-Pietsch, *Appl. Phys. Lett.* **75**, 106 (1999).
9. T. Bryllert, M. Borgstrom, L.-E. Wernersson, W. Seifert, and L. Samuelson, *Appl. Phys. Lett.* **82**, 2655 (2003).
10. G. Kießlich, P. Samuelsson, A. Wacker, and E. Schöll, *Phys. Rev. B* **73**, 033312 (2006).
11. J. Koch, and F. von Oppen, *Phys. Rev. Lett.* **94**, 206804 (2005).
12. G. Kießlich, A. Wacker, and E. Schöll, *Nonequilibrium Carrier Dynamics in Semiconductors Proc. 14th Int. Conf., July, 2005, Chicago, USA Series: Springer Proc. Phys., Vol. 110* (2006).
13. M. Gattobigio, G. Iannaccone, and M. Macucci, *Phys. Rev. B* **65**, 115337 (2002).
14. P. Barthold, F. Hohls, N. Maire, K. Pierz, and R. J. Haug, *Phys. Rev. Lett.* **96**, 246804 (2006).

Quantum Dot Array Energy Spectrum Tuning With Laser Pulse Action

A. V. Dvurechenskii[1], A. I. Yakimov[1], V. A. Volodin[1], M. D. Efremov[1], A. I. Nikiforov[1], G. Yu. Mikhalyov[1], E. I. Gatskevich[2], and G. D. Ivlev[2]

[1] Institute of Semiconductor Physics, Siberian Branch of the Russian Academy of Sciences, Lavrentiev prospect 13, 630090 Novosibirsk, Russia

[2] Institute of Electronics, National Academy of Sciences of Belarus, 22, Logoiskii Trakt, 220090 Minsk, Belarus

Abstract. Space-charge spectroscopy has been used to study the hole energy spectrum of array of Ge quantum dots (QD's) coherently embedded in a Si matrix and subjected *ex situ* to a ruby laser ($\lambda = 694$ nm) nanosecond pulsed action. The obtained results give evidence for a substantial reduction of the QD's size dispersion and for a narrowing distribution of the hole energy levels stimulated by nanosecond laser irradiation.

Keywords: Quantum dot, laser annealing, germanium, silicon, energy levels.
PACS: 73.21 La, 73.40 Gk, 73.63 Kv

INTRODUCTION

The basic technique to grow quantum dots (QD's) nanostructure is molecular beam epitaxy, which commonly gives size inhomogeneity of QD's within a 20% range. The self-assembling imply the appearance of nanoclusters (QD's) with defined parameters: size, shape, space between nanoclusters, and their arrangement. At present, particular attention is being given to the size distribution in array of QD's, because this parameter is responsible for quantized state energy level dispersion being apparent in optical and electrical properties. The conventional way to tune the parameters of QD's array (size, shape and density) is variation of growth conditions by the alteration of substrate temperature and molecular flux. However, to establish a way to get sufficiently uniform QD's size still remains a critical issue. This should be solved since well defined sizes with small dispersion are generally required for any unique physical experiments and practical applications. In this work we present the results of investigation of nanosecond pulsed laser action on Ge/Si quantum dot heterostructures. The idea is to dissolve smaller size Ge nanoclusters in Si matrix by pulsed laser melting of Ge QD's and intermixing with surrounding solid Si. The melting point of Ge (958.5 C) is rather less than of Si one (1410 C). So, the short pulsed heating allows melting Ge nanoclusters inside solid Si. Regrowth time following melting is defined by the cooling of Si layer due to heat diffusion into Si substrate.

This time is comparable with laser pulse duration in nanosecond scale of laser pulses. So, the smaller Ge QD's may be easier dissolved due to larger interface/volume ratio [1].

EXPERIMENTAL TECHNIQUE

The samples were grown by molecular beam epitaxy on a Si (001). The areal density of the dots was estimated to be about 3×10^{11} cm^{-2} and the dot uniformity approximately 17%. A 80 ns pulse ruby laser (fundamental wavelength 694 nm) with optical system formed the light beam of 4.5 mm in diameter and inhomogeneity not worse than 5%. The energy density was taken as a threshold for Si surface melting inducing in our experiments near 1 J/cm^2. Laser beam energy reproduced with accuracy better than 2%. A pyrometer sensor detected thermal radiation from the central part of the laser-heated area to measure the brightness temperature on Si surface. From the capacitance-voltage characteristics, temperature- and frequency dependent admittance measurements, the energies of holes confined in Ge QD's were determined. The Raman spectra were measured at room temperature using a computer-controlled setup. For the capacitance and conductance measurements, Ti contacts were deposited on top of the samples through a shadow mask to form a Schottky diode.

CP893, *Physics of Semiconductors, 28th International Conference*
edited by W. Jantsch and F. Schäffler
© 2007 American Institute of Physics 978-0-7354-0397-0/07/$23.00

RESULTS AND DISCUSSIONS

A striking feature observed with Raman spectra (Fig.1) is the reduction of the width of the Ge-Ge band in the laser annealed samples. As the number of laser pulses increases to 10, the full width at half maximum of the Ge-Ge peak is reduced by a factor of about 1.5. Since the position of the Raman peak is determined by the optical phonon confinement effect and elastic strain distribution, this result implies that the nanosecond laser annealing can improve the homogeneity of the structural characteristics of Ge nanoclusters.

Temperature- and frequency-dependent admittance measurements in combination with standard admittance spectroscopy processing techniques allow us to define holes activation energies of the QD's. For all samples, the activation energy decreases with decreasing of the bias voltage U_B, and the range of energy variation ΔE, in the interval U_B where the capacitance plateau in capacitance-voltage measurements is observed, diminishes after the laser action (Fig. 1). With increasing of the reverse bias, the chemical potential scans through the density of hole states in the QD's layer. At higher reverse bias, the chemical potential crosses deeper states in the dots. In QD's, which can be charged by more than two carriers and in which conclusively higher energy levels than the ground state are occupied, the dependence of the activation energy on the QD's occupation is usually attributed to the state-filling effect. However the effect of state-filling is not relevant in a system of small QD's which are studied in present work and contain no more than two holes. Thus, the change of the activation energy with bias may be attributed to the dispersion of the hole ground state eigenenergy due to the size distribution of the QD's. Following this interpretation, the parameter ΔE should reflect the spread of hole energy levels in array of the dots. Reducing of ΔE after the laser treatment allows to conclude that the pulsed laser action does lead to the decrease of the hole energy dispersion. After the laser treatment, the hole level value tends to increase. This is explained by the increase of the average QD's size in ensemble due to laser-induced dissolving the small Ge islands and swelling out the large Ge dots because of the atomic intermixing at the Ge/Si interface. Fitting the obtained capacitance-voltage characteristics by numerically simulated curves gave the energies of holes confined in Ge QD's and their energy dispersion which were in good agreement with values determined by admittance spectroscopy.

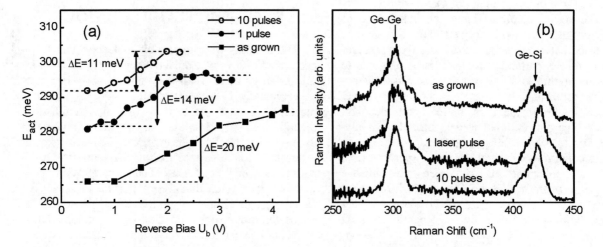

FIGURE 1. (a) Bias dependent activation energies of hole emission rate before and after pulsed laser processing. (b) Raman spectra of Ge QD's samples before and after pulsed laser annealing

ACKNOWLEDGMENTS

This work has been supported by Russian Foundation of Basic Research (Grant 06-02-81001) and Integration project of SO RAN.

REFERENCES

1. A.I. Yakimov, A.V. Dvurechenskii, V.A. Volodin, M.D. Efremov, A.I. Nikiforov, G.Yu. Mikhalyov, E.I. Gatskevich, G.D. Ivlev, *Phys. Rev. B* **72**, 115318 (2005).

Scanning Gate Measurements on a Coupled Quantum Dot - Quantum Point Contact System

A. E. Gildemeister*, T. Ihn*, R. Schleser*, K. Ensslin*, D. C. Driscoll† and A. C. Gossard†

*Solid State Physics Laboratory, ETH Zürich, 8093 Zürich, Switzerland
†Materials Departement, University of California, Santa Barbara, CA-93106, USA

Abstract. We use the metallic tip of a low-temperature scanning force microscope as a movable gate to study a quantum dot and an adjacent quantum point contact. By scanning the tip we can add single electrons to the dot and detect them with the quantum point contact. Additionally, we detect other charging events which we attribute to charge traps.

Keywords: quantum dot, quantum point contact, scanning gate microscopy
PACS: 73.21.La, 73.23.Hk

Quantum point contacts (QPCs) and quantum dots are cornerstones of semiconductor nanostructures. Conductance quantization in QPCs [1] and charge quantization in quantum dots [2] are their distinctive features at low temperatures in clean samples. In the right regime the QPC conductance is sensitive to single elementary charges and QPCs have been used to detect charge in nearby quantum dots [3]. Local spectroscopy has been reported of both QPCs and quantum dots. Among the experimental results are single electron charging of quantum dots [4, 5, 6] and charge detection with QPCs [7, 8].

In this paper we present results from a scanning probe study of a capacitively coupled system of a quantum dot and a QPC. Both devices are fully gate controlled and we can measure their conductances simultaneously. By moving the tip of a scanning force microscope (SFM) we add single electrons to the dot and use the QPC transconductance to detect them. In addition, we find that charge traps in the sample accept single electrons. This could be the reason for frequently observed parametric charge rearrangements in these samples.

Our sample was prepared in a GaAs/AlGaAs heterostructure with a two-dimensional electron gas (2DEG) residing 34 nm below the surface. The mobility is about 450000 cm^2/Vs and the electron density is 4×10^{11} cm^{-2} at 4.2 K. We used local anodic oxidation with a room-temperature SFM [9] to define a quantum dot of about 150 nm geometrical diameter and an adjacent QPC.

We scanned the PtIr tip of an SFM over the sample surface to spatially map the conductance. The SFM is operated in a dilution refrigerator [10] and the electronic temperature in the experiments presented here was about 500 mK. No magnetic field was applied and we used standard lock-in techniques to measure conductances.

Using lateral gates we tuned the quantum dot to the Coulomb blockade regime, so that individual electrons could tunnel on or off the dot. The QPC was adjusted to a conductance below its first plateau where it is very sensitive to changes of the electrical potential. For example, charging the quantum dot with an additional electron leads to a reduction of the QPC conductance. Even more sensitive is the QPC transconductance, which we measured by applying a small AC voltage of 0.5 mV to a gate on the opposite side of the quantum dot and detecting the QPC conductance at the same frequency. This technique is frequently used to detect charge on the quantum dot. However, the QPC is of course sensitive to all charging events in its proximity.

Fig. 1 shows three scanning gate images measured in parallel in a single 15 hour long scan. The tip, which acts as a plunger gate, was biased to +425 mV and scanned over the sample surface at a constant height of 100 nm.

The quantum dot is mostly in Coulomb blockade and shows few rings of high conductance (Fig. 1 a)). We see high conductance where the tip potential brings a charge state of the dot in resonance with the Fermi levels of source and drain. As we move the tip across one of these rings the charge on the dot changes by one electron. We know from additional measurements with different tip biases that the tip potential is attractive, i.e., we add single electrons to the dot as we move the tip closer. From calculations as well as other measurements we know that the tip-potential is bell-shaped. Therefore the outer rings, where the potential is steep, are relatively sharp and the innermost ring is broadened as the potential flattens off.

The QPC's conductance (Fig. 1 b)) increases gradually as the attractive tip approaches it. On top of this we see ring-shaped kinks in the QPC conductance.

CP893, *Physics of Semiconductors, 28th International Conference*
edited by W. Jantsch and F. Schäffler
© 2007 American Institute of Physics 978-0-7354-0397-0/07/$23.00

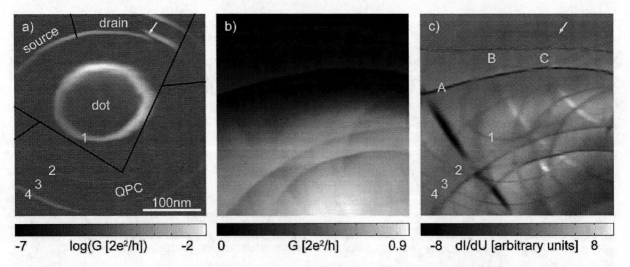

FIGURE 1. Simultaneously measured scanning gate images of a) the quantum dot conductance b) the QPC conductance and c) the QPC transconductance. Black lines in a) mark the approximate location of the oxide lines that define the structure. The rings of high conductance in a) (1-4) appear where the dot charge changes by one electron. In b) we see that the QPC's conductance increases smoothly with some additional kinks as the tip approaches it. In the transconductance c) we see rings corresponding to charging the dot (1-4) plus additional charging events. A-C and the arrows are explained in the main text.

These are even better resolved in the QPC transconductance (Fig. 1 c)) where about 20 ring-shaped features can be discerned. We distinguish two groups. Four rings (labelled 1-4) are centered around the quantum dot and coincide with the rings seen in the dot conductance. While three of these rings are only seen partially in the dot conductance due to noise, they show up fully in the transconductance of the QPC. The other rings cannot be explained by charging of the quantum dot since their centers lie outside of the dot. They may be divided into two sub-groups. Some rings (e.g. A) are centered roughly around the QPC, coincide with equipotential lines of the QPC, and could be due to resonances of the QPC. We will focus on the remaining rings, which can neither be explained by charging of the dot nor by resonances in the QPC.

Most of these rings are of similar strength and sharpness as those associated with the quantum dot. Therefore we attribute the rings to electrons charging traps located at a similar distance from the QPC. We again find groups of concentric rings, which suggests that some of the traps may be multiply charged. Closer inspection reveals anticrossings where different rings intersect (arrows), a sign of capacitive coupling between the charge traps and between the traps and the dot. We also find two rings (B,C) of positive rather than negative transconductance, a sign that traps can also be positively charged as the tip approaches.

We measure about 15 of these rings and we estimate the QPC to be sensitive to roughly twice the scanned area of $0.5 \ \mu m^2$. From this we calculate a trap density of $n_t \approx 30 \ \mu m^{-2}$ and an average distance of $d_t \approx 2\sqrt{\pi/n_t} \approx$

600 nm between two traps. The sample has a doping density of $n = 120000 \ \mu m^{-2}$ and a mean free path of $\ell = 4.7 \ \mu m$. The trap density is below 0.1% of the doping density, confirming the good quality of the sample.

Doping atoms in the remote doping layer or background impurities could act as the charge traps observed here and these might cause the well-known charge rearrangements. Further measurements addressing the dependence of the charging events on tip height and voltage are necessary to clarify the nature of the traps.

In conclusion, we have shown that the metallic tip of an SFM can charge a quantum dot with single electrons and that a nearby QPC can detect these as well as charging events in other charge traps.

REFERENCES

1. B. J. van Wees *et al.*, *Phys. Rev. Lett.* **60**, 848–850 (1988).
2. L. P. Kouwenhoven *et al.*, *Proceedings of the NATO Advanced Study Institute on Mesoscopic Electron Transport*, Kluwer, 1997, pp. 105–214.
3. M. Field *et al.*, *Phys. Rev. Lett.* **70**, 1311–1314 (1993).
4. M. T. Woodside *et al.*, *Science* **296**, 1098–1101 (2002).
5. A. Pioda *et al.*, *Phys. Rev. Lett.* **93**, 216801 (2004).
6. P. Fallahi *et al.*, *Nano Lett.* **5**, 223–226 (2005).
7. R. Crook *et al.*, *Phys. Rev. B* **66**, 121301 (2002).
8. A. Pioda *et al.*, *cond-mat\0607161* (2006).
9. R. Held *et al.*, *Appl. Phys. Lett.* **71**, 2689 (1997).
10. A. E. Gildemeister *et al.* (2006), manuscript in preparation.

Quantum information processing using designed defects in 2D antidot lattices

Jesper Pedersen, Christian Flindt, Niels Asger Mortensen and Antti-Pekka Jauho

MIC – Department of Micro and Nanotechnology, NanoDTU,
Technical University of Denmark, Kongens Lyngby, Denmark

Abstract. We have recently proposed to use designed defects in antidot lattices for quantum information processing. Here we present numerical results for the band structure and the density of states of a periodic antidot lattice, and we show how localized states appear in the band gaps, when defects are introduced in the structure. These localized states may potentially form the building blocks of a scalable quantum computation architecture.

Keywords: Quantum information processing, quantum dots, antidot lattices
PACS: 03.67.Lx, 73.63.Kv, 73.61.Ey

Since the original proposal by Loss and DiVincenzo in 1998 gate-defined quantum double-dot systems have been under intensive study as a suitable candidate for quantum computing [1]. Inspired by this idea we have recently proposed to use bound states which form at defects in an antidot lattice for quantum information processing [2]. Given the available fabrication methods we believe that the suggested structure offers high scalability. Here we present numerical results for the band structure and the density of states (DOS) of a periodic antidot lattice, and we show how localized states appear in the band gaps, when defects are introduced.

Consider a two-dimensional electron gas at a GaAs heterostructure superimposed with a triangular lattice of antidots with lattice constant Λ. In the effective-mass approximation the two-dimensional single-electron Schrödinger equation reads

$$\left[-\frac{\hbar^2}{2m^*}\nabla_{\mathbf{r}}^2 + \sum_i V(\mathbf{r}-\mathbf{R}_i) \right] \psi_n(\mathbf{r}) = E_n\psi_n(\mathbf{r}) \qquad (1)$$

where the sum runs over all antidots i, positioned at $\mathbf{R}_i$. Each antidot is modelled as a circular potential barrier of height V_0 and diameter d, i.e., $V(\mathbf{r}) = V_0$ for $r < d/2$, and zero elsewhere. Assuming that V_0 is so large that the eigenfunctions ψ_n do not penetrate into the antidots, Eq. (1) simplifies to

$$-\frac{\hbar^2}{2m^*}\nabla_{\mathbf{r}}^2 \psi_n(\mathbf{r}) = E_n\psi_n(\mathbf{r}) \qquad (2)$$

with the boundary condition $\psi_n = 0$ in the antidots.

We first consider the perfectly periodic structure defined by the Wigner-Seitz cell shown as the shaded area in the upper inset of Fig. 1. The band structure is calculated by solving Eq. (2) on the finite-size domain of the Wigner-Seitz cell, using Bloch's theorem to impose

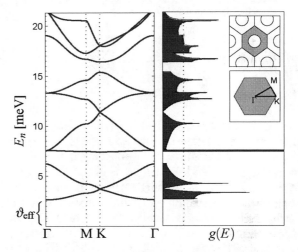

FIGURE 1. Left: Band structure of the periodic structure calculated for $d/\Lambda = 0.5$. Energies are given for GaAs with $\hbar^2/2m^* \approx 0.6$ eVnm^2 and a lattice constant of $\Lambda = 75$ nm. Right: Density of states. The dotted line indicates the free electron DOS. Insets show (upper) the Wigner-Seitz cell and (lower) the first Brillouin zone.

periodic boundary conditions. Solving differential equations on finite-size domains given well-defined boundary conditions is a well-suited problem for available finite element software packages. The calculated band structure is shown in Fig. 1 along the high-symmetry axes indicated in the lower inset of the figure. The band gap around $E \approx 6$ meV opens up at $d/\Lambda \approx 0.35$, whereas the higher-energy band gap around $E \approx 15.5$ meV only occurs for $d/\Lambda > 0.45$. On the figure we have also indicated the gap ϑ_{eff} below which no states exist for the periodic structure. Also shown is the DOS, which is calculated using the linear tetrahedron method in its symmetry corrected form [3, 4]. Recall that the DOS is calculated via

CP893, *Physics of Semiconductors, 28th International Conference*
edited by W. Jantsch and F. Schäffler
© 2007 American Institute of Physics 978-0-7354-0397-0/07/$23.00

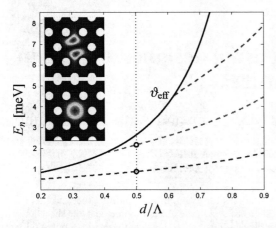

FIGURE 2. Energy spectrum for an antidot lattice with a single defect. The three lowest eigenvalues are shown as a function of d/Λ. The full line indicates the height ϑ_{eff} of the effective potential giving an upper limit to the existence of bound states. Inset: Localized eigenfunctions corresponding to the eigenvalues indicated with circles.

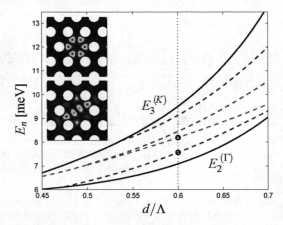

FIGURE 3. Energy spectrum near the lowest band gap for an antidot lattice with a single defect. The eigenvalues are shown as a function of d/Λ. The full lines indicate the band gap edges, giving an upper and lower limit to the existence of bound states. Inset: Localized eigenfunctions corresponding to the eigenvalues indicated with circles.

the Brillouin zone integral

$$g(E) = \int_{\text{FBZ}} d^2k \, \delta(E - E(\mathbf{k})). \tag{3}$$

The linear tetrahedron method involves a discretization of the integration domain into grid points in k-space $\{\mathbf{k}_i, i = 1, ..., N\}$ defining nonoverlapping triangular elements. On each grid point $E(\mathbf{k})$ is evaluated, and the DOS integral over each triangle calculated analytically using linear interpolation between the triangle vertices. Finally the FBZ integral is replaced by a sum of integrals over each triangular element. The symmetry corrected form ensures that the multiplicity of the high-symmetry points on the grid is the same as their individual geometrical multiplicity by extending the domain of integration beyond the subdomain enclosed by the three high-symmetry points.

We now turn to the case where a single antidot has been left out of the lattice. We refer to the missing antidot as a defect. The system resembles that of a photonic crystal, where one or several localized electromagnetic modes form at the location of a core defect. Finite-element calculations of the discrete spectrum of an antidot lattice with a single defect are shown in Fig. 2. The gap ϑ_{eff} (defined on Fig. 1) gives an upper limit to the existence of bound states and can be considered as the height of an effective two-dimensional spherical potential well in which the localized states reside. In Fig. 3 we show similar calculations of localized states residing in one of the higher-lying band gaps of the periodic structure. As expected a defect in the lattice leads to the formation of a number of localized states at the location of the defect. As can be seen on both figures the number of

localized states can be controlled experimentally by fabricating a structure with a certain value of the ratio d/Λ. For GaAs with $d/\Lambda = 0.5$ and $\Gamma = 75$ nm the energy splitting of the two lowest states is $\Delta E = E_2 - E_1 \approx 1.1$ meV, which is much larger than $k_B T$ at subkelvin temperatures and the level structure is thus protected against thermal dephasing.

One can imagine fabricating large antidot lattices with several coupled defect states that may serve as either charge (orbital) or spin qubits. In Ref. [2] we have calculated numerically the tunnel coupling between two neighboring defect states and shown how it can be varied over several orders of magnitude using a suitable split gate. We are currently in the process of extending these calculations to include the exchange coupling between electron spins in neighboring defect states, and we are investigating how global properties of an antidot lattice may be used to couple distant defect states.

In conclusion, we have presented a new architecture consisting of coupled defects states in an antidot lattice which we believe may be relevant for future large-scale quantum information processing.

REFERENCES

1. D. Loss and D. P. DiVincenzo, *Phys. Rev. A* **57**, 120 (1998).
2. C. Flindt, N. A. Mortensen and A.-P. Jauho, *Nano Lett.* **5** **(12)**, 2515-2518 (2005).
3. G. Lehmann and M. Taut, *Phys. Status Solidi B* **54**, 469 (1972).
4. J. Hanna, M. Watanabe and T. Kato, *J. Phys. Condens. Matter* **2**, 7455 (1990).

Linear and Nonlinear Transport in Single Magnetic-Ion-Doped Quantum Dots

Fanyao Qu[1,2] and P. Vasilopoulos[1]

[1]Concordia University, Department of Physics, 7141 Sherbrooke Ouest, Montréal, Québec, H3G 1M8, Canada
[2]Universidade Federal de Uberlândia, Instituto de Física, 38400-902, Uberlândia-MG, Brazil

Abstract. A quantum theory of single-electron tunneling through a II-VI quantum dot (QD), doped with single Mn^{2+} ion and weakly coupled to ferromagnetic (FM) leads in Coulomb blockade regime, has been developed. We find that tunneling magnetoresistance (TMR) can be well controlled by bias voltage and strongly enhanced by the electron-Mn exchange interaction and spin selectivity of the leads.

Keywords: Quantum dot, electronic transport, Coulomb blockade, Magnetoresistance
PACS: 72.20. Ht, 72.20.-i, 73.20. Mf

INTRODUCTION

Studying single electron tunneling through a quantum dot (QD) reveals a series of fascinating phenomena,[1-3] such as, charging effects, Coulomb blockade (CB), spin blockade (SB), voltage controlled spin-polarization, tunneling magneto-resistance (TMR), quantum tunneling of magnetization and Kondo effects. An ability to incorporate a few magnetic Mn^{2+} ions into a controlled electronic environment, such as a self-assembled QD with tunable number of carriers, would make an important breakthrough in spintronics devices because it allows one to manipulate and detect individual spins.[4-6] The *s-d* exchange interaction between the magnetic ions and the electrons, confined to a QD and lived in the leads, causes spin-disorder scattering, spin splitting of electronic state, and formation of magnetic polarons. Thereby diluted magnetic QDs provide both new mechanisms for modulating the polarization of current and also new means for investigating nanoscale magnetic excitations.[7] In this paper, we study the effects of interplay between exchange interaction and Zeeman coupling on electronic transport through a single Mn^{2+} ion doped two-dimensional quantum dot weakly coupled to two reservoirs by tunneling barriers.

THEORETICAL MODEL

The full Hamiltonian of hybrid system reads $\hat{H} = \hat{H}_L + \hat{H}_R + \hat{H}_D + \hat{H}_T$. Here, $\hat{H}_{L/R}$ describes electrons with spin in the left/right leads. The electrons in the dot are described by $\hat{H}_D = \hat{H}_0 + \hat{H}_{spin}$,[6] where $\hat{H}_0$ ($\hat{H}_{spin}$) corresponds to spin-independent (spin-dependent) Hamiltonian of electron-Mn hybrid system. $\hat{H}_T$ is the spin-dependent hybridization of the QD to the electrodes. We assume that the system is in the strong Coulomb blockade and in the sequential tunneling regime. Then the population number N_e of electrons can take on only the values of 0 and 1. For $N_e=1$, $\hat{H}_{spin} = -J_{ss}\vec{S}\cdot\vec{M} - (g_e S_z + g_{Mn}M_z)\mu_B B$, where, $\vec{S}$ ($\vec{M}$) is the spin of electron (Mn^{2+} ion), J_{ss} is exchange interaction strength in the electronic *s*-shell and magnetic field B is along z-axis. Since $\left[J_z, \hat{H}_{spin}\right] = 0$, the eigenvalue m of J_z is a good quantum number, with $\vec{J} = \vec{S} + \vec{M}$ the total spin of the hybrid system. Hence, the eigenstates of Hamiltoinan $\hat{H}_{spin}$, characterized by m, take the form

$$|m\rangle^{(\pm)} = a_{m,\downarrow}^{(\pm)}\left|\downarrow\right\rangle\left|m+\frac{1}{2}\right\rangle + b_{m,\uparrow}^{(\pm)}\left|\uparrow\right\rangle\left|m-\frac{1}{2}\right\rangle,$$

here $|m| \leq 2$, $\left|\uparrow\right\rangle$ ($\left|\downarrow\right\rangle$) indicates the spin state of an electron with spin-up (spin-down), and

$$a_{m,\downarrow}^{(\pm)} = \left\{\left[\left(M+\frac{1}{2}\right)^2 - m^2\right]\middle/2\delta m(\delta m \mp m')\right\}^{1/2} \text{ and }$$

$$b_{m,\uparrow}^{(\pm)} = \mp\frac{1}{\sqrt{2}}\left(1 \mp m'/\delta m\right)^{1/2}.$$ We find the corresponding energies in units of J_{ss}, given by $\widetilde{E}(m, \lambda) = \left(1/2 - 2mg_{Mn}\widetilde{B} + \lambda\delta m\right)/2$, where $\lambda = \pm 1$,

CP893, *Physics of Semiconductors, 28th International Conference*
edited by W. Jantsch and F. Schäffler
© 2007 American Institute of Physics 978-0-7354-0397-0/07/$23.00

823

$$m' = m + (g_e - g_{Mn})\widetilde{B}, \delta m = \sqrt{(M+1/2)^2 + m'^2 - m^2}$$
$$\widetilde{B} = \mu_B B / J_{ss}.$$

An electron that leaves or enters the dot through the left (right) tunnel barrier induces transitions between the $|i\rangle$ and $|j\rangle$ state and provides the energy difference $\Delta E(m, \lambda) = E_j - E_i$. After some algebra, we find the transition rates

$$\Gamma_{j,i}^{L/R}(\sigma, \lambda) = t_\sigma^{L/R} \left[\left| a_{m,\downarrow}^{(\pm)} \right|^2 \delta_{\sigma,\downarrow} \delta_{M_z, m+\frac{1}{2}} + \left| b_{m,\uparrow}^{(\pm)} \right|^2 \delta_{\sigma,\uparrow} \delta_{M_z, m-\frac{1}{2}} \right].$$

$$\left\{ f_{L/R}(\Delta E(m,\lambda) - \mu_{L/R}) \delta_{n_j, n_i+1} + [1 - f_{L/R}(\Delta E(m,\lambda) - \mu_{L/R})] \delta_{n_j, n_i-1} \right\}$$

where the $f_{L/R}(E)$ is Fermi-Dirac distribution function, characterizing the occupation of electron levels in the left (electrochemical potential μ_L) and the right (μ_R) reservoir. It is noted that the selection rules for the allowed transitions are $\Delta m = \pm 1/2$ and $\Delta M_z = 0$. Then spin-polarized current I_σ is calculated by

$$I_\sigma = e/2 \sum_{i,j(i \neq j)} \left[\Gamma_{i,j}^L(\sigma) - \Gamma_{i,j}^R(\sigma) \right] (N_j - N_i) P_j,$$ where, N_k is the

number of electrons in the k-th state, and P_j the probability of finding the QD in the state j will deviate from its equilibrium value for a given drain-source voltage $V_{SD} = (\mu_L - \mu_R)/e$. The stationary non-equilibrium populations P_i obey

$$\sum_{j(j \neq i)} \left[\Gamma_{i,j}(\sigma) P_j - \Gamma_{j,i}(\sigma) P_i \right] = 0, \text{ with } \Gamma_{i,j} = \Gamma_{i,j}^L + \Gamma_{i,j}^R.$$ The

tunneling magnetoresistance is determined by $TMR \equiv (G_{FM} - G_{AF})/G_{AF}$, where G_{AF} and G_{FM} denote the total differential conductance in the antiparallel (AF)- and parallel (FM)-alignment of magnetizations in the left and right leads. We assume that in the AF-alignment the magnetization of the right electrode is reversed, i.e., $t_\pm^R = \alpha t_0 (1 \pm \Delta_R)/2$ for FM alignment, and $t_\pm^R = \alpha t_0 (1 \mp \Delta_R)/2$ for the AF one, $t_\pm^L = t_0 (1 \pm \Delta_L)/2$ where Δ_R (Δ_L) describes the spin selectivity of the contacts between the right (left) lead with a QD, t_0 is a parameter and α refers to the asymmetry between the right and left leads. For comparison, we have derived the TMR for a pure QD,

$$TMR = -1 + \sum_{j=-1}^{+1} A_j^+ \bigg/ \sum_{j=-1}^{+1} A_j^-, \qquad (1)$$

with $A_j^\pm = (1 + j\Delta_L)(1 \pm j\Delta_R)/[(1 + j\Delta_L) + \alpha(1 \pm j\Delta_R)].$

RESULTS AND DISCUSSION

The TMR depends strongly on the bias voltage, the transmittances of the barriers, the relative orientation of the magnetization between the electrodes, and the electron-Mn exchange interaction strength. Fig. 1 shows the voltage dependence of TMR at T=4 K and B=10⁻⁴ T for asymmetric leads with α=0.6, Δ_L=0.9 at several values of Δ_R. For comparison, the corresponding TMR of an undoped QD are also presented as the dashed black line. We find that the TMR increases with increasing either applied bias voltage or spin-selectivity Δ_R. Moreover, it is strongly enhanced by the electron-Mn exchange interaction, as shown in the region located to the right of the dashed black curve.

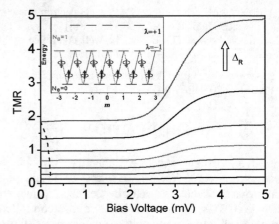

FIGURE 1. Voltage dependence of the TMR at T=4 K and B=10⁻⁴ T for asymmetric leads with α=0.6, Δ_L=0.9 in several values of Δ_R. The dashed black curve separates the regions of enhanced (to their right) and suppressed (to their left) TMR. The white arrow indicates the growth-direction of Δ_R. Inset shows a scheme of the zero-field energy levels for the $N_e=0$ and $N_e=1$ multiplets.

ACKNOWLEDGMENTS

F. Qu thanks P. Hawrylak for valuable discussions. This work was supported by the Canadian NSERC Grant No. OGP0121756.

REFERENCES

1. Daniela Pfannkuche and Sergio E. Ulloa, *Phys. Rev. Lett.* **74**, 1194-1197 (1995).
2. Dietmar Weinmann, Wolfgang Häusler and Bernhard Kramer, *Phys. Rev. Lett.* **74**, 984-987 (1995).
3. Jiwoong Park, et al., *Nature* **417**, 722 (2002).
4. A.L. Efros, M. Rosen and E. I. Rashba, *Phys. Rev. Lett.* **87**, 206601 (2001).
5. Besombes, Y. Leger, L. Maingault, D. Ferrand and H. Mariette, J.Cibert. *Phys. Rev. Lett.* **93**, 207403 (2004).
6. Fanyao Qu and P. Hawrylack, *Phys. Rev. Lett.* **95**, 217206 (2005).
7. C. Gould, A. Slobodskyy, T. Slobodskyy, P. Grabs, D. Supp, P. Hawrylak, Fanyao Qu, G. Schmidt and L.W. Molenkamp, *Phys. Rev. Lett.* **97**, 017202 (2006).

Energy Level Engineering of Coupled InAs Quantum Dot Structures

J. S. Kim[1], E. K. Kim[1], W. G. Jeong[2], S. S. Kim[3], H. M. Cheong[3] and I. K. Han[4]

[1]*Department of Physics and Quantum-Function Spinics Lab., Hanyang University, Seoul 133-791, Korea*
[2]*Department of Materials Engineering, Sungkyunkwan University, Korea*
[3]*Department of Physics, Sogang University, Korea*
[4]*Nano Device Research Center, Korea Institute of Science and Technology, Seoul 130-650, Korea*

Abstract. Photoluminescence, capacitance-voltage (C-V), and deep-level transient spectroscopy (DLTS) measurements were performed to investigate the optical and electrical properties of the vertically coupled InGaAs/InGaAsP/InP quantum dot (QD) system depending in an electric field. Two groups of activation energies, $0.36 \sim 0.37$ eV and $0.41 \sim 0.44$ eV for small and large QDs, appear in coupled QD samples by varying with the applied electric field. From the results, the quantum energy states of nearby QDs appear to couple and decouple as the gate bias conditions vary.

Keywords: deep level transient spectroscopy, vertical coupling, quantum dots, energy level, InGaAs/InGaAsP/InP
PACS: 73.21.La, 68.65.+g, 81.15.Gh

INTRODUCTION

Quantum dot (QD) is a zero dimensional nanostructure of which energy band structure is a kind of potential well. The QD can restrict free motion of carriers in all three spatial dimensions. As the result, it has similar properties just like hydrogen atom or particle in a box [1]. Then, it can be considered as an artificial atom with discrete energy state, delta function like density of the state, and high carrier confinement [2]. Indeed, the properties of QDs are controllable different from ordinary atoms. Electrons or holes in QD system can have quantum states (i.e. spin and energy states, etc.) like electrons in a hydrogen atom. In recent, many research groups are investigating fundamental properties of single and vertically stacked QD systems to applying quantum information devices such as a quantum bit or a quantum logic gate by using the properties of the QDs [3-5]. In this study, we have been studied fundamental electrical and optical properties of vertically stacked InAs/InP or InAs/GaAs QD systems, by performing capacitance-voltage (C-V), deep-level transient spectroscopy (DLTS) and photoluminescence (PL) methods.

EXPERIMENT

The InGaAs/InGaAsP/InP QDs were grown on nominally exact (001) InP substrate by using metal-organic chemical vapor deposition (MOCVD) under an operating pressure of 76 Torr. The photoluminescence wavelength and the optical properties were optimized by controlling the compositions of the InGaAs QDs and the InGaAsP barrier layers and by varying the spacing between QD stacks. 1-μm-thick InP buffer was grown on an *n*-InP substrate at 620 °C. The temperature was then lowered to the QD growth temperature (540 °C), and the InGaAsP barrier layers and QDs were grown. The density of QDs appeared to be about 1×10^{10} cm^{-2} in the atomic force microscope (AFM) measurement, and their height and lateral sizes were about 3.5~6 nm and 35~45 nm, respectively. In the samples used in this study, the QDs located in the lower layer were larger than those located in the upper layer QDs, which could be controlled by varying the growth conditions. The QD stacks were separated by 10-nm InGaAsP spacers. Following the QD multistacks and the upper InGaAsP capping layer, a 120-nm-thick InP capping layer, were grown at a growth temperature of 620 °C.

For the C-V and the DLTS measurements, we fabricated metal-insulator-semiconductor diode samples to prevent leakage current due to low barrier height in metal Schottky contacts to InP [6].

RESULTS AND DISCUSSION

CP893, *Physics of Semiconductors, 28th International Conference*
edited by W. Jantsch and F. Schäffler
© 2007 American Institute of Physics 978-0-7354-0397-0/07/$23.00

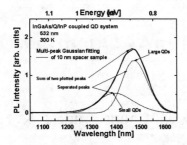

FIGURE 1. PL spectrum of InGaAs/InGaAsP/InP vertically coupled QD sample.

Figure 1 shows the result of PL measurements for InGaAs/InGaAsP/InP as-grown QD samples measured at room temperature. The PL spectra does not show two separate peaks, but rather a smooth signal as is the general tendency of QDs affected by thermal fluctuations at room temperature. However, the broad peak seems to have an overlapped shape consisting of two peaks with a difference of about 75 nm. From the results, two kinds of QDs with different dimensions exist and have different energy levels with an energy difference of more than about 50 meV.

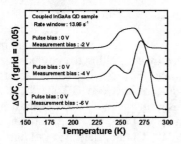

FIGURE 2. DLTS spectra of the vertically coupled InGaAs QD sample measured under different bias conditions from -2 to -6 V for a rate window of 13.86 s^{-1}.

TABLE 1. DLTS parameters of the coupled QDs.

Bias conditions	Signal origin	Activation energy (eV)
0 V ~ -2 V	Small QD	0.37
	Large QD	0.41
0 V ~ -4 V	Small QD	0.36
	Large QD	0.42
0 V ~ -6 V	Small QD	0.37
	Large QD	0.44

The bias dependence DLTS spectra for the vertically coupled InGaAs/InGaAsP QD sample are shown in Fig. 2. These spectra have two main peaks, and their origins seem to be two kinds of QDs because there are no defects in the InP or InGaAsP layers in this temperature regions and these peak positions are different from those for InAs/InP QD samples [6]. In DLTS measurements, the activation energy represents a difference between the conduction band edge and electron bound state energy levels of the QDs. The

activation energies and emission cross-sections were extracted by using Arrhenius plot with DLTS signal.

In this figure, two DLTS signals, a low-temperature peak and a high-temperature peak, are greatly separated under a large measurement bias, but are overlapped under a small bias. The extracted DLTS parameters are summarized in Table 1. The activation energy differences between the small and large QD signals are 40 meV (0.37 eV and 0.41 eV) for a -2 V measurement bias and 60 meV (0.37 eV and 0.43 eV) for a -4 V measurement bias. Thus, the two energy levels of the vertically coupled QDs are more closely related at the low reverse bias. The band structures with applied biases are shown in Fig. 3. These results show the same tendency as was seen in the optical properties measured by another research group [5]. The energy states of the vertically stacked QDs system can be controlled by using the gate bias; thus, they can be applicable to a solid quantum bit.

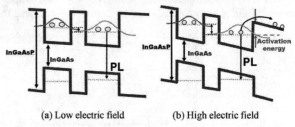

(a) Low electric field   (b) High electric field

FIGURE 3. Schematic band structures of the coupled QD sample with applied electric field

ACKNOWLEDGMENTS

This work was supported by NRL Program and KOSEF q-Psi at Hanyang University, the Dual Project of the Ministry of Commerce, Industry and Energy of Korea, and the 2nd step Brain Korea 21 project in 2006.

REFERENCES

1. L. Jacak, P. Hawrylak and A. Wójs, *Quantum dots*, New York: Springer, 1998, pp. 1-3.
2. C-W. Jiang and M. A. Green, *J. Appl. Phys.* **99**, 114902 (2006)
3. H. J. Krenner, M. Sabathil, E. C. Clark, A. Kress, D. Schuh, M. Bichler, G. Abstreiter, and J. J. Finley, *Phys. Rev. Lett.* **94**, 57402 (2005).
4. J. Lee, H. N. Spector, W. C. Chou, and C. S. Chu, *J. Appl. Phys.* **99**, 113708 (2006).
5. G. Ortnera, M. Bayera, A. Kressb, A. Forchelb, Y.B. Lyanda-Gellerc, and T.L. Reineckec, *Physica E* **21**, 171 (2004).
6. E. K. Kim, J. S. Kim, H. Hwang, K. Park, E. Yoon, J. H. Kim, I-W. Park, and Y. J. Park, *Jpn. J. Appl. Phys.* **43**, 3825 (2004).

Fano effect in a ring-dot system with tunable coupling

A. Fuhrer[*,†], P. Brunsheim[†], T. Ihn[*], M. Sigrist[*], K. Ensslin[*], W. Wegscheider[**] and M. Bichler[‡]

[*]*Solid State Physics Laboratory, ETH Zurich, CH-8093 Zurich, Switzerland*
[†]*Solid State Physics/Nanometer Consortium, Lund University, Sweden*
[**]*Institut für experimentelle und angewandte Physik, Universität Regensburg, Germany*
[‡]*Walter Schottky Institut, Technische Universität München, Germany*

Abstract. The interplay between the Fano effect and the Aharonov–Bohm effect has been studied in a system where a Coulomb-blockaded quantum dot is side-coupled to an open quantum ring. The Fano resonance lineshapes observed in the current through the ring can be tuned with an external magnetic field penetrating the ring area and the corresponding Fano-parameter q is found to be periodic with the Aharonov–Bohm period of the ring.

Keywords: quantum dots, Fano effect, Aharonov–Bohm effect, quantum interference
PACS: 73.23.-b, 73.21.La, 73.21.Hb

The Aharonov–Bohm effect [1] and the Fano effect [2] are two fundamental quantum interference effects in mesoscopic physics that allow the detection and investigation of phase-coherence and decoherence. While the former leads to magneto-oscillations in the conductance of a device [3], the latter produces asymmetric resonant lineshapes in energy (or gate voltage) [4, 5]. Recently, structures have been investigated in which quantum dots coupled to quantum rings allow to study the interplay between both effects in detail [6, 7].

Here we present measurements of the Fano effect in a quantum ring that is tunnel coupled to a quantum dot [7]. When the dot is in the Coulomb blockade regime, but strongly coupled to the open ring, Fano line shapes are observed in the current through the ring as the electron number in the dot changes by one. The symmetry of the Fano resonances is found to depend on the magnetic flux penetrating the area of the ring and on the strength of the ring–dot coupling.

The sample (Fig. 1 inset) is fabricated by direct local oxidation of the surface of a GaAs heterostructure with a two-dimensional electron gas using an atomic force microscope (AFM) [8]. Below the thick bright lines the two-dimensional electron gas is depleted. An 8 nm titanium film on top of the sample is further structured with the AFM into seven individual top gate electrodes. This allows for a unique degree of tunability of the electron number in the dot via gate 'igd', the electron density in the ring and the coupling to source and drain. Furthermore, the narrow top gate electrode labeled 'tgc' allows us to tune the coupling between the two structures and thereby adjust the q-parameter of the Fano-scatterer represented by the dot which is side coupled to one arm of the ring.

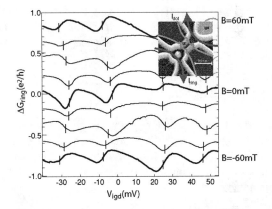

FIGURE 1. Fano resonances in the ring conductance as a function of the dot plunger gate voltage for a series of magnetic field values covering two Aharonov–Bohm periods. Inset: sample geometry.

This device allows us to investigate the transport properties of a tunable Fano scatterer embedded in a two terminal ring structure and link the change in the voltage V_{tgc} to a real q-parameter which we can tune from $|q| = 1$ to $|q| = 0$. We measure the current through the ring, I_{ring}, and through the dot, I_{dot}, with standard low-frequency lock-in techniques in a dilution refrigerator at an electron temperature of 100 mK.

Figure 1 shows a series of traces of the ring conductance G_{ring} measured at different magnetic fields between $B = -60$ mT and $+60$ mT as a function of the voltage V_{igd} on the dot plunger gate. The displayed magnetic field range covers two Aharonov–Bohm periods ($\Delta B_{\text{AB}} = 61$ mT). In each trace the positions of the conductance resonances of the dot are marked by vertical

CP893, *Physics of Semiconductors, 28th International Conference*
edited by W. Jantsch and F. Schäffler

dashed lines. These resonance positions shift in V_{igd} with magnetic field due to orbital effects in the quantum dot. The ring conductance shows asymmetric resonant Fano-lineshapes at these positions. Using the magnetic field, the lineshapes of a particular resonance can be tuned from maximally asymmetric (implying a Fano-parameter $q = 1$) to a dip (implying $q = 0$). After changing the magnetic field by one Aharonov–Bohm period, the original lineshape is restored (three thick lines) confirming that the Fano-parameter is periodic in magnetic field. The fact that corresponding traces taken at positive and negative magnetic field are nearly identical, i.e., $G_{ring}(B, V_{igd}) = G_{ring}(-B, V_{igd})$, is a result of the effective two-terminal nature of the conductance measurement.

In Fig. 2 we plot corresponding data for I_{dot} and I_{ring} for a small range of V_{igd} and two magnetic field values. The dot current was fitted using a Lorentzian line shape

$$I_{dot} = \frac{I_{max}}{1 + \varepsilon^2},$$

with $\varepsilon = (V_{igd} - V_{igd0})/(\Gamma/2)$ allowing the determination of the line width Γ, the resonance position V_{igd0} and the resonance height I_{max}. The Fano-lineshapes were fitted according to

$$I_{ring} = I_0 + \frac{I_1}{q^2 + 1} \frac{(\varepsilon + q)^2}{1 + \varepsilon^2} \quad (1)$$

giving the Fano-parameter q, the amplitude prefactor I_1 and the incoherent background current I_0. It can be seen that the data is described by the above equations remarkably well giving the following values for the Fano parameters q:

B (mT)	V_{igd0} (mV)	q
30	-26.7	0.34
30	-3.3	0.52
0	-27.8	-0.7
0	-5.4	-0.36

At temperatures above $T = 0.65$ K the Fano effect disappears while the Aharonov–Bohm interference in the ring persists up to $T = 4.2$ K. We find excellent agreement between the experimental observations and a more elaborate single-channel scattering matrix model and can link our model parameters to the usual Fano expression in eq. (1) [7].

We have further investigated how decoherence arises in the structure due to the additional contacts on the dot which allow us to probe the energy positions of the discrete dot levels independently of the current through the ring. Following Ref. [9] to include decoherence in the model we find good agreement with the experimental data [7].

Our experiment together with the model is a major step in understanding Fano effects in mesoscopic systems in

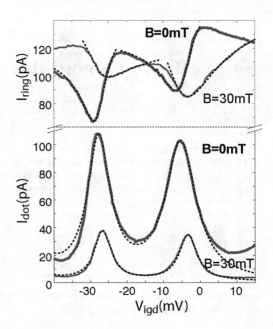

FIGURE 2. Comparison of two selected quantum dot resonances at two magnetic field values as seen in I_{dot} and in I_{ring}. Dashed lines are fits as described in the text.

general and more specifically in understanding the role of Fano type interference in ring geometries with quantum dots, a topic that is intensively discussed in many recent theoretical and experimental papers.

ACKNOWLEDGMENTS

Financial support from the Swiss Science Foundation (Schweizerischer Nationalfonds) is gratefully acknowledged. We also acknowledge valuable discussions with Hongqi Xu.

REFERENCES

1. Y. Aharonov and D. Bohm, Phys. Rev. **115**, 485 (1959).
2. U. Fano, Phys. Rev. **124**, 1866 (1961); Nuovo Cimento **12**, 156 (1935).
3. T. Ihn *et al.*, Advances in Solid State Physics, Vol. 43, ed. B. Kramer, Springer Verlag, New York, p. 139, 2003.
4. J. Gores *et al.*, Phys. Rev. B **62**, 2188 (2000).
5. A.C. Johnson *et al.*, Phys. Rev. Lett. **93**, 106803 (2004).
6. K. Kobayashi *et al.*, Phys. Rev. Lett. **88**, 256806 (2002).
7. A. Fuhrer *et al.*, Phys. Rev. B **73**, 205326 (2006).
8. M. Sigrist *et al.*, Appl. Phys. Lett. **85**, 3558 (2004).
9. C. Benjamin and A.M. Jayannavar, Phys. Rev. B **65**, 153309 (2002).

A high-performance full-configuration-interaction study of Wigner crystallization in quantum dots

Massimo Rontani* and Guido Goldoni*,†

*INFM National Research Center S3, Via Campi 213/A, 41100 Modena, Italy
†Dipartimento di Fisica, Università degli Studi di Modena e Reggio Emilia, Modena, Italy

Abstract. We study the transition between liquid and solid electron phases of a two-dimensional quantum dot by performing extensive full-configuration-interaction calculations. From the analysis of pair correlation functions we find evidence of localization for values of the dimensionless density parameter $\lambda \approx 4$.

Keywords: Quantum Dots, Electron Correlation, Full Configuration Interaction, Wigner molecule
PACS: 73.21.La, 73.20.Qt, 31.25.Eb, 31.25.Jf

Semiconductor quantum dots (QDs) are systems where key parameters controlling electron-electron interaction, such as density, confinement potential, electron number, etc. may be artificially tuned in the laboratory [1, 2, 3, 4]. Therefore, their study can give a new insight into few-body physics. A convenient and yet remarkably accurate [1] starting point for theory is the envelope-function and effective-mass two-dimensional (2D) interacting Hamiltonian:

$$H = \sum_i^N H_0(i) + \frac{1}{2} \sum_{i \neq j} \frac{e^2}{\kappa |r_i - r_j|}, \quad (1)$$

with

$$H_0(i) = \frac{p_i^2}{2m^*} + \frac{1}{2} m^* \omega_0^2 r_i^2. \quad (2)$$

Here, N is the number of free conduction band electrons localized in the QD, e and κ are respectively the electron charge and static relative dielectric constant of the host semiconductor, r is the position of the electron, p is its canonically conjugated momentum, ω_0 is the natural frequency of a 2D harmonic trap. The eigenstates of the SP Hamiltonian (2) are known as Fock-Darwin (FD) orbitals [1]. The typical QD lateral extension is given by the characteristic dot radius $\ell_{QD} = (\hbar/m^*\omega_0)^{1/2}$, ℓ_{QD} being the mean square root of r on the FD lowest-energy level. As we keep N fixed and increase ℓ_{QD} (decrease the density), the Coulomb-to-kinetic energy dimensionless ratio [5] $\lambda = \ell_{QD}/a_B^*$ [$a_B^* = \hbar^2\kappa/(m^*e^2)$ is the effective Bohr radius] increases as well, driving the system into the Wigner regime. In this limit electrons are localized in space and arrange themselves in geometrically ordered configurations to minimize electrostatic energy [1, 6, 3, 4]. This order foreruns the 2D Wigner solid, which is obtained letting $\lambda \to \infty$ and keeping the density constant.

The critical density and the nature of the crossover between QD solid and liquid phases have been much de-

bated in the recent literature [5, 7, 8, 9, 10, 11, 3, 12]. Up to now, only Quantum Monte Carlo (QMC) simulations seemed to provide accurate enough ground state energies for large λ and small N [5, 9, 10, 11, 12]. On the other hand, the configuration interaction (CI) approach gives access also to the low-energy spectrum, the few-body wave functions, and their quantum numbers. So far, the application of CI has been limited by the large number of Slater determinants required to represent the Hilbert space in the regime of the Wigner crystallization [8].

We have performed extensive Full CI (FCI) calculations to monitor the liquid-solid transition in a broad density range, using a recently developed high-performance parallel code.[1] The considered regime was too computationally demanding for previous CI calculations [8]. Our predictions are validated by the excellent agreement between our CI results for ground state energies [3] and those obtained via QMC in Ref. [5]. Moreover, we are able to monitor the low-energy spectrum as the density is varied. Here we analyze the ground-state wave function in a few significant cases.

In order to break the circular symmetry of the dot and then observe electron localization, we compute the spin-resolved pair correlation function $P_{s,s_0}(r, \varphi; r_0, \varphi_0)$, which is the conditional probability[2] of finding an electron with spin $s = \uparrow, \downarrow$ at $r \equiv (r, \varphi)$ given another one is fixed at r_0 with spin s_0. Figure 1 displays the "angular" correlation function $P_{s,s_0}(r, \varphi; r_0, \varphi_0)$ vs. φ at certain spin orientations for the three-electron ground state at $\lambda = 4$. The fixed position r_0 was chosen at the maximum of the electron density, displaced out of the dot

---

[1] Code website: www.s3.infm.it/donrodrigo.
[2] See Ref. [2] for rigorous definitions and Ref. [3] for full details on the FCI calculation. The normalization is given by the condition $\int dr\, dr_0\, P_{s,s_0}(r, \varphi; r_0, \varphi_0) = 1$.

CP893, *Physics of Semiconductors, 28th International Conference*
edited by W. Jantsch and F. Schäffler

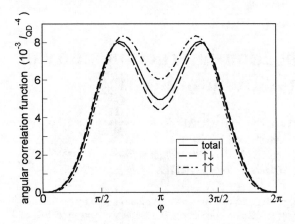

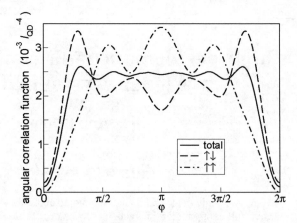

FIGURE 1. Angular spin-resolved pair correlation function $P_{s,s_0}(r,\varphi;r_0,\varphi_0)$ vs. azimuthal angle φ for the doublet ground state for $N = 3$ and $\lambda = 4$. The length unit is ℓ_{QD}. The spin-independent correlation function $P(r,\varphi;r_0,\varphi_0)$ (continuous line) is summed over all spin projections s and s_0 and is normalized according to Eq. (4) of Ref. [2]. The FCI diagonalization was performed starting from the 36 (spin-degenerate) lowest-energy Fock-Darwin orbitals.

FIGURE 2. Angular spin-resolved pair correlation function $P_{s,s_0}(r,\varphi;r_0,\varphi_0)$ vs. azimuthal angle φ for the triplet ground state for $N = 8$ and $\lambda = 4$. For conventions cf. Fig. 1. In the FCI calculation 21 Fock-Darwin orbitals were used.

This paper is supported by Supercomputing Project INFM-CINECA 2006 and MIUR-FIRB RBIN04EY74.

center [$P_{s,s_0}(r,\varphi;r_0,\varphi_0)$ depends on $\varphi - \varphi_0$ in virtue of circular symmetry]. Let us first focus on the total correlation function P (solid line of Fig. 1), i.e. the spin-independent conditional probability: it clearly shows the exchange and correlation hole around $\varphi = 0$ ($\varphi = \pi$), together with two well-resolved peaks approximately at angles $\varphi = 2\pi/3, 4\pi/3$. Such a "Wigner molecule" [1] is consistent with the classical arrangement made of three particles sitting at the vertices of an equilateral triangle [13]. The crystallization is confirmed by the substantial overlap of the total correlation function P with spin-resolved $P_{\uparrow\downarrow}$ (dashed line) and $P_{\uparrow\uparrow}$ (dot-dashed line). Indeed, in the Wigner limit the system becomes classical and the spin degree of freedom irrelevant [6]. Note that $P_{\uparrow\uparrow}$ is more "squeezed" than $P_{\uparrow\downarrow}$ since exchange interaction is more effective than Coulomb correlation in keeping electrons far apart.

By repeating an analogous calculation for the eight-electron ground state, we see in Fig. 2 that now the peak-to-valley ratio of P is reduced with respect to Fig. 1. The reason is that, keeping λ fixed, the density increases with N because the confinement potential is soft [1]. Still we are able to resolve 6 peaks of P (solid line). This time the overall picture is consistent with a classical molecule made of seven electrons at the vertices of a regular heptagon plus one electron at the dot center [13].

We performed similar analyses for several values of $N \leq 8$ and $\lambda \leq 10$, finding a common crystallization threshold around $\lambda \approx 4$. Such a prediction agrees with results of Ref. [5].

REFERENCES

1. S. M. Reimann, and M. Manninen, *Rev. Mod. Phys.* **74**, 1283 (2002).
2. M. Rontani, F. Troiani, U. Hohenester, and E. Molinari, *Solid State Commun.* **119**, 309 (2001), special Issue on Spin Effects in Mesoscopic Systems.
3. M. Rontani, C. Cavazzoni, D. Bellucci, and G. Goldoni, *J. Chem. Phys.* **124**, 124102 (2006).
4. M. Rontani, Theory of electron spectroscopies in strongly correlated semiconductor quantum dots (2006), available as cond-mat/0602263.
5. R. Egger, W. Häusler, C. H. Mak, and H. Grabert, *Phys. Rev. Lett.* **82**, 3320 (1999).
6. M. Rontani, C. Cavazzoni, and G. Goldoni, *Computer Physics Commun.* **169**, 430 (2005).
7. R. Egger, W. Häusler, C. H. Mak, and H. Grabert, *Phys. Rev. Lett.* **83**, E462 (1999).
8. S. M. Reimann, M. Koskinen, and M. Manninen, *Phys. Rev. B* **62**, 8108 (2000).
9. A. V. Filinov, M. Bonitz, and Y. E. Lozovik, *Phys. Rev. Lett.* **86**, 3581 (2001).
10. A. Harju, S. Siljamäki, and R. M. Nieminen, *Phys. Rev. B* **65**, 075309 (2002).
11. B. Reusch, and R. Egger, *Europhys. Lett.* **64**, 84 (2003).
12. A. Ghosal, A. D. Güçlü, C. J. Umrigar, D. Ullmo, and H. U. Baranger, *Nature Physics* **2**, 336 (2006).
13. V. M. Bedanov, and F. M. Peeters, *Phys. Rev. B* **49**, 2667 (1994).

Effects of Electron-Phonon Interaction on Quantum Transport Through Single Molecule Transistor

Zuo-Zi Chen*, Hai-Zhou Lu*, Rong Lü* and Bang-fen Zhu[†,*]

*Center for Advanced Study, Tsinghua University, Beijing 100084, P. R. China
†Department of Physics, Tsinghua University, Beijing 100084, P. R. China

Abstract. The effects of the electron-phonon interaction on the nonequilibrium transport through a single molecule transistor or certain quantum dots are systematically studied, with focus on the quantum resonant tunneling, Kondo effect, and Fano effect. We find that the broken particle-hole symmetry in such system can be identified from the phonon sidebands in the spectral function at very low temperature. In the Kondo regime, two types of Kondo phonon-satellites with different asymmetric shapes are distinguished and related to the electron or hole spin- singlet, respectively. Since phonon acts as a "which way" detector, the phonon-assisted tunneling channel has no Fano interference with the reference electronic channel.

Keywords: Electron-Phonon Interaction; Single Molecule Transistor; Nonequilibrium transport; Kondo effect; Fano effect
PACS: 72.15.Qm, 85.65.+h, 73.63.Kv, 71.38.-k

there is no phonon satellites (4)resonances pining at,
...

Recently, the Kondo effect and Fano effect have been successfully realized in the quantum transport through the single-molecule-based electron transistor (SMT) or semiconductor quantum dots (QDs).[1, 2, 3] The local electron-phonon interaction (EPI) has also manifested itself in some of these experiments. The impacts of EPI on such processes have also been studied theoretically; however, with different emphasis, several approaches may lead to results somewhat different. In this note, we briefly report our recent investigations on the effects of the EPI on the quantum resonant tunneling, Kondo effect, and Fano effect in the nonequilibrium transport through the SMT or QDs by combining the improved canonical transformation for the EPI and the extended equation of motion approach for the nonequilibrium Green functions. [4, 5, 6]

The system is described by the Anderson-Holstein model. To deal with the EPI nonperturbatively, a canonical transformation is adopted,[4] which is appropriate when the tunneling coupling is much weaker than the EPI. Then the electron part can be decoupled from the phonon environment, and the greater and lesser Green functions are separated into two parts rigourously, i.e., $G_\sigma^{>(<)}(t) = \bar{G}_\sigma(t)e^{-\Phi(\pm t)}$, where $\bar{G}^{>(<)}$ are governed by the renormalized electron Hamiltonian $\bar{H}_{el}$, and $\Phi(t)$ comes from the phonon contribution,

$$\Phi(t) = g[N_{ph}(1 - e^{i\omega_0 t}) + (N_{ph} + 1)(1 - e^{-i\omega_0 t})]. \quad (1)$$

Using the identity $A_\sigma = i(G_\sigma^> - G_\sigma^<)$, the spectral function is determined and thus the transport properties. Compared with the usual approximation $G_\sigma^r(t) \approx \bar{G}_\sigma^r(t)e^{-\Phi(t)}$,[7] in which $\Phi(t) \approx \Phi(-t)$ is

granted, the present formalism is more accurate particularly at very low temperature where N_{ph} is almost zero. In addition, in evaluating $\bar{G}_\sigma^{>(<)}$ by the equation of motion technique, we has extended the usual truncation approximation to deal with the Kondo system below the Kondo temperature, out of equilibrium and with finite Zeeman splitting.

In the resonant tunneling regime, we find the profile of local spectral function is sensitive to the gate and bias voltages at very low temperature. [4] For example, when the local level lies below (above) the Fermi levels in the left and right leads $\mu_{L(R)}$, the phonon sidebands can only appear below (above) this level. If the local level lies between two Fermi surfaces, the phonon sidebands may develop on both sides, but the profiles may exhibit sharp discontinuity. The sensitive of the phonon sidebands on the gate and bias voltage can be understood by considering two limit cases at zero temperature. For finite EPI on an isolate dot (no hopping exists between dot and leads), the particle number within the dot is fixed to be 1 or 0. Thus the phonon sideband appears only below (above) the dot level because only phonon emission is allowed. As for the case of finite hopping without the EPI, the spectral function is insensitive to the $\mu_{L(R)}$, however the particle number in the dot can be tuned from 0 to 1 continuously by adjusting the lead Fermi levels. Thus for the general cases with both finite EPI and hopping, by adjusting the gate and bias voltages one can change the particle-hole distribution within the dot and thereby manipulate the phonon sidebands. In other word, the broken particle-hole symmetry in such system can be identified from the phonon sidebands. As a consequence, there is no phonon satellite appeared in the differential conductance at zero temperature when the bias voltage is smaller

CP893, *Physics of Semiconductors, 28th International Conference*
edited by W. Jantsch and F. Schäffler
© 2007 American Institute of Physics 978-0-7354-0397-0/07/$23.00

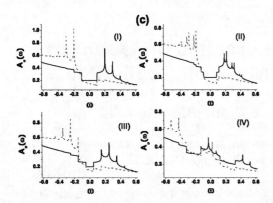

FIGURE 1. (color online) The spin-resolved spectral function (black solid line for spin up, red dash line for spin down component) for several bias voltages, in which finite Zeeman splitting, on site-U and EPI are considered.

than one phonon energy.

In the Kondo regime for the QDs or SMT system, the spectral function exhibits the sharp Kondo resonance peaks pinned at $\mu_{L(R)}$. The EPI will split these Kondo resonances into a set of Kondo-phonon-satellites pining at $\mu_{L(R)} \pm n\hbar\omega_0$. The Kondo satellites on different sides show up different asymmetric shapes and are found to be associated with different types of spin singlets.[5] For example, the Kondo satellite at $\mu_{L(R)} + n\hbar\omega_0$ comes form the phonon-assisted spin exchange processes between the local electron and excited lead electrons, while the satellite at $\mu_{L(R)} - n\hbar\omega_0$ is related to the spin exchange processes between the local hole and excited lead holes. Moreover, when the spin-degeneracy of the SMT level is lifted by applying a local magnetic field, the Kondo satellites in the spin resolved spectral function are found to disappear on one side of the main peak, and fade out on the opposite side for other spin component. This indicates that in the presence of finite Zeeman splitting, the Kondo resonance in the spectral function with different spin index comes from different spin exchange processes. When the bias voltage turns on, each Kondo peak is separated into two sub-peaks related to two Fermi levels, respectively. These two sub-sets of Kondo satellites separate from each other further when the bias increases, resulting in the peculiar pattern as shown in Fig.1. The Kondo satellites superpose over the phonon sidebands of the local level as discussed above, jointly responsible for the sharp and peculiar peaks in the spectral function and differential conductance under extremely low temperature. A question naturally raised is whether the EPI affects the coherence properties through the QDs or SMT system. To answer this, a two-channel resonant tunneling model is studied, in which a narrow channel is coupled to a local vibration, while another broad channel without EPI is taken as the reference one. It is found while the Fano effect between the two channels is renormalized by the EPI, there is no quantum interference between the phonon-assisted channel and the reference channel. This results from the fundamental principle of the complementarity of quantum mechanics in the quantum transport process, because the phonon acts as a detector from which the "which way" information can be determined. This "coherence loss" feature is generally true for the boson-fermion mixture, which at low temperatures may be used as an intrinsic tool to verify the which-way effect of quantum mechanics. A closely related transport experiment in the single wall Carbonnanotube has been proposed.[6]

In summary, the impacts of EPI on the transport through the SMT or QDs system have been systematically studied with special attention paid on the quantum, many-body, and coherent properties. We find that at low temperature, since the asymmetry between phonon-absorption and phonon-emission processes, the broken particle-hole symmetry in the SMT or QDs may manifest itself in the phonon sidebands of the spectral function, and the Kondo-phonon-satellites can be divided into two types that are associated with the electron or hole spin-singlets. Besides, the coupling between the electron and phonons will change the coherent properties of electrons by the "which way" effect.

ACKNOWLEDGMENTS

We would like to acknowledge Hui Zhai and Chaoxing Liu for helpful discussions. This work is supported by the Natural Science Foundation of China (Grant No. 10374056, 10574076), and the Program of Basic Research Development of China (Grant No. 2001CB610508).

REFERENCES

1. H. Park, J. Park, A. K. L. Lim, et al., Nature (London), 2000, **407**:57
2. L. H. Yu, Z. K. Keane, J. W. Ciszek, et al., Phys. Rev. Lett., 2004, **93**:266802
3. B. J. LeRoy, S. G. Lemay, J. Kong, and C. Dekker, Nature (London), 2004, **432**:371-37
4. Z. Z. Chen, R. Lü, and B. F. Zhu, Phys. Rev. B, 2005, **71**: 165324, and references therein
5. Z. Z. Chen, H. Z. Lu, R. Lü, and B. F. Zhu, J. Phys.: Condens. Matter 18 (2006) 5435-5446, and references therein
6. Haizhou Lu, Zuo-Zi Chen, Rong Lü, and Bang-fen Zhu, to be submitted.
7. J. X. Zhu and A. V. Balatsky, Phys. Rev. B, 2003, **67**: 165326

Constant Capacitance-DLTS on InAs-Quantum Dots embedded in Schottkydiodes

A. Schramm*, J. Schaefer*, S. Schulz* and W. Hansen*

*Institute of Applied Physics, University of Hamburg, Jungiusstrasse 11, 20355 Hamburg, Germany

Abstract. Electron escape from self-assembled InAs quantum dots (QDs) in GaAs is studied. We apply constant capacitance deep level transient spectroscopy (CC-DLTS) to investigate the electric field dependence of the activation energies. As a major advantage for interpretation of the results in contrast to conventional DLTS the electric field of the quantum dot layer remains constant in CC-DLTS experiments. The results of conventional DLTS results are well reproduced.

Deep Level Transient Spectroscopy (DLTS) has been employed to probe the electronic states in QDs[1, 2, 3, 4, 5]. In previous work it has been found that the activation energies may depart from the level separation between ground state in the QDs and the continuum of the GaAs matrix as a result of tunnelling from intermediate states[2] or thermionic tunneling[4]. Accordingly, the electric field dependence is found to be much stronger than would be expected from the Poole-Frenkel effect[4]. In view of the strong electric field dependence it is highly desirable to determine the emission rates with a technique in which the electric field remains constant while the charge emission from the dots is probed. In contrast to conventional DLTS, in CC-DLTS the field of the dot-layer charges is kept constant.

In our experiments we use slightly n-doped ($N_D = 4 \times 10^{15}$ cm^{-3}) Schottky diodes grown with solid-source MBE on (001) GaAs that contain a layer of self-assembled InAs quantum dots $z_Q = 750$ nm below the surface. AFM maps of a reference dot layer grown on the surface with the same growth parameters as for embedded dots yield a dot density of $N_{QD} = 4 \times 10^9$ cm^{-2}. For Schottky contacts, 50 nm chromium was evaporated with 1 mm diameter.

In a simple one-dimensional model, in which the charges in the dots are considered a two-dimensional charge sheet with homogeneous density n_Q, the extension of the depletion zone z_D is

$$z_D = \sqrt{\frac{2}{eN_D}(\varepsilon\varepsilon_0(V_{bi} - V_r) + en_Qz_Q)}. \quad (1)$$

Here V_{bi} is the built-in potential, V_r the bias at the diode, ε the dielectric constant of the GaAs matrix, and n_Q/N_{QD} is the occupation of the dots. In conventional DLTS experiments the charge emission from the dot layer is probed via measurement of the the diode capacitance,

which is inversely proportional to z_D. Accordingly, the electric field $F_Q = eN_D(z_D - z_Q)/(\varepsilon\varepsilon_0)$ changes during the measurement. In CC-DLTS a control loop generates a voltage transient $V_r(t)$ that keeps the depletion width and thus F_Q constant while the electrons escape from the dots. As can be seen from above equation at constant z_D the voltage transient directly reflects the time evolution of the electron occupation in the dots. It is important to note, that in case of multiply charged dots above F_Q fails to well describe the field at small distance from the dots. If the distance becomes smaller than the inter-dot distance the Coulomb field of nearest dot becomes increasingly important.

In contrast to common CC-DLTS setups, in which fast real-time feedback circuits are applied, we use a computer based iterative feedback system similar to the one described in [6]. The voltage transients are generated in an iterative procedure with a 16 bit D/A converter.

In Fig. 1 we compare experimental CC-DLTS (a) and DLTS measurements (b) obtained in double-boxcar technique[7] from the voltage and the capacitance transients, respectively. The reverse voltages V_r in (b) are chosen such that the equilibrium capacitance with empty dots correspond to the capacitances C_∞ used in (a). The delay times t_1 and t_2 of the double boxcar filter define an escape time $\tau_{ref} = (t_2 - t_1)/ln(t_2/t_1)$ at the maxima in the spectra. In the CC-DLTS measurements we clearly observe two maxima between $T = 50$ K and 90 K which are associated to the emission of electrons from the s-state occupied with one or two electrons, respectively. Both maxima shift to lower temperatures with decreasing V_r. Note, that in (a) the amplitudes of the s-peaks hardly change. This is due to the fact that in CC-DLTS experiments the signal strength ΔV_r according to equation (1) only depends on the change of the charge density Δn_Q.

The broad maximum at temperatures below $T < 50$ K

CP893, *Physics of Semiconductors, 28th International Conference*
edited by W. Jantsch and F. Schäffler
© 2007 American Institute of Physics 978-0-7354-0397-0/07/$23.00

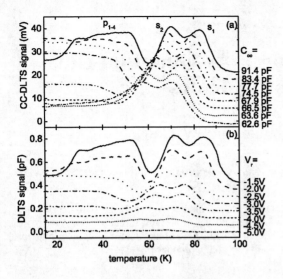

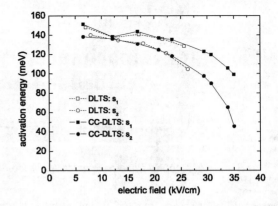

FIGURE 2. Activation energies derived with an Arrhenius analysis from CC-DLTS and DLTS measurements vs the electric field F_Q calculated as described in the text.

FIGURE 1. CC-DLTS (a) and DLTS (b) spectra of a Schottky diode with embedded QDs. The signals in (a) and (b) are determined from the difference $\Delta V = V_r(t_2) - V_r(t_1)$ and $\Delta C = C(t_2) - C(t_1)$, respectively. To improve clarity, the spectra are offset in (a) by 3 mV and in (b) by 0.05 pF, respectively. The reference time is $\tau_{ref} = 4$ ms

is associated to the emission of electrons from the p-shell [5]. At decreasing C_∞ (lower V_r) the p-maxima vanish since in higher electric fields competing tunnelling processes set in. Accordingly, the signal gradually becomes temperature independent[8].

The DLTS spectrum in Fig. 1(b) recorded at $V_r = -1.5$ V is very similar to the corresponding CC-DLTS spectrum. Note however, that with decreasing V_r the peak heights of the spectra strongly decrease in (b). The decreasing capacitances at decreasing V_r lead to a reduced signal in DLTS experiments. Apart from this, the s-maxima behave quite similar in (a) and (b) with increasing electric field (reduced V_r or C_∞, respectively).

The shift of the DLTS maxima to lower temperatures with decreasing reverse voltages is explained with a decrease of the activation energies with increasing electric field F_Q. In Fig. 2 the field dependence of the activation energies derived from the reference-time dependence of the s_1- and s_2-peaks is presented for both techniques. For the CC-DLTS data the electric field is easily calculated. In contrast, in order to determine the field from V_r for the DLTS data it is necessary to assume a dot occupation of 1 and 2 for the s_1 and s_2 peak, respectively. The data demonstrate that the activation energies obtained from both techniques agree very well. Note, however, that the field range accessible with CC-DLTS is significantly larger.

In conclusion, we compare CC-DLTS and DLTS data of the thermal electron emission from self-assembled InAs quantum dots in order to study the electric field dependence of emission rates. By means of the gate voltage the electric field F_Q can be well controlled. The similarity of the spectra confirm that the occupation dependence of this field hardly affects the determination of the emission rates. For the sample presented here F_Q increases by 0.5 kV/cm if the dot occupation changes by one electron per dot. This is a small value on the scale on which changes of the activation energy are resolved. We conclude that the difference of the significantly higher emission rates observed, e. g., for doubly occupied dots with respect to singly occupied ones arises from the Coulomb potential at close proximity to the dots.

REFERENCES

1. Anand, S., Carlsson, N., Pistol, M.-E., Samuelson, L., and Seifert, W., *Appl. Phys. Lett.*, **67**, 3016 (1995).
2. Kapteyn, C. M. A., Heinrichsdorff, F., Stier, O., Heitz, R., Grundmann, M., Zakharov, N. D., Werner, P., and Bimberg, D., *Phys. Rev. B*, **60**, 14265 (1999).
3. Engström, O., Malmkvist, M., Fu, Y., Olafson, H. O., and Sveinbjörnsson, E. O., *Appl. Phys. Lett.*, **83**, 3578 (2003).
4. Schulz, S., Schnüll, S., Heyn, C., and Hansen, W., *Phys. Rev. B*, **69**, 195317 (2004).
5. Schramm, A., Schulz, S., Schaefer, J., Zander, T., Heyn, C., and Hansen, W., *Appl. Phys. Lett.*, **88**, 213107 (2006).
6. Okamoto, Y., Yonekura, H., Morimoto, J., and Miyakawa, T., *Rev. Sci. Instrum.*, **67**, 809 (1995).
7. Lang, D. V., *J. Appl. Phys.*, **45**, 3023 (1974).
8. Schulz, S., Schramm, A., Heyn, C., and Hansen, W., *Phys. Rev. B*, **in Press** (2006).

Current instabilities in resonant tunneling quantum dot structures

Kathy Lüdge and Eckehard Schöll

Technische Universität Berlin, Institut für Theoretische Physik, Hardenbergstr. 36, 10623 Berlin, Germany

Abstract. We investigate nonlinear charge transport through quantum dots embedded in a double barrier resonant tunneling structure. Depending upon the parameters of the circuit in which the device is operated, our model predicts various current instabilities: switching between a low current and a high current state, or self-generated current and voltage oscillations exhibiting both a Hopf bifurcation and a global homoclinic bifurcation.

Keywords: Quantum dots, resonant tunneling, current instabilities
PACS: 73.21.La,85.35.Gv,72.20.Ht

Due to improvements in semiconductor growth technologies, the fabrication and industrial application of quantum dot (QD) structures have become more and more important. Related to this, also the current transport through devices consisting of layers with QDs has attracted considerable interest. As the size of a single QD is of the order of 10 nm, the Coulomb charging energy U is much larger than the typical energy scale of the system, and single electron or hole tunneling effects become visible in the current (I)-voltage (V) characteristics. In particular single peaks at low bias in the I(V) characteristic have been found. These peaks have been shown to result from Coulomb blocking effects leading to strong negative differential conductance [1].

In this work we investigate the current transport through QDs embedded in a double barrier structure that is operated in an external circuit with a dc bias voltage V_0 and a series resistance R and a parallel capacitance C (right inset in Fig.1). We show that the performance of such nonlinear devices crucially depend on the chosen external circuit parameters, so that they can be used either as switches or as self-sustained current oscillators.

To analyze the dynamics of the QD system, a Master equation approach for sequential tunneling through two parallel, electrostatically coupled QDs (see left inset in Fig. 1) is used [1]:

$$\frac{d}{dt}\underline{P} = \underline{\underline{M}}(V)\underline{P} \tag{1}$$

$$C\frac{d}{dt}V = \frac{V_0 - V}{R} - \langle I(\underline{P}, V)\rangle \tag{2}$$

where the four-dimensional vector $\underline{P}$ is composed of the occupation probabilities P_v for the Fock states $v = (n_1, n_2)$ ($n_i \in \{0, 1\}$) of the QDs $i = 1, 2$ and the 4×4-matrix $\underline{\underline{M}}$ consists of the transition rates for tunneling into or out of the QD system which contain the occupation of the contacts and the tunneling rates $\Gamma^i_{e/c}$ and

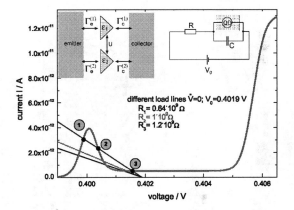

FIGURE 1. Current–voltage characteristic of the QD structure. Load lines are shown for three different values of R. The fixed points are denoted by circled numerals. The insets show the QD configuration (left) and the attached circuit (right).

depend upon the voltage drop V across the QD structure. The dynamic degree of freedom of V due to Kirchhoff's circuit equation (2) is also taken into account. Here $\langle I \rangle$ is the average current.

We perform a linear stability analysis of the fixed points of this five–dimensional system (1), (2). Interesting effects are found if the nullclines of the external circuit and of the QD system, i.e. the load line and the QD I(V) characteristic, intersect such that three operating points (fixed points, labeled 1,2,3 in Fig.1) exist.

For the case of a positive capacitance C we can show that oscillatory instabilities caused by a Hopf bifurcation cannot occur. Nevertheless there is a saddle-point (2) on the negative conductivity branch that separates the basins of attraction for the two stable nodes on the high (1) and low current (3) branch, respectively. Thus, the resonant

CP893, *Physics of Semiconductors, 28th International Conference*
edited by W. Jantsch and F. Schäffler

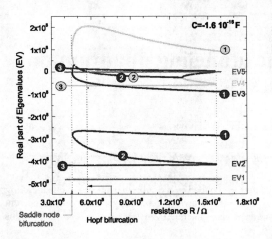

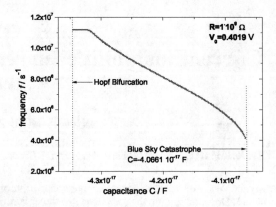

FIGURE 2. Eigenvalues (EV) of the 5–dimensional system at all three fixed points (marked with circled numerals) as a function of R for $C = -1.6 \times 10^{-16}$ F, $V_0 = 0.4019$ V.

FIGURE 4. Frequency of limit cycle oscillations between the Hopf and the global bifurcation ($R = 10^9 \Omega$, $V_0 = 0.4019$ V).

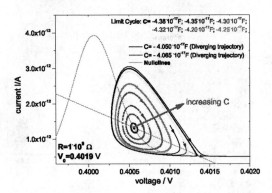

FIGURE 3. Oscillations in the (I,V) phase space for different values of C ($R = 10^9 \Omega$, $V_0 = 0.4019$ V).

tunneling QD structure could be used as a fast switching device, where switching is achieved by either varying the external voltage V_0 or the series resistance R.

For negative capacitance, which can easily be realized by an active circuit consisting of operation amplifiers [2, 3], a Hopf bifurcation leading to uniform limit cycle oscillations can be found. The eigenvalues λ of the system for $C = -1.6 \times 10^{-16}$ F are shown in Fig. 2. The operating points 1 and 3 are always unstable (Re$\lambda > 0$), while the fixed point 2 exhibits a Hopf bifurcation where the pair of complex conjugate eigenvalues EV3 and EV4 crosses from Re$\lambda < 0$ to Re$\lambda > 0$. With increasing $|C|$ the oscillation amplitude of the limit cycle increases while its shape transforms from an elliptic to a strongly nonlinear relaxation-type shape. Fig. 3 shows transients obtained from eqs.(1),(2) for different values of C. At a

certain value of C the limit cycle collides with the saddle-point 3 on the low current branch and disappears. This represents a global homoclinic bifurcation (or blue-sky catastrophe), where the oscillation abruptly ceases with a finite amplitude, while the frequency tends to zero. The frequency of the limit cycle oscillations is shown in Fig. 4. Beyond this global bifurcation the system is unstable and has no stable fixed point.

Comparing the performance of this resonant tunneling device with a conventional double barrier resonant tunneling diode (DBRT) using a quantum well [4], some similarities but also essential differences are found. The most important difference is the shape of the I(V) characteristic which is Z-shaped for the DBRT but N-shaped for the QD device. Thus for voltage-clamp the QD device does not exhibit bistability. Further, in the DBRT the oscillatory regime is terminated by an inverse Hopf bifurcation which ensures the existence of at least one stable fixed point, whereas in the QD device complex bifurcation scenarios including global bifurcations occur, and there are parameter sets for which no stable fixed points exist.

This work was supported by DFG within Sfb 555.

REFERENCES

1. G. Kießlich, A. Wacker, and E. Schöll, Physica B **314**, 459 (2002)
2. National Semiconductor Application Note 31, Feb. 1978, Op Amp Circuit Collection
3. A. D. Martin, M. L. F. Lerch, P. E. Simmonds, and L. Eaves, Appl. Phys. Lett. **64**, 1248 (1994)
4. E. Schöll, A. Amann, M. Rudolf, and J. Unkelbach, Physica B **314**, 113 (2002)

Recombination, Transport and Loss Mechanisms in p-doped InAs/GaAs Quantum Dots

I. P. Marko[1], N. F. Massé[1], S. J. Sweeney[1], and A. R. Adams[1], N. Hatori[2], M. Sugawara[2]

[1]Advanced Technology Institute, School of Electronic and Physical Sciences, University of Surrey, Guildford, Surrey, GU2 7XH, UK
[2]Optical Semiconductor Devices Lab. Fujitsu Laboratories LTD. 10-1 Morinosato-Wakamiya, Atsugi, 243-0197 Japan

Abstract. The results on the temperature dependence of the radiative and non-radiative recombination processes in p-doped and undoped quantum dot (QD) lasers suggest that the observed characteristics of p-doped QDs are caused by an increase in the effective conduction band off-set due to Columbic attraction of the extra holes and so an increased localization of electrons in the dots. This leads to an increase in the temperature at which the carriers are able to establish thermal equilibrium from T=200K in the undoped devices to ≥320K in the p-doped samples. Interestingly this can be used to advantage since, as the temperature increases, the improved efficiency associated with better transport between the dots can be exactly offset by the increasing rate of Auger recombination, thus leading to a temperature stable operation around room temperature.

Keywords: quantum dot laser, p-doping, recombination mechanisms, non-radiative recombination, carrier transport.
PACS: 72.20.Jv, 78.60.–b, 79.20.Fv, 85.35.Be

INTRODUCTION

The electronic and optical processes occurring in semiconductor quantum dots are extremely complex. Firstly, the carriers are isolated in the individual dots and therefore, depending on the temperature, they are unable to properly achieve a thermal equilibrium distribution. Secondly, QD size distribution leads to a distribution in optical transition energies that also inhibits interactions between the dots via photon emission and absorption. These properties are very important technologically because semiconductor quantum dot systems show great promise as single photon emitters or as lasers. It has been demonstrated recently that p-type modulation doping of InAs/GaAs quantum dots significantly improves the temperature performance of QD semiconductor lasers that might be used in optical fibre communications [1-2]. However the process is complex and is also accompanied by an increased threshold current density compared to undoped devices [3]. The results we present here are aimed to understand the specific influence of p-doping on temperature performance of 1.3 μm QD lasers.

RESULTS AND DISCUSSION

The detailed analysis of the temperature dependence of the threshold current, I_{th}, and its radiative component, I_{rad}, determined as a value of integrated unamplified spontaneous emission (SE), L, (measured from a window milled in a substrate contact of p-doped and undoped devices) showed that their complex behaviour (see fig. 1) can be explained simply assuming that the radiative recombination and non-radiative Auger recombination rates are strongly modified by thermal redistribution of carriers between the dots [4]. The large differences between the devices at T<320 K arise due to the trapped holes in the p-doped devices. This is confirmed by measurements of temperature dependence of the full width at half maximum (FWHM) of SE line corresponding to the ground state (GS) optical transitions, which is given in fig. 2. The results demonstrate a broader carrier distribution at low T and lack of carrier thermalisation with increasing T in the p-doped device until about T=320-350 K, where the difference between both devices almost disappears.

CP893, *Physics of Semiconductors, 28th International Conference*
edited by W. Jantsch and F. Schäffler
© 2007 American Institute of Physics 978-0-7354-0397-0/07/$23.00

The measurements of the spontaneous and stimulated emission rates as a function of temperature and high hydrostatic pressure also show that Auger recombination is an extremely important process near room temperature (RT) and causes the same temperature dependence of I_{th} in both laser types above RT [3, 4]. This can be used to advantage since, as the T increases, the improved efficiency associated with better transport between the dots can be exactly offset by the increasing rate of Auger recombination, thus leading to a temperature stable operation around room temperature as shown in fig. 1.

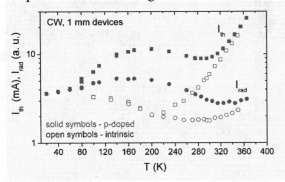

FIGURE 1. Temperature dependence of I_{th} and I_{rad} for the p-doped and undoped QD devices.

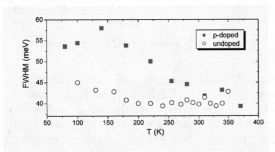

FIGURE 2. FWHM of the GS spontaneous emission line for the p-doped and undoped QD lasers as a function of temperature.

The large differences between the devices below RT arise due to the trapped holes in the p-doped devices. These both greatly increase Auger recombination involving holes excitation at low temperatures and decrease electron thermal escape due to their Coulombic attraction which increases the barrier height for the electrons [4].

In order to explain fully the difference between the observed characteristics of the undoped and p-doped devices, we also studied the temperature dependence of gain [5] and external differential efficiency, η_d (see fig. 3). We observed smaller values of η_d in the p-doped devices and non-linear light-current (LI) characteristics at RT. The p-doped devices also showed small increase of η_d and improved linearity of LIs with increasing T up to 350-370K supporting the idea of the improved carrier thermalisation. In contrast, η_d in the undoped devices was more temperature sensitive and decreased with increasing T.

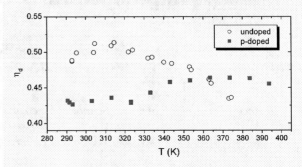

FIGURE 3. External differential efficiency of the p-doped and undoped QD lasers as a function of temperature.

All these observations are in very good agreement with the measured values of optical loss, α_i, both at RT and 350 K, which showed that α_i is about 10 cm^{-1} in the p-doped devices at both temperatures. However, in the undoped devices α_i increased from ~5cm^{-1} at 293K to ~10cm^{-1} at 350K. Therefore, we think that further transitions involving the excitation of holes from the confined states to continuum states derived from the spin-split-off bands (inter-valence band absorption) must be taken into consideration.

ACKNOWLEDGMENTS

The authors gratefully acknowledge the EPSRC (UK) and the Nuffield Foundation (NAL/00695/G) for supporting this work and Dr. A. Andreev for the helpful discussions.

REFERENCES

1. M.Sugawara, N.Hatori, M.Ishida, H. Ebe, Y.Arakawa, T.Akiyama, K.Otsubo, T.Yamamoto, Y.Nakata, J. Phys. D:Appl. Phys., 38, 2126 (2005).
2. I. I. Novikov , N.Y. Gordeev, L. Y. Karachinskii, M. V. Maksimov, Y. M. Shernyakov, A. R. Kovsh, I. L. Krestnikov, A. V. Kozhukhov, S. S. Mikhrin, N. N. Ledentsov, Semiconductors, 39, 477 (2005)
3. I. P. Marko, A. R. Adams, S. J. Sweeney, I. R. Sellers, D. J. Mowbray and M. S. Skolnick, H. Y. Liu and K. M. Groom, IEEE Select. Top. Quantum Electr., 11(5), 1041 (2005)
4. I. P. Marko, N. F. Massé, S. J. Sweeney, A. D. Andreev and A. R. Adams, N. Hatori, M. Sugawara, Appl. Phys. Lett., 87, 211114 (2005).
5. N. F. Massé, S. J. Sweeney, I. P. Marko, and A. R. Adams, N. Hatori, M. Sugawara, submitted to Appl. Phys. Lett. (2006).

Influence of Electron-Phonon Interaction on Fano Resonance in Aharonov-Bohm Interferometer

Akiko Ueda and Mikio Eto

Faculty of Science and Technology, Keio University, 3-14-1 Hiyoshi, Kohoku-ku, Yokohama 223-8522, Japan

Abstract. We theoretically study the effect of electron-phonon (e-ph) interaction on a Fano resonance in an Aharonov-Bohm interferometer with an embedded quantum dot. We examine the bias-voltage (V) dependence of the decoherence, using Keldysh Green function method and perturbation with respect to e-ph interaction. With optical phonons of energy ω_0, only the elastic process takes place when $eV < \omega_0$, in which electrons emit and absorb phonons virtually. The process suppresses the resonant amplitude. When $eV > \omega_0$, the inelastic process is possible which is accompanied by real emission of phonons. It results in the dephasing and broadens the resonant width. With acoustic phonons, the asymmetric shape of the Fano resonance grows like a symmetric one as the bias voltage increases, in qualitative accordance with experimental results.

Keywords: Fano resonance, Quantum dot, Aharonov-Bohm interferometer, Electron-phonon interaction, Decoherence, Keldysh Green function
PACS: 71.38.-k, 73.21.La, 73.23.-b

INTRODUCTION

In semiconductor quantum dots, preservation of quantum coherence is an important issue for the application to the quantum information processing. To examine the coherence, transport measurements have been reported using an Aharonov-Bohm (AB) ring with an embedded quantum dot as an interferometer [1, 2, 3]. When the high-order interference takes place inside the ring, an asymmetric shape of a Fano resonance is observed [3], which is caused by the interference between a discrete level (in a quantum dot) and the continuum of states (in an AB ring). When the bias voltage increases, the asymmetric resonant shape becomes a symmetric one, which implies that the finite bias significantly reduces the coherence. To elucidate the dephasing effect on the Fano resonance, we theoretically investigate the effect of electron-phonon (e-ph) interaction, which is one of major dephasing mechanisms under finite bias [4].

MODEL

Our model for the AB interferometer is shown in the inset of Fig. 1. There are two transport paths between external leads. One path connects the leads through a quantum dot by t_L and t_R and the other path connects the leads directly by $We^{i\varphi}$, where φ is the phase of the magnetic flux inside the ring. In this paper, we fix $t_L = t_R$ and $\varphi = 0$. In a quantum dot, an energy level (ε_0) can be tuned by a gate voltage. We define the linewidth of the energy level by $\Gamma = 2\pi\nu(t_L^2 + t_R^2)$, where ν is the density of states in the leads. The transmission probability through the ref-

erence arm is $T_r = 4\xi/(1 + \xi)^2$ with $\xi = \pi^2\nu^2W^2$. We set $T_r = 0.18$. A dotted line in Fig. 1 indicates the conductance in the absence of e-ph interaction. We observe a Fano resonance with dip and peak [5].

We consider e-ph interaction inside the quantum dot. The Hamiltonians of the interaction and phonons are written as $H_{e-ph} = \sum_q M_q(a_q + a_{-q}^\dagger)d^\dagger d$, $H_{ph} = \sum_q \omega_q a_q^\dagger a_q$, where $a_q^\dagger$ and a_q ($d^\dagger$ and d) are creation and annihilation operators of a phonon with momentum q (an electron in the dot). Owing to an oscillating factor $\langle d|e^{iq\cdot r}|d\rangle$ in M_q, phonons with wave number $|q| < 2\pi/L$ effectively couple to electrons, where L is the size of the quantum dot. The bias voltage between leads is given by $eV = \mu_L - \mu_R$. We fix $\mu_L = eV$ and $\mu_R = 0$.

To calculate the current under finite bias, we adopt Keldysh Green function formalism [6]. We treat e-ph interaction by the perturbation expansion and self-consistent Born approximation [4].

CALCULATED RESULTS

First, we consider the case of longitudinal optical phonon ($\omega_q = \omega_0$). We treat the e-ph interaction by the second-order perturbation. We define the coupling strength of the e-ph interaction as $\zeta = \sum_q M_q^2$. In Fig. 1, we plot the differential conductance, dI/dV, as a function of ε_0. The temperature is set to $T = 0$. We consider the cases of $eV = 0.5\Gamma$ ($eV < \omega_0 = 2\Gamma$; dashed line) and 3Γ ($eV > \omega_0$; solid line). When $eV < \omega_0$, a real process of phonon emission cannot take place at $T = 0$. Even in this case, the amplitude of Fano resonance diminishes. This is due to the elastic process in which electrons emit and ab-

CP893, *Physics of Semiconductors, 28th International Conference*
edited by W. Jantsch and F. Schäffler
© 2007 American Institute of Physics 978-0-7354-0397-0/07/$23.00

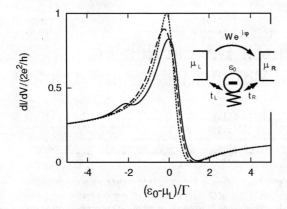

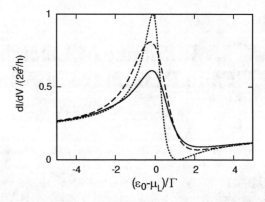

FIGURE 1. Differential conductance as a function of the dot level ε_0 with optical phonons. The phonon energy is $\omega_0 = 2\Gamma$, whereas the strength of e-ph coupling is $\zeta = 0.8\Gamma$. The bias voltage is $eV = 0.5\Gamma$ (dashed line) and 3Γ (solid line). The dotted line indicates the conductance in the absence of e-ph interaction. Inset: Model for an AB interferometer with an embedded quantum dot.

FIGURE 2. Differential conductance as a function of the dot level ε_0 with acoustic phonons. The coupling constant is $g = 0.05$. The dot size is fixed at $L = c_s/(2\Gamma)$. The bias voltage is $eV = 0.5\Gamma$ (dashed line) and 2Γ (solid line). The dotted line indicates the conductance in the absence of e-ph interaction.

sorb phonons virtually. This process does not cause dephasing, but disturbs the coherent transport through the quantum dot and hence suppresses the resonance. When $eV > \omega_0$, both elastic and inelastic processes are possible. The inelastic process in which electrons actually emit phonons results in dephasing and decreases the lifetime of the dot state [4]. In consequence, the width of Fano resonance is broadened although the broadening is not clearly seen in Fig. 1.

Next, we consider the acoustic phonons. For this case, we extend the self-consistent Born approximation to the Keldysh Green function. M_q is given by $M_q = g\pi^2 c_s^2/(V|q|)\langle d|e^{iq\cdot r}|d\rangle$, where g is the coupling constant, V is the system volume and c_s is the sound velocity. The dispersion relation of phonons is $\omega_q = c_s|q|$. We set $g = 0.05$ and the dot size $L = c_s/(2\Gamma)$. The differential conductance is plotted in Fig. 2, as a function of the energy level ε_0. The bias voltage is $eV = 0.5\Gamma$ (dashed line) and 2Γ (solid line). In contrast to the case of optical phonons, the inelastic process always exists, which is accompanied by the real emission of phonons. A subpeak structure is not observed since the acoustic phonon has a continuous spectrum. The resonant amplitude decreases with increasing the bias voltage as in the case of optical phonon. This should be mainly ascribable to the elastic process. The resonant width is more broadened with increasing bias voltage, which is due to the inelastic process. These effects are more prominent with larger bias since more phonons can participate in the e-ph interaction. Particularly, the resonant dip becomes almost invisible with high bias and as a result, the asymmetric shape of the Fano resonance grows like a symmetric one, which is in qualitative accordance with the experimental

results [3].

CONCLUSION

We have investigated the influence of e-ph interaction on Fano resonance under finite bias. Using Keldysh Green function method and perturbation with respect to e-ph interaction, we have obtained the bias-voltage (V) dependence of the decoherence. With optical phonons of energy ω_0, we distinguish elastic and inelastic processes. When $eV < \omega_0$, only the elastic process takes place in which electrons emit and absorb phonons virtually. The process suppresses the resonant amplitude, whereas it does not change the resonant width. When $eV > \omega_0$, the inelastic process is possible, which broadens the resonant width. With acoustic phonons, the suppression of resonant amplitude and broadening of the resonant width are more prominent with an increase in the bias. The asymmetric resonant shape becomes like a symmetric one, in qualitative accordance with the experimental results.

This work is supported in part by a Grant in Aid for the 21st century Center of Excellence for Optical and Electronic Device Technology for Access Network from the Ministry of Education, Culture, Sports, Science, and Technology in Japan.

REFERENCES

1. A. Yacoby *et al.*, *Phys. Rev. Lett.* **74**, 4047 (1995).
2. R. Schuster *et al.*, *Nature (London)* **385**, 417 (1997).
3. K. Kobayashi *et al.*, *Phys. Rev. Lett.* **85**, 256806 (2002).
4. A. Ueda *et al.*, *Phys. Rev. B* **73**, 235353 (2006).
5. A. Ueda *et al.*, *J. Phys. Soc. Jpn. Suppl. A* **72**, 157 (2003).
6. A.-P. Jauho *et al.*, *Phys. Rev. B* **50**, 5528 (1994).

Thermoelectric power in coherent transport as a tool for transmission-phase measurement

Takeshi Nakanishi[*,†] and Takeo Kato[†]

*National Institute of Advanced Industrial Science and Technology, 1 Umezono, Tsukuba 305-8568, Japan, and CREST, JST, 4-1-8 Hon-machi, Kawaguchi, Saitama 332-0012 Japan
†Institute for Solid State Physics, University of Tokyo, 5-1-5 Kashiwanoha, Kashiwa, Chiba 277-8581, Japan

Abstract. Thermoelectric power of a quantum dot is studied in a coherent region. Pronounced peaks are shown in the thermoelectric power, corresponding to a transmission zero in the conductance. Phase information of wavefunction in the quantum dot can be extracted from peak-and-dip structures of the thermoelectric power without the use of a magnetic field.

Keywords: thermoelectric power, quantum dot, conductance, Landauer formula, Mott formula, Fano effects
PACS: 73.23.Hk, 73.50.Lw, 72.15.Jf

A series of systematic experiments for a quantum dot (QD) embedded in an Aharonov-Bohm (AB) ring [1, 2] has shown that the phase of AB oscillations changes by π across a resonance peak as expected by coherent transmission of electrons through the QD. A surprising and unexpected finding is that the phase becomes the same between adjacent peaks by the presence of a phase lapse by π between those peaks. Recent observation of Fano-type asymmetric conductance peaks has also revealed that the adjacent peaks tend to have the same phase [3, 4]. In order to understand the phase lapse, the existence of 'zero transmission' coefficient has been pointed out theoretically [5].

In this paper, we show that measurement of a thermoelectric power (TEP) is suitable for detection of zero transmission in coherent transport through a QD. We also show that, by observation of zero transmission points, the phase information of the wavefunction in the QD can be obtained without the use of a magnetic field.

The conductance and TEP for quasi-one-dimensional systems is obtained from the Landauer formula as

$$G(\mu,T) = \frac{e}{\pi \hbar} \int d\varepsilon T(\varepsilon) \left[-\frac{\partial f}{\partial \varepsilon} \right], \quad (1)$$

$$S(\mu,T) = -\frac{k_B \beta}{e} \frac{\int d\varepsilon T(\varepsilon)(\varepsilon - \mu)[-\partial f/\partial \varepsilon]}{\int d\varepsilon T(\varepsilon)[-\partial f/\partial \varepsilon]}, \quad (2)$$

with transmission probability $T(\varepsilon)$, the Fermi distribution function f, and the Fermi energy μ in leads. The Sommerfeld expansion with taking up to the first order to T gives the Mott formula

$$S_M(\mu,T) = -\frac{\pi^2}{3} \frac{k_B^2 T}{e} \frac{1}{G(\mu,T)} \frac{\partial G(\mu,T)}{\partial \mu}. \quad (3)$$

From this expression, we can expect that transmission zeros induce a singular behavior in energy dependences of TEP due to suppression of conductance in the denominator.

We first consider transmission through a quantum dot by the Hamiltonian

$$H = \sum_{k,\alpha} \varepsilon_{k,\alpha} C_{k,\alpha}^\dagger C_{k,\alpha} + \sum_j \varepsilon_j d_j^\dagger d_j + \sum_{k,\alpha,j} [V_{\alpha,j} C_{k,\alpha}^\dagger d_j + H.c.], \quad (4)$$

where the operators $c_{k,\alpha}$ refer to electronic states in the left and right leads ($\alpha = L, R$) and the operators d_j describe QD levels. Following to the derivation by Silva et al. [6], one obtains the transmission coefficient and calculates TEP as well as conductance for a non-interacting electron model [7]. Transmission probabilities exhibit resonance peaks with the conventional Breit-Wigner line-shape with a width Γ. Transmission probability vanishes (transmission zero) with the phase lapse between adjacent transmission peaks j and $j + 1$ for the case that the relative coupling sign, $\sigma \equiv \text{sign}(V_{L,j} V_{R,j} V_{L,j+1} V_{R,j+1})$, equals $+1$, while no phase lapse occurs between them for $\sigma = -1$. Corresponding to the transmission zeros, we have shown a significant enhancement of TEP and then jump from positive to negative. The peak and the dip of the TEP around the transmission zero are $\pm (\pi/\sqrt{3})(k_B/e) \sim \pm 1.81(k_B/e)$ for temperatures lower than a level spacing Δ. The prominent structure shows clearly the transmission zero, while it is hard to see it in the tail of conductance. For high temperatures $k_B T \gg \Gamma$ we have observed a sawtooth shape of TEP with amplitude of $\sim (k_B/e)(\Delta/2k_B T)$ as predicted in a sequential tunneling regime [8].

Next we consider another example of the zero transmission. When the double-slit condition is valid, the transmission through an AB ring with a QD on one arm and a reference path on the other is given by $t = t^0 + t^d$, where t^0 is a transmission coefficient through a contin-

CP893, *Physics of Semiconductors, 28th International Conference*
edited by W. Jantsch and F. Schäffler
© 2007 American Institute of Physics 978-0-7354-0397-0/07/$23.00

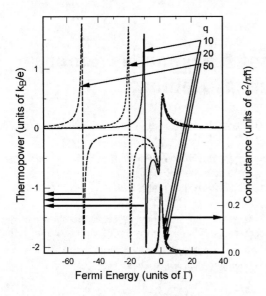

FIGURE 1. TEP and conductance for the Fano-type transmission with $q = 10$ (solid line), 20 (dotted line) and 50 (dashed line) in low temperature $k_B T = 0.2\Gamma$.

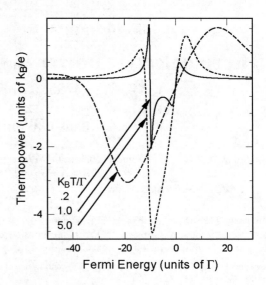

FIGURE 2. Temperature dependence of TEP for the Fano-type transmission with $q = 10$.

uum state of the reference path, essentially independent of energy [4]. The transmission $t^d = \alpha/(\varepsilon/\Gamma + i)$ through a QD shows the Breit-Wigner line-shape, where the peak energy is chosen as the origin of ε. Total transmission probability is given by

$$T(\varepsilon) = |t|^2 = |t^0|^2 \frac{|\varepsilon/\Gamma + q|^2}{(\varepsilon/\Gamma)^2 + 1}, \qquad (5)$$

with a Fano parameter $q = \alpha/t^0 + i$ that relates on the phase of QD states through the constant α. Note that, we can chose real q in the presence of time-reversal symmetry. Then conductance shows the asymmetric Fano line shape. For large $q = 10, 20$ and 50, however, calculated conductance with the normalization $|t^0|^2 = 1/(|q|^2 + 1)$ shown in Fig. 1 is almost symmetric and difficult to distinguish. Actually the Fano line shape converges in symmetric Breit-Wigner line shape in the limit of infinite q. The Fano parameter q can be observed from the transmission zero, where transmission probability vanishes at $\varepsilon = -q\Gamma$ due to the interference of Fano effects, although it is not clearly seen in the tail of conductance. On the other hand, calculated TEP's shown in Fig. 1 exhibit a significant enhancement at $\varepsilon = -q\Gamma$, and then jump from positive to negative. At $\varepsilon = 0$, corresponding to the peak of conductance, TEP shows an additional small structure. With the increase of temperature, thermal averaging smears these structures for $k_B T > \Gamma$, as shown in Fig. 2.

Transmission zeros are expected to be sensitive to dephasing in the QD. For TEP of QD's with short dephasing time, the picture of an inelastic co-tunneling will become valid by suppression of higher-oder hopping pro-

cesses, and then pronounced peaks and dips of TEP will disappear [9].

In summary, we have shown pronounced structures in the thermoelectric power that gives us phase information of wavefunction in the quantum dot. Because of its simpleness, observation of zero transmission by TEP's has advantages for detection of phase information in comparison with conductance measurement of the Aharonov-Bohm ring with a quantum dot in the magnetic field. Furthermore the structure in TEP's is clearly observed even when the transmission zero is well separated from resonance peaks. This can not be revealed from the conductance, which may be too small to accurately measure in the tail of these peaks.

REFERENCES

1. A. Yacoby, M. Heiblum, D. Mahalu, and H. Shtrikman, Phys. Rev. Lett. **74** (1995) 4047.
2. R. Schuster, E. Buks, M. Heiblum, D. Mahalu, V. Umansky, and H. Shtrikman, Nature **385** (1997) 417.
3. K. Kobayashi, H. Aikawa, S. Katsumoto, and Y. Iye, Phys. Rev. Lett. **88** (2002) 256806.
4. T. Nakanishi, K. Terakura and T. Ando, Phys. Rev. B **69** (2004) 115307.
5. H.-W. Lee, Phys. Rev. Lett. **82** (1999) 2358.
6. A. Silva, Y. Oreg, and Y. Gefen, Phys. Rev. B **66** (2002) 195316.
7. T. Nakanishi and T. Kato, J. Phys. Soc. Jpn., to be submitted.
8. C. W. J. Beenakker and A. A. M. Staring, Phys. Rev. B **46** (1992) 9667.
9. M. Turek and K. A. Matveev, Phys. Rev. B **66** (2002) 115332.

Quantum dots defined in InAs quantum wires by local gate electrodes

C. Fasth, A. Fuhrer and L. Samuelson

Solid State Physics/Nanometer Consortium, Lund University, P.O. Box 118 Lund, Sweden

Abstract. Single and double quantum dots are fabricated by inducing tunnelbarriers in homogenous InAs nanowires with local gates. By depositing the nanowires onto a grid of thin gold electrodes the potential landscape in the nanowire can be controlled in detail with the applied gate voltages. Control over the size of a single quantum dot(s) containing a single electron is shown and double quantum dot stability diagrams indicate good control over multiple dot systems along a nanowire.

Keywords: quantum dots, nanowires, double dots
PACS: 73.23.Hk, 73.21.La, 73.21.Hb, 73.63.-b

Single and double quantum dots are currently widely investigated in order to understand molecular interactions between two such artificial atoms and for their potential applications as quantum gates and qubits. We present low-temperature transport measurements on tunable few-electron quantum dots induced in homogeneous InAs quantum wires.

The nanowires are grown by chemical beam epitaxy, seeded by Au aerosol particles, and have a diameter of 50 nm. Previous electrical transport measurements show the wires to be n-type, most likely due to unintentional doping through carbon incorporation during nanowire growth [1]. The doping level is on the order of 10^{18} cm^{-3}. To achieve local control over the electron density in the nanowires, they are deposited onto thin parallel gold electrodes (30 nm wide and with a 30 nm gap between them), which are defined by electron beam lithography (EBL). The electrodes are covered with a 18 nm thick SiN dielectric film to provide electrical insulation. Before nanowire deposition the SiN is etched away from the electrode ends to enable contacting. In a further EBL step, the nanowires and the underlying electrodes are contacted using Ni/Au contacts, see Fig. 1(a).

Quantum dots are induced by electrical depletion of the wire using the local gate electrodes. This scheme has permitted the realization of fully gate-defined and controllable multiple quantum dots along the nanowire[2].

In the present device, five of the electrodes under the wire (g1, g2, g3, g4, g5) are contacted and used as barrier or plunger gates [see Fig. 1(a)]. All other gates ('outer') beneath the wire are also contacted and set to a common voltage of $+2.2$ V. To define a single quantum dot, we tune V_{g1} and V_{g3} to negative voltages in order to locally induce tunnel barriers in the wire. V_{g2} can then be used as a plunger gate voltage to control the number of electrons on the quantum dot formed between the barriers.

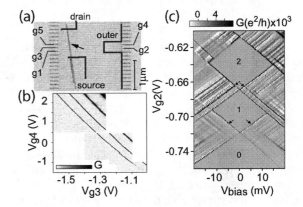

FIGURE 1. (a) Scanning electron microscopy image of the device. The positions of the EBL-defined Ni/Au gates and contacts are indicated with solid black lines and the contacted part of the nanowire is pointed out by an arrow. (b) Conductance map at low bias showing the transition from a geometrically small to a large quantum dot. The first electron conductance peak in visible throughout the process. (c) Differential conductance measured as a function of bias and plunger gate (gate 2) voltage, showing Coulomb diamonds. Here $V_{g1} = -2.56$ V, $V_{g3} = -1.17$ V, $V_{g4} = -0.5$ V and $V_{g3} = 2.5$ V. For $V_{bias} > 0$, electrons are injected from the source contact.

To show the versatility of the device design, we gradually transfer the barrier function from gate g3 to gate g4, by tuning the V_{g3} more positive while simultaneously tuning V_{g4} more negative, until the quantum dot extends over both g2 and g3. In this process, part of which is shown in Fig. 1(b), we continuously monitor the system to ensure that the last electron on the dot can still be reached. In Fig. 1(c), we show the differential conductance as a function of bias and V_{g2} measured at an intermediate point in the transition, where the barrier function is shared by g3 and g4.

Figure 1(c) shows the lowest two Coulomb diamonds

CP893, *Physics of Semiconductors, 28th International Conference*
edited by W. Jantsch and F. Schäffler
© 2007 American Institute of Physics 978-0-7354-0397-0/07/$23.00

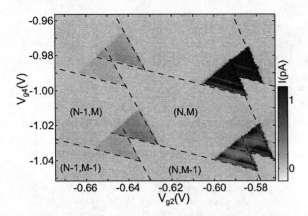

FIGURE 2. Current through the nanowire when a double dot is induced using negative gate voltages on V_{g1}, V_{g3} and V_{g5}. The applied bias $V_{bias} = 5mV$ allows for transport in triangular shaped regions around the triple points defining the corners of the hexagonal shaped regions of stable electron number (N,M).

for electron numbers N=1 and N=2. For $V_{g2} < -740$ mV, no further diamonds are observed and the diamond borderlines continue in a straight line. This indicates that the induced quantum dot is really empty. The differential conductance at finite bias shows a multitude of peaks, each corresponding to a new transport channel entering the bias window. Most of the weak and densely spaced lines at high bias do not originate in quantum dot states, but instead correspond to a modulation of the dot current due to fluctuations in the lead resistance. This can be understood when considering the low-dimensional character of the source and drain leads with a relatively short mean free path of $\ell_e \approx 100$ nm and a coherence length at $T = 100$ mK which we expect to exceed the length of the nanowire ($\ell_\phi \approx 200$ nm at $T = 8$ K[3]). Coherent backscattering then leads to the observed conductance fluctuations which typically depend strongly on the applied magnetic field. Magnetoconductance measurements (not shown) of the evolution of the excited states at finite bias as a function of magnetic field allow us to identify which states actually belong to the quantum dot and which states do not. The first excited states of the one- and two-electron dot are indicated with arrows in Fig. 1(c). In the case of two electrons, one electron already occupies the quantum dot while the other is transported through either the singlet or one of the triplet states.

Tuning the gate voltages V_{g1}, V_{g3} and V_{g5} to negative voltages and using V_{g2} and V_{g4} as plunger gates allows us to induce a double quantum dot in the nanowire. Figure 2 shows a typical measurement of the hexagonal stability diagram of a double quantum dot at $V_{bias} = 5$ mV. At this bias voltage the triple points expand into triangular regions where transport can take place e.g. going from (N-1,M-1) to (N-1, M) to (N, M-1) and back to (N-1,M-1) for the lowest triple point. In this case the electron

number was not known exactly but is expected to be N,M < 5.

In conclusion we have demonstrated good control over coupling and dot size in few-electron single and double quantum dots along an InAs nanowire. This is expected to allow us to investigate spin effects that arise due to the strong spin-orbit interaction in these InAs quantum dots and will let us asses the suitability of such systems for future spintronics applications.

ACKNOWLEDGMENTS

This work was supported by the Swiss National Science Foundation (SNF), the Swedish Foundation for Strategic Research (SSF) and the Swedish Research Council (VR).

REFERENCES

1. B. J. Ohlsson, M. T. Björk, A. I. Persson, C. Thelander, L. R. Wallenberg, M. H. Magnusson, K. Deppert, and L. Samuelson, *Physica E* **13**, 1126 (2002)
2. C. Fasth, A. Fuhrer, M. T. Björk, and L. Samuelson, *Nano Lett.* **5**, 1487 (2005)
3. A. E. Hansen, M. T. Björk, C. Fasth, C. Thelander, and L. Samuelson, *Phys. Rev. B* **71**, 205328 (2005)

Influences of Vibrations to Fano Resonances in a C_{60}

Shigeo Fujimoto and Yuhei Natsume

Graduate School of Science and Technology, Chiba University,
1-33, Yayoi-cho, Inage-ku, Chiba 263-8522, Japan

Abstract. In order to investigate Fano effects in mesoscopic system without a referential path, we discuss conduction spectra in transport processes through a fullerene C_{60} on the basis of theoretical calculation. Asymmetric Fano resonances are obtained in conductance through the C_{60} with gerade (breathing) vibrational mode. This result suggests that the C_{60} plays a role of interferometer by itself.

Keywords: quantum dot, fullerene, Fano effect, coherent transport
PACS: 73.23.Ad; 73.63.Kv

INTRODUCTION

Recent development of nanoscale technology has been enabled us to investigate various types of quantum-mechanical systems, such as quantum dots (QDs) and an Aharonov-Bohm (AB) ring etc. In particular, some problems which is concerned with quantum-mechanical interference effect has fascinated us. In the last several years, to investigate the effects in such systems, transport measurements by the use of an AB ring with a QD in the one branch have been carried out. In these experiments, an asymmetric shape of the Fano resonances [1] has been reported [2]. In addition, Fano-type interferences through a QD without external interference circuits have been observed in the latest experiments of mesoscopic systems; semi-open QD and T-shaped QD etc. are used [3, 4]. From the viewpoint of theoretical aspects, Fano effect in mesoscopic systems has been also studied. In paticular, the existence of two types of transport channels, weakly and strongly coupled states, is discussed in Ref. [5].

It should be noted that Fano effect is caused by the quantum-mechanical interference between continuum states and discrete levels. Since Fano effect is the interference phenomenon, multiple transmission channels should play an important role to the phenomenon. For the purpose of the making clear the effect of multiple channels, we adopt a C_{60} to the typical example for the theoretical investigations.

Because the C_{60} is highly symmetric molecule, it has many levels with multiple degeneracy in its electronic states. Furthermore, such levels are essentially coupled with intramolecular vibrations. When the degeneracy is resolved, the other transmission channels are expected to appear. As a result, various channels contributing to Fano resonances are provided for conduction processes.

Conductance-voltage characteristics through a C_{60} on silicon have been calculated by G.-C. Liang et al. [6].

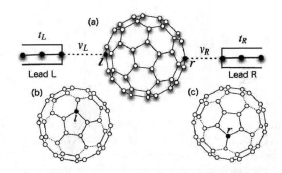

FIGURE 1. (a) Schematic illustration of a system which is discussed in this report. A fullerene C_{60} is sandwiched between two conductive leads. The left (right) lead is attached to fullerene's site l (r). These leads are diametrically connected with the C_{60}. (b) Left and (c) right side of the C_{60}. The dashed lines indicate selected bonds $< ij >'$.

They have investigated contact effects in the conduction process. However, interference effects caused by multi-paths, such as Fano resonaces, have not been discussed.

In this work, we discuss theoretically Fano effects without inteference circuits, such as an AB ring, in conductance through a C_{60}.

MODEL AND METHOD

We discuss theoretically transport processes through a C_{60} as schematically illustrated in Fig. 1.

The Hamiltonian of a C_{60}, $H_c = H_c^0 + H_c'$, is expressed as

$$H_c^0 = -t \sum_{\substack{<ij> \in \\ \text{all bonds}}} \left(c_i^\dagger c_j + h\,c \right) - eV_g \sum_i n_i, \qquad (1)$$

$$H_c' = -t\delta \sum_{<ij>'} \left(c_i^\dagger c_j + h\,c \right) \qquad \delta = t'\,t - 1, \qquad (2)$$

CP893, *Physics of Semiconductors, 28th International Conference*
edited by W. Jantsch and F. Schäffler
© 2007 American Institute of Physics 978-0-7354-0397-0/07/$23.00

where t and t' are transfer energies between sites for a C_{60}, δ is the deviation of the transfer energy between carbon sites, and V_g is gate potential, which shifts the energy of the C_{60}. We give a transfer energy t' to selected bonds $< ij >'$ shown in Fig. 1 (b) and (c) according to patterns of gerade-type (i.e. breathing) vibrational mode, which has the rotational symmetry for the transmission direction. The deviation of transfer energy between carbon sites is treated as the 2nd order perturbation, because we consider the coherent transport process with the essential influence of vibrations. In the present expression of this picture, this is the lowest order perturbation.

The calculation is based on the Green's function method by the use of the tight-binding approximation [7, 8]. The present conduction process is expressed by Green's functions. The Green's function of a C_{60} is described as

$$G^c_{lr}(\varepsilon\ eV_g) = \sum_n \frac{\langle l|n\rangle \langle n|r\rangle}{\varepsilon - \varepsilon_n + eV_g + i(\Gamma^l_n + \Gamma^r_n)\ 2}$$
$$\left[1 + \sum_{m \neq n} \frac{|\langle m|H'_c|n\rangle|^2}{(\varepsilon_n - \varepsilon_m)^2}\right] \quad (3)$$

where ε_n and $|n\rangle$ are the eigenvalue and eigenstate of Eq. (1). Peak width Γ^i_n ($i \in l\ r$) in the denominator of the Eq. (3) means energy broadening due to the coupling between leads and the C_{60}. By the use of these Green's functions, we can calculate the conductance through the system $G(\varepsilon\ eV_g) = (2e^2\ h) \cdot T(\varepsilon\ eV_g)$, where the transmittance $T(\varepsilon\ eV_g)$ is expressed as

$$T(\varepsilon\ eV_g) = 4v^2_L v^2_R \left|G^c_{lr}(\varepsilon\ eV_g)\right|^2 \mathrm{Img}_L(\varepsilon)\,\mathrm{Img}_R(\varepsilon) \quad (4)$$

Here v_L (v_R) is the coupling constant between left (right) lead and the fullerene C_{60}. In Eq. (4), g_L and g_R are the semi-infinite Green's functions at the edges of the left and right leads, respectively: $g_j(\varepsilon) = \left(\varepsilon - i\sqrt{4t^2_j - \varepsilon^2}\right)\ 2t^2_j$ $(j \in L\ R)$

RESULTS AND DISCUSSION

By broadenings and splittings for the electronic levels result from intra- and inter-level couplings, interference effects appear even for the case without a referential path of an AB ring. As clearly seen in Fig. 2, we can find close overlapping between the weak peak and the tail of the strong peak; two transport channels are opened simultaneously around $eV_g \sim -1\ 24t$. In this situation, the interference effect between electrons pass through the 2 channels play an important role in conduction spectra. In fact, spectra with and without interference terms embody quite different features as shown by solid and dashed lines in Fig. 2; a significant dip is found for the weak

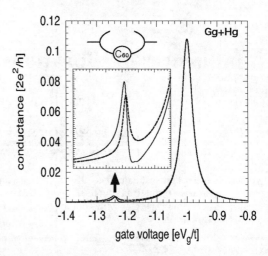

FIGURE 2. Conductance through a C_{60} without a referential path of an AB ring. The contribution from gerade (breathing) vibrational mode is taken into account. The value of δ is 0.3. To see the distinctive effect of interference, we draw two lines; While solid line shows conductance with interference effect, dashed line denotes that without it, which is simple summation of the resolved spectra of electronic levels.

peak in the spectrum with interference terms. We recognize that these characteristic shapes are caused by Fano effect. Actually, this situation satisfies the condition of Fano effect; while the phase of the transmission through the weak peak changes by π, the phase via the tail of the strong peak is unchanged. As a result, the weak peak behaves as a discrete level, whereas the tail of the strong peak plays a role of continuum states. Consequently, an asymmetric Fano peak is obtained without the referential path of an AB ring in the conduction spectrum.

In conclusion, we point out that the referential path of an AB ring is not required for the interference if molecules are satisfied with the condition of Fano effect by themselves.

REFERENCES

1. U. Fano, Phys. Rev. **124**, 1866 (1961).
2. K. Kobayashi, H. Aikawa, S. Katsumoto and Y. Iye, Phys. Rev. Lett. **88**, 256806 (2002).
3. K. Kobayashi, H. Aikawa, S. Katsumoto and Y. Iye, Phys. Rev. B **70**, 035319 (2004).
4. H. Aikawa, K. Kobayashi, A. Sano, S. Katsumoto and Y. Iye, J. Phys. Soc. Jpn. **73**, 3235 (2004).
5. T. Nakanishi, K. Terakura and T. Ando, Phys. Rev. B **69**, 115307 (2004).
6. G.-C. Liang and A. W. Ghosh, Phys. Rev. Lett. **95**, 076403 (2005).
7. S. Datta, *Electronic Transport in Mesoscopic Systems* (Cambridge University Press, Cambridge, 1995).
8. Y. Meir and N. S. Wingreen, Phys. Rev. Lett. **68**, 2512 (1992).

Strain and electronic structure interactions in realistically-scaled quantum dot stacks

Muhammad Usman[1], Shaikh Ahmed[1],
Marek Korkusinski[2], Clemens Heitzinger[1], and Gerhard Klimeck[1]

[1]School of Electrical and Computer Engineering, Purdue University, West Lafayette IN, 47907 USA
[2]Institute for Microstructural sciences National Research Council of Canada, Ottawa KIA 0R6, Canada

Abstract. Self-assembled quantum dots (DQ) can be grown as stacks where the QD distance can be controlled with atomic layer control. This distance determines the interaction of the artificial atom states to form artificial molecules. The design of QD stacks becomes complicated since the structures are subject to inhomogeneous, long-range strain and growth imperfections such as non-identical dots and inter-diffused interfaces. This study presents simulations of stacks consistent of three QDs in their resulting inhomogeneous strain field. The simulations are performed with NEMO 3-D which uses the valence force field method to compute the strain and the empirical $sp^3d^5s^*$ tight binding method to compute the electronic structure. Strain is shown to provide a very interesting mixing between states and preferred ordering of the ground state in the top-most or bottom most quantum dot subject to growth asymmetries.

Keywords: NEMO-3D, atomistic VFF model, Hamiltonian.
PACS: 73.21.La

INTRODUCTION AND APPROACH

Self-assembled quantum dots (QDs) in the InAs/GaAs material system like to grow on top of one another allowing for a simple creation of QD stacks [1]. Isolated atomic-like states are expected to transition into molecular-like states with decreasing QD distance. QD stacks therefore form a very interesting laboratory to explore basic quantum mechanics as well as a potential device structure for optical devices such as lasers and detectors.

The modeling and simulation of such QD stacks bears several difficulties. One should not assume that the devices are formed with perfect interfaces and perfect composition. Interface inter-diffusion and gradients in the composition are to be expected. Besides such imperfections, just crystal symmetry alone will determine some of the coupling mechanisms between the QD. Therefore it is not fundamentally sufficient to model the devices with jellium methods such as k.p or effective mass approaches.

The Nanoelectronic Modeling tool (NEMO 3-D) [2,3] was built to handle systems of large size with atomistic resolution. It has shown the capability to simulate strain in systems of up to 64 million atoms in an atomistic valence force field (VFF) method. A modified Keating potential that accounts for anharmonicity [4] is used in VFF. The electronic structure calculation is typically performed with the $sp^3d^5s^*$ empirical tight binding model which, due to its increased complexity compared to the VFF strain model, has only been demonstrated for systems up to 21 million atoms. The design space of a three dot quantum dot system and the physics of interaction of strain and wave function coupling is explored.

RESULTS

Quantum dot stacks consistent of three QD layers are simulated (see insets of Fig 1). The InAs quantum dots are disk shaped with height 1.5nm positioned on a 0.5nm thick wetting layer. Two QD stacks are considered: identical dots of width 5nm and a system of 5/6/7nm width, increasing in the growth direction. The substrate thickness under the first wetting layer is kept constant at 30nm and the cap layer on top of the topmost dot is kept at 10 nm for all simulations. The bottom-most atomic layer is fixed to GaAs lattice constant, periodic boundary conditions are assumed in the lateral dimensions and the topmost surface atoms are allowed to "breathe" freely. The largest system considered here requires the strain calculation of ~660,000 atoms. The electronic structure is computed

CP893, *Physics of Semiconductors, 28th International Conference*
edited by W. Jantsch and F. Schäffler
© 2007 American Institute of Physics 978-0-7354-0397-0/07/$23.00

in a smaller domain that just encompasses the central dots and a buffer region. To avoid the formation of surface states by the dangling bonds of the artificially cut simulation domain the resulting "numerical surface" atoms are passivated [5]. The largest electronic structure domain considered here is ~205,000 atoms. The lateral extent of the simulations is chosen very small here at 12nm for the very small QDs. Simulations with larger dots and larger lateral dimensions are under way.

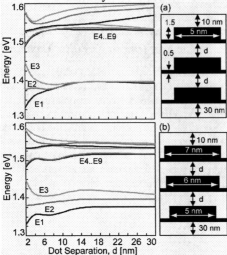

Fig 1: Electron state energies in the quantum dot molecule as a function interdot separation for two different QD stacks.

Figure 1a shows the electron state energy as a function of inter-dot separation for nominally identical dots. In a system without inhomogeneous strain one would expect the identical dots to have degenerate eigenstate energies for large dot separations. Strain breaks the degeneracy even for large systems. The strain field clearly extends over the distance of 30nm quantum dot separation. As the dot separation is narrowed the dots interact with each other mechanically through the strain field as well as quantum mechanically through wavefunction overlaps. The set of lowest states E1-3 as well as the excited states E4-9 clearly show the state repulsion of bonding and anti-bonding molecular states for short inter-dot distances.

Figure 1b shows the corresponding trace of eigen energies for the stack of non-identical dots. The states are non-degenerate for all inter-dot distances, however the formation of molecular states can be seen in the separation of the eigen states as the distance decreases. The set of E4-9 excited states show a slightly different admixture of states compared to Figure 1a.

Figure 2 shows cross-sectional cuts in the growth direction and one lateral direction through the middle of the 3D wavefunctions. The wavefunctions are quite clearly separated into the individual dots with little overlap across the dots for dot separations of 30 and

15nm. For 2nm and 4nm, wavefunction overlap can be observed.

Whether or not the coupled dot system favors the top-most or bottom-most QD to peak the ground state wavefunction is a complicated interplay of strain, QD size, and wavefunction overlap. Only a detailed simulation can reveal that interplay.

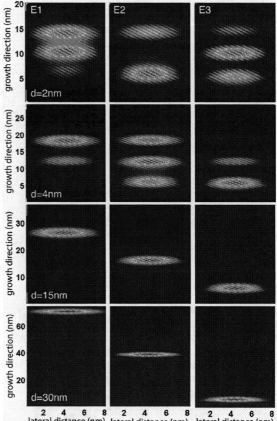

Fig 2: First three electron states wavefunction magnitudes (columns) with QD 2, 4, 15 and 30nm separation (rows) for non-identical dots (Figure 1 b).

CONCLUSIONS

QD stacks consistent of three QDs are analyzed. Non-trivial strain and electronic structure coupling is revealed with an analysis of the eigen energies and eigen states of the artificial molecule system. More detailed analysis on the strain distribution is needed to fully explain the movement of the electron states as a function of quantum dot distance.

REFERENCES

[1] Michler, P, Ed., Springer, Berlin, (2003).
[2] Klimeck, G, et al, Comp. Mod. in Eng. and Sci., 3, 601 (2002).
[3] OL Lazarenkova, et al, Appl. Phys. Lett. 85, 4193 (2004).
[4] Oyafuso, F, et al, J of Computational Electronics, 1, 317,(2002).
[5] Seungwon Lee, et al, Phys. Rev. B 69, 045316 (2004)

Symmetry Breaking and Fine Structure Splitting in Zincblende Quantum Dots: Atomistic Simulations of Long-Range Strain and Piezoelectric Field

Shaikh Ahmed[1], Muhammad Usman[1], Clemens Heitzinger[1], Rajib Rahman[1], Andrei Schliwa[2], and Gerhard Klimeck[1]

[1]*Network for Computational Nanotechnology, Purdue University, W. Lafayette, IN 47907, USA*
[2]*Institut für Festkörperphysik, Technische Universität Berlin, Germany*
E-mail: ssahmed@purdue.edu

Abstract. Electrons and holes captured in self-assembled quantum dots (QDs) are subject to symmetry breaking that cannot be represented in with continuum material representations. Atomistic calculations reveal symmetry lowering due to effects of strain and piezo-electric fields. These effects are fundamentally based on the crystal topology in the quantum dots. This work studies these two competing effects and demonstrates the fine structure splitting that has been demonstrated experimentally can be attributed to the underlying atomistic structure of the quantum dots.

Keywords: Quantum dots, Strain, Piezoelectricity, Crystal Symmetry.
PACS: 73.21.La

INTRODUCTION

Existing nanofabrication techniques create QDs in a variety of types and sizes. Among them, semiconductor QDs grown by self-assembly (SADs), trapping electrons as well as holes, are of particular importance in quantum optics, since they can be used as detectors of infrared radiation, optical memories, single photon sources, and lasers. At device sizes of tens of nanometers effects of atomistic granularity cannot be neglected. Surface roughness, unintentional doping, or distortions of the crystal lattice, if not taken into account, can have a deleterious impact on the device design.

Spectroscopic analysis of self-assembled quantum dots demonstrates polarized transitions between confined hole and electron levels. While the continuum models (effective mass or *k.p*) can reliably predict aspects of the single-particle energy states, they fail to capture the non-degeneracy and optical polarization anisotropy of the energy states in the (001) plane [1]. The symmetry in quantum dots realized from III-V materials is lowered due to two fundamental symmetry breaking mechanisms: 1) the underlying crystal, which lacks inversion symmetry, and 2) the presence of strain which induces piezoelectric charges. Strain in self-assembled

quantum dots is a long-range phenomenon and the dot states depend strongly on both the size of the strain domain and the boundary conditions. Both sources of symmetry breaking influence the fine structure splitting (splitting of the bright exciton) in self-assembled quantum dots. In this work, the impact of various factors on the symmetry breaking/lowering and fine structure splitting in atomistally represented self-assembled zincblende quantum dots is studied.

SIMULATION APPROACH

The study has been carried out through atomistic simulations using the Nanoelectronic Modeling tool NEMO-3D [2] capturing both the fundamental quantum character of charge carriers and the classical, long-distance strain effects on equal footing. Since the strain is long-ranged, its realistic determination requires a large computational domain. To tackle this problem for an embedded InAs quantum dot NEMO-3D uses the atomistic VFF Keating model containing up to 64 million atoms or $(110nm)^3$. Interatomic distance changes obtained are used to influence the $sp^3d^5s^*$ tight-binding electronic Hamiltonian defined in a subdomain containing up to 21 million atoms or $(78nm)^3$ (matrix size of order of 4×10^8). Such system

CP893, *Physics of Semiconductors, 28th International Conference*
edited by W. Jantsch and F. Schäffler
© 2007 American Institute of Physics 978-0-7354-0397-0/07/$23.00

sizes require use of parallel clusters or other HPC resources.

The dome-shaped QDs in this study (schematic shown in Fig. 1) have diameters and height within a range of 4.0 − 20.0 nm and 1.7 − 8.0 nm respectively, and are positioned on a 0.6-nm-thick wetting layer (dark regions). The simulation of strain is carried out in the large computational box (width D and height H), while the electronic structure computation is usually restricted to the smaller domain (width d and height h). All the strain simulations fix the atom positions on the bottom plane to the GaAs lattice constant, assume periodic boundary conditions in the lateral dimensions, and open boundary conditions on the top surface. The inner electronic box assumes closed boundary conditions with passivated dangling bonds.

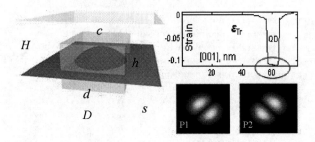

Fig 1. (Left) Schematic view of the QD nanostructure, with two simulation domains: central for electronic structure, and larger for strain calculations. (Right) Strain distribution along [001] and the introduced optical anisotropy in the first set of excited electron states P_1/P_2.

RESULTS AND DISCUSSION

Atomistic strain and relaxation modifies the effective confinement volume in the device and hence modulates the energy states. Fig. 1 (right panel) shows the net strain distribution along the [001] direction in a typical dome shaped quantum dot. The presence of the gradient in the strain profile introduces unequal stress in the zinc-blende lattice structure along the depth, breaks the equivalence of the [110] and [1$\underline{1}$0] directions, and breaks the degeneracy of the P_1/P_2 first excited states.

The simulation results also show a significant dependence of the dot states and magnitude of fine-splitting on the substrate layer thickness (underneath the dot) and the cap layer (above the dot). The strain in the QD system therefore penetrates *deeply* into the substrate and *cannot be neglected*. Fig. 2 shows such observed dependency where $E0$ is the ground state energy and dE is the magnitude of the fine structure splitting in the P electronic states due to the inclusion of atomistic strain and relaxation. The wavefunction

orientation remains unchanged irrespective of the included substrate depth.

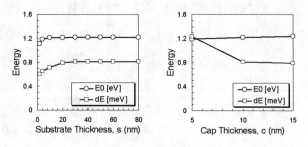

Fig 2. (Left) Substrate thickness dependence of the ground state and the P_1/P_2 energy splitting. Other structural parameters remain constant (h = 4 nm, d = 20 nm, c = 10 nm). (Right) The impact of cap layer thickness (with deep substrate thickness, s = 50nm).

The presence of off-diagonal strain tensor elements leads to the generation of a piezoelectric field, which is incorporated in the simulations as an external potential by solving the Poisson equation on the zincblende lattice. The relevant parameters for the piezoelectric calculation are taken from ref [1]. The piezoelectric potential has been found to introduce a global shift in the energy spectrum potentially strong enough to flip the optical orientation in certain sized quantum dots. In those cases the piezoelectric potential dominates over that resulting from the inclusion of atomistic strain in the simulations.

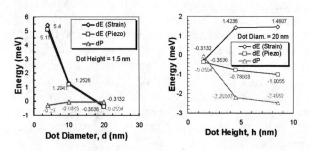

Fig 3. Influence of strain and piezoelectricity as a function of dot diameter (left) and dot height (right) on the fine-splitting and polarization of states.

REFERENCES

1. Gabriel Bester and Alex Zunger, *Physical Review* B, 71, 045318, (2005).
2. G. Klimeck, F. Oyafuso, T. Boykin, R. Bowen, and P. von Allmen, Computer Modeling in Engineering and Science, 3, 601, 2002.

*Supported by the Indiana 21st Century Fund and National Science Foundation under Grant No. EEC-0228390.

Exciton states and magnetooptical transitions in stacks of InGaAs/GaAs self-assembled quantum rings

M. Tadić*,† and F. M. Peeters†

*Faculty of Electrical Engineering, University of Belgrade, PO Box 3554, 11120 Belgrade, Serbia
†Department of Physics, University of Antwerp (Campus Groenenborger),
Groenenborgerlaan 171, B-2020 Antwerp, Belgium

Abstract. Electron, hole, and exciton states in the stacks composed of three strained (In,Ga)As quantum rings were computed. We found considerable influence of strain on both the single particle and exciton spectra, while the oscillator strength for exciton recombination is reduced by the magnetic field.

Keywords: quantum ring, quantum dot, exciton
PACS: 73.21.La

Recently, it has been demonstrated that certain modifications of the Stranski-Krastanov growth sequence can change the morphology of lens-shaped quantum dots into quantum rings [1, 2]. Fabrication of these rings promoted interest in the excitonic Aharonov-Bohm effect, which was predicted to occur in one-dimensional rings [3]. The fabricated rings have typically an outer radius between 30 and 60 nm and height of about 2 nm [4]. Inhomogeneous strain is present in the structure, which as recently found facilitates growth of rings in vertical stacks [5], similar to the case of quantum dots.

In the present study, we employ the 4-band $\mathbf{k} \cdot \mathbf{p}$ model to compute the hole states in these stacks, composed of three strained (In,Ga)As quantum rings of rectangular cross section. In order to compute the exciton states, we use an exact diagonalization approach, while the continuum mechanical model is employed to compute the strain distribution. We investigate: (1) the spatial localization of the holes as function of the spacer thickness; (2) the influence of the relocation of the electrons and holes due to the localization of the exciton; (3) the variation of the lowest exciton energy states of different angular momenta in a normal magnetic field; (4) the variation of the oscillator strength for exciton recombination with the magnetic field.

The continuum mechanical model is employed to compute the strain distribution [6]. In order to describe the electronic structure of the conduction band, the nonparabolic bulk-like corrections to the conduction band effective mass were adopted [7]. Furthermore, mixing between the heavy holes and light holes is explicitly taken into account in the 4-band effective-mass model. Valence-band states are classified according to the value of the z projection of the total angular momentum and parity. Exciton states are organized in quartets [6].

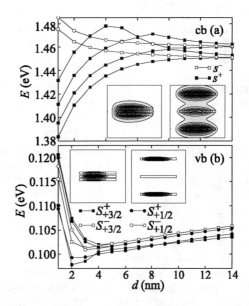

FIGURE 1. The eigenergies of (a) the electron s states and (b) the hole $S^{\pm}_{+3/2}$ and $S^{\pm}_{+1/2}$ states. The insets show the probability density distributions for $d = 1$ and $d = 14$ nm.

We consider the stacks of (In,Ga)As rings [5], which have the outer radius $R_o = 50$ nm, the inner radius $R_i = 10$ nm, the height $h = 2$ nm, while $x = 0.5$ is chosen for the composition inside the dot. Other material and structural properties are given in Ref. [8]. The spacer thickness is varied from $d = 1$ to 14 nm.

Dependence of the eigenenergies of the $s^{\pm}$ states on the spacer thickness is shown in Fig. 1(a). The electron states are obviously organized in triplets. Furthermore, the ground electron state exhibits an overshoot on the ground state of the single quantum dot, with the peak at $d = 12$ nm. The lifting of the energy of the ground

CP893, *Physics of Semiconductors, 28th International Conference*
edited by W. Jantsch and F. Schäffler
© 2007 American Institute of Physics 978-0-7354-0397-0/07/$23.00

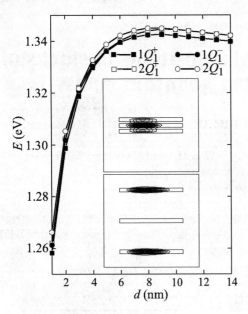

FIGURE 2. The lowest exciton energy levels. For the notation see Ref. [6].

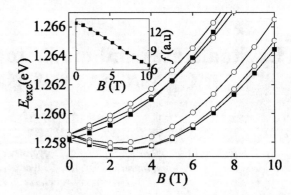

FIGURE 3. The lowest energy exciton states in the normal magnetic field. The inset shows the variation of the oscillator strength.

state is mainly due to the long range character of e_{zz} component of the strain tensor [6]. Because of strain and the band mixing [6], the hole states shown in Fig. 1(b) are arranged as doublets for large d. The insets in Figs. 1(a) and 1(b) display the distributions of the probability density of the ground states for $d = 1$ and $d = 14$ nm. As *a priori* expected, overlaps between the electron and hole clouds of the individual quantum dots is considerable at $d = 1$ nm, while at $d = 14$ nm, the electrons are localized mainly in the satellite dots. This implies that the reconstruction of the wave functions towards the case of the single quantum dot is not complete at $d = 14$ nm.

Asymmetric splitting of the hole states observed in Fig. 1 is responsible for the splitting of the exciton energy levels. Because of the doublet arrangement of hole states, the exciton states appear as doublets. Furthermore, there exists an overshoot on the ground exciton energy of the single quantum dot. One should note that the ground state shown in Fig. 2 is optically active for the in-plane polarized light. The increase of the transition energy in the stack of self-assembled rings was recently observed [5], and might appear due to the poor control of the dimensions of the individual rings in the stack. However, as demonstrated in Fig. 2, the increase of the transition energy might arise due to the presence of strain, and therefore may partially account for the observed variation of the experimental photoluminescent spectra in Ref. [5].

Fig. 3 shows the exciton states in the normal magnetic field. Both displayed quartets exhibit diamagnetic shift, while no Aharonov-Bohm effect is found in the ground exciton state. This is the result of the type-I character of

the exciton and the large width of the quantum rings. The oscillator strength of the ground exciton state, shown in the inset in Fig. 3, is halved when the magnetic field B increases from 0 to 10 T.

In summary, we performed 4-band effective-mass calculation of the exciton states in stacks of strained (In,Ga)As/GaAs nanoscopic rings. We found that the asymmetric splitting of the hole states in the stack profoundly influences the exciton states. No Aharonov-Bohm oscillations were found in the ground exciton level, and also the oscillator strength for the exciton recombination monotonously decreases when B increases.

This work was supported in part by the EU-NoE: SANDiE, the Belgian Science Policy, and the Ministry of Science and Environmental Protection of the Republic of Serbia.

REFERENCES

1. J. M. Garcia, G. Medeiros-Ribeiro, K. Schmidt, T. Ngo, J. L. Feng, A. Lorke, J. Kotthaus, and P. M. Petroff, Appl. Phys. Lett. **71**, 2014 (1997).
2. A. Lorke, R. Johannes Luyken, A. O. Govorov, J. P. Kotthaus, J. M. Garcia, and P. M. Petroff, Phys. Rev. Lett. **84**, 2223 (2000).
3. R. A. Römer and M. R. Raikh, Phys. Rev. B **62**, 7045 (2000).
4. D. Haft, C. Schulhauser, A. O. Govorov, R. J. Warburton, K. Karrai, J. M. Garcia, W. Schoefeld, and P. M. Petroff, Physica E **13**, 165 (2002).
5. D. Granados, J. M. Garcia, T. Ben, and S. I. Molina, Appl. Phys. Lett. **86**, 071918 (2005).
6. M. Tadić, F. M. Peeters, and K. L. Janssens, Phys. Rev. B **65**, 165333 (2002); M. Tadić and F. M. Peeters, *ibid*, **70**, 195302 (2004).
7. J. I. Climente, J. Planelles, and W. Jaskólski, Phys. Rev. B **68**, 075307 (2003).
8. M. Tadić and F. M. Peeters, Phys. Rev. B **71**, 125342 (2005).

Observation of the singlet and triplet states in a hybrid vertical-lateral double dot

T. Hatano[a], Y. Tokura[a,b], S. Amaha[a], T. Kubo[a] and S. Tarucha[a,c]

[a]Tarucha Quantum Spin Information with Quantum Dots, ICORP, JST, Atsugi-shi, Kanagawa 243-0198, Japan
[b]NTT Basic Research Laboratories, Atsugi-shi, Kanagawa 243-0198, Japan
[c]Department of Applied Physics, Univ. of Tokyo, Hongo, Bunkyo-ku, Tokyo 113-8656, Japan

Abstract. We fabricated a hybrid vertical-lateral double dot and measured the linear and nonlinear single electron transport properties to study a inter-dot tunnel and exchange coupling. The inter-dot tunnel coupling was tunable for a double dot containing just a few electrons with center gate voltage as a parameter. For the large tunnel coupling, we observed an excited state close to the ground state that formed an effective two-electron state in the excitation spectrum, and assigned the ground and excited states to the spin singlet and triplet states, respectively.

Keywords: tunnel coupling, exchange coupling, double dot, Coulomb oscillations, excitation spectrum
PACS: 73.63.Kv, 73.23.Hk

INTRODUCTION

A double quantum dot (DQD) [1-4] can contain an electronic system suitable for manipulating the spin effects, because various inter-dot coupling strengths, e.g., tunnel coupling t and exchange coupling J, can be well manipulated by external parameters. In particular, control of J is a key prerequisite in spin-based quantum computing [5]. J is the energy separation between the spin singlet and triplet states, and depends on t and the inter- and intra- dot Coulomb energies. t is determined by the overlap of the electron wave functions between two dots, and can be modulated as a function of gate voltage and magnetic field. Recently, an experimental study of exchange coupling was reported for lateral DQDs, and J was derived from the observed coherent oscillations [6]. In this work we used a hybrid vertical-lateral DQD device to study the tunnel and exchange coupling with center gate voltage as a parameter. We obtained the charging diagram to show that the inter-dot tunnel coupling is tunable by controlling the center gate voltage, and also that the exchange-coupled singlet and triplet states are visible in the excitation spectrum.

EXPERIMENTS

Our device consists of two laterally coupled vertical dots with four split gates (Fig. 1) [4]. Two of the gates (side gates) are used to tune the electron number in each dot independently, and the remaining two gates (center gates) are used to tune the inter-dot tunnel coupling. Current flows in the vertical direction through the two dots which are connected in parallel. The conductance was measured for the DQD device in a dilution refrigerator with a bath temperature of 20 mK.

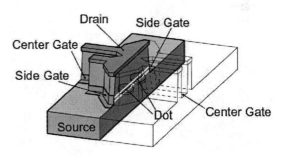

Fig.1 Schematic of the hybrid vertical-lateral double dot device.

Figure 2 is a gray scale plot of the differential conductance, dI_{sd}/dV_{sd} vs. source-drain voltage V_{sd} and left (right) side gate voltage V_{sL} (V_{sR}) in (a) ((b)). Several diamond shaped-regions or Coulomb diamonds are clearly seen. However, there are no Coulomb diamonds for V_{sL}, $V_{sR} < -2$ V, indicating that the dots are empty. This measurement denotes that the

CP893, *Physics of Semiconductors, 28th International Conference*
edited by W. Jantsch and F. Schäffler
© 2007 American Institute of Physics 978-0-7354-0397-0/07/$23.00

electron numbers, N_L and N_R, in the left and right dots, are varied one by one, starting from zero [7].

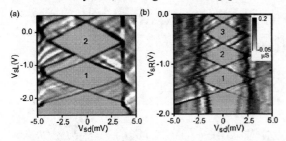

Fig.2 Differential conductance dI_{sd}/dV_{sd} vs. V_{sd} and V_{sL} (V_{sR}) measured (a) for the left dot with V_{sR} = -1.4 V and center gate voltage V_c = -1.3 V and (b) for the right dot with V_{sR} = -2.4 V and V_c = -0.6 V.

Figure 3 is a gray scale plot of the linear conductance as a function V_{sL} and V_{sR} measured for V_c = -1.2V (a) and -0.5 V (b). Here we set V_{sd} = 8 μV. In (a) both N_L and N_R are reduced to zero. However, the Coulomb oscillation peaks for changing N_L (vertical lines) and those for changing N_R (horizontal lines) cross almost perpendicularly. This implies that the two dots are almost decoupled, probably because the electrons are well localized in the center of each dot, and also because the V_c of -1.2 V is too negative. On the other hand, when V_c was made more positive to increase the inter-dot tunnel coupling, diagonal gaps or 'anticrossings' appeared at the Coulomb oscillation vertices, resulting in the hexagonal stability diagram shown in Fig. 3(b). These anticrossings arise from the inter-dot Coulomb interaction as well as the inter-dot tunnel coupling.

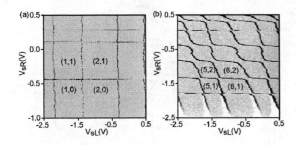

Fig.3 Linear conductance vs. V_{sL} and V_{sR} measured for V_c = -1.2 V (a) and -0.5 V (b).

Finally we made V_c more positive and measured the excitation spectrum. The result can be found is in Fig. 4, which shows a gray scale plot of the differential conductance $(dI_{sd}/dV_{sL} + dI_{sd}/dV_{sR})/\sqrt{2}$ at V_c = -0.3 V and V_{sd} = -300 μV. In this diagram, (N_L, N_R) transits from (6,2) to (7,3). For (6,2), two orbital states, and one orbital state are fully occupied in the left, and right dots, respectively. So for (7,3), an unpaired spin electron is located in each dot with the core of (6,2) [5].

Then the lower left (upper right) stripe indicates the one-electron state (two- electron state) above the core. The dark regions show the positive derivative, and highlight either the ground states or the excite states. The upper right stripe includes two dark lines. We assign the lower (upper) line to the singlet (triplet) state as the ground (excited) state [5]. The excitation energy ($\approx$ 140 μeV) compares well with the calculated J of 180 μeV.

SUMMARY

We observed that the inter-dot tunnel coupling in a hybrid vertical-lateral DQD is tunable by controlling the gate voltage, and also that the exchange-coupled singlet and triplet states are visible in the excitation spectrum.

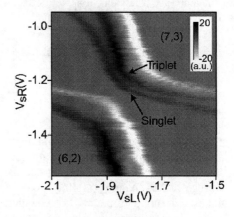

Fig. 4 Differential conductance $(dI_{sd}/dV_{sL} + dI_{sd}/dV_{sR})/\sqrt{2}$ as a function of two side gate voltages for V_c = -0.3 V and V_{sd} = -300 μV.

Acknowledgements

We thank S. Teraoka, T. Obata, Y. Sin, M. P. Ladriere, A. Shibatomi, T. Kodera, K. Yoshida, K. Ono, S. Sasaki, D. G. Austing and M. Stopa for experimental help and useful discussions. ST acknowledges financial support from DARPA grant no. DAAD19-01-1-0659 of the QuIST program, Grant-in-Aid for Scientific Research A (No. 40302799), SORST-JST and the IT Program, MEXT.

References

[1] S. Amaha et al., Solid State Commun. **119**, 183 (2001).
[2] A. W. Holleitner et al., Science **297**, 70 (2002).
[3] J. M. Elzerman et al., Phys. Rev. B **67**, 161308 (2003).
[4] T. Hatano et al. Phys. Rev. Lett. 93, 066806 (2004).
[5] G. Burkard et al., Phys. Rev. B **59**, 2070 (1999).
[6] J. R. Petta et al., Science **309**, 2180 (2005).
[7] S. Tarucha et al., Phys. Rev. Lett. 77, 3613 (1996).

Phase Information from Two-Terminal Conductance of Quantum Dot Systems

Tomohiro Otsuka[1], Hisashi Aikawa[1], Mikio Eto[1,2], Gyong L Khym[3], Kicheon Kang[3], Yasuhiro Iye[1], and Shingo Katsumoto[1]

[1]Institute for Solid State Physics, University of Tokyo, 5-1-5 Kashiwanoha, Chiba, 277-8581, Japan
[2]Faculty of Science and Technology, Keio University, 3-14-1 Hiyoshi, Kohoku-ku, Yokohama 223-8522, Japan
[3]Dept. Phys. and Institute for Condensed Matter Theory, Chonnam National University, Gwangju 500-757, Korea

Abstract. Two-terminal devices generally work as "leaky resonators" in coherent transport, which mixes up the quantum phase information from all parts of the devices, e.g., quantum dots (QDs) embedded in them. With the aid of appropriate theoretical modeling, however, we can extract important information on the phase from the total conductance. As typical examples, we present here experiments in a side-coupled QD, and a QD embedded in an Aharonov-Bohm (AB) ring. In the former, kinetic degrees of freedoms transverse and longitudinal to a quantum wire give rise to dramatic change in the interference effect. In the latter, "phase shift locking to $\pi/2$" appears as a plateau structure in the conductance. Specialized theoretical models give reasonable explanations to these effects, bringing important information on the phase of the electron wavefunctions in the QDs.

Keywords: Quantum dots, Coulomb blockade, Fano effect, Kondo effect.
PACS: 73.21.La, 73.23.Hk, 73.63.Kv

The phase of a wavefunction is a most important concept in wave-mechanics. Various interference effects in mesoscopic physics are direct consequences of phase difference. A sharp contrast between mesoscopic conductors and ordinary wave interferometers lies in the constraint of unitarity in two-terminal devices. In other words, the two-terminal devices usually work as "leaky resonators" rather than simple inter-ferometers. This situation makes the output complicated and gives significant distortion on the phase information. On the other hand, the two-terminal devices have apparent advantage in the amplitude of interference signals.

In this article, we show that we can extract important undistorted phase information from two-terminal conductance with the aid of appropriate theoretical models. Especially the phase shifts through quantum dots (QDs) are of interest because they carry essential knowledge of electronic states in them and many body effects, which arise from indirect interaction between conduction electrons via QDs.

The quantum interference circuits and the QDs used in the present study were made from two-dimensional electron system at an AlGaAs/GaAs hetero-interface. The circuits and the dots were defined by wet-etching or lithography-made metallic gates.

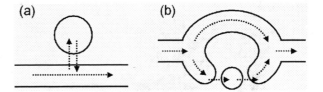

FIGURE.1 Schematic diagrams of interference circuits used in the present experiments. (a) T-shaped stab resonator. (b) AB ring with a quantum dot in one of the arms.

In Fig.1, we show two types of interferometers adopted in the experiments. In the side-coupled geometry (Fig.1(a)), the size of the dot can be extremely small by applying negative voltage to the plunger gate with keeping a finite coupling to the quantum wire. This feature makes it possible to explore the interference effect in few-electron QD regime. However, because the interference and the resonance occur in a very narrow region, the control of the parameters of the interferometer is inevitably associated with variation of other parameters. On the other hand in an Aharonov-Bohm (AB) ring structure shown in Fig.1(b), the phase difference between the two arms can be easily tuned by the flux piercing the ring without changing other parameters though it is

CP893, *Physics of Semiconductors, 28th International Conference*
edited by W. Jantsch and F. Schäffler

hard to measure the transport in the few-electron regime.

In the side coupled geometry (Fig.1(a)), we measured the conductance (G_w) through the quantum wire as a function of the plunger gate voltage (V_p) of the QD and the gate voltage of the wire (V_w), which determines the width of the constriction. Roughly G_w varies stepwise in V_w and the effect of interference appears as an additional variance, which responds to V_p. Fig.2 shows such variance ΔG_w as a function of V_p and V_w. The peak structures in the oscillation of ΔG_w versus V_p show the charging-Fano mixed effect and the steep decrease in the amplitude of such structure around $V_p = -1V$ indicates that the electrons in the dot are depleted for V_p lower than $-1V$, that is, the electron number $n = 0$. From this starting point, we can count n one by one.

From the interval of the Fano peaks, we estimate the addition-energy of an electron, which is apparently larger for $n = 2$ and 6. They are the numbers to form the first and the second shell structure of the two-dimensional harmonic oscillator, indicating circular confining potential. An interesting feature appearing in Fig.2 is the abrupt inversion in the line shape of the Fano peaks in the middle of the first plateau, to which we give a convincing theoretical explanation based on a tight binding model. The detail will be given elsewhere.

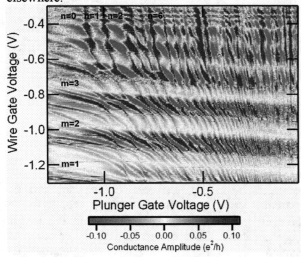

FIGURE 2. Color plot of ΔG_w as a function of V_p and V_w. The electron number in the dot and the conductance plateau number are indicated by n and m respectively. The temperature is 30mK.

Next we report the Fano-Kondo effect in a QD embedded in an AB ring. We first optimize the QD gate voltage to form the Kondo state in the lower arm. Then we opened the upper reference path to observe the Fano-Kondo effect. To get the coherent portion in the conductance, we subtracted the mid-line of the AB

oscillation from the bare conductance. Fig.3(a) shows the results around 0.5T, in which clear mixed line shape of the Fano-Kondo effect appeared. The theories for perfect one-dimensional electron paths predict "frequency doubling" in the middle of the valley due to the Onsager reciprocity for two terminal devices. However the experimental result seems to be free from the constraint and is similar to that predicted for four terminal devices. A clear sign of $\pi/2$ phase shift locking is observed in the middle.

In order to explain the result, we have considered a minimal model of two-channel AB ring with a QD with a single electron level (Fig.3(b)). The main feature of this model is the existence of the two interacting channels with different enclosing area and this causes the breaking of the "phase rigidity" in appearance. We have adopted a finite-U slave boson mean-field approximation for the Kondo effect and calculated the conductance at zero temperature. The calculated line shape (Fig.3(c)) is in good agreement with the experiment in (a), manifesting that the model grabs the essence of the phenomenon. The result also certificates that the anomaly in the middle is due to the $\pi/2$ phase shift locking. The successful analysis demonstrates that the conductance through two-terminal interferometers can provides useful information on the quantum phase.

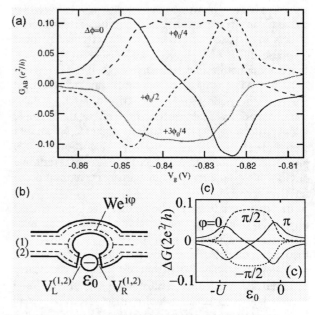

FIGURE 3. (a): Coherent part of conductance, which responds to the AB flux in the interferometer in Fig.1(b). The temperature is 45mK. The base magnetic field is 0.49T and ϕ_0 is the flux quantum h/e. (b): Theoretical model for calculation. To take account of the finite medium magnetic field, we consider edge channels and a direct channel. (c): Calculated conductance for the model shown in (b). The parameters are taken to imitate the results in (a).

Coherent Transport Through a Quadruple Point in a Few Electron Triple Dot.

L. Gaudreau[1,2], A.S.Sachrajda[1], S.Studenikin[1], P.Zawadzki[1], A.Kam[1], and J.Lapointe[1]

[1] National Research Council, 1200 Montreal Road, Ottawa Canada K1A 0R6
[2] Université de Sherbooke, Quebec , Canada J1K 2R1

Abstract. A few electron double electrostatic lateral quantum dot can be transformed into a few electron triple quantum dot by applying a different combination of gate voltages. Quadruple points have been achieved at which all three dots are simultaneously on resonance. At these special points in the stability diagram four occupation configurations are possible. Both charge detection and transport experiments have been performed on this device. In this short paper we present data and confirm that transport is coherent by observing a π phase shift in magneto-conductance oscillations as one passes through the quadruple point.

Keywords: Triple Quantum Dots, Coherent Transport, Quantum information
PACS: 73.21.La, 73.63.-b, 73.63.Kv

INTRODUCTION

Few electron lateral quantum dots and coupled quantum dots are considered promising candidates for quantum information applications as charge and spin qubits[1]. Recently, for the first time, a few electron triple quantum dot system was realized[2] and the stability diagram mapped out using charge detection techniques[3] down to the (0,0,0) regime (where (l,m,n) refer to the number of electrons l,m,n in each of the dots respectively). In this short paper we provide evidence that transport through this system is coherent when all three dots are in resonance.

EXPERIMENT AND RESULTS

Details of the device[4,5,6], the charge detection techniques[2] employed as well as a description of tuning procedures are provided in reference 2. In order to observe transport phenomena through the triple dot the electron arrangement was shifted by (0,1,2) from the empty (0,0,0) configuration. The three quantum dot potentials (A,B,C) were arranged in a ring with dots A and B coupled to one lead and dot C coupled to the other. A schematic of this arrangement is included in figure 1. Both DC transport experiments and charge detection measurements using an adjacent quantum point contact were performed. Figure 1 shows a zoom of the stability diagram of the triple dot in the regime

of interest at settings where a quadruple point (i.e. where four electronic configurations are resonant) has been formed at point X. The regime studied in reference 2 is closer to the (0,0,0) regime and all charge transfer lines (i.e. at which electrons transfer between dots) were visible making setting the quadruple point experimentally straightforward. At the regime in figure 1, however, the charge transfer lines between dots A and B were not detectable and the quadruple points were set through a careful analysis of the line slopes, line amplitudes and the lengths of the observable charge transfer lines (bright lines in the figure). More details will be provided elsewhere. The inset shows a wider charge detection region in which the change in slope and intensity of the more horizontal lines (associated with dots A and B) at the quadruple point can clearly be observed. The left hand plot is obtained from charge detection experiments whilst the right hand greyscale is a low bias transport measurement over the same regime. The electron configurations are also shown. Note that the charge transfer processes between dots A and B (e.g. (1,1,2) to (0,2,2)) are not visible directly but are inferred from the analysis as mentioned above.

Several points need to be stressed in the data. The quadruple point is set at point X. A charge reconfiguration[2] occurs (0,2,2) to (1,1,3) as the boundary at C is crossed. Magneto-transport measurements have been performed in detail at points

CP893, *Physics of Semiconductors, 28th International Conference*
edited by W. Jantsch and F. Schäffler
© 2007 American Institute of Physics 978-0-7354-0397-0/07/$23.00

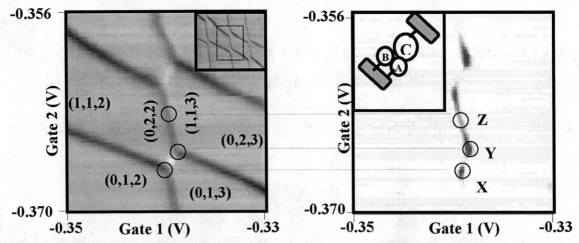

FIGURE 1. Charge detection and transport measurements through a quadruple point (X) in a triple dot circuit (see text for details). The insets contain a wider charge detection region and a schematic of the quantum dot circuit.

X, Y and Z. A wide variety of phenomena was observed. The phenomena include magneto-conductance fluctuations which undergo π phase changes (as may be expected from phase rigidity[7] in two terminal measurements) and visibility modulations of these fluctuations. Figure 2 shows one example. A high bias measurement (300µeV) is made through the quadruple point passing from (0,1,2) to (0,1,3). During passage through the quadruple point (where transport occurs) two other electronic configurations also become resonant (0,2,2) and (1,1,2). A broad conductance peak with structure is observed (inset of figure 2). At either edge of the peak magnetoconductance oscillations with a period 28mT can be seen (see figure) but differing by a π phase change. On the peak center itself a more complicated behavior occurs involving additional periods. The fluctuations persist up to 700mK.

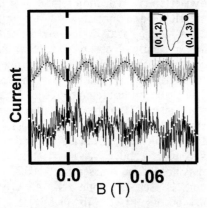

FIGURE 2. Magneto-conductance oscillations at a quadruple point (see text for details). Maximum peak current was 35 pA.

CONCLUSIONS

Transport measurements have been performed on a triple quantum dot circuit, analogous to a quantum ring. Magnetoconductance fluctuations were observed at quadruple points accompanied by a variety of phenomena related to coherent transport such as π phase changes of the Aharanov-Bohm like oscillations.

ACKNOWLEDGMENTS

We would like to acknowledge fruitful discussions with Pawel Hawrylak, Marek Korkusinski, Aashish Clerk and Karyn Lehur. ASS and AK acknowledge support from the Canadian Institute for Advanced Research. ASS acknowledges funding from NSERC.

REFERENCES

1. D. Loss and D. P. DiVincenzo, Phys. Rev. A **57**, 120 (1998).
2. Gaudreau L. et al. Phys.Rev.Lett. (to be published 21st July 2006)
3. M. Field *et al.*, Phys. Rev. Lett. **70**, 1311 (1993).
4. M. Ciorga *et al.*, Phys. Rev. B. **61**, R163315 (2000).
5. J. M. Elzerman *et al.*, Phys. Rev. B **67**, 161308 (2003).
6. A. K. Huttel, S. Ludwig, H. Lorenz, K. Eberl, and J. P. Kotthaus, Phys. Rev. B **72**, 081310 (2005).
7. Yacoby A., Schuster,R. and Heiblum M, Phys. Rev. B **53** (1996) 9583.

Spatial Localization of an Optical Near Field Dressed by Coherent Phonons

Yuji Tanaka* and Kiyoshi Kobayashi*,†

*Department of Physics, Tokyo Institute of Technology, 2-12-1 O-okayama, Meguro-ku, Tokyo 152-8551, Japan
†CREST, Japan Science and Technology Agency

Abstract. We present a quantum-field theoretical model to explain the experimentally suggested spatial localization of photons associated with coherent phonons in an optical near-field probe system. Considering the localized phonon modes, due to the impurity in a one-dimensional system, we obtained the temporal evolution of the localization of photons, which depends on the photon-phonon coupling constant, as well as the hopping constant of photons. The result shows that photons move and localize at the impurity sites when the hopping constant is comparable to the photon-phonon coupling.

Keywords: Dressed state, localized photon, one-dimensional system, time evolution.
PACS: 78.67.-n, 42.50.Ct, 71.23.An, 71.38.-k

INTRODUCTION

An optical near field, which is an electromagnetic field localized around material on a nanometer scale, is free from the diffraction limit of light, and has recently been used to explore optical responses of single or coupled semiconductor quantum dots and single molecules, and to fabricate nanostructures [1]. In order to fabricate nanophotonic devices, it is critical to control the size and position of the nanostructures. Optical near-field approaches promise to solve this problem. Superradiance, as a cooperative phenomenon, of a quantum-dot chain system excited by an optical near field, and energy transfer to a dipole-forbidden level in a coupled quantum-dot system, showing the breakdown of the long wave approximation, have been reported as inherent phenomena of an optical near field [2, 3]. A nanophotonic switch based on these phenomena has been demonstrated experimentally [4]. As fundamental physics, however, the light-matter interaction on a nanometer scale has not been formulated fully and selfconsistently beyond the long wave approximation. In addition, the role of a phonon has not been clarified for nanomaterials interacting with optical near fields.

In this paper, we present a quantum-field theoretical model to explain the experimentally suggested spatial localization of photons associated with coherent phonons in an optical near-field probe system [5]. The system is simply modeled as a one-dimensional two-level molecular chain coupled with photon and phonon fields. An optical near field is expressed by a photon not only localizing at each molecular site but also hopping to the nearest-neighbor sites [6].

MODEL AND RESULTS

The model under consideration can be described using the following Hamiltonian:

$$
\begin{aligned}
\hat{H} &= \sum_{i=1}^{N} \hbar\omega \hat{a}_i^\dagger \hat{a}_i \\
&+ \left\{ \sum_{i=1}^{N} \frac{\hat{p}_i^2}{2m_i} + \sum_{i=1}^{N-1} \frac{1}{2} k(\hat{x}_{i+1} - \hat{x}_i)^2 + \frac{1}{2} k\hat{x}_1^2 + \frac{1}{2} k\hat{x}_N^2 \right\} \\
&+ \sum_{i=1}^{N} \hbar\chi \hat{x}_i \hat{a}_i^\dagger \hat{a}_i + \sum_{i=1}^{N-1} \hbar J(\hat{a}_i^\dagger \hat{a}_{i+1} + \hat{a}_{i+1}^\dagger \hat{a}_i),
\end{aligned} \tag{1}
$$

where the creation and annihilation operators of a photon localized at site i are denoted as $\hat{a}_i^\dagger$, and $\hat{a}_i$, the displacement and conjugate momentum operators of the lattice vibration are expressed as $\hat{x}_i$ and $\hat{p}_i$, respectively. The third and fourth terms in Eq. (1) represent the photon-phonon interaction and photon hopping, respectively. Here, we assumed that the electronic polarization field is included in the photon field. Note that the first and last terms in Hamiltonian (1) describe a kind of polariton effect.

Using the canonical transformation generated by an anti-Hermitian operator defined as [7]

$$
\hat{S} = \sum_j \sum_q \frac{\chi_{jq}}{\Omega_q} \left(\hat{b}_q^\dagger - \hat{b}_q\right) \hat{a}_j^\dagger \hat{a}_j, \tag{2}
$$

we rewrite Hamiltonian (1), which can be described in terms of a quasi-particle–a localized photon dressed by the coherent phonon as follows:

$$
\hat{H} = \sum_i \hbar\omega \hat{\alpha}_i^\dagger \hat{\alpha}_i - \sum_p \sum_i \sum_j \hbar \frac{\chi_{ip}\chi_{jp}}{\Omega_p} \left\langle \hat{\alpha}_i^\dagger \hat{\alpha}_i \right\rangle \hat{\alpha}_j^\dagger \hat{\alpha}_j
$$

CP893, *Physics of Semiconductors, 28th International Conference*
edited by W. Jantsch and F. Schäffler

$$+ \sum_i \hbar J \left(\hat{\alpha}_i^\dagger \hat{\alpha}_{i+1} + \hat{\alpha}_{i+1}^\dagger \hat{\alpha}_i \right) + \sum_p \hbar \Omega_p \hat{\beta}_p^\dagger \hat{\beta}_p, \quad (3)$$

with

$$\hat{\alpha}_i^\dagger = e^{-\hat{S}} \hat{a}_i^\dagger e^{\hat{S}} = \hat{a}_i^\dagger \exp \left\{ -\sum_p \frac{\chi_{ip}}{\Omega_p} (\hat{b}_p^\dagger - \hat{b}_p) \right\}$$

and

$$\hat{\beta}_p^\dagger = e^{-\hat{S}} \hat{b}_p^\dagger e^{\hat{S}} = \hat{b}_p^\dagger + \sum_i \frac{\chi_{ip}}{\Omega_p} \hat{a}_i^\dagger \hat{a}_i,$$

where $\left(\hat{\alpha}_i^\dagger, \hat{\alpha}_i, \hat{\beta}_p^\dagger, \hat{\beta}_p \right)$ are the quasi-particle operators, $(\hat{b}_p^\dagger, \hat{b}_p)$ are the phonon operators of mode p with frequency Ω_p, and χ_{ip} is the photon-phonon coupling constant.

On the basis of the Hamiltonian (3), we discuss the spatial localization of an optical near field. We normalized the coupling constant J in terms of χ in the following calculation. As shown in Fig. 1, the one-dimensional system has localized phonon modes due to doped molecules with different mass in the chain, as these have higher energies than the delocalized ones. A photon in the $\hat{a}_i^\dagger |0\rangle$ state can excite these localized phonon modes, and hop to other sites, depending on the coupling constants J and χ. Figure 2 illustrates one such case. When the coupling constant J is comparable to $(\hbar/k)(\chi/N)^2$ photons move between the impurity sites and then localize at the sites. This indicates that an optical near field can localize at the edge of the probe tip after hopping between the sites of impurity and the interaction with localized phonon modes.

CONCLUDING REMARKS

We have presented a quantum-field theoretical model, and pointed out that the spatial localization of an optical near field originates from the interplay of a photon and localized phonon modes. A localized photon dressed by the coherent phonon, as discussed here, would be verified experimentally as a nonadiabatic, or multi-phonon assist process, such as in the photodissociation of molecules with an optical near field.

ACKNOWLEDGMENTS

This work was supported in part by the 21st Century COE program at Tokyo Institute of Technology "Nanometer-Scale Quantum Physics" and by a Grant-in-Aid for Scientific Research from the Ministry of Education, Culture, Sports, Science and Technology, Japan.

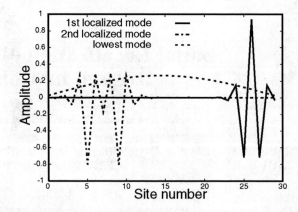

FIGURE 1. First and second localized modes of lattice vibration and the lowest delocalized mode.

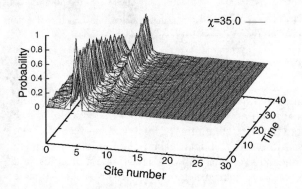

FIGURE 2. Photon probability found at each site as a function of time.

REFERENCES

1. Y. Yamamoto, M. Kourogi, M. Ohtsu, V. Polonski, and G. H. Lee, *Appl. Phys. Letters* **76**, 2173–2175 (2000); K. Matsuda, T. Saiki, S. Nomura, M. Mihara, Y. Aoyagi, S. Nair, and T. Takagahara, *Phys. Rev. Lett.* **91**, 177401 (2003).
2. T. Kawazoe, K. Kobayashi, J. Lim, Y. Narita, and M. Ohtsu, *Phys. Rev. Lett.* **88**, 067404 (2002).
3. S. Sangu, K. Kobayashi, A. Shojiguchi, and M. Ohtsu, *Phys. Rev. B* **69**, 115334 (2004).
4. T. Kawazoe, K. Kobayashi, S. Sangu, and M. Ohtsu, *Appl. Phys. Letters* **82**, 2957–2959 (2003).
5. T. Kawazoe, K. Kobayashi, and M. Ohtsu, *J. Chem. Phys.* **122**, 024715 (2005); K. Kobayashi, T. Kawazoe, and M. Ohtsu, *IEEE Trans. on Nanotech.* **4**, 517–522 (2005).
6. A. Shojiguchi, K. Kobayashi, S. Sangu, K. Kitahara, and M. Ohtsu, *J. Phys. Soc. Jpn.* **72**, 2984–3001 (2003).
7. A. S. Davydov and G. M. Pestryakov, *phys. stat. sol.* (b) **49**, 505–512 (1972).

Current-injection lasing in T-shaped GaAs/AlGaAs quantum-wire lasers

Shu-man Liu[1], Masahiro Yoshita[1], Makoto Okano[1] and Hidefumi Akiyama[1,2]
Loren N. Pfeiffer[2] and Ken W. West[2]

[1]Institute for Solid State Physics, University of Tokyo, and CREST, JST, Chiba 277-8581, Japan
[2]Bell Laboratories, Lucent Technologies, 600 Mountain Avenue, Murray Hill, New Jersey 07974, USA

Abstract. Current-injection T-shaped GaAs/AlGaAs quantum wires lasers have been fabricated by a cleaved-edge overgrowth method with molecular beam epitaxy. Continuous single-mode operation at photon energy of ~1.5 eV has been demonstrated between 30 K up to 70 K from laser diodes with high-reflectivity coating on both cleaved facets. The lowest threshold current (I_{th}) of 0.27 mA has been achieved at 30K, which are attributed to the high quality of the 2D confined structure and hence very low internal losses of the optical cavities.

Keywords: Quantum wire lasers, Low threshold current
PACS: 78.67.Lt, 42.55.Px

INTRODUCTION

The quantum-wire lasers are expected to operate efficiently with low injection currents. Intensive experimental efforts have been made to verify and understand such low threshold current. Nevertheless, the physics arguments are still unclear, and further experiments are necessary on quantum-wire-laser samples with high controllability in material, optical, and electrical structures. In this work, we demonstrate low-threshold singe-mode lasing in 20-period T-shaped quantum wire (T-wire) lasers with high material quality and a new efficient current injection scheme.

EXPERIMENT

Current-injection T wire lasers were fabricated by the cleaved-edge overgrowth method with molecular beam epitaxy (MBE)[1]. Figure 1 shows a schematic view of the laser structure. The quantum wires were formed at the T-intersections of 20-period 14-nm-thick (001) $Al_{0.07}Ga_{0.97}As$ multiple quantum wells (MQWs) (stem wells) and a 6-nm-thick (110) GaAs quantum well (arm well). Laser bars of 500 μm cavity length were cut from the wafer by cleavage with the cleaved facets perpendicular to the axis of the T-wires after MBE growth and metallization. The cavity facets were coated by the high reflectivity Au-layers after deposition of 70 nm SiO_2 insulating layer with plasma

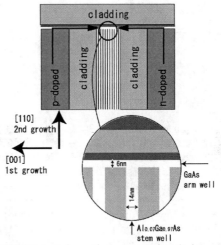

FIGURE 1. Schematic cross-sectional view of a T-wire laser structure. The arrows at the upper panel indicate the carrier injection from the doped layer to T-wire active region via the arm well.

assisted chemical vapor deposition.

In the laser structure, both electrons and holes are injected into the active region of 20 T-wires via only the arm well. This injection scheme is different from that reported by Wegscheider et al[2], in which electrons and holes are injected from the arm well and stem wells, respectively. Thus, the current in our laser structure is confined in the thin arm well, as shown by the arrows in the upper panel. Light emission from the laser diode was dispersed in a 0.75-m spectrometer and detected with a charge-coupled-device (CCD) camera. A photodiode detector was used to measure the output power.

RESULTS AND DISCUSSION

Figure 2 shows the current versus voltage (I-V) curve of the laser diode at temperatures from 5K to room temperature (r.t.), exhibiting typical diode characteristic. The soft turn-on of the I-V curve at temperatures below 30 K is probably due to carrier freezing in doped MQW and buffer layers. Figure 3 shows the single facet light output power characteristics for a 500 μm length laser diode as a

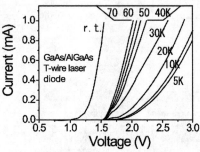

FIGURE 2. Diode current-voltage characteristics of a T-wire laser at various temperatures from 5K to room temperature (r.t.) indicated in the figure.

function of the bias current at 30 K, together with the output spectra at four different bias points below and above threshold, respectively. The threshold current (I_{th}) of the laser device is 0.27 mA and the mean differential quantum efficiency is 12% at 30K. The optical spectrum is modulated by Fabry-Pérot oscillations below the threshold current and turns into a single lasing mode at 1.554 eV after the current reaches the threshold current. The largest shift as the current increases to 1.5 mA is 1.2 meV, showing the stability of the lasing energy from our T-wire lasers. No emission or lasing from the stem wells has been observed at all injection currents investigated, indicating high injection efficiency. Single-mode lasing has been similarly observed at the cryostat temperatures between 30 and 70 K. If we assume internal quantum efficiency $\eta_i= 1$ on the basis of high injection efficiency and negligibly small nonradiative decay, the measured η_d of 12% at 30 K gives an estimation of internal loss $\alpha_i = 0.32$ cm^{-1}. The I_{th} of 0.27 mA at 30 K for 20 T-wires corresponds to 0.014 mA per 500-μm-long single-wire. Thus the threshold carrier density is estimated to be 7×10^5 cm^{-1} per single-

wire by using separately measured carrier lifetime of 0.4 ns and the assumed $\eta_i= 1$. This estimated result agrees well with our separate experimental results on optically pumped T-wire lasers [2-5].

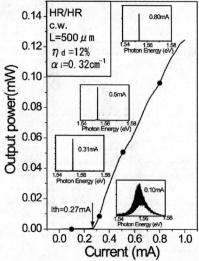

FIGURE 3 Light power–current characteristics and emission spectra at different bias currents for a high-reflection (HR) coated T-wire laser diode under c.w. operation at 30K. The threshold current (Ith), the estimated differential quantum efficiency (η_d) and internal loss (α_i) has been indicated in the figure.

SUMMARY

We have presented low-threshold current-injection lasers using 20-period T-wires of high material quality as gain medium and a simple but efficient current injection scheme, which contribute to the low threshold current and hence low threshold current density and low internal loss in our c.w. operated laser diodes.

REFERENCES

1. L. Pfeiffer, K. W. West, H. L Stormer, J. P Eisenstein, K. W. Baldwin, D. Gershoni, and J. Spector, Appl. Phys. Lett. **56**, 1697-1699 (1990)
2. W. Wegscheider, L. N. Pfeiffer, K. W. West, and R. E. Leiberguth, Appl. Phys. Lett. **65**, 2510-2512 (1994).
3. H. Akiyama, L. N. Pfeiffer, M. Yoshita, A. Pinczuk, P. B. Littlewood, K.W. West, M. J. Matthews and J. Wynn, Phys. Rev. B **67**, 041302R (2003)
4. Y. Takahashi, S. Watanabe, M. Yoshita, H. Itoh, Y. Hayamizu, H. Akiyama, L. N. Pfeiffer and K. W. West, Appl. Phys. Lett. **83**, 4089-4091 (2003).
5. M. Yoshita, Y. Hayamizu, H. Akiyama, L. N. Pfeiffer and K. W. West, submitted.

Band-edge divergence and Fermi-edge singularity in an n-type doped T-shaped quantum wire

T. Ihara[1], M. Yoshita[1], H. Akiyama[1], L. N. Pfeiffer[2] and K.W. West[2]

[1]*Institute for Solid State Physics, University of Tokyo and CREST, JST, Chiba 2778581, Japan*
[2]*Bell Laboratories, Lucent Technologies, Murray Hill, NJ 07974, USA*

Abstract. We studied photoluminescence-excitation (PLE) spectra of one-dimensional (1D) electron systems in an n-type modulation-doped single quantum wire at various temperatures from 5K to 50K. At low temperature (5K), we observed a single absorption onset, which corresponds to the Fermi edge of degenerate 1D electron gas. As the temperature was increased, this Fermi-edge absorption onset disappeared, while another absorption onset appeared at lower energy, which became a sharp peak at 50K. We assigned this peak to the 1D band-edge absorption induced by the inverse square root divergence of 1D density of states (DOS).

Keywords: Quantum wires; Electron density of states; Photoluminescence; Fermi-edge singularity
PACS: 73.21.Hb, 73.20.At, 78.67.Lt, 78.55.Cr

INTRODUCTION

Band-edge divergence of one-dimensional (1D) density of states (DOS) is one of the intriguing characters of 1D electron systems formed in an n-type doped quantum wire. One of the earlier theories [1] predicted that, in the presence of degenerate 1D electron gas, the optical spectra exhibit a sharp band-edge peak induced by 1D DOS divergence with many-body Coulomb enhancements near the Fermi edge (Fermi edge singularity; FES). While experimental investigation of FES has been reported [2], the appearance of the band-edge divergence has not been verified yet. In this work, we study the temperature-elevated photoluminescence (PL) and PL-excitation (PLE) spectra of 1D electron systems formed in an n-type doped T-shaped quantum wire.

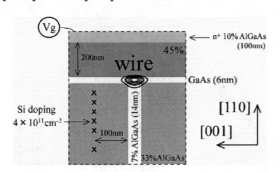

FIG. 1 Schematic view of n-type doped quantum wire sample.

SAMPLES AND EXPERIMENTS

Fig.1 shows the sample structure of an n-type doped GaAs quantum wire. Cleaved-edge overgrowth with molecular beam epitaxy and growth interrupt annealing were used to fabricate the single quantum wire sample with a 14nm x 6nm cross-sectional size [3]. The electron density of the wire can be tuned by applying gate voltage (V_g). Micro-PL and PLE measurements on the wire were performed with a excitation from cw titanium-sapphire laser with a 1μm spot size. The direction of PL detection was perpendicular to the laser excitation and their polarization were orthogonal to each other to improve signal-to-noise ratio.

RESULTS AND DISCUSSION

Solid curves in Fig. 2 indicate normalized PLE spectra at various temperatures in the presence of dense 1D electron gas. The gate voltage was fixed to 0.7V, which corresponds to the electron density of about 6 x 10^5 cm^{-1} in the quantum wire. At low temperature (5K), we observed a single absorption onset at 1.575eV with a long low-energy tail. We assigned this onset as the Fermi edge (FE), which separates the occupied and unoccupied state in the conduction band. A large absorption by the arm well showed its low-energy tail at around 1.578eV. As the

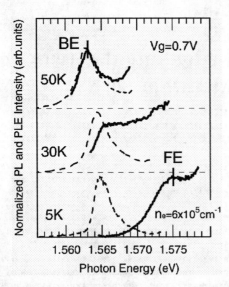

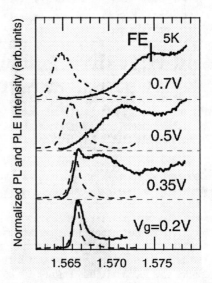

FIG. 2 Normalized PL (dotted curves) and PLE (solid curves) spectra of 1D electron gas at various temperatures. BE and FE corresponds to the band edge and Fermi edge, respectively.

FIG. 3 Normalized PL (dotted curves) and PLE (solid curves) spectra of 1D electron gas at various gate voltages.

temperature was increased, the FE onset was smeared and another absorption onset was formed at 1.565eV. At 50K, this onset increased its intensity and formed a sharp peak structure. We assigned this peak to the band-edge (BE) van Hove singularity induced by the inverse square root 1D-DOS divergence.

Normalized PL spectra are shown in Fig. 2 by dotted curves. At 5K, we observed an asymmetrical broad PL peak at 1.565eV. We assigned this PL peak to the band-edge emission. The energy gap of 10meV between PL peak and PLE onset at FE corresponds to Burstein-Moss shift. As the temperature was increased, the PL peak shifted to lower energy without any remarkable change in its lineshape. This red shift with increasing temperature also appears in bulk GaAs. At 50K, we found that the PL and PLE peak appeared exactly at the same energy of band edge denoted by BE.

We also studied electron density dependence of PLE spectra at low temperature (5K), using the same sample of a doped quantum wire. The solid curves in Fig. 3 indicate the normalized PLE spectra at various Vg. The top line at Vg = 0.7V corresponds to the high-density, which is the same as the bottom line of Fig. 2. As we have already mentioned, the single absorption onset (FE) at Vg = 0.7V corresponds to the Fermi edge. As the density was decreased, the FE onset shifted to lower energy. At Vg = 0.35V, band-edge absorption peak appeared at low-energy side (1.5665eV), and a characteristic double peak structure was formed. As the density was further decreased, the Fermi edge peak merge into the tail of the band-edge peak, and formed

a single asymmetrical absorption peak structure at Vg = 0.2V.

The sharp absorption peak (BE) at 50K in Fig. 2 and the double peak structure at 0.35V in Fig. 3 are surely characteristic of 1D electron systems. As we have mentioned above, these structures can be understood by the divergence of 1D DOS. In fact, the band edge absorption of 2D electron systems exhibits rather broader lineshape due to the step functional 2D DOS.

CONCLUSION

Low-temperature PL and PLE spectra are studied in an n-type modulation-doped T-shaped single quantum wire with a gate to tune electron densities. With non-degenerate 1D electron gas, band-edge absorption exhibits a sharp band-edge-divergence of 1D density of states (DOS). When the dense 1D electron gas is degenerate at a low temperature, we observe a Fermi-edge absorption onset.

REFERENCES

1. F. J. Rodríguez and C. Tejedor, Phys. Rev. B **47**, 1506 (1993).
2. J. M. Calleja, A. R. Goñi, B. S. Dennis, J. S. Weiner, A. Pinczuk, S. Schmitt-Rink, L. N. Pfeiffer, K. W. West, J. F. Müller, and A. E. Ruckenstein, Solid State Commun. **79**, 911 (1991).
3. H. Akiyama, L. N. Pfeiffer, A. Pinczuk, K. W. West, and M. Yoshita, Solid State Commun. **122**, 169 (2002).

Raman study of InAs/InP quantum wires

T. Angelova[1], A. Cros[1], A. Cantarero[1], D. Fuster[2], Y. González[2] and L. González[2]

[1] *Instituto de Ciencia de los Materiales, Universidad de Valencia, P.O. Box 22085, 46071 Valencia, Spain*
[2] *Instituto de Microelectrónica de Madrid (CNM-CSIC), Isaac Newton 8, 28760 Tres Cantos, Madrid, Spain*

Abstract. We present a Raman study of the vibrational modes in InAs/InP (001) quantum wires. The energy of the observed phonon modes evidences the confinement properties of the wires, their strain anisotropy and the effect of atomic intermixing. Resonance effects in confined and interface phonons are discussed for excitation in the vicinity of the E_1 critical point. The observed vibrations and their variation with sample characteristics are in agreement with the conclusions of previous structural and optical characterization performed in the same samples.

Keywords: Quantum Wires, Raman scattering, strain.
PACS: 70.30-j, 78.67, 68.65.La

INTRODUCTION

Interest in the optical properties of self-assembled InAs/InP quantum wires (QWrs) and quantum dots (QDs) directly grown by the Stranski-Krastanow method has been motivated because of their promising applications for optoelectronic devices operating in the 1.30-1.55 μm wavelength range employed in fiber optical telecommunication systems.

During the last years, it has been demonstrated that Raman spectroscopy is a valuable tool for nanostructure characterization, providing information about strain, composition and electronic structure [1, 2]. In this work we have investigated the structural and electronic properties of multilayers of InAs/InP QWrs as a function of the thickness of the InP spacer layer (d). Two series of InAs QWrs covered by a 20 nm thick InP cap layer were grown on (001) InP by solid-source molecular beam epitaxy. The first series was grown at a temperature of 380 °C (denoted in what follows as low temperature, LT), and consists of three samples with d = 5, 10 and 20 nm. The second series was grown at a higher temperature (515 °C, referred as HT), with d = 3, 5, 10 and 20 nm. The resulting QWrs are oriented along [1$\bar{1}$0] [3]. Raman measurements were performed with a Jobin-Yvon T64000 spectrometer equipped with a nitrogen cooled charge coupled device detector. The spectra were taken at room temperature in $z(x,x)\bar{z}$ and $z(x,y)\bar{z}$ configurations, where x||[110], y||[1$\bar{1}$0] and z||[001].

The 488 nm line of an Ar$^+$ laser served as excitation source. A 100x microscope objective was used to focus the light to a 1 μm spot on the sample surface, and collect the scattered signal to the spectrometer. For measurements around the resonance, eight emission lines of the Ar$^+$ laser were used, covering a range from 2.4 eV to 2.73 eV.

RESULTS AND DISCUSSION

The polarized Raman spectra of the HT sample with d = 5 nm are shown in Figure 1. The plasma line at 221.0 cm^{-1} marked as P in the Figure has been used to calibrate the spectra. The observed peaks can be grouped in a low energy (ω<250 cm^{-1}) and a high energy region (ω>300 cm^{-1}). Considering first the characteristics of the high energy side, the peaks at 342 and 303 cm^{-1} can be attributed to InP longitudinal optical (LO) and transverse optical (TO) phonon modes. The broad peak near 310 cm^{-1}, observed more clearly in parallel polarization, corresponds to an interface mode (IF) in which the P atoms have maximum amplitude of vibration. Turning our attention to the low energy part, three confined LO phonon modes related to InAs can be observed between 220 and 240 cm^{-1}. They have been labeled as LO$_1$, LO$_3$ and LO$_5$ in the Figure. The assignment of the order of the confined modes has been performed by comparison with the bulk dispersion curves. The energy of LO$_1$ is almost coincident with that of bulk LO mode (239.8 cm^{-1}), indicating that the QWrs are

CP893, *Physics of Semiconductors, 28th International Conference*
edited by W. Jantsch and F. Schäffler

almost relaxed. The broad structure at 229 cm^{-1} observed only under $z(x,x)\bar{z}$ polarization can be attributed to IF phonon modes where As vibrations dominate. Taking into account the selection rules of Raman scattering in bulk zinc-blende semiconductors, only LO phonons should be allowed in parallel polarization. We have found that the vibrational modes arising from the QWrs violate these selection rules. The interface phonons, however, follow them as expected [4].

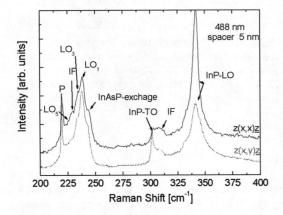

FIGURE 1. Polarized micro-Raman spectra of InAs/InP QWrs from the HT series with d = 5 nm.

The peak denoted as InAsP-exchange has been tentatively attributed to the exchange of As and P atoms during growth. This phonon mode has been assigned considering its behavior with spacer thickness (its energy increases with d [1]) and annealing temperature [5]. The intensity of this mode is related to the growth conditions, and increases with growth temperature [3]. Furthermore, the frequency of this mode is shifted upwards in the HT series with respect to that of LT, indicating a larger atom intermixing when growth is performed at high temperature, in accordance with the work of *Fuster et a*l [6].

Figure 2 displays micro-Raman spectra corresponding to the LT series with d = 10 nm in parallel polarization for different excitation energies. The intensity of the InAs related modes was normalized to that of the InP LO mode. A resonance enhancement of the LO$_1$ phonon mode was observed in the vicinity of 2.5-2.62 eV. This is probably due to the proximity of the E$_1$ electronic transition of InAs which is found at 2.61 eV for the bulk at 300 K [7]. However, the intensity of the InAs - IF mode seems to increase further with increasing wavelength, indicating that the resonance may occur at somewhat higher energies for this mode. This can be understood taking into account the mixed InAs-InP nature of this

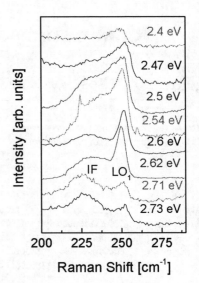

FIGURE 2. Micro-Raman spectra of InAs/InP QWrs recorded at room temperature with several laser wavelengths for the d = 10 nm sample (LT series).

vibration and considering that the E$_1$ electronic transition of bulk InP is known to be at 3.1 eV at 300 K [8].

ACKNOWLEDGMENTS

The authors are thankful to the Ministry Education and Science of Spain (MAT2003-00399), the Generalitat Valenciana, and the European Network SANDIE (NMP4-CT-2004-500101) for financial support.

REFERENCES

1. L. Artús, R. Cuscó, S. Hernández, A. Patané, A. Polimeni, M. Henini and L. Eaves, *Appl. Phys. Letters* **77**, 3556 (2000).
2. W. Lei, Y. Chen, B. Xu, X. Ye, Y. Zeng and Z. Wang, *Nonotechnology* **16**, 1974 (2005).
3. D .Fuster, "Crecimiento y caracterización de hilos cuánticos de InAs/InP" Ph.D. Thesis, University of Valencia, 2006.
4. M. Cardona and G. Günterodt, "Optical Properties", in *Light Scattering in Solids,* edited by Springer Berlin, 1982-1996, pp 365-371.
5. S. Tripathy, C. Chia, J, Dong and S. Chua, *Electrochem. and Solid-State Llett.* **8**, 194-197 (2005).
6. D. Fuster, M. González, L. González, Y. González, T. Ben, A. Ponce, S. Molina and J. Matínez-Pastor, *Appl. Phys. Letters* **85**, 1424 (2004).
7. R. Carles, N. Saint-Cricq, J. Renicci, A. Zwick and M. Renucci, *Phy. Rev. B* **22**, 6120 (1980).
8. P. Lautenschlager, M. Garriga and M. Cardona, *Phy. Rev. B* **36**, 4813 (1987).

Raman Scattering in GaN/AlN Multiple Quantum Disk Nanocolumns

T. Sekine[*,†], S. Suzuki[*], M. Tada[**], T. Nakazato[**], A. Kikuchi[**,†] and K. Kishino[**,†]

[*]Department of Physics, Sophia University, Tokyo 102-8554, Japan
[†]CREST, Japan Science and Technology Agency, Kawaguchi, Saitama 332-0012, Japan
[**]Department of Electrical and Electronics Engineering, Sophia University, Tokyo 102-8554, Japan

Abstract. We have studied phonon modes in GaN/AlN multiple quantum disk nanocolumns, which are self-organized on Al_2O_3 and Si substrates by RF-MBE, by means of Raman scattering. The Raman spectrum drastically changes with increasing thickness of the GaN quantum disk. We find the confined, quasi-confined and interface phonon modes, which are not observed in the usual GaN/AlN superlattice thin film. They are activated by confinement in the columnar nanostructures and a multiple-scattering process.

Keywords: Raman scattering, phonon, nanocolumns, GaN/AlN multiple quantum disks
PACS: 72.10Di, 73.21Cd, 73.21Hb, 73.61Ga, 73.63Bd

Recently, the semiconductor columnar nanostructures, i.e., nanocolumns, have aroused great attention because of their potential uses in both the mesoscopic research and the development of nanodevices. Yoshizawa et al.[1] first succeeded in growing GaN nanocolumns on Al_2O_3 by rf-plasma-assisted molecular beam epitaxy (RF-MBE) through a self-organization process. This method was applied to the growth of a novel columnar nanostructure, GaN/AlGaN heterostructure nanocolumns with GaN multiple quantum disks (MQDs).[2] Moreover, Kikuchi et al.[3] fabricated InGaN/GaN MQD nanocolumn light-emitting diodes on n-type Si substrates.

In spite of remarkable progress in the growth of GaN and GaN-related nanocolumns and in the fabrication technologies of the devices using these materials, some basic properties of the nanocolumns including lattice dynamics still remain poorly studied. In this work, we study phonon mode behavior in GaN/AlN MQD nanocolumns by means of Raman scattering.

GaN/AlN MQD nanocolumns with hexagonal wurtzite crystal structures were self-organized on (0001) Al_2O_3 and (111) Si substrates by RF-MBE method.[2] The schematic structure of typical GaN/AlN MQD nanocolumns is illustrated in Fig. 1. The nanocolumns were grown at high density of about 10^{10} columns/cm². The average column diameter ranges from 40 to 100 nm and the height is about 2 μm. The 514.5-nm line of Ar^+-ion laser was incident on the c plane of the sample and Raman spectra were recorded in quasibackscattering geometry at room temperature.

Figure 2 shows Raman spectra in GaN/AlN MQD nanocolumns with various thicknesses of GaN and AlN quantum disks (QDs). However, the thickness of AlN QD may be regarded as almost constant when compared

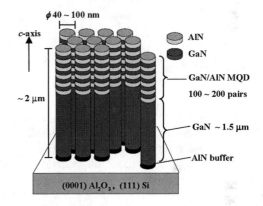

FIGURE 1. Schematic structure of typical GaN/AlN MQD nanocolumns.

with that of GaN QD. When the GaN QDs are thin, three peaks are observed at 531, 597, and 645 cm⁻¹, in addition to the Raman-active E_2 phonon of bulk GaN. The 597- and 645-cm⁻¹ peaks gradually disappear with increasing thickness of GaN QD. On the other hand, two new peaks appear at about 550 and 579 cm⁻¹ and shift gradually to the low-frequency side with increasing thickness of GaN QD. Simultaneously the intensity of the E_2 phonon of GaN drastically increases. Moreover, a broad peak appears around 810 cm⁻¹. In the 52.2/23.0-Å sample we observed two new peaks at 485 and 708 cm⁻¹. In the 710/500-Å sample a peak having a low-frequency tail was observed at 574 cm⁻¹ in addition to a small broad peak at 645 cm⁻¹. All of the new peaks were not observed in a usual GaN/AlN superlattice (SL) film grown by RF-MBE, which has fifty pairs of GaN/AlN.

Gleize et al.[4] calculated the dispersion of polar

CP893, Physics of Semiconductors, 28th International Conference
edited by W. Jantsch and F. Schäffler
© 2007 American Institute of Physics 978-0-7354-0397-0/07/$23.00

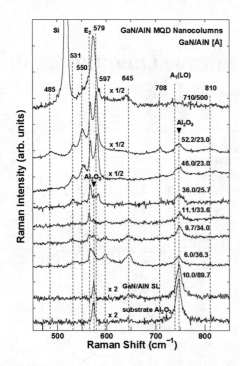

FIGURE 2. Raman spectra of GaN/AlN MQD nanocolumns. Raman spectra of GaN/AlN SL film and substrate Al_2O_3 are also shown for comparison.

optical phonons along the layer direction in wurtzite GaN/AlN heterostructure SL in the framework of the dielectric continuum model. The extraordinary phonons are classified into three kinds of phonon modes; nondispersive confined modes in either one of two layers, dispersive quasi-confined modes confined in one type of layer and evanescent in the other, and interface modes localized at the interfaces of two layers and decaying exponentially from the interfaces in both layer.

In the nanocolumns we should consider the phonon wave function to be confined along the radial direction of column. Although the result of Gleize *et al.* cannot be simply applied to the present experimental result, we try to assign the new peaks. The 550-cm^{-1} peak, appearing between $\omega_{A_1(TO)}^{GaN} = 531$ cm^{-1} and $\omega_{E_1(TO)}^{GaN} = 557$ cm^{-1} when the GaN QDs are thick, is assigned to a quasi-confined mode existing strongly within the GaN layers.[4] Similarly, the 531-cm^{-1} peak, whose frequency corresponds to A_1(TO) phonon of bulk GaN, also is a quasi-confined mode. The 645-cm^{-1} peak comes from a quasi-confined mode in the AlN layers, because it is observed between $\omega_{A_1(TO)}^{AlN} = 614$ cm^{-1} and $\omega_{E_1(TO)}^{AlN} = 673cm^{-1}$ and the scattering efficiency is large when the GaN QDs are thin. The two new peaks at about 579 and 597 cm^{-1} originate from interface modes, because they appear between $\omega_{E_1(TO)}^{GaN} = 557$ cm^{-1} and $\omega_{A_1(TO)}^{AlN} = 614$

cm^{-1}. Moreover, the broad peak at 810 cm^{-1} comes from interface modes.

The E_2 and A_1(LO) peaks at 565 and 739 cm^{-1} are proper confined modes in the GaN/AlN MQD nanocolumns. Moreover, we observed two more peaks at 485 and 708 cm^{-1} in the 52.2/23.0-Å sample. The 708-cm^{-1} peak possessing a low-frequency tail may be assigned to the Fröhlich mode, which is a surface phonon located at the side surface of column.[5] It appears probably because the GaN QDs are thick and the effects of the MQD structures weaken. The 485-cm^{-1} peak cannot be understood at present, because its frequency is lower than $\omega_{A_1(TO)}^{GaN} = 531$ cm^{-1} and any quasi-confined and interface modes are not allowed in this region.

We could not observe confined, quasi-confined, and interface modes in the GaN/AlN SL film, as shown in Fig. 2. The phonon wave vector along the radial direction, $q_\perp$, is zero in the backscattering geometry, but $\sim 6 \times 10^5$ cm^{-1} at most, taking into account a possibility that the laser light could be incident on the side of column in the multiple scattering. Then the frequencies of the quasi-confined modes at $q_\perp d \sim 0.6$ in the GaN/AlN SL film with a period of the SL, $d \simeq 100$ Å, are nearly equal to the E_1(TO) phonons of bulk materials.[4] We observed that the quasi-confined modes at 550 and 645 cm^{-1} were split from the GaN E_1(TO) and AlN E_1(TO) phonons, respectively; it is probably due to not only the quantization of the wave vector along the c axis but also that of $q_\perp$ by confinement of wave function in the nanocolumns when $q_\perp d \sim \pi d/r \sim 1$. Here r is the column radius. In the 710/500-Å sample, i.e., when $\pi d/r \gg 1$, only one peak having a low-frequency tail was observed around 574 cm^{-1}, which may be understood in terms of the relaxation of the $q = 0$ selection rule due to partial confinement in the columnar microcrystal.[6] Moreover, the multiple-scattering process enhances the scattering efficiency in the columnar nanostructures.[5]

The observed Raman peaks are sharp, and the frequencies of the proper confined phonon modes hardly changed in the MQD nanocolumns when compared with the corresponding phonons of bulk GaN. These facts indicate the presence of heterointerfaces between the GaN and AlN layers and the strains are relieved at the barriers.

REFERENCES

1. M. Yoshizawa *et al.*, *Jpn. J. Appl. Phys.* **36**, L459-L462 (1997).
2. M. Yoshizawa *et al.*, *J. Cryst. Growth* **189/190**, 138-141 (1998).
3. A. Kikuchi *et al.*, *Jpn. J. Appl. Phys.* **43**, L1524-L1526 (2004).
4. J. Gleize *et al.*, *Phys. Rev. B* **60**, 15985-15992 (1999).
5. T. Sekine *et al.*, *e-J. Surf. Sci. Nanotech.* **4**, 227-232 (2006).
6. H.-L. Lie *et al.*, *Chem. Phys. Lett.* **345**, 245-251 (2001).

Spatially-resolved Photoluminescence Imaging of CdS and GaAs/AlGaAs Nanowires

L.M. Smith[1], Thang B. Hoang[1], L.V. Titova[1], H.E. Jackson[1], J.M. Yarrison-Rice[2],
J.L. Lensch[3], L.J. Lauhon[3], Y. Kim[4], H. J. Joyce[4] and C. Jagadish[4]

[1]*Department of Physics, University of Cincinnati, Cincinnati, OH*
[2]*Physics Department, Miami University, Oxford, OH*
[3]*Department of Materials Science and Engineering, Northwestern University, Evanston, IL*
[4]*Department of Electronic Materials Engineering, Research School of Physical Sciences and Engineering,
Australian National University, Australia*

Abstract. We use low temperature spatially resolved photoluminescence imaging to study optical properties and electronic states of single CdS and GaAs/AlGaAs core-shell nanowires.

Keywords: Nanowires, nanostructures, photoluminescence spectroscopy, defect luminescence.
PACS: 61.46.-w, 78.67.-n

Vapor-Liquid-Solid (VLS) grown semiconductor nanowires (NWs) have recently begun to be incorporated into a number of electronic and optical devices [1-3]. Detailed information about structural uniformity and electronic structure of the NWs important for any such devices can be provided by single NW spatially-resolved PL imaging. .Because of the large surface-to-volume ratio inherent in NWs, even small surface or structural variations can have a large impact on their electronic states. Passivating the surface of the NWs by growing a shell of the higher gap material has been shown to dramatically improve NW luminescence efficiency by spatially separating the NW core states from the surface [4]. Here we describe low temperature spatially resolved photoluminescence (PL) imaging of both single uncoated CdS nanowires and core-shell GaAs/AlGaAs nanowires.

CdS NWs were synthesized by VLS from 50 nm Au catalysts [5]. AFM measurements of several single CdS NWs from 10 to 15 μm in length show a broad range of structural variations from straight and smooth NWs to ones with kinks and lobes. GaAs/AlGaAs core-shell NWs 6-8 μm-long were prepared by MOCVD starting with a 30 nm gold catalyst. In AFM images, the NWs appear straight and tapered, with few surface imperfections. For single NW PL measurements, CdS NWs were excited by 2.5 mW of a 458 nm Ar+ laser, and GaAs/AlGaAs NWs – by equivalent power density of 750 nm Ti:S laser. In

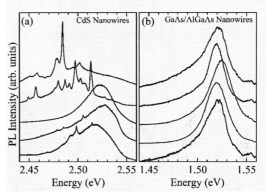

FIGURE 1. PL spectra of single CdS (a) and GaAs-AlGaAs NWs. The spectra have been normalized for clarity.

order to illuminate entire NWs, the laser was defocused to a 10 μm spot. A 50×/0.5NA long working length microscope objective was used to project magnified images of the single wire PL onto the entrance slit of the spectrometer. The spatial resolution of our PL imaging setup is 1.5 μm. All measurements were done at 10 K.

Low temperature PL spectroscopy of individual NWs provides important information about their electronic structure. Figure 1 displays PL spectra of several CdS (Fig. 1a) and GaAs-AlGaAs (Fig. 1b) NWs. The variety of structures observed by AFM in CdS NW are reflected in the PL spectra. Uniform wires display dominant near band edge (NBE) PL near 2.52 eV in a broad band (FWHM 33-45 meV) (see

CP893, *Physics of Semiconductors, 28th International Conference*
edited by W. Jantsch and F. Schäffler

three bottom spectra in Fig. 1a), while disordered NWs exhibit sharp emission lines at lower energy (top two spectra in Fig 1a.)

The PL spectra of all studied GaAs/AlGaAs NWs (Fig. 1b) display a single band edge peak at 1.521 ± 0.003 eV with 23 ± 3 meV FWHM which corresponds to free exicton emission in bulk epilayers. GaAs/AlGaAs core-shell NWs display PL over an 1- to 2-orders of magnitude higher intensity than bare GaAs nanowires. In addition, (not shown) bare GaAs nanowires also show significant defect PL at lower energy.

Fig. 2 shows 2D PL images (spatial position vs. emission energy) of single CdS (Fig. 2a) and GaAs-AlGaAs (Fig. 2b) nanowires. The vertical axes of the images correspond to the spatial position along the wires, while the horizontal axes show the emission energy.

In Fig. 2a we show a PL map from a non-uniform CdS NW with several bends, kinks and lobes.[6,7] The spectral map clearly indicates that narrow emission lines are associated with particular positions along the NW. Fig. 2b shows several spectral cross-sections at three different positions along the NW (A, C, B-D). The NBE emission also appears on the 2D map as a broad high energy shoulder which emits uniformly along the NW.

Time-resolved measurements [6] show that the lifetime of NBE emission from all CdS NWs is less than 80 ps, significantly smaller than the known 500 ps exciton lifetime in bulk CdS [8], suggesting the presence of non-radiative defects, or surface states. On the other hand, the defect-related emissions exhibit lifetimes ranging from 300 to 700 ps, possibly indicating that defect-localized excitons are protected from such non-radiative states.

Fig. 2c shows a 2D PL map of a single GaAs-AlGaAs NW. The PL intensity varies along the length of the NW with the most intense PL emission observed from a small (~1.3 μm) portion of the NW. On the other hand, the peak energy and emission profile is uniform as shown by the two spectra shown in Fig. 2d. Both spectra contain a single free exciton peak. No evidence of localized defect emission is observed in this or any other studied GaAs-AlGaAs NW.

The high PL efficiency and absence of defect states of core-shell NWs compared to their bare counterparts, shows that surface passivation dramatically improves NW optical properties. However, the measured lifetime of excitons in GaAs/AlGaAs NWs is still less than 80 ps suggesting that there are still significant non-radiative recombination centers in these NWs. Identifying those defects and minimizing their concentration should further improve the quantum efficiency in GaAs/AlGaAs NWs.

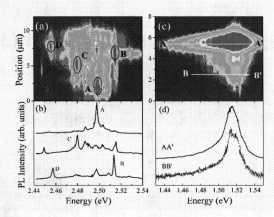

FIGURE 2. 2D PL map (a) and spectra taken along several positions (b) along the CdS NW; 2D PL map (c) and spectra taken along several positions (d) along the GaAs-AlGaAs NW.

In conclusion, we have shown that spatially resolved low temperature PL imaging of single NWs provides information about the nature and properties of the electronic states in these structures which is crucial for the development of the NW-based photo-electronic devices. In bare CdS NWs, localized defect states are evidenced by narrow excitonic emission lines. The emission energy of the core-shell GaAs-AlGaAs NWs is uniform along the nanowire axis although the intensity may vary. These results indicate that the core-shell NWs are more uniform and their emission properties more predictable, thus making them better candidates for the NW photonic device applications.

We acknowledge support of the NSF through DMR 0071797 and 0216374, PRF through the ACS, and the Australian Research Council. JLL acknowledges the support of a NSF Graduate Fellowship.

1. Y. Gu, E.-S. Kwak, J. L. Lensch, J. E. Allen, T. W. Odom, and L. J. Lauhon, *Appl. Phys. Letters,* **87**, 043111-043113 (2005).
2. Carl J. Barrelet, Andrew B. Greytak, and Charles M. Lieber, *Nano Letters* **4**, 1981-1985 (2004).
3. Ritesh Agarwal, Carl J. Barrelet, and Charles M. Lieber, , Nano Letters 5, 917-920 (2005).
4. J. Noborisaka, J. Motohisa, S. Hara, and T. Fukui, *Appl. Phys. Letters* **87**, 093109-093111 (2005).
5. C.J. Barrelet, Yue Wu, David. C. Bell, and C. M. Lieber, *J. Am. Chem. Soc.* **125**, 11498-11499 (2003).
6. L.V. Titova, Thang Ba Hoang, H.E. Jackson, L.M. Smith, J.M. Yarrison-Rice, J.L. Lensch, L.J. Lauhon, *Appl. Phys. Lett.* **89**, 053119 (2006).
7. L.V. Titova, Thang Ba Hoang, H.E. Jackson, L.M. Smith, J.M. Yarrison-Rice, J.L. Lensch, L.J. Lauhon, in press, *Appl. Phys. Lett,* condmat/0606428 .
8. D.G. Thomas and J.J. Hopfield, *Phys. Rev. Lett.* **7**, 316-319 (1961).

Optical Spectroscopy Of Charged Quantum Dot Molecules

M. Scheibner[1], A. S. Bracker[1], E. A. Stinaff[1], M. F. Doty[1], D. Gammon[1], I. V. Ponomarev[1], T. L. Reinecke[1], V. L. Korenev[2]

[1]Naval Research Laboratory, Washington DC, 20375 USA
[2]A. F. Ioffe Physical Technical Institute, St. Petersburg, 194021 Russia

Abstract. Coupling between two closely spaced quantum dots is observed by means of photoluminescence spectroscopy. Hole coupling is realized by rational crystal growth and heterostructure design. We identify molecular resonances of different excitonic charge states, including the important case of a doubly charged quantum dot molecule.

Keywords: Quantum Dot Molecules, Tunnel Coupling, Photoluminescence Spectroscopy.
PACS: 78.67.HC, 73.21.La, 78.47.+p, 78.55.Et

INTRODUCTION

Molecular optical spectra can be very complex, but clever chemical synthesis, symmetry principles, and selection rules allow spectral assignments even for complicated molecules. With semiconductor quantum dot molecules (QDMs), the advantage of perfect ensemble homogeneity is lost. However crystal growth and heterostructure design provide a powerful tool to continuously tune the atom-like physical properties of quantum dots (QDs) [1-5]. Building on our recent result for hole coupling in a singly positively charged QDMs [1, 2], we present the optical signatures of hole coupling for a doubly positively charged QDM. This case is of great interest as it could be utilized as a two qubit system. In addition, we provide a simple and intuitive scheme for the assignment of spectral lines in QDMs and show how the QDM spectra allow us to obtain further information on the molecular structure.

SAMPLE AND EXPERIMENT

We have performed photoluminescence (PL) spectroscopy on individual InAs/GaAs QDMs. The QDMs were formed by the subsequent growth of two closely spaced layers of self-assembled QDs, where the QDs of the second layer nucleate preferably on top of QDs in the first layer, forming 'diatomic' molecules. The relative bandgaps of the QDs are defined by truncating the QDs to a well-defined height, using an indium flush technique. The dimensions of the QDM we studied here are h_B=4.0 nm, h_T=2.5 nm for the heights of the bottom and top

QD respectively and d=4.0 nm for the barrier width. Here we use a n-type field tunable heterostructures to modify the interdot band offsets in the conduction and the valance band. This allows us to tune the hole levels into resonance applying a positive electric field. The off resonant electrons are localized in the bottom QD only.

The QDMs were excited quasi-resonantly with a continuous wave titanium sapphire laser tuned below the energy of the wetting layers. The PL-signal was spectrally dispersed by a half meter monochromator, equipped with a 1200 mm^{-1} line grating, and detected with a charged coupled device (CCD) camera. The overall spectral resolution was 50 μeV. The QDMs were kept a constant temperature of T=10 K.

CHARGED QDMS

The optical spectra of charge tunable single QDs have been studied intensively and provide the basis for understanding the spectra of QDMs. These spectra exhibit a characteristic sequence of PL-lines which can be associated with specific charge states of the QD [6]. The PL-line of the neutral exciton is accompanied by a PL-line typically 1-4 meV higher in energy and another PL-line typically 5-7 meV lower in energy. These are identified to originate from the positively and the negatively charged excitons (trions), respectively. The same sequence can be found in the spectra of QDMs [1].

Figure 1a shows the part of a QDM spectrum which contains the neutral exciton (X^0) and the positive trion (X^+) transitions as function of electric

CP893, Physics of Semiconductors, 28th International Conference
edited by W. Jantsch and F. Schäffler
© 2007 American Institute of Physics 978-0-7354-0397-0/07/$23.00

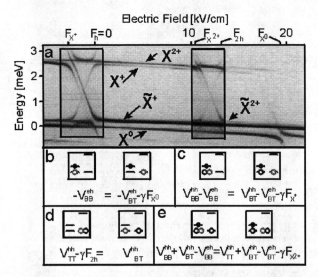

FIGURE 1. a) Optical spectrum of a QDM as function of electric field. This spectral map contains single exciton PL-transitions which arise when the QDM is uncharged, singly or doubly positively charged. 5 times smaller field steps were used inside the black boxes. b)-e) illustration of the conditions for hole level resonances for the neutral exciton (b), positive trion (c), two holes (d) and doubly positively charged exciton. The tunneling hole is marked red.

field. The molecular character is proven by the presence of strongly field dependent PL-lines (slope $\pm\gamma$ [7]), which arise from interdot e-h recombination, and anticross with less field independent PL-lines (intradot e-h recombination) [1-5]. Anticrossings are a clear sign of quantum mechanical tunnel coupling. In the case of the positive trion these features arrange in an 'x'-shaped pattern.

We have shown recently that this 'x'-pattern arises from the fact that both the initial (X^+) and the final (single hole) state of the trion transitions can exist not only with all charges in the bottom QD but also in a configuration with one hole in the top QD [1]. It follows that anticrossings can occur in the initial state as well as in the final state. These molecular resonances are realized at different electric fields because of a difference between electron and hole Coulomb potentials.

The relative positions of the various anticrossings in electric field follow from the resonance condition. It demands that the tunneling particle experiences the same net potential in both QDs. Without loss of generality we chose the resonance of the single hole to be realized at zero field ($F_h=0$). The relative fields of the resonances of neutral exciton, F_{X^0}, and the positive trion, F_{X^+}, are to first approximation given by (see Figs. 1 b and c) $F_{X^0} = (V_{BB}^{eh} - V_{BT}^{eh})/\gamma$ and

$F_{X^+} = F_{X^0} + (V_{BT}^{hh} - V_{BB}^{hh})/\gamma$, considering only direct Coulomb interactions $V_{ij}^{\alpha\beta}$ between two particles α and β, that are located in dot i and dot j, respectively.

If an e-h recombination takes place in the bottom QD while the top QD contains an additional charge, the resulting PL energy is similar to PL energy of the same transition without this additional charge. The intradot e-h recombination of the positive trion ($\tilde{X}^+$) where one of the holes is located in the top QD is such a transition and it is close in energy to the neutral exciton PL-line. In general, the influence of an additional charge in the top QD on the exciton transition in the bottom QD is to first approximation determined by the difference between the Coulomb interaction of the bottom dot electron and hole with this charge.

Like the neutral exciton (X^0) the positive trion PL-line (X^+) is accompanied by a higher energy partner. In terms of the above model this PL-line can be assigned to a doubly positively charged exciton (X^{2+}), where one hole is in the top QD. It is also possible to have two holes in the top QD while an e-h pair remains in the bottom QD. Consequently, the intradot recombination associated with this configuration ($\tilde{X}^{2+}$) should be close in energy to the X^0 and $\tilde{X}^+$ PL-lines. Close examination of the field dependent PL-map reveals this line and a second 'x'-pattern (see Figs. 1a, d and e).

From the position in field where the anticrossings of the X^{2+} transition in this particular QDM occur (Figs. 1 d and e) it follows that $V_{BB}^{hh} \approx V_{TT}^{hh} + 8$ meV. This indicates a larger average separation of the holes when they are in the top QD than when they are in the bottom QD. Thus, in this QDM the top dot is vertically thinner but laterally larger than the bottom dot.

ACKNOWLEDGMENTS

We acknowledge the financial support by NSA/ARO, CRDF, RFBR, RSSF, and ONR. M.F.D., I.V.P and E.A.S, are NRC/NRL Research Associates.

REFERENCES

1. E. A. Stinaff, *et al.*, *Science* **311**, 636 (2006)
2. M. Scheibner, *et al.* cond-mat/0607241
3. H. J. Krenner, *et al.*, *Phys. Rev. Lett.* **94**, 057402 (2005)
4. G. Ortner, et al., *Phys. Rev. Lett.* **94**, 157401 (2005)
5. H. J. Krenner, *et al.*, cond-mat/0604659 (2006)
6. B. Urbaszek, *et al. Phys. Rev. Lett.* **90**, 247403 (2003)
7. The slope of the interdot PL-lines is given by $\gamma=e(d+(h_B+h_T)/2)$, where e is the elementary charge.

Theory of Spin States of Quantum Dot Molecules

I. V. Ponomarev[1], T.L. Reinecke[1], M. Scheibner[1], E.A. Stinaff[1], A. S. Bracker[1], M.F. Doty[1], D. Gammon[1], and V.L. Korenev[2]

[1] *Naval Research Laboratory, Washington DC, 20375, USA*
[2] *A.F. Ioffe Physical Technical Institute, St. Petersburg, Russia*

Abstract. The photoluminescence spectrum of an asymmetric pair of coupled InAs quantum dots in an applied electric field shows a rich pattern of level anticrossings, crossings and fine structure that can be understood as a superposition of charge and spin configurations. We present a theoretical model that provides a description of the energy positions and intensities of the optical transitions in exciton, biexciton and charged exciton states of coupled quantum dots molecules.

Keywords: Coupled quantum dots, spin states, coherent coupling, exchange interaction
PACS: 78.67.Hc, 73.21.La, 78.47.+p, 78.55.Et

INTRODUCTION

Optical manipulation of spins in the self-assembled InAs coupled quantum dots (CQDs) is of interest in connection with gates in quantum information applications. These systems could lead to ultrafast control of spin qubits. To this end it is important to obtain a detailed understanding of the spin states in CQDs. Recent photoluminescence (PL) spectroscopy [1,2,3] of CQDs controlled by an applied electric field reveals a richer diversity in spectral line patterns than in their single quantum dot counterparts. Here we present a theoretical model that accounts well for the rich optical spectra. We derive an effective Hamiltonian that describes the low energy excitations of this system in terms of a small number of physical parameters.

THE MODEL

Self-assembled InAs/GaAs QDs are strongly confined cylindrical-like structures with a vertical size $h\sim2-6$ nm and a lateral size $a\sim10-40$ nm. Their sizes are almost an order of magnitude smaller than those of electrostatically defined QDs ($h\sim10$, $a\sim400$ nm). Due to a stronger confinement the self-assembled dots have larger single-particle energy separations that result in better protection from environment for the lowest levels and in many cases allow a perturbative treatment of Coulomb interactions between the particles. On the other hand, optical excitation means that two different kinds of particles are involved (electrons and holes). Therefore, the number of physically important parameters becomes larger compared to transport experiments in electrostatically defined QDs [3].

Although the two QDs in the samples under investigation here [1,2] were grown with nominally the same vertical heights, the top (T) QD usually has a higher exciton ground energy due to inherent asymmetry of the dots. The asymmetric nature of these CQDs means that electron and hole resonances occur at different electric fields. When the field brings the hole levels into resonance, the electron levels shift out of resonance and the electron remains localized in one dot.

We take the electron to be in its ground state $\varphi_B^e(\mathbf{r}_e)$ that is located primarily in the bottom (B) quantum dot. The truncated single particle basis for holes consists of the two lowest orthonormal s-states $\varphi_B^h(\mathbf{r}_h)$ and $\varphi_T^h(\mathbf{r}_h)$ in the two dots. Bra-ket notations for these single-particle states are $|B^e>, |B^h>, |T^h>$. For the electron spin functions we use the notation $|\alpha^e>, |\beta^e>$ for spin projections $S_z^e = \mp \frac{1}{2}$. The heavy hole spin function ($J_z = \pm 3/2$) is treated as a fermion with the pseudo-spin ½. For the two-particle spin states we use orthogonal set of singlet and triplet spin wave functions $|s_{ij}>, |\tau_{ij}^{(m)}>$, where $m=\pm1,0$.

CP893, *Physics of Semiconductors, 28th International Conference*
edited by W. Jantsch and F. Schäffler
© 2007 American Institute of Physics 978-0-7354-0397-0/07/$23.00

We take the applied electric field, F, to change only the difference between two hole energies by $f = |e| F \tilde{d}$, where e is the charge of the electron and $\tilde{d} = d + (h_B + h_T)/2$ is the distance between centers of two dots. The zero of electric field is taken to occur when the two hole energies would cross in the absence of coupling between the dots. The many-body basis configurations for each molecule are constructed from antisymmetrized products of single-particle states.

In the envelope function approximation and in the effective atomic units, the many-particle Hamiltonian of the CQDs charge states consists of three parts:

$$\hat{H} = \sum_{\alpha, l} \mathbf{h}_l^{\alpha} + \sum_{\alpha, \beta, l, m} V_C \left(\left| \mathbf{r}_{\alpha l} - \mathbf{r}_{\beta m} \right| \right) + \hat{H}_{exch}^{eh}, \quad (1)$$

where $\alpha = e$ or h; $l, m = 1, \ldots$ The first sum gives the single-particle Hamiltonians for electrons and holes, the second part gives the Coulomb interactions between particles, and the third part is electron-hole exchange that has the form of the short-range effective Hamiltonian $A \sum_{i,j} \delta \left(\mathbf{r}_{ei} - \mathbf{r}_{hj} \right) \hat{\sigma}_{ez}^{(i)} \hat{\sigma}_{hz}^{(j)}$, where A is a coupling constant, $\hat{\sigma}_{e(h)z}^{(i)}$ are Pauli matrices, and z is along the growth direction which has the strongest confinement direction for electrons and holes. The single-particle Hamiltonians have the following matrix elements: $\left\langle B^{\alpha} \left| \mathbf{h}^{\alpha} \right| B^{\alpha} \right\rangle = \varepsilon_{\alpha}$, $\left\langle T^h \left| \mathbf{h}^h \right| T^h \right\rangle = \varepsilon_h - f$,

$\left\langle B^h \left| \mathbf{h}^h \right| T^h \right\rangle = t_h$, where ε_{α} are the electron or hole confinement energies in the bottom QD, and t_h is the hole tunneling rate. The Coulomb part of the many-particle Hamiltonian generates Coulomb intergrals:

$V_{ijkl}^{\alpha, \beta} = \pm \int d\mathbf{r} d\mathbf{r}' \left| \mathbf{r} - \mathbf{r}' \right|^{-1} \varphi_i^{\alpha *}(\mathbf{r}) \varphi_k^{\beta *}(\mathbf{r}') \varphi_j^{\alpha}(\mathbf{r}) \varphi_l^{\beta}(\mathbf{r}').$ The electron-hole exchange interaction is given by $J_{ij}^{eh} = A \int d\mathbf{r} \left| \varphi_B^e \right|^2 \varphi_i^{h *} \varphi_j^h.$

We find from calculations for model dot and barrier potentials that there is a hierarchy in magnitudes of the parameters $t_h, V_{ijkl}^{\alpha \beta}, J_{ij}^{eh}$, which is determined by their different dependences on distance between QDs.

Positive Trion X^+

As an illustration here we consider the case of a positive trion X^+ in a QDM [1, 2]. In order to obtain PL energy transitions we calculate the initial (with 2 holes + 1 electron) and the final states (with 1 hole). Two singlets and one triplet form the basis many-particle states of the initial X^+ Hamiltonian:

$\left| 1 \right\rangle = \left| B^e B_1^h B_2^h; \beta^e s_{12}^h \right\rangle$, $\left| 2 \right\rangle = \left| B^e 2^{-1/2} \left(B_1^h T_2^h + T_1^h B_2^h \right); \beta^e s_{12}^h \right\rangle$,

$\left| 3, 4, 5 \right\rangle = \left| B^e 2^{-1/2} \left(B_1^h T_2^h - T_1^h B_2^h \right); \beta^e \tau_{12}^{(0,+1,-1)h} \right\rangle$. The final states after electron-hole recombination are obtained by diagonalizing the single hole Hamiltonian in the basis of states $| B^h >, | T^h >$. Transitions between initial and final states give the energy positions of PL spectrum. We find that they give a good description of the experimental spectra (see Fig. 1) and that they determine the characteristic "X" pattern seen in the experiment [1,2].

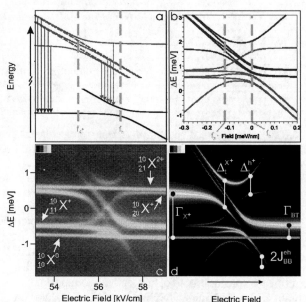

FIGURE 1. (a) The dependence of eigenenergies on electric field for the initial and the final Hamiltonians. The distance between QDs is 6 nm. The fields for the minimal trion and hole splittings are shown by green dashed lines. (b) and (d) are the calculated PL energy spectrum and intensities. (c) Experimental intensities for X^+ charge configuration with $d = 6$ nm. Some states belonging to different charge states (such as X^{2+}) also appear in spectrum. Far from resonances the PL energies can be qualitatively described by labeling, where $_{p,q}^{n,m} X^+$ denotes the spin configuration of the initial state with $n(m)$ electrons and $p(q)$ holes in the bottom(top) dot. The particles involved in e-h recombination are underlined.

ACKNOWLEDGMENTS

We acknowledge the support by DARPA and ONR.

REFERENCES

1. E.A. Stinaff et al., *Science* **311**, 636–639 (2006).
2. M. Scheibner et al., cond-mat/0607241 (2006).
3. H.J. Krenner et al., *Phys.Rev. Letters* **94**, 057402 (2005).

Time-Resolved Optical Spectroscopy of Tunnel Coupled Lateral Quantum Dot Molecules

C. Hermannstädter*, G. J. Beirne*, L. Wang†, A. Rastelli†, O. G. Schmidt† and P. Michler*

*Institut für Strahlenphysik, Universität Stuttgart, Allmandring 3, 70569 Stuttgart, Germany
†Max-Planck-Institut für Festkörperforschung, Heisenbergstr. 1, 70569 Stuttgart, Germany

Abstract. The two laterally coupled quantum dots, also referred to as lateral quantum dot molecules, exhibit a characteristic photoluminescence spectrum consisting of six dominant emission lines that are due to neutral and charged excitonic as well as biexcitonic recombination. All of these lines are found to originate from the same single quantum emitter following photon statistics measurements. Using a parallel electric field we are able to control the quantum coupling between the dots. This control manifests itself as an ability to reversibly switch the relative intensities of the two neutral excitonic transitions, which results in a possible application of the molecules as tunable single-photon emitters. To further investigate the exact origin of the photoluminescence lines we have also investigated the decay times of the molecule emission.

Keywords: coupled quantum dots, dot molecules, tunable single-photon source, time-resolved optical spectroscopy
PACS: 78.55.Cr, 78.67.Hc, 73.21.La, 78.47.+p

The control of quantum coupling along the growth direction in vertically stacked quantum dot molecules (QDMs), using electric fields has been observed [1], [2]. The novel QDMs used in this work are fabricated as lateral pairs of closely spaced self-assembled InGaAs quantum dots (QDs) [3]. Atomic force microscopy measurements show that each QDM consists of two structurally distinct QDs, which are aligned along the $[1\bar{1}0]$ direction with a density as low as 5×10^7 cm^{-2} [4]. The in-plane geometry allows for the application of lateral electric fields, either along or perpendicular to the QDM coupling-axis, simply by processing electrodes on the sample surface.

Typical photoluminescence (PL) spectra from a QDM are presented in Fig. 1 (a-b). At low excitation power density (PD) the spectrum consists of two intense lines, named X1 and X2, and two less intense lines, Y and Z. All four lines exhibit a linear dependence on PD with respect to their integrated PL intensities, which leads us to assume that X1 and X2 are due to neutral excitonic transitions. Y and Z on the other hand, are thought to be due to charged excitonic transitions. At higher PDs, two additional lines, XX1 and XX2, appear and exhibit a super-linear PD dependence indicating that they originate from biexcitonic transitions.

Photon statistics measurements were carried out to confirm, firstly, the single-photon nature of the six lines and, secondly, that they all originate from the same quantum source. Second-order autocorrelation measurements have been performed on the QDM lines under both cw and pulsed excitation conditions. All results show a pronounced suppression of coincidence events at $\tau = 0$ in the related Poisson-normalized autocorre-

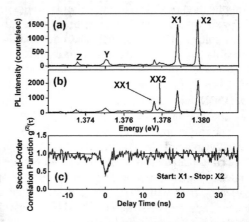

FIGURE 1. QDM A at T = 4 K, under non-resonant cw excitation at 1.54 eV: **(a)** PL spectrum at 450 Wcm^{-2} PD; **(b)** PL spectrum at 750 Wcm^{-2} PD; **(c)** $g^{(2)}(\tau)$ at 750 Wcm^{-2} PD with a Poisson level of 118 counts/channel.

lation function $g^{(2)}(\tau) = \frac{\langle : I(t) \cdot I(t+\tau) : \rangle}{\langle : I^2(t) : \rangle}$, i.e. photon anti-bunching with values below 0.5, which clearly indicates single-photon emission. In addition, second-order cross-correlation functions have been measured pairwise between the six molecule lines and these measurements also show photon antibunching with values below 0.5 for all configurations at $\tau = 0$ for $g^{(2)}(\tau) = \frac{\langle : I_a(t) \cdot I_b(t+\tau) : \rangle}{\langle : I_a(t) \cdot I_b(t) : \rangle}$, where a and b label the START and STOP photons. This proves that the lines originate from the same single quantum source (e.g. Fig. 1 (c)), as emission from two independent dots would not be correlated. Also, cascaded emission has been observed indicating the existence of

CP893, *Physics of Semiconductors, 28th International Conference*
edited by W. Jantsch and F. Schäffler
© 2007 American Institute of Physics 978-0-7354-0397-0/07/$23.00

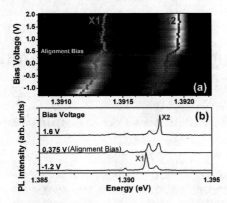

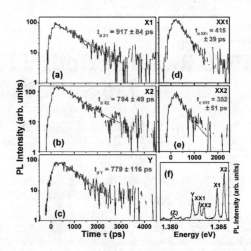

FIGURE 2. Anomalous Stark shift and switching of QDM B excitons at T = 4 K, under non-resonant fs-pulsed excitation at 1.51 eV and 50 Wcm^{-2}: **(a)** PL intensity as a function of energy and bias, the symbols mark the peak centers, the solid lines are guides to the eye showing the expected behavior if no coupling was present; **(b)** PL spectra at 1.6 V, 0.375 V and -1.2 V.

FIGURE 3. Time-resolved PL of the characteristic emission lines **(a-e)** and PL spectrum **(f)** of QDM C, all at T = 4 K, under non-resonant fs-pulsed excitation at 1.49 eV and 400 Wcm^{-2}.

two biexciton-exciton-cascades, XX1-X1 and XX2-X2 [4], as expected.

The application of a lateral electric field parallel to the coupling-axis of the molecules is realized by applying static bias voltages to two parallel electrodes and allows for reversible switching of the emission from X1 to X2 with both peaks being equally intense at the alignment bias of 0.375 V, as shown in Fig. 2. At the alignment bias the QDM has the maximum degree of coupling between the two dots since at this voltage the single-particle electron ground states of the individual dots are energetically aligned. In general, the switching in the QDMs occurs independent of the polarity of the applied bias. It does, however, depend on the relative orientation of the electric field with respect to the QDM coupling-axis and, as expected, no switching could be observed for electric fields applied perpendicular to this axis. These observations are in good agreement with a 1D-model and lead us to the assumption that electron-tunneling is the predominant coupling mechanism in the QDMs. Another important observation is an anomaly in the Stark shift of the exciton emission energies as seen in Fig. 2 (a), which is about 60-80 μeV at the alignment point. This value allows for an estimate of the QDM coupling energy of about 150 μeV.

Time-resolved single-photon counting (TCSPC) measurements have been performed on all molecule lines in order to learn more about the decay characteristics and to support the aforementioned denotation of the Y and Z lines as being due to charged excitonic recombination. The following decay times have been found for the excitons X1, X2: (800-1200)$\pm$100 ps, the biexcitons XX1, XX2: (250-500)$\pm$50 ps, and Y and Z: (600-900)$\pm$100 ps. In agreement with results on single QDs [5], the biexciton decay times are about half those of the excitons as a

result of the second possible decay channel. The decay times of Y and Z are intermediate, in accordance with single dot results. The shorter decay time of these two lines compared to X1 and X2 is thought to be due to the extra carrier confined in the QDM that also leads to an increased number of available decay channels. This observation supports the denotation of Y and Z as emission from charged excitons.

In conclusion, this work demonstrates the presence of quantum coupling in lateral QDMs and the ability to control the QDM single-photon emission using electric fields. This makes the QDM a good candidate for application as a wavelength-tunable single-photon emitter. Furthermore, the origin of the lines constituting the characteristic QDM PL emission have been studied using photon statistics and TCSPC experiments.

The authors acknowledge financial support from the Deutsche Forschungsgemeinschaft (SFB/TR 21 and FOR 730).

REFERENCES

1. H. J. Krenner, M. Sabathil, E. C. Clark, A. Kress, D. Schuh, M. Bichler, G. Abstreiter and J. J. Finley, Phys. Rev. Lett. **94**, 057402 (2005).
2. G. Ortner, M. Bayer, Y. Lyanda-Geller, T. L. Reinecke, A. Kress, J. P. Reithmaier and A. Forchel, Phys. Rev. Lett. **94**, 157401 (2005).
3. R. Songmuang, S. Kiravittaya and O. G. Schmidt, Appl. Phys. Lett. **82**, 2892 (2003).
4. G. J. Beirne, C. Hermannstädter, L. Wang, A. Rastelli, O. G. Schmidt and P. Michler, Phys. Rev. Lett. **96**, 137401 (2006).
5. R. M. Thompson, R. M. Stevenson, A. J. Shields, I. Farrer, C. J. Lobo, D. A. Ritchie, M. L. Leadbeater and M. Pepper, Phys. Rev. B **64**, 201302 (2001).

Optical near-field mapping of bright and dark quantum dot states

Ulrich Hohenester*, Guido Goldoni† and Elisa Molinari†

*Institut für Physik, Karl–Franzens–Universität Graz, Universitätsplatz 5, 8010 Graz
†INFM–S³ and Dipartimento di Fisica, Università di Modena e Reggio Emilia, Via Campi 213/A, 41100 Modena, Italy

Abstract.
We theoretically investigate scanning nearfield optical microscopy (SNOM) of semiconductor quantum dots. In the nearfield regime bright and dark excitonic states become mixed, opening new channels for the coupling to the electromagnetic field. As a consequence, ultra-narrow luminescence lines appear in the spectra, corresponding to very long lived excitonic states.

Keywords: quantum dots, scanning nearfield optical microscopy (SNOM)
PACS: 73.21.La,78.67.-n,71.35.-y

Scanning near-field optical microscopy (SNOM) is an experimental technique that combines the advantages of nanometric resolution of scanning-probe microscopy with the unique properties of optical spectroscopy. This is achieved by quenching light through the tip of an optical fiber and exciting the probe in the near-field, hereby overcoming the diffraction limit of light by several orders of magnitude [1, 2]. Near-field spectroscopy has been successfully used for the measurement of single and coupled semiconductor nanostructures [3, 4, 5], molecules [6, 7], or metallic nanostructures [8, 9]. If the spatial near-field resolution falls below the extension of confined quantum systems, it becomes possible to directly map out the spatial probability distribution of the wavefunction. This was recently achieved by Matsuda et al. [10] for quantum dots where the quantum confinement is induced by local monolayer fluctuations in the thickness of a semiconductor quantum well. With $\Psi_x(r_e, r_h)$ the electron-hole wavefunction of the quantum dot, the matrix elements for the optical nearfield transitions are of the form [11, 12]

$$\int dr\, E_\omega(r_{\text{tip}} - r)\Psi_x(r, r),\qquad(1)$$

with $E_\omega(r_{\text{tip}} - r)$ the electromagnetic distribution around the nearfield tip. In contrast to the far-field, where the matrix elements governing the light-matter coupling are determined by the quantum states alone, in the near-field the pertinent matrix elements (1) become a convolution of the quantum states with the electro-magnetic field profile of the SNOM tip. This allows to break in the near-field the usual optical selection rules, and to excite dark states whose excitation is forbidden by symmetry in the far-field.

In our calculations we consider quantum confined states induced by monolayer fluctuations in the thickness of a GaAs/AlGaAs semiconductor quantum well [10, 11]. Since the confinement length (several tens of nm) is much larger than both the lattice constant and the excitonic Bohr radius, we adopt the usual envelope function and rigid-exciton (rigid-biexciton) approximations, the latter assuming that the correlated electron-hole wavefunctions factorize into a center-of-mass and a relative part given by that of the quantum well [11]. The insets of Fig. 1 show the real-space maps of the square modulus of the biexciton ground (B_0) and first excited (B_1) states, respectively, for a prototypical square-like confinenement potential (dashed lines) as a function of the center-of-mass coordinates. The wavefunction symmetries resemble those of a particle-in-a-box problem with s and p symmetry states. Similar results are found for the gound and excited exciton states X_0 and X_1, respectively.

We now assume that the heterostructure is excited through a strongly inhomogeneous field emitted by a fiber tip at the two different spots A and B shown in the inset of the Fig. 1. For convenience we consider a two-photon excitation of biexcitons, where, because of the large biexciton binding energy $\delta E_b \sim 4$ meV [13], the luminescence from the $B \to X$ and $X \to 0$ recombinations is red- and blue-shifted, respectively, and can thus be spectrally discriminated. We also assume that the luminescence is detected somewhere in the far-field (not necessarily through the SNOM tip). Figure 1 shows the corresponding luminescence spectra. For tip position A (center of the dot) the field does not break the symmetry of the underlying quantum states. Accordingly, only the ground state biexciton B_0 can be

CP893, *Physics of Semiconductors, 28th International Conference*
edited by W. Jantsch and F. Schäffler
© 2007 American Institute of Physics 978-0-7354-0397-0/07/$23.00

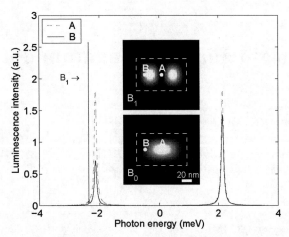

FIGURE 1. Luminescenece spectra of excitons and biexcitons for a prototypical quantum dot and for two different positions A and B of the SNOM tip. The insets report the real-space map of the ground and first excited biexciton states B_0 and B_1, respectively. At tip position A the luminescence spectra are governed by two strong peaks attributed to the decay of the exciton and biexciton states of lowest energy. At tip position B an additional, ultra-narrow peak appears, which is attributed to the excited, far-field forbidden biexciton state B_1.

excited, whereas the transition to B_1 is forbidden because of symmetry, as in the far-field case. Correspondingly the luminescence spectra consist of two equally strong peaks associated to the $B_0 \rightarrow X_0$ and $X_0 \rightarrow 0$ transitions. The line broadenings are due to photon emissions and are as large as $\Gamma \sim 100$ μeV for the large coherence volumes of the exciton and biexciton states. Note that the far-field luminescence spectrum (not shown here) is almost identical.

When the dot is excited at tip position B, which does not coincide with the symmetry center of the heterostructure, an additional ultra-narrow peak appears, indicated with B_1 in Fig. 2B, which is due to the excitation of the biexciton B_1. Because this dark state couples weakly to photons, its lifetime is orders of magnitude larger than that of the bright B_0 state. At the lowest excitation powers the broadening of this additional peak is dominated by phonon scattering ($\Gamma \sim 1$ μeV for zero temperature). However, its appearence in the luminescence spectrum indicates a substantial excitation-induced mixing of biexciton and exciton states, as also evidenced by the approximately $1:9$ ratio between the oscillator strengths of the dark and bright transitions. With increasing excitation power this mixing becomes stronger and the peaks are further broadened. In Ref. [12] we investigate the dependence of the B_1 transition on excitation power and temperature, and find an ac-Stark effect and a splitting of the line at relatively small Rabi energies. Similarly to the Mollow spectrum of a driven two-level system, this splitting is due to a strong light-biexciton coupling and occurs when the line broadening Γ becomes comparable to the effective Rabi frequency. The essentials of these findings are expected to prevail for dot confinements with lower symmetry.

Dark-state transitions in the near-field spectra are expected to constitute a genuine property of carrier complexes in large nano systems, where the large active dot volume results in a strong enhancement of the light-matter coupling, relatively short lifetimes of bright states, and a pronounced mixing of excitonic states in presence of laser excitation. In the future, similar wavefunction mapping is expected to become possible for other scanning probe techniques, such as optical nano antennas [14], which might pave the way for optical nano imaging of molecules or biological structures.

REFERENCES

1. M. A. Paesler, and P. J. Moyer, *Near-Field Optics: Theory, Instrumentation, and Applications*, Wiley, New York, 1996.
2. B. Hecht, B. Sick, U. P. Wild, V. Deckert, R. Zenobi, O. J. F. Martin, and D. W. Pohl, *J. Chem. Phys.* **112**, 7761 (2000).
3. E. Betzig, J. K. Trautman, T. D. Harris, J. S. Weiner, and R. L. Kostelak, *Science* **251**, 1468 (1991).
4. H. F. Hess, E. Betzig, T. D. Harris, L. N. Pfeiffer, and K. W. West, *Science* **264**, 1740 (1994).
5. J. R. Guest, T. H. Stievater, Gang Chen, E. A. Tabak, B. G. Orr, D. G. Steel, D. Gammon, and D. S. Katzer, *Science* **293**, 2224 (2001).
6. W. E. Moerner, T. Plakhotnik, T. Irngartinger, U. P. Wild, D. W. Pohl, and B. Hecht, *Phys. Rev. Lett.* **73**, 2764 (1994).
7. C. Hettich, C. Schmitt, J. Zitzmann, S. Kühn, I. Gerhardt, and V. Sandoghdar, *Science* **298**, 385 (2002).
8. C. Chicanne, T. David, R. Quidant, J. C. Weber, Y. Lacroute, E. Bourillot, A. Dereux, C. Golas de Francs, and C. Girard, *Phys. Rev. Lett.* **88**, 097402 (2002).
9. C. Ropers, D. J. Park, G. Stibenz, G. Steinmeyer, J. Kim, D. S. Kim, and C. Lienau, *Phys. Rev. Lett.* **94**, 113901 (2005).
10. K. Matsuda, T. Saiki, S. Nomura, M. Mihara, Y. Aoyagi, S. Nair, and T. Takagahara, *Phys. Rev. Lett.* **91**, 177401 (2003).
11. U. Hohenester, G. Goldoni, and E. Molinari, *Appl. Phys. Lett.* **84**, 3963 (2004).
12. U. Hohenester, G. Goldoni, and E. Molinari, *Phys. Rev. Lett.* **95**, 195429 (2005).
13. A. Zrenner, L. V. Butov, M. Hagn, G. Abstreiter, G. Böhm, and G. Weimann, *Phys. Rev. Lett.* **72**, 3382 (1994).
14. J. N. Farahani, D. W. Pohl, H. J. Eisler, and B. Hecht, *Phys. Rev. Lett.* **95**, 017402 (2005).

Collective And Individual Emissions For InGaAs Quantum Dots In Photonic Crystal Nanocavity

W.-Y. Chen[1], H.-.S Chang[1], W.-H. Chang[1], T.-P. Hsieh[2], J.-I. Chyi[2], and T. M. Hsu[1]

1) Department of Physics, National Central University, Jhong-Li, Taiwan
2) Department of Electrical Engineering, National Central University, Jhong-Li, Taiwan
Tel: +886-3-4227151ext65320, Fax: +886-3-4251175, jerry@phy.ncu.edu.tw

Abstract. We investigate the collective and individual emissions from $In_{0.5}Ga_{0.5}As$ quantum dots (QDs) in single-defect photonic crystal nanocavities. The cavity mode collectively excited by the QD ensemble shows a pair of dipole-like modes with definite linear polarizations. Single exciton emission lines are resolved under low excitation power. By monitoring the power dependence of individual QD emissions, a nearly tenfold light enhancement for on-resonance QDs is observed. The polarization states of individual QDs are also investigated. It is found that either a pure dipole mode or a mixture of both dipole modes could be excited by an individual dot. These behaviors are attributed to the random distribution of QD location in the nanocavity

Keywords: quantum dots, photonic crystal
PACS: 42.70.Qs, 78.67.Hc

Coupling of spontaneous emissions (SE) from semiconductor quantum dots (QDs) into cavity modes of an optical microcavity[1] is a key step to develop QD-based single photon sources.[2-4] In the weak-coupling regime, the SE rate will be enhanced due to the Purcell effect.[5] Significant enhancement can be achieved when the cavity offers high quality factor (Q) and/or small mode volume (V_m). If the QDs are on-resonance, i.e., spectral and spatial match with cavity mode, the enhancement can reach its maximum. In recent years, focused attention has turned to the use of photonic crystal (PC) nanocavities. For properly designed PC nanocavities, very high Q ($> 10^4$) together with a very small V_m of the order of cubic wavelength in material $[\sim(\lambda/n)^3]$ are theoretically predicted. This feature is particularly appealing since such high Q/V_m ratios may further push the QD-cavity interaction into the strong-coupling regime and realize the cavity-quantum electrodynamic (cavity-QED) phenomena.

In this work, the optical properties of $In_{0.5}Ga_{0.5}As$ QDs in H1 PC nanocavities are reported. Both the collective behaviors and individual properties of the QDs are investigated under different excitation conditions. The cavity mode, collectively excited by the QD ensemble, shows a pair of dipole-like modes. By monitoring the power dependence of individual QD emissions, a nearly tenfold enhanced SE rate for on-resonance QDs is observed. The polarization states of individual QDs are also investigated. It is found that either a pure dipole-like mode or a mixture of both

eigenmodes could be excited by individual QDs. These behaviors are attributed to the random distribution of QD location in the nanocavity.

The sample was grown on a (001) GaAs substrate using a low-pressure metal-organic chemical-vapor deposition reactor. The active region consisted of three layers of self-assembled $In_{0.5}Ga_{0.5}As$ QDs with 20-nm GaAs spacers at the center of a 190-nm-thick GaAs membrane layer. The QD density was about $\sim 3 \times 10^{10}$ cm^{-2}. After growth, the PC patterns were fabricated by using an e-beam lithography system and a dry etching system. A series of hexagonal PC structures were fabricated with different lattice constants (a=0.27-0.37 μm) and air hole radii (r=0.1-0.1 μm). The H1 nanocavities were formed by removing one air hole from the center of the hexagonal PC. Scan electron micrographs of the fabricated PC nanocavity was shown in Fig. 1(a).

Low-temperature microphotoluminescence (μ-PL) was used to characterize the optical emissions from the QDs in the nanocavities. The sample was held in a helium-flow cryostat at T=4-5 K. The QDs were optically excited by a He-Ne laser (633nm) through a microscope objective. The PL signals were collected by the same objective and analyzed by a spectrometer equipped with a liquid-nitrogen-cooled charge-coupled device. An achromatic waveplate was also used to eliminate the polarization selectivity of the gratings.

Figure 1(b) shows a typical PL spectrum from the

CP893, *Physics of Semiconductors, 28th International Conference*
edited by W. Jantsch and F. Schäffler

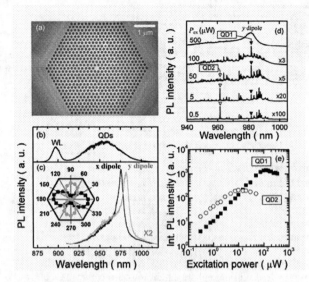

FIGURE 1. (a) The SEM image of a PC nanocavity. (b) The μ-PL spectrum taken from unprocess region. (c) The μ-PL for an H1 nanocavity. Inset: polar plot of the PL intensity as a function of polarization angle. (d)The evolutions of y-polarized PL spectra with the pumping laser power. The spectra were normalized by the indicated factors. (e) The intensities of excitation emissions from QD1 and QD2 as functions of the pumping power.

unprocess region. A broad QD emission band (920-1000 nm) and a wetting-layer peak (900 nm) can be observed. Figure 1(c) shows the μ-PL spectra for a H1 PC nanocavity with a=0.34 μm and r/a=0.38 at polarization angle along x and y directions. A feature of cavity resonance can be found near 980 nm. Polarization analysis reveals that the cavity resonance consists of a pair of linearly polarized modes at 975 and 982 nm. As shown in inset of fig. 1(c), these two modes are orthogonally polarized along the x and y directions, which are the x- and y- dipole modes for the H1 PC nanocavity. When the excitation power is reduced, a series of sharp lines become observable, which are shown in Fig. 1(d). These emission lines come from the exciton emissions from individual QDs of different sizes. By comparing the saturation power of QD1 (on-resonance) and QD2 (off-resonance), the enhancement of SE rate can be obtained. Figure 1(e) shows the emission intensity of QD1 and QD2 as a function of excitation power. The saturation power of QD1 is about ten times higher then QD2, indicating a nearly tenfold enhancement of the SE rate in QD1.

Now we take a closer look at polarization states of individual QDs (Fig. 2(a)). The polarizations of these lines are found to be randomly distributed. This feature is noticeable in Figs. 2(b) to 2(d), where the polarization characteristics for three selected QDs

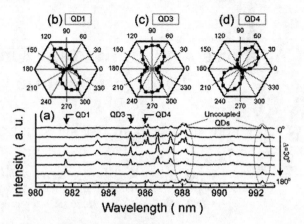

FIGURE 2. (a) The evolutions of emission lines with the polarization angle. (b)-(d) Polar plot of the PL intensity for three selected QDs.

are displayed. For example, the case of QD3 can be characterized as a pure y-dipole mode. However, for QD1 and QD4, the polarization angles deviate significantly from the y direction. Their polarization is a superposition of both modes. These behaviors are attributed to the random distribution of location QD in the nanocavity.

The optical properties of collective and individual emissions from $In_{0.5}Ga_{0.5}As$ QDs in H1 PC nanocavities were investigated. The cavity mode collectively excited by the QD ensemble shows a pair of orthogonally polarized dipole modes. A nearly tenfold enhancement of the SE rate was observed. The study of the polarization state of individual QDs suggests that QD-cavity interactions are different from dot to dot, due to the random distribution of QD locations in the nanocavity.

This work was supported by the National Science Council of Taiwan under Grant No. NSC-93-2120-M-008-001 and by CNST of UST.

REFERENCES

1. K. J. Vahala, *Nature (London)* **425**, 839 (2003).
2. P. Michler, A. Kiraz, C. Becher, W. V. Schoenfeld, P. M. Petroff, L. Zhang, E. Hu, and A. Imamoğlu, *Science* **290**,2282 (2000).
3. E. Moreau, I. Robert, J. M. Gérard, I. Abram, L. Manin, and V. Thierry-Mieg, *Appl. Phys. Lett.* 79, 2865(2001).
4. M. Pelton, C. Santori, J. Vučković, B. Zhang, G. S. Solomon, J. Plant, and Y. Yamamoto, *Phys. Rev. Lett.* **89**, 233602 (2002).
5. E. M. Purcell, *Phys. Rev.* **69**, 681 (1946).

Optical Properties Of Exciton Charge States In InGaAs Quantum Dots Grown By Metalorganic Chemical Vapor Deposition

H.-S.Chang[1], W.-H.Chang[1], W.-Y.Chen[1], T.-P.Hsieh[2], J.-I.Chyi[2], and T.M.Hsu[1]

[1]Department of Physics, National Central University, Jhong-li, 32001 Taiwan, Republic of China
[2]Department of Electrical Engineering, National Central University, Jhong-li, 32001 Taiwan, Republic of China

Abstract. The impact of residual impurities on neutral and charged exciton complexes in single InGaAs quantum dots (QDs) grown by metalorganic chemical vapor deposition were investigated. We show that the formation of a charged exciton can be controlled by using resonant excitation to the residual impurity level. This optical excitation scheme is useful for the selective generation only charged excitons in initially neutral QDs without sophisticated sample designs.

Keywords: self-assembled quantum dots, microphotoluminescence, photon antibunching, single photon sources.
PACS: 73.21.La, 78.67.Hc, 71.35.-y, 78.55.Cr

INTRODUCTION

Optical spectroscopy of single semiconductor quantum dots (QDs) has recently been the subject of intensive investigation.[1] This technique not only provides direct access to the underlying atomlike properties of single QDs, but also opens up possibilities of utilizing QDs as building blocks for quantum information applications, such as single photon emitters and quantum logic gates. For many of the proposed applications, few-particle exciton states of single QDs are of great importance. The few-particle exciton states arise from different charge configurations in a QD, including neutral excitonic species as well as their charged counterparts. Of particular interest are singly, charged excitons, which are free from the electron-hole exchange splitting due to their singlet spin states[2] and hence are well suited for single-photon emitters without fine structures[3]. In addition, the single spins left after trion recombination are also useful for spin-based quantum information processing. In this respect, controlling the QD charge state appears to be an important step toward these applications.

In this work, we investigate the neutral and charged exciton complexes in single InGaAs QDs grown by metalorganic chemical vapor deposition (MOCVD). We show that the formation of charged excitons can be selectively generated by optical resonant excitation to the residual impurity level. The fine structures caused by QD-impurity interactions are also addressed.

EXPERIMENTS

Our sample was grown on a n^+ GaAs substrate by a low-pressure MOCVD. After a 500-nm undoped GaAs buffer layer, a layer of $In_{0.5}Ga_{0.5}As$ QDs was then grown at at 500 °C. The InGaAs coverage was carefully controlled to ~4.2 MLs, yielding a low QD density of about 10^8-10^9 cm^{-2}. The QDs were finally capped by a 80-nm undoped GaAs layer. Further isolation of individual QDs was achieved by fabricating an aluminum shadow mask with an array of 300-nm apertures using electron-beam lithography. μPL was performed at 5-8 K on these apertures using a Ti-sapphire laser focused via a microscope objective. Luminescence was collected by the same objective lens and analyzed by a 0.64 m triple monochromator equipped with a charged-coupled device (CCD) camera.

RESULTS AND DISCUSSIONS

Figure 1 shows the μPL spectra obtained from one of the fabricated apertures under different excitation energies (E_{ex}). For E_{ex}=1520 meV, two emission lines are observed. Two emission lines at 1328.8 meV and 1323.8 meV are identified as neutral exciton (X) and

CP893, *Physics of Semiconductors, 28th International Conference*
edited by W. Jantsch and F. Schäffler
© 2007 American Institute of Physics 978-0-7354-0397-0/07/$23.00

negative charged exciton (X^-), according to their linear power dependence of intensity and their asymmetric antibunching behavior in photon cross-correlation measurements[4]. When E_{ex} is reduced to the WL energy (E_{WL}=1363 meV), only the X line can be observed. This implies that the QD is initially neutral in the absence of laser excitation. The formation of X^- was usually related to the presence of impurities in the QD surrounding. For the MOCVD-grown sample used here, the unintentionally doped carbon impurities may play a prominent role. Of particular interest is that when E_{ex}=1494 meV, i.e., the resonant energy of carbon acceptor level, selective generation of only X^- becomes possible. The resonant laser light can be absorbed by the carbon acceptors. Since most of the photogenerated holes are trapped by the carbon impurities, the formation of neutral X is very unlikely, leading to the preferential generation of only X^- in the QD.

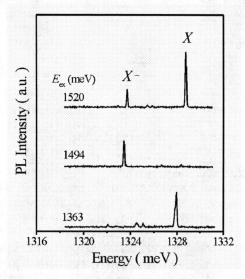

FIGURE 1. Single QD spectra under different E_{ex}'s.

We study the QD-impurity interaction by resonant excitation to the impurity level at different excitation powers (P_{ex}), which is shown in Fig. 2(a). The spectrum is dominated by X^- line in low P_{ex} regime. The intensity of X^- line saturated at P_{ex}=30 μW (P_{sat}), which is shown in Fig. 2(b). The X line and biexciton ($2X$) line become visible when $P_{ex}>P_{sat}$. We note that we identified $2X$ line according to its quadratic power dependence of intensity. The emission energies of the X^- and X lines (E_{X^-} and E_X) also varied with P_{ex}, which are shown in Fig. 2(c). We found that E_{X^-} displays a sigmoid energy shift and an abrupt change at P_{sat}. For the case of E_X, it further shows a peak doublet near P_{sat}, exhibiting a fine structure splitting of about ~160 μeV [see the insert of Fig. 2(c)]. We ascribe these observations to the interaction between the QD and charged impurity nearby[1].

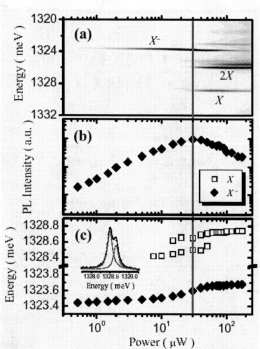

FIGURE 2. (a) The power evolution of a single QD spectra for E_{ex}=1494 meV. (b) The intensity of X^- as a function of P_{ex}. (c) The energies of X^- and X lines as a function of P_{ex}.

CONCLUDSIONS

We have applied μPL spectroscopy to study the neutral and charged exciton complexes in single InGaAs QDs grown by MOCVD. We show that the residual carbon acceptors can act as medium for selective generation of only charged excitons in initially neutral QDs by using resonant excitation's to the impurity level. We also observe fine-structure splittings induced by the QD-impurity interactions, which should be considered for further applications.

ACKNOWLEDGMENTS

This work was supported by the National Science Council of the Republic of China under Grant No. NSC-94-2120-M-008-001.

REFERENCES

1. A. Lemaître, A.D. Ashmore, J.J. Finley, D.J. Mowbray, M.S. Skolnick, M. Hopkinson, and T.F. Krauss, Phys. Rev. B **63**, 161309(R) (2001).
2. M. Bayer *et al.*, Phys. Rev. B **65**, 195315 (2002).
3. R.M. Stevenson, R.M. Thompson, A.J. Shields, I. Farrer, B.E. Kardynal, D.A. Ritchie, and M. Pepper, Phys. Rev. B **66**, 081302(R) (2002).
4. S. M. Ulrich *et al.*, Phys. Rev. B **71**, 235328 (2005).

The Influence of Surface Phonons on Polaron States in Quantum Dots

A.Yu. Maslov, O.V. Proshina, A.N. Rusina

A.F.Ioffe Physical Technical Institute, 194021, St.-Petersburg, Russia

Abstract. The influence of the surface phonons on the polaron effect in a quantum dot is investigated. We consider the polar quantum dot embedded into the polar matrix. The polaron energy shift for the electron and hole ground states is calculated. It is shown that the contribution of the surface phonons may exceed the bulk phonon contribution.

Keywords: Polanon, quantum dot, surface phonons.
PACS: 71.38.+I; 78.66-w; 73.20.Dx

In ionic materials the strong electron-phonon interaction leads to the polaron effects [1]. These effects should be enhanced in the quantum dots. The most significant manifestation of the polaron effects is the sequences of intensive phonon replicas in optical spectrum [2-4]. The theoretical explanation of the enhanced polaron effects in quantum dots often based on the interaction of the charge carriers with bulk optical phonons only. On the other hand the important characteristic feature of the nanostructures is the difference in the dielectric properties of materials used. It leads to the existence of surface (or interface) phonons. The influence of surface phonons on the polaron effects is not clear yet. In paper [5] it is declared that the role of surface phonon is very small when carriers are localized inside the dot. But it is shown in the paper [6] that the interaction with surface phonons strongly reduces the polaron effects in a case when the polar quantum dot is embedded into non-polar matrix.

In this paper we present a results of detail investigations the influence of the surface phonons on polaron states in spherical quantum dot. We use continues dielectric model to solve this problem. Both the quantum dot and surrounding matrix are considered as polar materials. The spectrum of surface phonons in this case was calculated theoretically in [7]. The strong confinement regime for the charge carriers is considered. It means, that the carriers are localized inside the dot. More over, the quantum dot radius R is smaller than the radius of bulk polaron a_0,

$$\frac{R}{a_0} \ll 1 \qquad (1)$$

In this case quantum numbers of the energy levels and the wave functions of carriers are determined by the quantum dot parameters. The electron-phonon interaction leads to the significant changes in the energies of size quantization levels, so called the polaron energy shifts.

We use two different approaches to the calculation of the polaron energy shifts. The first one based on the direct calculation of polaron shift from the total Hamiltonian of the system,

$$\hat{H} = \hat{H}_e + \hat{H}_{ph} + \hat{H}_{e-ph}. \qquad (2)$$

Here H_e being the Hamiltonian of the charge carrier in the quantum dot, H_{ph} describes the real phonon spectrum of the system and the H_{e-ph} takes into considerations the interaction of the carriers with bulk and surface phonons. We use the adiabatic approximation to solve this problem.

The second approach based on the interaction of the carriers with the classical phonon field. This field includes all phonon branches but without any detailed elaboration of them. This method is less accurate but more simple in calculation. Both methods give very similar results with some unimportant differences in numerical factors.

CP893, *Physics of Semiconductors, 28th International Conference*
edited by W. Jantsch and F. Schäffler
© 2007 American Institute of Physics 978-0-7354-0397-0/07/$23.00

For the electron state we consider the simple parabolic energy spectrum with effective mass m_e. The polaron energy shift) $E^{(e)}$ for the spherically symmetric electron states is found to be equal to

$$\Delta E_i^{(e)} = -\frac{e^2}{R}\left(\frac{a_i^{(e)}}{\varepsilon_1^*} + \frac{b_i^{(e)}}{\varepsilon_2^*}\right) \qquad (3)$$

where the optical dielectric function ε_k^* is determined by the relation $1/\varepsilon_k^* = 1/\varepsilon_{k,\infty} - 1/\varepsilon_{k,0}$, ε_0, ε_∞ being the static and high frequency dielectric functions, correspondingly. The index k=1 means the quantum dot and the index k=2 means the surrounding matrix. For the electron ground state the numerical factors a and b are equal to

$$a_1^{(e)} = \frac{1}{2} - \frac{Si(2\pi)}{2\pi} + \frac{Si(4\pi)}{4\pi} \approx 0.39,$$

$$b_1^{(e)} = \frac{1}{2} \qquad (4)$$

Here $Si(x)$ being the integral sine.

In the limiting cases the Equation (3) gives the known results. If we put $\varepsilon_1^* = \varepsilon_2^*$, than the system has the bulk phonons only, end Eq. (3) coincides with the results of paper [8]. When the surrounding matrix is not polarized ($1/\varepsilon_2^* = 0$), one can obtain the results of paper [6]. This is the minimum polaron energy shift for the quantum dot from definite material in any matrix. It should be emphasized that the Eq. (3) predicts the noticeable polaron energy shift in the quantum dot fabricated from non-polar material ($1/\varepsilon_1^* = 0$) embedded into the polar matrix. This polaron energy shift creates by the interaction of the electron with surface phonons only.

There are some differences in polaron energy shifts for hole states due to the degenerated valence band structure in typical semiconductors. We consider the hole energy levels in a framework of Luttinger Hamiltonan. The ground state wave function of the hole is a superposition of two parts with s- and d-symmetry [9]. As a result, there exist an additional contribution in polaron energy shift. For the hole ground state it is equal to

$$\Delta E_1^{(h)} = -\left[\frac{a_1^{(h)}(\beta)}{\varepsilon_1^*} + \frac{0.5}{\varepsilon_2^*} + \left(1 - \frac{\varepsilon_2^*}{\varepsilon_1^*}\right)\frac{c_1^{(h)}(\beta)}{2\varepsilon_1^* + 3\varepsilon_2^*}\right]$$

$$(5)$$

where the numerical factors $a_1^{(h)}$ and $c_1^{(h)}$ depends on the light to heavy hole masses ratio $\beta = m_l/m_h$. These dependencies are presented in [10].

The last term in Eq. (5) connected to the interaction of the hole with surface phonons. One can see that the sign of this term depends on the dielectric properties of the quantum dot and surrounding matrix.

To conclude, the surface phonons plays an important role in the polaron effects in quantum dots. The energy of the interaction of the carriers with surface phonons is comparable with the interaction with the bulk phonons. The corresponding choose of the dielectric properties of the matrix gives the possibility both to increase or to decrease the polaron effects. Our approach gives the possibility to examine the influence of the surface phonons on polaron states in other nanostructures.

ACKNOWLEDGMENTS

The paper is supported by the Russian Foundation for Basic Research, Russian Federal Program of Leading Scientific Schools and the Academic Program "Quantum Nanostructures".

REFERENCES

1. S.I. Pekar, *Untersuchungen uber die Electronentheorie Kristalle*, Akademie Verlag, Berlin, 1954.
2. M.C. Klein, F. Hache, D. Ricard, C. Flytzanis, *Phys. Rev. B*, **42** 11123 (1990).
3. V. Jungnickel, F. Henneberger, *J. Luminescence*, **70** 238 (1996).
4. I.P. Ipatova, A.Yu. Maslov, O.V.Proshina, *Semiconductors*, **33** 765, (1999).
5. K. Oshiro, K. Akai, M. Matsuura, *Phys. Rev. B*, **59** 10850 (1999).
6. A.L. Vartanian et al., *J. Phys.: Cond. Matt*, **14** 13357 (2002).
7. D.V. Melnikov, W.B. Fowler, *Phys. Rev. B*, **64** 245320 (2001).
8. I.P. Ipatova, A.Yu. Maslov, O.V. Proshina, *Surface Science*, **507-510** 598 (2002).
9. Al. L. Efros, *Phys. Rev. B*, **46** 7448 (1992).
10. A.Yu. Maslov, O.V. Proshina, A.N. Rusina, to be published.

Order-N electronic structure calculation of n-type GaAs quantum dots

S. Nomura[*,†] and T. Iitaka[†]

[*]*CREST-JST and Institute of Physics, University of Tsukuba,*
1-1-1 Tennodai, Tsukuba, 305-8571, Japan
[†]*RIKEN (The Institute of Physical and Chemical Research),*
2-1 Hirosawa, Wako, 351-0198, Japan

Abstract. We present a novel method for calculating electronic properties of large and complex systems based on a local density approximation by using a combination of Chebyshev polynomial expansion and time-dependent method. The electron density is obtained without calculating eigenenergies and eigenstates with the computational time which scales as $O(N)$. This method is applied to calculate the electronic structure of a model n-type GaAs quantum dots.

Keywords: quantum dot, local density approximation, order-N
PACS: 71.15.-m, 71.55.Eq

INTRODUCTION

Order-N electronic structure calculation methods have been attracting interests of researchers. One of such methods utilizes a combination of Chebyshev polynomial expansion method [1] and time-dependent method [2] (CPE-TDM). The electron density is obtained without calculating eigenenergies and eigenstates. The computational time of CPE-TDM scales as $O(N)$, as compared with that of the conventional method such as conjugate gradient method (CGM), which grows as $O(N^2)$ with increase in the system size N. Thus CPE-TDM enables us to calculate large systems which require prohibitively large computational time by CGM. CPE-TDM was applied to calculate the optical properties of hydrogenated Si nanocrystals containing more than 10,000 atoms within the empirical pseudopotential formalism [3] and the ESR spectrum of $s = 1/2$ antiferromagnet Cu benzoate [4], which have proved the advantage of CPE-TDM. However, CPE-TDM has not been applied to calculation of the electronic structure within a local density approximation (LDA). In this paper, we report on an implementation of CPE-TDM for a calculation of the electronic structure of n-type GaAs quantum dots (QDs) within a LDA formalism.

METHOD OF CALCULATION

The model Hamiltonian of the system is

$$H = \frac{\mathbf{p}^2}{2m^*} + \frac{1}{2}m^*\omega_0^2 r^2 + V_c(\mathbf{r}) + V_H(\mathbf{r}) + V_x(\mathbf{r}) \quad (1)$$

where m^* is the effective mass of the electrons, $\omega_0 = 3$ meV, and, $V_c(\mathbf{r})$, $V_H(\mathbf{r})$, and $V_x(\mathbf{r})$ are the vertical confining potential, the Hartree potential, the exchange potential, respectively. The model structure is a 20 nm-wide GaAs quantum well sandwiched by undoped $Al_xGa_{1-x}As(x = 0.3)$ barriers. The electrons are assumed to be supplied from 5 nm-thick Si-doped $Al_xGa_{1-x}As$ layer, located 20 nm above the GaAs quantum well layer. The Fermi-energy (E_F) is taken as the origin of the energy. The number of the electrons in a QD is not fixed to an integer number and is determined by E_F and the potential energy. A 3D mesh of $64 \times 64 \times 8$ is used for the calculation of the electron density, and $64 \times 64 \times 16$ is used for the calculation of the potentials. The Hamiltonian is discretized in real space by the higher-order finite difference method [5].

A random phase vector as defined by $|\Phi\rangle \equiv \sum_{n=1}^{N} |n\rangle \xi_n$, where $\{|n\rangle\}$ is a basis set and ξ_n is a set of random phase variables, is used as an initial state. This was shown to give results with the smallest statistical error [6]. Here Φ is a $N_x \times N_y \times N_z$ column vector for a system defined by a real-space uniform grid of $N_x \times N_y \times N_z$. The electron density $n(\mathbf{r})$ is extracted by the Fermi operator function $f(H) = 1/[e^{\beta(H-E_F)} + 1]$ as

$$n(\mathbf{r}) = \langle \mathbf{r}|f(H)|\Phi\rangle. \quad (2)$$

The Fermi operator is evaluated by the Chebyshev polynomial expansion,

$$f(H)|\Phi\rangle = \sum_k a_k(\beta)T_k(H)|\Phi\rangle. \quad (3)$$

Actually the electron density is calculated with j_{max} sets of $|\Phi\rangle$ as $n(\mathbf{r}) = \sum_{j=1}^{j=j_{max}} \langle \mathbf{r}|f(H)|\Phi_j\rangle / j_{max}$. The Hartree and exchange potentials are calculated using $n(\mathbf{r})$.

CP893, *Physics of Semiconductors, 28th International Conference*
edited by W. Jantsch and F. Schäffler

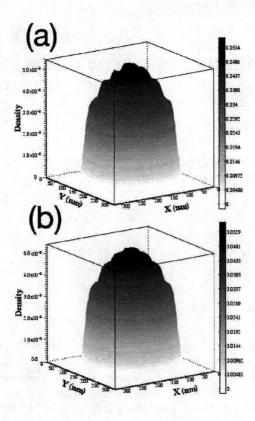

FIGURE 1. The electron density distribution obtained by (a) CPE-TDM and by (b) CGM.

The density of states (DOS) is calculated by a time evolution method as given by

$$\rho(\omega) = -\frac{1}{\pi} \text{Im}(\langle\langle \langle\Phi|G(\omega + i\eta)|\Phi\rangle \rangle\rangle), \quad (4)$$

where $G(\omega + i\eta)$ is the real-time Green's function and $\langle\langle \cdot \rangle\rangle$ stands for statistical average. The DOS is calculated with k_{max} sets of $|\Phi\rangle$. The energy resolution η is chosen to be 0.5 meV.

RESULTS AND DISCUSSIONS

Model calculations are performed for GaAs QDs containing about 77 electrons. The number of the self-consistent iterations is fixed to 100 for both the CGM and CPE-TDM calculations. The potential is converged to $|V_H(\mathbf{r}) - V_H^{new}(\mathbf{r})| < 0.003$meV for the CGM calculation. The electron density distributions are shown in Fig. 1 for CPE-TDM with $j_{max} = 64$ and CGM. The calculated electron density distribution reasonably agrees with the result by CGM within the statistical fluctuations. The Friedel-type spatial oscillations of the electron density[7]

are reproduced in both the results by the CPE-TDM and CGM.

The total number of electrons (N_e) is calculated to be 76.8, 76.7, 77.1, 76.8 for the cases of $j_{max} = 8, 16, 32$, and 64, respectively, which is compared with $N_e = 77.1$ calculated by CGM. The statistical fluctuation of N_e is reduced due to the self-averaging effect.

In summary, it has been demonstrated that CPE-TDM can be applied to a LDA calculation of a model QD system despite the presence of the statistical fluctuations of the calculated quantities originated from the random phase vectors. It has been shown that the random phase vectors is useful if the statistical fluctuations are controlled by carefully choosing the parameters for the calculations. Our linear scale method opens up possibilities for calculating the electronic and optical properties of large and complex systems, such as QD arrays with interaction between QDs and devices employing the Rashba type spin-orbit interaction. Finally, because the Green's function can be effectively estimated by CPE-TDM, the properties of the electronic system such as the DC and Hall conductivities, and the optical absorption spectra, are obtained within $O(N)$ computational costs.

ACKNOWLEDGMENTS

This work was partly supported by the Grant-in-Aid for Scientific Research from Japan Society for the Promotion of Science. Computational support by RIKEN Super Combined Cluster System is gratefully acknowledged.

REFERENCES

1. R. Kosloff and H. Tal-Ezer, *Chem. Phys. Lett.* **127**, 223 (1986); S.Goedecker, *Rev. Mod. Phys.* **71**, 1085 (1999).
2. T. Iitaka, *Phys. Rev. E* **49**, 4684 (1994).
3. S. Nomura et al., *Phys. Rev. B* **56**, R4348 (1997);T. Iitaka et al., *Phys. Rev. E* **56**, 1222 (1997).
4. T. Iitaka and T. Ebisuzaki, *Phys. Rev. Lett.* **90**, 047203 (2003).
5. S. Nomura and Y. Aoyagi, *Phys. Rev. Lett.* **93**, 096803 (2004).
6. T. Iitaka and T. Ebisuzaki, *Phys. Rev. E* **69**, 057701 (2004).
7. J.H. Luscombe, A.M. Bouchard, and M. Luban, *Phys. Rev. B* **46**, 10262 (1992).

Comparison of Carrier Lifetime for InAs Quantum Dots in the Quaternary Barriers on InP Substrate

J. Park[1], Y. D. Jang[1], H. Lee[1], D. Lee[1], S. H. Pyun[2], W. G. Jeong[2], J. W. Jang[3], J. S. Kim[4] and D. K. Oh[4]

[1]Department of Physics, Chungnam National University, Daejeon 305-764, Korea
[2]Department of Materials Engineering, Sungkyunkwan University, Suwon, Korea
[3]NanoEpi Technologies, Gyonggi Technopark, Ansan, Korea
[4]Electronics and Telecommunication Research Institute, Daejeon 305-350, Korea

Abstract. We have found that the carrier lifetime of an InAs/InGaAsP quantum dot (QD) on an InP substrate is twice that of an InAs/InAlGaAs QD on the same substrate, although the ground-state energy levels and barrier heights of these QDs are comparable. The carrier lifetime of the InAs/InAlGaAs QD within the ground state PL band is shorter as the detection wavelength is longer. On the contrary, it shows the same carrier lifetime for the InAs/InGaAsP QD. The difference is interpreted in terms of the smaller conduction band-offset in InAs/InGaAsP QDs compared to InAs/InAlGaAs QDs.

Keywords: quantum dot, carrier lifetime, band offset.
PACS: 78.66.–w, 78.67.–n, 78.67.Hc

INTRODUCTION

Recently, high-performance quantum dot (QD) devices on InP (100) substrate, such as InAs/InGaAsP QD laser diodes (LDs), InAs/InAlGaAs QD LDs and InAs/InGaAsP QD semiconductor optical amplifiers were reported at wavelengths around 1.5 μm. [1,2,3]

In this work, we compare the optical characteristics of InAs/InGaAsP and InAs/InAlGaAs QDs. We show that these QDs exhibit significantly different carrier lifetimes, and interpret the difference in terms of the different band-offset of the two QD systems.

EXPERIMENTS AND DISCUSSIONS

An InAs/InGaAsP QD sample (QD1) was grown on a nominally exact (100) InP substrate by metal-organic chemical vapor deposition. Lattice matched InGaAsP (λ_g = 1.1 μm) was used as a barrier material. A small amount of gallium, about 0.6% in mole fraction, was added in the InAs QD. The average diameter and height of QD1 are 32 nm and 3.4 nm, respectively. The dot density of QD1 is 1.1×10^{11}/cm^2. QD1 have five periods of QD layer and the thickness of each InGaAsP barrier is 40 nm. InAs/InAlGaAs single layer QD sample (QD2) was grown by

molecular beam epitaxy on an InP (100) substrate. The InAlGaAs barrier (λ_g = 1.1 μm) was lattice matched to InP. A transmission electron micrograph picture shows that the size of QD2 is about (26.0 ± 1.0) nm in diameter and (3.0 ± 0.5) nm in height. The dot density of QD2 is ~ 6×10^{10}/cm^2.

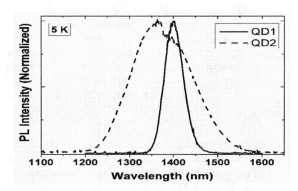

FIGURE 1. PL spectra of InAs/InGaAsP QD(QD1) and an InAs/InAlGaAs QD(QD2) at 5 K.

Figure 1 shows the photoluminescence (PL) spectra of two QD samples measured at 5 K. The PL peak positions of the two QD samples are located at around 1400 nm. The PL peaks at room temperature are also located around the same wavelength, ~1500 nm. From

CP893, *Physics of Semiconductors, 28th International Conference*
edited by W. Jantsch and F. Schäffler
© 2007 American Institute of Physics 978-0-7354-0397-0/07/$23.00

the above results, these QD samples constitute a good set to systematically compare the optical properties. The full width at half maximum (FWHM) of QD1 is 31 meV, indicating that this QD was grown uniformly. The FWHM of QD2, however, is 109 meV, likely due to large size-fluctuations of QD.

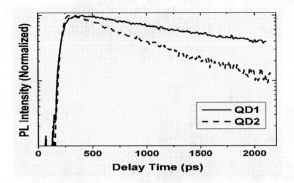

FIGURE 2. Decay curves of InAs/InGaAsP QD(QD1) and an InAs/InAlGaAs QD(QD2) at the PL peak at 10 K.

As shown in Fig. 2, the carrier lifetime for QD1 is 1.8 ns, QD2 shows a carrier lifetime of 0.7 ns at the PL peak. The shorter carrier lifetime observed for QD2 compared to QD1 is most likely due to the larger conduction band-offset in the InAs/InAlGaAs system compared to the InAs/InGaAsP system. The unstrained conduction band-offset for InAs/InGaAsP is 40%, which is significantly smaller than the CB offset of 67% for InAs/InGaAlAs.[4] According to the result of simple calculation with the uniform strain, the conduction band-offset is 0.160 eV for InAs/InGaAsP and 0.367 eV for InAs/InAlGaAs.[5] The conduction band energy depends only on isotropic pressure. The heavy hole is well confined inside the QD since its effective mass is heavy. Due to the smaller conduction band-offset, QD1 has the large penetration of the electron wavefunction into the barrier, reduced electron-hole overlap, and as a result, a longer carrier lifetime. In contrast, QD2, which has the larger conduction band-offset, shows the relatively shorter carrier lifetime.

Figure 3 shows the decay curves of QD1 and QD2 through the PL band. In Fig. 3(a), the decay times of QD1 in the ground state PL band are the same through the whole PL band. On the contrary, the decay times of QD2, shown in Fig. 3(b), vary across the PL band: the shorter decay time at the longer wavelength. We expect that this decay time variation results from the difference of the electron wave function confinement as a different-sized QDs and the large size fluctuation of QD, especially the growth direction. The electron wavefunction confinement is more sensitive to the variation of the QD sizes, as shown in Fig. 3(b), as

well as the fact that the size fluctuation of QD2 is larger than that for QD1.

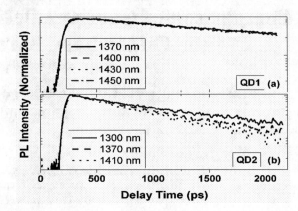

FIGURE 3. Decay curves of QD1 (a) and QD2 (b) at a different detection wavelength through the GS PL band.

SUMMARY

We have observed that the carrier lifetime of InAs/InGaAsP QD is twice longer than that of InAs/InAlGaAs QD. The observed behavior is explained in terms of the smaller conduction band-offset of the InAs/InGaAsP QD compared to the InAs/InAlGaAs QD. Furthermore, the carrier lifetime of the InAs/InAlGaAs QD in the ground state PL band varies because of relatively large conduction band offset.

ACKNOWLEDGMENTS

This work was supported by the Basic Research Program (Grant No. R01-2003-000-10268-0) of the Korea Science and Engineering Foundation and, in part, the National Research Laboratory Program (Grant No. 2004-02403).

REFERENCES

1. J. W. Jang, S. H. Lee, I. C. Lee, W. G. Jeong, R. Stevensen, P. D. Dapkus, N. J. Kim, M. S. Hwang, and D. Lee , *Appl. Phys. Lett.* **85**, 3675 (2004)
2. F. Lelarge, B. Rousseau, B. Dagens, F. Poingt, F. Pommereau, and A. Accard, *IEEE Photon. Technol. Lett.* **17**, 1369 (2005)
3. T. Akiyama, M. Ekawa, M. Sugawara, H. Sudo, K. Kawaguchi, A. Kuramata, H. Ebe, K. Morito, H. Imai, and Y. Arakawa, in *Optical Fiber Communications Conference (OFC 2004)*, Postdeadline Paper, 692 (2004)
4. T. Ishikawa, and J. E. Bowers, *IEEE J. Quantum Electron.* **30**, 562 (1994)
5. D. Bimberg, and M. Grundmann, *Quantum Dot Heterostructures* (Wiley, New York, 1999)

A theoretical and experimental study of λ>2 µm luminescence of quantum dots on InP substrate

F. Doré[1], J. Even[1], C. Cornet[1], A. Schliwa[2], N. Bertru[1], O. Dehaese[1], I. Alghoraibi[1], H. Folliot[1], R. Piron[1], A. Le Corre[1], S. Loualiche[1]

[1] Laboratoire d'Etude des Nanostructures à semiconducteurs (UMR-FOTON6082)
Insa de Rennes, 20 Avenue des Buttes de Coesmes, 35043 Rennes Cedex, France
[2] Festkörper Institut, Teschniche Universität Berlin Institut für Festkörperphysik,
Technische Universität Berlin, Hardenbergstrasse 36, 10623 Berlin, Germany
francois.dore@univ-rennes1.fr

Abstract. Theoretical and experimental studies of the electronic properties of InAs(Sb) quantum dots (QDs) grown by molecular beam epitaxy (MBE) on InP(100) substrate are presented. Eight-band **k•p** calculations including strain and piezoelectric effects are performed on InAs/InP(100) quantum dot (QD) structure to study the influence of the quantum dot height. Photoluminescence (PL) spectroscopy experiments show promising results. High arsine flow rate during the growth of InAs QDs makes possible long emission wavelength beyond 2 µm. Emission wavelength as long as 2.35 µm is observed with InAsSb QDs.

Keywords: Quantum dots, Midinfrared, Indium Phosphide
PACS: 73.21.La, 78.67.Hc, 81.07.Ta, 71.15.-m, 78.55.Et

INTRODUCTION

Mid-infrared semiconductor lasers emitting at room temperature are of great interest in various fields like free-space optical telecommunications, gas sensing or reconstructive surgery. On InP substrates, the technologically-matured InGaAsP QWs system is limited to 2 µm optical wavelength [1]. This spectral barrier can be broken down by the incorporation of Sb which leads to a large gap decreasing. Quantum dot (QD) formation allows to accommodate large mismatches without formation of dislocations. Consequently, in order to extend the wavelength emission on InP substrates beyond 2 µm, we propose to use InAsSb QDs. Laser emission from InAsSb QDs grown on InP have been recently reported at 1.96 µm [2]. In this paper we investigate theoretically using the eight-band **k•p** model the impact of QDs heignt on their optical properties. We finally report results of PL experiments on InAs/InGaAsP and InAsSb/InGaAs QDs structures exhibiting room temperature (RT) PL beyond 2 µm.

CALCULATIONS

Excitonic properties are calculated for self-organized QDs based on a three-dimensional implementation of the eight-band **k•p** model and a configuration interaction scheme thus accounting for the inhomogeneous strain distribution, the piezoelectric effect, inter- and intraband mixing and Coulomb interactions [3]. In the calculations, we assume the QDs to have a truncated cone profile, where the total height of the pyramid is equal to 8.8 nm (30 monolayers (ML), where 1ML ~ 0.29 nm on (100) substrate), the baselength is equal to 35 nm.

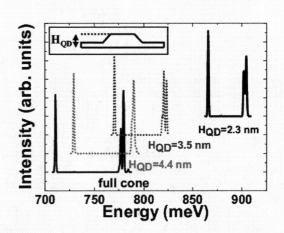

FIGURE 1. Excitonic absorption spectra calculated in an eight-band **k•p** model for InAs/InP (100) QDs, as a function of the QD height.

Figure 1 displays calculated exciton absorption spectra for QDs of different height on InP(100)

CP893, *Physics of Semiconductors, 28th International Conference*
edited by W. Jantsch and F. Schäffler
© 2007 American Institute of Physics 978-0-7354-0397-0/07/$23.00

substrate (the WL height in this case is taken equal to 4 ML). Calculated exciton absorption spectra are plotted with a polarization along the [1 −1 0] axis, as this axis is an QDs in-plane axis for both substrates. The spectra show a blueshift of 135 meV for the ground state transition energy upon reducing the QD height from a pointed cone-shaped QD down to 8 ML truncated-one.

EXPERIMENTAL RESULTS

We investigated two different materials associations: InAs/InGaAsP and InAsSb/InGaAs. Samples without antimony have been grown by gas source MBE. In this paper, the flow rates are given in units of standard cubic centimeters per second (sccm). Samples with antimony have been grown by solid source MBE.

By optimizing growth parameters of InAs nanostructures embedded in Q1.18 alloy, PL has been observed beyond 2 μm at RT [4].

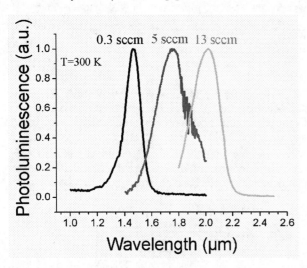

FIGURE 2. Room temperature PL spectra of single InAs/InGaAsP/InP(100) quantum nanostructures layer grown with different arsine flow rates.

Figure 2 presents three PL peaks of InAs/Q1.18/InP(100) nanostructures samples obtained with different arsine flow rates during the nanostructures growth. As already mentioned on InP(311) [5], we observe a red-shift induced by increasing arsenic pressure. Sample grown with a 0.3 sccm arsine flow rate exhibits a PL peak centred below 1.5 μm. 1.76 μm was obtained from the sample grown with 5 sccm As₂ flux whereas a 12 sccm flow rate shifts the maximum of PL peak to 2.03 μm. It corresponds to an increase of InAs nanostructures size confirmed by atomic force microscopy measurements (0.7 nm, 13 nm and 20 nm for height and a radius of

23 nm, 37 nm and 40 nm respectively for the 3 fluxes 0.3 sccm, 5 sccm and 13 sccm). Note that the longest wavelength is close to the theoretical limit of about 3 μm corresponding to the room temperature gap of bulk InAs lattice-matched to InP [6].

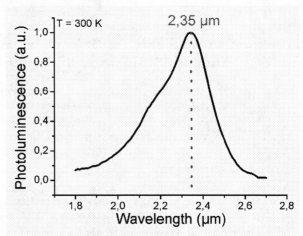

FIGURE 3. Room temperature photoluminescence spectrum of single InAsSb/InGaAs/InP(100) quantum nanostructures layer.

As suggested above, we introduced antimony in the growth process of InAs active material to increase emission wavelength of our structures. Figure 3 exhibits PL spectrum of a sample containing InAsSb quantum dots layers embedded in an InGaAs alloy lattice-matched to InP. An emission wavelength close to 2.4 μm has been reached at RT.

ACKNOWLEDGMENTS

This work was supported by the SANDiE Network of Excellence (Contract No. NMP4-CT-2004-500101) of the sixth Framework Program of the European Commission.

REFERENCES

[1] D. Bimberg, M. Grundmann and N. N. Ledentsov, *Quantum Dot Heterostructures*, (Wiley, 1998)
[2] T. J. Rotter, A. Stintz and K. J. Malloy, IEE Proc. Optoelectron. **150**, 318 (2003)
[3] C. Cornet, A. Schliwa, J. Even, F. Doré et al., accepted for publication in Phys. Rev. B.
[4] F. Doré, C. Cornet et al., Phys. Stat. Sol. (c) **3**, pp. 524-527 (2006).
[5] P. Caroff et al., Jap. J. of Appl. Phys. **44**, n° 33 (2005).
[6] C. Cornet, F. Doré et al., J. Appl. Phys. **98**, 126105 (2005)

Fine structure of electron-hole complexes in single semimagnetic quantum dots

A. V. Chernenko[*], A. S. Brichkin[*], V. D. Kulakovskii[*], E. A. Chekhovich[*], S. V. Ivanov[†] and A. V. Toropov[†]

[*]*Institute of Solid State Physics, Chernogolovka, Moscow Region, 142432, Russia*
[†]*Ioffe Physico-Technical Institute, St. Petersburg, 194021, Russia*

Abstract.
  Photoluminescence spectra of CdSe/ZnSe/ZnMnSe semimagnetic quantum dots were studies in Faraday and Voigt geometries in the magnetic field up to 11 T at T=1.6 K. Incorporation of the nonmagnetic ZnSe layer between CdSe quantum dot layer and semimagnetic barriers reduced the strength of *sp-d* exchange interaction and hence broadening of emission lines that obscures an observation of the fine structure of electron-hole complexes. This allows one to identify exciton, biexciton and trion lines in the spectra of quantum dots and study their fine structure. An account of both *sp-d* and electron-hole exchange interactions are required in order to describe the Zeeman splitting and polarization behavior of the spectra.

Keywords: quantum dots, diluted magnetic semiconductors, magnetooptics
PACS: 75.75.+a, 05.40.-a, 75.50.Pp, 78.67.Hc

INTRODUCTION

The electron-hole (*e-h*) exchange interaction is dramatically enhanced in 0D structures due to the strong dimensional confinement. Together with narrow linewidth of single quantum dots (QDs) photoluminescence(PL) lines it allows one clear observation of the fine structure of *e-h* complexes. Contrary, the observation of *e-h* exchange splitting in semimagnetic or diluted magnetic semiconductor (DMS) QDs is obscured by the large width of PL lines connected to fluctuations of magnetic ions moments interacting with charge carriers. It is possible to decrease the linewidth by means of a spatial separation of the magnetic ions and QD's electrons and holes. Here we report about the observation of fine structure of PL lines of semimagnetic QDs with weak exchange interaction due to an incorporation of the additional nonmagnetic ZnSe between MBE grown CdSe QDs and ZnMnSe semimagnetic barrier.

QDS MAGNETOLUMINESCENCE SPECTRA

The samples studied are CdSe self-assembled QDs grown by MBE on ZnSe cladding layers. The CdSe layer is separated from DMS $Zn_{0.89}Mn_{0.11}Se$ barrier by an additional nonmagnetic ZnSe layer of 1.6 nm nominal thickness. In order to obtain the PL signal an opaque metal mask containing small periodically arranged aperture holes of various sizes was deposited onto the top of the sample straight over the QD layer. Additional infor-

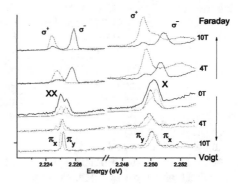

FIGURE 1. PL spectra of the sample under study recorded in various magnetic fields in Faraday and Voigt geometries at high level of laser excitation. The lines denoted as X and XX correspond to the exciton and biexciton recombination, respectively

mation about sample preparation can be found elsewhere (see [1] and reference therein). The sample was excited by ultraviolet line of Ar ion laser $\lambda = 355$ nm and the PL signal was analyzed by a monochromator combined with CCD camera.

  Typical PL spectra of the sample are shown in Figs. 1 and 2. The doublet line X corresponding to the exchange-split exciton recombination is observed in the QD spectrum presented in Fig.1 at B=0 T and low level of optical excitation. In the magnetic field perpendicular to the sample plane the lines exhibit strong Zeeman splitting and acquire circular polarization. With an increased ex-

CP893, *Physics of Semiconductors, 28th International Conference*
edited by W. Jantsch and F. Schäffler

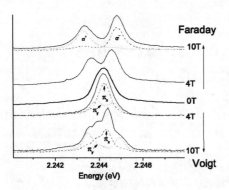

FIGURE 2. Polarization spectra of the X^- trion line in Faraday and Voigt geometries in various magnetic fields.

citation power a new doublet XX with opposite order of polarization appears in the spectrum ~ 22 meV below the exciton line. The intensity of this doublet superlinearly depends on the excitation power. We associate this doublet with the recombination of biexciton from the same QD.

Besides exciton and biexciton doublets a singlet line corresponding to the trion (X^-) recombination is observed in the spectra shown in Fig.2 at B=0 T. The trion one splits into two lines in the Faraday geometry one. The dependence of PL intensity and polarization on B is very similar to that observed for excitons. Time-resolved measurements revealed that the lifetime of the exciton line is equal to that of the trion line, whereas it as much as twice longer than the lifetime of the XX line.

In the magnetic field parallel to the sample plane (Voigt geometry) the initially singlet trion line splits into a quartet of lines as shown in Fig.2. Polarization measurements indicate that the inner and outer pairs of the quartet are orthogonally polarized to each other. The polarization of the lines does not depend on the direction of the magnetic filed, but is determined by internal axes of the QDs.

The behavior of these lines in the magnetic field in the Voigt geometry is similar to that observed by Koudinov at al. in nonmagnetic CdSe QDs [2]. The line polarization behavior is explained as a result of *hh-lh* mixing due to the low symmetry potential (lower than C_2) caused by both the shape of QDs and the symmetry of the strain distribution. However, the magnitude of the Zeeman splitting in our case is substantially larger due to *sp-d* exchange interaction. The analysis of Zeeman splitting of exciton lines in the Faraday geometry reveals that the actual temperature of Mn system is relatively high, $T \sim 25$ K, and the magnetic polaron effect broadening the lines is negligible in our case [1].

The *sp-d* exchange affects the Zeeman splitting of PL

lines or, in other words, modifies the effective electron and hole g-factors. The *sp-d* exchange interaction does not change the sign of the electron effective g-factor whereas it can change the sign of the hole effective g-factor g^h_{eff}. This is true for the both geometries. Thus, the influence of *e-h* as well as *sp-d* exchange interaction on PL lines should be taken into account to calculate the Zeeman splitting of the exciton, biexciton and trion lines.

Note, that our case is qualitatively different from that studied by Besombes et.al. [3] where the influence of the single Mn ion incorporated into QD on carriers' g-factors is negligible. Contrary to this, in our case the sign and magnitude of the g-factors is determined by the *sp-d* exchange interaction provided by tens or even hundreds of Mn ions.

Calculations within the developed model indicate that the effective hole g-factor in the Voigt geometry $g^\perp_h$ that responsible for the hole levels splitting in the Voigt geometry indeed changes the sign in DMS QDs similar to g_z. The theory fits experimental data under assumption that the penetration of electron and holes wave-functions into the DMs barrier is different.

In the exciton, the *lh-hh* mixing can change the polarization of exchange splitted doublets. The intensity of lines from the pair becomes as follows $I_1 \propto (\cos(\Phi/2 - \phi) + k\gamma\cos(\Phi/2 - 2\theta + \phi))^2$ and $I_2 \propto (\sin(\Phi/2 - \phi) + k\gamma\sin(\Phi/2 - 2\theta + \phi))^2$ respectively. Where θ is the angle determined by the deformation mixing of *hh-lh* states (matrix element of the mixing $\propto \gamma e^{\pm i2\theta}/\Delta_{lh-hh}$) whereas $\Phi/2$ is the angle determining the axis of the *e-h* exchange interaction, ϕ is the light polarization angle, the meaning of k and γ are the same as in [2]. The analysis of the spectra indicates that the polarization of the most exciton lines are higher than 95%, which means that the angles $\Phi/2$ and 2θ are usually close to each other.

In conclusion, the study of magnetoPL spectra structure of CdSe/ZnSe/ZnMnSe QDs with weak *sp-d* exchange interaction allowed to observe the fine structure of excitons, biexcitons, trions and investigate the effect of *sp-d* exchange interaction on it.

ACKNOWLEDGMENTS

This work was supported by Russian Foundation for Basic Research. We are thankful to A.V.Koudinov for helpful discussion.

REFERENCES

1. P.S. Dorozhkin *et al.* APL 86, 062507(2005).
2. A.V.Koudinov *et.al.* PRB 70, 241305(R) (2004).
3. L.Besombes *et.al*, PRL 93, 207403(2004).

Near-field magneto-optics of quantum dots

Anna Zora*, Constantinos Simserides† and Georgios Triberis*

*University of Athens, Physics Department, Panepistimiopolis, Zografos, GR-15784, Athens, Greece
†University of Patras, Materials Science Department, Panepistimiopolis, Rio, GR-26504, Patras, Greece

Abstract. Encouraged by the latest experimental developments as well as by the theoretical interest on the near-field (NF) optics of semiconductor quantum dots (QDs), we present our most recent theoretical results on the NF optical absorption and photoluminescence (PL) of single and coupled III-V QDs subjected additionally to an external magnetic field of variable orientation and magnitude. The zero-magnetic-field "structural" QD symmetry can be destroyed varying the magnetic field orientation. The asymmetry induced by the magnetic field -except for specific orientations along symmetry axes- can be uncovered in the near-field but not in the far-field spectra. Hence, we predict that NF magnetoabsorption experiments, of realistic spatial resolution, will be in the position to bring to light the QD symmetry.

Keywords: excitons, absorption, magnetoexcitons, quantum dots, Near-field, NSOM
PACS: PACS numbers: 71.35.Cc,71.35.Ji,73.21.La,87.64.Xx

PREAMBLE

We summarize the elements of our systematic study of the near-field magnetoabsorption of single and double quantum dots (QDs) [1]. It is inspired by the experimental [2] and theoretical [3] progress in the near-field (NF) optics of QDs achieved recently. Although the illumination of a nanostructure with a NF probe in conjuction with the simultaneous application of an external magnetic field may become a challenge to experimentalists, we hope that our results will encourage this adventure.

The analysis of QDs subjected to a magnetic field, has been the subject of many recent publications. Usually in order to facilitate the calculation, the magnetic field is applied along a symmetry axis. Our computational scheme allows us to study QDs of any given geometry, under magnetic field of any orientation. We are not limited to analytically solvable problems like the famous Fock-Darwin system. Hence, we are free to explore the interplay between the *spatial confinement* imposed by the QD geometry and the *magnetic confinement* governed by the magnitude and the orientation of the magnetic field. Here, we briefly discuss single QDs which possess zero-magnetic-field ("structural") cylindrical symmetry, with a square quantum well along the z axis (of width z_0), and parabolic confinement in the xy plane. However, we emphasize on the NF magnetoabsorption spectra under "in-plane" magnetic field which *destroys* this "structural" cylindrical symmetry.

THEORY IN BRIEF

Within our theoretical framework [1]: (a) We calculate the single-particle states of electrons and holes subjected to a magnetic field of variable magnitude and orientation, for a QD of arbitrary geometry, using an expansion into plane waves within a periodicity box. (b) We compute the Coulomb matrix elements for the interaction between electrons and holes. (c) We evaluate the excitonic eigenstates. (d) We calculate the NF absorption or PL spectra. In this short article we merely give an example of the *magnetic field orientation* importance, i.e. we will emphasize its significance, especially in *symmetry breaking*.

Under a "perpendicular" magnetic field applied in the z direction, the system is rotationally symmetric relative to the z axis, i.e. the QD retains its cylindrical symmetry. The total eigenenergies are given by $E_{xy} + E_z$. The z axis eigenenergies are determined by the QW, i.e. $E_z = E_i$, where i is a natural number. Because of the parabolic confinement in the xy plane, application of a "perpendicular" magnetic field along the z axis changes the height of the energetic staircase and removes the degeneracy proportionally to B (Fock - Darwin), i.e. the xy plane eigenenergies become: $E_{xy} = E_{n_\rho, m_l} = \hbar\Omega(2n_\rho + |m_l| + 1) \pm \hbar\omega_B m_l/2$. The plus (+) sign corresponds to electrons, and the minus (−) sign to holes, while $\Omega^2 = \omega_B^2/4 + \omega_{pc}^2$. The energy scale $\hbar\omega_{pc}$ stems from the "spatial" parabolic confinement in the xy plane, while $\hbar\omega_B = \hbar eB/m^*$ is related to the "magnetic confinement". n_ρ is a natural number and m_l is an integer. Due to the rotational symmetry relative to the z axis under a "perpendicular" magnetic field, the z component of the angular momentum (with eigenvalues $\hbar m_l$) is conserved.

Under an "in-plane" magnetic field, applied along the x or the y axis, the symmetry of the system is broken i.e. it is no longer cylindrical. This is a case where an analytical solution of the single-particle problem is not straightforward, a case underlining the power of our numerical procedure. Under "in-plane" magnetic field,

CP893, *Physics of Semiconductors, 28th International Conference*
edited by W. Jantsch and F. Schäffler
© 2007 American Institute of Physics 978-0-7354-0397-0/07/$23.00

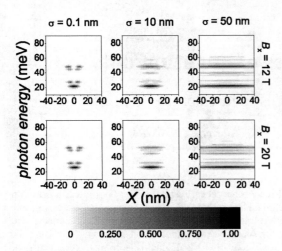

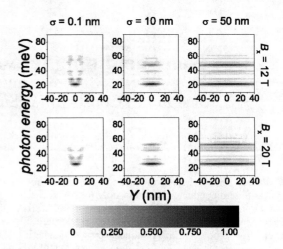

FIGURE 1. The magnetic field is *not* applied along the symmetry axis z, but along the axis x, *destroying* the QD "structural" symmetry. A scan along X, keeping $Y = 0$, is presented here.

FIGURE 2. The same QD and magnetic field orientation with Fig. 1. Now a scan along Y, keeping $X = 0$, is presented. This is not equivalent to the scan along X, keeping $Y = 0$, presented in Fig. 1. This assymetry is evident for $\sigma = 10$ nm i.e. in the near field, but cannot be revealed in the far field e.g. for $\sigma = 50$ nm.

none of the components of the angular momentum is conserved. In analogy with QWs [4] one would expect the influence of an "in-plane" magnetic field to increase with the QW width.

RESULTS AND PROSPECTS

In Fig. 1 we consider a single QD with a square quantum well ($z_0 = 30$ nm) along the z axis, and parabolic confinement in the xy plane. The local absorption, $\alpha(X, \hbar\omega)$, as a function of the tip position along the x axis, X (nm), and the photon energy measured with respect to the bandgap, $\hbar\omega$ (meV) is presented. We keep $Y = 0$. Each column corresponds to different spatial resolution, $2\sqrt{2\ln 2}\sigma \approx 2.35\sigma$. Each row corresponds to a different value of the "in-plane" magnetic field, B_x. In this example, the zero-magnetic-field "structural" cylindrical symmetry has been broken by the "in-plane" magnetic field. In Fig. 2 we consider the same single QD and magnetic field orientation with Fig. 1. Now $\alpha(Y, \hbar\omega)$ is illustrated, keeping $X = 0$. Since the zero-magnetic-field "structural" cylindrical symmetry has been broken by the "in-plane" magnetic field, this Y scan ($X = 0$) is not equivalent to the X scan ($Y = 0$) illustrated in Fig. 1. This assymetry can be brought to light for $\sigma = 10$ nm i.e. in the near field, but cannot be revealed in the far field e.g. for $\sigma = 50$ nm.

Within the framework of our approach we apply Kuhn and Rossi formula for the PL intensity [5] for the case of QDs. Comparison of our theoretical results with far-field experimental data [6] as well as predictions for the near

field will be hopefully published elsewhere [7].

ACKNOWLEDGMENTS

Work supported by the Hellenic Ministry of Education under the program "Heracletus". CS dedicates his contribution to the memory of John Polygiannakis.

REFERENCES

1. C. Simserides, A. Zora, G. Triberis, *Phys. Rev. B* **73**, 155313 (2006). See also http://users.uoa.gr/~csimseri/ or http://www.matersci.upatras.gr.
2. K. Matsuda, T. Saiki, S. Nomura, M. Mihara and Y. Aoyagi, *Appl. Phys. Lett.* **81**, 2291 (2002); K. Matsuda, T. Saiki, S. Nomura, M. Mihara, Y. Aoyagi, S. Nair, and T. Takagahara, *Phys. Rev. Lett.* **91**, 177401 (2003).
3. U. Hohenester, G. Goldoni, and E. Molinari, *Appl. Phys. Lett.* **84**, 3963 (2004); E. Runge and C. Lienau, *Phys. Rev. B* **71**, 035347 (2005).
4. C. Simserides, *J. Comput. Electron.* **2**, 459 (2003); *Phys. Rev. B* **69**, 113302 (2004).
5. T. Kuhn and F. Rossi, *Phys. Rev. B* **46**, 7496 (1992).
6. M. Bayer, A. Schmidt, A. Forchel, F. Faller, T. L. Reinecke, P. A. Knipp, A. A. Dremin, V. D. Kulakovskii, *Phys. Rev. Lett.* **74**, 3439 (1995).
7. A. Zora, C. Simserides, G. Triberis, *unpublished*.

Effect of Surface Oxidation on Optical Absorption of Silicon Nanocrystallites

Ikurou Umezu[1,2], Motohiko Koyama[1], Takehito Yoshida[3] and Akira Sugimura[1,2]

[1] Department of Physics, Konan University, Kobe 658-8501, Japan
[2] Quantum Nanotechnology Laboratory, Konan University, Kobe 658-8501, Japan
[3] Department of Mechanical Engineering, Anan National College of Technology, Anan 774-0017, Japan

Abstract. We prepared surface hydrogenated silicon nanocrystallites by pulsed laser ablation of Si target in hydrogen gas to measure and to discuss correlation between native oxidation and optical absorption. At early stage of exposure to the atmosphere, subgap absorption at around 2 eV was observed. This subgap absorption changed to about 3 eV by further exposure. These absorption bands correspond to the PL emission bands at 2 and 3 eV observed for the surface oxidized Si nanocrystallites. The natural surface oxidation creates defects and their energy level discontinuously change with degree of natural oxidation.

Keywords: silicon nanocrystal, optical absorption, photoluminescence, surface oxidation
PACS: 78.67.-n, 81.07.Bc, 81.15.Fg, 73.21.La

INTRODUCTION

Effects of surface oxidation on the optical properties are very important issues for silicon nanocrystallites. Many researches are focused on the photoluminescence (PL) properties since visible PL from nc-Si is attractive phenomena.[1,2] Although measurement of optical absorption is most simple and reliable method to estimate density of states, research focused on the optical absorption is relatively scarce. One of the reasons is that measurements are performed on the porous Si in many cases, and it is necessary to peel porous layer from substrate to measure optical absorption. Although many reports evaluate optical band gap by PL measurement, this is not appropriate for defect related PL such as defect created by surface oxidation.[3] Detailed measurements of the optical absorption spectra and comparison with the theoretical works are important to understand the effect of oxidation on the density of state of this material. We deposited surface hydrogenated Si nanocrystallites on the synthetic quarts substrate by pulsed laser ablation (PLA) in hydrogen gas[4,5] to measure and to discuss correlation between natural oxidation and optical absorption.

EXPERIMENT

The hydrogenated Si nanocrystallites were prepared by PLA in H_2 background gas. After a chamber was evacuated less than 1.0×10^{-5} Pascal, high purity (99.9999%) H_2 gas was introduced into the vacuum chamber. A fourth harmonic of pulsed Nd:YAG laser beam was focused onto the single-crystalline Si target. The wavelength, pulse width, repetition rate, fluence of the laser beam at the Si target were 266 nm, 10 ns, 10 Hz, 1.5 J/cm^2, respectively. The sample prepared by this method was surface hydrogenated Si nanocrystallites which diameter is about 4-5 nm.[4,5] The substrates are synthetic quarts and Si wafer for UV-visible and IR transmission measurements.

RESULTS AND DISCUSSION

The samples are exposed to the atmosphere for 95 days to evaluate an effect of native oxidation. The changes in the optical absorption spectra with exposure time for the specimens deposited at 560 and 1100 Pascal are shown in Fig. 1. Absorption at subgap energy region (1~3eV) was appeared. The Si-O bond density and peak frequency measured by FT-IR increased with the exposure time. The Si-O absorption was observed even at 0 days. This indicates oxidation

CP893, *Physics of Semiconductors, 28th International Conference*
edited by W. Jantsch and F. Schäffler
© 2007 American Institute of Physics 978-0-7354-0397-0/07/$23.00

start just after exposure to the atmosphere. The IR peak frequency at 0 days is 1050 cm^{-1} and it shifts to 1080 cm^{-1} at 3 days. This indicates that composition of native oxide changed from sub-oxide (SiO$_x$;x<2) to nearly stoichiometric (SiO$_2$) composition.

We assumed Gaussian type of subgap absorption spectra and these spectra was subtracted from original spectra. The resulting spectra are shown in Fig. 2. The subgap absorption and subtracted spectra are shown by dotted and broken lines. Subgap absorption exists at around 2.1 eV appeared at low exposure time and it moves to at around 3 eV for further exposure. Although these spectral deconvolution have large ambiguity, change in the peak energy from about 2 to 3 eV is obvious. The subtracted spectra correspond to the band to band optical absorption spectra. The optical gap energy shifted to higher energy by native oxidation. The recession of the optical bandgap energy by surface oxidation is pointed out by some theoretical works.[6-9] We can not observe decrease in the optical gap energy. This indicates that the effect of decrease in the size is larger than that of recession of optical gap energy.

We previously reported PL peak wavelengths of native oxidized nc-Si:H are at around 650 and 400 nm (~2 and 3 eV).[4] The PL peak energy discontinuously changed from 2 to 3 eV. This discontinuous change in the energy corresponds to the change in the optical-gap energy. The subgap absorption bands have strong correlation with these PL emission bands. These results indicate that the change in the subgap absorption energy and PL peak energy is due to the creation of defect center by oxidation and the energy of defect level change with the degree of oxidation.

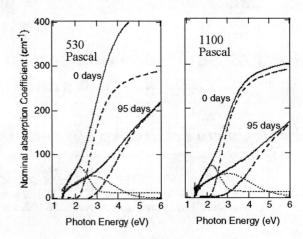

FIGURE 2. Deconvolution of the absorption spectra.

CONCLUSIONS

We measured band-to-band and defect absorption of the surface hydrogenated silicon nanocrystallites. Careful observation enables us to distinguish defect absorption from band-to-band absorption. The peak energy of the defect center changed by degree of oxidation and it is consistent with the change in the PL center.

ACKNOWLEDGMENTS

This work was partially supported by a Grant-in-Aid for Scientific Research from the Japan Society for the Promotion of Science, Nippon Sheet Glass Foundation for Materials Science and Engineering, and The Hirao Taro Foundation of the Konan University Association for Academic Research.

REFERENCES

1. D.J. Lockwood. *Light Emission in Silicon*, San Diego : Academic Press, 1998
2. S. Ossicini, L. Pavesi and F. Priolo. *Light Emitting Silicon for Microphotonics* , Berlin, Springer 2003
3. M.V. Wolkin, J. Jorne, P.M. Fauchet, G. Allan and C. Delerue: *Phys. Rev. Lett* 82, (1999) 197.
4. K. Matsumoto, M. Inada, I. Umezu and A. Sugimura, *Jpn. J. Appl. Phys.* 44, (2005) 8742-8746.
5. T. Makino, M. Inada, I. Umezu and A. Sugimura, *J. Phys. D* 38, (2005) 3507-3511.
6. E. Degoli, G. Cantele, E. Luppi, R. Margi, D. Ninno, O. Bisi and S. Ossicini, *Phys. Rev. B* 69, (2004) 155411.
7. L.E. Ramos, J. Furthmuller and F. Bechstedt, *Phys. Rev. B* 70, (2004) 033311.
8. M. Nishida, *Phys. Rev. B* 69, (2004) 165324.
9. I. Vasiliev, J.R. Chelikowsky and R.M. Martin: *Phys. Rev. B* 65, (2002) 121302(R).

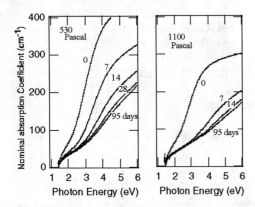

FIGURE 1. The change in the optical absorption spectra by exposure to the atmosphere for the samples prepared at 530 and 1100 Pascal.

InN/GaN quantum dots: Electronic and optical properties

S. Schulz*, S. Schumacher*,† and G. Czycholl*

*Institute for Theoretical Physics, University of Bremen, 28359 Bremen, Germany
†Currently at: College of Optical Sciences, University of Arizona, Tucson, Arizona 85721, USA

Abstract. In the framework of a tight-binding model we investigate the electronic and optical properties of self-assembled nitride quantum dots (QDs). Coulomb and dipole matrix elements are calculated from the single-particle wave functions, which include the underlying wurtzite crystal structure on an atomistic level. These matrix elements are used for the evaluation of optical properties. For different dot sizes of the investigated lens-shaped InN/GaN QDs, we analyze the excitonic absorption and emission spectra. Furthermore the influence of the intrinsic and strain-induced electrostatic built-in field on the spectra is addressed. For a small lens-shaped InN/GaN QD we predict a vanishing exciton ground state emission. For larger QDs, a bright ground state emission is found but with reduced oscillator strength.

PACS: 78.67.HC, 73.22.Dj, 71.35.-y

Semiconductor quantum dots (QDs) are subject of intense experimental and theoretical research. As a new material system, group-III nitrides are of particular interest due to their wide range of emission frequencies from red to ultraviolet. As a technologically promising manifestation of zero-dimensional heterostructures we study self-assembled QDs.

We consider a lens-shaped InN QD, which is grown in the (0001)-direction on top of an InN wetting layer and embedded in a GaN matrix. The one-particle states are calculated by means of a tight-binding (TB) model, which provides a powerful approach to the electronic states of low-dimensional heterostructures on an atomistic level [1]. In our work we use an sp^3 basis per spin direction and lattice site $\mathbf{R}$, for details see Ref. [2]. Since we are interested in more general aspects, we neglect the strain-induced displacement of the atoms. For the chosen dot geometry, a more realistic inclusion of strain effects does not change the symmetry of the system, so that our general statements should also hold if the strain-field was included in our approach. The spontaneous polarization of the wurtzite lattice and the strong strain-induced piezoelectric field are treated as outlined in Ref. [3]. In order to investigate the influence of the dot size on the single-particle and excitonic properties, we study three different lens-shaped QDs with diameters $d = 4.5, 5.7, 7.7$ nm and heights of $h = 1.6, 2.3, 3.0$ nm, respectively.

The circular symmetry of the investigated QD geometry around the z-axis preserves the intrinsic C_{3v} symmetry of the underlying wurtzite crystal lattice. In contrast to a lens-shaped QD with a zincblende structure, this symmetry leads to an exact two-fold degeneracy of the p-shell (exited states) for electrons and holes. In case of the electron states, the dominant orbital character stems from the single s-orbital, while for the hole states a strong inter-mixing of different atomic p-orbitals is observed. These effects cannot be accounted for in single-band effective mass approaches and require a multiband treatment like $\mathbf{k} \cdot \mathbf{p}$, pseudopotential or a tight-binding approach. Under the influence of the electrostatic built-in field, the electron single-particle states are shifted towards the top of the QD whereas the hole states move to the bottom of the nanostructure. In case of the largest QD, a clear spatial separation of electron and hole wave functions is observed. This leads to a decrease in the dipole matrix elements. For the intermediate and largest QD with built-in field, the hole ground state is formed by the two degenerate states Φ_1^h and Φ_2^h (p-shell) whereas the first excited state Φ_3^h (s-shell) is nondegenerate. This behavior is interchanged with decreasing QD size, and for the smallest QD, the ground state is formed by the s-shell. Such a behavior in the ordering of energy levels is also reported for other QD systems [4].

To study the optical properties of the nanostructure, the calculation of dipole and Coulomb matrix elements is required. In case of an empirical TB model, the atomic orbitals are not explicitly known and therefore we approximate the Coulomb matrix elements by:

$$V_{ijkl} = \sum_{\mathbf{RR'}} \sum_{\alpha\beta} c_{\mathbf{R}\alpha}^{i*} c_{\mathbf{R'}\beta}^{j*} c_{\mathbf{R'}\beta}^{k} c_{\mathbf{R}\alpha}^{l} V(\mathbf{R}-\mathbf{R'}), \quad (1)$$

$$\text{with} \quad V(\mathbf{R}-\mathbf{R'}) = \frac{e_0^2}{4\pi\varepsilon_0\varepsilon_r|\mathbf{R}-\mathbf{R'}|} \quad \text{for} \quad \mathbf{R} \neq \mathbf{R'}$$

$$\text{and} \quad V(0) = \frac{1}{V_{uc}^2} \int_{uc} d^3r\, d^3r' \frac{e_0^2}{4\pi\varepsilon_0\varepsilon_r|\mathbf{r}-\mathbf{r'}|} \approx V_0. \quad (2)$$

The expansion coefficients $c_{\alpha,\mathbf{R}}^i$ are related to the ith one-particle wave function $\Phi_i(\mathbf{r}) = \sum_{\alpha,\mathbf{R}} c_{\alpha,\mathbf{R}}^i \phi_{\alpha,\mathbf{R}}(\mathbf{r})$ which is given in terms of the atomic orbitals $\phi_{\alpha,\mathbf{R}}(\mathbf{r})$ localized at the lattice site $\mathbf{R}$. In this manner, justified by the long ranged slowly varying character of the Coulomb interaction, we only take into account its variation on a

CP893, *Physics of Semiconductors, 28th International Conference*
edited by W. Jantsch and F. Schäffler
© 2007 American Institute of Physics 978-0-7354-0397-0/07/$23.00

larger length scale (magnitude of lattice constants) but not within one unit cell [2]. The calculation of the onsite integral, Eq. 2, can be done quasianalytically [5].

Besides the Coulomb interaction, the dipole matrix elements between electron and hole wave functions are an essential ingredient for the calculation of optical spectra. In contrast to the Coulomb matrix elements, the short range contributions dominate the dipole matrix elements. The precise structure of the atomic orbitals cannot be neglected for the calculation of these matrix elements. Therefore it is necessary to connect the calculated TB-coefficient $c^i_{\alpha,R}$ to the underlying basis orbitals. To this end we use numerically orthogonalized Slater orbitals [2], which fulfill the basic requirements of an orthogonal TB model regarding locality, symmetry and orthogonality of the basis orbitals. Furthermore, to treat the slight nonlocality of the dipole operator and in particular the anion-cation structure of the crystal, the dipole matrix elements are calculated up to second-nearest neighbors. From this we obtain that the only relevant dipole matrix elements in our system are $\mathbf{ed}^{eh}_{s,p_x} = \mathbf{ed}^{eh}_{s,p_y}$ and $\mathbf{ed}^{eh}_{p_x,s} = \mathbf{ed}^{eh}_{p_y,s}$ with the light polarization vector $\mathbf{e} = \frac{1}{\sqrt{2}}(1,1,0)$. The resulting selection rules cannot be explained within a single-band effective mass-approach.

With the determined dipole and Coulomb matrix elements, the calculation of optical spectra can directly be performed starting from the many-body Hamiltonian as given in, e.g., Ref. [6]. To keep the discussion simple, we included only the first three bound electron and hole states in the configuration-interaction (CI) calculation [6]. The excitonic absorption and emission spectra, calculated by Fermi's golden rule, are depicted for the smallest and the largest QD in Fig 1. The excitonic absorption for the small QD with (solid line) and without (dashed line) the built-in field is shown in Fig. 1(a). According to the dipole selection rules, the lower energy line is dominated by contributions where the electron is exited in the s-shell and the hole in the p-shell, and vice versa for the high energy line. Under the influence of the built-in field, the whole spectrum is red-shifted. In addition, the built-in field leads to a spatial separation of electron and hole wave functions and therefore the oscillator strengths are drastically reduced. For the small QD no exciton ground state emission is observed, as discussed in detail in Ref. [7] and shown in Fig. 1 (c). Figure 1(b) shows the excitonic absorption spectrum with (solid line) and without (dashed line) the built-in field for the large QD. Compared to the small QD, the separation of electron and hole wave functions is much more pronounced and therefore the reduction of the oscillator strength and the redshift in energy is much larger. For the large QD with the built-in field the ground state is a two-fold degenerate state (p-shell). Therefore the main contribution to the exciton ground state is formed by the electron in

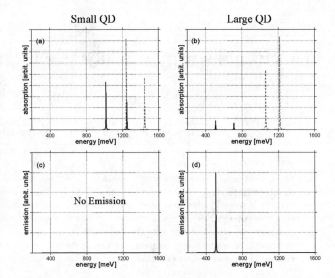

FIGURE 1. (a) Excitonic absorption for the small QD with (solid line) and without (dashed line) the influence of the built-in field. (b) Same as (a) but for the large QD. Excitonic ground state emission for the small (c) and the large (d) QD with the influence of the built-in field. Without the built-in field, the ground state emission also vanishes for the large QD and is consequently not shown.

the s-shell, and the hole in the p-shell. In contrast to the small QD, a nonvanishing exciton ground state emission can be observed, which is depicted in Fig. 1(d). Without the built-in field no emission is observed.

To avoid the strong reduction of the oscillator strength by spatial separation of electron and hole wavefunctions, one possible solution, which is discussed in the literature, is the growth of smaller QD structures. However, our results demonstrate that the growth of smaller QD structures might turn out to have limitations concerning optical purposes.

REFERENCES

1. R. Santoprete, B. Koiller, R. B. Capaz, P. Kratzer, Q. K. K. Liu, and M. Scheffler, *Phys. Rev. B* **68**, 235311 (2003).
2. S. Schulz, S. Schumacher, and G. Czycholl, *Phys. Rev. B* **73**, 245327 (2006).
3. S. De Rinaldis, I. D'Amico, and F. Rossi, *Phys. Rev. B* **69**, 235316 (2004).
4. A. Bagga, P. K. Chattopadhyay, and S. Ghosh, *Phys. Rev. B* **71**, 115327 (2005).
5. I. Schnell, G. Czycholl, and R. C. Albers, *Phys. Rev. B* **65**, 075103 (2002).
6. N. Baer, P. Gartner, and F. Jahnke, *Eur. Phys. J. B* **42**, 231 (2004).
7. N. Baer, S. Schulz, S. Schumacher, P. Gartner, G. Czycholl, and F. Jahnke, *Appl. Phys. Lett.* **87**, 231114 (2005).

Rough InAs/GaAs Quantum Dots

M. G. Bezerra[1,2], G. A. Farias[2], J. A. K. Freire[2] and R. Ferreira[1]

[1] *Laboratoire Pierre Aigrain, Ecole Normale Supérieure, 24 Rue Lhomond F-75005 – Paris, France*
[2] *Departamento de Fisica, Universidade Federal do Ceara, CP 6030, 60455-900 Fortaleza, Ceara, Brazil*

Abstract. We consider the effect of static disorder modeled by interface roughness in the intra-band FIR absorption of semiconductor quantum dots. We show that a broad PL profile appears for realistic disorder parameters and analyze its role on the linear polarization of the absorption response.

Keywords: Quantum Dots, Optical properties, Static Disorder
PACS: 71.20.Nr ; 73.63.Kv ; 74.25.Gz

INTRODUCTION

The self-assembled quantum dots (QDs) offer a wide range of potential applications for optoelectronic devices such as semiconductor lasers, single electron transistors and optical memories [1]. Yet, the use of an ensemble of QDs is in some cases limited by inhomogeneous broadening. Indeed, despite the important advances in the growth techniques, state-of-the-art samples still display QDs with important ($\approx$10%) size fluctuations. These fluctuations are usually modelled by slight variations of the dot geometric and material parameters (basis radius, height, composition, ...).. We consider in this work the role of interface roughness on the electronic states of quantum dots: to the best of our knowledge, their role in quantum dots has, so far, not been discussed (see e.g. [2] for a study in quantum wells). These effects are often neglected and expected to be much less important than fluctuations related to the mean size of the dots, because : (i) the low laying electron and hole bound states are usually well confined within the QD and only slightly explore the barrier region, and (ii) roughness preserve the mean QD volume. However, interface roughness should constitute the ultimate inhomogeneous static perturbation to a QD ensemble. We show here that they can play an important role in the optical response of an either single QD and an ensemble of (nominally identical) QDs.

We use a simple effective mass model to evaluate the low laying confined QD states. In the following we shall focus on the electron states in the conduction band. We use the following parameters in the calculations: isotropic effective mass $m^*/m_0 = 0.067$; offset discontinuity between the QD and the GaAs regions Ve = 413 meV. The QD is modelled by a truncated cone of height 25Å, basis radius 100Å and basis angle 70°, floating on a one ML (3.33 Å thick) wetting layer. We compute initially the first 5 bound states (of S, P and D-like symmetries) of a perfect dot, i.e., for which the confinement potential is a piece-wise constant function of the electron position [3]. We then use these states as a basis for diagonalizing two different perturbations. The first one is an anisotropic correction for a quantum dot of in-plane elliptical shape. The small and large radii of the ellipse are respectively taken as 95Å and 105Å. The corresponding anisotropic correction couple the non-degenerated S and D states and also the two degenerated P states. The anisotropic splitting ΔE_P of the P levels has been observed in magneto-optical experiments in the FIR domain done in QDs doped with one electron [4]. For our QD we calculate $\Delta E_P = 3.5$ meV.

The second term is the disorder perturbation. The roughness is modelled as a random deviation of the perfect confining geometry, as given e.g. by the presence of protrusions of one material into the other, namely, of the dot into the barrier and vice-versa, in such a way that the mean roughness potential vanishes. More precisely, the dot radius of the rough QD is a random function of the in-plane angle (θ), with deviation with respect to the perfect QD radius given by:

CP893, *Physics of Semiconductors, 28th International Conference*
edited by W. Jantsch and F. Schäffler
© 2007 American Institute of Physics 978-0-7354-0397-0/07/$23.00

$$\delta R(\theta) = 2\sigma_R \sqrt{\frac{L_C}{\overline{R}}} \sum_{n>0} e^{-\left(\frac{nL_C}{2\overline{R}}\right)^2} \cos[n\theta + \phi_n] \quad (1)$$

where σ_R is the variance and L_C the correlation length of the small random deviation of the radius around its mean value $\overline{R}(\theta)$ ($|\delta R| \ll \overline{R}$).

We consider the FIR absorption of a doped QD from its ground state towards its first two excited states. For a perfect elliptical dot, these are the two energy splitted P-like states; its absorption spectrum is linearly polarized, account to the elongated shape. We define the polarization ratio as P = (OSx-OSy)/(OSx+OSy), where "x" and "y" refer to the in-plane directions with large and small dot radii respectively and OS is proportional to the dipolar oscillator strength for the transitions. Thus, the polarization spectrum of the perfect dot has two lines with +1 (lower energy) and –1 (higher energy) values.

We show in figure 1 the linear polarization spectrum of an ensemble of 100 independent rough QDs (for 100 runs using equation (1)). The two panels are for two values of the variance and for fixed L_C = 40Å.

The roughness related perturbation admix all the bound state. It leads to several features in the polarization spectrum. Let us consider initially the "weak" disorder case displayed in the upper panel. First of all, the intra-level couplings renormalize the energies of the QD states, and contribute to an (average) increase of the ΔE_P splitting. Secondly, the polarization spectrum becomes slightly broader, because of the different coupling strengths related to the different realizations of the rough interface. Third, because of the symmetry-breaking, the "x" and "y" nature of the P levels become less and less marked with increasing disorder, and the magnitude of the (average) polarization decreases, even thought the lower and higher energy bands do still preserve a preferential polarization sign.

These three effects are greatly enhanced for a stronger disorder, as shown in the lower panel in the figure 1. We observe a polarization spectrum with the same qualitative characteristics as obtained for an ensemble of non-rough QDs with size fluctuation: two lines with broadening of the same order of the ΔE_P splitting with preferential "x" and "y" polarizations in the lower and higher energy sides respectively.

ACKNOWLEDGMENTS

One of us (MGB) would like to thank the CAPES (Brazil) for financial support. The Laboratoire Pierre Aigrain is "Unité mixte de Recherche du CNRS (UMR8551) et des Universites Paris 6 et Paris 7".

REFERENCES

1. Y. A. Arakawa and H. Sakaki, Appl. Phys. Lett. 40, 939 (1982)
2. M. C. A. Lima, G. A. Farias and V. N. Freire, Phys Rev. B52, 5777 (1995)
3. R. Ferreira and G. Bastard, Appl. Phys. Lett. 74, 2818 (1999)
4. S. Hameau, Y. Guldner, O. Verzelen, R. Ferreira, G. Bastard, J. Zeman, A. Lemaitre, J-M. Gerard, Phys. Rev. Lett. 83, 4152 (1999)

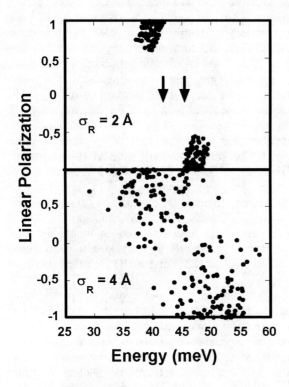

FIGURE 1. Linear polarization of the FIR absorption involving the first two excited states of an ensemble of 100 independent rough QDs, for two different values of the variance. L_C = 40 Å. The arrows indicate the energy positions of the two transitions of the perfect elliptical QD, with polarizations respectively +1 and –1 for the lower and higher energy absorptions.

Electron states and magnetophotoluminescence of elongated InAs/GaAs quantum dots

V. Křápek[*], K. Kuldová[†], J. Oswald[†], A. Hospodková[†], E. Hulicius[†] and J. Humlíček[*]

[*]Faculty of Science, Masaryk University, Kotlářská 2, 611 37 Brno, Czech Republic
[†]Institute of Physics, ASCR, Cukrovarnická 10, 162 53 Praha 6, Czech Republic

Abstract. We have calculated the electronic structure of a single InAs/GaAs quantum dot in a perpendicular magnetic field. Considerable sensitivity of the shift of energy levels in magnetic field to a lateral elongation of the dots is demonstrated and a possibility to retrieve the elongation from magnetophotoluminescence spectra is discussed. Sensitivity analysis shows that spectra with at least two well resolved bands are needed for a reliable determination of the elongation.

Keywords: quantum dots, magnetophotoluminescence, elongation
PACS: 73.21.La,73.22.Dj,73.43.Cd

Determination of morphology of quantum dots (QDs) is presently subject of intense interest due to its strong influence on the QD electronic structure. The lateral elongation of the QDs is of particular interest, since it influences their optical properties, in particular the polarization of absorption and emission. The QDs suitable for the applications are buried, which embarrasses the determination of their lateral profile by standard structural methods [1]. On the other hand, photoluminescence (PL) in perpendicular magnetic field probes directly the shape of electron wave functions, and is therefore usable even for the buried dots. We present the calculations of the electron states in elongated QDs in the perpendicular magnetic field and discuss the possibility to measure the elongation and exciton effective mass by the magneto-PL.

Since the lateral confinement of carriers in flat QDs is usually much weaker than the vertical confinement, it is reasonable to treat them independently and approximate the former one by a two-dimensional (2D) anisotropic harmonic potential. This approach has been widely and successfully applied for circular dots, see e.g. [2]. We denote the lower harmonic frequency ω_0, the higher one $L\omega_0$, where L is the ratio of larger and smaller lateral dimensions of the dot, called elongation below. Assuming QD elongated in x direction, the Hamiltonian for perpendicular magnetic field reads

$$-\frac{\hbar^2}{2m^*}\Delta_{xy} + \frac{1}{2}m^*\left(\omega_0^2 x^2 + L^2\omega_0^2 y^2 + \frac{1}{4}\omega_c^2 r^2\right) - \frac{1}{2}\omega_c l_z,$$

where m^* is the particle effective mass, $l_z = xp_y - yp_x$ is the projection of the angular momentum onto the field direction, and $\omega_c = eB/m^*$ is the cyclotron frequency. Solutions are found using exact diagonalization; for $L = 1$ they result in the well-known Fock-Darwin states.

The transition energies generally depend on the effective masses and harmonic frequencies of both electrons and holes; however, according to our calculations, the energies are very precisely (better than to 1 meV) determined by the total harmonic frequency and by the reduced effective mass of the electron-hole pair.

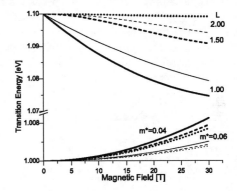

FIGURE 1. The field dependence of transition energies calculated for $\omega_0 = 100\,\text{meV}$, $m^* = 0.04m_0$ (thick lines) and $0.06m_0$ (thin lines), and $L = 1.0$ (solid lines), 1.5 (dashed lines), and 2.0 (dotted lines).

Figure 1 displays the calculated field dependences of the two lowest bands for different m^* and L. High values of the elongation and effective mass lead to smaller energy shifts with increasing field; the dependence on the mass is more pronounced for the lowest transition, while the dependence on the elongation is more pronounced for the first higher transition. The model parameters ω_0, m^*, and L can be determined from the measured magneto-PL spectra displaying at least two well resolved transitions; we have already applied this approach to both circular and elongated MOVPE grown dots [3], [4].

CP893, *Physics of Semiconductors, 28th International Conference*
edited by W. Jantsch and F. Schäffler

We proceed further with calculating the errors of the parameters assuming that ω_0 is known precisely (note that it can be determined with a fairly small error from the energy separation of the two lowest transition), and the transition energies measured for magnetic fields from 0 T to 30 T with the step of 3 T with a random error of magnitude of 1 meV (2 meV) for the lowest (first higher) transition, respectively. For reasonable values of m^* (from $0.03\,m_0$ to $0.06\,m_0$) and L (from 1 to 2), the maximum relative errors of the m^* and L are 11 % and 5 % for $\omega_0 = 100$ meV, and 3 % and 4 % for $\omega_0 = 20$ meV. As expected, the largest relative errors are found for the parameter values with the most flat energy dependencies; i.e., $m^* = 0.06\,m_0$ and $L = 2$. For these values, the correlation of the estimates is 1 % (-28 %) for ω_0 of 20 meV (100 meV), respectively. Small values of the correlation are crucial for the accurate determination of the parameters.

When the higher transitions are not detected, it is still possible to obtain ω_0 and m^* for the circular dots [5]. However, if the dots *are* elongated, then even for ω_0 known, the values of L and m^* cannot be determined simultaneously due to their large correlation, which can easily exceed 99 %. The relative errors of the parameter estimates are then several tens of percent, or even more. This is illustrated in Fig. 2, where the field dependence for selected values of the parameters is reproduced using different sets of the parameters ω_0, m^*, L. Lines differing in ω_0 and m^* are distinguishable on the scale of meV and therefore simultaneous determination of both parameters is possible; on the other hand, the opposite is true for the lines differing in m^* and L.

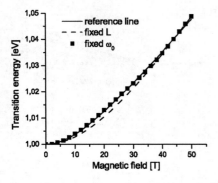

FIGURE 2. The transition energies calculated for the following values of the parameters: $\omega_0 = 20$ meV, $m^* = 0.045\,m_0$, $L = 1$ (solid line); $\omega_0 = 50$ meV, $m^* = 0.034\,m_0$, $L = 1$ (fixed L; dashed line); $\omega_0 = 20$ meV, $m^* = 0.040\,m_0$, $L = 1.5$ (fixed ω_0; squares).

We have tested the accuracy of the 2D harmonic potential approach by comparing its results with those obtained by a more accurate method. We have chosen a circular QD with the two lowest transitions at 1.0 and

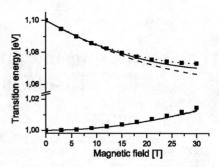

FIGURE 3. The energy shifts calculated for the dot with the lowest transition energies of 1.0 and 1.1 eV. The lines represent full 3D solution for the lens- (solid), cylinder- (dashed), and cone-shaped (dotted) dot. The corresponding 2D solution ($\omega_0 = 100$ meV, $m^* = 0.031\,m_0$, $L = 1$) is shown by squares.

1.1 eV as a reference system. The full three-dimensional (3D) problem was solved within the single-band effective mass approximation including a realistic strain field. This calculation also predicts the value of the effective mass: $m^* = 0.031\,m_0$. The results for different QD shapes together with the results of corresponding 2D calculation ($\omega_0 = 100$ meV, $L = 1$) are displayed in Fig. 3. The results are fairly close, e.g., the best 2D fit of the real lens–shaped QD is obtained for the parameters $m^* = 0.033\,m_0$ and $L = 1$, which means the relative systematic error lower than 10 %. In general, the 2D approximation tends to overestimate the shift of the lowest transition and underestimate that of the first higher transition, i.e., it overestimates the effective mass and underestimates the elongation. However, the 2D harmonic–potential approach can be considered a reasonable approximation.

ACKNOWLEDGMENTS

This work was supported by the GAAV grant B101630601, the GACR grant 202/06/0718, and by the Institutional Research Programs MSM021622410 and AV0Z10100521.

REFERENCES

1. R. Songmuang, S. Kiravittaya, and O. G. Schmidt, *J. Cryst. Growth* **249**, 416 (2003).
2. A. Wojs and P. Hawrylak, *Phys. Rev. B* **53**, 10841 (1996).
3. K. Kuldová, V. Křápek, A. Hospodková, O. Bonaventurová Zrzavecká, J. Oswald, E. Hulicius, and J. Humlíček, *Mater. Sci. Eng. C* **26**, 983 (2006)
4. V. Křápek, K. Kuldová, J. Oswald, A. Hospodková, E. Hulicius, and J. Humlíček, submitted to *Appl. Phys. Lett.*
5. C. Cornet, C. Levallois, P. Caroff, H. Folliot, C. Labbe, J. Even, A. Le Corre, S. Loualiche, M. Hayne, and V. V. Moshchalkov, *Appl. Phys. Lett.* **87**, 233111 (2005).

Delocalized Electron States in Quantum Dot Molecules

T. van Lippen, R. Nötzel, A. Yu. Silov and J.H. Wolter

COBRA Inter-University Research Institute, Eindhoven University of Technology
P.O. Box 513, 5600 MB Eindhoven, the Netherlands

Abstract. We demonstrate 2-dimensional coupling of the electron states in lateral quantum dot molecules by excitation density and temperature dependent micro-photoluminescence (PL) spectroscopy. The 2-dimensional coupling manifests itself in a quasi-continuous density of states due to delocalized electron states. It accounts for broad PL bands observed in excitation density dependent micro-PL and provides low-energy carrier redistribution channels between localized states, as evident from the temperature dependent micro-PL measurements.

Keywords: quantum dot, electronic coupling, quantum dot molecule
PACS: 78.67.Hc, 73.21.La, 78.55.Cr, 81.15.Hi

INTRODUCTION

There is strong interest in coupling and coherence of quantum dot (QD) structures to create artificial matter and to obtain new functional units for applications. In strongly coupled QD configurations, the wave functions delocalize due to tunneling, leading to extended states described by a coherent superposition of individual QD wave functions. Lateral QD coupling has been observed in the two limiting cases of a pair of QDs [1] and high-density QD layers [2]. Here we demonstrate 2-dimensional coupling of the electron states in lateral QD molecules (QDMs) containing on average 4 QDs [3,4] by excitation density and temperature dependent micro-photoluminescence (PL) spectroscopy. This intermediate regime, when fully understood, is anticipated to provide the most complex, advanced functionalities with analogies to the properties of quantum clusters [5].

EXPERIMENTAL

The QDMs, grown by solid-source molecular beam epitaxy on GaAs (311)B substrates, consist of closely spaced ordered InAs QDs with adjustable number. They are formed by self-organized anisotropic strain engineering of an (In,Ga)As/GaAs superlattice template and the ordering of InAs QDs on top due to local strain recognition. For a detailed description see Refs. 3 and 4. The n- (p-) type modulation-doped QDMs were obtained by inserting 30 nm Si (Be) doped GaAs separated by 8 nm undoped GaAs above the QDMs. A low number of QDMs with average 4 QDs per molecule was selected through aluminum masks with 1×1 μm^2 square openings fabricated by electron beam lithography. Excitation by a Ti:sapphire laser and detection were performed through a microscope objective. A triple monochromator and an (In,Ga)As charge coupled device were used to disperse and detect the PL with high spectral resolution

RESULTS & DISCUSSION

In excitation density dependent micro-PL spectra of the p-type modulation-doped QDMs taken at 3.5 K , Fig. 1(a), two discrete sets of sharp (< 1meV) peaks superimposed on top of broad (~ 15 meV) PL bands are observed. The number and intensity of the sharp peaks within each set and the intensity of the broad PL bands increase with excitation density. The n-type modulation-doped QDMs, on the other hand, only reveal broad PL bands of similar width, intensity similarly increases with excitation density, see Fig. 1(b). As a function of temperature, the number and intensity of the sharp peaks of the p-type modulation-doped QDMs decreases, see Fig. 2 (a). The sharp peaks vanish around 60 K and the intensity of the broad PL bands increases with a maximum in the temperature range of 80 – 110 K before it drops at higher temperatures. The observation of the broad PL bands down to low excitation density and temperature is a clear signature of the recombination of excitons in extended states forming a quasi-continuous density of states, while the superimposed sharp features originate from localized states therein [6]. With increase of the

CP893, *Physics of Semiconductors, 28th International Conference*
edited by W. Jantsch and F. Schäffler
© 2007 American Institute of Physics 978-0-7354-0397-0/07/$23.00

excitation density, the intensity of the broad PL bands increases and additional sharp peaks arise at higher and lower energies which are, similar to isolated QDs, attributed to localized bi-excitons and charged excitons. The width of the sharp peaks is in the order of a few hundred μeV, significantly broader than that reported for isolated QDs [7], which indicates interaction with the energetically close extended states in the presence of relatively weak confinement or localization.

With moderate increase of the temperature, the localized excitons redistribute through the extended states creating low-energy carrier redistribution channels. This results in the observed gradual reduction of the number of sharp peaks. Further temperature rise then leads to an increase of the intensity of the broad PL bands due to thermally activated occupation of the extended states. The overall shift of the PL spectra to lower energy is caused by the dependence of the band gap energy on the temperature. The absence of sharp features for the n-type modulation-doped QDMs, see Fig. 2(b), is attributed to the occupation of the localized states as well as the extended electron state up to the Fermi energy, given by the doping level. As the localized states are distributed in energy over the range of the extended states, their sharp emission peaks are buried beneath the stronger emission due to the occupied extended electron states, and only the broad PL bands from individual QDMs are observed. As a function of excitation density and temperature, the broad PL bands behave very similar to those of the p-type modulation-doped QDMs with comparable width, confirming the similar extended energy level structure in those QDMs with the same number of QDs.

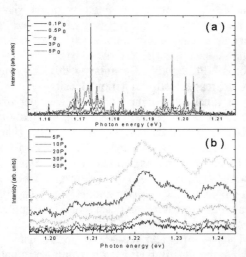

FIGURE 1. Excitation density dependent micro-PL taken at 3.5 K of the p-type (a) and n-type (b) modulation-doped QDMs. $P_0 = 1$ kW/cm^2.

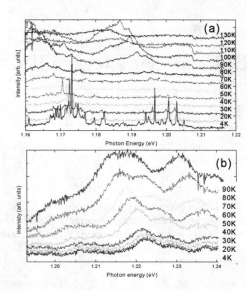

FIGURE 2. Temperature dependent micro-PL spectra of the p-type (a) and n-type (b) modulation-doped QDMs. The excitation density is 5 P_0 (a) and 10 P_0 (b). The cut-off at 1.207 eV is caused by the intermediate slit of the monochromator.

CONCLUSIONS

We have studied excitation density and temperature dependent micro-PL of ordered lateral QDMs, demonstrating extended electron states. Micro-PL spectra of the p-type modulation-doped QDMs exhibit discrete sets of sharp PL peaks on top of broad PL bands. Number and intensity of the sharp peaks increase with excitation density. Only broad PL bands are observed for the n-type modulation-doped QDMs with similar behavior. These findings are consistently explained by state filling in the presence of extended electron states. They are formed due to lateral electronic coupling of the QDs within the QDMs and appear as a quasi-continuous density of states. They account for the broad PL bands and provide low-energy carrier redistribution channels between localized states observed in the excitation density and temperature dependent micro-PL measurements. This opens a route for experimental investigations of the quantum behavior of carriers in artificial QDMs, with possible application in future quantum functional devices.

REFERENCES

[1] G.J. Beirne *et al.* Phys. Rev. Lett. **96**, 137401 (2006)
[2] S. Lan *et al.* Phys. Rev. B **61**, 16847 (2000)
[3] T. van Lippen *et al.* Appl. Phys. Lett. **85**, 118 (2004)
[4] T. van Lippen *et al.* J. Appl. Phys. **97**, 44301 (2005)
[5] T. Maier *et al.* Rev. Mod. Phys, **77**, 1027 (2005)
[6] F. Intonti *et al.* Phys. Rev. B **63**, 075313 (2001)
[7] R. Nötzel *et al.* Nature **392**, 56 (1998)

Excitonic Fock-Darwin Spectrum Of A Single Quantum Dot

A. Babiński[1], M. Potemski[2], S. Raymond[3], J. Lapointe[3], Z. R. Wasilewski[3], and J.M.Baranowski[1]

[1]*Institute of Experimental Physics, Warsaw University, Hoza 69, 00-681 Warsaw, Poland*
[2]*Grenoble High Magnetic Field Laboratory, CNRS, BP-166, 38042 Grenoble Cedex 9, France*
[3]*Institute for Microstructural Sciences , NRC, Ottawa, K1A 0R6, Canada*

Abstract. Optical spectroscopy of a highly-excited single InAs/GaAs self-assembled quantum dot (QD) has been performed. The multiexcitonic emission from the *s*-, *p*-, and *d*-shells of the dot is observed and investigated in magnetic field up to 14T. Effects of interaction between the multiexcitonic configurations and the asymmetry of localizing potential are clearly visible when single-particle states become nearly degenerate: at $B=0$ and at a field-induced level-crossing. It is shown that the Fock-Darwin pattern modified with phenomenological parameters related to the effects explains the field-evolution of the emission.

Keywords: Quantum Dots, Optical Spectroscopy.
PACS: 78.67.Hc, 78.55.Cr, 75.75.+a

INTRODUCTION

Semiconductor quantum dots (QDs) offer a unique opportunity to study electron-electron interactions in strongly confined systems. So far, these studies were mainly limited to investigations of the emission related to the ground states in QDs [1]. More input may be expected from the analysis of multiexcitonic configurations in QDs. The optical emission from a highly-excited single QDs and its evolution in magnetic field are investigated in this work.

EXPERIMENTAL RESULTS

The sample investigated in this work was grown by molecular beam epitaxy on an n$^+$-GaAs substrate. It contains a single layer of InAs/GaAs QDs [2]. The structure was annealed after growth (30 s at 850° C) to shift the emission into the sensitivity range of a CCD camera and to decrease the confining potential in the QDs [3]. A set of mesa structures was prepared on the sample to limit the number of dots addressed optically. The details of experimental setup have been presented elsewhere [4].

The evolution of the photoluminescence (PL) spectra from a submicron-size mesa as a function of the excitation power is shown in Fig. 1. The spectrum obtained at the lowest excitation power (~1 W/cm^2) is dominated by two emission lines, attributed to single excitons in a dot of different charge states. Their weak satellites are most likely due to respective biexcitons.

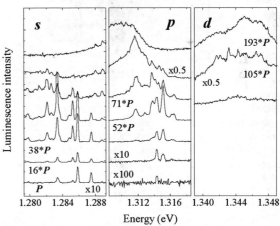

FIGURE 1. Power-dependence of the luminescence from a single InAs/GaAs dot. The lowest excitation power density P=~1 W/cm^2.

At higher energy a weak emission line can also be observed, which is related to the *p*-shell. With increasing excitation power new *s*-shell-related and *p*-shell-related emission lines emerge. These involve multi-excitonic complexes with more than 3 excitons, giving rise to emission associated with the *s*- as well as the *p*-shell [5]. Further increase of excitation power

CP893, *Physics of Semiconductors, 28th International Conference*
edited by W. Jantsch and F. Schäffler
© 2007 American Institute of Physics 978-0-7354-0397-0/07/$23.00

results in new emission lines in both s-related and p-related energy-range. The highest excitation results in further change of the s-related and p-related emission, as well as in a new emission band at higher energy, which is due to the d-shell of the dot.

The attribution of the emission lines to particular shells of the dot is unambiguously supported by their evolution in magnetic field, which is shown in Fig.2. The s-related emission lines shift diamagnetically in magnetic field. The p-related lines either red-shift either blue-shift in magnetic field, and the d-related emission splits into three components.

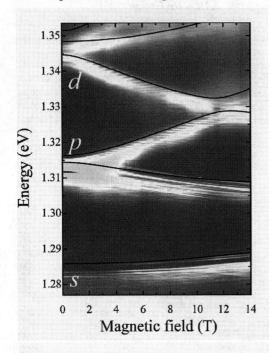

FIGURE 2. Luminescence from the s-, p-, and d-shells of a single InAs/GaAs dot in magnetic field up to 14T. The simulation based on the FD model modified by the zero-field splitting of the p- and d-shells and p-d interaction in high magnetic field is shown with red lines.

DISSCUSSION

The overall pattern of the PL-evolution in magnetic field resembles the Fock-Darwin (FD) spectrum [6], previously observed in PL experiments on large numbers of dots [7]. The observation of discreet emission lines uncovers new details of the optical signature of a multiexciton system. These are the zero-field splitting between the p-related emission lines, which in magnetic field red- and blue-shift and the interaction between the p-, and d-related emission lines induced by magnetic field. The zero-field splitting of the p- (and d-) related lines is due to electron-electron interaction [8] and to a possible asymmetry of localizing potential [9]. The splitting can

be reproduced in a simple perturbation theory by the introduction of a phenomenological interaction parameter to the single-particle FD model. In a similar way, the interaction between the p- and d-related emission lines can be described. Those parameters, as well as the reduced electron-hole mass found from experiment ($\mu=0.057m_0$) can be used to construct the modified FD pattern (see continuous lines in Fig. 2), which surprisingly well describes our experimental data [10].

CONCLUSIONS

Spectroscopic measurements of a highly excited single InAs/GaAs QD are presented. Sharp emission lines due to multiexcitonic complexes related to the s-, p-, and d-shells of the dot have been identified and investigated in magnetic field. The orbital Zeeman splitting of the emission from p- and d-shells and the effects of the electron-electron interaction and/or the asymmetry of the lateral potential have been observed. It has been shown that the magnetic field evolution of the emission from the highly-excited QD can be well described by a modified single-particle excitonic FD model.

ACKNOWLEDGMENTS

Valuable discussions with P. Hawrylak and W. Sheng are kindly acknowledged. Financial support from Polish budget for science (1 P03B 014 29) and from EC (ICA1-2002-70010, RITA-CT-2003-505474) is acknowledged.

REFERENCES

1. *Optics of Quantum Dots and Wires,* edited by G. W Bryant and G. S. Solomon, Boston, London: Artech House, 2005.
2. Z.R. Wasilewski, S. Fafard, and J. P. McCaffrey, *J. Cryst. Growth* **201/202,** 1131 (1999).
3. S. Fafard and C. Ni. Allen, *Appl. Phys. Lett.* **75,** 2374 (1999).
4. A.Babiński, *Acta Phys. Pol. A,* **110,** 275 (2006).
5. M. Bayer, O. Stern, P. Hawrylak, S. Fafard, and A. Forchel, *Nature* (London) **405,** 923 (2000).
6. V. Fock, *Z. Phys.* **47,** 446 (1928), *C. G. Darwin, Proc. Cambridge Philos. Soc.* **27,** 86 (1930).
7. S. Raymond *et al,* Phys. Rev. Lett. **92,** 187402 (2004).
8. P. Hawrylak, *Phys. Rev. B* **60,** 5597 (1999).
9. G. Bester and A. Zunger, *Phys. Rev. B* **71,** 045318 (2005).
10. A.Babinski, M.Potemski, S.Raymond, J.Lapointe, and Z.R.Wasilewski, Phys. Rev. B, **74,** 155301 (2006).

Low-density quantum dots embedded in photonic-crystal nanocavities for single-photon generations

Wen-Hao Chang*, Wen-Yen Chen†, Hsiang-Szu Chang†, Tung-Po Hsieh**, Jen-Inn Chyi** and Tzu-Min Hsu†

*Department of Electrophysics, National Chiao Tung University, Hsinchu 300, Taiwan
†Department of Physics, National Central University, Chung-li 320, Taiwan
**Department of Electrical Engineering, National Central University, Chung-li 320, Taiwan

Abstract. An efficient single-photon source based on low-density InGaAs quantum dots in a photonic-crystal nanocavity is demonstrated. The single-photon source features the effects of photonic band gap, yielding a *single-mode* spontaneous emission coupling efficiency as high as β=92% and a linear polarization degree up to p=95%. This appealing performance makes it well-suited for practical implementation of polarization-encoded schemes in quantum cryptography.

Keywords: quantum dots, single-photon sources, photon antibunching, cavity QED
PACS: 78.67.Hc, 42.50.Dv, 42.50.Pq, 42.70.Qs

Semiconductor quantum dots (QDs) incorporated in monolithic microcavities are promising systems of solid-state single-photon emitters for applications in the field of quantum information, particularly in quantum cryptography. By taking the advantage of cavity quantum electrodynamics (c-QED) effects, the emitted photons from single QDs can be efficiently funnelled into a specific cavity mode, hence achieving efficient, fast, or even directional single-photon emissions. Among various QD-cavity systems, photonic crystal (PC) cavity may be the most promising system, due not only to their capability of offering high-Q factor and small mode volume, but also the greatest design freedom. Besides, PC structures also promise to fully control the spontaneous emission (SE) dynamics, through the modification of available optical modes by the PC surrounding. This novel feature will make a PC-based single-photon emitter to achieve a very high SE coupling factor (β), well suited for practical applications.

In this work, we report an efficient single-photon source based on low-density InGaAs QDs ($\sim 3/\mu m^2$) embedded in a 2D PC nanocavities. The cavity design is based on a L3 defect within a triangular PC lattice fabricated into a 180-nm GaAs membrane by electron-beam lithography and dry etching. A layer of low-density $In_{0.5}Ga_{0.5}As$ QDs, grown by MOCVD through a careful control of coverage, was inserted in the center of the membrane layer. The air-hole periodicity and radius are $a = 300$ nm and $r = 0.31a$, respectively. The L3 cavity was formed by introducing three missing air holes in a line [see Fig. 1(a)]. The two air holes at both edges were displaced outward by a shift s varied systematically from 0 to $0.25a$.

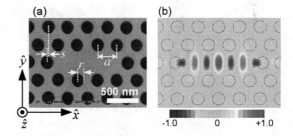

FIGURE 1. (a) Scanning electron micrograph of the fabricated nanocavity. (b)The calculated electric field profile (E_y) of the shallow donor-type cavity mode confined in the L3 cavity with s=0.1a. The color scale is normalized to max($|E_y|$).

Optical emissions were characterized by micro-photoluminescence (μPL) at 5-8 K. Analysis of cavity emissions show that the resonant wavelength shifts systematically from 938 to 962 nm, as s varying from 0 to $0.15a$. According to 3D-FDTD calculations [Fig. 1(b)], we identified the cavity mode as a shallow donor-type defect mode. Figure 2(a) shows the μPL spectra obtained from one of the fabricated nanocavities as a function of excitation power P_{ex}. According to the QD density, each cavity would contain only 1-2 dots. We select in Fig. 2(a) a cavity displaying two sets of lines, corresponding to emissions from two different single QDs (labeled QD1 and QD2), to highlight different behaviors of on- and off-resonance QDs. Single-exciton (X) and biexciton ($2X$) lines of QD1 have been identified according to their power dependence of intensity shown in Fig. 2(b). For the off-resonance QD2, single-exciton (X') and biexciton ($2X'$) lines also show similar power dependence, except a much weaker intensity and a several

CP893, *Physics of Semiconductors, 28th International Conference*
edited by W. Jantsch and F. Schäffler
© 2007 American Institute of Physics 978-0-7354-0397-0/07/$23.00

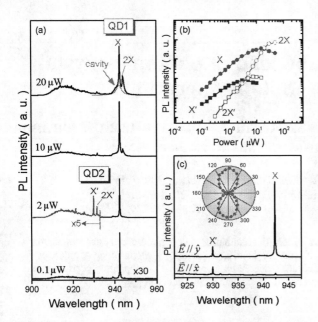

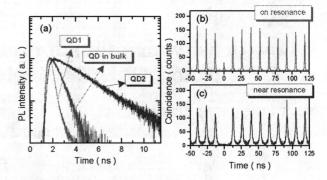

FIGURE 3. (a) Time-resolved μPL traces of QDs on-resonance (QD1), off-resonance (QD2) and in bulk without the PC effects. (b) The measured photon correlations from QD1 and (c) from another QD in a nominally the same cavity but with a larger detuning.

FIGURE 2. (a) μPL spectra of a nanocavity with $s=0.1a$ under different P_{ex}. (b) The power dependence of emission lines from QD1 and QD2. (c) Polarization-resolved spectra with electric field $\vec{E}$ parallel to $\hat{x}$ and $\hat{y}$ directions. The inset shows a polar plot of the X-line intensity as a function of polarization angle.

times lower saturation power for the X' line. The cavity mode structure can be observed under higher P_{ex}'s and matches spectrally with the X line. The QD-cavity coupling can be further confirmed by the polarization analysis. As shown in Fig. 2(c), the X line of QD1 is strongly y-polarized with a polarization degree up to $p = 95\%$, matching well with the cavity polarization.

Time-resolved μPL of single QDs by are shown in Fig. 3(a). The measured lifetimes for exciton lines of QD1 and QD2 were $\tau_1 = 0.21$ ns and $\tau_2 = 2.52$ ns, corresponding to a threefold enhanced ($\times 3$) and a fourfold suppressed ($\times 1/4$) SE rate for on- and off-resonance QDs, respectively, as comparing with the intrinsic lifetime of $\tau_0 = 0.65$ ns for QDs without the PC effects. This result demonstrates a full control of the SE dynamics of single QDs based on PC nanocavities. The measured lifetimes can be utilized to estimate SE coupling efficiency, $\beta = (\gamma - \gamma_{PC})/\gamma$, where the total SE rate γ is view as the sum of rates into cavity mode γ_C and into the PC surrounding γ_{PC}. Assuming $\gamma_{PC} \approx 1/\tau_2$, the single-mode coupling efficiency would be $\beta \approx 1 - (\tau_1/\tau_2) = 92\%$. Such a high β factor highlights the importance of the use of PC nanocavity. The photonic gap of the PC makes the emitted photons to be predominantly funnelled into the cavity mode, despite the cavity Q is not high. This is in striking contrast to other solid-state cavities, in which a high coupling efficiency relies mainly on a high-Q cavity

to achieve a larger Purcell enhancement.

Triggered single-photon generations were achieved by pulsed excitation on the QDs and characterized by a Hanbury-Brown and Twiss (HBT) type setup. For the histogram obtained from X line of QD1 [Fig. 3(b)], a clear signature of photon antibunching was observed. The nonzero $g^{(2)}(0) \sim 0.2$ most likely arise from the coupling of WL emissions into the cavity mode. We have also investigated another single QD in a nominally the same cavity, but with a larger detuning and hence a longer emission lifetime (1.2 ns). In this case, the multiphoton event was further reduced to $g^{(2)}(0) \sim 0.01$ [Fig. 3(c)], corresponding to a hundredfold suppressed multiphoton emissions as comparing with a Poissonian source. This implies that using a near-resonance QD can eliminate the background level considerably, however, at the expense of larger timing jitters due to the relatively longer emission lifetime.

In summary, we demonstrate an efficient single-photon source based on low-density InGaAs QDs embedded in linear-type PC nanocavities. Our single-photon source shows a high coupling efficiency, a high polarization degree, low multiphoton emission rates, as well as reduced timing jitters. This appealing performance makes it well-suited for practical implementation of polarization-encoded schemes in quantum cryptography.

This works is supported by the National Science Council of the Republic of China under Grant No. NSC-94-2120-M-008-001.

REFERENCES

1. T.-P. Hsieh et al., *Nanotechnology* 17, 512 (2006).
2. W.-H. Chang, et al., *Phys. Rev. B* 72, 233302 (2005)
3. W.-H. Chang, et al., *Phys. Rev. Lett.* 96, 117401 (2006)

Electro-Optical Characterization of Self-Assembled InAs/GaAs Quantum Rings Embedded in P-i-N and Schottky Diodes

A.G. Taboada[1], F. Suárez[1], D. Granados[1], T. J. Badcock[2], D. J. Mowbray[2], K. M. Groom[2], B. Alén[1], J.M. García[1] and M.L. Dotor[1]

1. Instituto de Microelectrónica de Madrid (CNM-CSIC), Isaac Newton 8 (PTM), 28760-Tres Cantos, Spain

2 Department of Physics, University of Sheffield, Sheffield, United Kingdom S3 7RH

Abstract. In this work we present measurements of excitation of the photoluminescence (PLE), photocurrent (PC) and electroluminescence (EL) in ring shaped nanostructures grown by MBE embedded in two different electro-optical devices: a Schottky diode and a P-i-N diode. This characterization will be used to improve QRs laser devices.

Keywords: Quantum Rings, Schottky and P-i-N diode, PLE, PC, EL.
PACS: 73.21, 71.35.Cc, 78.30.Fs

INTRODUCTION

The zero-dimensional semiconductor systems have been thoroughly investigated during the past years. Ring shaped nanostructures grown by solid source molecular beam epitaxy (MBE) [1] opened new perspectives for quantum-optical devices as well as fundamental physics research due to their unique optical and electric properties [2,3] (Fig1). Carrier transport plays an important role in determining the properties of these optical devices. In this work special attention has been devoted to the emission and absorption processes of charge carriers by the nanostructures embedded in electro-optical devices.

EXPERIMENTAL SET-UP

The electronic structure both for the ensemble and single quantum rings [3] has been determined using photoluminescence (PL) and capacitance-voltage (CV) in previous measurements. This characterization was used to develop QRs laser devices. Lasing emission was achieved up to 150 K [4]. In this work we present results on the same structure using photocurrent (PC) and excitation of the photoluminescence spectroscopy (PLE) using a incandescent lamp; and electroluminescence (EL) spectroscopy with a germanium detector.

The samples were grown by MBE. Self assembled quantum rings are fabricated partially capping an original layer of quantum dots. The strained InAs islands are destabilizes with a thin layer of 2 nm thick of GaAs, driving to the quantum rings (QR) formation. Details of the growth of the quantum rings can be obtained elsewhere [1].

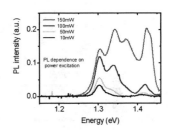

FIGURE 1. AFM 2μm x 2μm image of uncapped QRs (left) and QRs PL spectra dependence on power excitation (right).

To apply the bias a metal-insulator-semiconductor Schottky diode is proccessed. A highly doped ($2x10^{18}$ cm^{-3}) GaAs:Si buffer acts as back contact to inject carriers to study the conduction band properties. The QR are embedded between a GaAs tunnel barrier 25 nm thick; and a GaAs layer followed by an AlAs/GaAs short period super lattice which acts as blocking barrier to reduce leakage currents. The thickness of this barrier is 150nm. A semi-transparent schottky contact gate (50Å Ni + 50Å Cr) is deposited on top of the structure.

The P-i-N Diode.

The EL and PC signals have been measured at different temperatures from a three vertical QR

CP893, *Physics of Semiconductors, 28th International Conference*
edited by W. Jantsch and F. Schäffler
© 2007 American Institute of Physics 978-0-7354-0397-0/07/$23.00

stacked layers embedded in a P-i-N diode. The n+ and p+ cladding layers are formed by gradual Si and Be doping respectively. The separate confinement heterostructures is formed by a AlAs/GaAs graded index short period superlattices waveguide. In the active region, three stacked layers of QR spaced by 10 nm of GaAs have been used. Au–Ge–Au and Cr–Au have been used for the n and p contacts, respectively [4].

RESULTS

The PLE characterization allows us to determine the relaxation and recombination processes in the intra-gap electronic structure. We have observed a strong absorption below the gap, both in the WL and in the excited states of the QR´s.

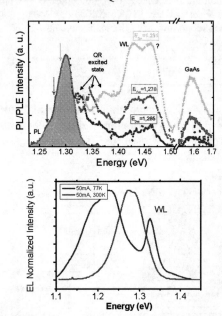

FIGURE 2. PLE absorption spectra at three different energies and PL spectra (up) and EL collected at 77K and 300K (bottom).

Using the P-i-N diode we have measured EL emission from nanostructures in the range of temperatures from 5 K to 300K (Fig2, lower panel). The wetting layer shows a strong contribution to the EL emission above 150K and high injection currents.

We have observed contributions to the PC from the ground and excited states of the QR, wetting layer and GaAs in both devices. PC experiments have been conducted as a function of applied reverse bias, excitation power and temperature.

Dark currents are low enough to allow for photocurrent signal detection levels below few pA at the QR energies. The optical efficiency and carrier

extraction is bigger in the P-i-N diode due to the larger number of layers and the improved band alignment at reverse voltages.

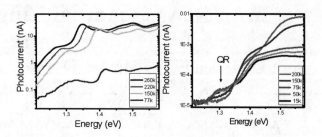

FIGURE 3. PC collected in the P-i-N diode (left) and in the Schottky diode (right) at from T=15K to 260K.

CONCLUSIONS

The energy level proximity of the WL and the QRs favors that the thermo-ionic emission processes currents acquire importance in EL at high temperatures. This effect can explain why QR P-i-N laser structures don't show lasing emission above 150 K.

We have observed contributions to the PC and PLE signal from states below the GaAs band edge, which enable the study of the intragap electronic structure.

ACKNOWLEDGMENTS

This work was financed by Spanish MCyT under NANOSELF II project (TEC2005-05781-C03-01), NANOCOMIC project (S 0505ESP 0200), NANIC project (NA2004-09109-C04-01), INGENIO 2010-Consolider GENESISFV project (CSD2006-00004) and by SANDIE Network of excellence (Contract nº NMP4-CT-2004-500101 group TEP-0120)

REFERENCES

1. D.Granados and J.M. García, Appl. Phys.Lett. 82, 2401 (2003)

2. A.Lorke, R. J.Luyken, A.O. Govorov, J.P. Kotthaus, J.M.García and P.M.Petroff , Phys. Rev Lett. 84 2223-2226 (2000)

3. B.Alén, J. Martínez-Pastor, D.Granados and J.M. García, Phys. Rev. B 72, 155331 (2005)

4. F. Suárez, D. Granados, M. Dotor and J. M García, Nanotechnology, 15, S126-S130, (2004)

Electronic Raman Scattering in InAs/AlAs Quantum Dot Structures

A.G. Milekhin[1], A.I. Toropov[1], A.K. Bakarov[1], M. Lentze[2], J. Geurts[2] and D.R.T Zahn[3]

[1]Institute of Semiconductor Physics, Novosibirsk, 630090, Lavrentjev av.13, Russia
[2]Physikalisches Institut der Universität Würzburg, 97074 Würzburg, Germany
[3]Institut für Physik, Technische Universität Chemnitz, D-09107 Chemnitz, Germany

Abstract. We present a resonant Raman study of periodical structures with InAs quantum dots (QDs) in AlAs matrix focusing on zero-dimensional inter-subband spin and charge density excitations (SDEs and CDEs, respectively), as well as coupled intersubband plasmon-phonon modes. The behaviour of the SDE and CDE mode frequencies as a function of temperature, excitation energy and applied magnetic field is discussed.

Keywords: quantum dots, electronic excitations, Raman scattering.
PACS: 78.67.Hc, 78.66.Fd

INTRODUCTION

Electronic Raman scattering by quasi-zero-dimensional systems has been extensively studied in recent years [1 and ref. therein]. However, the electronic excitations in self-assembled quantum dot superlattices are rather less investigated so far.

We present a Raman study of inter-subband single-particle excitations (SPEs) and charge density excitations (CDEs) in periodical structures with InAs QDs embedded in AlAs.

EXPERIMENTAL

The nanostructures under investigation were grown by molecular beam epitaxy on (001)-oriented GaAs substrates. The Stransky-Krastanov growth mode was employed for self-assembling QDs at a substrate temperature of 510 °C. The nanostructures consist of 10 InAs QD layers of 2.5 ML nominal thickness separated by 5-nm-thick AlAs. Delta-doping with Si atoms ($N_{Si}=2\cdot10^{12}$ cm^{-2}) 2 nm beneath each QD layer was used to populate the QD ground state.

The Raman spectra were measured in a backscattering geometry using a Dilor XY triple spectrometer with different excitation lines of Ar$^+$ and Kr$^+$ lasers at temperatures from 1.7 to 300 K. A dye laser (DCM) was used to approach the resonance with interband transitions in InAs QDs. The Raman spectra were analyzed in both polarized and depolarized geometries in Stokes and anti-Stokes regions. The spectral resolution was 2 cm^{-1} over the entire spectral range.

Magnetic fields up to 6 T were applied perpendicular to the growth axis of the structures (Voigt geometry).

RESULTS AND DISCUSSION

Fig.1 shows Raman spectra of sample measured in the $z(xx)\bar{z}$ and $z(xy)\bar{z}$ scattering geometries at different temperature in the vicinity of a resonance with interband transitions in QDs. The features observed in the spectra near 250, 295, 390 cm^{-1} are attributed to LO phonons in InAs QDs, GaAs substrate, and interface phonons in AlAs layers [2]. Besides the phonon features, broad and intensive lines are observed in the low frequency region of the spectra measured in Stokes and anti-Stokes (not shown here) $z(xy)\bar{z}$ and $z(xx)\bar{z}$ geometries at about 150 and 250 cm^{-1}, respectively interpreted as being due to inter-subband SDE and CDE excitations.

The wave-vector independence of CDEs and SDEs energies measured in the range of $(0.9 \div 1.9)\cdot10^5$ cm^{-1}

CP893, *Physics of Semiconductors, 28th International Conference*
edited by W. Jantsch and F. Schäffler

(not shown here) confirms their zero-dimensional character.

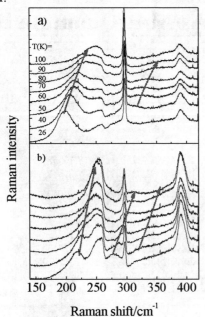

FIGURE 1. Raman spectra of InAs/AlAs QD structures measured in the $z(xy)\bar{z}$ -a) and $z(xx)\bar{z}$ -b) scattering geometries at different temperatures.

With increasing temperature the frequency position of the SDEs and CDEs lines increases. This increase is explained by the size selective resonant Raman scattering by an array of non-unifrom QDs. With increasing temperature the energy of interband transitions in InAs QDs decreases, therefore, the QDs of smaller size which have higher interband transition energies come into resonance with the excitation energy. The smaller QDs have larger intersubband energies leading to increasing frequencies of the SDEs and CDEs lines.

With increasing temperature the frequencies of the electronic excitations approach that of optical

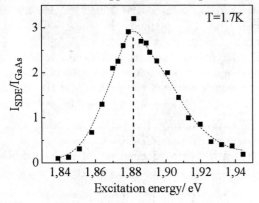

FIGURE 2. Normalised intensity of the Raman peak due to SDEs versus excitation energy.

and interface phonons in InAs QDs resulting in the appearance of plasmon-phonon modes [3] as indicated by arrows in Fig.1.

A sharp asymmetric resonance profile was obtained for the SDEs peak (Fig.2) with a maximum at about 1.88 eV which corresponds to the energy of interband transition in QDs and a full-width at half-maximum of only about 40 meV. The intensity of the SDE peak was normalized with repect to the LO phonon line of GaAs. No change of the SDEs frequency position as a function of excitation energy was observed. The peak asymmetry is presumably caused by the influence of high energy electronic states.

The complex spectrum of electronic excitations was observed when a magnetic field was applied (Fig.3). For example, the SDE_1 line appears to split and evolves into two modes while the energy of the CDE_2 and CDE_1 modes increases. New broad features associated with inter-Landau level transitions in the QDs appear at high magnetic field (above 4T).

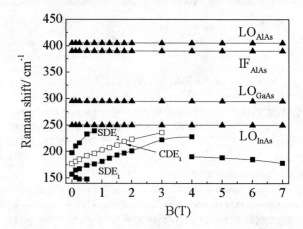

FIGURE 3. Magnetic field dependence of the SDE and CDE peak frequencies measured at T=1.7K. Phonon peak positions are shown by triangles. The horizontal lines show phonon energies in QDs, AlAs matrix and GaAs substrate.

ACKNOWLEDGMENTS

This work was supported in part by the Russian Foundation for Basic Research (grant 06-02-90870 Mol a).

REFERENCES

1. C. Schüller, C. Steinebach, D. Heitmann, *Sol. State. Comm.* **119**, 323-331 (2001).
2. A.G. Milekhin, A.I. Toropov, A.K. Bakarov et al. *Phys. Rev. B* **70** 085314 (2004).
3. P.A.Knipp, *Surf.Science* **361/362**, 818-825 (1996).

Resonant emission of a single InAs/GaAs quantum dot in a waveguiding configuration

Romain Melet*, Roger Grousson*, Valia Voliotis*,†, Dimitri Roditchev*, Aristide Lemaitre**, Anthony Martinez** and Abderrahim Ramdane**

*Institut des NanoSciences de Paris, CNRS UMR 7588, Université Pierre et Marie Curie et Denis Diderot, Campus Boucicaut, 140 rue de Lourmel, 75015 Paris, France
†also at: Université Evry Val d'Essonne, Boulevard F. Mitterand, 92025 Paris, France
**Laboratoire de Photonique et Nanostructures, CNRS, Routes de Nozay, 91460 Marcoussis, France

Abstract. By means of confocal spectroscopy, optical properties of InAs/GaAs quantum dots embedded in a waveguide are studied. This new experimental configuration appears to be very promising in the framework of quantum computation in order to manipulate resonantly the fundamental state of a quantum dot. Preliminary experiments which allow us to validate this new set-up have been performed. Micro-photoluminescence in a wave guiding configuration on a single QD and absorption measurements of an ensemble of dots are also presented.

Keywords: Quantum dot, Micro-photoluminescence, Waveguide
PACS: 78.67.Hc, 78.55.Cr, 78.40.Fy

INTRODUCTION

Quantum dots (QDs) are the focus of a great interest in the context of quantum information processing [1]. Atomic-like properties of QD, such as discret eigenstates, long coherence time [2], have now been demonstrated and make this system a valuable candidate in the search for a solid state qubit. Many steps toward practical realization of quantum computation have now been achieved, such as Rabi rotation [3], or experimental realization of the Deutsch-Jozsa algorithm [4].

The most reliable way to take advantage of the long coherence time (T_2) of QDs levels is to focus on the fundamental transition of the dot which is the one who possesses the longest T_2.

One major challenge in optical experiments such as micro-photoluminescence (μPL) [5] is to excite a transition and detect its emission *at the same energy* because it is impossible to separate photons emitted from the studied structure from excitation photons.

In this paper we present optical properties of InAs/GaAs QDs studied with an original experiment based on μPL and guided optics [6] which will allow to uncouple excitation light and emission of a single QD.

EXPERIMENTAL SET UP

The sample consists of an InAs/GaAs QDs layer embedded in a waveguiding structure grown by molecular beam epitaxy on a GaAs substrate. An InAs layer is embedded in a 600 nm GaAs layer between a 1 μm thick GaAlAs barriers. This structure forms a waveguide, the GaAs layer being its core. The density of QDs varies in the sample from 10^5 per micron to a few QDs per micron. In order to obtain a one dimensional guiding structure, 2 μm wide ridges are made on the surface of the sample by reactive ion etching (RIE).

Thanks to this sample structure and with a specifically designed three-optical access cryostat, it is possible at low temperature (10 K), to excite QDs by focusing the excitation into the waveguide, parallel to the QDs layers, and to detect its emission in a direction perpendicular to the excitation (see the inset of figure 3). With this experimental configuration, it is possible to detect luminescence from QDs without being hindered by the laser as in an usual backscattering μPL experiment. This configuration allows moreover to perform transmission experiments and to obtain the absorption coefficient of the structure.

EXPERIMENTAL RESULTS

First, we present μPL experiments as a function of the excitation power, performed on a sample with a QDs concentration of the order of 10^3 dots per micron. The excitation energy is tuned in the absorption of the GaAs layer. In figure 1a is shown a μPL spectrum of an ensemble of QDs recorded at low excitation power. We observe emission only from the QDs, there is no emission from the wetting layer (WL). By increasing excitation power (fig. 1b) we observe that the wetting layer emission at 1.42 eV emerges and that the maximum of the QDs emis-

CP893, *Physics of Semiconductors, 28th International Conference*
edited by W. Jantsch and F. Schäffler

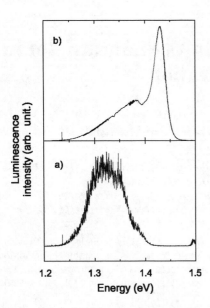

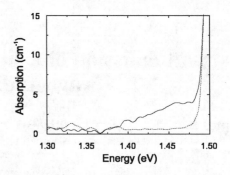

FIGURE 2. Absorption spectrum for transverse electric (TE) (dotted line) and transverse magnetic (TM) (solid line) wave.

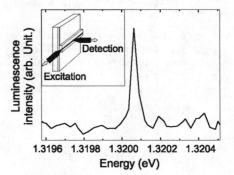

FIGURE 1. Micro-luminescence spectrum a) at low excitation power (65 $W.cm^{-2}$), b) at high excitation power (130 $kW.cm^{-2}$).

FIGURE 3. Guided micro-luminescence spectrum of a single InAs QD. The inset shows a schematic view of the experimental configuration.

sion shifts toward higher energy. The behavior of the WL is well understood in terms of saturation of QDs levels. At low excitation power the density of photo-created carriers is too low to fill all the QD states. When increasing the excitation power, all the dot levels are filled because of the Pauli exclusion principle so that the remaining carriers stay in the WL and recombine from there. This observation demonstrates a highly efficient transfer of photo-created carriers between WL ans QDs in this kind of structure.

The high energy shift of the QD luminescence is explained by the progressive filling of excited p-states of the QDs.

Figure 2 shows the absorption spectrum of the structure. This spectrum is obtained by measuring the transmission of a white light through the waveguide. The main observation is that the absorption in the WL is strongly dependent on the polarization of incident light: only TM polarized light is absorbed, in contrast with what should be expected for a quantum well [7], if one assumes that the WL is a narrow quantum well. The origin of this non trivial polarization selection rules is not clear for the moment. Given the measured absorption coefficient of 3 cm^{-1} and the filling factor of the wetting layer, we obtain an absolute absorption coefficient of 3800 cm^{-1}.

Finally in figure 3, we show a μPL spectrum of a single QD obtained in the *guided excitation configuration*, the excitation energy being resonant with the WL emission. This result demonstrates the feasibility of the *guided micro-photoluminescence* experiment in order to

excite and observe emission of a single QD.

CONCLUSION

We have demonstrated the feasibility of the guided μPL experiment which is a very promising solution for an all optical manipulation of solid state qubit at resonance. The preliminary results on absorption show intriguing polarization selection rules which need further investigation.

The next step is to perform resonant excitation of a single QD and achieve coherent control of its fundamental transition.

REFERENCES

1. E. Biolatti *et al*, *Phys. Rev. Lett.* **85**, 5647 (2000)
2. D.Birkedal *et al*, *Phys. Rev.Lett* **87**, 227401 (2001)
3. T. H. Stievater *et al*, *Phys. Rev. Lett.* **87**, 133603 (2002)
4. P. Bianucci *et al*, *Phys. Rev. B* **69**, 161303 (2004)
5. T. Guillet *et al*, *Phys. Rev. B* **68**, 045319 (2003)
6. R. Grousson *et al*, *Semicond. Sci. Technol.* **8**, 1217 (1993)
7. V. Voliotis *et al*, *Phys. Rev. B*, **52**, 10725 (1995)

Phonon-induced Exciton Dephasing in Quantum Dots and Quantum Dot Molecules

E. A. Muljarov[*,†] and R. Zimmermann[*]

[*]Institut für Physik der Humboldt-Universität zu Berlin, Newtonstraße 15, 12489 Berlin, Germany
[†]A.M. Prokhorov General Physics Institute RAS, Vavilova 38, Moscow 119991, Russia

Abstract. The phonon-induced dephasing in quantum dots is due to two basic sources: real and virtual phonon-assisted transitions between excitonic states. We calculate the time-dependent optical polarization and absorption in single and coupled quantum dots. We show that, depending on the energy distance between exciton levels in quantum dots, the dephasing can be dominated either by real acoustic phonon-assisted transitions, or by virtual transitions.

Keywords: Dephasing, electron-phonon interaction, quantum dots, excitons
PACS: 78.67.Hc, 71.38.-k, 71.35.-y

Interaction between excitons and lattice vibrations (phonons) leads to a dephasing of the optical polarization in semiconductor nanostructures. Dephasing in quantum dots (QDs) and QD molecules (QDMs) has been studied by time-integrated four-wave mixing measurements [1]. Recently we have developed a novel approach to solve the coupled exciton-acoustic phonon problem and calculated the measured optical response in QDs using the cumulant expansion [2, 3, 4].

In the present work we study the two major mechanisms leading to the dephasing in QDs and QDMs: real and virtual phonon-assisted transitions between excitonic states. Dephasing due to real transitions is always accompanied by exciton relaxation to other levels. Virtual transitions do not change the level occupation and thus result in pure dephasing.

The Hamiltonian of excitonic states in a QD linearly coupled to acoustic phonons has the form [3]

$$H = \sum_n \hbar\omega_n |n\rangle\langle n| + \sum_{\mathbf{q}} \hbar\omega_q^{ac} a_{\mathbf{q}}^\dagger a_{\mathbf{q}} + \hbar V, \quad (1)$$

$$V = \sum_{n,m} |n\rangle\langle m| \sum_{\mathbf{q}} M_{nm}(\mathbf{q})(a_{\mathbf{q}} + a_{-\mathbf{q}}^\dagger), \quad (2)$$

where $\hbar\omega_n$ is the bare exciton transition energy, and $M_{nm}(\mathbf{q}) \propto \sqrt{q}\langle n|D_c e^{i\mathbf{q}\mathbf{r}_e} - D_v e^{i\mathbf{q}\mathbf{r}_h}|m\rangle$ the exciton-acoustic phonon matrix element. The linear polarization can be written as an infinite perturbation series

$$P(t) = \sum_n |\mu_n|^2 e^{-i\omega_n t} \left\langle n\Big|\mathscr{T}\exp\left\{-i\int_0^t d\tau V(\tau)\right\}\Big|n\right\rangle, \quad (3)$$

which we calculate exactly or approximately, using the cumulant expansion:

$$P(t) = \sum_n |\mu_n|^2 \exp\{K_n(t)\}. \quad (4)$$

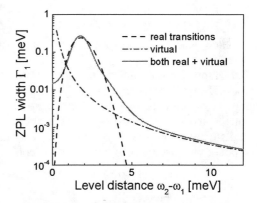

FIGURE 1. Broadening of the exciton ground state ZPL as a function of the exciton level distance in a spherical InAs QD, calculated at $T = 100$ K with account for only real transitions (in first order), only virtual transitions, and for both real and virtual transitions up to second order in the cumulant.

In the long-time limit the cumulant behaves as $K_n(t) \to -S_n - i\tilde{\omega}_n t - \Gamma_n t$, where $\tilde{\omega}_n$ is the polaron shifted exciton transition frequency and Γ_n the broadening of the zero-phonon line (ZPL). A perturbation series for the cumulant $K_n(t)$ is reconstructed from the plain expansion Eq. (3). This series ends already in first order in the independent boson model (BM) [5] which accounts for only diagonal terms in the exciton-phonon interaction: $M_{nm}(\mathbf{q}) = \delta_{nm}M_{nn}(\mathbf{q})$. However, in this case the ZPL has zero width, $\Gamma_n = 0$.

The broadening of the ZPL is exclusively due to the non-diagonal interaction. In first order, the cumulant expansion reproduces exactly Fermi's Golden rule for the *real* phonon-assisted transitions: $\Gamma_1^{(1)} = \pi N_{\text{Bose}}(\Delta\omega)\sum_{\mathbf{q}}|M_{12}(\mathbf{q})|^2\delta(\Delta\omega - \omega_q^{ac})$, where the ground state dephasing rate $\Gamma_1^{(1)}$ is given here for

CP893, *Physics of Semiconductors, 28th International Conference*
edited by W. Jantsch and F. Schäffler

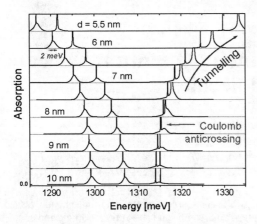

FIGURE 2. Absorption spectrum (linear scale) of an asymmetric InGaAs QDM calculated at $T = 10$ K for different interdot distances d. The peaks of the ZPLs are truncated.

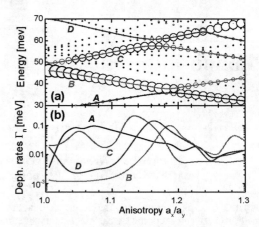

FIGURE 3. P-shell exciton energy levels in a pancake InGaAs QD as a function of the in-plane shape anisotropy (a); the ground exciton state is at -31.4 meV. Dephasing rates Γ_n of four optically active states at $T = 10K$ (b); their oscillator strength is given in panel (a) by the circle area.

a system of two excitonic levels only (Fig. 1, dashed curve). As $M_{12}(\mathbf{q})$ decays with $\mathbf{q}$ due to the localization of the exciton wave functions in a QD, $\Gamma_1^{(1)}$ also drops quickly with $\Delta\omega = \omega_2 - \omega_1$.

In spite of this 'phonon bottleneck' effect, *virtual* transitions are always present in QDs and lead to a non-vanishing broadening of the ZPL everywhere (Fig. 1, dash-dotted curve). They contribute in the next (second) order and are taken into account within the exactly solvable model of the quadratic exciton-phonon coupling [2]

$$V_Q = |1\rangle\langle 1| \sum_{\mathbf{pq}} \sum_{n \neq 1} \frac{M_{1n}(\mathbf{p})M_{n1}(\mathbf{q})}{\omega_1 - \omega_n}(a_{\mathbf{p}} + a_{-\mathbf{p}}^\dagger)(a_{\mathbf{q}} + a_{-\mathbf{q}}^\dagger).$$
(5)

V_Q is found by mapping the non-diagonal coupling into an effective diagonal one which allows us to use advantages of the BM. Solving the full Hamiltonian Eqs. (1,2) up to second order in the cumulant, we take into account both real and virtual transitions (Fig. 1, full curve) [3].

For the ground exciton state in typical QDs, virtual processes are the major mechanism of the dephasing, since the energy distances to higher confined states are much larger than the typical energy range of the acoustic phonons coupled to the QDs. In contrast, the energy distance between excited states in QDs and QD molecules can be small thus allowing real phonon-assisted transitions between the levels to come into play, too.

The absorption of a QDM due to the lowest four exciton states is shown in Fig. 2. The lower two states are quite isolated in energy; thus their absorption bands have very narrow ZPLs, like that of the ground state in a single QD. On the other hand, the upper two states can be close to each other, and real transitions between them are possible. As a result, at $T = 10K$ the uppermost state has a much larger ZPL width than the other states. Nevertheless, when the Coulomb anticrossing is reached (at the in-

terdot distance of 8.5 nm), its ZPL width suddenly drops and never restores at larger d. This is due to a change of the symmetry of states, owing to the Coulomb interaction.

A similar behavior of the dephasing takes place for excited states in isolated QDs, see Fig. 3. For small in-plane anisotropy, the brightest state B of the so-called p-shell in a pancake QD is well separated from all other states and thus has a rather small (at low temperatures) dephasing rate Γ determined only by virtual transitions. In fact, real transitions are exponentially small in this case. However, they are of paramount importance for the dephasing of many other closely lying exciton levels. For example, another bright state C has a relatively large dephasing rate, the latter being very sensitive to the anisotropy parameter. This is due to quick changes of the energy distance between state C and other states (both bright and dark) which participate in real transitions.

In conclusion, a complicated interplay between level spacing and phonon coupling leads to a rich dephasing scenario in QDs and QD molecules.

REFERENCES

1. P. Borri, W. Langbein *et al.* Phys. Rev. Lett. **87**, 157401 (2001); P. Borri, W. Langbein *et al.* Phys. Rev. Lett. **91**, 267401 (2003).
2. E. A. Muljarov and R. Zimmermann, Phys. Rev. Lett. **93**, 237401 (2004).
3. E. A. Muljarov, T. Takagahara, and R. Zimmermann, Phys. Rev. Lett. **95**, 177405 (2005).
4. E. A. Muljarov and R. Zimmermann, Phys. Status Solidi (b) **243** (2006).
5. G. Mahan, *Many-Particle Physics*, Plenum, New York (1990).

Temperature Dependence Of The Exciton Homogeneous Linewidth In CdTe and CdSe Self-assembled Quantum Dots: Limit Of Single Photon Source Operation

Kuntheak Kheng, Sebatian Moehl, Ivan-Christophe Robin, Laurent Maingault, Régis André, and Henri Mariette

CEA-CNRS Group Nanophysique et Semiconducteurs
CEA-Grenoble /SP2M, 17, avenue des Martyrs, 38054 Grenoble Cedex 9, France

Abstract. Excitonic emission in single CdTe/ $Zn_{0.7}Mg_{0.3}Te$ and CdSe/ZnSe quantum dots has been obtained up to 160 K and 220 K respectively. The study of the linewidth thermal broadening allows us to estimate the temperature limit of single photon emission in CdTe and CdSe QDs.

Keywords: II-VI semiconductors, quantum dots, thermal broadening, phonons.
PACS: 71.35.Pq, 78.67.Hc, 78.55.Et

INTRODUCTION

The high Coulomb interaction between confined carriers makes semiconductor quantum dots (QDs) very promising as active medium of single photon emitters. It allows distinguishing (at least at low temperature) the single exciton emission from the biexciton emission, which is crucial for single photon emission. As practical applications require room temperature operation, the separation of the two emission lines must remain larger than the thermal broadening of the optical linewidths. As compared to the more extensively investigated III-V QDs, II-VI QDs (as CdTe and CdSe) present the advantage of a larger exciton binding energy and should allow separation of the two emission lines up to higher temperatures. In this contribution, from the study of the temperature dependence of the single dot emission we estimate the temperature limit of single photon emission in CdTe and CdSe QDs

EXPERIMENTAL DETAILS

The QDs are grown by atomic layer epitaxy of CdSe (CdTe) on ZnSe ($Zn_{0.7}Mg_{0.3}Te$) barriers. QD formation is then induced by deposition/desorption of amorphous Se (Te) for CdSe/ZnSe QDs and amorphous Te for CdTe/$Zn_{0.7}Mg_{0.3}Te$ QDs. For CdTe QDs, we have shown that the incorporation of Mg in

ZnTe barriers enhances the carriers confinement and allows reaching higher temperature for the radiative recombination regime. Details on the growth of these structures can be found in Ref [1] and [2] respectively.

The photoluminescence (PL) of individual QDs is excited with the 488 nm line of an argon laser (above barrier excitation) and collected through a large numerical-aperture microscope objective and aluminium shadow masks with 0.2–1.0 μm apertures. The PL is then dispersed by a 1 meter monochromator and detected by a nitrogen cooled Si charge-coupled-device matrice matrix providing a spectral resolution of 70 μeV.

RESULTS AND DISCUSSION

Fig. 1 shows the emission spectra of single CdTe (a) and CdSe (b) QDs for increasing temperature. Single dot emission has been obtained up to 160K for CdTe QDs and to 220K and CdSe QDs. First, let us note that the macro-PL of the studied QD samples can be recorded up to room temperature, but the micro-PL quenches at much lower temperature. The reason of this quenching is that thermal escape of carriers out of QDs and non radiative recombination in the trapping process of photo-generated carriers lead to preferential emission from higher states (continuum states in the wetting layer). The homogeneous lineshape is typically composed of a Lorentzian zero-phonon line

CP893, *Physics of Semiconductors, 28th International Conference*
edited by W. Jantsch and F. Schäffler
© 2007 American Institute of Physics 978-0-7354-0397-0/07/$23.00

at low temperature and an broad acoustic phonon band [3, 4] that increases with temperature.

Fig. 2 plots the Full Width at Half Maximum (FWHM) of the single dot lines as a function of temperature. In the low temperature regime (<50K) the FWHM is defined by the zero-phonon linewidth [5]. In this case the FWHM increases with temperature due to the activation of *inelastic* scattering of carriers by phonons and it can be described by FWHM(T)=FWHM(0)+γ_AT+γ_O/(exp($\hbar\omega_{LO}$/kT)-1)

where γ_A and γ_O are the coupling constants with acoustic and LO phonons respectively [6].

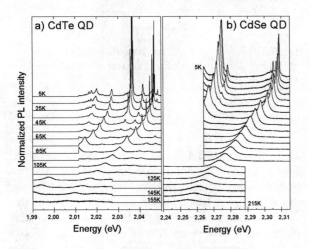

FIGURE 1. Evolution of the photoluminescence spectrum of (a) CdTe and (b) CdSe single QD with temperature.

Above 70K the lineshape is completely dominated by the broad acoustic phonon band, that is the main broadening mechanism is the *elastic* interaction of carriers with acoustic phonons (pure dephasing) [3]. In this case we observe that the linewidth increases linearly with temperature. The linear fit gives a slope of 66μeV/K for the CdSe QD and 79μeV/K for the CdTe QD.

The CdTe QD linewidth is smaller than that of CdSe QD at low temperature indicating that the effect of phonon coupling is stronger in CdSe. However, due to the higher slope of the CdTe QD thermal broadening, the CdSe QD linewidth becomes smaller above 150 K. The extrapolation of the FWHM to 300K gives FWHM$_{CdSe}$=18 meV for the CdSe QD and FWHM$_{CdTe}$=19.4 meV for the CdTe QD.

For single photon source application, the linewidth must remain smaller than the biexciton binding energy (exciton-biexciton line separation). This condition can be fulfilled by a CdSe QD at room temperature since the biexciton binding energy is in the range 20-26meV in our structure. However for CdTe QDs the mean

biexciton binding energy is 13 meV and the extrapolation of the FWHM reaches this value at about 200K.

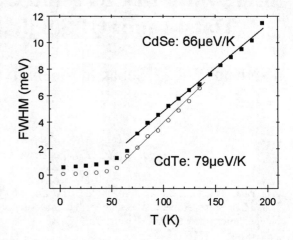

FIGURE 2. Thermal linewidth broadening of CdSe (square) and CdTe (circle). Lines are linear fit of the FWHM evolution in the high temperature range.

In conclusion, single photon source can operate up to room temperature with CdSe QDs, but it is limited to about 200K with CdTe QDs. However, in contrast to CdSe materials, CdTe materials offer the possibility to grow in situ Bragg mirrors to fabricate micropillar with high quality factor [7].

REFERENCES

1. I. C. Robin, R. André, H. Mariette, S. Tatarenko, Le Si Dang, J. M. Gérard, and E. Bellet-Amalric, Physica E 26, 119 (2005)
2. S. Moehl, L. Maingault, K. Kheng, and H. Mariette, Appl. Phys. Lett. 87, 033111 (2005)
3. L. Besombes, .K Kheng, L. Marsal and H. Mariette, Phys. Rev. B63, 155307 (2001)
4. I. Favero *et al.*, Phys. Rev. B 68, 233301 (2003)
5. Note that the zero-phonon linewidth is also slightly broadened by the fluctuating electric field produced by photo-created carriers (spectral diffusion).
6. S. Rubin, T. L. Reinecke, and B. Segall, Phys. Rev. B 42, 11218 (1990)
7. J. M. Gérard *et al*, Appl. Phys. Lett. 61, 459 (1996)

Ex-situ control of fine-structure splitting and excitonic binding energies in single InAs/GaAs quantum dots

R. Seguin, A. Schliwa, T. D. Germann, S. Rodt, K. Pötschke, U. W. Pohl and D. Bimberg

Institut für Festkörperphyik, Technische Universität Berlin, Hardenbergstr. 36, 10623 Berlin

Abstract. A systematic study of the impact of annealing on the electronic properties of single InAs/GaAs quantum dots (QDs) is presented. We are able to record single QD cathodoluminescence spectra and trace the evolution of one and the same QD over several steps of annealing. A systematic reduction of the excitonic fine-structure splitting is reported. In addition the binding energies of different excitonic complexes change dramatically. The results are interpreted in terms of a change of electron and hole wavefunction shape and mutual position.

Keywords: single quantum dots, annealing, cathodoluminescence
PACS: 78.67.Hc, 73.21.La, 71.35.Pq, 78.60.Hk

Self-assembled quantum dots (QDs) are building blocks for numerous novel devices including single photon emitters and storage devices [1]. It is of largest importance to tailor their opto-electronical properties for optimal device performance. Annealing can considerably alter the electronic structure of QDs [2, 3, 4]. Here, the first systematic study of the influence of such an annealing process on the emission characteristics of *one and the same* QD for two consecutive steps of annealing is presented. Excitonic binding energies and fine-structure splittings are determined.

The InAs QDs were grown by MOCVD in GaAs matrix on GaAs(001) substrates. For the QDs nominally 1.9 monolayers of InAs were deposited followed by a 540 s growth interruption. During the growth interruption the QDs undergo a ripening process [5]. Due to its long duration, most QDs gain in size leading to an ensemble peak centered at 1.06 eV. However, some small QDs remain as they represent the material reservoir for the ripening process of the larger QDs. This leads to an ultra-low QD density ($< 10^7$ per cm^2) in the 1.25-1.35 eV spectral range (Fig. 1).

The sample was examined using a JEOL JSM 840 scanning electron microscope equipped with a cathodoluminescence setup providing temperatures as low as 6 K. The luminescence was dispersed by a 0.3 m monochromator equipped with a 1200 lines/mm grating. The light was detected with a liquid-nitrogen cooled Si charge-coupled-device camera. The minimal linewidth as given by the setup was $\approx$140 μeV. Using a lineshape analysis, the energetic position of a single lines could be determined withtin an accuracy better than 20 μeV.

In order to relocate the QDs after annealing, circular mesas with 24 μm in diameter were etched into the sample surface (Fig. 1). The consecutive annealing steps

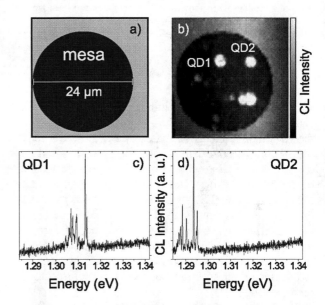

FIGURE 1. a) Schematic top view of the mesa structure. b) Maxima of monochromatic intensity between 1.284 and 1.342 eV visualize the position of the QDs. Four QDs are located in this particular mesa, corresponding to a QD density of 10^6 QDs per cm^2 in this spectral range. c) / d) Spectra of QDs 1 and 2.

lasted five minutes at 710 and 720 °C respectively, performed under As atmosphere in order to stabilize the sample surface.

Fig. 2 shows the influence of the annealing steps on a particular QD. Neutral excitons (X), biexcitons (XX) and charged (positively (X+), negatively (X-)) excitons could be identified following Ref. [6]. For easier comparison the energetic position of the X line has been shifted to 0 meV. Fig. 2 shows that the XX shifts to lower energies with respect to the X line, changing its character from

CP893, *Physics of Semiconductors, 28th International Conference*
edited by W. Jantsch and F. Schäffler
© 2007 American Institute of Physics 978-0-7354-0397-0/07/$23.00

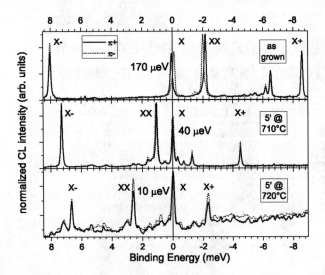

FIGURE 2. The effect of two annealing steps on the spectrum of a single QD is shown. 0 eV corresponds to the respective exciton recombination energy (1.2738 eV for as grown, 1.3002 for 710 °C, and 1.3174 eV for 720 °C). Additionally, the respective excitonic fine structure splitting is shown to decrease from 170 ± 20 μeV to 10 ± 20 μeV.

anti-binding (-2.1 meV) to binding (2.6 meV) with a total change in binding energy $\Delta E_{XX}^{bind} = 4.7$ meV. Likewise, the X+ binding energy increases by $\Delta E_{X+}^{bind} = 6.3$ meV. The X- on the other hand shows the opposite trend becoming less binding with its binding energy decreasing by $\Delta E_{X-}^{bind} = -1.3$ meV. Additionally the excitonic fine-structure splitting (FSS) was recorded. For this particular dot it decreased from 170 to ≈ 10 μeV, i.e. a value below our experimental accuracy. The general trend of decreasing FSS and increasing XX binding energy after annealing has also been observed by Young et al. However, they did not record the spectra of identical QDs before and after annealing [2].

The binding energies of these complexes are a function of the wavefunction shape and their mutual position affecting the direct Coulomb energies and the degree of correlation. The energy contribution due to correlation E^{corr} foremost depends on the number of bound states and the sublevel spacing. In our case there is a trade off between the decreasing number of bound states with annealing ($E^{corr} \downarrow$) and the slightly decreasing sublevel spacing ($E^{corr} \uparrow$). Therefore we approximate E^{corr} to be constant during annealing and analyze the change of binding energies in terms of the direct Coulomb integrals and their change alone:

$$\Delta E_{X+}^{bind} = \Delta J_{eh} + \Delta J_{hh} + (\Delta E_{X+}^{corr} = 0) \quad , \quad (1)$$

$$\Delta E_{X-}^{bind} = \Delta J_{eh} + \Delta J_{ee} + (\Delta E_{X-}^{corr} = 0) \quad , \quad (2)$$

$$\Delta E_{XX}^{bind} = 2\Delta J_{eh} + \Delta J_{ee} + J_{hh} + (\Delta E_{XX}^{corr} = 0), \quad (3)$$

where J_{ab} describes the Coulomb energy between the wavefunctions ψ_a and ψ_b.

The left hand values are taken from experiment. As a first approximation, the electron wavefunction does not change with annealing due to its small effective mass, leading to the additional assumption $\Delta J_{ee} = 0$. Since the right hand side of the equation system 1-3 has rank two only, we can solve eqs. 1 and 2 and use eq. 3 as a test. Eqs. 1 and 2 yield $\Delta J_{hh} = 7.6$ meV and $\Delta J_{eh} = -1.3$ meV respectively. These values are well confirmed by eq. 3. J_{hh} describes the Coulomb repulsion of the spin-degenerate hole groundstates and has therefore a negative value. A positive ΔJ_{hh} hence is a sign of an extension of the hole groundstate wavefunction upon annealing. J_{eh} describes the the Coulomb attraction between electron and hole groundstate having a positive value. For the ΔJ_{eh} one would expect a value half as large as $-\Delta J_{hh}$ since the hole wavefunction increases its extent and the electron extent remains virtually unchanged. But this is only true if electron and hole preserve their mutual position and their shapes. In contrast, our results can be understood if we assume that both wavefunctions are originally oriented along orthogonal directions like [110] and [110] and loose this misorientation during annealing. In an elongated QD electron and hole wavefunctions are aligned into the direction of the elongation. Hence the large FSS plus the required misorientation of electron and hole wavefunction point at an interface-mediated anisotropy resulting from the lack of inversion symmetry of the underlying zinc-blende lattice. Annealing destroys the clearly defined interfaces and the confinement anisotropy vanishes. Model calculations show, that piezoelectric fields are insensitive to annealing.

In conclusion, we have recorded emission spectra of single QDs and followed their evolution under an annealing procedure. We have shown, that it is possible to alter the electronic structure of the QDs on the order of meV in a controlled manner. Our results can be understood by a change of electron and hole wavefunction shape and mutual position. We have thus demonstrated a powerful tool to tailor single QDs' electronic properties for their use in potential applications.

This works was supported by the DFG via SfB 296 and the SANDiE Network of Excellence of the European Commision, Contract No. NMP4-CT-2004-500101.

REFERENCES

1. e. g. O. Benson et al., *Phys. Rev. Lett.* **84**, 2513 (2000); S. Cortez et al., *Phys. Rev. Lett.* **89**, 207401 (2002).
2. R. J. Young et al., *Phys. Rev. B* **72**, 113305 (2005).
3. Langbein et al., *Phys. Rev. B* **69**, 161301(R) (2004).
4. A. I. Tartakovskii et al., *Phys. Rev. B* **70**, 193303 (2004).
5. U. W. Pohl et al., *Phys. Rev. B* **72**, 245332 (2005).
6. S. Rodt et al., *Phys. Rev. B* **71**, 155325 (2005).

Multi-Electronic Structures in GaAs Quantum Dots

M. Yamagiwa[1,2], F. Saito[1], M. Kurasawa[1], T. Kihira[1], Y. Ogawa[1], F. Minami[1], and N. Koguchi[2]

[1]*Department of Physics, Tokyo Institute of Technology, Meguro-ku, Tokyo 152-8551, Japan*
[2]*Quantum Dot Research Center, National Institute for Materials Science, 1-2-1 Sengen, Tsukuba 305-0047, Japan*

Abstract. We have studied the micro-photoluminescence spectra of strain-free GaAs/AlGaAs single quantum dots, coupled with magnetic field dependence, time-resolved, and photon correlation measurements. The experimental behavior can be well explained by a model calculation based on the successive relaxation of multi-excitons.

Keywords: quantum dot, exciton, multi-exciton, micro-photoluminescence, droplet epitaxy, GaAs.
PACS: 73.63.Bd, 73.22.-f, 78.55.-m.

A strongly excited single quantum dot (SQD) exhibits a photoluminescence (PL) spectrum with a rich structure of sharp emission bands, which is a manifestation of the multi-electronic interactions in the SQD's discrete energy levels. We have studied the micro-PL (μPL) spectra of strain-free GaAs/AlGaAs SQDs, coupled with magnetic field dependence, time-resolved, and photon correlation measurements. Based on our findings, we have proposed a theoretical model for the systematic assignment of the multi-excitonic emissions, and determined the multi-electronic interaction parameters.

The sample under study in this work consists of GaAs QDs held in an AlGaAs matrix, and were grown by droplet epitaxy using a molecular beam epitaxy system [1,2]. The QD density and base size of this sample are 7×10^8 cm^2 and 40 nm, respectively.

The sample was cooled using low-vibration He cryostats, which provided temperatures down to 5 K. The excitation beam, which excite above the barrier bandgap for all experiments, is focused onto the sample by a 50$\times$ objective lens; the PL is picked up by the same objective, dispersed by a monochromator, and recorded with a charge coupled device camera.

Figure 1 shows the SQD PL spectra as a function of the excitation power, using a frequency-double YLF laser emitting at 2.35 eV as an excitation source. The single excitonic emission (notated as X_1) is observed at the weak excitation power limit. With increasing excitation power, several peaks (notated as X_2, X_{3a}, X_{3b}), which are considered as multi-excitonic emissions, appear at the lower energy side of the X_1 peak with spacings of the order of 1 meV.

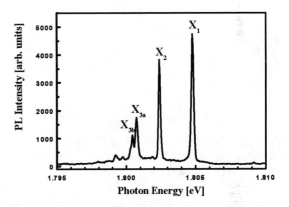

FIGURE 1. A typical μPL spectrum of a SQD under strong excitation (6.7 μW).

In order to designate the multi-excitonic origins of the X_1, X_2 and $X_{3a,b}$ peak assignments, we studied the magnetic field dependence of these peaks under strong cw excitation. The sample and the objective lens were placed in a superconducting split-coil magnet system so that the magnetic field ($\leq$5T) was aligned normal to the sample (Faraday configuration). By applying a magnetic field, the X_1, X_2 and $X_{3a,b}$ lines exhibited a diamagnetic shift (Fig. 2a) and a Zeeman splitting (Fig. 2b). The X_1 and X_2 lines exhibit the same diamagnetic shift. This indicates that the X_2 line originated from a biexcitonic emission, because the diamagnetic shift for the biexcitonic emission is given by the difference of the shift of the initial biexcitonic state, which is theoretically twice that of the single exciton [3,4], and of the final excitonic state.

CP893, *Physics of Semiconductors, 28th International Conference*
edited by W. Jantsch and F. Schäffler
© 2007 American Institute of Physics 978-0-7354-0397-0/07/$23.00

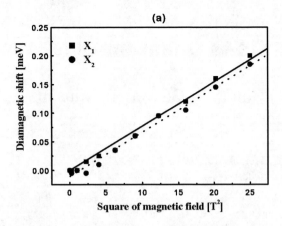

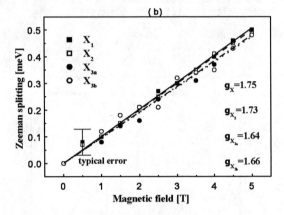

FIGURE 2. (a) The diamagnetic shifts of the X_1 and X_2 lines versus the square of the magnetic field. The lines are a linear fit to B^2. (b) The Zeeman splittings of the X_1, X_2, and $X_{3a,b}$ lines versus the magnetic field.

The Zeeman splitting of the X_2 and $X_{3a,b}$ lines exhibit the same behavior as the X_1 line: this can be interpreted completely in that the splittings of multi-excitonic emissions result from a Zeeman splitting of the single exciton state [5], which is the end state for the biexciton (X_2) and $X_{3a,b}$ lines.

Thus, the X_2 and $X_{3a,b}$ lines originated from multiexcitonic complexes which seemed to show a cascade emission ending with the single exciton state. We conducted time-resolved measurements on a SQD in order to verify this sequential emission. A 150 fs-pulse width Ti-sapphire pulsed laser, emitting at 1.55 eV with a 76 MHz repetition rate, was frequency-doubled to non-resonantly excite a SQD. A portion of the excitation beam served as the start signal for a time-amplitude converter (TAC); the PL peak photons were detected via a monochromator and an avalanche photodiode at its output slit, which generated the stop signal. The output of the TAC was fed into a multi-channel analyzer and integrated to acquire the time evolution of the PL intensity for each peak. The sequential rise in PL intensity is indicative of the cascaded emission involving these peaks. By using the PL photon as both the start/stop signal in the above setup, autocorrelation measurements were performed on an SQD, which revealed a pronounced "antibunching" for the emission from the X_1 peak, indicating the single photon emission from a SQD. Preliminary studies of the cross-correlations between X_1 and X_2 peaks show promise of a more detailed cascade picture.

Finally, we propose a theoretical model that systematically explains the measured PL spectrum taking into account the number of exchange interactions depending on the carrier population. In this model, it is considered that the spectral redshifts of multi-exciton line are caused by the number of exchange interactions, which increase with the number of carriers. This concept is built on the fact that the differences between the multi-exciton direct Coulomb terms are much smaller than the exchange terms for the optical transition between confined multi-exciton states. Therefore, the sum of exchange interaction energies lowers the energy of the N+1 multi-exciton levels more than it lowers the energy of the N multi-exciton levels, thus causing successive redshifts in the transition energies. By comparing the measured PL spectrum and the optical transitional energies in this model, we can determine the electron-electron and hole-hole exchange interaction parameters, which are the order of 1meV, while the electron-hole exchange interaction parameter is <1meV.

ACKNOWLEDGMENTS

This work was supported by a 21st Century COE Program at Tokyo Tech "Nanometer-Scale Quantum Physics" by the Ministry of Education, Culture, Sports, Science and Technology, by the Grant-in-Aid for Scientific Research from the Ministry of Education, Culture, Sports, Science and Technology of Japan, and by the Strategic Information and Communications R&D Promotion Scheme.

REFERENCES

1. N. Koguchi, S. Takahashi, and T. Chikyow, J. Cryst. Growth **111**, 688 (1991).
2. M. Yamagiwa, N. Sumita, F. Minami, and N. Koguchi, J. Lumin. **108**, 379 (2004).
3. A. Kuther, M. Bayer, A. Forchel, A. Gorbunov, V. B. Timofeev, F. Schäfer and J. P. Reithmaier, Phys. Rev. B **58**, R7508 (1998).
4. S. N. Walck and T. L. Reinecke, Phys. Rev. B **57**, 9088 (1998).
5. F. Saito, M. Yamagiwa, K. Ikeda, Y. Ogawa, F. Minami, and N. Koguchi, J. Lumin. **119**, 565 (2006).

A microscopic theory for the optical properties of semiconductor quantum-dot systems

M. Lorke, J. Seebeck, P. Gartner and F. Jahnke

Institute for Theoretical Physics, University of Bremen, Germany

Abstract. A microscopic theory is used to study the optical absoprtion and gain spectra of semiconductor quantum dots. The dephasing of a coherent excitation and line-shifts of the interband transitions due to carrier-carrier Coulomb interaction and carrier-phonon interaction are determined from a quantum kinetic treatment of correlation processes. Our theoretical model predicts a new phenomenon in quantum-dot systems, namely a reduction of the optical gain with increasing carrier density.

Keywords: quantum dots, optical properties
PACS: 78.67.Hc, 71.35.Cc

INTRODUCTION

In recent years semiconductor quantum dots (QDs) have emerged as new active materials for optoelectronic devices. Possible applications include LED's, lasers, or amplifiers [1, 2]. In quantum information technology QDs have been successfully used to generate single photons or correlated photon pairs [3, 4, 5]. A central issue in different applications are dephasing processes. They determine the homogeneous linewidth of the QD resonances, limit the coherence properties of QD lasers and their ultrafast emission dynamics, and have a strong influence on coherent optical nonlinearities. Optical studies of QDs have recently been focused on self-assembled systems which are typically grown in the Stranski-Krastanoff mode. The resulting QDs are randomly distributed on a two-dimensional wetting layer (WL). The coupling of the QD states to the WL states is an important source for scattering and dephasing.

For the theoretical description of the QD system we use a quantum-kinetic theory that takes into account both the dephasing due to carrier-carrier Coulomb interactions and due to carrier-phonon interaction.

THEORETICAL MODEL

We consider a InGaAs QD system that consist of two confined shells both for electrons and holes, which due to their angular momentum properties we denote as s-shell and p-shell. Schematically the single-particle energy spectrum is given in Fig. 1. The unrenormalized s-shell and p-shell states are located -142 meV (-115 meV) and -66 meV (-55 meV) for electrons (holes) below the WL bandedge, respectively. We solve equations for the interband transition amplitude ψ_α, where α denotes either a localized QD or a delocalized WL state.

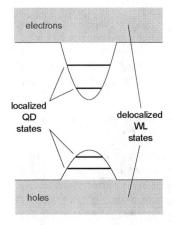

FIGURE 1. Schematic drawing of energy levels in the quantum-dot (QD) on wetting-layer (WL) system.

The Fourier transform of the coherent interband transition amplitude ψ_α obeys the equation

$$(\hbar\omega - \varepsilon_\alpha^e - \varepsilon_\alpha^h)\psi_\alpha + \hbar\Omega_\alpha(1 - f_\alpha^e - f_\alpha^h)$$
$$= iS_\alpha^{c-c}(\omega) + iS_\alpha^{c-p}(\omega) . \qquad (1)$$

The functions $f_\alpha^{e,h}$ are the carrier populations of the state α for electrons or holes, and Ω_α is the renormalized Rabi energy. With S_α^{c-c} and S_α^{c-p} we denote the Correlation contributions due to carrier-carrier Coulomb and carrier-phonon interaction respectively. For details confer Ref. [6]. As we are interested in the high temperature, high carrier density regime we consider only LO phonons, that require in QD systems a description in the polaron picture [7]. From the solution of Eq. (1) we calculate the total polarization and the optical susceptibility $\chi(\omega)$ of the system.

CP893, *Physics of Semiconductors, 28th International Conference*
edited by W. Jantsch and F. Schäffler
© 2007 American Institute of Physics 978-0-7354-0397-0/07/$23.00

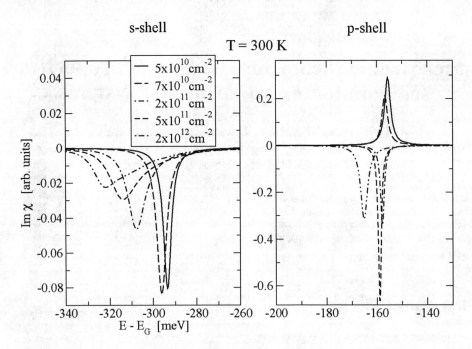

FIGURE 2. Imaginary part of the optical suscepibility for the s-shell and p-shell resonances for various carrier densities and a temperature of 300K. The energy axis is given relative to the WL bandgap energy

NUMERICAL RESULTS

In Fig. 2 the absoprtion (obtained from the optical susceptibility) is shown for the given QD parameters and a temperature of 300K. For the s-shell we observe optical gain already for low carrier densities. We find a substantial broadening of the QD transitions of several meV which is in good agreement with recent photoluminescence measurements of single QDs [8].

A closer examination of the spectra in Fig. 2 reveals a novel behavior in intrinsic QD gain. For $n \geq 7 \times 10^{10} cm^{-2}$, the s-shell QD peak gain actually decreases with increasing carrier density. The same behaviour is found for the p-shell at larger carrier densities. This can be traced back to the fact, that the inversion factor $(1 - f_\alpha^e - f_\alpha^h)$ becomes fixed when both electron and hole populations approach unity. However the dephasing, that controls the linewidth, can increase due to the presence of the WL states. This saturation of the inversion is significantly more pronounced in QD than in QW or bulk systems because of the density of states of the 0-d versus the 2-d or 3-d system. One gathers from this results that intrinsic QD gain properties are strongly governed by dephasing. This behaviour is not known in any other gain material and could lead to new effects in semiconductor QD laser structures. However a large inhomogeneous broadening can mask the gain reduction effect, as the peak gain of the inhomogeneously broadend spectra is more sensitive to the area underneath the gain curve as to the gain maximum of the homogeneous result. As a consequence the gain reduction behavior should be observable in QD system with small inhomogenous broadening or ideally in experiments on single QDs.

ACKNOWLEDGMENTS

We gratefully acknowledge financial support from the DFG research group "Quantum optics in semiconductor nanostructures" and a grant for CPU time at the Forschungszentrum Jülich (Germany).

REFERENCES

1. Y. Masumoto, and T. Takagahara, editors, *Semiconductor Quantum Dots*, Springer-Verlag, Berlin, 2002, 1. edn.
2. P. Michler, editor, *Single Quantum Dots*, Springer-Verlag, Berlin, 2003, 1. edn.
3. P. Michler, A. Imamoglu, M. D. Mason, P. J. Carson, G. F. Strouse, and S. K. Buratto, *Nature* **406**, 968 (2000).
4. E. Moreau, I. Robert, L. Manin, V. Thierry-Mieg, J. M. Gerad, and I. Abram, *Phys. Rev. Lett.* **87**, 183601 (2001).
5. M. Pelton, C. Santori, J. Vuckovic, B. Zhang, G. S. Solomon, J. Plant, and Y. Yamamoto, *Phys. Rev. Lett.* **89**, 233602 (2002).
6. M. Lorke, T. R. Nielsen, J. Seebeck, P. Gartner, and F. Jahnke, *Phys. Rev. B* **73**, 085324 (2006).
7. J. Seebeck, T. R. Nielsen, P. Gartner, and F. Jahnke, *Phys. Rev. B* **71**, 125327 (2005).
8. M. Bayer, and A. Forchel, *Phys. Rev. B* **65**, 041308(R) (2002).

Electronic structure of the dilute nitrogen quantum dots

Stanko Tomić

Computational Science and Engineering Department, CCLRC Daresbury Laboratory, Cheshire WA4 4AD, UK

Abstract. We present a theoretical study of the electronic and optical properties of InGaAsN/GaAs quantum dot (QD) structures. The calculations are based on a 10×10 **k·p** band-anti-crossing Hamiltonian, incorporating valence, conduction and nitrogen-induced bands. Numerical results for the model system of capped pyramid shaped quantum dot with {101} facets on a thin wetting layer are presented. Theoretical results show lowering of the fundamental optical transition upon introduction of nitrogen. With appropriate tailoring of the indium and nitrogen concentration this system could be a potential candidate for 1.55 μm emission on GaAs substrate.

Keywords: Semiconductor quantum dots, dilute nitrogen structures.
PACS: 73.21.La, 78.67.Hc, 71.20.Nr

INTRODUCTION

The In(Ga)AsN semiconductor quantum dots (QD) with dilute amount of nitrogen are promising candidates for the active region in next generation optoelectronic devices [1-3]. Recent advances in growth techniques facilitate the fabrication of self-assembled QDs with a very small amount (<4%) of nitrogen substitutional impurities in the QD region or in capping layer [4,5]. We present here a theoretical study of the electronic and optical properties of the dilute nitrogen InGaAsN/GaAs(N) quantum dot (QD) structures at the low temperature, based on a 10 band **k·p** band-anti-crossing (BAC) Hamiltonian [6]. The strong interaction between the N resonant states and the conduction band edge means that the conventional 8-band **k·p** method cannot be applied directly to (In,Ga)AsN and related heterostructures. The electronic structure is calculated below by extending the conventional 8-band **k·p** Hamiltonian to a 10-band model. To describe the electronic structure of InGaAsN, two (spin-degenerate) nitrogen-related bands were added to the usual two conduction and six valence bands in the conventional 8-band model [6-8]. Improved agreement was shown between the electron effective mass predicted by the 10 band BAC model and that observed experimentally when there are no cluster states close by in energy with which the InGaAsN CBE can interact [7,8]. This finding justifies that, away from nitrogen cluster states, the 10 band BAC model provides an excellent description not just of the energy gap but also of the band structure along all 3 directions of the **k** vector.

RESULTS AND DISCUSSION

To quantify the influence of nitrogen on the band structure we proceed the analysis with the set of samples, each of which has a different amount of nitrogen and the same In content of $y=70\%$ in the QD region. Fig. 1 shows the band edge energies along the [001] direction of the three samples with different content of N in the QD: (a) $x=0$, (b) $x=2\%$ and (c) $x=4\%$. Due to dominant effects of BAC interaction and a reduced strain the conduction band is strongly affected. The sample with $y=70\%$ and $x=4\%$ has an even deeper CB potential in the QD than the pure InAs/GaAs dot, inducing more tightly confined electron states. At the same time a better confinement in the CB is achieved with significantly reduced lattice mismatch of 4.03% (6.68% in InAs/GaAs). The valence band structure is only slightly affected by nitrogen.

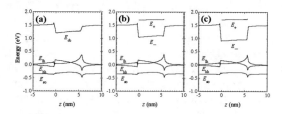

FIGURE 1. Band structure along the [001] direction through the center of the QD for three samples with the same indium concentration, $y=70\%$, and different amounts of nitrogen: (a) N-free, (b) $x=2\%$, and (c) $x=4\%$.

CP893, *Physics of Semiconductors, 28th International Conference*
edited by W. Jantsch and F. Schäffler
© 2007 American Institute of Physics 978-0-7354-0397-0/07/$23.00

To achieve a longer wavelength of the $e0$-$h0$ transition than in the pure InAs QD, we study the sample with 4% of N in $In_{0.7}Ga_{0.3}As$. As expected, the effect of increased nitrogen concentration further increases the CB offset by about ~280 meV relative to the corresponding N-free sample, Fig. 1(c). The CB minimum is at E_{-}=0.787 eV, reducing the optical transition energy to $e0$-$h0$ = 1.033 eV, which is ~77 meV smaller than in pure InAs/GaAs QDs. In contrast to the N-free and y=70% QD, the dipole matrix element for the [100] polarization drops by about 45%, and the polarization anisotropy is unchanged. The pronounced reduction of the dipole matrix element upon introduction of nitrogen is explained in terms of strong nitrogen related band mixing to the conduction band Γ-character of the host material. The comparison, with the N-free $In_{0.7}Ga_{0.3}As$ QD, in terms of the character-decomposed electron ground state wave functions is given in Fig. 2. In y=70% and x=4% QD the electron ground state is composed predominantly of the s-like states, with a 31.7%/57.9% ratio between the nitrogen and the host material conduction band character, while the remaining 10.4% belongs to the p-like characters in the VB. The hole ground state is mostly of heavy hole character (81.2%) with negligible admixture of the nitrogen band (8.11×10^{-4}%)

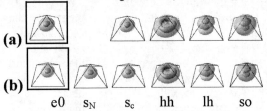

FIGURE 2. Projection of the electron ground state wave function onto their basis states: (a) N-free and y=70%, (b) x=4% and y=70%.

To illustrate the influence of nitrogen on the confinement, we compare the charge densities of the first few CB and VB states in the y=70% and N-free sample against those in y=70% and x=4% QD. A stronger confinement of the first three states in the CB of x=4% QD is observed. Since the amplitude of nitrogen character $|s_N>$ in dilute nitrogen heterostructures increases with increasing confinement [7], an improved localization of higher states, $e1$ and $e2$, in $In_{0.7}Ga_{0.3}As_{0.96}N_{0.04}$/GaAs QD has been observed too. A slightly better confinement of the VB states in N-free sample is attributed mainly to a stronger influence of strain. Finally, we briefly discuss the influence of quantum size effects on the $e0$-$h0$ transition energy, and ground state optical matrix element of QDs. We change pyramid base length from 20 to 36 lattice constants of GaAs, and monitor the variation of the $e0$-$h0$ transition energy in the $In_{0.7}Ga_{0.3}As_{0.96}N_{0.04}$/GaAs QD. Difference in the $e0$-$h0$

transition energy, relative to InAs QDs, decrease from 77 meV for the small dots (b=11.3 nm) to the 51 meV for the large dot (b=20.4 nm). For the largest (b=20.4 nm) QD with x=4% the $e0$-$h0$ transition energy is estimated to be 0.894 eV (~1.39 μm), while it Coulomb energy is 15 meV. At room temperature the emission moves further towards longer wavelengths. However, the shift will be smaller than in conventional III-V QD, because the dilute-N level reduces the E_g temperature sensitivity. By comparing our theoretical results with experimental findings we observe: (i) for y=70% and x=4% QD samples grown at 520°C [which results in h~8 nm (b ~16 nm)][4] the PL wavelength is 1.27μm, while we predict the wavelength of 1.32 μm for the same (y,x) and b=30a (17 nm); (ii) the reported dependence of measured wavelengths (in the range from 1.28 μm to 1.45 μm at T=10 K)[4] on the growth temperature (QD size) is in good agreement with theoretical predictions for direct transition wavelengths (1.2 to 1.39 μm), having in mind the uncertainty of the QD size, shape and In and N profiles; (iii) for the sample with y=70%, x=2% and lateral dot dimension of 15 nm the measured micro-PL is ~1.15 μm (1.08 eV), which is halfway between the predictions for the N-free and x=4% QDs of similar size; (iv) the theoretical results for the QDs with the N in the barrier region [6], can partly explain the observed increase of the emission wavelength and a radical lowering of the PL emission intensity with increased N concentration in the capped layer above the QD [5], due to weakened quantum size effects and strong degradation of the confinement ability respectively.

CONCLUSIONS

With appropriate tailoring of the indium and nitrogen concentration this system could be a potential candidate for 1.55 μm emission on GaAs substrate, particularly at the room temperature. We conclude that several possible routes toward 1.55 μm wavelength emission would be: further increase of the indium content in nitrogen reach ~4% QD, the increase of the QD size/volume, or vertically aligned and coupled dilute nitrogen QDs.

REFERENCES

1. C.Y. Liu et al, *Appl. Phys. Lett.* **88**, 081105 (2006).
2. Q. Gao et al, *Electron. Solid-State Lett.* **8**, G57 (2005)
3. Z.Z. Sun et al, *Appl. Phys. Lett.* **85**, 1469 (2004).
4. M. Sopanen et al, *Appl.Phys.Lett.* **76**, 994 (2000).
5. O. Schumann, et al, *Phys. Rev. B* **71**, 245316 (2005).
6. S. Tomić, *Phys Rev B* **73**, 125348 (2006).
7. S. Tomić et al, *Phys. Rev. B* **69**, 245305 (2004).
8. S. Tomić et al, *Phys. Rev. B* **71**, 233301 (2005).

Anti-Stokes Photoluminescence and Enhanced Raman Scattering from InSb Quantum Dots and Nanowires

Terumasa Horiuchi and Noboru Wada

Department of Mechanical Engineering, Faculty of Engineering, Toyo University
Kawagoe City, Saitama, Japan 350-8585

Abstract. InSb quantum dots, nanowires and bulk crystals were examined by Raman and photoluminescence spectroscopies varying the laser-power density. Surprisingly strong anti-Stokes photoluminescence was found, especially from the dot samples. Moreover, enhanced second-order Raman scattering was observed, which depended on both the laser power density and samples. The second-order Raman enhancement may be caused by the excitons created by photoirradiation.

Keywords: InSb, nanowire, quantum dot, hot luminescence, second-order Raman scattering
PACS: 71.55.Eg, 73.21.Hb, 73.21.La, 78.55.-m, 78.30.-j

INTRODUCTION

The dynamics of hot carriers in semiconductors has been an intensive research subject for the last few decades [1]. In particular, narrow-gap semiconductors may exhibit intriguing physical properties when confined in a limited space, since the carriers generally have high mobilities and large mean-free paths; quantum effects may appear at relatively high temperatures. Of special interest are the carrier-phonon and phonon-phonon interactions within the nano-structures. Here, hot luminescence and second-order Raman scattering from InSb in quantum-dot (QD), nano-wire and bulk forms are reported.

EXPERIMENT AND RESULTS

InSb quantum dots and nanowires were fabricated on Si substrates by a vapor-transport method using a focused-ion beam (FIB) system [2]. Those samples together with bulk InSb crystals were examined using a CW Ar-ion laser (λ=514.5 nm) with a CCD-coupled monochromator in the back-scattering geometry. The laser power used was up to 8 mW with a focused spot size ~1 μm on the samples (the maximum laser power density on the sample surface was estimated to be ~10^6 W/cm^2).

Photoluminescence (PL) spectra shown in Figure 1 were taken almost in the same experimental conditions with the laser power P=3 mW. The InSb QDs (with 100-400 nm in diameter) appeared to emit quite strong

Stokes PL, whereas the InSb nanowires (with 50-200 nm in diameter and ~1 μm in length) emitted less and the bulk emitted the least. Especially noted here is that there were significant anti-Stokes PL intensities observed, as shown in the insert in Fig. 1. The range of the anti-Stokes PL extended to 465 nm or ~2000 cm^{-1} away from the laser energy. The anti-Stokes PL should originate from the hot-carrier-phonon scattering [3]. In fact, when the samples were cooled from room temperature to 10K, the anti-Stokes PL intensity decreased drastically, proving that the phonons were

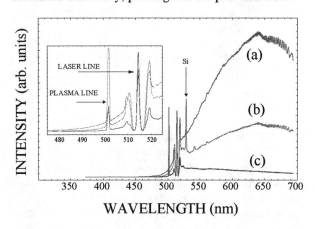

FIGURE 1. PL spectra at room temperature taken from (a) InSb QDs, (b) nanowires, (c) bulk. The insert is an expansion around the exciting laser line. The Si peaks were from the Si substrates. The dips in the intensity at the laser line were caused by the notch filters used.

CP893, *Physics of Semiconductors, 28th International Conference*
edited by W. Jantsch and F. Schäffler

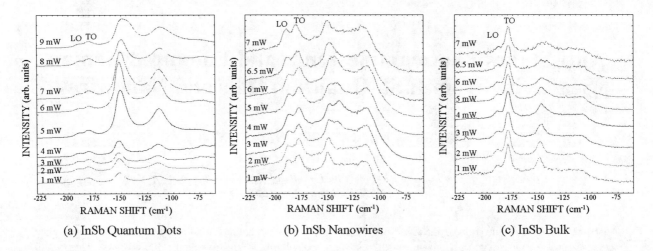

FIGURE 2. Laser-power dependent anti-Stokes Raman spectra taken at room temperature from (a) InSb QDs, (b) nanowires and (c) a single crystal. The CW-laser powers indicated were measured at the samples. The spectra were scaled so that the intensities of LO and TO phonon peaks appeared to be the same. Because of the notch filters used, the spectra above -100 cm^{-1} were spurious.

involved in the up-conversion process.

Fig. 2 shows power dependence of the Raman spectra from the InSb samples mentioned above. Fig. 2(a) depicts the Raman spectra from the InSb QDs, where the photo-excited hot carriers should be confined in the dots. Surprisingly strong second-order Raman scattering peaks were observed in addition to the LO and TO phonon peaks at -190 and -180 cm^{-1}, respectively. The peak at -150 cm^{-1} may be attributed to TO-TA, whereas the peak at -115 cm^{-1} may be assigned to 2TA [4]. As the laser power increased, the relative intensities of those second-order Raman peaks dramatically increased and the peak positions red-shifted. The peaks also became quite broad at higher laser powers.

As seen in Fig. 2(b), the second-order Raman intensities of InSb nanowires relative to the LO and TO phonon peaks appeared to be much less than those of the QDs. As the laser power increased, the peak at -150 cm^{-1} red-shifted and appeared to become two peaks, which might be related to the 1D geometrical shape of nanowires. Further increase in the power caused the two-peak feature to become one peak again.

In bulk InSb crystals, the second-order Raman features appeared to be generally less pronounced than those of the QDs and nanowires, as shown in Fig. 2(c). Red-shifting and broadening with increasing the laser power were still observed in the bulk sample. It is noted here, however, that the second-order Raman features in bulk InSb were quite sensitive to the location of the laser beam spot, e.g., crystalline edge or center.

Because of the high laser power density, a vast amount of hot carriers are created locally and should be heavily involved in the carrier-carrier and carrier-

phonon scattering process. The strong anti-Stokes PL observed should originate from the hot-carrier-phonon scattering process.

Excitons have been shown to enhance the Raman cross section by several orders of magnitudes [5]. In confined geometry, an extremely high exciton density may be expected, since the carries cannot escape from the restricted region. We propose that the photo-excited excitons may be responsible for the extremely strong second-order Raman scattering in QDs and nanowires.

ACKNOWLEDGMENTS

This work was partly supported the Ministry of Education, Science, Sports and Culture, Grant-in-Aid for Scientific Research. Also, the special research grant from Toyo University is gratefully acknowledged. We are very grateful to Profs. K. Tsubaki and T. Hanajiri and for useful discussions.

REFERENCES

1. J. Shah, *Ultrafast Spectroscopy of Semiconductors and Semiconductor Nanostructures,* (Springer-Verlag, 1997).
2. M. Ishizuka, T. Horiuchi and N. Wada, *Narrow Gap Semiconductors*, edited by J. Kono and J. Léotin, Taylor & Francis, 2006, p. 125-130.
3. N. Wada, A.C.H. Rowe and S.A. Solin, *Physics of Semiconductors*, edited by Jośe Menéndez and Chris G. Van de Walle, AIP, 2005, p.135-136.
4. W. Keifer, W. Richter and M. Cardona, Phys. Rev. B **12**, 2346 (1975).
5. P.Y. Yu and M. Cardona, *Fundamentals of Semiconductors,* (Springer-Verlag, 2001).

Exciton Aharonov-Bohm Effect in Embedded Nanostructures

M. Grochol, F. Grosse and R. Zimmermann

Institut für Physik der Humboldt-Universität zu Berlin, Newtonstrasse 15, 12489 Berlin, Germany

Abstract. Exciton properties in an embedded semiconductor nanoring under perpendicular magnetic field are investigated. Due to the unique nonsimply connected topology of the exciton wave function, oscillations of the transition energies with magnetic field (exciton Aharonov-Bohm effect) and a persistent current appear. The amplitudes of these effects depend on the effective strength of the Coulomb interaction.

Keywords: Exciton, Aharonov-Bohm Effect, Persistent current
PACS: 71.35.Ji, 78.67.Hc, 71.35.Cc, 73.23.Ra

Recent progress in the growth of semiconductor nanostructures and especially nanorings [1, 2] enables the investigation of effects related to the nonsimply connected geometry of the electronic wave function under applied magnetic field B, e. g. the Aharonov-Bohm effect [3] (ABE). The ABE has been observed for electrons in self-assembled InAs/GaAs nanorings [4]. The ABE due to excitons has not been confirmed fully yet since there are contradictory experimental results measured on type II InP/GaAs quantum dots [5, 6]. Previous theoretical investigations have been predominantly based on a model ring with zero width and its variations [7]. Recently, we have taken into account the finite width of nanorings, and performed detailed investigations [8]. An intimate relation between the oscillatory component of the exciton energy with magnetic field and the induced persistent current has been revealed. Furthermore, the exciton emission kinetics has been investigated, predicting photoluminescence quenching with B-field [9].

Excitons in a nanoring are described here within the envelope function formalism and applying the effective mass approximation. Since the nanoring is embedded in a narrow quantum well, the single sublevel approximation holds. In-plane cylindrical symmetry is assumed. After integrating over the motion in the confinement direction and using the relative Coulomb gauge of the B-field, the in-plane Hamiltonian in polar coordinates reads

$$
\begin{aligned}
\hat{H} &= \sum_{a=e,h} \left[-\frac{\hbar^2}{2m_a} \frac{1}{r_a} \frac{\partial}{\partial r_a} \left(r_a \frac{\partial}{\partial r_a} \right) + \right. \\
&\left. \frac{1}{2m_a r_a^2} \left(-i\hbar \frac{\partial}{\partial \phi_a} - q_a \frac{eB}{2} r_a^2 \right)^2 + V_a(r_a) \right] \\
&+ V_C(r_e, r_h, \phi_e - \phi_h),
\end{aligned}
$$ (1)

where $V_C(r_e, r_h, \phi_e - \phi_h)$ is the averaged Coulomb potential and e(h) stands for electron (hole). Changing the angular coordinates to $\phi = \phi_e - \phi_h$ and $\Phi = \frac{1}{2}(\phi_e + \phi_h)$, the total wave function can be factorized

$$
\Psi(r_e, r_h, \phi, \Phi) = \psi(r_e, r_h, \phi) \frac{e^{im\Phi}}{\sqrt{2\pi}}.
$$ (2)

Using the definition of the optical oscillator strength f_α of the state $|\alpha\rangle$, it can be easily seen that only states with total angular quantum number $m = 0$ are optically active (bright) [8].

The persistent current (PC) I_α induced by the exciton in the state $|\alpha\rangle$ can be calculated as the expectation value of the azimuthal component of the current operator,

$$
\begin{aligned}
\hat{J}_{a,\phi}(r, \phi) &= \frac{q_a}{2m_a} \left[\left(-i\hbar \frac{1}{r_a} \frac{\partial}{\partial \phi_a} - \frac{q_a B r_a}{2} \right) \delta(\mathbf{r_a} - \mathbf{r}) \right. \\
&\left. + \delta(\mathbf{r_a} - \mathbf{r}) \left(-i\hbar \frac{1}{r_a} \frac{\partial}{\partial \phi_a} - \frac{q_a B r_a}{2} \right) \right] ; \quad (3)
\end{aligned}
$$

$$
I_\alpha = \int dr \, \langle \alpha | \hat{J}_{e,\phi}(r, \phi) + \hat{J}_{h,\phi}(r, \phi) | \alpha \rangle.
$$ (4)

We investigate the following in-plane type-II structure: An InP nanoring embedded in a 4 nm wide $Ga_{0.51}In_{0.49}P$ quantum well sandwiched between AlAs barriers. Due to the different lattice constants of InP and $Ga_{0.51}In_{0.49}P$, there is non-zero strain which modifies the conduction and valence band offsets (the hole potential plotted in the inset of Fig. 1a). Strain is included within the approximation of isotropic elasticity [10].

The lowest bright exciton energies for a ring with inner and outer radius of $r_1 = 10$ nm and $r_2 = 20$ nm are shown in Fig. 1a. Two states (1 and 4) show only a monotonic increase of the energy with magnetic field. The first one is the ground state at $B = 0$ T, and the hole is found outside the ring at $r < r_1$ (Fig. 1d, type-II behavior). State 4 has a much larger oscillator strength since the hole is found inside the ring like the electron (Fig. 1c, type-I behavior). This increases the energy due to the ring-like

CP893, *Physics of Semiconductors, 28th International Conference*
edited by W. Jantsch and F. Schäffler
© 2007 American Institute of Physics 978-0-7354-0397-0/07/$23.00

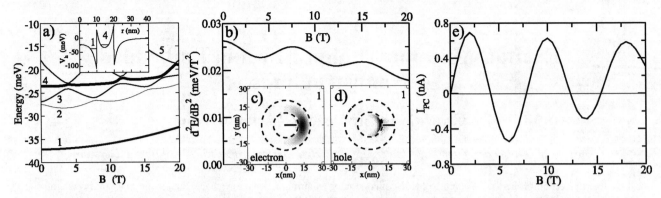

FIGURE 1. a) The lowest bright exciton energies of the InP/GaInP nanoring. The oscillator strength is schematically indicated by the line width (the oscillator strengths of states 1 and 4 differ by a factor of ten). Inset: The hole potential including strain. b) The second derivative of the lowest bright state energy (1) with respect to the B-field. Below, the electron (c) and the hole (d) correlated density of the state 1 at $B = 0$ T is plotted. The position of the second particle is fixed as shown by a horizontal bar. The ring boundaries are displayed as dashed circles ($r_1 = 10$ nm and $r_2 = 20$ nm). e) Persistent current as a function of magnetic field for state 1.

barrier for the hole (inset of Fig. 1a). The oscillatory behavior is clearly seen for excited states (2, 3, and 5, hole outside the ring) since they have enough kinetic energy to overcome the Coulomb attraction of electron and hole and to sample the whole ring. We note that there is a small overlap between states 2, 3, 4, and 5 which leads to the avoided crossing as clearly seen.

Usually, only the energy of the lowest bright state can be easily measured. Its energy dependence on the B-field has a quadratic component at least for small B, but this component is usually much stronger than any oscillatory one. Forming the second derivative of the energy with respect to B allows to extract the oscillatory component in a clear way (Fig. 1b).

The amplitude of the oscillations is determined by the wave function topology and in particular by the probability to find electron and hole on opposite sides of the ring. Due to the Coulomb interaction this probability decays exponentially on the scale of the exciton Bohr radius a_B. This is illustrated in Fig. 1c and 1d, where electron and hole correlated densities are plotted. Due to $r_1 > a_B$ the ring topology of the wave function is very weak, in correspondence to the small oscillation amplitude.

Finally, we look at the persistent current induced by excitons in the lowest bright state (one exciton per nanoring is assumed). Oscillations with the same period as in the second derivative (Fig. 1b) are observed. Their amplitude decreases as the ring topology becomes weaker with stronger magnetic field. The measurement of the PC would reveal unambiguously the ring topology of the wave function: A current flows only if the wave function is nonsimply connected. However, such a measurement is much more complicated compared to the optical measurement.

To conclude, we have demonstrated on a model example how the non-trivial ring topology of the exciton wave function manifests itself in various measurable quantities like oscillation in energy or persistent current. However, our results predict that such measurements would be extremely difficult.

REFERENCES

1. J. M. García, G. Medeiros-Ribeiro, K. Schmidt, T. Ngo, J. L. Feng, A. Lorke, J. Kotthaus, and P. M. Petroff, *Appl. Phys. Lett.* **71**, 2014 (1997).
2. T. Mano, T. Kuroda, S. Sanguinetti, T. Ochiai, T. Tateno, J. Kim, T. Noda, M. Kawabe, K. Sakoda, G. Kido, and N. Koguchi, *Nano Lett.* **5**, 425 (2005).
3. Y. Aharonov, and D. Bohm, *Phys. Rev.* **115**, 485 (1959).
4. A. Lorke, R. J. Luyken, A. O. Govorov, J. P. Kotthaus, J. M. García, and P. M. Petroff, *Phys. Rev. Lett.* **84**, 2223 (2000).
5. E. Ribeiro, A. O. Govorov, J. W. Carvalho, and G. Medeiros-Ribeiro, *Phys. Rev. Lett.* **92**, 126402 (2004).
6. M. P. F. de Godoy, P. F. Gomes, M. K. K. Nakaema, F. Iikawa, M. J. S. P. Brasil, R. A. Caetano, J. R. Madureira, J. R. R. Bortoleto, M. A. Cotta, E. Ribeiro, G. E. Marques, and A. C. R. Bittencourt, *Phys. Rev. B* **73**, 033309 (2006).
7. A. V. Chaplik, *JETP Lett.* **62**, 900 (1995).
8. M. Grochol, F. Grosse, and R. Zimmermann, *submitted* (2006).
9. M. Grochol, F. Grosse, and R. Zimmermann, *phys. stat. sol. (b), accepted (Proc. EXCON 7, Winston-Salem)* (2006).
10. J. H. Davies, *J. Appl. Phys.* **84**, 1358 (1998).

Temperature dependence of photoluminescence of CdSe/ZnSe quantum dots grown on GaAs and Si/Ge virtual substrates

E. E. Onishchenko, V. S. Bagaev, I. P. Kazakov, and M. M. Rzaev

P.N.Lebedev Physics Institute, Russian Academy of Sciences, Leninskii pr. 53, 119991 Moscow, Russia

Abstract. We have carried out temperature-dependent studies of the photoluminescence properties of a set of CdSe/ZnSe quantum dot structures grown on conventionally used GaAs(100) substrates and Si(100)/Ge virtual substrates. Both single-layer and multilayer QD structures have been studied. It was shown that the conventional MBE technique allows to grow CdSe/ZnSe QDs having the activation energy of luminescence quenching as large as 200 meV.

Keywords: quantum dots, virtual substrates, luminescence
PACS: 78.55.-m, 78.67.Hc

INTRODUCTION

Growth of self-assembled II-VI quantum dots (QDs) on Si/SiGe substrates is of crucial importance for the integration of optoelectronic devices with the mainstream silicon-based technology. A new technique of growth of high-quality CdSe/ZnSe QD structures on so-called "virtual" Si(100)/Ge substrates has been recently developed by our group [1]. Si/Ge virtual substrate is a sequence of Si and Ge epitaxial layers grown on Si substrate which has a Ge-layer with relatively high structural quality as a cap layer (ZnSe and Ge have similar lattice constants). It is of importance for design of II-VI QD blue-green laser structures and light-emitting devices integrated with the silicon-based technology and operating at room temperature to study the influence of sample parameters on the temperature dependence of their luminescent properties.

EXPERIMENTAL AND RESULTS

Samples consisted of five periods of CdSe/ZnSe QDs with CdSe layer with nominal thicknesses of 2 and 3.3 monolayers (ML) separated by ZnSe spacer layers with thickness of 20 nm have been grown on virtual Si/Ge substrates (see details in [1]). The reference set of samples was grown on conventionally used GaAs (100) substrates. Three samples with single

CdSe layers with nominal thicknesses of 1, 2, and 3.3 ML also have been grown on GaAs substrates under similar growth conditions. Regardless the substrates used, the multilayer QD samples exhibit a high photoluminescence (PL) efficiency at low temperatures [1]. QD multilayers grown on different kind of substrates exhibit activation energies of PL quenching in the range from 90 to 120 meV. PL of the samples grown on Si/Ge substrates is detectable up to room temperature.

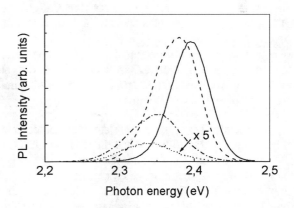

FIGURE 1. PL spectra of CdSe/ZnSe QD sample with a CdSe layer nominal thickness of 3.3 monolayers at 5 K (solid line), 100 K (dashed line), 200 K (dashed-dotted line) and room temperature (dotted line).

CP893, *Physics of Semiconductors, 28th International Conference*
edited by W. Jantsch and F. Schäffler
© 2007 American Institute of Physics 978-0-7354-0397-0/07/$23.00

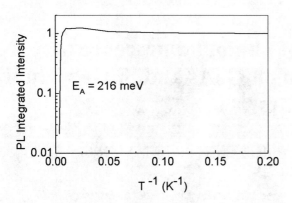

FIGURE 2. Temperature dependence of integrated PL intensity of CdSe/ZnSe QD sample with a CdSe layer nominal thickness of 3.3 monolayers.

In contrast to the case of QD multilayers, the activation energies of PL quenching for single-layer QD samples lie within a wide range. For the single-layer QD samples with thin CdSe layers (1 and 2 ML) the activation energies are equal to 75 and 140 meV, respectively. These values are sufficiently similar to those for QD multilayers, in principle. However, the properties of single-layer QD sample with the thickest CdSe layer are rather unexpected: PL is still rather efficient at room temperature (Fig. 1). The temperature dependence of integrated PL intensity for this sample is shown in Fig. 2. The activation energy is more than 200 meV for this structure. To the best of our knowledge, such a value of the activation energy is the highest one reported in literature for CdSe/ZnSe QDs (for example, the activation energy for CdSe/ZnSe QDs grown by the use of a special method to induce large QDs formation is 163 meV [2]). It is worthwhile to note that the measurement of the PL temperature dependence of the sample has been carried out at sufficiently low excitation power (0.5 mW) and excitation density (< 10 W/cm^2).

In principle, it is possible to relate the enhancement of activation energy to the formation of larger QDs (or QDs with greater Cd content) in this sample. But, likely, it is not the case: the spectral position of emission band for the sample has a blue-shift more than 150 meV with respect to a sample with just the same CdSe layer thickness grown on GaAs substrate. It is known that the activation energy for II-VI QD multilayers can differ from that for single-layer QDs even for nominally equal thickness of QD layer material. Usually, the activation energy for multilayers is higher. Nevertheless, an opposite situation can take place. So, it was shown for CdTe/ZnTe QDs (which are similar to CdSe/ZnSe QDs in many respects) that, in some cases, the activation energy can decrease for

QD multilayers with respect to single-layer QDs due to the change of strain distribution pattern within QD structure [3]. The activation energy in CdTe/ZnTe structures is defined by a potential well depth for holes [4]. The change of a strain distribution pattern which takes place as a result of presence of several QD layers causes the change of the potential well depth for holes. A similar situation can take place for CdSe/ZnSe QDs. A particular strain distribution pattern for the single-layer QD sample under discussion likely is as follows: the potential well for holes is rather deep (deeper than in multilayer QD samples with the same nominal thickness of CdSe layer).

The enhancement of the exciton binding energy can be the second reason of an unusually high value of the activation energy. It has been shown theoretically and experimentally that the exciton binding energy in QD can exceed 4-5 times this value for bulk material under appropriate conditions (appropriate relation between an exciton Bohr radius and a lateral QD size) [5]. Possibly, such conditions occur in the sample. Note that the exciton binding energy for bulk ZnSe is large (20 meV). Obviously, the combination of increase of the potential depth for holes and increase of the exciton binding energy should lead to the enhancement of activation energy of luminescence quenching.

In conclusion, we have shown that the use of virtual Si/Ge substrates may be promising, in principle, for the growth of CdSe/ZnSe-based optoelectronic devices integrated with the silicon-based technology and operating at room temperature.

ACKNOWLEDGMENTS

This work was supported by the RFBR grant N 06-08-00958.

REFERENCES

1. E. E. Onishchenko, M. M. Rzaev, I. P. Kazakov. *Phys. Stat. Sol. (c)* **3**, 905 (2006).
2. I. C. Robin, R. Andre, H. Marriete, S. Tatarenko, Le Si Dang, J. M. Gerard, E. Bellet-Amalric, *Physica E* **26**, 119 (2005).
3. E. E. Onishchenko, V. S. Bagaev, V. V. Zaitsev, E. I. Makhov, *Physica E* **26**, 153 (2005).
4. F. Tinjod, K. Kheng, J. Joel, H. Mariette, *Physica E* **17**, 68 (2003).
5. M. Bayer, S. N. Walck, T. L. Reinecke, A. Forchel, *Phys. Rev B* **57**, 6584 (1998).

Analytical Determination of Exciton Energy in GaN/AlN Quantum Dots

D.P. Williams[1], A.D. Andreev[2] and E.P. O'Reilly[1]

[1]*Tyndall National Institute, Lee Maltings, Cork, Ireland*
[2]*Advanced Technology Institute, University of Surrey, Guildford GU2 7XH, UK*

Abstract. Using previously derived analytical expressions for the polarization field in nitride quantum dots (QDs), we show that the potential in the growth direction can be approximated as linear, with the slope of this linear potential depending only on the aspect ratio of the dot. Disagreement in the sign of the piezoelectric coefficient e_{15} causes significant uncertainty in the calculated potential.

Keywords: GaN quantum dots; polarization potential; exciton energy.
PACS: 73.21.La, 77.65.Ly

INTRODUCTION

The wurtzite (hexagonal) crystal structure of the III-nitride semiconductors leads to large built-in electric fields, caused by both the spontaneous and piezoelectric polarization[1], giving a near-linear dependence of exciton energy on dot size[2]. We have previously presented analytical expressions for the polarization potential along the central axis of cylindrical and truncated cone QDs[3]. We use these analytical expressions here to show that the potential in the growth direction can be approximated as linear within the dot for a wide range of dot height to radius aspect ratios. We also show that the potential can be approximated as quadratic in the plane perpendicular to the growth direction. The linear potential is used to represent the band edge profile as a triangular well in the growth direction, which allows the Schrödinger equation to be solved analytically, in terms of Airy functions along the growth direction and simple harmonic oscillator (SHO) wavefunctions within the growth plane. Because the slope of the potential along the growth direction depends only on the aspect ratio of the dot, the ground state exciton energy decreases linearly with increasing dot height, provided the aspect ratio is conserved while the dot height is varied.

RADIAL AND AXIAL POTENTIAL

Our previous work[3,4] on built-in polarization fields in nitride QDs has shown that the field in the z direction [which we take to be the (0001) growth

direction] has the most significant effect on the confinement potential, reaching 6 – 8 MV/cm in GaN/AlN QDs, with the in-plane field of ~1 MV/cm providing additional lateral confinement. We therefore begin our approximation by separating the potential into a radial part and an axial (z direction) part.

The solid curve in Fig. 1 shows the calculated potential in a GaN/AlN truncated cone dot, plotted as a function of r just above the base of the dot. Since the wavefunctions of carriers in nitride QDs are confined well within the dot, close to the central axis[4], it is only necessary to accurately approximate the potential in the region of small r. The dashed curve shows a SHO

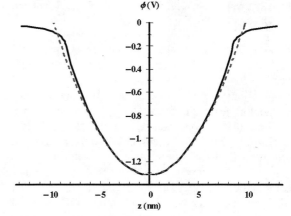

FIGURE 1. Polarization potential as a function of r, just above the base of a GaN/AlN truncated cone dot with base radius 8.5nm, top radius 2 nm and height 3.6 nm. The dashed curve is an harmonic oscillator fit to the potential.

CP893, *Physics of Semiconductors, 28th International Conference*
edited by W. Jantsch and F. Schäffler
© 2007 American Institute of Physics 978-0-7354-0397-0/07/$23.00

approximation to the potential, calculated using the analytical approach described in Appendix A of ref. [3]. For both truncated cone and cylindrical dots, the error introduced by this approximation is typically 1% or less for values of r less than about half the radius of the dot at the given z value, confirming the validity of this approximation for the present analysis.

Turning now to the axial, or z direction, previous calculations have shown the potential variation is near linear along this direction for a wide range of realistic dot dimensions, sizes and compositions[3-5]. We derived in [5] a linear approximation for the potential along the z axis of a cylindrical QD, as a function of the QD aspect ratio $f = h/R$, where h is the cylinder height and R the cylinder radius. Fig. 2 shows that the error introduced by this linear approximation is less than 1% for values of f smaller than about 0.45 in the case of GaN/AlN QDs, confirming the validity of the linear approximation for the axial potential.

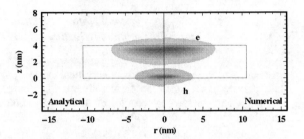

uncertainty in the sign of the shear piezoelectric coefficient, e_{15}. Values of e_{15} in the literature range from e_{15} = -0.48 to +0.35 C/m^2 [5,6]. The polarization field is independent of e_{15} in a quantum well, but can vary by as much as 10-20% in a QD, depending on the assumed sign of e_{15}. This emphasizes the need for further measurement and analysis to develop a reliable set of material parameters for the nitrides.

FIGURE 3. Contour plot in the r-z plane of the electron (red, top) and hole (blue, bottom) wavefunctions in a cylindrical QD, with the analytical (numerical) solution on the left (right).

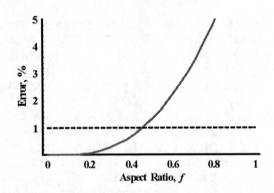

FIGURE 2. Maximum error of the linear approximation to the polarization potential in a cylindrical QD, as a function of the QD aspect ratio, f.

Figure 3 compares the approximate electron and hole wavefunctions calculated using the model potential for a GaN/AlN QD with the numerical wavefunctions calculated using the full expression for the potential, for a cylindrical QD with h = 4 nm and R = 10.5 nm (f = 0.38). It can be seen that the analytical approach provides an excellent description of the electron and hole wavefunctions, confirming its validity as a means to estimate the exciton recombination energy in GaN-based QDs. The analytically calculated exciton recombination energy is within 0.1 eV of the numerical result over a wide range of dot sizes. Because the slope of the polarization potential is constant for a given dot aspect ratio, f, this leads to an approximately linear variation in exciton energy with dot height for fixed f.

We finally note that there is greater uncertainty in the predicted magnitude of the polarization field in a GaN QD compared to a GaN quantum well, because of

CONCLUSIONS

We conclude that the potential in the growth direction can be approximated as linear in a GaN/AlN QD, with the slope of this linear potential depending only on the aspect ratio of the dot. Disagreement in the sign of the piezoelectric coefficient e_{15} introduces uncertainty in the calculated potential, emphasizing the need for more reliable material parameters for the nitrides.

ACKNOWLEDGMENTS

We gratefully acknowledge support from Science Foundation Ireland and the Irish Research Council for Science, Engineering and Technology (D.P.W.)

REFERENCES

1. F, Bernardini, V. Fiorentini and D. Vanderbilt, *Phys. Rev. B* **56**, 10024 (R) (1997).
2. J. Simon, N.T. Pelekanos, C. Adelmann, E. Martinez-Guerrero, R. André, B. Daudin, L.S. Dang and H. Mariette, *Phys. Rev. B* **68**, 035312 (2003)
3. D.P. Williams, A.D. Andreev, E.P. O'Reilly and D.A. Faux, *Phys. Rev. B* **72**, 235318 (2005).
4. A.D. Andreev and E.P. O'Reilly, *Phys.Rev. B* **62**, 15851 (2000).
5. D.P. Williams, A.D. Andreev and E.P. O'Reilly, *Phys. Rev. B* **73**, 241301(R) (2006).
6. G. Bu, D. Ciplys, M. Shur, L.J. Schowalter, S. Schujman and R. Gaska, *Appl. Phys. Lett.* **84**, 4611 (2004).

Carrier dynamics of electrons in n-type modulation-doped InAs/GaAs quantum dot structure studied using THz time-domain spectroscopy

Seung Jae Oh[1], Chul Kang[1], In Hee Maeng[1], Nam Ki Cho[2], Jin Dong Song[2], Won Jun Choi[2], Jung Il Lee[2], and Joo-Hiuk Son[1*]

[1]Physics Dept., University of Seoul, Seoul 130-743, Korea
[2]Korea Institute of Science & Technology, P.O.Box 131, Cheongryang, Seoul, Korea
E-mail: *joohiuk@uos.ac.kr

Abstract. We have investigated the carrier transport dynamics of n-type modulation-doped InAs/GaAs quantum dots (QDs) using terahertz time-domain spectroscopy (THz TDS) in order to estimate the total number of electrons captured by the QDs. The THz transmission of the sample with QDs is larger than that of the sample without QDs, which implies that the conductivity of sample with QDs is lower than that without QDs. From the THz waveforms and subsequent analysis, the density and mobility of free electrons, which are not captured by the QDs, have been obtained.

Keywords: terahertz electromagnetic waves, quantum dots, carrier transport dynamics
PACS: 78.66.-w

INTRODUCTION

The study of the carrier dynamics in an InAs/GaAs quantum dot (QDs) structure is important for their application in optoelectronic devices such as infrared detectors and laser diodes [1,2] because the density and mobility of the electrons captured or escaped from the confined states of the QDs affect the characteristics of such devices.

THz time domain spectroscopy (THz-TDS) has been used as a useful technique for studying carrier dynamics in a doped semiconductor up to a few THz [3]. In contrast to Fourier Transform-Infrared (FT-IR) spectroscopy which requires an iterative numerical process such as the Kramers-Kronig relation to extract the complex optical constants, THz-TDS yields accurate complex optical constants because it uses coherent electromagnetic pulses. THz-TDS also has a higher signal to noise ratio (> 5,000) than FTIR.

In this paper, we have investigated the carrier transport dynamics of n-type modulation doped InAs/GaAs quantum dots (QDs) using THz-TDS [3] in order to estimate the total number of electrons captured by the QDs. We have also studied the temperature dependence.

EXPERIMENT METHOD

We generate and detect THz electromagnetic pulses using the photoconductive switching and sampling techniques, respectively. The configuration of the THz-TDS setup used in this study is explained in Ref. 3.

Two samples with 30-pair modulation-doped layers were prepared; one is with QDs (#1) and the other is without QDs (#2). Each modulation-doped QD layer consisted of a 50nm-thick GaAs, an InAs/GaAs QD layer, a 15 nm-thick GaAs cap, a 3 nm-thick Si-doped GaAs ($n=1\times10^{18}$ cm^{-3}) and another 10 nm-thick GaAs, sequentially from the bottom. The sample without QDs has the same modulation-doped structure except the QD layers.

THz time-domain signals before and after transmitting samples are converted into frequency-domain signals by Fourier transform. The phase difference and power reduction give the real and imaginary indices of refraction respectively. The square of the complex refractive index is equivalent to the complex dielectric constants, which is related to the electrical constants such as the real and imaginary conductivities as given in Eq. (1) below :

CP893, *Physics of Semiconductors, 28th International Conference*
edited by W. Jantsch and F. Schäffler
© 2007 American Institute of Physics 978-0-7354-0397-0/07/$23.00

TABLE 1. Fitting parameter of the Drude model, Note: ω_p : Plasma frequency(THz), Γ : Damping rate(THz), n : the number of carrier density($\times 10^{16}$ cm^{-3}), μ : mobility (cm^2/Vs), n_s , the number of carrier density per unit area($\times 10^{11}$ cm^{-2})

Parameter	$\omega_p/2\pi$	$\Gamma/2\pi$	n	μ	n_s
with QDs	7.59	1.16	4.79	3601	1.07
Without QDs	8.10	0.81	5.45	5157	1.23

$$\varepsilon(\omega) = \varepsilon_{GaAs} + i\frac{\sigma(\omega)}{\omega\varepsilon_0}, \qquad (1)$$

where $\varepsilon(\omega)$ is the complex dielectric constant, ε_{GaAs} is the dielectric constant of GaAs at the infinity, $\sigma(\omega)$ is the conductivity, and ε_0 is the free space permittivity.

RESULTS

Fig.1 shows that the real conductivity of sample #1 is lower than that of the sample #2 as expected by the larger THz transmission by the sample #1. That implies that InAs/GaAs QDs act as charge traps and the electrons confined in the QDs are not mobile.

The complex conductivity of the semiconductors including free carriers is described by the Drude model as

$$\sigma(\omega) = i\varepsilon_0\omega_p^2/(\omega+i\Gamma), \qquad (2)$$

where ω_p , Γ are the plasma frequency and the damping rate, respectively. These parameters are obtained by the model fit to the experimental data as shown in Fig. 1, which yield the carrier densities (N) and mobilities (μ) with relations of $\mu = e/m^*\Gamma$ and $\omega_p^2 = Ne^2/\varepsilon_0 m^*$ where e is the unit charge, m^* is the effective mass of electrons. The fitting parameters are shown in Table 1. The carrier densities are 4.79×10^{16}cm^{-3} and 5.45×10^{16} cm^{-3} for the sample #1 and #2 at room temperature, respectively. Therefore, considering the total thickness of the epitaxial layers and the number of the modulation-doped layers, the carrier density trapped by the InAs/GaAs QD layer at room temperature is deduced to be 1.6×10^{10} cm^{-2}. We have also measured the THz absorption of sample #1 on various temperature conditions. As the temperature is lowered from 300K to 20K, the absorption decreases monotonically although a doped GaAs has the highest absorption at around 100K because of the highest electron mobility at the temperature. This means that the conductivity of sample #1 is reduced at lower temperatures because the QDs capture more electrons and, consequently, there are less free electrons.

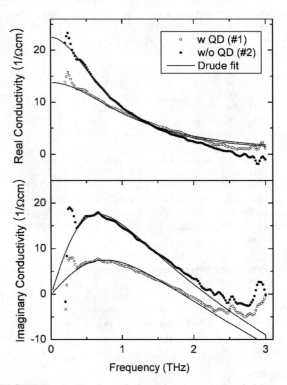

FIGURE 1. Real and imaginary conductivities of modulation-doped GaAs structures with and without InAs/GaAs QDs at room temperature.

CONCLUSIONS

We have studied the carrier transport dynamics of n-type modulation-doped InAs/GaAs QDs. The carrier densities and mobilities with and without QDs are obtained by the Drude model fit, whose differences originate from the carrier capure by QDs. And the THz absorption changes due to QDs on various temperature conditions are also shown.

REFERENCES

1. A. D. Stiff, S. Krishna, P. Bhattacharya and S. W. Kennerly, *IEEE J. Quantum Electron.*, **37**, 1412 (2001).
2. O. B. Shchekin and D. G. Deppe, *Appl. Phys. Lett*, **80**, 2758 (2002).
3. C. Kang, I. H. Maeng, S. J. Oh, J. -H. Son, T. –I. Jeon, K. H. An, S. C. Lim and Y. H. Lee, *Appl. Phys. Lett.*,**87**, 041908-1 (2005).

Effect of Carrier Migration on the Photoluminescence of CdTe/ZnTe Quantum-Dot Superlattices

Victor S. Bagaev[1], Evgeny E. Onishchenko[1], and Grzegorz Karczewski[2]

[1]P.N.Lebedev Physics Institute, Russian Academy of Sciences, Leninskii pr. 53, 119991 Moscow, Russia
[2]Institute of Physics, Polish Academy of Sciences, Al. Lotnikow 32/46, 02-668 Warszawa, Poland

Abstract. We have studied the photoluminescence of CdTe/ZnTe quantum-dot superlattices in a wide temperature range for different excitation power. It has been established that a drastic change of the luminescence spectra takes place for QD superlattices with thin ZnTe spacers already at low temperatures. This means that an intense carrier migration takes place as within clusters of ordered QDs so over the whole QD ensemble already at low temperatures. Such an unusual behavior can be explained on the base of the peculiarities of the CdTe/ZnTe system band-gap diagram.

Keywords: quantum dots, carrier migration, luminescence
PACS: 73.21.La, 78.55.-m, 78.67.Hc

INTRODUCTION

Studies of the temperature dependence of the optical properties of a self-assembled quantum dot (QD) ensemble can give information on how optically injected carriers are distributed within the ensemble and the processes which govern this distribution. We have studied the photoluminescence (PL) of CdTe/ZnTe quantum-dot multilayer structures in a wide temperature range for different excitation power. The peak position, width, and shape of PL band along with integrated PL intensity were analyzed.

EXPERIMENTAL DETAILS AND RESULTS

The QD superlattices were grown by MBE on semi-insulating GaAs (100) substrates. A ZnTe or CdTe buffer layer with thickness of about 5 μm was grown followed by QD superlattices consisting of different numbers of CdTe layers with a nominal thickness of 2.5 or 3 monolayers (ML) separated by ZnTe spacer layers with a definite thickness (ranged from 5 to 75 ML for different samples). A detailed description of samples grown on CdTe buffer layers and of those grown on ZnTe buffer layers can be found in [1] and [2], respectively. High-resolution transmission electron microscopy studies have shown

that in such structures an individual QD plane represents a layer of ZnCdTe solid solution containing Cd-enriched nanoislands (QDs). It was shown that in the case of ZnTe spacer with a thickness less than 25 ML, correlation in the QD positions appears both in the growth and lateral directions [3]. Regions of 3D-ordered QD clusters and areas of randomly distributed QDs coexist in such samples. Thus, there are both

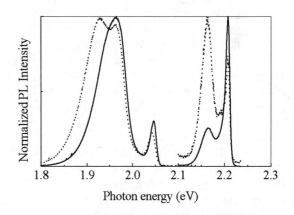

FIGURE 1. Normalized PL spectra of CdTe/ZnTe QD superlattices grown on CdTe (right; nominal thickness of CdTe layer – 2.5 ML, ZnTe spacer thickness – 12 ML) and ZnTe (left; nominal thickness of CdTe layer – 3 ML, ZnTe spacer thickness – 10 ML) buffer layer at the lowest (dotted line) and high (solid line) excitation power density at 5 K.

CP893, *Physics of Semiconductors, 28th International Conference*
edited by W. Jantsch and F. Schäffler
© 2007 American Institute of Physics 978-0-7354-0397-0/07/$23.00

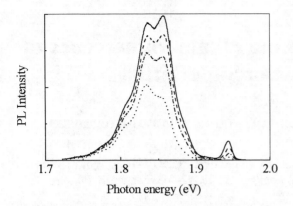

FIGURE 2. PL spectra of the CdTe/ZnTe QD superlattice with the thinnest ZnTe spacer at different temperatures: 5 K – solid line, 10 K – dashed line; 20 K – dashed-dotted line; 30 K – dotted line.

"isolated" (which have no closely spaced QDs in adjacent QD layers) and stacked QDs in the same sample.

An additional longer-wavelength emission band appears in the PL spectrum of QD structures with a rather small thickness of ZnTe spacer layers (Fig. 1). It can be attributed to excitons localized at correlated QDs in the adjacent QD planes. The main reasons of the position shift of the stacked QD emission band with respect to the emission band position of isolated QDs are a modification of QD strain state under QD stack formation and changes in QD size and composition. The additional emission band can have a rather complicated shape that changes significantly with excitation power (for the samples with thinnest ZnTe spacers). In this case the PL band peak position shifts to higher energy as the excitation power increases. This evidences that the coupling between QDs within a QD cluster takes place. It has been established also that even small temperature increase (up to 20-30 K) results in the substantial modification of this band shape (Fig. 2). Moreover, a change of the whole PL spectrum can occur in the samples with thin ZnTe spacers at low temperatures: in some samples the emission band of isolated QDs practically disappears from the PL spectrum at 30-40 K. It means that an intense carrier migration takes place as within clusters of ordered QDs so over the whole QD ensemble already at such low temperatures.

The behavior observed can be explained on the base of the peculiarities of CdTe/ZnTe system band-gap diagram. It is known that changes in the temperature dependence of the peak position energy and spectral width of a QD emission band are governed by thermally stimulated carrier transfer processes and hence depend on the depth of the confining potential. Valence-band offset for the CdTe/ZnTe system is controlled mainly by elastic strain caused by the large lattice mismatch between CdTe and ZnTe. Respectively, the depth of a potential well for holes in QD is determined by elastic strain to a great extent. Variation of sample parameters (a buffer layer material, a thickness of barrier layers and so on) should lead to the change of the QD superlattice strain state and, consequently, affects strongly the potential well depth for holes. For the QD samples with thin ZnTe spacers, ZnCdTe layers containing CdTe islands are less strained with respect to the samples with relatively thick spacers. Correspondingly, a potential well depth for heavy holes in QDs decreases for such samples (specifically, in some structures the potential well depth for a hole is determined mainly by Coulomb interaction with an electron). In particular, it reveals itself in decrease of the activation energy of PL quenching with a ZnTe spacer thickness decrease. A small value of the activation energy means that even a slight temperature increase is able to stimulate the thermal escape of a hole from a particular QD and, hence, to stimulate holes migration within QD ensemble. It leads to rapid redistribution of carriers (and excitons) within QD ensemble with the temperature increase (carrier migration between QDs favors a drift of carriers toward larger QDs having lower emission energy) and, consequently, to a drastic change of the QD superlattice emission spectra.

In conclusion, we have shown that, due to the pecularities of CdTe/ZnTe system band-gap diagram, an intense carrier migration (both in lateral and in growth direction) takes place in CdTe/ZnTe QD superlattices with small thicknesses of ZnTe spacer layers already at low temperatures. It causes a rather unusual temperature dependence of such QD superlattice photoluminescence.

REFERENCES

1. E. E. Onishchenko, V. S. Bagaev, V. V. Zaitsev, E. I. Makhov, *Physica E* **26**, 153 (2005).
2. E. E. Onishchenko, V. S. Bagaev, G. Karczewski S. P. Kozyrev, I. V. Kucherenko, N. N. Mel'nik, V. S. Vinogradov, L. K. Vodop'yanov. *Phys.Stat.Solidi (c)* **3**, 881 (2006).
3. S. Mackowski, G. Karczewski, T. Woitowitz, J. Kossut, S. Kret, A. Szczepanska, G. Prechtl, W. Heiss, *Appl. Phys. Lett.* **78**, 3884 (2001).

Resonant Raman scattering on optical phonons confined in spherical semiconductor nanocrystals: ODP interaction and polaron effects

A.G. Rolo[1], R.P. Miranda[1], M.I. Vasilevskiy[1] and C. Trallero-Giner[2]

[1] Centro de Física, Universidade do Minho, Campus de Gualtar 4710-057 Braga, Portugal
[2] Departamento de Física Teórica, Universidad de La Habana, Vedado 10400, La Habana, Cuba

Theoretical and experimental results concerning Raman-active optical phonon modes and exciton-phonon (e-ph) interaction in nearly spherical nanocrystals (NC's) of II-VI and III-V semiconductors are presented. A continuum lattice dynamics model for confined phonons and the effective mass approximation for electronic states in the NC's were used in the calculations. Both Fröhlich and optical deformation potential (ODP) mechanisms of the e-ph interaction were considered. Based on the computed e-ph interaction constants, Raman spectra have been calculated within standard perturbation theory and polaron approaches. The experimental studies were performed on NC films fabricated using wet chemistry methods. The results, as well as those obtained for other NC systems, published in the literature, are in good agreement with the theoretical predictions.

Keywords: phonon, exciton, quantum dot, Raman scattering
PACS: 78.67.DE; 63.22.+m; 63.20.Kr

INTRODUCTION

During the last decade, several techniques have shown the ability to produce nanometer-sized crystalline particles of several elemental, II-VI and III-V semiconductor materials. From the point of view of their electronic properties, semiconductor NC's are quantum dots (QD's) with narrow atomic-like energy spectra as demonstrated by single QD spectroscopy experiments [1]. The e-h states in QD's can be described in the framework of the effective mass approximation (EMA) starting from the bulk material electronic structure [2] unless the NC's are too small (~1nm in size).

Phonons in QD's have also been studied in detail, although to a less extent than electrons and holes. Their importance is determined by the role played by the electron-phonon (e-ph) interaction in several optical and transport phenomena. One of the fundamental questions about phonons is the applicability of bulk crystal lattice dynamics to NC's containing just several hundreds of atoms. Secondly, are the electron-phonon (e-ph) interaction mechanisms the same in QD's as in the bulk materials? From a more applied point of view, there are at least two reasons to study phonons in QD's. First, to what extent is the Raman spectroscopy, the most common technique to study phonons, sensitive to QD size and crystalline quality? We tried to answer these questions by means of experimental and theoretical work that took several years. In this communication, we present an overview of our results concerning optical phonons confined in nearly spherical NC's of polar (II-VI and III-V) semiconductor materials.

THEORETICAL BACKGROUND

Spatial quantization of optical phonon modes in a spherical QD was considered theoretically on the basis of a continuous equation of motion, originally proposed in Ref. [3], and a Poisson equation for the electrostatic potential coupled to the mechanical displacement. Solving these coupled equations in spherical coordinates and applying appropriate boundary conditions allow one to obtain a complete set of confined optical phonon modes (see, for example, Ref. [4]). These modes are classified according to three "spherical" quantum numbers n, l and m. It is important to note that the confined optical phonon modes have a mixed longitudinal-transverse-interface nature. They are degenerate with respect to m unless anisotropy of the QD material is taken into account. It can be shown from general symmetry consideration that modes with $l=0,2$ are Raman-active if the underlying e-ph interaction is of the Fröhlich type, i.e, proportional to the (scalar) electrostatic potential [5].

With the EMA wavefunctions known for the lowest exciton states in a QD made of a typical zinc-blend material [2], the calculation of the e-ph matrix elements is straightforward. Given these, one can apply the formalism presented, for example, in Ref. [5] to calculate the Raman cross-section under resonance conditions. It turns out, however, that, because of the discrete nature of the exciton states in QD's and the intensity of the e-ph interaction, polaron corrections to the energy spectrum are important [6]. It is more secure to calculate Raman scattering spectra within a non-perturbative approach based on the polaron concept as proposed in Ref. [7].

For some materials, such as InP, another e-ph interaction mechanism can be important, namely the optical deformation potential (ODP) one. The Hamiltonian of this interaction is proportional to the displacement and the proportionality coefficient is a vector of (4×4) matrices (see e.g. [8]). Consequently, phonon modes with $l=1,3$ are Raman-active via this mechanism.

RESULTS AND DISCUSSION

The main results can be summarized as follows:
(i) For most polar materials the Fröhlich type e-ph interaction in NC's is by far the most important. In this case, only $l=0$ and $l=2$ phonon modes (with different n) contribute to the scattering. The latter is only active for the cross polarization configuration. Since the most intensively scattering modes have the frequencies just a few cm^{-1} below the bulk optical phonon frequency, it is not possible to resolve them experimentally because of the NC size distribution. In practical terms, for instance, for probing the NC size and shape deviations, it can be an advantage to excite many exciton states (instead of resonantly exciting just the ground state) because the analysis of the Raman lineshape is simpler in this case [9].

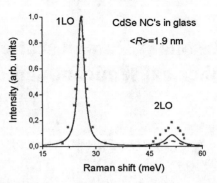

FIGURE 1. Raman scattering spectra calculated in the perturbation theory (dashed line) and polaron approaches (solid line). The points are experimental data from Ref. [5].

(ii) The Raman spectra of InP NC's, for a wide range of NC sizes, exhibit two intense modes and not just one as it takes place for II-VI QD's. The puzzling second (TO-type) mode is accounted for the strong ODP e-ph interaction in this material and its lower ionicity, comparing to the II-VI semiconductors. The $l=1$ TO-type modes give considerable contribution to the Raman scattering and are responsible for the peculiar spectral peak.

(iii) The most important polaron effect in the Raman scattering is the enhancement of the higher order (2LO and 3LO) modes, compared to the standard perturbation theory results. Taking it into account allows for a better description of previously published experimental dats on multiphonon scattering by CdSe QD's as shown in Fig. 1.

ACKNOWLEDGMENT

Travel support from the Calouste Gulbenkian Foundation is acknowledged.

REFERENCES

1. S. A. Empedocles, D. J. Norris and M. G. Bawendi, Phys. Rev. Lett. **77**, 3873 (1996).
2. Al. L. Efros et al, *Phys. Rev.* B **54**, 4843 (1996).
3. M. Barbiker, *J. Phys. C* **19**, 683 (1986).
4. M. I. Vasilevskiy, *Phys. Rev.* B **66**, 195326 (2002).
5. R. Rodriguez-Suarez et al, *Phys. Rev.* B **62**, 11006 (2000).
6. M. I. Vasilevskiy, E. V. Anda and S. S. Makler, *Phys. Rev.* B **70**, 35318 (2004).
7. M. I. Vasilevskiy, R. .P. Miranda, E. V. Anda and S. S. Makler, *Semicond. Sci.Technol.* **19**, S312 (2004).
8. A. Dargys, *Semicond. Sci.Technol.* **20**, 733 (2005).
9. M. I. Vasilevskiy et al, *J. Phys.: Condens. Matter* **13**, 3491 (2001).

Micro-photoluminescence of isolated hexagonal GaN/AlN quantum dots : role of the electron-hole dipole

R. Bardoux[1], T. Guillet[1], P. Lefebvre[1], T. Taliercio[1],
T. Bretagnon[1], B. Gil[1] and F. Semond[2]

[1] *Groupe d'Etude des Semiconducteurs - CNRS - Université Montpellier II.*
CC 074. Place Eugène Bataillon. F-34095 Montpellier Cedex 5. France
[2] *Centre de Recherche pour l'Hétéro-Epitaxie et ses Applications - CNRS.*
Rue Bernard Grégory. F-06560 Valbonne. France

Abstract. We present single dot spectroscopy of hexagonal GaN/AlN self-assembled quantum dots (QDs) grown by MBE along the (0001) axis. The GaN quantum dots are grown on an AlN epilayer on Si (111) substrate, with dot densities between 10^8 and 10^{11} cm^{-2}. We study the micro-photoluminescence spectra of a few quantum dots. In the energy range corresponding to the smaller dots we observe several groups of peaks, each group corresponding to the emission of a unique quantum dot. These groups are identified through their time-correlated spectral diffusion. The measured linewidth of the transition is 2 meV (resolution limited).

Keywords: Quantum dot, GaN. micro-photoluminescence, spectral diffusion
PACS: 78.55-m, 78.67.Hc, 73.21.La, 78.55.Cr

Group III nitride quantum dots (QDs) have attracted a lot of attention for their light emitting properties in the blue and UV range. The understanding of the spectroscopy of a single quantum dot is of great interest for the comprehension of their radiative recombination, especially for the realization of single photon sources. Among them, hexagonal GaN/AlN self-assembled QDs are polar due to the large internal electric field, leading to an important electron-hole dipole and a strong modification of the recombination dynamics compared to non-polar QDs [1].

We present here the study of the micro-photoluminescence (μPL) of single QDs and the influence of the environment on their spectra. The GaN QDs are grown on an AlN epilayer on Si (111) substrate and covered with an AlN cap layer. A misorientation angle of the substrate allows us to control the dot density between 10^8 and 10^{11} cm^{-2}. A macro-photoluminescence study shows two populations in the QD height distribution, one around 2.8nm (3.2eV) and a second are around 1.6nm (3.7eV). The samples are then covered with an aluminium mask presenting 0.5 μm diameter apertures in order to isolate a few QDs.

Figure 1.a presents the μPL spectrum obtained on one of the apertures of the mask. The sample is excited with a continuous frequency-doubled Argon laser at 244 nm (5.07 eV). Sharp peaks are observed as well as a broad background. The sharp peaks originate from the QDs present beneath the aperture. We associate the broad underlying spectrum, which is similar to the tail of the macro-PL spectrum, to neighboring QDs which are not properly discriminated by the mask.

Figure 1.b presents the time evolution of this μPL spectrum over 3000 s. The energy of each peak exhibits continuous and discrete variations of the order of 1 meV. The white rectangles indicate well-resolved fluctuations which are observed for 2 or 3 of the peaks only. These fluctuations, called spectral diffusion, are related to slight modifications of the electrostatic environment of the QDs, which modify the local electric field and induce small Stark shifts of the transition energy, as already observed in II-VI QDs [2,3].

The fact that the 3 transitions labeled A_1, A_2 and A_3 fluctuate in the same way at the same time shows that they are associated to excitons (or excitonic complexes, e.g. X^+, X^-) experiencing the same local electric field, i.e. they originate from the same QD. Similarly, the transitions C_1 and C_2 are associated to a second QD C, distinct from QD A. The transitions labeled B do not present clear shifts, so that we cannot conclude whether one or more QDs are involved. Fig 1

CP893, *Physics of Semiconductors, 28th International Conference*
edited by W. Jantsch and F. Schäffler

therefore presents the spectrum of 3 or 4 QDs, each one emitting at different energies separated by 3 to 7 meV. These transitions are usually related to different excitonic complexes in II-VI QDs, however we cannot exclude other explanations, like the excitonic fine structure. Further studies are required in order to unambiguously identify them.

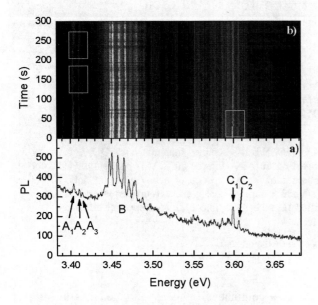

FIGURE 1. a) µPL spectrum of a few GaN QDs; b) Time evolution (false colors) of this spectrum over 3000s, with an acquisition time of 10 s.

Spectral diffusion occurs on different timescales, and we have here exhibited its signature over seconds to minutes. When this spectral diffusion takes place faster than the acquisition time of the spectra, it induces an inhomogeneous broadening of the transitions. This explains the rather large line-widths (10 meV) observed in polar GaN QDs up to now [4]. Here we observe much smaller line-widths, down to our experimental resolution of 2 meV in fig. 1, and 1 meV in other spectra obtained on the same sample.

In conclusion, we were able to isolate a few GaN/AlN QDs and to study their spectra in µPL. We identified the peaks related to the same QD by analyzing their spectral diffusion. The detailed understanding of these transitions will be the object of further investigations.

REFERENCES

1. T. Bretagnon, P. Lefebvre, P. Valvin, R. Bardoux, T. Guillet, T. Taliercio, B. Gil, N. Grandjean, F. Semond, B. Damilano, A. Dussaigne, and J. Massies, *Phys. Rev. B* **73**, 113304 (2006)

2. V. Türck, S. Rodt, O. Stier, R. Heitz, R. Engelhardt, U. W. Pohl, D. Bimberg, and R. Steingrüber, *Phys. Rev. B* **61**, 9944 (2000).
3. L. Besombes, K. Kheng, L. Marsal, and H. Mariette, *Phys. Rev. B* **65**, 121314 (2002)
4. T. Nakaoka, S. Kako, and Y. Arakawa, *Phys. Rev. B* **73**, 121305 (2006)

Photoluminescent Properties of InAs Quantum Dots Grown by MOVPE on an $In_xAl_yGa_{1-x-y}As$ Layer and their Dependence on the Layer Stoichiometry

Julio G. Mendoza-Alvarez[1], Mauricio P. Pires[2], Sandra M. Landi[2], Patricia L. Souza[2], Jose M. Villas-Boas[3], Nelson Studart[4]

[1]*Departamento de Fisica. Cinvestav-IPN. Apdo. Postal 14-740. Mexico DF 07000. Mexico*
[2]*Labsem, CETUC, PUC-Rio. Marques de Sao Vicente 225, Rio de Janeiro. Brazil*
[3]*Department of Physics and Astronomy. Ohio University, Athens, Ohio 45701-2979. USA*
[4]*Departamento de Fisica. Universidade Federal de Sao Carlos, SP, 13565-905. Brazil*

Abstract. In this paper we report on the growth, using MOVPE (Metal Organic Vapor Phase Epitaxy), of a layer of InAs quantum dots (QDs) on top of quaternary layers of $In_{0.53}Al_yGa_{0.47-y}As$ lattice-matched to InP substrates, with a variable stoichiometry due to the variation in the Al concentration. It has been recently reported that as the Al concentration in the quaternary layer increases, smaller InAs QDs are obtained, and also that the peak of the luminescence emission shifts to longer wavelengths up to around 2.1 microns [1]. In this work we present results on the PL characterization for a set of InAs QDs/$In_{0.53}Al_yGa_{0.43-y}As$ samples, for aluminum concentrations of y = 0, 0.058, 0.11 and 0.165. PL spectra were measured changing the laser excitation power and the sample temperature in the range from 16K up to room temperature. From the analysis of the PL spectra we observe that at low temperatures the emission band is composed of two contributions centered at around 0.64 and 0.673 eV which shift to higher energies as the Al concentration in the layer increases as a result of the increase in the energy barrier height between the dot and the InAlGaAs layer. We discuss the nature of the transitions involved in the PL bands and their behavior with the laser power and temperature, using a 1D theoretical model that takes into account the energy position of the quantized electronic levels in the InAs QDs due to the band offsets and to the strain effects at the InAlGaAs-InAsQD-InP interfaces.

Keywords: Optical properties of quantum dots; MOVPE-growth of InAs QDs; self-assembly quantum dots
PACS: 78.67.Hc; 81.15.Gh; 81.16.Dn

INTRODUCTION

The use of InP substrates instead of GaAs has made it possible to reach wavelengths emissions for InAs QDs layer of up to 1.9 microns, suitable for fiber optic communication systems and infrared devices. The application of these InAs QDs for optoelectronic devices requires the achievement of samples with a high density of QDs with a narrow size distribution and good optical properties. It is also desirable to get a large refractive index change between the InAs QDs active region and the semiconductor layer behind them to improve the temperature characteristics, because of a wider energy separation of the quantum confined levels, and a deep potential well. This can be accomplish growing the InAs QDs layer on top of a semiconductor with a wider bandgap energy than the traditional InGaAs lattice-matched to InP, such as a quaternary layer of $In_{0.53}Al_yGa_{0.47-y}As$ with a stoichiometry such that it is lattice-matched to InP.

EXPERIMENTAL

Samples were grown by MOVPE with phosphine (PH_3), arsine (AsH_3), trimethyl-indium (TMI), trimethyl-gallium (TMG), and trimethyl-aluminum (TMA) as precursors, and hydrogen as carrier gas. Fe-doped (SI) InP (001) wafers were used as substrates. A 150 nm-thick InP buffer layer was grown initially at 630 °C after which the reactor was cooled-down to 600 °C; then a 500 nm-thick $In_{0.53}Al_yGa_{0.47-y}As$ was grown with a III/V ratio of 30. The temperature was ramped-down to 500 °C during a 5-minutes period without growth to keep the well-defined terrace structure before dot deposition. 2.5ML InAs dot material was deposited on the surface at a growth rate of 0.5ML/s and then the surface was annealed for 12 s under an

CP893, *Physics of Semiconductors, 28th International Conference*
edited by W. Jantsch and F. Schäffler
© 2007 American Institute of Physics 978-0-7354-0397-0/07/$23.00

arsine flow. At this point, the samples were either cooled down under arsine containing atmosphere, or capped with 50nm InP during which the temperature was ramped up to 600 °C. A set of samples with four values of Al concentration was grown, for y-values of: 0.0, 0.058, 0.11 and 0.165. For the photoluminescence (PL) measurements, the 488 nm-line of an Ar^+ laser was used as the exciting source, and a LN_2-cooled Ge photodetector couple to a lock-in amplifier was used to detect the PL emission from the InAs QD's.

RESULTS AND DISCUSSION

The PL spectra samples with different Al concentration in the InAlGaAs layer are shown in Fig. 1. For the InAs QD layer grown on an $In_{0.53}Ga_{0.47}As$ layer, the PL spectrum show a band centered at 0.64 eV and a shoulder at 0.673 eV, with FWHM values of 25 and 17 meV, which is an indication that the layer of InAs QDs has a good crystalline quality.

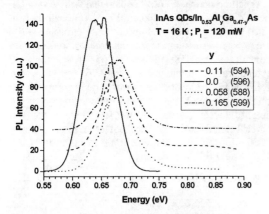

FIGURE 1. PL spectra for the InAs QD layers grown on top of an InAlGaAs layer for various Al concentrations.

For the InAs QD layers grown on quaternary InAlGaAs layers, there is a blue-shift to higher energies to around 0.68-0.69 eV due to the shift of the quantized energy levels inside the dot to higher energies because of the increase in the energy barriers of the QD when the Al concentration increases in the quaternary layer.

For the InAs QD layer (sample 588) grown on the $In_{0.53}Al_{0.11}Ga_{0.36}As$ layer, there is a peak at 0.675 eV, a shoulder at 0.72 eV and a broad band at 0.82 eV; we assign the main peak as due to the e_1-hh_1 transition, the shoulder to the e_1-lh_1, and the broad band as due to radiative emission from the $In_{0.53}Al_{0.11}Ga_{0.36}As$ layer. For a 5-fold increase in the laser power excitation the transition energy peaks remained essentially the same, and the ratio between the intensity from the e_1-lh_1 and the e_1-hh_1 increases by a factor of four, probably indicating a saturation effect of the heavy holes-related states.

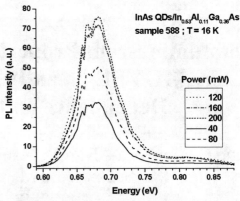

FIGURE 2. Dependence of the PL spectra for sample 588 on the laser power excitation.

We have used a simple 1D effective-mass model for the InP/InGaAlAs/InAs/InP structure as shown in Fig. 3. The calculation of the band structure takes into account the strain fields which are produced around the InAs QDs due to the difference in lattice constants between the InAs, the InGaAlAs and the InP layers. We have calculated the band offset using the method as described by Su-Huai Wei and Alex Zunger [2]. The parameters we use are taken from ref. [3] and we used an interpolation to obtain the parameter for the quaternary compound. To obtain the eigenstates for both valence and conduction band we expanded the effective potential in a base of a large quantum well and diagonalized the effective Hamiltonian. We truncated our bases when the eigenvalues had converged with certain precision.

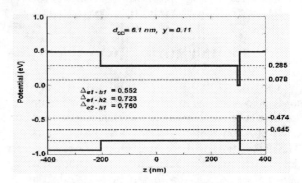

FIGURE 3. Energy levels for the InAs QD grown on an InAlGaAs layer and covered by a 50 nm-thick InP layer.

REFERENCES

1. M. Borgstrom, M.P. Pires, T. Bryllert, S. Landi, W. Seifert, P.L. Souza, *J. Cryst. Growth* **252**, 481-485 (2003)
2. Su-Huai Wei and Alex Zunger, *Appl. Phys. Lett,* **72**, 2011-2013 (1998)
3. I. Vurgaftmana, J.R. Meyer, and L.R. Ram-Mohan, *J. Appl. Phys* **89**, 5815 (2001).

Electron-Hole Separation of Zero-Dimensional Excitons in A Single Self-Organized InAs Quantum Dot Studied Under Normal and In-Plane Electric Fields

M. Ohmori, K. Torii, N. Kondo, and H. Sakaki

Institute of Industrial Science, University of Tokyo, 4-6-1 Komaba, Meguro-ku, Tokyo, 153- 8505, Japan

Abstract. The Stark shift of a single self-organized InAs quantum dot is measured under the top and side gate voltages using a novel GaAs mesa structure. By measuring the shift as a function of the top gate voltage, we estimate the electron-hole separation in a dot along the growth direction. It is shown that this separation changes quite sensitively when the side gate voltage is applied. Possible mechanisms are discussed.

Keywords: Quantum dot, Stark effect
PACS: 78.55.Cr, 78.67.Hc, 73.21.-b

INTRODUCTION

A zero-dimensional exciton confined in a single self-organized InAs quantum dot (QD) has been extensively investigated because of its importance both in fundamental physics and applications, including QD-based single photon emitters [1] and detectors [2]. Earlier works have shown that the electron-hole pair in such a QD is often polarized, as the built-in strain and/or the local accumulation of In atoms around the dot modify the confining potential [3]. Hence, one needs to clarify why and how such an exciton is polarized and establish ways to control the spatial separation of electron and hole. Here we report our attempt to control the polarization state of a QD exciton by placing a single InAs QD in a novel GaAs mesa structure.

SAMPLE AND EXPERIMENT

The wafer for our sample was grown by molecular beam epitaxy on a highly doped n$^+$ GaAs (100) wafer, which acts as a back contact. The InAs QD layer is placed in the middle of a 400 nm thick GaAs layer, which is sandwiched by 400 nm thick (substrate side) and 180 nm thick (top side) GaAs/AlGaAs (2 nm/18 nm) superlattice buffer layers. These buffer layers prevent the perpendicular carrier flow. The top part of the sample is covered by a 20 nm thick GaAs cap layer. To facilitate single QD spectroscopy, the density of QDs was controlled to be as low as about 1×10^6 cm^{-2}

by employing the post-growth-annealing technique [4]. Figure 1 shows a schematic crossectional view of our InAs QD sample shaped into an inverted mesa structure. We formed a top and two side contacts by depositing a 5-nm-thick semitransparent NiCr layer. Photo-luminescence (PL) spectra of the QD were recorded at $T = 11$ K using He-Ne laser as excitation source.

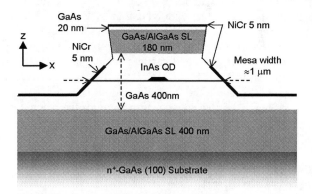

FIGURE 1. Schematic cross-sectional view of the sample. An InAs QD is embedded in an inverted mesa structure with three NiCr Schottky electrodes.

RESULT AND DISCUSSION

Figure 2 shows the Stark shift of PL from the ground state exciton measured as a function of top gate voltage V_T under various side gate voltages V_S. Parabolic fits to the data for each shift are also shown.

CP893, *Physics of Semiconductors, 28th International Conference*
edited by W. Jantsch and F. Schäffler
© 2007 American Institute of Physics 978-0-7354-0397-0/07/$23.00

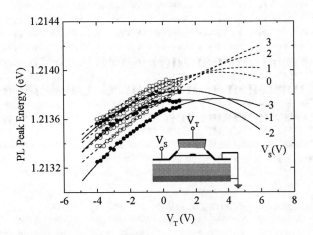

FIGURE 2. The Stark shift induced by the top gate voltage V_T measured under various side gate voltages V_S.

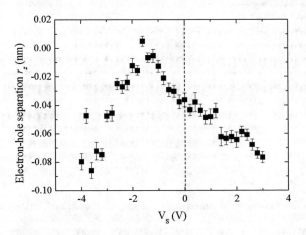

FIGURE 3. The side gate voltage dependence of electron-hole separation r_z.

The Stark shift data are well described by $E_p(F) = E_0 + pF + \beta F^2$, where p and β represent the permanent exciton dipole and the polarizability of the state, respectively [3]. We evaluate the growth direction (z-axis) component of dipole by assuming that the QD is located at the center of the mesa, and by calculating the electric field F_z, including a built-in electric field of the Schottky contact.

The electron-hole separation $r_z = p_z/e$ is determined as a function of V_S and plotted in Fig. 3. The negative sign of r_z implies that the electron component of the wave function lie below the hole at $F_z = 0$. At $V_S = 0$ V, r_z is found to be about -0.04 nm, which is much smaller than the value reported earlier by Fry et al. [3]. This indicates that the actual electric field is suppressed on our sample by some mechanisms; for example, photo-generated carriers accumulated at the top and bottom GaAs/AlGaAs hetero junctions may substantially screen the field. We should consider also the influence of the voltage drop through the Ohmic loss of NiCr thin electrode since it may reduce the bias effect.

Note that, when $V_S > 0$, $|r_z|$ increases from 0.04 to 0.08 nm. It should be also noted that, when $V_S < 0$, $|r_z|$ decreases to almost 0 nm at $V_S = -1.6$ V, and then increases as V_S. This asymmetry is likely to result from the asymmetric position of the QD and built-in electric field. If the position of the QD is on the right hand side in the mesa structure, the internal electric field has an in-plane component along the direction of the x-axis in Fig. 1. Therefore, in-plane electric field F_x is zero at $V_S = -1.6$ V.

It is quite notable that the electron-hole separation $|r_z|$ increases as $|F_x|$. This means that the application of in-plane electric fields enhances the z-component of the electron-hole separation. This suggests that, as the in-plane field increases, the hole moves toward the upper edge of truncated pyramidal dot [5], where the confinement is locally enhanced possibly due to the local accumulation of strains and/or indium atoms.

In summary, the Stark spectroscopy on a single InAs quantum dot in the presence of both normal and in-plane electric fields has been performed and analyzed. It has been found that the electron-hole separation of a zero-dimensional exciton in the dot is influenced sensitively by in-plane electric fields, suggesting the complexed spatial distributions of both strains and the In composition in this system.

ACKNOWLEDGMENTS

The authors express sincere thanks for the following four grants: the Grant-in-Aid for Special Promotion Research on "Quantum Dots", the Grant-in-Aid for Scientific Research on "Quantum Rings", the MEXT IT Program, and the 21C. COE Program.

REFERENCES

1. Z. Yuan, B. E. Kardyna, R. M. Stevenson, A. J. Shields, C. J. Lobo, K. Cooper, N. S. Beattie, D. A. Ritchie, and M. Pepper, *Science* **295**, 102 (2002).
2. A. J. Shields, M. P. O'Sullivanb, I. Farrer, D. A. Ritchie, R. A. Hogg, M. L. Leadbeater, C. E. Norman and M. Pepperb, *Appl. Phys. Lett.* **76** 3673 (2000).
3. P. W. Fry, E. Itskevich, D. J. Mowbray, M. S. Skolnick, J. J. Finley, J. A. Barker, E. P. O'Reilly, L. R. Wilson, I. A. Larkin, P. A. Maksym, M. Hopkinson, M. Al-Khafaji, J. P. R. David, A. G. Cullis, G. Hill, and J. C. Clark, *Phys. Rev. Lett.* **84**, 733 (2000).
4. I. Kamiya, I. Tanaka, O. Ohtsuki, and H. Sakaki, *Physica E* **13**, 1172 (2002).
5. D. M. Bruls, J. W. A. M. Vugs, P. M. Koenraad, H. W. M. Salemink, and J. H. Wolter, *Appl. Phys. Lett.* **81** 1708 (2002).

Observation of PL intensity modulation in self-assembled Quantum Rings (QR) under strong pulsed magnetic fields

Alfonso G. Taboada[1], Daniel Granados[1], Victor V. Moshchalkov[2], Manus Hayne[2,3] and Jorge M. García[1]

1 Instituto de Microelectronica de Madrid, CNM-CSIC, Tres Cantos, Spain
2 Katholieke Universitiet Leuven, Celestijnenlaan 200D, B-3001 Leuven Belgium
3 Lancaster University, Lancaster LA1 4YB, UK

Abstract. We present photoluminescence (PL) measurements of self-assembled In(Ga)As QRs in strong pulsed magnetic fields. The results show a striking modulation of the intensity. This modulation of the emission can be attributed to an effect predicted by Govorov et al.: a mechanism for the topological phase of a neutral particle, a polarized exciton confined to a semiconductor quantum ring. The magnetic-field induced phase strongly affects the excitons in the QR, resulting in switching between bright exciton ground states and novel dark states.

Keywords: Quantum Rings, Quantum dots, Aharonov-Bohm effect, Magneto-Photoluminescence.
PACS: 68.65.Hb, 68.65.-k, 75.45.+j, 78.20.Ls, 78.30.Fs

INTRODUCTION

The optical Aharonov-Bohm [1] effect originates from the difference between the phases acquired by the electron and hole wave functions as the magnetic flux threads a ring. It is possible to fabricate defect free self-assembled quantum rings (QR) from an original layer of self-assembled quantum dots (QD) in which these phase effects can be tested, such a modification on the emission intensity and exciton lifetime. Due to their different effective masses the electron and hole are polarized in the radial direction and confine different number of magnetic flux quanta in their different trajectories. It is predicted [2] that this will produce a strong modulation of the oscillator strength of the excitonic transition, giving rise to theoretical "dark windows" when the applied magnetic field is changed.

EXPERIMENTAL SET-UP

The samples are grown by solid source molecular beam epitaxy (MBE). Self-assembled quantum rings are fabricated by partially capping an original layer of quantum dots with a thin layer of 2 nm thick of GaAs. Details of the growth of the quantum dots (QD) and quantum rings (QR) can be obtained elsewhere [3]. The QR or QD are embedded between a GaAs tunnel barrier 25 nm thick; and a 30 nm GaAs layer followed by an AlAs/GaAs short period super lattice (SPSL). The thickness of this barrier is 150nm. A highly silicon doped (2×10^{18} cm^{-3}) GaAs layer is first grown as a back-contact for these sample as they have also been used for capacitance-spectroscopy measurements. The QR density is approximately 5×10^{9}cm^{-3}.

Magneto-Photoluminescence (M-PL) has been performed with pulsed fields of ~30 msec and up to 50 T generated by a bank of capacitors which are discharged in a coil around the sample in a cryostat at liquid helium (4K) or at 2K when the cryostat is pumped. An optical fiber transports the excitation signal of an Ar laser. A bundle of fibers collect the M-PL emission and is guided to a CCD camera which can sample up to 127 spectra during the magnetic pulse. Pumping power of QR samples has been selected so only one contribution from the fundamental states is observed. The magnetic field is applied perpendicular to the surface of the sample, i.e. parallel to the growth direction (001) and perpendicular to the ensemble of rings. The homogeneity of the size distribution of rings is estimated both from separate PL and Atomic Force Microscope (AFM) measurements to be better than 10%.

RESULTS

The M-PL results of an ensemble of QD are presented in figure 1. A colored contour plot is employed to display all the PL spectra in an uprising part of a magnetic field shot. A monotonous increase of the position of the PL maxima is observed. This maximum can be fitted using an excitonic model [4] to a function with a parabolic contribution in the low field regime and a linear part for high fields. The same results have been reported in similar types of QD and correspond to the diamagnetic shift competition between magnetic

CP893, *Physics of Semiconductors, 28th International Conference*
edited by W. Jantsch and F. Schäffler
© 2007 American Institute of Physics 978-0-7354-0397-0/07/$23.00

length confinement and the confinement potential of the nanostructure, from which the exciton radius and effective mass can be extracted.

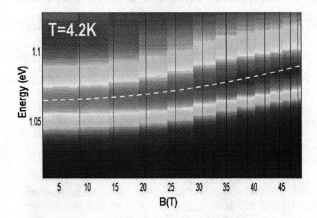

FIGURE 1. Contour plot for a QD sample. No oscillations are observed. Dashed line i

Table 1 shows these values compared to the ones extracted in a similar analysis performed with a QR sample.

TABLE 1. Exciton radius measured by M-PL.

Nanostructure	Exciton radius	Effective mass
QD	5.21 nm	$0.134m_0$
QR	6.33 nm	$0.110m_0$

Figure 2 displays the M-PL data for a QR sample. Clear modulation on the intensity is observed at 22T, also around 38T there is another subtle effect.

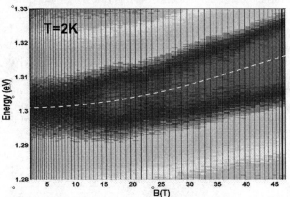

FIGURE 2. Contour plot for a QR sample. Oscillations in intensity are observed at 22T and at 38T.

The variations in the intensity can also be clearly observed in figure 3-a. The PL intensity is plotted vs. the magnetic field. An oscillation is observed at 22T and traces of a non monotonous behavior around 38T. Figure 3-b is a plot of the difference between the experimental data of three different measurements and

the fit to the model employed to describe the modeled QD diamagnetic shift. Clear signature of an oscillatory behavior is observed at 22T and at ~38 T.

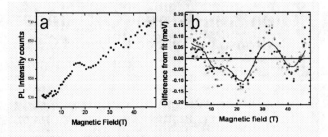

FIGURE 3. a) Intensity plot of PL vs. Magnetic Field. As observed in figure 2, there are oscillations in the intensity. b) Plot of the difference between the experimental data of three different measurements and the fit to the model employed to describe the modeled QD diamagnetic shift. The blue line is the smoothed average of the three measurements. A clear signature of an oscillatory behavior is observed at 22T and at ~38 T.

CONCLUSIONS

Magneto-PL has been measured in a sample fabricated with self-assembled quantum rings. Clear deviations of the behaviour of the QR sample respect to the QD sample are observed. A possible mechanism for the oscillation in the intensity is the Aharanov-Bohm effect related to the electrons and the holes trapping different amounts of magnetic flux, and leading to the existence of dark excitonic windows. This is a clear signature of a non-trivially connected geometry of the confinement potential which reveals the quantum nature of the ensemble of mesoscopic system.

ACKNOWLEDGMENTS

Projects: NANOSELF-II (TEC2005-05781-C03-01), NANOCOMIC (S 0505ESP 0200), NANIC (NA2004-09109-C04-01), INGENIO 2010-Consolider QOIT (CSD2006-00019), by SANDIE (Contract nº NMP4-CT-2004-500101) and EC EuroMagNET (Contract no. RII3-CT-2004-506239).

REFERENCES

1. Y. Aharonov and D. Bohm, Phys. Rev 11,485-91(1959)
2. A.O. Govorov, S.E. Ulloa, K. Karrai and R.J. Warburton PRB 66, 0831309 (R) (2002).
3. D. Granados and J.M. García, Applied Physics Letters. 82, 2401 (2003)
4. Hayne et al., Physica B 346-347, 421 (2004)

Observation of a Long-Range Interaction between Semiconductor Quantum Dots

E.W. Bogaart, J.E.M. Haverkort, and R. Nötzel

Eindhoven University of Technology, Department of Applied Physics
P.O. Box 513, 5600MB Eindhoven, The Netherlands

Abstract. We demonstrate electromagnetic interaction between distant quantum dots (QDs), as is observed from transient pump-probe differential reflectivity measurements. The QD-exciton lifetime is measured as a function of the probe photon energy and shows a strong resonant behavior with respect to the QD density of states. The observed exciton lifetime spectrum reveals a subradiance-like coupling between the QD, with a 12 times enhancement of the lifetime at the center of the ground state transition. This effect is due to a mutual electromagnetic coupling between resonant QDs, which extends over distances considerably beyond the nearest neighbor QD-QD separation.

Keywords: quantum dots, time-resolved, cooperative phenomena, electromagnetic interaction.
PACS: 78.47.+p, 42.50.Fx, 78.67.Hc

The manipulation of the spontaneous lifetime of an emitter, e.g., an excited quantum dot (QD), is of particular interest for fundamental physics as well as for future applications in quantum logic devices [1]. Modification of the local density of electromagnetic states in the vicinity of the emitter, known as the Purcell effect, by inserting the emitter into a nanocavity [2,3] allows for inhibition and enhancement of the spontaneous emission lifetime.

Optical excitation of a QD-exciton has a profound impact on the QD permittivity near its resonance. The permittivity of an excited QD can be modeled [4] with a Lorentzian contribution and has a calculated peak value of $\varepsilon_{QD} \sim 10^6$ at resonance [4,5], which is much larger than the permittivity of the GaAs host medium ($\varepsilon_h = 11.5$). Thus, excited QDs form a high contrast permittivity landscape providing strong dipole scattering of the electromagnetic fields [6]. In other words, an excited QD strongly modifies the local polarization for resonant light, which is likely to couple with other excited QDs. Hence, the initially isolated QDs are collectively coupled by the electromagnetic field.

We demonstrate a long-range electromagnetic interaction between spectrally identical QDs. From time-resolved differential reflection data, in which the QD reflectance is monitored as a function of the probe photon energy [7], we observe a significant enhancement of the exciton lifetime in a semiconductor QD ensemble without any external manipulation of the electromagnetic field. This collective effect is comparable in magnitude with the lifetime enhancement reported for a single QD-exciton within an artificial nanocavity [2,8]. Our observations indicate that the QDs mutually couple over distances considerably beyond the nearest neighbor separation.

The experiments are performed on self-assembled InAs/GaAs QDs grown by molecular beam epitaxy on a (100) GaAs substrate. The nanostructure studied here, is the same sample as reported in Ref. 7. Atomic force microscopy images of uncapped QDs reveal the formation of QDs with a density of 2.8×10^{10} cm^{-2}.

The QD-exciton lifetime is investigated by means of pump-probe time-resolved differential reflection spectroscopy [7]. The QDs are non-resonantly excited using short laser pulses from a 2 ps mode-locked Ti:sapphire laser, creating free carriers which are subsequently captured in the QDs. The carrier-induced differential reflection $\Delta R/R_0$ is monitored by tuning the probe laser into resonance with the transition energy of the QD ensemble [7]. The 2 ps probe pulses are generated from an optical parametric oscillator, synchronically pumped by the Ti:sapphire laser.

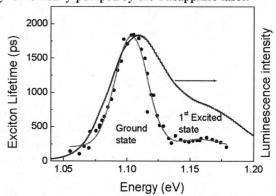

Figure 1. Exciton lifetime and photoluminescence intensity versus the exciton transition energy (300 W/cm^2, 5 K). The resonant-like behavior is due to electromagnetic coupling of energetically identical QDs.

The main consequence of the electromagnetic coupling due to the collective polarizability of the structure [6,9] is a profound modification of the

CP893, *Physics of Semiconductors, 28th International Conference*
edited by W. Jantsch and F. Schäffler
© 2007 American Institute of Physics 978-0-7354-0397-0/07/$23.00

exciton lifetime, as is depicted by the spectrum in Fig. 1. The exciton lifetime spectrum shows a pronounced resonant-like behavior with a 12 times enhancement near the center of the ground state energy distribution at 1.107 eV. Surprisingly, also for the QD first excited state at 1.163 eV an enhancement of the exciton lifetime is observed.

Another pronounced effect is that the exciton lifetime spectrum is considerably narrower than the photoluminescence (PL) spectrum. Analysis of the lifetime spectrum using Gaussian fits reveals a spectral width of the ground (excited) state of 27 meV (23 meV) while the spectral width of the PL is 44 meV.

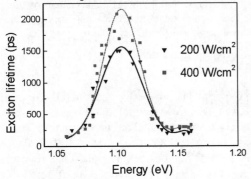

Figure 2. *Excitation density dependence of the exciton lifetime at 200 and 400 W/cm², obtained at 5 K.*

Figure 2 shows additional evidence for an electromagnetic coupling between optically excited QDs. The exciton lifetime exhibits a strong dependence on the pump excitation density. We observe a maximum exciton lifetime of 1.5 ns at 200 W/cm² pump excitation which increases to 2.1 ns at 400 W/cm² pump excitation. The strong dependence of the exciton lifetime on the pump power indicates that the exciton lifetime is governed by the fraction of excited QDs within the sample. Thus, the strength of the electromagnetic coupling can be optically tuned. The experimental results as depicted in Figs. 1 and 2 are clearly in contradiction with the conventional hypothesis of a weak electromagnetic coupling of QDs.

In order to explain and to analyze the observed lifetime enhancement, we use and significantly extend the electromagnetic response theory for a periodic array of identical and spherical QDs [6] with an effective exciton volume V_{QD}. Calculations show that the exciton emission rate $\Gamma^{coupled}$ of a QD-array - with transition energy $\hbar\omega_0$ - can be written as

$$\Gamma^{coupled} = \Gamma^{isolated} - \frac{k_0\sqrt{\varepsilon_h}\,\omega_{QD}V_{QD}}{2d_{QD}^2}. \quad (1)$$

Here $\Gamma^{isolated}$ is a weighted sum of the dephasing rate [10] and the radiative emission rate of a single isolated QD. k_0 and d_{QD} denote the vacuum wave vector and the spacing of the QDs within the two-dimensional periodic lattice, respectively, and ω_{QD} is the phenomenological parameter proportional to the QD oscillator strength [6]. Equation (1) shows that the lifetime $1/\Gamma^{coupled}$ is governed by the lattice spacing d_{QD}.

The resonant and optically excited QDs form a sub-ensemble which can be approximated by an ordered array [11] with an average lattice spacing d^{res}_{QD}. This means that the whole QD ensemble is divided into smaller sub-ensembles each with their own sub-ensemble density $N(\omega_j)$. The average distance between the QDs within each sub-ensemble depends on the location of these QDs within the overall size distribution, and is governed by $1/d^{res}_{QD} = N(\omega_j) = \sqrt{N_{QD}}\,G(\omega_j)$. N_{QD} denotes the area QD density and $G(\omega)$ is a Gaussian line shape function representing the inhomogeneously broadened density of states of the QD ensemble. Hereby Eq. (1) is written as

$$\Gamma^{coupled}(\omega) = \Gamma^{isolated}(\omega) - 2\frac{k_0\sqrt{\varepsilon_h}\,\omega_{QD}V_{QD}}{2}N_{QD}G^2(\omega). \quad (2)$$

Equation (2) proves the observed functional behavior, as observed from Figs. 1 and 2. The additional factor two in the second term on the righthand side of Eq. (2) takes into account the QD spin degeneracy. Equation (2) also predicts that the width of the exciton lifetime spectrum is a factor $\sqrt{2}$ narrower than the QD distribution $G(\omega)$ due to the quadratic dependence. This prediction is indeed observed experimentally (see Fig. 1)

Applying the electromagnetic response theory to our QDs, our observed 12 times enhancement of the exciton lifetime corresponds to an average distance of $d^{res}_{QD} = 490 \pm 20$ nm between the radiatively coupled QDs at the center of the QD-size distribution, as is illustrated in Fig. 1. We note that the wings of the QD-exciton lifetime spectrum are thus governed by an even larger separation between the mutually interacting QDs.

REFERENCES

1. D. Loss and D.P. DiVincenzo, *Phys. Rev. A* **57**, 120 (1998).
2. K.J. Vahala, *Nature* **424**, 839 (2003).
3. D. Englund *et al.*, *Phys. Rev. Lett.* **95**, 013904 (2005).
4. S. Schmitt-Rink *et al.*, *Phys. Rev. B* **35**, 8113 (1987).
5. S.A. Maksimenko *et al.*, *Semicond. Sci. Technol.* **15**, 491 (2000).
6. G.Ya. Slepyan *et al.*, *Phys. Rev. B* **64**, 125326 (2001).
7. E.W. Bogaart *et al.*, *Phys. Rev. B* **72**, 195301 (2005).
8. T. Baba *et al.*, *Appl. Phys. Lett.* **85**, 3989 (2004).
9. V. Bondarenko *et al.*, *Phys. Rev. B* **71**, 115304 (2005).
10. P. Borri *et al.*, *Phys. Rev. Lett.* **87**, 157401 (2001).
11. B.N.J. Persson, *Phys. Rev. B* **34**, 8941 (1986).

Electronic Structure of Long Wavelength (>1.3μm) GaAsSb-capped InAs Quantum Dots

T. J. Badcock[1], D. J. Mowbray[1], E. Nabavi[1], H. Y. Liu[2], M. J. Steer[2], M. Hopkinson[2], M. Hayne[3,4], T. Nuytten[4] and V. V. Moshchalkov[4]

[1]Department of Physics and Astronomy, University of Sheffield, Sheffield S3 7RH U.K.
[2]Department of Electronic and Electrical Engineering and EPSRC National Centre for III-V Technologies, University of Sheffield, S1 3JD, U.K.
[3]Physics Department, Lancaster University, Lancaster, LA1 4YB, U.K.
[4]INPAC-Institute for Nanoscale Physics and Chemistry, Pulsed Field Group, Katholieke Universiteit, Leuven, Celestijnenlaan 200D, Leuven B-3001, Belgium

Abstract. It is demonstrated that capping InAs self-assembled quantum dots with a thin GaAsSb layer allows the emission to be extended beyond 1.5μm at room temperature. This behaviour is attributed to the formation of a type-II system for Sb composition above ~15%. Magneto-optical spectroscopy suggests that the type-II excitons remain compact and it is postulated that strain modulation of the GaAsSb layer results in hole localization immediately above the quantum dots.

Keywords: quantum dots, magneto-optics, excitons.
PACS: 73.21.La, 78.67.Hc, 73.61.Ey

INTRODUCTION

The emission of InAs self-assembled quantum dots (QDs) grown within an InGaAs matrix can be tuned over the wavelength range ~1.1-1.3μm. Such dots have now been used as the basis of high performance injection lasers, operating in the 1.3μm telecommunications band[1]. However, there is considerable interest in extending the emission to the second telecommunications band at 1.55μm. In this paper we demonstrate emission beyond 1.5μm based on InAs QDs capped with a thin GaAsSb layer.

EXPERIMENTAL DETAILS

The samples consist of InAs QDs grown on (001) GaAs substrates by MBE. The dots are formed by depositing 3 monolayers of InAs and are capped with 6nm of GaAsSb, where the Sb composition varies between 14 and 26%. Photoluminescence (PL) and photoluminescence excitation (PLE) spectra were excited with light from a tungsten-halogen bulb dispersed by a monochromator. Ar$^+$ laser excited PL spectra were recorded in a pulsed magnet system with fields up to 50T.

RESULTS

Previous work[2,3] has shown that structures with an Sb composition above ~15% exhibit a strong blue shifting emission with increasing laser excitation power. This behaviour indicates the formation of a type-II system, believed to occur with electrons confined in the QDs but holes confined in the GaAsSb layer. Further evidence for the formation of a type-II system is provided by PL and PLE spectroscopy. Figure 1 shows PL and PLE spectra recorded at 4.2K for samples with different Sb compositions. In addition to LO phonon features, which are specific to the 14% sample around 1120nm, the PL and PLE spectra exhibit three main features. The emission in the region 1200 to 1500 nm, which redshifts strongly with increasing Sb composition, is attributed to the type-II transition. The absorption at ~1200 nm for the three highest Sb samples, with corresponding emission for the 14% sample, is attributed to the type-I QD transition. Finally, the absorption in the region ~900-1050 nm, which redshifts relatively weakly with

CP893, *Physics of Semiconductors, 28th International Conference*
edited by W. Jantsch and F. Schäffler
© 2007 American Institute of Physics 978-0-7354-0397-0/07/$23.00

increasing Sb composition, is attributed to a type-I

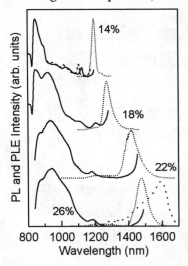

FIGURE 1. PL (dotted) and PLE (solid) spectra recorded at 4.2K. The dashed line shows the 300K PL of the 26% sample.

transition within the GaAsSb layer. The increasing Stokes' shift between the PL and the absorption at ~1200nm hence represents the energy difference between the hole states in the QD and cap layer. Also shown in Fig. 1 is the room temperature PL of the 26% sample.

Type-II transitions are expected to have a small oscillator strength due to the spatial separation of the electron and hole wavefunctions. To probe the spatial extent of the exciton wavefunction we use the fact that the diamagnetic shift, observed in the limit where the magnetic energy is less than the exciton binding energy, is proportional to the square of the exciton radius[4]. Figure 2 shows diamagnetic shifts plotted against the square of the magnetic field for four samples. The data is recorded for the Faraday geometry with the field applied along the growth direction. Although the diamagnetic coefficient varies between samples there is no obvious correlation with Sb content and the data is consistent with exciton radii for all samples within ±20% of that of the 14% sample. Hence the magneto-optical data implies that the electron and hole remain in close proximity in the type-II structures. The reason for this remains unclear but may be related to the lateral modulation of the strain state of the GaAsSb cap layer. If this has a constant composition and thickness it will experience a compressive stain between the dots but a tensile strain above the dots. The tensile strain will result in a local potential minimum for holes, causing them to be localized immediately above the dots and close to the confined electrons.

It is also notable that the transition to a linear field dependence, which occurs when the magnetic length

falls below $0.707a_0$ with a_0 the exciton Bohr radius, is not observed for any of the samples. This places an upper limit for the inplane value of a_0 of ~6nm for both the type-I and type-II excitons.

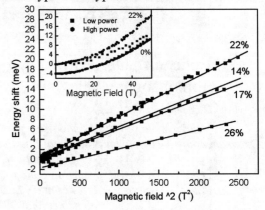

FIGURE 2. PL emission energy plotted against the square of magnetic field. Inset: laser power dependence of a type-I and type-II structure. The two sets of data for the 0% sample have been offset by -4meV for clarity.

One significant difference between the type-I and type-II structures (Sb composition <15% or >15%) is the dependence of the diamagnetic shift on laser power. This is shown in the inset to Figure 2 which shows the field dependence of the PL for two samples: one with an InGaAs cap layer (0% Sb) and the other with a 22% Sb cap. Whilst the former exhibits a power independent response, the latter exhibits a significantly different shift rate for low and high laser powers. This power dependent diamagnetic shift arises from carrier induced electrostatic band bending in the type-II system which alters the spatial separation of the electron and hole wavefunctions. A further difference between the type-I and type-II structures is that the latter exhibit an initial negative shift of ~ 2-3meV at low fields in both the Faraday and Voigt geometry. The reason for this difference is unclear.

In conclusion, emission from InAs quantum dots can be extended beyond 1.5μm by capping with a thin GaAsSb layer. The long wavelength emission results from the formation of a type-II system. Magneto-optical spectroscopy indicates that the type-II excitons remain relatively compact.

This work is supported by EPSRC grant GR/S49308/01 and the EU Network of Excellence SANDiE NMP4-CT-2004-500101

REFERENCES

1. H Y Liu et al Appl. Phys. Lett. **85**, 704 (2004)
2. H Y Liu et al Appl. Phys. Lett. **86**, 143108 (2005)
3. H Y Liu et al J. Appl. Phys. **99**, 046104 (2006)
4. M Hayne Physica B **346**, 421 (2004)

Optical Studies of Non-linear Absorption in Single InGaN/GaN Quantum Dots

A. F. Jarjour[1], R. A. Taylor[1], R.W. Martin[2], I.M. Watson[3], R.A. Oliver[5], G.A.D. Briggs[4], M.J. Kappers[5] and C.J. Humphreys[5]

1Clarendon Laboratory, University of Oxford, Parks Road, Oxford, OX1 3PU, UK.
2Department of Physics, University of Strathclyde, 107 Rottenrow, Glasgow G4 0NG, UK.
3Institue of Photonics, University of Strathclyde, 106 Rottenrow, Glasgow G4 0NW, UK.
4Department of Materials, University of Oxford, Parks Road, Oxford OX1 3PH, UK.
5Department of Materials, University of Cambridge, Pembroke Street, Cambridge CB2 3QZ, UK.

Abstract. Micro-photoluminescence properties of single InGaN/GaN quantum dots (QDs) are investigated using sub-bandgap excitation by 1 ps pulses from a Ti:sapphire laser. This results in almost complete suppression of background emission arising from the underlying quantum well to which the QDs are coupled. Photoluminescence excitation spectra undertaken using this technique show evidence of p-states. The non-linear intensity dependence of the emission is also discussed.

Keywords: InGaN, quantum dots, microphotoluminescence.
PACS: 78.67.Hc, 78.47.+p, 78.30.Fs

INTRODUCTION

In this paper we present a study of the photoluminescence (PL) properties of single InGaN/GaN QDs under multi-photon excitation. When compared to similar spectra obtained under single-photon excitation, it is found that the significant background present in these spectra is totally suppressed. Furthermore, multi-photon PLE measurements are presented.

EXPERIMENT

Experiments on two quite different quantum dot samples are reported here. Sample A was grown by R.A. Oliver *et al.*[1] by MOCVD employing a novel post-growth anneal in molecular nitrogen. The average dimensions of the dots are estimated to be 0.93 nm in height and 21.6 nm in diameter with an areal density of ~10^{10} cm^{-2}. The QDs in this sample were formed on top of a two-dimensional (2D) quantum well (QW) commonly referred to as a wetting layer (WL). Sample B consisted of arrays of selectively grown micro-pyramids topped by 5-periods of InGaN QWs of 2.0 nm thickness and GaN barriers of 6.0 nm thickness fabricated by I.M. Watson *et al.*[2]. The hexagonal-based pyramids were ~8 μm in height with base edges of ~5 μm and an areal density of 2×10^6 cm^{-2}.

Non-linear spectroscopy multi-photon spectroscopy provides the possibility of exciting transitions that are forbidden for one-photon excitation (OPE). It is also useful from a practical point of view as it enables a wide separation between the excitation and detection wavelengths. Here we use the term "non-linear excitation" (NE) for the process whereby the excitation energy falls in the bandgap of the structure, and hence only transitions by multiple-photon absorption are possible. In our experiments, this is achieved using 1-ps pulses from a tuneable Ti:sapphire laser with tuning resolution of ~1.5 meV and employing the same micro-PL setup described previously[2].

The sample was mounted in a temperature-controlled cryostat and the laser was focused by a ×36 microscope objective to a spot size of ~2 μm. The PL was collected by the same objective and directed to a 0.3 m spectrograph with a grating of 1200 grooves/mm, giving a spectral resolution of ~650 μeV. The spectrum was detected using a cooled CCD detector.

RESULTS AND DISCUSSION

We have examined the dependence of the QD emission on the NE wavelength at a fixed power in order to probe the existence of excited states. In fact, it would be expected that when the energy of multiple

CP893, *Physics of Semiconductors, 28th International Conference*
edited by W. Jantsch and F. Schäffler
© 2007 American Institute of Physics 978-0-7354-0397-0/07/$23.00

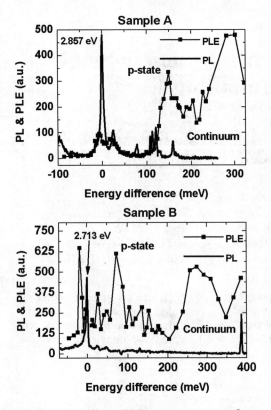

FIGURE 1. Non-linear PLE spectra (squares) for samples A (at 20 mW) and B (at 50 mW). PL spectra are also shown for comparison at the same excitation powers.

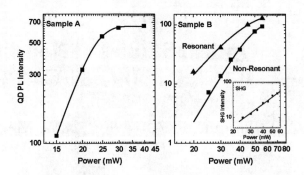

FIGURE 2. Intensity dependence of quantum dot emission (log-log scale). Sample A: excitation at 1.55eV. Sample B: Square symbols correspond to excitation at 1.55 eV, triangles to 1.39 eV. Inset shows intensity dependence of the second harmonic intensity.

fitted with the law:

$$I_{QD} = I_{sat}\left[1 - \exp\left[-\left(P/P_{sat}\right)^{d}\right]\right]$$

which corresponds to a multiple-order Poissonian absorption process. The best fit of the experimental data with the mentioned law gives the following values: for sample A, 4.51 ± 0.6 and for sample B 4.40 ± 0.6 under non-resonant excitation and 2.96 ± 0.2 under resonant excitation. This is not due to some artifact in the system. The inset in figure 2 shows the intensity of the SHG line (seen in the PL in figure 1 for sample B at the right) as a function of the excitation power. Here $d = 2.06 \pm 0.13$, the expected quadratic behaviour. These findings indicate that processes of higher order than 2 are involved in the NE. The slightly lower order under resonant excitation in Sample B is consistent with the assignment of this state a p-state of the same QD. Valence-band mixing and asymmetry in the QDs means that the polarization states of the different energy levels in the QDs can differ from the two circularly-polarized states which are the eigenstates of the total angular momentum in a structure with rotational symmetry, giving rise to more complex selection rules.

ACKNOWLEDGMENTS

This work is supported by the EPSRC (grant GR/S82176/01) part of QIPIRC (www.qipirc.org). We also acknowledge the Clarendon Fund /ORS scheme (A. F. J.) and from Peterhouse, Cambridge (RAO).

REFERENCES

1. R. A. Oliver, G. A. D. Briggs, M. J. Kappers, C. J. Humphreys, S. Yasin, J. H. Rice, J. D. Smith, and R. A. Taylor, *Appl. Phys. Letters* **83**, 755 (2003).
2. P. R. Edwards, R. W. Martin, I. M. Watson, C. Liu, R. A. Taylor, J. H. Rice, J. H. Na, J. W. Robinson, and J. D. Smith, *Appl. Phys. Letters* **85**, 4281 (2004).
3. T. Saito, Y. Arakawa, *Physica E* **15**, 169 (2002).

photons corresponds to the energy of an excited state, an enhancement of the non-linear absorption should occur. Figure 1 presents the PLE results obtained from the two QD samples A and B, together with the PL spectrum. A broad absorption is observed 302 meV and 274 meV above the QD energy in samples A and B, respectively. This peak is observed for several QDs in both samples and is attributed to absorption of continuum states. A resonance peak is observed for sample A at 149 meV above the QD and several resonance peaks are observed for sample B at energy separation from the QD of 73, 27 and -18 meV. Previous theoretical studies on hexagonal InGaN QDs report a separation between the first excited states and the ground state of 122 meV[3]. The modelled dot was bigger than those in sample A and smaller than those in sample B. Therefore, it is consistent to assign the peak at 149 meV for sample A and that at 73 meV for sample B to excited states (p-states).

In order to understand the order of the non-linearity, the intensity dependence of the QD emission on the NE power was measured. This dependence is presented in figure 2 for the QDs in figure 1. For sample A, only non-resonant excitation at 1.55 eV is examined. For sample B, two excitation energies are examined: at 1.55 eV (non-resonant excitation) and at 1.39 eV (resonant excitation corresponding to the state 73 meV above the dot). All the experimental data are

Ultrafast Spectral Hole Burning Spectroscopy of Exciton Spin Relaxation in Quantum Dots

T. Müller, T. Moldaschl, G. Strasser, and K. Unterrainer

Institute of Photonics & Center for Micro- and Nanostructures, Vienna University of Technology, Floragasse 7, A-1040 Vienna, Austria, Fax: ++43-1-58801-36299, Email: thomas.mueller@tuwien.ac.at

Abstract. The exciton spin relaxation within the radiative doublet of the exciton ground state in InAs/GaAs self-assembled quantum dots is studied via an ultrafast spectral hole burning technique. In the case of cross-polarized pump and probe pulses a spectral "antihole" emerges due to relaxation of the exciton spin. The measured relaxation time decreases rapidly from 1.15 ns at T = 5 K to 90 ps at 90 K, suggesting exciton-acoustic phonon interaction as the underlying spin relaxation mechanism.

Keywords: Ultrafast spectroscopy, Semiconductor quantum dots, Ultrafast processes in condensed matter
PACS: 73.20.Mf, 73.21.La, 78.47.+p, 78.67

INTRODUCTION

The carrier spin couples much weaker to the environment than the carrier wavefunction. Thus, spin states in semiconductor quantum dots (QDs) are a promising candidate for the implementation of future quantum logic devices. Indeed, very long (~ns) spin relaxation times have been found in III-V [1-3] and II-VI [4] self-assembled QDs. Studies of spin-polarized carriers confined in QDs have so far mainly been performed by time-resolved photoluminescence measurements on QD ensembles where spin populations are created using circularly polarized light excitation. In this contribution we report measurements of the spin relaxation in an ensemble of InAs/GaAs self-assembled QDs using an ultrafast spectral hole burning (SHB) technique [5].

EXPERIMENT

The investigated sample consists of 30 layers of InAs QDs with a dot density of approximately 2×10^{10} cm^{-2} per layer. In order to be accessible to our Ti:sapphire laser system, the exciton transitions were shifted to higher energies by rapid thermal annealing. Excitonic ground state luminescence from the dots at T = 5 K is observed at 1.281 eV with an inhomogeneous broadening of the transitions of ~45 meV (FWHM).

SHB measurements were performed using a mode-locked Ti:sapphire laser that delivers 80-fs pulses with a center frequency of 1.285 eV and a spectral width of ~14 meV (FWHM). A grating pulse shaper was used to produce 1.4 meV (FWHM) broad pump pulses and the change in the transmission induced by the pump was measured with a weaker 80-fs probe pulse. The probe was spectrally dispersed with a monochromator which allowed the determination of the changes induced at photon energies different from that of the pump. A motorized translation stage controlled the delay between the pump and probe pulses. In addition, half-wave-plates were used to independently adjust the linear polarizations of both pump and probe.

RESULTS

Figure 1 shows SHB signals recorded at T = 5 K. In these measurements a linear Π_y-polarized pump pulse is tuned to the maximum of the excitonic ground state transition. The polarization of the broadband probe pulse is tuned either perpendicular (upper trace) or parallel (lower trace) to the pump and the differential transmission change of the probe is measured at a temporal delay of 10 ps after excitation. In the first case, the SHB signal shows enhanced transmission at the pump photon energy, corresponding to a bleaching of the $|00\rangle$ ground state population. In the case of parallel polarizations of the two pulses, we observe (i) enhanced transmission at the pump photon energy, and (ii) reduced transmission, i.e., an "antihole", at energies below the pump photon energy [6]. The antihole arises from the population of the $|01\rangle$ exciton state which gives rise to absorption to the biexciton

CP893, *Physics of Semiconductors, 28*th *International Conference*
edited by W. Jantsch and F. Schäffler
© 2007 American Institute of Physics 978-0-7354-0397-0/07/$23.00

state |11> at an energy of ΔE below the exciton peak. We determine a biexciton binding energy of 4.2 meV.

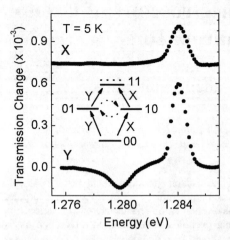

FIGURE 1. SHB signals for Π_x (upper trace) and Π_y - polarized probe pulses. The polarization of the pump is in both cases Π_y. Inset: Schematic drawing of the energy levels in a QD. |00> is the ground state; |10> and |01> correspond to the exciton states, which can be excited by Π_x - and Π_y - polarized light, respectively; and |11> denotes the biexciton state. The biexciton energy is less than twice the bare exciton energy, the difference between them being the biexciton binding energy ΔE.

The SHB signals strongly broaden at $T = 90$ K, and after deconvolution of the pump pulse we find a FWHM linewidth of 2.1 meV. Temperature dependent measurements show that the linewidth is determined by acoustic phonon-exciton interaction in the dots. The temporal evolution of the antihole at $T = 90$ K is shown in Figure 2 (a). With increasing pump-probe delay, the ratio of cross-polarized signal to co-polarized signal increases and reaches one for long delay times, as shown in the inset. It is obvious that the development of an antihole in the cross-polarized case is due to spin relaxation: As |01> excitons flip their spin, the |10> exciton state gets populated, giving rise to absorption to the biexciton state |11>. The spin relaxation rate Γ can be found from the equation $(A_\| - A_\perp)/(A_\| + A_\perp) \propto \exp(-2\Gamma\tau)$, where $A_\|$ and $A_\perp$ denote the antihole amplitudes for co- and cross-polarized probe light, and τ is the pump-probe delay time. A fit yields $1/\Gamma = 90$ ps. Figure 2 (b) presents the temperature dependence of the relaxation time. It increases rapidly from 90 ps to 1.15 ns as the temperature is reduced from 90 K to 5 K. At 5 K the spin relaxation time is more than two times longer than the exciton lifetime which remains approximately constant (~0.5 ns) over the investigated temperature range. The large change of the spin relaxation time suggests that phonon scattering related mechanisms become significant at high temperature. The observed temperature dependence is characterized by a small activation energy which strongly points to an acoustic phonon mediated spin flip process.

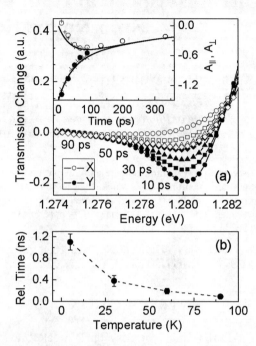

FIGURE 2. (a) Temporal evolution of the antihole at $T = 90$ K. Inset: Antihole amplitudes for co- and cross-polarized pump and probe pulses (symbols: experimental data; lines: results from a simple rate equation model). (b) Temperature dependence of the spin relaxation time.

ACKNOWLEDGMENTS

This work was supported by the Austrian Fond zur Förderung der Wissenschaftlichen Forschung (SFB-ADLIS, SFB-IRON) and the ECNoE program SANDiE.

REFERENCES

1. M. Paillard, X. Marie, P. Renucci, T. Amand, A. Jbeli, and J. M. Gérard, *Phys. Rev. Lett.* **86**, 1634 (2001).
2. A. S. Lenihan, M. V. Gurudev Dutt, D. G. Steel, S. Ghosh, and P. K. Bhattacharya, *Phys. Rev. Lett.* **88**, 223601 (2002).
3. H. Gotoh, H. Ando, H. Kamada, A. Chavez-Pirson, and J. Temmyo, *Appl. Phys. Lett.* **72**, 1341 (1998).
4. M. Scheibner, G. Bacher, S. Weber, A. Forchel, Th. Passow, and D. Hommel, *Phys. Rev. B* **67**, 153302 (2003).
5. T. Müller, G. Strasser, and K. Unterrainer, *Appl. Phys. Lett.* **88**, 192105 (2006).
6. A. S. Lenihan, M. V. Gurudev Dutt, D. G. Steel, S. Ghosh, and P. Bhattacharya, *Phys. Rev. B* **69**, 045306 (2004).

Spin storage and readout in self-organized quantum dots

T. Warming*, W. Wieczorek*, M. Geller*, D. Bimberg*, G. E. Cirlin†,
A. E. Zhukov† and V. M. Ustinov†

*Institut für Festkörperphysik, Technische Universität Berlin, Hardenbergstrasse 36, 10623 Berlin, Germany
†A. F. Ioffe Physico-Technical Institute, Russian Acadamy of Sciences, 26 Polytekhnicheskaya, St. Petersburg 194021, Russian Federation

Abstract. We demonstrate optical charging of spectrally selected subensembles of self-organized quantum dots with single charge carriers. By circularly polarized excitation in an applied magnetic field, we are able to address the spin of single electron in the quantum dot. A spin-flip of the electron is observed after excitation in the upper Zeeman level.

Keywords: quantum dot, charging, spin storage, spectral hole burning
PACS: 78.67.Hc, 71.70.Ej, 72.25.Dc

Self-organized QDs may present a basis for future single-electron memories [1] and spin-based quantum computation [2, 3]. One QD stores one information bit represented by a stored charge carrier [4, 5] or its spin [6]. In spin-based quantum computation, the electron spin can act as a quantum bit. Addressing a few or just single QDs in a macroscopic sample and controlling the spin and charge state of carriers will be essential for these applications.

Here we address spectrally subensembles of QDs having the same ground state transition energy by resonant excitation [4, 5, 7]. In this work we focus on the controlling of the spin of the stored electrons using circular polarized excitation in a magnetic field. The experimental scheme is as follows. A Ti:Sapphire laser (referred to as write-laser, W) continuously charges a subensemble of QDs with excitons. These excitons decompose in an applied electric field: the holes leave the QDs by tunneling, the electrons remain in the QDs, because their tunneling is repressed by an $Al_{0.35}Ga_{0.65}As$ barrier below the QD layer. A charged QD shifts its absorption to the transition energy of the negative trion, X^-, at $\Delta E_{X^-} = +6$ meV. Additional charging of QDs with more than a single carrier is prevented due to the fact that the energy shift is larger than the line width of W. The actual QD occupation is now probed by absorption of photons from a second light source (referred to as read-source, R) and the photocurrent is measured using standard lock-in technique. R is a tungsten lamp, dispersed by a 0.275 m double grating monochromator. The difference between the photocurrent with and without W (ΔI_{PC}) reflects the changes in absorption induced by W. At the energetic position of W a spectral hole is observed (compare Fig. 1) because QDs with a transition at this energy are charged. The absorption by the charged QDs is seen at $\Delta E_{X^-} = +6$ meV as an spectral antihole.

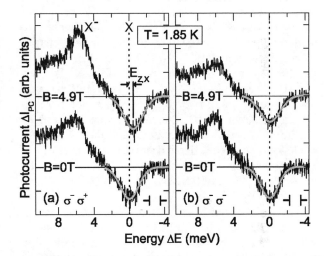

FIGURE 1. Photocurrent spectra ΔI_{PC} for sample E dependent on the applied magnetic field B for $\sigma^-\sigma^+$ (a) and $\sigma^-\sigma^-$ (b) excitation. The curves are vertically shifted for clarity. The gray curves show Gaussian fits to the data.

The investigated p-i-n-structures (p region as the top layer) are grown on s/i-GaAs substrates by molecular beam epitaxy (MBE) at 585 °C with a single layer of self-organized InAs QDs in the center of a 300 nm thick intrinsic region. The QDs were formed by deposition of 2.5 ML of InAs on GaAs at 485 °C, yielding an areal density of $\sim 5 \cdot 10^{10}$ cm^{-2}. To repress the tunneling of the electrons a 75 nm thick $Al_{0.35}Ga_{0.65}As$ tunnel barrier was included below the QD layer, separated from the QDs by a 7 nm thick GaAs layer. Mesa structures with a diameter of 800 μm were fabricated. A photoluminescence experiment (not shown here) shows the ensemble maximum of the QD ground state transition at 1.15 eV with a FWHM of 90 meV at 7 K. For magnetic field measurements in Faraday config-

CP893, *Physics of Semiconductors, 28th International Conference*
edited by W. Jantsch and F. Schäffler
© 2007 American Institute of Physics 978-0-7354-0397-0/07/$23.00

uration ($B \leq 4.9$ T) the samples were investigated in a superconductive split-coil magneto cryostat at $T = 1.85$ K, using super fluid He.

In the following experiments, W and R are circularly polarized, to selectively address the spin of stored electrons. At $B = 0$ T, a superposition of the X states $1/\sqrt{2}(|+1\rangle \pm |-1\rangle)$ is excited, whereas at sufficiently large B spin-polarized excitons are generated [8]. The polarization of W determines the spin of stored electrons. The spin polarization is detected via the absorption selection rules of the X^- transition. The X^- can only be formed by excitation of two electrons with antiparallel spin. All four possible configurations for W and R are considered in the following. In our notation, the configuration $\sigma^-\sigma^+$ means that W is σ^- and R is σ^+ polarized.

The ΔI_{PC} spectra for configuration $\sigma^-\sigma^+$ and $\sigma^-\sigma^-$ are shown in Fig. 1(a) and Fig. 1(b).

The spectral area of the X^- is discussed. At $B = 0$ T, the X^- is observed at about $\Delta E_{X^-} = +6$ meV for all four configurations. At $B = 4.9$ T, the X^- becomes more pronounced for $\sigma^-\sigma^+$ excitation, whereas it weakens for $\sigma^-\sigma^-$ excitation, see Fig. 1(a) and Fig. 1(b). To quantify this observation, the spectral area of the X^- is determined between $\Delta E = +9.2$ meV and $+3.6$ meV and normalized to its value at $B = 0$ T, see Fig. 2. For crosspolarized excitation $\sigma^-\sigma^+$, the spectral area increases by a factor of 1.3 with an increase in B from 0 T to 4.9 T, while for $\sigma^+\sigma^-$ excitation it decreases by a factor of 0.9. For copolarized excitation $\sigma^-\sigma^-$, the spectral area decreases by a factor of 0.8, whereas for $\sigma^+\sigma^+$ excitation it increases by a factor of 1.3.

At $B = 0$ T, mixed X states are excited. Consequently, half the QDs are charged by W with electrons having spin $+1/2$ (spin-up) and half having spin $-1/2$ (spin-down). R leads to an X^- formation with probability 1/2 for each of the charged QDs, as it excites as well mixed X states. In total, half of the charged QDs are detected via the X^- transition. At sufficiently large B, a σ^- W excites the X state $|-1\rangle$ and the QDs are only charged with spin-up electrons. A σ^+ R leads to an X^- formation in all charged QDs, as antiparallel electron spin states are excited, see Fig. 2. Consequently, the spectral area of X^- increases with an increase in B. For a σ^- R, the formation of an X^- is forbidden as W and R excite parallel electron spin states, see Fig. 2. Consequently, the spectral area of X^- decreases.

For a σ^+ W, we observe a spin-flip of the stored, initially spin-down electron. This conclusion is drawn from the observation that the spectral area increases for copolarized excitation $\sigma^+\sigma^+$, while it decreases for crosspolarized excitation $\sigma^+\sigma^-$. A σ^+ W charges QDs with spin-down electrons occupying the upper Zeeman level followed by a subsequent spin-flip to the lower Zeeman level, see Fig. 2. Hence, the formation of an X^- is allowed by excitation with a σ^+ R (spectral area in-

creases) whereas it is forbidden for a σ^- R (spectral area decreases). The initial occupation of the upper Zeeman level can be proven by analyzing the energetic position of the spectral hole [7]. If W and R address different spin states, the Zeeman splitting $E_{Z,X}$ is seen as energetic shift between W and the spectral hole, measured with R (compare Fig. 1). If W and R are addressing the same spin state the spectral hole is at the same energetic position as W. The spin-flip of the electron to the lower Zeeman level occurs during its retention time in the QD, which is on the order of 100 ms.

In summary, we demonstrated spin- and spectral- selective optical charging of subensembles of QDs with single electrons. In spectral hole burning experiments we showed that the spin of single electrons stored in charged QDs can be addressed selectively using circularly polarized excitation in a magnetic field. A spin-flip to the lower Zeeman level was observed when QDs were charged with electrons in the upper Zeeman level.

Parts of this work were supported by the SANDiE Network of Excellence of the European Commission, Contract No. NMP4-CT-2004-500101 and by Deutsche Forschungsgemeinschaft in the framework of SFB 296.

Norm. area of X⁻			Electron occupation	
Write	σ^-	σ^+	σ^-	σ^+
Read σ^+	1.3	1.3	[schematic]	[schematic]
σ^-	0.8	0.9	[schematic]	[schematic]

FIGURE 2. Normalized area of the negative trion (X^-) for all configurations of write-laser and read-source and schematic pictures of the occupation of the Zeeman split electron levels.

REFERENCES

1. S. Muto, *Jpn. J. Appl. Phys.* **34**, L210 (1995).
2. D. Loss and D. P. DiVincenzo, *Phys. Rev. A.* **57**, 120 (1998).
3. T. Calarco *et al*, Phys. Rev. A. **68**, 012310 (2003).
4. R. Heitz *et al*, Physica E **21**, 215 (2004).
5. M. Kroutvar *et al*, Appl. Phys. Lett. **83**, 443 (2003).
6. M. Kroutvar *et al*, Nature **432**, 81 (2004).
7. W. Wieczorek *et al*, Appl. Phys. Lett. **88**, 182107 (2006).
8. M. Bayer *et al*, Phys. Rev. B **65**, 195315 (2002).

Probing spin states in AlGaAs/GaAs few-electron quantum dots by inelastic light scattering

S. Kalliakos[1], C. Pascual García[1], V. Pellegrini[1], A. Pinczuk[2,3], B. S. Dennis[3], L. N. Pfeiffer[3], K. W. West[3], M. Rontani[4], G. Goldoni[4], E. Molinari[4]

1 NEST CNR-INFM and Scuola Normale Superiore,Via della Faggiola 19, 56126 Pisa, Italy
2 Dept of Physics, Dept of Appl. Phys. and Appl. Math.,
Columbia University, New York, New York
3 Bell Labs, Lucent Technologies, Murray Hill, New Jersey
4 S3 CNR-INFM and Università degli Studi di Modena and Reggio Emilia, 41100 Modena, Italy

Abstract. Resonant inelastic light scattering provides a venue for the study of spin transitions and interactions in quantum dots (QDs) with few electrons. Here we present the observation of inter-shell excitations in GaAs/AlGaAs nanofabricated QDs containing four electrons. The ground state with four electrons dictated by Hund's rule is a triplet with total spin $S = 1$ so that peculiar to this configuration there are two monopole inter-shell spin modes with changes $\Delta S = \pm 1$ that connect the triplet state to the excited states with $S = 0$ and $S = 2$, respectively. We present light scattering spectra that offer evidence of these excitations. The light scattering spectra are interpreted by numerical evaluations within a full configuration interaction approach.

Keywords: Quantum Dots, Electron Correlation, Inelastic Light Scattering
PACS: 73.20Mf, 73.21La, 78.30-j

Semiconductor QDs have been proposed as building blocks for spintronic devices and for the creation and manipulation of quantum bits at the nanoscale [1, 2]. QDs represent a unique laboratory where few-particle fundamental quantum effects can be studied.

The description of the electronic properties of QDs with few electrons requires a treatment beyond mean-field Hartree-Fock (HF) theory that incorporates correlation effects. Electronic states have been studied in transport [3] and interband optical experiments [4]. These works have uncovered the role of the electron-electron interaction as the number of electrons in the QD is changed. In this paper, we present resonant inelastic light scattering experiments that probe low-lying inter-shell electronic spin and charge excitations in nanofabricated QDs with four electrons. According to Hund's rule, the ground state (GS) of this configuration is a triplet with $S = 1$. Electronic inter-shell spin excitations with $\Delta S = +1$ and $\Delta S = -1$ are observed. We argue that the splitting of the inter-shell excitations is a direct manifestation of the correlations among electrons [5].

The samples were fabricated from a 25nm-wide, one-side modulation-doped $Al_{0.1}Ga_{0.9}As$/GaAs quantum well (QW) with measured low-temperature electron density $n = 1.1 \times 10^{11}$ cm^{-2} and mobility of 2.7×10^6 cm^2/Vs [5]. An array of QDs with 210 nm

diameter was defined by electron-beam lithography and produced by inductive coupled plasma reactive ion etching. Resonant inelastic light scattering experiments where preformed at $T = 1.8$ K in a backscattering configuration using a tunable Ti-Sapphire laser. The scattered light was collected into a triple grating spectrometer with CCD multichannel detection.

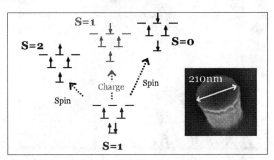

FIGURE 1. Schematic representation of the low-lying spin and charge inter-shell excitations in a quantum dot (QD) with four electrons. From the ground state with $S = 1$ (blue colour) there are two possible spin excitations ($\Delta S = \pm 1$, black colour) and one charge excitation ($\Delta S = 0$, red colour), respectively. A SEM picture of the etched QD is also shown.

Taking the growth direction as the z-axis, the QD potential in the x-y plane in the dot can be considered as parabolic and it originates from the electron capture

CP893, *Physics of Semiconductors, 28th International Conference*
edited by W. Jantsch and F. Schäffler
© 2007 American Institute of Physics 978-0-7354-0397-0/07/$23.00

at surface states. This creates an effective confinement width much smaller than the geometrical diameter of the QDs. It is well known that the single-particle QD levels are provided by Fock-Darwin (FD) orbitals [6] with energies given by $E_{n,m} = \hbar\omega_0(2n + |m| + 1)$ where $n = 0,1,2...$, $m = 0,\pm 1,..$ are the radial and azimuthal quantum numbers, respectively. $\hbar\omega_0$ is the electron harmonic confinement energy. The FD shells are defined by an integer value of $N_{shell} = 2n + |m|$ with a well-defined atomic parity. Parity selection rules in QDs indicate that monopole transitions with $\Delta M = 0$ ($\Delta N_{shell} = 2, 4,...$) are active in light scattering experiments in a backscattering geometry [7].

Figure 1 shows a schematic view of ground and excited states, together with a SEM image the etched pillar. In the case of four electron occupation, there are three possible electronic inter-shell excitations. First, a spin excitation from the ground state with $S = 1$ to an excited state with $S = 2$ ($\Delta S = +1$), then a charge excitation with $\Delta S = 0$ and finally another spin excitation to a singlet state with $S = 0$ ($\Delta S = -1$). The latter excitation (corresponding to a triplet-to-singlet transition) is peculiar to the QD with four electrons.

In light scattering experiments, spin excitations are probed with crossed polarization between the incident and scattered light while parallel polarizations are required to probe charge excitations [8]. Figure 2 (a) reports representative spectra in which pairs of peaks are seen at energies close to 4 and 7-8 meV and interpreted as monopole excitations with $\Delta S = 1$ (spin) and $\Delta S = 0$ (charge). In addition, a sharp peak in the spin channel at 5.5 meV is assigned to the spin mode with $\Delta S = -1$ that occurs because the ground state is a triplet state. Such a spin excitation is split from the $\Delta S = +1$ mode seen at lower energy by the difference in exchange and correlation contributions. This assignment is supported by calculations within the full configuration-interaction theory (FCI), as shown in Figure 2 (b) [5, 9].

In conclusion, we presented inelastic light scattering measurements of inter-shell excitations in doped nanofabricated QDs with four electrons. Triplet-to-singlet spin transition of the four electron QDs has been identified. From these experiments, inelastic light scattering emerges as a powerful method to study spin effects in few-electron QDs.

We acknowledge support from the Italian Ministry of Foreign Affairs, Italian Ministry of Research (FIRB-RBAU01ZEML), European Community's Human Potential Program (HPRN-CT-2002-00291), National Science Foundation (DMR-03-52738), Department of Energy (DE-AIO2-04ER46133). We are grateful to SENTECH-Berlin for allowing us to use the ICP-RIE machine.

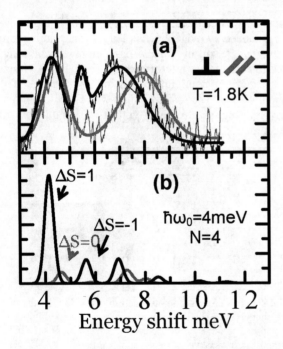

FIGURE 2. (Color online) (a) Experimental polarized (red) and depolarized (black) resonant inelastic light scattering spectra. Incident laser energy is 1567 meV and the excitation intensity is I=0.08 W/cm^2. Fits of the data with three Gaussians are shown. (b) Theoretical spectra for four electrons. Gaussian distributions with a phenomenological standard deviation $\sigma = 0.18$ meV were used. Best fitting is obtained with $\hbar\omega_0 = 4$ meV.

1. D. Loss and D. P. DiVincenzo, *Phys Rev. A* **57**, 120 (1998).
2. J. M. Taylor, H.-A. Engel, W. Dür, A. Yacoby, C. M. Marcus, P. Zoller, M. D. Lukin, *Nature Phys.* **1**, 177 (2005).
3. L. P. Kouwenhoven, D. G. Austing and S. Tarucha, *Rep. Prog. Phys.* **64**, 701 (2001).
4. M. Kroutvar, Y. Ducommun, D. Heiss, M. Bichler, D. Schuh, G. Abstreiter and J. J. Finley *Nature* **432**, 81 (2004).
5. C. P. Garcia, V. Pellegrini, A. Pinczuk, M. Rontani, G. Goldoni, E. Molinari, B. S. Dennis, L. N. Pfeiffer and K. W. West, *Phys. Rev. Lett.* **95**, 266806 (2005).
6. S.M. Reimann and M. Manninen, *Rev. Mod. Phys.* **74**, 1283 (2002).
7. C. Schüller, K. Keller, G. Biese, E. Ulrichs, L. Rolf, C. Steinebach, D. Heitmann, and K. Eberl, *Phys. Rev. Lett.* **80**, 2673 (1998)
8. V. Pellegrini and A. Pinczuk, *Solid State Commun.* **119**, 301 (2001).
9. Details of the method can be found in M. Rontani *et al.*, *J. Chem. Phys.* **124**, 124102 (2006).

Spin Lifetime in Electron-Doped InP Quantum Dots

Y. Masumoto, B. Pal, S. Oguchi and M. Ikezawa

Institute of Physics, University of Tsukuba, Tsukuba 305-8571, Japan

Abstract. Spin relaxation of electrons doped in InP quantum dots was studied by means of luminescence pump-probe and Hanle measurements. Optical pumping makes spins of doped electrons to be oriented in parallel to the helicity of the circularly polarized excitation. The luminescence pump-probe showed the spin orientation of the doped electrons decay on a millisecond time-scale. Hanle measurement clarified the spin dephasing relaxation time of doped electrons is 1.7 ns which is explained by the frozen fluctuation of nuclear spins.

Keywords: Spin, Quantum Dot, InP
PACS: 78.67.Hc; 71.35.Pq; 72.25.Fe

Electron spins in quantum dots (QDs) are good candidates for the quantum memory in the quantum information technology, because transferring the quantum information from the photon polarization to the electron spin polarization is direct and one-to-one. Electrons in QDs are expected to have long spin lifetime and doped electrons in QDs have infinite lifetime. We investigated time-resolved optical orientation of charge tunable InP QDs and found that the spins of the doped electrons are oriented under the circularly polarized excitation and are preserved in part for up to sub-millisecond [1]. In this work, we report nanosecond dephasing time of the spins by means of Hanle measurement as well as up to millisecond preservation of the spin by means of photoluminescence (PL) pump-probe in the same QDs.

The samples studied are charge tunable one-layer InP self-assembled QDs grown on n^+-GaAs substrates. The excitation source was a cw Ti:sapphire laser and the PL was detected by a photomultiplier with a 2-channel gated photon counter (GPC). A photoelastic modulator (PEM) was used to produce right and left circular polarization alternatively at 42 kHz in the detection path or the excitation path. The number of electrons in the QDs was varied with the change of the electric bias applied across the quantum structure. Trionic quantum beats in PL showed that each InP QD contains one doped electron on an average at the electric bias of $-0.1 \sim -0.2$V [2].

Under the electric bias of -0.1V, the negative circular polarization (NCP) was observed in PL of InP QDs under the circularly polarized quasi-resonant excitation and the longitudinal magnetic field of 0.1T. Time-resolved study of the PL circular polarization showed that NCP started at 100ps and is preserved within the recombination lifetime [1]. The NCP is explained by considering the optical pumping of the spins of doped electrons under the circularly polarized excitation and the simultaneous spin flip-flop process of a photogenerated electron-hole pair in P-QDs in which the spin of the doped electron is ori-

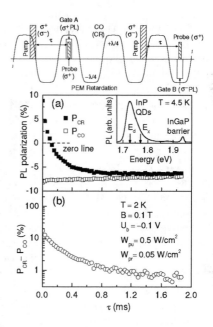

FIGURE 1. (Upper Sketch): Synchronization of retardation in a PEM, probe pulses, and gates of a GPC. (Main Panel): Probe PL polarization for co- (P_{CO}) and cross- (P_{CR}) circularly polarized pump-probe **(a)**, and the difference $P_{CR} - P_{CO}$ vs. pump-probe delay (τ) **(b)**. PL spectrum is shown in the inset.

ented in parallel to the helicity of the circularly polarized excitation [1, 3]. For the time-resolved optical orientation of doped electrons in the time region far beyond the PL lifetime, a pump-probe PL was used [3].

The timing of the pump, probe pulses and the gate of the photon counter is shown at the upper part of Fig.1. We measured the probe PL polarization for co-circularly polarized pump-probe (P_{CO}) and cross-circularly polarized pump-probe (P_{CR}) as a function of pump-probe time delay τ. The experimental data are shown in the main panel of Fig.1. The difference $P_{CR} - P_{CO}$ is a good mea-

CP893, Physics of Semiconductors, 28th International Conference
edited by W. Jantsch and F. Schäffler
© 2007 American Institute of Physics 978-0-7354-0397-0/07/$23.00

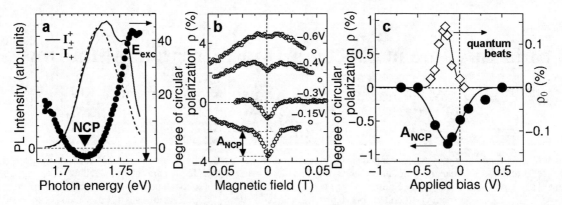

FIGURE 2. **a.** Circularly polarized PL spectra and circular polarization spectrum of InP QDs. **b.** PL circular polarization of the electrically biased InP QDs under the transverse magnetic field (Hanle curve). **c.** Amplitude of the sharp Hanle dip and that of trionic quantum beat as a function of applied electric bias.

sure of the pump induced spin orientation of the doped electrons. A semi-logarithmic plot of $P_{CR} - P_{CO}$ shows that the spin orientation of doped electrons decays non-exponentially and that the spin polarization decays on a millisecond time-scale. Spin relaxation rate increases with the increase of the temperature and the longitudinal magnetic field. The temperature dependence suggests two-phonon processes as the dominant spin relaxation mechanism in QDs at the elevated temperatures.

Under quasi-resonant excitation, PL of singly electron doped InP QDs showed NCP at the Stokes shift of 49 meV even under zero magnetic field, as shown in Fig.2a. We measured the Hanle effect of the sample under the transverse magnetic field. The Hanle curves of singly electron doped InP QDs taken in the magnetic field up to 6 T and under the electric bias of -0.1V are described by the expression, $\rho(B) = A_0 + A_{NCP}/[1 + (B/B_1)^2] + A_2/[1 + (B/B_2)^2] + A_3/[1 + (B/B_3)^2]$, where $B_i = \hbar/g_i\mu_B T_{2,i}^*$, $(i = 1, 2, 3)$, and $T_{2,i}^*$ is the spin lifetime. Fitting parameters are, $A_0 = 0.10\%$, $A_{NCP} = -1.43\%$, $B_1 = 4.5$ mT, $A_2 = -3.97\%$, $B_2 = 128$ mT, $A_3 = 2.30\%$, and $B_3 = 1.54$ T. Lorentzians having half width at the half maximum (HWHM) of B_2 and B_3 are observed in neutral InP QDs and are assigned to depolarization of excitons and holes, respectively [4]. The Hanle curves precisely measured in the low field regime up to 62.5 mT are displayed in Figs.2b. Simultaneously with the enhancement of the trionic quantum beat, a sharp dip appeared on a broader Lorentzian in the Hanle curve and the amplitude of the sharp dip of negative circular polarization, A_{NCP}, is enhanced around the applied bias of -0.2 V, as is shown in Figs.2b and 2c. The clear coincidence between NCP and trionic quantum beat shows sharp Hanle dip is reflected by the long spin dephasing time of doped electrons in QDs. The sharp Lorentzian dip has HWHM of 4.5 mT. The HWHM of $B_1 = 4.5$ mT of the sharp Hanle dip corresponds to the electron spin coherence time of τ

= 1.7 ns, because electron g-factor in InP QDs is 1.5. This observation clearly indicates the spin coherence time of doped electrons in InP QDs is 1.7 ns. The recombination lifetime in InP QDs is 250 ps by the time-resolved PL measurement [1]. The 1.7 ns spin dephasing time of the doped electron is much longer than the recombination lifetime. The time is almost consistent with the estimated electron spin dephasing time in the randomly distributed frozen fluctuation of the nuclear hyperfine field [5]. It is almost consistent with the dispersion of the hyperfine field caused by nuclear spin fluctuation measured from a clear zero-field dip (HWHM = 15mT) in the plot of the circular polarization vs. the longitudinal magnetic field. Dephasing rate increases with the increase of temperature, and its temperature dependence suggests the two-phonon process for dephasing of the electron spin.

This work was supported by the Grant-in-Aid for the Scientific Research #13852003 and #18204028 from the MEXT and "R&D promotion scheme funding international joint research" promoted by NICT of Japan.

REFERENCES

1. M. Ikezawa, B. Pal, Y. Masumoto, I. V. Ignatiev, S. V. Verbin, and I. Ya. Gerlovin, *Phys. Rev. B* **72**, 153302-1–4 (2005).
2. I. E. Kozin, V. G. Davydov, I. V. Ignatiev, A. V. Kavokin, K. V. Kavokin, G. Malpuech, H. -W. Ren, M. Sugisaki, S. Sugou, and Y. Masumoto, *Phys. Rev. B* **65**, 241312(R)-1–4 (2002).
3. B. Pal, M. Ikezawa, Y. Masumoto, and I. V. Ignatiev, *J. Phys. Soc. Jpn.* **75**, 54702-1–5 (2006).
4. Multicomponent Hanle curves for electrons and excitons were observed in *Phys. Rev. B* **66**, 153409-1–4 (2002) by R. I. Dzhioev et al. and *Phys. Solid State* **40**, 2024–2030 (1998) by V. P. Kochereshko et al.
5. I. A. Merkulov, Al. L. Efros, and M. Rosen, *Phys. Rev. B* **65**, 205309-1–8 (2002).

Spin mixing for one and two electron states in quantum dots

T. Grange*, R. Ferreira*, G. Bastard*, E. A. Zibik[†], P. J. Phillips[**], L. R. Wilson[†] and M. S. Skolnick[†]

*Laboratoire Pierre Aigrain, Ecole Normale Supérieure, 24 rue Lhomond, 75005 Paris, France
[†]Department of Physics and Astronomy, University of Sheffield, Sheffield S3 7RH, United Kingdom
[**]FOM Institute Rijnhuizen, PO Box 1207, NL-3430BE, Nieuwegein, Netherlands

Abstract. We consider the role of one-electron spin-dependent couplings on the energy relaxation triggered by polaron disintegration in quantum dots charged with two electrons.

Keywords: quantum dot, polaron, spin
PACS: 73.21.La,71.38.-k,78.67.Hc

One electron confined in a self-assembled InAs/GaAs semiconductor quantum dot (QD) strongly interacts with the longitudinal optical (LO) vibrations of the crystal. This leads to the existence of QD polaron states. These states have been observed through intra-band magneto-optical transmission experiments in the far-infrared [1, 2]. Polarons, however, are not stable entities, because of intrinsic anharmonicity couplings affecting the LO phonons [3, 4]. Time-resolved experiments have allowed the measurement of the lifetime of QD polarons, which is typically of the order of a few tens of ps [5, 6]. The existence of polaron coupling and its intrinsic instability provides a comprehensive framework for understanding the energy relaxation problem in quantum dots.

Recent experiments report the existence of polaron states for quantum dots loaded with two electrons [7]. Moreover, pump-probe experiments at low temperature (4K), which probe the population recovery of the ground state, show a clear biexponential decay of the far-infrared signal, as shown in fig. 1. The initial fast decay time of the 2-electron sample ($\simeq$30ps) is shorter than the one measured for 1-electron ($\simeq$45ps). However, the long time recovery, absent in the 1-electron sample, occurs on a much longer time scale ($\simeq$ 1ns). We show here that the biexponential behavior is related to the existence of singlet and triplet states for dots hosting two electrons. The incident radiation excites the singlet spin state, which may either relax directly to the ground state producing the shorter decay component or relax to the lower energy triplet states. Once in the spin triplet states, relaxation to the ground state is partly blocked, giving rise to the long decay time.

The two-electron singlet and triplet states of the QD are calculated by diagonalizing the direct and exchange Coulomb interactions within a truncated basis of the first three bound one-electron states of a QD: $|s\rangle$, $|p_x\rangle$ and $|p_y\rangle$. The scheme of the low-lying two-electron states

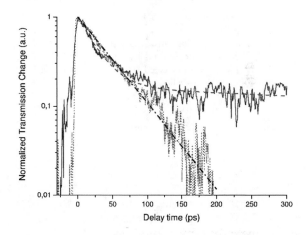

FIGURE 1. Transmission of the probe as a function of the time delay with the pump. Experimental measurement for 1 electron in (red) dotted line and for 2 electron in (blue) solid line. The (black) dot-dashed line is a monoexponential fit of the 1 electron measurement. The (green) dahed line is the numerical simulation for 2 electron described in the text.

is presented in fig. 2 [singlet (triplet) states appear on the left (right) side]. In this figure, $V_A > 0$ is the energy splitting of the $|p_x\rangle$ and $|p_y\rangle$ one-electron states due to the in-plane anisotropy of the QD, and $-V_E < 0$ is the orbital exchange energy that splits singlet and triplet states. For typical quantum dots $V_E > V_A$, and thus the $|sp_x\rangle^T$ and $|sp_y\rangle^T$ sets of triplet states have lower energies than the first excited singlet state $|sp_x\rangle^S$.

Coupling of electrons to LO phonons generate singlet and triplet polaron states. The matrix element at the origin of the polaron is $\sqrt{2}$ stronger for the singlet as

CP893, *Physics of Semiconductors, 28th International Conference*
edited by W. Jantsch and F. Schäffler
© 2007 American Institute of Physics 978-0-7354-0397-0/07/$23.00

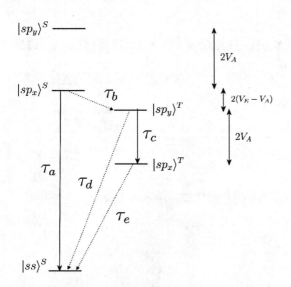

FIGURE 2. Energy diagram of a quantum dots charged with 2 electrons. The superscript S and T stand for singlet and triplet respectively. The solid and dashed arrows are respectively spin-conserving and spin-flip relaxation mechanisms.

compared to the one-electron one :

$$\langle s^1 s^2, 1 | V_F^1 + V_F^2 | \frac{s^1 p_x^2 + p_x^1 s^2}{\sqrt{2}}, 0 \rangle = \sqrt{2} \langle s, 1 | V_F | p_x, 0 \rangle$$

(1)

where $|l^1, l^2, n\rangle$ is a state with the first and second electron in l^1 and l^2 orbital states and having n LO phonon modes entering in the formation of the polaron (V_F is the Fröhlich coupling). As a consequence, the first excited singlet polaron has a larger one-LO phonon component and thus an anharmonic lifetime shorter than the corresponding one-electron polaron probed with the same photon energy in a QD hosting only one electron ($\hbar\omega$ = 55 meV in fig. 1). The triplet polaron states in fig. 2 are on the contrary stable, since the Fröhlich coupling is spin-diagonal. We end-up in this way with a series of independent singlet and triplet polarons. Since coupling to FIR light is also spin-conserving, the only difference in pump-probe experiments would be a faster monoexponential decay in 2-electrons samples with respect 1-electron ones.

In order to explain the long time slow decay in fig. 1, we have to take into account a possible exchange of population between the photoexcited singlet state and the lower energy triplet states. To this aim, we consider the Dresselhaus coupling [8, 9], which is an intrinsic (bulk-related) spin-mixing coupling for the one-electron states of the QD. Indeed, it has been shown to lead to a spin-mixing of the one-electron states and trigger the spin-flip energy relaxation between Zeeman-split spin levels

of QDs in the presence of a magnetic field [11, 12]. The bulk Dresselhaus interaction reads $V_D = \gamma\sigma.\Omega$, where σ is the electron spin in terms of Pauli matrices, $\Omega_x = k_x(k_y^2 - k_z^2)$, ... with k the electron wavevector operator ($k \rightarrow -i\nabla$), and γ a material dependent constant : $\gamma_{GaAs} = 7$ a.u. and $\gamma_{InAs} = 26$ a.u. [10] .

The dashed arrows in fig. 2 correspond to different scattering processes between singlet and triplet polaron states, which become allowed when we consider the Dresselhaus coupling : singlet-to-triplet relaxation assisted by acoustical phonons (deformation potential coupling; τ_b) and triplet-to-singlet disintegration of triplet polarons (anharmonic coupling; τ_d and τ_e). The solid arrows are spin-conserving paths: singlet polaron disintegration (τ_a) and relaxation assisted by acoustical phonons between anisotropy-split triplet states (τ_c). We present in fig. 1, dashed line, the calculation of the population recovery of the ground state after population at t = 0 of the first excited singlet state, and accounting for the different spin-conserving and spin-flip energy relaxation paths. The slow decay at long times is mainly governed by the two spin-flip processes between the singlet and triplet subspaces. The spin-flip rates are roughly proportional to γ^2 : we have used $\gamma = 18$ a.u. in the simulation, which is compatible with the bulk GaAs and InAs values. These results underline the importance of spin-related couplings in the energy relaxation of quantum dots loaded with two or more electrons.

REFERENCES

1. S. Hameau, Y. Guldner, O. Verzelen, R. Ferreira, G. Bastard, J. Zeman, A. Lemaître, and J.M. Gérard, Phys. Rev. Lett. **83**, 4152 (1999).
2. S. Hameau *et al.* , Phys. Rev. B **65**, 085316 (2002).
3. X.-Q. Li, H. Nakayama, and Y. Arakawa, Phys. Rev. B **59**, 5069 (1999).
4. O. Verzelen, R. Ferreira, and G. Bastard, Phys. Rev. B **62**, R4809 (2000).
5. S. Sauvage, P. Boucaud, R. P .S. M. Lobo, F. Bras, G. Fishman, R. Prazeres, F. Glotin, J. M. Ortega, and J. M. Gérard, Phys. Rev. Lett. **88**, 177402 (2002).
6. E. A. Zibik, L. R. Wilson, R. P. Green, G. Bastard, R. Ferreira, P. J. Phillips, D. A. Carder, J-P. R. Wells, J. W. Cockburn, M. S. Skolnick, M. J. Steer, and M. Hopkinson, Phys. Rev. B **70**, 161305(R) (2004).
7. B. Carpenter *et al.*, Submitted to Phys. Rev. B
8. G. Dresselhaus, Phys. Rev. **100**, 580 (1955).
9. M. I. D'yakonov and V. Y. Kachorovski, Sov. Phys. Semicond. **20**, 110 (1986).
10. M. Cardona, N. E. Christensen, and G. Fasol, Phys. Rev. B **38**, 1806 (1988).
11. A. V. Khaetskii and Y. V. Nazarov, Phys. Rev. B **64**, 125316 (2001).
12. M. Kroutvar, Y. Ducommun, D. Heiss, M. Bichler, D. Schuh, G. Abstreiter and J. J. Finley, Nature **432**, 81 (2004).

Selective optical generation of a coherent acoustic nanocavity mode

M. F. Pascual Winter[*,†], G. Rozas[*], B. Jusserand[†], B. Perrin[†], A. Fainstein[*],
P. O. Vaccaro[**] and S. Saravanan[**]

[*]*Centro Atómico Bariloche & Instituto Balseiro, C.N.E.A., 8400 S. C. de Bariloche, Río Negro, Argentina*
[†]*Institut des Nanosciences de Paris, UMR CNRS 7588, Université Pierre et Marie Curie, Campus Boucicaut,*
140 Rue de Lourmel, 75015 Paris, France
[**]*ATR Wave Engineering Laboratories, 2-2-2 Hikaridai, Keihanna Science City, Kyoto 619-0288, Japan*

Abstract. We report the first experimental evidence of selective generation of a confined acoustic mode in a $Ga_{0.85}In_{0.15}As$ nanocavity enclosed by two $Ga_{0.85}In_{0.15}As$/AlAs phonon Bragg mirrors. Femtosecond pump-probe experiments reveal the generation of a cavity mode within the acoustic mini-gap of the mirrors, in addition to their folded acoustic modes. Selective generation of the confined mode alone is achievable for certain energies below the absorption of the quantum wells in the phonon mirrors. These energies are experimentally identified with the cavity spacer electronic transitions. The amplitude of the acoustic nanocavity mode can be controlled by detuning the excitation from the spacer transitions. The present work finds a direct interest in the seek of monochromatic MHz-THz acoustic sources.

Keywords: acoustic, cavity, phonon, semiconductor, pump&probe
PACS: 63.22.+m, 78.47.+p, 42.60.Da, 78.66.Fd

Acoustic nanocavities, which strongly confine MHz-THz sound waves in a spacer enclosed by two phonon Bragg mirrors (superlattices), have proved their interest in the study and manipulation of the electron-phonon and photon-phonon interactions[1]. They are also envisaged as an amplification system for monochromatic acoustic sources in the MHz-THz range[2]. Incoherent confined cavity modes have been experimentally observed through Raman scattering experiments on nanocavities embedded in optical microcavities[1]. Moreover, nanocavities' acoustic transmission and effective confinement properties have been recently evidenced by means of femtosecond pump-probe (p-p) techniques[3]. The aim of the present work is to study the possibility of selectively generating a coherent cavity mode via optical femtosecond impulsions.

We have comparatively studied an acoustic nanocavity and a superlattice (SL). The latter consisted of 24 periods of a $Ga_{0.85}In_{0.15}As$/AlAs unit cell grown on a [001]-oriented GaAs substrate. The SL period was chosen to have the first zone-center mini-gap at ~ 0.54 THz. In order to maximize this mini-gap, the widths of the $Ga_{0.85}In_{0.15}As$/AlAs layers followed the $\frac{\lambda}{4}/\frac{3\lambda}{4}$ relation, where λ is the wavelength (in each material) corresponding to the center of the mentioned mini-gap. This results in layer widths of 21Å/78Å respectively. On the other hand, the acoustic cavity differed from the SL in its central $Ga_{0.85}In_{0.15}As$ layer width which made a $\lambda/2$ spacer. An intermediate $Al_{0.5}Ga_{0.5}As$ stop-layer was included between the substrate and the heterostructure in order to allow for the chemical etching of the substrate.

Laser energy dependent p-p experiments have been performed on both samples at room temperature. Femtosecond pump and probe pulses from a mode-locked Ti:sapphire laser were focused on the same side of the sample (the heterostructure side). Fig. 1 shows the Fourier transform (FT) amplitude of the detected temporal signal, normalized to the non-modulated photodiode voltage; this ratio is proportional to the reflectivity modulation $\Delta R/R$ of the probe beam[4]. Frames (a) and (b) in the figure display the results obtained on the SL and cavity samples, respectively. The number to the left of each spectrum indicates the incident energy in eV. In the 1.734 eV SL spectrum we observe three main peaks. Two of them correspond to folded longitudinal acoustic phonon modes whose wavevector q doubles the incident photon wavevector k_i, and have been labeled $q = 2k_i$. A third peak at an intermediate energy correspond to a folded acoustic phonon with $q = 0$, i.e. at the first Brillouin mini-zone center. Just one mode of the zone center doublet is present due to a parity selection rule. A sharp peak at 0.656 THz (labeled with an asterisk in Fig. 1) is an artifact due to the laser power stability system. For lower laser energies the whole spectrum amplitude decreases until complete extinction at 1.589 eV. This is the expected behavior since we are exploring the SL fundamental transition energy region. We have verified through room temperature photoluminescence (PL) experiments that the SL emission is centered at 1.72 eV.

As for what the cavity concerns, we can see in Fig.

CP893, *Physics of Semiconductors, 28th International Conference*
edited by W. Jantsch and F. Schäffler
© 2007 American Institute of Physics 978-0-7354-0397-0/07/$23.00

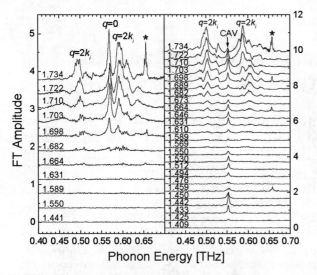

FIGURE 1. Fourier transform amplitude of the normalized reflected probe intensity from the SL (a) and cavity (b) samples. For each spectrum the incident laser energy is expressed in eV.

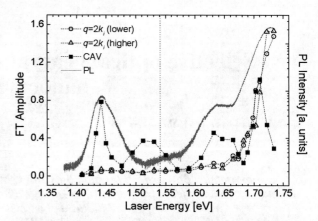

FIGURE 2. FT amplitude of different phonon modes: lower energy $q = 2k_i$ (open circles), higher energy $q = 2k_i$ (open triangles) and cavity mode (filled squares), compared to the PL spectra (gray line).

1 (b) that the spectra are qualitatively different. Aside from the $q = 2k_i$ modes of the two SL's that make the cavity mirrors, there is an additional peak approximately centered with respect to the $q = 2k_i$ doublet. It can be identified as the cavity confined mode. The $q = 0$ mode is not observed and not expected either, since its even parity with respect to the cavity spacer midpoint makes it Raman inactive. The incident energy dependence of the FT amplitude of the $q = 2k_i$ modes has been plotted in Fig. 2 with empty symbols [a circle (triangle) for the mode of lower (higher) energy]. The $q = 2k_i$ modes display the same behavior seen for the SL in Fig. 1 (a): a steep fall at high energies and rather constant negligible values for decreasing energies. On the other hand, the cavity mode displays a different incident energy dependence, depicted in Fig. 2 with filled squares. Its amplitude does not monotonically decrease with decreasing laser energy; it presents several local maxima instead. The first maximum is reached at 1.442 eV, and other local maxima are found at 1.521, 1.631 and 1.710 eV. The former is easily identified with the fundamental transition of the $\lambda/2$ spacer quantum well. Since the emission of such a quantum well is expected in the same energy region as the substrate's emission, room temperature PL experiments have been performed on samples where the substrate had been chemically removed. The results are presented as the gray line in Fig. 2 (right axis). We recognize the spacer fundamental transition at 1.443 eV, in agreement with the FT amplitude maximum. The $\lambda/4$ quantum wells in the acoustic mirrors give the PL peak at 1.728 eV. In order to locate higher transitions of the spacer, photoluminescence excitation (PLE) experiments have been carried out at liquid He temperatures.

We have measured an energy difference of 98 meV between the fundamental and first excited transition. Neglecting temperature effects in the relative energy positions of the transitions, the first excited transition for the spacer quantum well is expected at 1.541 eV at room temperature (dotted vertical line in Fig. 2). This is compatible with our observation of a FT amplitude maximum of the cavity mode in the p-p experiment at laser excitation of 1.521 eV. The higher maxima can be attributed to even higher quantum well transitions.

Summarizing, we have presented the first experimental evidence of selective generation of an acoustic nanocavity mode. This mode has been optically excited through femtosecond laser pulses, ensuring the coherence of the resulting acoustic vibration. The selectivity is attained by tuning the incident energy to the cavity spacer electronic transitions, which should fall below any other transition in the heterostructure. The detuning provides as well a way of controlling the intensity of the generated confined mode.

MFPW acknowledges support from the Programme Alβan, the European Union Programme of High Level Scholarships for Latin America, scholarship No.(E05D051993AR).

REFERENCES

1. M. Trigo, A. Bruchhausen, A. Fainstein, B. Jusserand and V. Thierry-Mieg, Phys. Rev. Lett. **89**, 227402 (2002).
2. P. A. Fokker, J. I. Dijkhuis and H. W. de Wijn, Phys. Rev. B **55**, 2925 (1997).
3. A. Huynh, N. D. Lanzillotti-Kimura, B. Jusserand, B. Perrin, A. Fainstein, M. F. Pascual Winter, E. Peronne and A. Lemaître, this conference proceedings.
4. A. Bartels, T. Dekorsy, H. Kurz and K. Köhler, App. Phys. Lett. **72**, 2844 (1998).

Pump-probe spectroscopy of CuCl exciton-biexciton system in a slab: Aspect of EIT interpretation

Mamoru Sakaue* and Kikuo Cho†

*Fujitsu Laboratories Ltd., Nanotechnology Research Center, Atsugi 243-0197 Japan
†Toyota Physical and Chemical Research Institute, Aichi, Nagakute 480-1192 Japan

Abstract. Theory of pump-probe process for weakly confined exciton-biexciton system is revisited from the viewpoint of EIT proposed recently by Chesi et al. In order to clarify the reason why the EIT window does not come out sharp enough, we study a more detailed model of the dielectric function of a slab by renormalizing the transitions among the size quantized exciton-biexciton levels. Numerical analysis shows that this model gives a better description of EIT behavior than that of "renormalized bulk dielectric function with generalized ABC's" used by Chesi et al.

Keywords: Electromagnetically induced transparency (EIT), pump-probe process, size quantization, renormalized dielectric function
PACS: 78.20.Bh,71.35.Gg,42.65.-k,78.67.-n

INTRODUCTION

In the presence of pump light resonantly coupled with exciton-biexciton transition, there occurs pump-induced changes in the optical spectra of excitons in the frequency region satisfying energy momentum conservation. The physical mechanisms involved in this phenomenon are two-photon absorption, dynamical Stark effect, pump-induced broadening, and so on. For a bulk system, these mechanisms are described by a renormalized dielectric function

$$\varepsilon(\vec{k}, \omega) = \varepsilon_b + \frac{\varepsilon_b \Delta_{LT}}{E_x(\vec{k}) - \hbar\omega - i\gamma - \Sigma}. \quad (1)$$

This is just the dielectric function of an exciton with energy dispersion $E_x(\vec{k})$, if we omit the correction term

$$\Sigma = \frac{\beta}{E_b(\vec{k} + \vec{k}_p) - \hbar\omega - \hbar\omega_p - i\gamma_b}, \quad (2)$$

which accounts for the pump-induced transition between the exciton and biexciton (energy dispersion $E_b(\vec{k})$) states satisfying wave vector conservation in the presence of pump light ($\vec{k}_p, \omega_p$) with coupling strength β.

If one fixes $\vec{k}$, this dielectric function resembles the susceptibility of three-level system with a condition of EIT (electromagnetically induced transparency) [1]. From this analogy, Chesi et al. [2] proposed an EIT type interpretation of the pump probe spectrum when the pump induced change appears in the middle of total reflection range. In spite of the continuous distribution of exciton wave vectors, they find a transmission window which might be interpreted as EIT of exciton-biexciton system. However, this window is much broader than the

typical cases of EIT in atomic systems, and the theoretical method used for this calculation (three branch bulk polaritons based on (1) together with generalized additional boundary conditions (ABC's) [3]) is known half successful in interpreting the observed pump-probe spectra of thin and thick samples of CuCl [4, 5].

With this background in mind, we revisit this problem in terms of a new renormalized nonlinear susceptibilty for size quantized excitons and biexcitons. In a slab, the wave vector conservation is relaxed, and those pairs of exciton-biexciton states with slightly non-conserving wave vectors also contribute to the pump-induced effects. In the weak confinement regime, we have extended the microscopic calculation of the third-order nonlocal nonlinear susceptibility [6], deriving a renormalized form of susceptibility which corresponds to the slab version of (1). Then we find that (2) is replaced with

$$\Sigma_{k,k'}(\omega, \omega_p) = \frac{\varepsilon_b \Delta_{LT} |J/I|^2}{\pi} \sum_{k''} \frac{\tilde{F}_{k,k''}^{(1)}(-\omega_p)\tilde{F}_{k'',k'}^{(1)}(\omega_p)}{E_b(\vec{k''}) - \hbar\omega_p - \hbar\omega - i\gamma_b}, \quad (3)$$

where

$$\tilde{F}_{k,k'}^{(1)}(\omega_p) = \frac{1}{d} \int_0^d dz\, \vec{E}(z, \omega_p) \sin kz \sin k'z. \quad (4)$$

Here $\vec{E}(z, \omega_p)$ denotes the internal pump field in the slab of thickness d, and I and J are defined in terms of the transition dipole moments involving excitons and biexcitons. The effect of the relaxed wave vector conservation is seen in the factor $\tilde{F}_{k,k'}^{(1)}(\omega_p)$, which, in the limit of large slab thickness, gives the same dielectric function as (1) with an extension allowing the presence of forward and internally reflected pump light. In this way, the thickness dependent relaxation of the wave vector conservation is

CP893, *Physics of Semiconductors, 28th International Conference*
edited by W. Jantsch and F. Schäffler

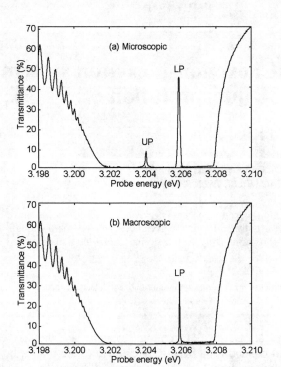

FIGURE 1. Transmittance spectra of a CuCl slab of 1.5 μm thickness obtained by (a) microscopic theory and by (b) macroscopic theory with generalized ABC allowing the internal reflection of pump light. Transmission window originating from the upper polariton is labeled by UP, and that from the lower polariton is labeled by LP.

well described this extension. The assumption of "generalized ABC's" [3] used in the analysis of Chesi et al. is avoided in this nonlocal formulation of nonlinear response, so that the theoretical foundation becomes more reliable. We call this scheme "microscopic" theory and the one used by Chesi et al. "macroscopic" one, and compare the consequences of these schemes in the transmission spectrum.

Numerical result of transmittance spectrum for a slab of 1.5 μm thickness is shown in Figure 1(a). The pump energy is fixed at 3.168 eV and the pump power is 7 kW·cm^{-2}. Sharp transmission windows are observed at 3.204 eV originated from the evanescent component of the upper polariton, and at 3.206 eV from the lower polariton. The sharpness of the windows are caused by the EIT type interference of the transitions among the size quantized exciton and biexciton levels and the ground state satisfying both the energy and momentum conservation. If the relaxed momentum conservation represented by the k and k' dependence of $\Sigma_{k,k'}$ is ignored, i.e., if the momentum conservation is recovered, the spectrum becomes similar to that obtained by Chesi et al. [2].

The main difference in analytical forms of the microscopic theory from the macroscopic theory used before

[2, 3] is concerned with the treatment of the internally reflected pump light. In order to confirm the role of internally reflected pump light, we calculate the same spectra by the macroscopic theory including the effects of the internal reflection of pump light. The obtained result for $\beta = 2.0 \times 10^{-9}$ eV^2 in Figure 1(b) shows a good agreement with the microscopic theory. Though the UP window is missing for this parameter, it appears for $d > 3$ μm. From this result, it is concluded that the interference between the exciton-biexciton transitions in the presence of the incident and internally reflected pump light causes the sharp EIT windows.

In summary, we studied the EIT mechanisms of the exciton-biexciton system in CuCl slabs by a microscopic theory where the transitions among the size quantized exciton-biexciton levels are renormalized in the nonlinear susceptibility. The momentum conservation, as well as energy conservation, in pump-induced transitions is an important factor to have sharp EIT windows. Especially, the interference between the transitions induced by incident and internally reflected pump light is the key mechanism of sharp EIT.

ACKNOWLEDGMENTS

The authors are grateful to Prof. La Rocca for a useful discussion. This work was supported in part by the grant of Japan Science and Technology Agency.

REFERENCES

1. E. Arimondo, *Coherent Population Trapping in Laser Spectroscopy*, Elsevier Sci. B. V., 1996.
2. S. Chesi, et al., *Phys. Rev. Lett.* **91**, 057402 (2003).
3. K. Cho, *J. Phys. Soc. Jpn.* **54**, 4444 (1985).
4. T. Mita, et al., *Solid State Commun.* **44**, 1003 (1982).
5. M. Kuwata, et al., *Solid State Commun.* **45**, 937 (1983).
6. N. Matsuura, and K. Cho, *J. Phys. Soc. Jpn.* **64**, 651 (1995).

All-optical Quantum Coherent Control of Electron Spin in Semiconductor Quantum Dots

Gabriela M. Slavcheva and Ortwin Hess

Advanced Technology Institute, School of Electronics and Physical Sciences, University of Surrey, Guildford, GU2 7XH, Surrey, United Kingdom

Abstract. We develop and apply a new dynamical model for rigorous description of circularly (elliptically) polarized ultrashort optical pulse interactions with the resonant nonlinearities in semiconductor optical waveguides. The method is based on self-consistent solution in the time domain of the vector Maxwell equations for electromagnetic wave propagation coupled via macroscopic polarization to the coherent time-evolution equations of a discrete N-level system in terms of the real pseudospin (coherence) vector. We investigate theoretically the optically-induced ultrafast resonant coherent spin dynamics in a singly charged semiconductor quantum dot. Onset of Rabi oscillations at sufficiently high excitation intensities is demonstrated numerically resulting in suppression of the spin relaxation and a longer decay time of the polarized photoluminescence.

Keywords: ultrafast spin dynamics, coherent and non-linear optics, optical orientation, coherent control, quantum dots, trion, self-induced transparency, solitons, pseudospin vector, Maxwell-Bloch equations.
PACS: 72.25.Fe, 72.25.Rb, 78.67.-n, 78.67.Hc, 42.50.Md, 42.65.Sf, 42.50.Hz, 42.81.Dp

INTRODUCTION

The all-optical spin orientation using circularly polarized optical pulses is a technique of key importance for coherent generation and manipulation of spin-polarised states in semiconductor nanostructures. Coherent quantum control of the electron spin confined in singly charged semiconductor quantum dots (QDs) has recently attracted significant interest because it allows coherent preparation and detection of the single electron spin states on a time scale shorter than typical spin decoherence times. Despite the recent progress made [1], the coherent optical generation and read out of single electron spin states remains a challenging task from experimental point of view. In this paper we address the problem by employing a novel dynamical model of the ultrafast optical circularly polarized pulse interactions with the resonant nonlinearities in a QD.

THEORETICAL MODEL

The electromagnetic wave incident to the generic quantum (0-D or 2-D) system is propagating along the quantization direction z and is elliptically polarized in a plane perpendicular to it. The optical wave centre carrier frequency is tuned in resonance with the fundamental

heavy-hole transition in a QW/trion transition in a singly charged QD (Fig. 1).

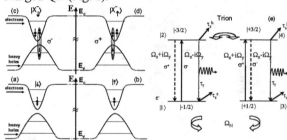

FIGURE 1. Schematic representation of the initial electron states in a single singly-charged quantum dot (a,b) and the ground trion state created by σ^-(c) and σ^+(d) light; (e) Energy-level diagram of a negatively charged exciton (trion) state in a single quantum dot. The levels are labeled by the total angular momentum projection J_z. The coherent optical transitions excited by σ^--and σ^+- polarized light, the spontaneous optical transitions and the spin-relaxation processes involved in the dynamics are designated by arrows.

The dipole-allowed transitions correspond to total angular momentum projection difference $\Delta J_z = \pm 1$ and the fundamental energy gap is $\hbar\omega_0$. The resonant nonlinearity is modeled by an ensemble of four-level systems with density N_a. The time-evolution of the quantum system in an external perturbation in terms of the SU(4) Lie group [4] is given by:

CP893, *Physics of Semiconductors, 28th International Conference*
edited by W. Jantsch and F. Schäffler
© 2007 American Institute of Physics 978-0-7354-0397-0/07/$23.00

$$\frac{\partial S_i}{\partial t} = f_{ijk}\gamma_j S_k - \frac{1}{T_i}\left(S_i - S_{ie}\right) \qquad (1)$$

where the system damping is accounted for by phenomenological non-uniform relaxation times T_i, f is the fully antisymmetric tensor of the structure constants, and the pseudospin S and the torque vector γ are expressed in terms of the λ-generators of SU(4) algebra. The system Hamiltonian is constructed similar to [2] and thus a system describing the time-evolution of the 15-dimensional state vector is obtained. The vector Maxwell equations for the optical wave propagation [2,3] coupled via polarisation to the pseudospin equations (1) are solved self-consistently in the time domain employing the FDTD technique [7].

SIMULATION RESULTS

Trion optically-induced spin dynamics

We apply the model to modulation-doped lens-shaped quantum dots with lateral dimensions largely exceeding the height (Fig. 1). Intense resonant ultrafast optical pulse drives the transitions between the electron and trion states.

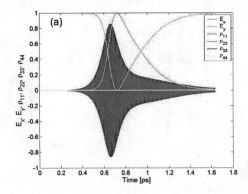

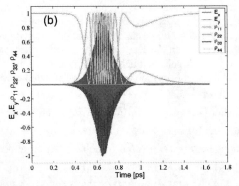

FIGURE 2. Time evolution of the σ^- optical pulse E-field components and the corresponding spin population of all four states. ρ_{22} represents the trion $|-3/2\rangle$ state population for initial spin-down state proportional to the σ^--polarized photoluminescence (initial field amplitude: (a) $E_0=5\times10^6$ Vm^{-1}; (b) $E_0=4\times10^7$ Vm^{-1}).

The system under investigation is a GaAs/AlGaAs self-assembled modulation-doped MBE-grown QD with 5 nm height [1] sandwiched between two 50 nm $Al_{0.3}Ga_{0.7}As$ barriers. The circularly polarized pulse centre frequency $\omega_0= 2.4\times10^{15}$ rad.s^{-1} is tuned in resonance with the energy splitting between the ground electron and trion state [1], corresponding to a wavelength $\lambda=787$ nm and the pulse duration is $T_p=1$ ps modulated by hyperbolic secant envelope. We shall be interested in the low-temperature regime. Transitions between the lower-lying initial electron levels occur due to the hyperfine interaction of the electron spin with the frozen random configuration of the nuclear spins of the lattice ions [6] with spin decoherence times set to 0.5 ns [8]. Transitions between the upper-lying levels also occur due to the hole-spin relaxation in the trion state which is a two-phonon assisted process with relaxation time ~ 1 μs [6]. The trion radiative decay time is set $\tau_r=100$ ps and the crossed transitions are not allowed. In Fig. 2 the initial spin population is assumed to reside in state $|1\rangle$ with $|\downarrow\rangle$ orientation. The evolution of the population ρ_{22} of $|-3/2\rangle$ trion state represents a measure of the intensity of the σ^--polarized photoluminescence, since the rate of the σ^- photon emission is $\sim \rho_{22}/\tau_r$. We demonstrate numerically the appearance of Rabi oscillations at high excitation intensities that suppress the electron spin relaxation [6]. This in turn leads to longer decay times of the photoluminescence and therefore to the possibility of detecting the spin state with greater accuracy. If the initial spin population resides in $|3\rangle$ with $|\uparrow\rangle$ orientation, the optical excitation with the same σ^--polarization does not affect the second system and the spin population of the $|-3/2\rangle$ trion state remains close to zero. This allows differentiation between the two polarizations of the detected polarized photoluminescence and therefore a high-precision measurement of the spin state.

REFERENCES

1. A. Hartmann *et al.*, *Phys. Rev. Lett.* **84**, 5648 (2000); R.J. Warburton *et al.*, *Nature* (London) **405**, 926 (2000) ; J. G. Tischler *at al.*, *Phys. Rev. B* **66**, 081310 (2002); D. Rugar *et al.*, *Nature* (London), **430**, 329 (2004); M Xiao *et al.* , *ibid.*, **430**, 435 (2004).
2. G. Slavcheva and O.Hess, *Phys. Rev. A* **72**, 053804 (2005).
3. G. Slavcheva, J.M. Arnold, I. Wallace, and R. W. Ziolkowski, *Phys. Rev. A* **66**, 063418 (2002).
4. F.T. Hioe and J. H. Eberly, *Phys. Rev. Lett.* **47**, 838 (1981).
5. R. P. Feynman, F. L. Vernon, and R. W. Hellwarth, *J. Appl. Phys.* **28**, 49 (1957).
6. A. Shabaev, Al. L. Efros, D. Gammon, and I. A. Merkulov, Phys. Rev. B **68**, 201305® (2003); I.A. Merkulov, Al. L. Efros, and M. Rosen, *Phys. Rev. B* **65**, 205309 (2002)
7. A. Taflove, *Computational Electrodynamics: The Finite-Difference Time-Domain Method*, Norwood, MA: Artech,, 1995.
8. S. E. Economou, R.-B. Liu, L. J. Sham, and D. G. Steel, *Phys. Rev. B* **71**, 195327 (2005).

Femtosecond polarization relaxation in CdSe nanocrystals

A. Tortschanoff[1], A. Al Salman[1], D. Tonti[1], M. B. Mohamed[1], G. van der Zwan[2], F. van Mourik[1], and M. Chergui[1]

[1]Laboratoire de Spectroscopie Ultrarapide, ISIC, Ecole Polytechnique Fédérale de Lausanne, CH-1015 Lausanne, Switzerland
[2]Vrije Universiteit Amsterdam, Analytical Chemistry and Applied Spectroscopy, Faculty of Sciences, de Boelelaan 1083, 1081 HV Amsterdam, Netherlands.

Abstract. We present ultrafast pump-probe studies on chemically prepared CdSe nanocrystals. Upon pulsed optical excitation we find pronounced oscillations, indicating strong coupling to a LO phonon mode. From the polarization dependence of the signal additional information about the very first coherent events of exciton dynamics is obtained. The observed anisotropy behaviour suggests strongly driven dynamics and rapid coherent motion.

Keywords: CdSe nanodots, anisotropy, ultrafast spectroscopy, exciton fine structure.
PACS: Replace 61.46.Hk, 63.22.+m, 61.20.Lc.

INTRODUCTION

Chemically prepared nanoparticles have attracted much interest in recent years and there is a lot of research concerning the nature and the dynamics of the excited states [1, 2] in these systems.

We studied the initial events in nano-particles upon resonant optical excitation to the lowest excited exciton state, using single color pump-probe spectroscopy. Further information about ultrafast dynamics and *coherent* initial properties at room temperature can be extracted by looking at the polarization dependence.

EXPERIMENTAL

Spherical CdSe colloidal nanocrystals (size range of 2-4 nm diameter) were prepared by a method similar to Talapin et al. [3], according to a procedure outlined elsewhere [4]. The dots we investigated in this work had a diameter of 4 nm and were dissolved in toluene. The absorption spectrum of the sample is shown in the inset of Figure 1.

Single color pump-probe experiments were performed using 50 fs pulses from an optical parametric amplifier which could be tuned across the red edge of the absorption band. Pump and probe beam were linearly polarized with a relative angle of 45° and, after passing the sample (contained in a 0.5 mm flow cell) the parallel and orthogonal components of the probe beam were separated by a cube polarizer and simultaneously detected with two photodiodes. From the parallel and orthogonal differential transmission (T_p and T_o, respectively), it is possible to calculate the isotropic response

$$S(t) = T_p(t) + 2T_o(t) \qquad (1)$$

as well as the time resolved anisotropy

$$r(t) = \frac{T_p(t) - T_o(t)}{T_p(t) + 2T_o(t)}. \qquad (2)$$

RESULTS AND DISCUSSION

Figure 1 shows the results from pump-probe measurements with the laser excitation tuned to two different positions in the lowest exciton band, as indicated in the inset.

The positive signal, we measure, corresponds to bleaching and stimulated emission contributions. No signatures of excited state absorption were found for these wavelengths. Upon resonant excitation on the red edge, we find pronounced oscillations with a period of 170 fs, which are damped out in about 1 ps. These oscillations result from the 205 cm^{-1} LO phonon mode of CdSe, which couples strongly to the optical transition.

CP893, *Physics of Semiconductors, 28th International Conference*
edited by W. Jantsch and F. Schäffler
© 2007 American Institute of Physics 978-0-7354-0397-0/07/$23.00

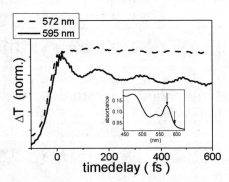

FIGURE 1. Ultrafast dynamics in the pump-probe signal of a CdSe nanodot with excitation at 572 nm (dotted line) and 595 nm (solid line). Curves are normalized and vertically displaced for clarity. Inset shows the absorption spectrum of the nanodot.

Figure 2 shows the results of time-resolved anisotropy measurements at the same wavelengths. After the pulse overlap region, the signal goes through a minimum and then rises up to a small final value, which stays constant on the ps timescale.

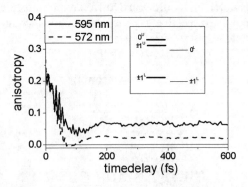

FIGURE 2. Ultrafast anisotropy dynamics in the pump-probe signal of a CdSe nano-dot with different excitation energies. The inset shows a level scheme of the lowest exciton fine-structure (see text for details).

According to theory [1,5] the lowest exciton band splits into five levels, due to electron-hole exchange interaction, the crystal field splitting and deviations from perfect spherical symmetry. These states have different symmetries and are commonly labeled according to the projection of their total angular momentum on the crystal c-axis [1] (c.f. inset of Figure 2). Two of these states are optically forbidden and from the three bright states, the 0^U state has a transition dipole moment parallel to the crystal c-axis, whereas the $\pm 1^{L,U}$ states are double degenerate and orthogonal to the c-axis [1]. From this symmetry splitting, we expect a small finite value of the anisotropy, as we see in our measurements after 150 fs. It is larger for excitation on

the red edge, where one can achieve selectivity for the plane polarized $\pm 1^L$ state.

The most remarkable feature in our experiments is the fact that the anisotropy initially goes through a minimum and rises up from zero, which cannot be explained within a kinetic scheme and clearly indicates a strongly driven coherent process. We believe this to be a signature of the formation of the thermalized exciton and its coupling to the lattice. Following this interpretation, the rise in anisotropy we observe, reflects the "dressing" or "renormalization" of the electron-hole pair [6], which occurs on the time scale of about 100 fs. While the electronic dephasing time of the primary photo-excited electron-hole pairs in CdSe nanocrystals is much less then 100 fs at room temperature [7], equilibration of the charge carriers with the lattice can be slower.

Upon pulsed excitation it takes a while for the electron to equilibrate with the lattice and "feel" the asymmetries, which determine the level splitting and lead to a rise in the anisotropy of the stimulated emission signal.

In conclusion, we presented preliminary ultrafast anisotropy pump-probe measurements, where a very fast rising anisotropy contribution was revealed, which we tentatively attribute to the equilibration of the "bare" excitation with the crystal lattice. Further investigations with better temporal resolution and at different temperatures and dot sizes are planned to verify the interpretation and elucidate the underlying processes and initial coherent effects in detail.

ACKNOWLEDGMENTS

This work was supported by the Swiss NSF via the NCCR: "Quantum Photonics" and Contracts 200020-105344, 205320-101825, and 2000-67912.02.

REFERENCES

1. A. L. Efros, M. Rosen, M. Kuno, M. Nirmal, D. J. Norris, M. Bawendi, Phys. Rev. B **54**, 4843 (1996)
2. U. Woggon, *Optical Properties of Semiconductor Quantum Dots,* Springer Tracts in Modern Physics, Vol. 136, 1996.
3. D. V. Talapin, A. L. Rogach, A. Kornowski, Nanoletters **1**, 207 (2001)
4. D. Tonti, F. van Mourik, and M. Chergui, Nanoletters **4**, 2483 (2004)
5. R. W. Schoenlein, D. M. Mittelman, J. J. Shiang, A. P. Alivisatos, C. V. Shank, Phys. Rev. Lett. **70**, 1014 (1993)
6. M. Hase, M. Kitajima, A. M. Constaninescu, H. Petek, Nature **426**, 51 (2003)
7. R. W. Schoenlein, D. M. Mittelman, J. J. Shiang, A. P. Alivisatos, C. V. Shank, Phys. Rev. Lett. **70**, 1014 (1993)

Anomalous Time Evolution of Exciton Coherence in Highly-stacked InAs Quantum Dots

J. Ishi-Hayase*, K. Akahane*, N. Yamamoto*, M. Kujiraoka*,†, K. Ema† and M. Sasaki*

*National Institute of Information and Communications Technology (NICT), 4-2-1 Nukui-Kitamachi, Koganei-shi, Tokyo 184-8795, Japan
†Department of Physics, Sophia University, 7-1 Kioi-Cho, Chiyoda-Ku, Tokyo 102-8554, Japan

Abstract. We perform a transient four-wave mixing experiment to investigate the initial dynamics of the time evolution of exciton coherence in highly-stacked InAs quantum dots. For short time delays, an oscillatory behavior with a period of 31 ps is observed only in the weak excitation regime. The excitation density and polarization dependence of this oscillation cannot be explained by the usual quantum beat phenomena such as biexcitonic and bright excitonic beats.

Keywords: quantum dots, transient four-wave mixing, coherent spectroscopy, quantum beat
PACS: 68.65.Hb, 42.65.-k

INTRODUCTION

The coherent properties and their manipulation of optical transition in self-assembled quantum dots (SAQDs) have recently received great interest, because they are of key importance in applications of QDs to quantum computing and coherent information processing. Transient four-wave mixing (FWM) is a powerful tool for studying coherent properties even in an inhomogeneously broadened QD ensemble[1]. We recently performed a FWM experiment using strain-compensated InAs SAQDs and investigated the dephasing mechanism for long time delays[2]. In this work, we have investigated, using FWM, the time evolution of exciton coherence in highly-stacked InAs SAQDs, with a special focus on the initial dynamics.

EXPERIMENTS

The sample consisted of 150 layers of InAs SAQDs embedded in 20-nm-thick InGaAlAs spacers grown on an InP(311)B substrate[3]. A schematic of the sample is shown in Fig. 1(a). To reduce the QD strain, our sample was fabricated using a novel strain compensation technique. This enabled us to stack over 100 QD layers, thereby significantly enhancing the FWM signal intensity compared to that of a single layer QD. Both side of our sample were antireflection-coated to prevent multiple reflections. The photoluminescence spectrum at 5 K had a peak of 0.900 eV, which is attributed to the exciton ground-state (GS) emission. The inhomogeneous broadening of the emission energy was 39 meV.

The time evolution of exciton coherence can be directly measured using the transient four-wave mixing

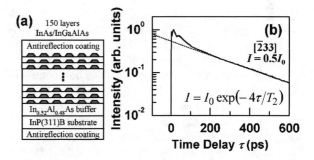

FIGURE 1. (a) Schematic of sample structure. (b) Time-integrated FWM signals versus τ at 5 K for $[\bar{2}33]$ polarization. Dotted line represents fitting curve calculated using a single exponential decay function.

(FWM) technique even in an inhomogeneously broadened QD ensemble. In our experiment, a time-integrated FWM signal in the direction of $2k_1 - k_2$ was recorded as a function of time delay (τ) between two excitation pulses with wave vectors of $k_{1,2}$. The FWM experiment was performed using ~ 0.8-ps optical pulses with a spectral width of ~ 2 meV produced by an optical parametric oscillator. The central energy of the excitation pulses was tuned to 0.888 eV, which was resonant with the inhomogeneously broadened exciton GS transition energy. In all measurements, the excitation intensities of the k_1 and k_2 pulses were identical, and both pulses were linearly polarized. The sample was kept in a closed-cycle He cryostat at 5 K. Neither an external magnetic field nor electric field were applied.

CP893, *Physics of Semiconductors, 28th International Conference*
edited by W. Jantsch and F. Schäffler
© 2007 American Institute of Physics 978-0-7354-0397-0/07/$23.00

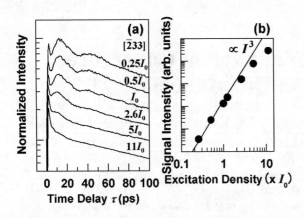

FIGURE 2. (a) FWM signals versus τ for various excitation densites I ($I_0 = 22$ kW/cm^2). Polarization of excitation pulses was in the [$\bar{2}$33] direction. (b) FWM signal intensity of slow component estimated for various I.

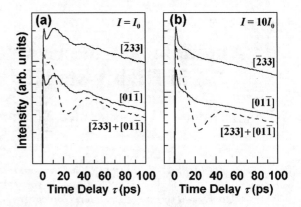

FIGURE 3. FWM signals versus τ at 5 K for various polarization directions of excitation pulses in (a) weak and (b) strong excitation regimes.

RESULTS AND DISCUSSION

Figure 1(b) shows a typical FWM signal in the weak excitation regime. The polarization of excitation pulses is in the [$\bar{2}$33] direction. For $\tau > 100$ ps, the observed FWM signal decays exponentially with a much longer time constant, which reflects the homogeneous broadening of the exciton GS transition. The corresponding dephasing time is estimated to be 1.1 ns. The results of detailed investigation on the slow decay component can be found elsewhere[2]. The fast decay component observed for $\tau < 100$ ps is caused by interaction between excitons and acoustic phonons with relatively higher energies.

Figure 2(a) shows the initial dynamics of the FWM signals up to $\tau = 100$ ps measured for various excitation intensities (I). In the weak excitation regime, below $I_0 = 22$ kW/cm^2, clear oscillations with strong damping are observed (hereafter referred to as "X beat"). As shown in Fig. 2(b), the FWM signal intensity is perfectly proportional to the third order of the excitation density for $I < I_0$, and thus the FWM signals are attributable to $\chi^{(3)}$ processes. The oscillation period of X beats is estimated to be approximately 31 ps, which corresponds to an energy of 130 μeV. In the strong excitation regime, $I > I_0$, the X beat gradually decreases with increasing excitation density and eventually vanished at $I > 10I_0$.

In SAQDs, two type of quantum beats have been observed when no external electric or magnetic field is applied. One is biexcitonic beat. However, the biexciton binding energy in InAs SAQDs is ~ 3 meV, which is much greater than that of the X beat. Therefore, the biexciton is not responsible for the X beat. The other quantum beat is the bright excitonic beat, which is observable under simultaneous excitation of two linearly-polarized exciton GSs. In our SAQDs, exciton GSs are polarized in the [01$\bar{1}$] and [$\bar{2}$33] directions. Therefore, bright excitonic beat should not be observed for the selective excitation for either [011] or [233] polarized GSs. To confirm this, we measured the polarization dependence of FWM signals in the weak and strong excitation regimes. As shown in Fig. 3, bright excitonic beats with a period of 50 ps appears only for the polarization tilted at 45 ° to the [011] ([233]) direction, as shown by the dotted lines in Fig. 3. This bright excitonic beat is observed even in the strong excitation regime, while the X beat disappears at the same excitation density. Moreover, the bright excitonic beat has a maximum at zero delay, as expected. This is very different from the X beat, which has a minimum at zero delay. These results clearly demonstrate that the X beat is not attributed to bright excitons. X beat is a new phenomenon that cannot be explained by any previously reported scheme. It is important to investigate its origin in order to clarify the coherent properties of excitons in SAQDs.

CONCLUSION

In conclusion, we measured transient FWM signals at 5 K in highly-stacked InAs SAQDs. In the weak excitation regime, a beat with a period of 31 ps was clearly observed. Based on the polarization and excitation density dependence, we found that the behavior of the beat was in contrast to the usual quantum beats observed in SAQDs.

REFERENCES

1. P. Borri, et al., Phys. Rev. Lett. **87**, 157401 (2001).
2. J. Ishi-Hayase, et al., Appl. Phys. Lett. **88**, 261907 (2006).
3. K. Akahane, et al., J. Cryst. Growth **245**, 31 (2002).

Polarization-Dependent Four-Wave Mixing Measurements in Highly-stacked InAs Quantum Dots

M. Kujiraoka*,†, J. Ishi-Hayase*, K. Akahane*, N. Yamamoto*, K. Ema† and M. Sasaki*

*National Institutes of Information and Communications Technology (NICT), 4-2-1 Nukui-Kitamachi, Koganei, Tokyo 184-8795, Japan
†Department of Physics, Sophia University, 7-1 Kioi-Cho, Chiyoda-Ku, Tokyo 102-8554, Japan

Abstract. We measure the polarization dependence of four-wave mixing (FWM) signals in highly-stacked InAs quantum dots on an InP(311)B substrate. Dephasing time T_2 and FWM signal intensity show large anisotropy for the crystal axes. The measured T_2 is determined only by the exciton population lifetime, and thus the polarization dependence of T_2 reflects the difference of the transition dipole moments related to bright exciton states with orthogonally linear polarizations.

Keywords: quantum dots; dephasing; coherent spectroscopy, optical anisotropy
PACS: 78.67.Hc; 78.47.+p; 42.50.Md

INTRODUCTION

Self-assembled quantum dots (SAQDs) are regarded as artificial atoms, and have opened a new and exciting field in quantum information technology[1]. In contrast to real atoms, the electron-hole exchange interaction lifts the degeneracy of optically active ("bright") exciton states which results in the energy splitting between these states. Such splitting has been observed in the single-dot photoluminescence (PL) spectroscopy with high spectral resolution. However, thus far there have been few reports describing the difference of homogeneous broadening between bright exciton states[2]. In this presentation, we measure the polarization dependence of dephasing time (T_2) by a transient four-wave mixing (FWM) technique in InAs SAQDs on an InP(311)B substrate in detail. Our results demonstrate that T_2 significantly depends on the polarization of excitation pulses reflecting the difference of T_2 between bright excitons states.

SAMPLE AND EXPERIMENTS

The sample in this work is fabricated by molecular beam epitaxy and contains 150 layers of InAs SAQDs embedded in 60 nm thick $In_{0.46}Ga_{0.11}Al_{0.43}As$ spacers [3]. To compensate for QD strain, the composition of spacers is precisely tailored and an InP(311)B substrate is used instead of a GaAs one. Owing to the strain compensation, QD density can be increased to $10^{12}/cm^2$ keeping the QD size uniformity, which improves a signal-to-noise ratio in optical measurements[1].

T_2 is measured by a transient FWM technique using 1.1 ps optical pulses emitted by an optical parametric

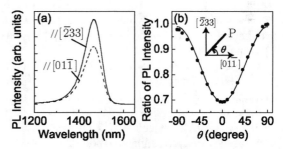

FIGURE 1. (a) PL spectra for polarizations along $[\bar{2}33]$ (solid line) and $[01\bar{1}]$ (dashed line), (b) Ratio of PL intensity for polarization θ (filled circles) and fitting results (solid line).

oscillator. The wavelength of excitation pulses is tuned to the central wavelength of the exciton ground-state (GS) emission, 1.468 μm [refer to Fig. 1(a)]. We measure time-integrated FWM signals in the direction of $2\boldsymbol{k}_1 - \boldsymbol{k}_2$ as a function of time delay τ between two excitation pulses. The excitation density is adjusted to 16 kW/cm², for which the nonlinear response is in the third-order regime.

RESULTS AND DISCUSSION

We first measure the polarization dependence of PL spectra at 3K under non-resonant and weak excitation. The dashed and solid curves in Fig. 1(a) show PL spectra for polarization along the $[\bar{2}33]$ and $[01\bar{1}]$ directions, respectively. PL bands observed at 1.468 μm in both polarization configurations are attributed to the exciton GS emission. The PL intensity shows clear polarization dependence, i.e., an optical anisotropy. The degree of polariza-

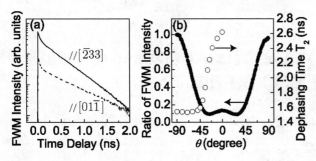

FIGURE 2. (a) FWM signals for polarization along $[\bar{2}33]$ (solid line) and $[01\bar{1}]$ (dashed line), (b) Polarization dependence of T_2 (open circles) and ratio of FWM intensity at θ (filled circles). The definition of θ is the same as Fig. 1

tion defined by $(I_{\mathrm{PL}}([\bar{2}33]) - I_{\mathrm{PL}}([01\bar{1}]))$ $(I_{\mathrm{PL}}([\bar{2}33]) + I_{\mathrm{PL}}([01\bar{1}]))$ is estimated to be approximately 19 %. Figure 1(b) plots the ratio of PL intensity at 1.468 μm for the polarization angle θ, where θ represents the angle between polarization and [011] directions. As shown by the solid line in Fig. 1(b), the result can be fitted by $I_{\mathrm{PL}}(\theta) = X \sin^2 \theta + Y \cos^2 \theta$ where X and Y corresponds to peak intensities of PL for polarization along $[\bar{2}33]$ and $[01\bar{1}]$, respectively.

This optical anisotropy indicates that QD rotational invariance is broken in our QDs. In this case, exciton ground states are split to two nondegenerate states. In our QDs, these states correspond to linearly polarized states along $[01\bar{1}]$ and $[\bar{2}33]$ which was confirmed by FWM measurements using cross-linearly polarized excitation pulses (not shown here). Observed optical anisotropy of PL spectra reflects the difference of the transition dipole moment related to $[01\bar{1}]$ and $[\bar{2}33]$ polarized states. The splitting energy between $[01\bar{1}]$ and $[\bar{2}33]$ polarized states is approximately 165 μeV which is estimated from the period of the quantum beats observed in FWM signals.

Figure 2(a) shows FWM signals at 3 K when the polarization of excitation pulses is along $[\bar{2}33]$ (solid line) and $[01\bar{1}]$ (dashed line). For $[\bar{2}33]$ ($[01\bar{1}]$) polarization, only $[\bar{2}33]$ ($[01\bar{1}]$) polarized exciton state contributes to FWM signals. Both of relaxation profiles and signal intensities are quite different by polarization directions. The open circles in Fig. 2(b) show T_2 as a function of θ. T_2 has a minimum 1.54 ns for $[\bar{2}33]$ polarization and a maximum 2.60 ns for $[01\bar{1}]$ polarization. These values can be converted to the homogeneous broadening γ_{ex} for $[\bar{2}33]$ and $[01\bar{1}]$ polarized states. Corresponding γ_{ex} are 0.85 μeV for $[\bar{2}33]$ polarized state and 0.50 μeV for $[01\bar{1}]$ polarized state. Our result demonstrates that the γ_{ex} for $[\bar{2}33]$ and $[01\bar{1}]$ polarized states are quite different from each other. Such difference has not been observed in a single-dot PL spectroscopy. The polarization dependence of T_2 can be reproduced by considering an ensemble average of the contribution of $[\bar{2}33]$ and $[01\bar{1}]$ polarized states.

This shows that observed T_2 for the polarization tilted to the $[\bar{2}33]$ and $[01\bar{1}]$ directions does not represents the intrinsic T_2 of eigenstates of excitons. Therefore, one have to pay careful attention to polarizations with respect to crystal axes in optical measurements to evaluate T_2 properly.

The dephasing time is determined from the exciton population lifetime T_1 and pure dephasing time T_2^{pure} as 1 $T_2 = 1$ $2T_1 + 1$ T_2^{pure}. From pump-probe measurements, T_1 is estimated to be 0.96 ns and 1.6 ns for $[\bar{2}33]$ and $[01\bar{1}]$ polarized states, respectively. This indicates that T_2 is almost determined by T_1, and thus the pure dephasing does not contribute to the measured T_2 so much at low temperature. Therefore, the polarization dependence of T_2 is governed by the polarization dependence of T_1. If an energy relaxation occurs via a radiative process, T_1 depends on a transition dipole moment. As discussed for the PL measurements, the transition dipole moment in our sample shows polarization dependence. Hence, the polarization dependence of T_2 originates from the anisotropy of transition dipole moments.

This is consistent for the results of temperature-dependent measurements of FWM signals. T_2 at 20K is not anisotropic. At finite temperature the phonon-exciton interaction is large and the contribution of the isotropic T_2^{pure} becomes significant. As a result, T_2 becomes isotropic.

The filled circles in Fig. 2(b) show the ratio of FWM intensity at the polarization angle θ. The result is much different from the polarization dependence of PL intensity and T_2. There is no report showing such a polarization dependence of FWM signal intensity. The mechanism will be discussed in a future publication.

CONCLUSION

We measure polarization dependence of FWM and PL signals in stacked InAs SAQDs on an InP(311)B substrate. Our QDs show large in-plane anisotropy as dephasing time T_2 varies from 1.54 to 2.60 ns and the degree of polarization is estimated to about 19 %. This demonstrates that one should consider polarizations in evaluating dephasing time T_2 properly. The measured T_2 is almost determined by the exciton population lifetime, and thus the polarization dependence of T_2 reflects the anisotropy of transition dipole moment at low temperature.

REFERENCES

1. J. Ishi-Hayase, et al., Appl. Phys. Lett. **88**, 261907 (2006).
2. W. Langbein, et al., Phys. Rev. **B 70**, 033301 (2004).
3. K. Akahane, et al., J. Cryst. Growth **245**, 31 (2002).

Phonon-Induced Exciton Dephasing in CdTe Self-Organized Quantum Dots

T. Kishimoto[1], H. Takahashi[1], Y. Ogawa[1], F. Minami[1], S. Kuroda[2] and K. Takita[2]

[1]Department of Physics, Tokyo Institute of Technology, Meguro-ku, Tokyo 152-8551, Japan
[2]Institute of Materials Science, University of Tsukuba, Tsukuba, Ibaraki 305-8573, Japan

Abstract. Time-resolved four-wave mixing technique (FWM) is used to study the phonon induced dephasing of the excitons in CdTe self-assembled quantum dots. The FWM signals show two different decay structures with fast and slow decay components, indicating a non-Lorentzian lineshape with a zero-phonon line and a broadband from exciton-acoustic phonon interaction in the spectral region. The dephasing of the zero-phonon line and the sideband components both show non-linear characteristics with respect to temperature. The experimental data are reproduced well by a theoretical model taking into account the carrier-acoustic phonon coupling.

Keywords: Four-wave mixing; Dephasing; CdTe
PACS: 42.50.Md, 71.38.-k, 78.55.Et, 78.67.Hc

INTRODUCTION

Quantum dots (QDs) are one of the major areas in semiconductor research. The homogeneous linewidth is basic characteristics for the interaction of light with matters. The QD system is insensitive to inelastic scattering by acoustic phonons due to the absence of suited states between the discrete energy levels, which results in a dephasing time limited by the radiative lifetime. The dephasing time is addressed mainly by measuring the homogeneous linewidth by a single-dot spectroscopy. The lineshape shows a non-Lorentzian with a zero-phonon line (ZPL) and a phonon sideband [1-3]. The radiative limit of the homogeneous linewidth of the photoluminescence (PL) spectra was not attained, probably due to a dynamical broadening caused by a spectral shift of the lines, i.e., spectral diffusion [4,5]. A narrow linewidth means a long dephasing time and its measurement is easily accessible from the time domain [5]. Here, we present the temperature dependence of dephasing obtained from FWM in CdTe self-assembled QDs. The polarization has a nonexponential decay dynamics with fast and slow components.

EXPERIMENT AND RESULTS

The samples used here were CdTe self-organized QDs grown on a (1 0 0) surface of ZnTe by molecular beam epitaxy [6]. The typical size of QDs is 20 nm in diameter and 2.5 nm in height. The density of the QDs is about 6×10^9 cm^{-2}. The laser source was an optical parametric oscillator, with pulse duration of ~150 fs, pumped synchronously by a mode-locked Ti:sapphire laser. The laser spectrum was centered on the exciton ground state transition. The FWM signal was detected in the $2k_2 - k_1$ direction in reflection geometry. The FWM signals have been measured at temperatures of $5K \leq T \leq 50K$. The decay profile showed no excitation power dependence, indicating that carrier-carrier scattering does not contribute to the dephasing process.

Fig. 1(a) shows the decay profiles of the FWM signals for several temperatures. The decay consists of an initial fast decay followed by a longer exponential decay. According to the PL spectra of the single QDs, which show the non-Lorentzian lineshape [1,3], we attribute the fast decay to the phonon sideband and slow one to the ZPL. With increasing temperature, the decay becomes faster and the sideband component increases. The sideband arises from the absorption or emission of the acoustic phonon. From the decay curves, we can extract the dephasing time T_2 of both components. The homogeneous linewidth $\Gamma (= 2\hbar/T_2)$ is shown versus temperature in Fig. 1(b,c). The full width at half maximum (FWHM) of the ZPL and the sideband are denoted as Γ_1 and Γ_2, respectively. Note that Γ_2 above 20 K are not plotted since the signal decay becomes faster than the pulse duration time. So we refer to the experimental data of PL measurements [3]. The linewidth is increased with temperature,

CP893, *Physics of Semiconductors, 28th International Conference*
edited by W. Jantsch and F. Schäffler
© 2007 American Institute of Physics 978-0-7354-0397-0/07/$23.00

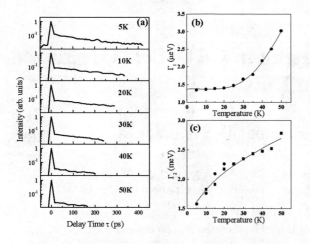

FIGURE 1. Time-integrated four-wave mixing at different temperatures (a). The FWHM of the ZPL (b) and of the phonon sideband (c) estimated from the measured dephasing time as a function of temperature. The points are the experimental data, and the line is the theoretical calculation. In (b) the squares are the experimental data of Ref. [3].

because the contribution of the phonon sideband becomes larger. Therefore, the sideband continues to increase with respect to the ZPL, further deviating from the shape of a Lorentzian.

To understand the effect of the temperature on the dephasing, we consider the temperature dependence of Γ_1 and Γ_2 as separate components of the dephasing. Γ_1 increases superlinearly with temperature. On the other hand, Γ_2 shows a sublinear dependence. In a QD the phonon coupling cannot be seen to be weak, and a nonperturbative treatment of the carrier-phonon coupling is required [2]. The theoretical lineshape for QDs is given by the Fourier transform of the dipole-dipole correlation function $P(t)$. By using the cumulant technique, we obtain the following expansion form [3]

$$P(t) = \exp[-i\omega_0 t - S(t)] \qquad (1)$$

$$S(t) = \int_0^t dt_1 \int_0^{t_1} dt_2 \langle V(t_1)V(t_2)\rangle = \int_0^t d\tau (t-\tau)\langle V(\tau)V(0)\rangle. \quad (2)$$

where $\hbar\omega_0$ is the transition energy, and $V(t)$ is the interaction Hamiltonian describing the fluctuations in the transition energy. The ZPL shape is governed by the long-time behavior of the function $S(t)$ [2]. The ZPL is found to have a Lorentzian lineshape with

FWHM $\Gamma_1 = \int_{-\infty}^{\infty} d\tau \langle V(\tau)V(0)\rangle$. To obtain the

temperature dependence of Γ_1, we take into account the linear and quadratic interactions of $\langle V(t)V(0)\rangle$.

The quadratic interaction, which arises the two-phonon process, contributes to the ZPL. The pure dephasing arises from the fluctuation of the excitonic energy due to emission and absorption of phonons at the same time. When virtual transitions to the next hole level occurs, Γ_1 is proportional to $\sinh^{-2}(\hbar\omega/2kT)$, where $\hbar\omega$

is the energy distance to the next hole level. In such a case, the theoretical line is approximated as

$$\Gamma_1 = \Gamma_0 + \Gamma \sinh^{-2}(\hbar\omega/2kT). \qquad (3)$$

The first term represents the temperature independent broadening. The best fit is obtained for $\Gamma_0 = 1.4$ μeV, $\Gamma = 5.6$ μeV and $\hbar\omega = 12$ meV.

The shape of the phonon sideband is determined by the short-time behavior of $S(t)$ [2]. The lineshape of the sideband becomes a gaussian with width $\Gamma_2 = 2\sqrt{2\ln 2}\sqrt{\langle V^2(0)\rangle}$. In this case, the lineshape is described by the linear term. Therefore, $\langle V^2(0)\rangle$ is found to be proportional to T. As the result, Γ_2 has $\sqrt{T}$ dependence. The experimental data obey the theoretical prediction.

CONCLUSIONS

The temperature dependence of the dephasing process in CdTe QDs is investigated. We find the dephasing time at low temperature is several hundred picoseconds, which corresponds to only a few μeV homogeneous broadening. The polarization decay shows nonexponential dynamics with two components, which correspond to the ZPL and the phonon sideband.

ACKNOWLEDGMENTS

This work was supported by a 21st Century COE Program at Tokyo Tech "Nanometer-Scale Quantum Physics" by the Ministry of Education, Culture, Sports, Science and Technology, by the Grant-in-Aid for Scientific Research from the Ministry of Education, Culture, Sports, Science and Technology of Japan, and by the Strategic Information and Communications R&D Promotion Scheme.

REFERENCES

1. L. Besombes, K. Kheng, L. Marsal and H. Mariette, Phys. Rev. B **63**, 155307 (2001).
2. E. A. Muljarov and R. Zimmermann, Phys. Rev. Lett. **93**, 237401 (2004).
3. K. Ikeda, Y. Ogawa, F. Minami, S. Kuroda, and K. Takita, Phys. Stat. Sol. C **3**, 874-877 (2006).
4. V. Türck, S. Rodt, O. Stier, R. Heitz, R. Engelhardt, U. W. Pohl, and D. Bimberg, Phys. Rev. B **61**, 9944-9947 (2000).
5. D. Birkedal, K. Leosson, and J.M. Hvam, Phys. Rev. Lett. **87**, 227401(2001).
6. Y. Terai, S. Kuroda, K. Takita, T. Okuno, Y. Masumoto, Appl. Phys. Lett. **73**, 3757-3759 (1998).

Energy Dependence of the Linear and Dynamical Photo-Induced Dichroisms of InAs/GaAs Quantum Dots

E. Aubry[1], F. Bernardot[1], J. Tribollet[1], C. Testelin[1],
M. Chamarro[1], and J.-M. Gérard[2]

[1] *Institut des NanoSciences de Paris – Universités Paris-6 et Paris-7, CNRS UMR 7588 –*
Campus Boucicaut – 140, rue de Lourmel – 75015 Paris – France
[2] *Nanophysics and Semiconductors Laboratory – CEA/DRFMC/SP2M –*
17, rue des Martyrs – 38054 Grenoble cedex – France

Abstract. We present pump-probe measurements of the photo-induced dynamics of the lowest electron-hole (e-h) transitions in ensembles of InAs/GaAs quantum dots, as a function of interband emission energy 1.30–1.40 eV. We used two different beam-polarization configurations to obtain information on the electronic structure of both e-h states, and on their relaxation and decoherence. In linear dichroism experiments, we address the population evolution of the e-h states: we measured two different e-h radiative times, with almost constant mean value 1 ns and ratio 0.8–0.9. In dynamical dichroism experiments, we observe the evolution of the coherence between the e-h states: we deduced an inhomogeneous decoherence time 10–25 ps, and an energy splitting monotonically decreasing with emission energy, from 80 to 20 µeV.

Keywords: Quantum dots. III-V semiconductors. Ultra-fast optical measurements.
PACS: 78.67.Hc 78.66.Fd 78.47.+p

SAMPLE AND SET-UP

The in-plane symmetry of the low-lying e-h states in InAs/GaAs self-assembled quantum dots (QDs), is reduced with respect to the in-plane symmetry of the corresponding quantum well states. This symmetry lowering induces a splitting of both e-h states *via* the anisotropic term of the long-range e-h exchange interaction, leading to a doublet linearly polarized[1,2] along the [110] and [1$\bar{1}$0] axes, and having slightly different oscillator strengths.[3] The studied sample is made of 40 layers of self-assembled InAs/GaAs QDs grown by molecular beam epitaxy. The mean density of the QDs is $4\ 10^{10}\ \text{cm}^{-2}$ per layer, with a typical dot height of 5 nm and a diameter of 15 nm. The photoluminescence (PL) spectrum[4] at 2 K shows a maximum at 1.34 eV and a full width at half maximum of about 60 meV.

In our experiments, pump and probe pulses have a duration of 2 ps. The average intensity of the pump is about $1\ \text{W/cm}^2$, and typically ten times larger than the probe intensity. Measurements are performed at 2 K. Two different pump-probe polarization configurations have been used[5]: the pump beam aligned with [110] or [1$\bar{1}$0], and the transmitted probe beam analysed along parallel and perpendicular directions, give photo-induced linear dichroism; the pump beam unaligned with [110] nor with [1$\bar{1}$0] builds up a quantum coherence between both e-h states, and the proper measurement of the transmission of an incident [110] probe beam, gives an oscillatory photo-induced dynamical dichroism.

LINEAR DICHROISM

Figure 1 shows the measured linear dichroism decay curves, for a pump and probe beam energy of 1.343 eV. The upper curve corresponds to a pump linearly polarized along the vertical direction with respect to the experimental set-up, and the lower one corresponds to a pump linearly polarized along the horizontal direction. Horizontal and vertical directions are parallel to the two crystallographic axes [110] and [1$\bar{1}$0]. The curves are non-symmetric with respect to the zero line, both in amplitude and in characteristic damping time; that is a consequence of the difference in the oscillator strengths of the e-h states. We measure a very short decay time of 20 ps and a longer one in the nanosecond scale. The short component disappears for higher-energy QDs, and is attributed to large-sized QDs excited in the second-excited states of the e-h

CP893, *Physics of Semiconductors, 28th International Conference*
edited by W. Jantsch and F. Schäffler
© 2007 American Institute of Physics 978-0-7354-0397-0/07/$23.00

pair[6]. The long-time decay is associated to the resonant excitation of the e-h states in small QDs, which is the studied situation.

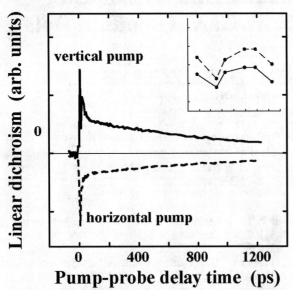

FIGURE 1. Photo-induced linear dichroism, at 1.343 eV. (Insert: both long-time decays *vs.* emission energy.)

Assuming a very long spin relaxation between the e-h states[7], mono-exponential fits of the long-time decays of Fig.1 give $\tau_V = 1038 \pm 18$ ps and $\tau_H = 1164 \pm 36$ ps, which leads to an oscillator strengths ratio $r = d_H^2/d_V^2 = \tau_V/\tau_H = 0.89 \pm 0.04$, according to the Fermi golden rule $\tau^{-1} \propto d^2$. These mean decay times are in good agreement with time-resolved PL[7] on the same sample, which have demonstrated an e-h radiative decay of about 1 ns, at 1.33 eV. In the emission energy range of the studied QDs (1.30–1.40 eV), τ_V and τ_H do not vary much around 1 ns (see insert in Fig.1), and the oscillator strengths ratio r remains within 0.8–0.9.

DYNAMICAL DICHROISM

Figure 2 shows the dynamical dichroism decay curve obtained with a circular pump beam, for a pump and probe beam energy of 1.343 eV. The signal-*vs.*-delay curve clearly shows a damped sine oscillation. Fitting of this curve to an exponentially damped sine function, give a period of 100 ± 20 ps, from which we deduce the mean energy splitting $\hbar\delta_1 = 41 \pm 8$ μeV between the linear e-h states. The fitting curve also gives a lower limit to the value of the decoherence time for a QD: $T_2^* = 16$ ps. This value, very small as compared to the radiative lifetime (around 1 ns), is likely to result from a wide distribution of the energy splitting $\hbar\delta_1$ over the collection of measured QDs, this distribution including possibly positive and negative energy splittings. Our results are consistent with time-resolved PL measurements[7] on the same sample, which yield $\hbar\delta_1 = 30 \pm 3$ μeV and $T_2^* = 30$ ps. They are also comparable to $T_2^* = 58$ ps and $\hbar\delta_1 = 40$ μeV obtained by Lenihan *et al.*[8]. Tartakovskii *et al.*[9] have obtained, at 10K, in self-assembled InAs QDs with a very narrow distribution of splitting energies, a decoherence time of 400ps, comparable to the lifetime.

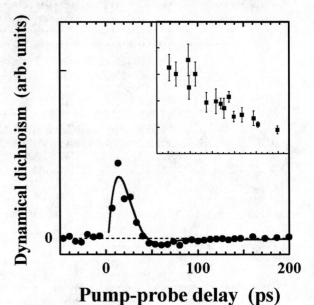

FIGURE 2. Photo-induced dynamical dichroism, at 1.343 eV. Dots represent experimental data for a circular pump; the line is a fitting to a damped sine function. (Insert: e-h energy splitting *vs.* emission energy.)

In the emission energy range of the studied QDs, from 1.30 eV to 1.40 eV, T_2^* remains within 10–25 ps, while the energy splitting $\hbar\delta_1$ monotonically decreases[10] from 80 μeV to 20 μeV (see insert in Fig.2). Similar decreasing $\hbar\delta_1$ with emission energy has already been observed.[11–14]

References

1. M. Bayer *et al.*, Phys. Rev. Lett. **82**, 1748 (1999)
2. L. Besombes *et al.*, Phys. Rev. Lett. **85**, 425 (2000)
3. A.J. Williamson *et al.*, Phys. Rev. B **62**, 12963 (2000)
4. J. Tribollet *et al.*, Phys. Stat. Sol. (c) **1**, 585 (2004)
5. F. Bernardot *et al.*, Phys. Rev. B **73**, 85301 (2006)
6. S. Hinooda *et al.*, Appl. Phys. Lett. **75**, 3530 (1999)
7. M. Sénès *et al.*, Phys. Rev. B **71**, 115334 (2005)
8. A.S. Lenihan *et al.*, Phys. Rev. Lett. **88**, 223601 (2002)
9. A.I. Tartakovskii *et al.*, Phys. Rev. Lett. **93**, 57401 (2004)
10. C. Testelin *et al.*, Phys. Stat. Sol. (c) (2006), to be published
11. W. Langbein *et al.*, Phys. Rev. B **69**, 161301(R) (2004)
12. R.J. Young *et al.*, Phys. Rev. B **72**, 113305 (2005)
13. A. Greilich *et al.*, Phys. Rev. B **73**, 45323 (2006)
14. R. Seguin *et al.*, Phys. Rev. Lett. **95**, 257402 (2005)

Two-Photon Excitation of Asymmetric GaN/AlGaN Quantum Discs

Kwan H Lee[1], Jong H Na[1], Stefan Birner[2], Sam N Yi[1], Robert A Taylor[1], Young S Park[3], Chang M Park[3], and Tae W Kang[3]

[1]Department of Physics, University of Oxford, Parks Road, Oxford, OX1 3PU, United Kingdom [2]Walter Schottky Institute and Physics Department, Technical University of Munich, D-85748 Garching, Germany [3]Quantum-functional Semiconductor Research Center, Dongguk University, Seoul 100-715, South Korea

Abstract. By using two-photon absorption spectroscopy we have performed time-integrated and time-resolved photoluminescence measurements on several coupled asymmetric GaN quantum discs, with embedded AlGaN barriers. We observe free-carrier screening, with an enhancement due to tunneling between the coupled quantum discs.

Keywords: GaN, two-photon excitation, nanocolumns, quantum discs.
PACS: 78.67.Bf, 78.47.+p, 78.30.Fs

INTRODUCTION

Self-organized GaN nanocolumns have gained interest in application for blue/ultra-violet wavelength optoelectronic devices. They possess desirable properties such as low defect density, good reproducibility, quantum confinement effects and can be produced using conventional growth techniques. These properties make nanocolumns an attractive basis for novel quantum optoelectronic devices (e.g. for quantum information processing [1]) and significant progress has been made towards practical devices [2].

Quantum well (QW) like structures grown at the tip of GaN nanocolumns are known as quantum discs (Q-discs) and demonstrate lateral confinement. By using two-photon absorption (TPA) spectroscopy we have performed time-integrated (TI-) and time-resolved (TR-) photoluminescence (PL) measurements on several coupled asymmetric GaN quantum discs. TPA is achieved using a high peak-power, pulsed laser, so that two-photons at wavelengths below the bandgap are absorbed simultaneously. Being a non-linear process, an attractive feature of two-photon excitation is the increased spatial resolution, relative to single photon excitation. We take advantage of this property to allow selective excitation and measurement of Q-discs. In III-nitride TPA spectroscopy has been limited to QW [3], but not nanocolumns.

SAMPLE DETAILS

GaN/AlGaN Q-discs samples studied were grown at the tip of a 2.7-μm-high GaN nanocolumn, with the nanocolumn and Q-disc grown by plasma assisted MBE on a Si (111) substrate without any buffer layer [4]. The GaN nanocolumns exhibited an average diameter of 100 nm and a density of $1 \times 10^9\ cm^{-2}$. The samples consisted of ten periods of two alternating GaN Q-disc thicknesses (4nm – DA and 3 nm – DB) separated by a 1.2 nm $Al_{0.5}Ga_{0.5}N$ barrier.

RESULTS

Details of the apparatus used for TI-PL and TR-PL measurements can be found in our earlier work [5]. The only changes being that excitation was performed at 415 nm for TPA.

Spectra as a function of excitation power ranging from 2.5 to 9 mW (at the focus) are presented in Fig. 1. We ensured that only a few Q-discs were excited by maximizing the intensity of the DA peak through precise movements of the piezo-stage. Further discussions of the spatial dependence will be given later. The inset in Fig. 1 shows the relationship between the peak intensity and excitation power for DA and DB peaks. The DB peak intensity displayed quadratic (slope = 2) dependence with excitation power (i.e. equivalent of linear PL dependence under

CP893, *Physics of Semiconductors, 28th International Conference*
edited by W. Jantsch and F. Schäffler
© 2007 American Institute of Physics 978-0-7354-0397-0/07/$23.00

single photon absorption conditions), while DA peak intensity displayed a higher order dependence (slope > 2) with excitation power. This observation is consistent with earlier studies involving GaAs/AlGaAs asymmetric QWs, which demonstrated nonlinear PL dependence with excitation power, due to carrier tunneling [6]. Lastly, results from next**nano**[3] computer modeling [7] demonstrate that carriers in DB are energetic enough to tunnel into DA, whilst carriers in DB are highly localized.

Figure 2 illustrates the increased spatial resolution offered by TPA spectroscopy by demonstrating that only several Q-discs (1 or 2) were excited by the beam. We excited the sample at 9 mW and observed the resulting TI-PL spectrum as the beam was moved laterally over the sample using the piezo-stage. Under these conditions, over region of interest, the DA peak intensity rapidly decreased for ~±200 nm radial movements from the peak. This is supported by the fact that the nanocolumns have an average diameter of ~100 nm and an average density of ~10/μm^2. Spatially dependent TI-PL spectra obtained under single photon (266 nm) excitation conditions excitation did not change the DA peak intensity significantly, even with ±1 μm lateral movements.

By using the increased spatial resolution offered by TPA spectroscopy, we performed TR-PL measurements on several Q-discs. Figure 3 show the TR-PL trace collected from the DA and DB peaks, at high (9 mW) and low (2.5 mW) excitation power. The TR-PL traces show a mono-exponential decay at low excitation power, with fitted lifetimes of 360 ps for DA and 310 ps for DB. At high excitation power the lifetimes decreased to 240 ps and 290 ps. In addition, DA trace showed a bi-exponential decay with a fast component of 140 ps.

The decrease in lifetime with increasing optical excitation could be explained by free-carrier screening [8], which compensates the built-in piezo- and pyroelectric field (responsible for the QCSE). The photo-generated free-carriers screen the built-in fields, which then leads to a reduction in the band structure tilt and consequently the overlap between electron and hole increases (decreased carrier lifetime). However this effect is more significant in DA due to the tunneling, which provides additional free-carriers. This observation is further supported by the TR-PL measurements on DA in the absence of electron tunneling – by deliberately moving the beam away from the nanocolumn by 400 nm, whilst under high excitation power. Here, DA lifetime increased to 280 ps, with a mono-exponential response, indicating a reduction in the free-carrier screening effect due to the tunneling. Such measurements are not possible under SPA spectroscopy, as discrete Q-discs could not be resolved for selective excitation.

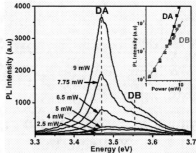

FIGURE 1. TI-PL and peak intensity dependence with excitation power (inset).

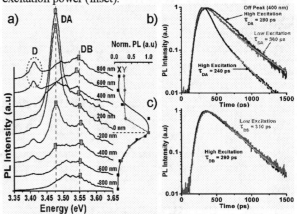

FIGURE 2. (a) Spatially dependant TI-PL spectrum. TR-PL trace for DA (b) and DB (c) under high and low excitation.

CONCLUSION

Using TPA we have been able to resolve several (1 or 2) coupled asymmetric GaN Q-disc structures and have studied the free-carrier screening in the Q-discs. The screening effect is enhanced due to carrier tunneling, which provides additional free-carriers.

ACKNOWLEDGMENTS

This research is part of the QIP IRC supported by EPSRC (GR/S82176/01). KHL thanks the support of the University College old members fund scholarship, Clarendon Fund bursary, Overseas Research Students award and M.A.G. Jones. YSP, CMP and TWK thanks QSRC and AOARD at Dongguk University.

REFERENCES

1. M. Zamfirescu et al., phys. stat. sol. (c) 2, 822 (2005)
2. A. Kikuchi et al., Jpn. J. Appl. Phys., 43, L1524 (2004)
3. F.-J. Kao et al., Opt. Lett., 24(20), 1407 (1999)
4. C. M. Park et al., Nanotechnology 17, 952 (2006)
5. J. H. Na et al., Appl. Phys. Lett., 86, 083109 (2005)
6. D. J. Leopold, M.M. Leopold, Phys. Rev. B, 42(17), 11147 (1990)
7. K. H. Lee et al., Appl. Phys. Lett, in print.
8. F.D. Sala, et al., Appl. Phys. Lett., 74(14), 2002 (1999)

Towards A Mid-Infrared Polaron Laser Using InAs/GaAs Self-Assembled Quantum Dots

S. Sauvage[1], P. Boucaud[1], F. Bras[1], G. Fishman[1], J.-M. Ortéga[2], J.-M. Gérard[3], G. Patriarche[4] and A. Lemaître[4]

1 IEF, CNRS UMR8622, Bâtiment 220, Université Paris-XI Sud, 91405 Orsay, France
http://pages.ief.u-psud.fr/QDgroup/index.html
2 CLIO-LURE, Bâtiment 209 D, Université Paris Sud, 91405 Orsay France
3 CEA-Grenoble, DRFMC-PSC, 38054 Grenoble Cedex 9, France
4 LPN, UPR 20, CNRS, Route de Nozay, F-91460 Marcoussis, France

Abstract. A three-level scheme based on S-P polaron intersublevel transitions in *n*-doped InAs/GaAs self-assembled quantum dots is proposed to obtain laser effect around 25 µm wavelength under optical pumping. The theoretical proposition is supported by the experimental knowledge of key input parameters: T1, T2, oscillator strenghs and polarizations. The intensity thresholds are predicted to be two orders of magnitude lower than for corresponding intersubband lasers and laser effect is expected to occur up to room temperature. The T2 dephasing time of the S-P$_+$ transition is measured by performing an optical Rabi oscillation experiment in resonance with the S-P+ transition. We show that the non-monotonous population dependence with pulse area and damping of the oscillation is only compatible with a T2~5 ps dephasing time, one order of magnitude longer than in quantum wells and one order of magnitude shorter than the 45 ps relaxation time of the s-p transition, demonstrating a non relaxation-limited decoherence for the transition.

Keywords: Quantum Dot, Polaron, Intersublevel, Intraband, Mid-Infrared, Optical Gain, Rabi Oscillation.
PACS: 42.55.Px 42.60.Lh, 78.45.+h, 71.38.Fp, 73.21.La

POLARON LASER SCHEME

The three-level laser scheme[1] is depicted in Figure 1-*Left* and based on the specific strong coupling regime which occurs for the Fröhlich electron-LO-phonon interaction,[2] leading in particular to the formation of mixed entangled electron-LO-phonon quasi-particles, i.e. polarons, as the discrete eigenstates of the system. To predict the laser performances, the S, P- and P+

confined electronic states are calculated in the framework of the three-dimensional resolution of the strain dependent 8 band **k.p** envelope function theory. One drastic consequence of the strong coupling regime is the very slow polaron relaxation between the P and S states, of the order of 50-70 ps at low temperature in agreement with experiment,[3] while much faster relaxation can be obtained between closely spaced P$_+$ and P. levels assisted by the irreversible emission of low energy acoustic phonons (Figure 1-*Middle*) as

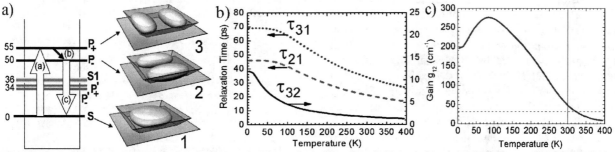

FIGURE 1. a) Polaron laser three-level scheme, b) Theoretical relaxation times as a function of temperature, c) Temperature dependence calculation of the optical gain at 25 µm wavelength for E_{23}=4 meV.

CP893, Physics of Semiconductors, 28th International Conference
edited by W. Jantsch and F. Schäffler
© 2007 American Institute of Physics 978-0-7354-0397-0/07/$23.00

shown experimentally recently in the literature.[4] Under optical pumping, the condition $\tau_{32} < \tau_{21}$ for population inversion $n_{P_-} - n_S > 0$ is fulfilled provided that the P states splitting be small enough, below 6 meV. For 80 quantum dots planes and $E_{32} = 4$ meV, optical gain of the order of 200 cm^{-1} is predicted in a monomode waveguide geometry (Figure 1-*Right*). When the temperature is increased, the strong reduction of τ_{32} as compared to τ_{31} and τ_{21}, originating from the small energy difference between level 2 and 3 as compared to kT, leads to even larger gains. Because of the long relaxation T1 times and the long T2 dephasing times (T2~5 ps, see next section), the intensity threshold of such a laser is expected to be two orders of magnitude smaller than the one of quantum wells.[1] Operation is also expected up to room temperature.

Note that vertically electronically coupled InAs/GaAs quantum dot molecules offer additional design parameters to continuously engineer the intersublevel electronic structure, beyond usual size, composition and geometry interplay as shown experimentally.[5] Quantum dot molecules open the route to control the relaxation as well as absorption and emission wavelengths in the mid-infrared spectral range.

OPTICAL RABI OSCILLATION

The T2 dephasing time is one of the key parameters driving the predicted laser performances. An optical Rabi oscillation experiment in resonance with the S-P$_+$ transition is performed to probe the polaron decoherence.[6] The 4 ps long pump pulses at 20 µm wavelength provided by the free electron laser CLIO (Orsay) are used to prepare state superposition in *n*-doped InAs/GaAs quantum dots. The pump pulse area (square root of the intensity) is controlled by inserting gold grid attenuators in the pump path. The population inversion is probed with synchronous spectrally degenerated weak probe pulses. The probe transmission variation $\Delta T/T$ is reported as filled dots in Figure 2 as a function of the pump pulse area. Probe transmission first increases with the pump area, reaches a maximum at around a π-pulse, then significantly decreases by 10% and finally slightly increases at the highest area value. The population inversion dependence with pump area is therefore non monotonous and attributed to the signature of an optical Rabi oscillation of the S and P$_+$ population.

The oscillation is obviously highly damped. To account for this feature, the system response is modeled using two-level optical Bloch equations accounting for the inhomogeneous contributions *i.e.* spatial distribution of the pulse intensity on the sample surface and the dipole distribution within the probed

quantum dot ensemble. Figure 2 shows that the agreement both on the absorption bleaching amplitude and oscillation contrast is only compatible with a T2~5 ps dephasing time (within a factor of 2), close to the pulse duration, one order of magnitude longer than in quantum wells and one order of magnitude shorter than 2T1=2x45 ps where T1 is the measured relaxation time. It corresponds to a homogeneous line width as small as 270 µeV and is expected to contribute to significantly increase the laser performances as compared to intersubband quantum well lasers.

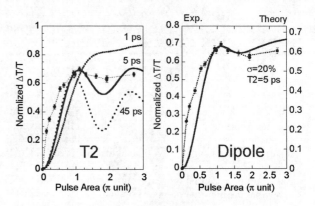

FIGURE 2. Probe transmission variation as a function of the pulse area (filled circles) compared with its predicted dependence obtained with 2-level optical Bloch equations accounting for the pulse area spatial profile and three different T2 times (*left*) and further considering the dipole distribution for a T2=5 ps time (*right*).

ACKNOWLEDGMENTS

SANDiE Network of Excellence of the European Commission, Contract No. NMP4-CT-2004-500101.

REFERENCES

1. S. Sauvage and P. Boucaud, *Appl. Phys. Lett.* **88**, 063106 (2006).
2. P. A. Knipp, T. L. Reinecke, A. Lorke, M. Fricke, P. M. Petroff, *Phys. Rev. B* **56**, 1516 (1997), S. Hameau, Y. Guldner, O. Verzelen, R. Ferreira, G. Bastard, J. Zeman, A. Lemaître, and J. M. Gérard, *Phys. Rev. Lett.* **83**, 4152 (1999).
3. S. Sauvage, P. Boucaud, R.P.S.M. Lobo, F. Bras, G. Fishman, R. Prazeres, F. Glotin, J. M. Ortega, J.-M. Gérard, *Phys. Rev. Lett.* **88**, 177402 (2002).
4. E. A. Zibik, L. R. Wilson, R. P. Green, G. Bastard, R. Ferreira, P. J. Philips, D. A. Carder, J.-P. R. Wells, J. W. Cockburn, M. S. Skolnick, M. J. Steer and M. Hopkinson, *Phys. Rev. B* **70**, 161305R (2004).
5. C. Kammerer, S. Sauvage, G. Fishman, P. Boucaud, G. Patriarche, A. Lemaître, *Appl. Phys. Lett.* **87**, 173113 (2005).
6. F. Bras, S. Sauvage, G. Fishman, and P. Boucaud, J.-M. Ortega, J.-M. Gérard, *Europhys. Lett.* **70**, 390 (2005).

Magneto-optical interband transitions in semiconductor quantum dots : evidence for excitonic polarons

V. Preisler*, T. Grange*, R. Ferreira*, L. A. de Vaulchier*, Y. Guldner*, F.J. Teran†, M. Potemski† and A. Lemaître**

*Laboratoire Pierre Aigrain, Ecole Normale Supérieure, 24 rue Lhomond, 75005 Paris, France
†Grenoble High Magnetic Field Laboratory, CNRS/MPI, 25 avenue des Martyrs, 38042 Grenoble Cedex 9, France
**Laboratoire de Photonique et Nanostructures, Route de Nozay, 91460 Marcoussis, France

Abstract. We investigate the interband transitions of self-assembled InAs/GaAs quantum dots by using resonant photoluminescence spectroscopy under strong magnetic field. Well defined resonances are observed in the spectra. A strong anticrossing between two transitions is observed, which cannot be accounted for by a purely excitonic model. The coupling between the mixed exciton-LO phonon states is calculated using the Fröhlich Hamiltonian. The excitonic polaron energies as well as the oscillator strengths of the interband transitions are determined. An anticrossing is predicted when two exciton-LO phonon states have close enough energies with phonon occupations which differ by one. A good agreement is found between the calculations and the experimental data evidencing the existence of excitonic polarons.

Keywords: quantum dot, polaron, exciton, phonon
PACS: 73.21.La,71.38.-k,78.67.Hc,78.20.Ls

Various experimental and theoretical works have demonstrated that carriers confined in InAs/GaAs quantum dots (QDs) are strongly coupled to the longitudinal optical (LO) vibrations of the underlying semiconductor lattice. For electrons (holes), this coupling leads to the formation of the electron (hole) polarons which can be evidenced by intraband magneto-optical transitions [1, 2, 3]. Optical interband transitions between valence and conduction states involve electron-hole pairs which are electrically neutral. Though the coupling between carriers and optical phonons is basically electrical (Fröhlich interaction), theoretical works have shown that excitons in QDs strongly couple to LO phonons [4, 5]. The eigenstates of the interacting exciton and phonon systems are the excitonic polarons which are predicted to give significant modifications of the energy levels and large anticrossings when two exciton-phonon states have close enough energies with phonon occupations which differ by one.

Experimental evidence of excitonic polarons have been reported in ref. [6] using photoluminescence excitation (PLE) at T=4K under strong magnetic field up to 28T on several ensembles of self-assembled InAs/GaAs QDs. We report here resonant photoluminescence (RPL) experiments on the same samples. In RPL spectroscopy, the excitation energy is less than the bandedge of the wetting layer, so that only subensembles of similar QDs are resonantly excited and contribute to the photoluminescence signal. Magneto-RPL spectra are presented in fig.1. The excitation energy is fixed as 1293 meV in or-

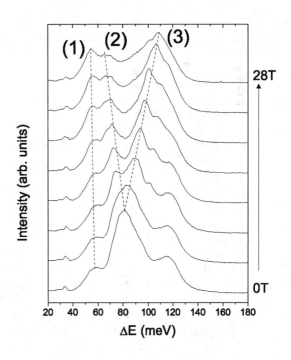

FIGURE 1. Magneto-RPL spectra at 4K from $B = 0$ to 28 T every 4T and for an excitation energy of 1293 meV. The dashed lines are guides for the eyes.

CP893, *Physics of Semiconductors, 28th International Conference*
edited by W. Jantsch and F. Schäffler
© 2007 American Institute of Physics 978-0-7354-0397-0/07/$23.00

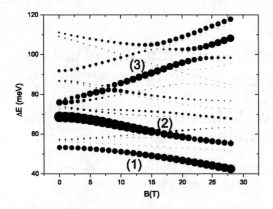

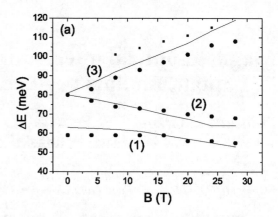

FIGURE 2. Calculated excitonic polaron energies and intensities as a function of the magnetic field . The area of the circles are proportional to the oscillator strengths.

FIGURE 3. Magnetic field dispersion of RPL resonances in dots. The solid lines are the calculated absorption peaks.

der to be resonant with the first excited transitions. An anticrossing of 12 meV between the two lowest energy transitions (1) and (2) is observed at a magnetic field of 20T. We will show that this behavior is a consequence of the strong coupling between excitons and phonons.

In fig. 2 we present the calculated polaron energy transitions. In order to calculate the excitonic polarons, we have used the dispersionless LO phonon approximation, which allows the very accurate calculation of polaron levels in QDs [2]. An LO phonon energy of $\hbar\omega = 36$ meV has been used. In addition to Fröhlich coupling terms, coulomb interactions and in-plane anisotropy have been taken into account. The energy dispersions and oscillator strengths of the polaron states, presented in Fig. 2, were calculated using an in-plane effective mass for electrons $m_e = 0.07 m_o$ and for holes $m_h = 0.22 m_o$, in agreement with FIR intraband magnetospectrocopy results. The other dots parameters were chosen in order to fit the experimental values of both the intraband s-p electronic (hole) transitions [47 meV (22 meV)] and the interband ground state energy (detection energy of 1215 meV).

The noninteracting exciton-phonon states are labelled $|n_e, n_h, N_\mathbf{q}\rangle$, where $|n\rangle = |s\rangle, |p^\pm\rangle$ are purely electronic levels. $|N_\mathbf{q}\rangle$ denotes the ensemble of the N LO-phonon states in the $\{\mathbf{q}\}$ modes. The Fröhlich Hamiltonian couples states which differ by one phonon. The diagonalisation of the Fröhlich interaction [6] gives the polaron states which are presented on fig. 2. In particular, the Fröhlich coupling between the states $|p_e^-, p_h^+, 0\rangle$ and $|s_e, p_h^+, 1\rangle$ give rise to the two polaron levels labelled (1) and (2). An anticrossing between (1) and (2) is observed as the magnetic field dependance is stronger for $|p_e^-, p_h^+, 0\rangle$ compared to $|s_e, p_h^+, 1\rangle$.

Fig. 3 shows a comparison between the observed RPL peak and the calculated absorption peaks. The calculated energy position as a function of magnetic field are found in good agreement with our data. In addition, when comparing the RPL results in fig. 1 with the calculated oscillator strength in fig. 2, we are able to predict the exchange of intensities between peaks (1) and (2) as the magnetic field increases.

In conclusion, we have investigated the interband transitions in self-assembled InAs/GaAs QDs by using magneto-RPL spectroscopy. We have calculated the coupling between the mixed exciton-LO phonon states using the Fröhlich Hamiltonian and we have determined the energies and oscillator strengths of the interband transitions. Our model accounts well for the experimental data, evidencing that the excitons and LO-phonons are in a strong coupling regime in QDs.

REFERENCES

1. S. Hameau, Y. Guldner, O. Verzelen, R. Ferreira, G. Bastard, J. Zeman, A. Lemaître, and J.M. Gérard, Phys. Rev. Lett. **83**, 4152 (1999).
2. S. Hameau, J.N. Isaia, Y. Guldner, E. Deleporte, O. Verzelen, R. Ferreira, G. Bastard, J. Zeman, and J.M. Gérard, Phys. Rev. B **65**, 085316 (2002).
3. V. Preisler, R. Ferreira, S. Hameau, L.A. de Vaulchier, Y. Guldner, M.L. Sadowski, and A. Lemaître, Phys. Rev. B **72**, 115309 (2005).
4. O. Verzelen, R. Ferreira, and G. Bastard, Phys. Rev. Lett. **88**, 146803 (2002).
5. R. Heitz, I. Mukhametzhanov, O. Stier, A. Madhukar, and D. Bimberg, Phys. Rev. Lett. **83**, 4654 (1999).
6. V. Preisler, T. Grange, R. Ferreira, L.A. de Vaulchier, Y. Guldner, F.J. Teran, M. Potemski and A. Lemaître, Phys. Rev. B **73**, 075320 (2006).

Bipolar charging in quantum dots array

Artem V Savelyev[*,†], Leonid Ya Karachinsky[*], Alexey S Shkolnik[*], Sara Pellegrini[**], Nikita Yu Gordeev[*], Alexander I Tartakovskii[†], Vadim P Evtikhiev[*], Georgy G Zegrya[*], Mikhail V Maximov[*], Victor M Ustinov[*], Ruben P Seisyan[*], Gerald S Buller[**] and Maurice S Skolnick[†]

[*]*A.F. Ioffe Physico-Technical Institute, Polytechnicheskaya 26, St.Petersburg, 194021, Russia*
[†]*Department of Physics and Astronomy, University of Sheffield, Hounsfield Road, Sheffield S3 7RH, United Kingdom*
[**]*School of Engineering and Physical Science, Heriot-Watt University, EH14 4AS, Edinburgh, United Kingdom*

Abstract. New type of carrier distribution among quantum dots - a spatially separated bipolar-charging state - has been studied experimentally and theoretically. Experimental methods such as pump-probe spectroscopy of electrically pumped samples and time-resolved photoluminescence were used. Theoretical approach based on a detailed statistics of carrier distribution was developed and proposed for interpretation of the experimental results.

Keywords: semiconductor quantum dots, charge carrier dynamics
PACS: 78.67.Hc, 73.50.Gr, 73.43.Cd, 78.47.+p

Semiconductor quantum dots (QDs) are very promising media for a variety of optoelectronic applications such as lasers, amplifiers single-photon emitters and quantum computers [1]. Charge carriers statistics is of great importance for the operation of those devices. Widely used filling factors f_n and f_p that describe the average filling of an electron/hole state in the QD do not reflect all details of carrier distribution among QDs. In Fig. 1 three possible states of the QD array are shown: the non-correlated distribution of electrons and holes (a), the positive-correlated distribution (b) and the negative-correlated distribution (c). Though all three states are described by $f_n = f_p = 1/2$ they have significantly different properties. Instead of the average filling numbers, a set of numbers $\{N_\alpha\}$ of QDs in each possible quantum state α is required to distinguish between (a)-(c) distributions.

An evolution of the QD with only one energy level for electrons (holes) is shown on fig. 1d. After an injection of e-h pairs into the matrix surrounding QDs carriers are captured into QDs and then they cannot escape from QD if temperature is low enough. When the time of radiative recombination is much smaller than the time of carrier capture into the chosen QD there are almost no QDs filled with e-h pairs. Due to stochastic nature of carrier captures [2] and the neutrality of an ensemble in average equal parts of QDs in the ensemble are charged with electrons and holes. Thus a new long lived type of carrier distribution is formed: the spatially-separated bipolar-charged (BC) state. Electrons and holes are located in the separated QDs, and an average filling of QDs is of the order of 1 (like Fig. 1c).

We have tested the presence of charged QDs in

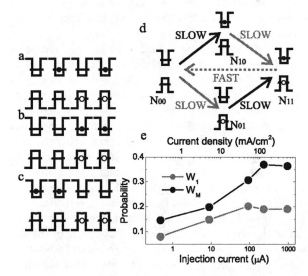

FIGURE 1. (a)-(c) The different types of carrier's distribution in the QD array. (d) Evolution of the chosen QD when e-h pairs injected in the semiconductor matrix. "00", "10","01","11" are possible QD states. (e) Probability to find single (W_1) or multiple (W_M) charged QD in the p-i-n laser diode.

the ensemble by means of ultrafast polarization-resolved pump-probe spectroscopy [3]. A conventional InAs/InGaAs/GaAs QD laser diode structure at helium temperature was under investigation. The difference in the spin dynamics between neutral and charged excitons leads to a formation of a long-lived polarized state of the QD ensemble, which then gives a clear evidence of

CP893, *Physics of Semiconductors, 28th International Conference*
edited by W. Jantsch and F. Schäffler
© 2007 American Institute of Physics 978-0-7354-0397-0/07/$23.00

QD charging [4]. We have observed the appearance of the long-lived polarization due to dc current injection [5] and calculated from that data part of single charged and multiple charged QDs in the ensemble (see fig. 1e). The observed crossover behavior from uncharged to charged state with increased pump level is due to the competition between processes of carrier captures into the chosen QD and carrier escapes from it. At low pump rate escapes dominate hence QDs is mostly uncharged.

A dynamics of distribution of the carriers in the QD ensemble can be described by vector master equation:

$$dN_\alpha/dt = \sum A_{\alpha\beta}(g_{c1}, g_{c2})N_\beta,$$

where A is the transition matrix and $A_{\alpha\beta}$ is the transition rate of QD from β to α state, $g_{c1}(g_{c2})$ - rate of carrier captures into the chosen QD. The former describes interaction of QD ensemble with matrix and directly depends on a carrier concentration in the matrix which is defined by neutrality conditions and a pump rate. At the stationary conditions when $d\vec{N}/dt = 0$ master equation can be reduced to the linear equation for $\vec{N}$ and then easily studied. Our analysis presents good quantitative explanation of the experimental results - at sufficient injection rate 55% of the QDs are charged.

The BC state can be formed even at room temperature after a short-pulse optical excitation of electron-hole pairs into the matrix due to stochastic nature of carrier captures [6,7]. That leads to the fluctuations of number of electrons and holes captured into the QDs. Just after injection pulse (Fig. 2a) direct radiative recombination (Fig. 2b) is the major process with characteristic time $\sim$ 1 ns though only some part of the injected carriers can recombine by that way. After a fast radiative recombination, the remaining carriers become spatially separated in different QDs and the BC state is formed (Fig. 2c). The following evolution has a much slower rate that is limited by the carrier escape time. Relaxation of the BC state can be monitored in the time-resolved photoluminescence (PL) decay experiments - results are shown in a Fig. 2d. Dynamical behavior of the BC state can also be studied in the frame of master equation. Electrons escape from QDs to matrix and then are re-captured into other QDs. In this case g_c becomes dependent on $\vec{N}$ and master equation becomes non-linear. Despite this analytical solutions still can be found for two important cases: homogeneous array of QDs and strongly inhomogeneous array where dispersion of electron energy is much higher than the temperature. In both cases PL decay demonstrates complicated non-exponential behavior that was clearly observed in the experiment.

The developed approach for carrier statistics in the QDs array is also important for understanding details of operation of optoelectronic devices. The temperature dependence of QD laser threshold current provides a good

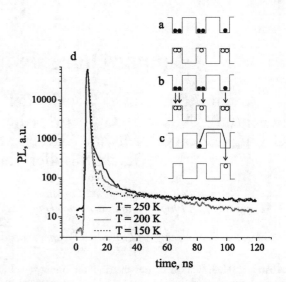

FIGURE 2. (a)-(c) Stages of QD ensemble evolution when carriers are injected in matrix by short-pulse optical excitation. (d) PL decay curved measured during the relaxation of BC state.

illustration of that. At sufficiently high temperature when quasi-equilibrium distribution is realized electron-hole Coulomb attraction leads to formation of positive correlated state (Fig. 1b). That effect exponentially depends on the temperature and leads to an unusual behavior: threshold current drops with increasing the temperature.

To conclude, a new type of carrier distribution - bipolar charging - when electrons and holes are located in separated QDs and its static and dynamic properties were studied experimentally and theoretically. These results will have strong impact on the interpretation of low-temperature data obtained on QDs. The developed theoretical approach is important for a deeper understanding of the properties of QD optoelectronic devices such as lasers operating far from equilibrium.

The authors acknowledge the financial support from the Russian Foundation for Basic Research (grant # 05-02-16922), L.Ya.K. acknowledges support from the President Grant for young scientists (MK-941.2005.2).

REFERENCES

1. Y. Arakawa and H. Sakaki, *Appl. Phys. Lett.* **40**, 939 (1982); S.S.Mihrin et al., *Semiconuctors* **36**, 1315 (2002); E.Biolatti et al., *Phys. Rev. Lett.* **85**, 5647 (2000).
2. M. Grundmann and D. Bimberg, *Phys. Rev. B* **55**, 9740 (1997).
3. A.I.Tartakovskii et al., *Phys. Rev. Lett.* **97**, 057401 (2004).
4. A.I.Tartakovskii et al., *Appl. Phys. Lett.* **85**, 2226 (2004).
5. A.V. Savelyev et al., *Appl. Phys. Lett.* **88**, 111104 (2006).
6. L.Ya.Karachinsky et al., *Appl. Phys. Lett.* **84**, 7 (2004).
7. A.S.Shkolnik et al., *Appl. Phys. Lett.* **86**, 211112 (2005).

Combined influence of Coulomb, exchange and phonon couplings on the line shape of quantum dot spectra

A. Krügel[*], V.M. Axt[*], T. Kuhn[*] and A. Vagov[†]

[*]*Institut für Festkörpertheorie, Westfälische Wilhelms-Universität, Wilhelm-Klemm-Str. 10, 48149 Münster, Germany*
[†]*Physics Department, Lancaster University, Lancaster, LA1 4YB, United Kingdom*

Abstract. We study single quantum dot (QD) four wave mixing (FWM) and pump probe (PP) spectra calculated numerically from the exact analytical solution for a four level QD model with pure dephasing. Due to Coulomb and exchange interaction the spectra exhibit a fine structure splitting of the exciton and biexciton lines. The combination of the different interaction contributions leads to new features such as biexciton contribution in PP spectra after co-circular excitation.

Keywords: quantum dots, nonlinear optical signals, pure dephasing
PACS: 63.20.ls,63.22.+m,71.35.-y,78.47.+p,78.67.Hc

Spectra from self assembled QDs exhibit characteristic differences compared to spectra from either atoms or higher dimensional semiconductor structures. They consist of narrow zero phonon lines (ZPLs) superimposed on a broad phononic background of non-Lorentzian shape corresponding to a fast non-exponential initial decay of the optical polarization. This initial decay is caused by elastic scattering processes between carriers and phonons, commonly referred to as pure dephasing processes, which are described theoretically by the independent boson model. Quantitative agreement between the measured short time decay of the time integrated FWM signal from an ensemble of InAs/GaAs self-assembled QDs and theoretical results within the two level independent boson model has been found for the case of co-circular short pulse excitation [1]. Recently, we have extended the theory to a four level QD model [2]. It includes the electronic ground state $|0\rangle$, the two linearly polarized exciton states $|x\rangle$ and $|y\rangle$ with the corresponding energies $\hbar\omega_{x/y} = \varepsilon_X \pm \Delta_{ex}/2$, split by the exchange energy Δ_{ex}, and the biexciton state $|B\rangle$ with energy $\hbar\omega_B = 2\varepsilon_X - \Delta_B$, Δ_B being the biexciton binding energy. The exact analytical solution for all density matrix elements in the time domain for the case of excitation by a series of ultrashort pulses is formally given in terms of a recursion formula which we have evaluated explicitly for the case of two pulse excitation, the first pulse with phase ϕ_1 arriving at time $t = -\tau$ and the second pulse with phase ϕ_2 arriving at $t = 0$. We have extracted the pump probe (PP) signal, proportional to $\exp\{i\phi_2\}$, and the four wave mixing (FWM) signal, proportional to $\exp\{i(2\phi_2 - \phi_1)\}$. Here we will present single dot FWM and PP spectra obtained from the exact analytical solution in the time domain concentrating on co-circular $\sigma^+\sigma^+$-excitation. In that case for QDs with

cylindrical symmetry, i.e. without exchange interaction, neither a biexcitonic contribution nor a σ^--aligned polarization could be expected. In this paper we study the role of fine structure splitting and biexciton binding on QD spectra, especially on the phononic background.

The explicit formula within the four level QD model for the FWM polarization after excitation with two co-circularly polarized pulses in the time domain is given in [3]. There it was already mentioned that for the case of vanishing exchange coupling it coincides with the result for the two level model. Even for non vanishing exchange coupling we find no biexcitonic contribution to the FWM signal within our limit of ultra-fast pulses. However, there are two ground state to exciton transitions (GETs) for the two linearly polarized excitons, respectively. Then, concentrating on the important feature for the present discussion, the $\sigma^\pm$-component of the FWM polarization has the form:

$$\langle \hat{P}^{\text{FWM}}_{++}\rangle_\pm = \theta(t)F^{\text{FMW}}(t,\tau)\left(e^{i\omega_x t} \pm e^{i\omega_y t}\right), \quad (1)$$

where $\theta(t)$ is the Heaviside step function and $F^{\text{FMW}}(t,\tau)$ is a function depending on the time t, the delay τ, the properties of the phonon system and on the pulse areas of the exciting pulses. For QDs deviating from a cylindrical symmetry the exciton states are non degenerate. Thus, after co-circular $\sigma^+\sigma^+$-excitation both, the σ^+- as well as the σ^--component of the FWM polarization are nonzero and exhibit two separate ZPLs. Their positions in the spectrum are given by the frequencies $\omega_{x/y}$. Both ZPLs have the same spectral weight and the same phononic background included in the function F^{FMW}. Since the characteristic energy scale of the phonon background is typically much larger than the fine structure splitting we find a strongly reduced phononic background in the σ^--component compared to the σ^+-signal. This can be seen

CP893, *Physics of Semiconductors, 28th International Conference*
edited by W. Jantsch and F. Schäffler
© 2007 American Institute of Physics 978-0-7354-0397-0/07/$23.00

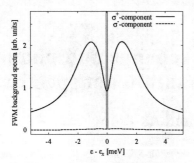

Figure 1. Absolute value of the FWM background spectra. The vertical black lines indicate the position of the ZPLs split by $\hbar\Delta_{\text{ex}} \approx 92\ \mu\text{eV}$.

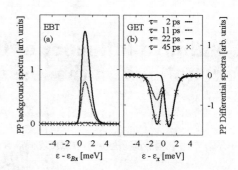

Figure 2. PP spectra for σ^+ detection polarization. (a): EBT for four different delay times τ. (b): Differential background of the GET. In both cases the temperature is $T = 1$ K and the pulse area of the pump pulse is $f_1 = \pi/100$. Their position of the ZPLs is the same as in Fig.1.

in Fig. 1 where we have plotted the absolute value of phononic FWM background spectra around the ZPLs for σ^+ detection polarization (solid) as well as for σ^- detection polarization (dashed). The vertical black lines indicate the positions of the ZPLs, which can be resolved separately in the experiment [4].

Let us now come to PP signals. In general PP spectra may be interpreted as absorption spectra of the second pulse. Thus they provide information about the occupations generated by the first pulse which at low temperature determine the shape of the phononic background around the GET and the exciton to biexciton transition (EBT). Since at low temperature the phonon side bands are not occupied one always finds absorption on the right hand side of the ZPL, due to transitions from the energetically lower zero phonon state into the sidebands of the energetically higher state, and gain on the left hand side of the ZPL stemming from transitions from the upper zero phonon state into the sidebands of the lower state. In Fig. 2 we have plotted for four different τ the phononic background spectra of the EBT (with transition energy $\varepsilon_{Bx} = \hbar(\omega_B - \omega_x)$) and, in order to concentrate on the nonlinear part, the differential background spectra of the GET. In the latter signal we observe above the ZPLs the reduction of the linear absorption and below the gain resulting from the excited excitons (the exact position of the two exciton ZPLs is the same as in the FWM case, but not of importance for the broad phononic background). For a pulse delay longer than the polaron dressing time but much shorter than the period corresponding to the exchange splitting $T_P = 2\pi\hbar/\Delta_{\text{ex}}$ (here $T_P \approx 45$ ps) both contributions are equal. This is because the exciton excited by the first σ^+ pulse is spin polarized and, thus, the second σ^+ pulse cannot excite the biexciton but only leads to stimulated emission into the ground state. Consequently, the EBT spectrum for $\tau = 2$ ps in Fig.2 (a) is equal to zero and the GET differential spectrum (Fig.2 (b)) is symmetric around $\varepsilon = 0$ meV. However, due to the exchange splitting, the spin state excited by the first

pulse is not an eigenstate but a quantum mechanical superposition of the two linearly polarized exciton states. It oscillates with the frequency $\Delta_{\text{ex}}/\hbar$ between the two spin polarizations. Thus, depending on the delay τ, it is possible to excite the biexciton by a second σ^+-pulse. For $\tau = 22$ ps $\approx T_P/2$ we find a strong signal of the EBT. This second pathway reduces the gain in the GET. $\tau = 11$ ps stands for the intermediate case while for $\tau = 45$ ps $\approx T_P$ the EBT signal vanishes again.

In this paper we have discussed PP and FWM spectra from single QDs calculated numerically from the exact analytical solution for a four level QD model coupled to phonons via pure dephasing processes. We have shown that the combined influence of Coulomb, exchange and phonon couplings leads to spectral features, such as biexcitonic absorption in PP signals after co-circular excitation and to the reduction of the phononic background in one polarization component of the FWM signal.

REFERENCES

1. A. Vagov, V. M. Axt, T. Kuhn, W. Langbein, P. Borri, and U. Woggon, *Phys. Rev. B* **70**, 201305(R) (2004).
2. V. M. Axt, T. Kuhn, A. Vagov, and F. M. Peeters, *Phys. Rev. B* **72**, 125309 (2005).
3. A. Krügel, V. M. Axt, and T. Kuhn, *Phys. Status Solidi B* (2006), in press.
4. M. Bayer, G. Ortner, O. Stern, A. Kuther, A. A. Gorbunov, A. Forchel, P. Hawrylak, S. Fafard, K. Hinzer, T. L. Reinecke, S. N. Walck, J. P. Reithmaier, F. Klopf, and F. Schäfer, *Phys. Rev. B* **65**, 195315 (2002).

Carrier Relaxation Dynamics 1.55 μm InAs/InP Quantum Dots Under High Resonant Excitation

C. Labbé, C. Cornet, H. Folliot, J. Even, P. Caroff, C. Levallois, O. Dehaese, A. Le Corre, S. Loualiche

Laboratoire d'Etude des Nanostructures à semiconducteurs (UMR-FOTON6082)
Insa de Rennes, 20 Avenue des Buttes de Coesmes, 35043 Rennes Cedex, France
christophe.labbe@insa-rennes.fr

Abstract. We studied the dynamic response of InAs/InP quantum dot transitions with a resonant pump-probe experiment. A 72-stacked InAs/InP quantum dot layer sample is grown on (311)B substrate. The variation of carrier radiative lifetimes with increasing excitation powers is measured and is attributed to the exciton and biexciton lifetime. The implications of such a difference on differential transmission are discussed, and finally exciton and biexciton lifetimes are measured to be about 1720 ps and 530 ps respectively.

Keywords: Quantum dots, Indium, Phosphide, dynamics, pump-probe
PACS: 78.67.Hc; 78.55.Cr, 78.47.+p

INTRODUCTION

InAs/InP quantum dots (QD), have demonstrated various interesting optical properties for the 1.55 μm operating wavelength, used for long haul telecommunications. The experimental and theoretical optical properties have been investigated as well as the effect of the QD lateral coupling.[1] Recently some dynamics studies have been carried out on InAs/InP on (100) substrate,[2,3] and on (311)B substrate.[4]

EXPERIMENTAL SETUP

Two samples of 12 and 72-stacked InAs/InP QD layers sample have been grown on InP(311)B substrate by gas-source molecular beam epitaxy. The first sample is a stack of 12 InAs/InP QD layers used for photoluminescence (PL) experiment. The second is a stack of 72 (6×12) InAs/InP QD layers, in order to obtain a sufficient absorption analogous to 12 quantum wells and to detect the differential transmission ratio (DTR).[5] We have used thick 150 nm InP spacers, to reduce the strain interaction between QD layers and its impact on the QD growth. Moreover every 12-stack was separated by a 500 nm InP spacer. For both samples, the growth conditions lead to an average dot diameter of 35 nm, a $5 \times 10^{10} cm^{-2}$ QD density and the dot height of 3 nm is set by the "double cap" epitaxy method.[6]

EXPERIMENTAL RESULTS

Photoluminescence of the 12 stack sample at high excitation power reveals ground and excited transitions (figure 1). The energy position of the excited states ES1 and ES2 are respectively at 9 and 14 meV from the ground state. The inset (Fig.1) shows the PL spectra under non-resonant excitation of the 12-stack InAs/InP QD at 4 K and RT. We can estimate the PL quantum efficiency at room temperature to be 0.27 by integrating the two PL intensities.

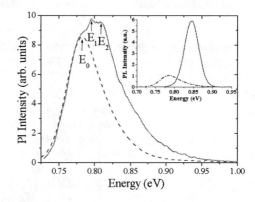

FIGURE 1. Low (dashed line) and high (solid line) excitation power PL measurements from the 12-stack InAs/InP sample. The three arrows mark the GS transition (E_0) and the excited-state transitions at $E_1=E_0+14$ meV and $E_2=E_0+26$ meV. The 4 K (dotted line) and RT (dashed line) PLs are illustrated in the inset.

CP893, *Physics of Semiconductors, 28th International Conference*
edited by W. Jantsch and F. Schäffler

At the maximum of the absorption at 1.540 μm wavelength (809 meV) corresponding to the E1 transition, we have performed time-resolved resonant pump-probe experiments to study the dynamic response of InAs/InP QD.[7] The carrier lifetime is shown on figure 2(a) as a function of the excitation density. First, a decrease followed by an increase of the lifetime with the excitation density and finally a subsequent decrease are observed. For an excitation density higher than 4.0×10^{13} photons/pulse.cm^2 the signal remains monoexponential ($\approx$550 ps).

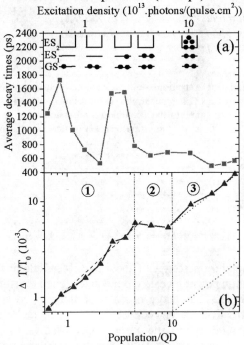

FIGURE 2. Excitation density (10^{13} photons/(pulse.cm^2)) and population/QD dependence for the QD monoexponential decay times at 1.54 μm (a) and the QD DTR (b). The population/QD is deduced from the excitation by a factor of 1.51×10^{-13}.

A correspondence can be performed in a first approximation to link the excitation power and the population per QD. We have measured optical losses of 69% attributed to diffusion and reflection on the sample surfaces and a quantum efficiency of 0.27 at room temperature. For a 72 stack QD layer sample, with 4400 cm^{-1} QD absorption[5], and a 3 nm QD height, the absorbed part of the incident intensity is found to be 9%.

High decay values are measured for a minimal population per QD equal to 1 or 3 (see diagram figure 2a) and low values to 2 or larger than 4. This leads to attribute to the exciton/triexciton the high values of decay times, and to attribute to biexciton/multiexciton low values of decay times.[8] Theses measured values of decay time around $\tau_x \approx 1700$ ps and $\tau_{xx} \approx 500$ ps

correspond to those found for exciton and biexciton on InAs/GaAs QD structure ($\tau_x \approx 1400$ ps - $\tau_{xx} \approx 600$ ps),[9] and on our system ($\tau_x \approx 1700$ ps).[4]

By increasing the pump power up to 4 charge carriers per QD, the exciton bleaching of ES2 should be observed. Nevertheless, assuming ES2 as a highly degenerated reservoir level, the measurements can be interpreted.[10] The pump (and the probe), centered at 805 meV, excites the GS (795 meV) and the ES1 (809 meV), but also this reservoir level ES2 (817 meV) due to the large $\Delta E_{FWMH} = 10$ meV of the probe. We cannot measure the decay times (τ^2_x), because such a reservoir, containing more than two states per QD, absorbs the pump but also the probe.

Figure 2b represents the DTR measured at about the maximum intensity of the DTR intensity. Three steps are visible on the curve (noted 1,2,3 on the figure 2b). The first domain corresponds to the absorption of both GS and ES1. The second step highlights the saturation of these two states by a DTR almost constant during about 6 carriers per QD. Parallel to this saturation, a part of the pump and the probe is absorbed by the upper reservoir levels (ES2), containing more than two states per QD. After a population of 10 carriers per QD, the reservoir levels, due to their own saturation, start to transmit the probe. We can see on the third step of the curve, the DTR increasing again. The decay lifetimes remains multiexcitonic.

ACKNOWLEDGMENTS

This work was supported by the SANDiE Network of Excellence (Contract No. NMP4-CT-2004-500101) of the sixth Framework Program of the European Commission.

REFERENCES

[1] C. Cornet, C. Platz et al., Phys. Rev. B **72**, 35342 (2005).
[2] B. Salem, G. Bremond et al., Physica E **17**, 124 (2003).
[3] E. W. Bogaart, R. Notzel et al., Appl. Phys. Lett. **86**, 173109 (2005).
[4] P. Miska, J. Even et al., Appl. Phys. Lett. **86**, 111905 (2005).
[5] C. Cornet, C. Labbé et al., Appl. Phys. Lett. **85**, 5685 (2004).
[6] C. Paranthoen, N. Bertru et al., Appl. Phys. Lett. **78**, 1751 (2001).
[7] C. Cornet, C. Labbé et al., Appl. Phys. Lett. **88**, 171502 (2006).
[8] E. Dekel et al., Phys. Rev. B **61**, 11009 (2000).
[9] E. Moreau, I. Robert et al., Phys. Rev. Let. **87**, 183601 (2001).
[10] C. Kammerer, G. Cassabois et al., Phys. Rev. B **65**, 033313/1 (2002).

Coupling, Relaxation and Coherent Emission in Semiconductor Double Quantum Dots

H Y Ramírez [+], A S Camacho[+] and L C Lew Yan Voon*

[+] *Universidad de Los Andes, Carrera 1 No. 18ª-10, Departamento de Física, Bogota, Colombia.*
* *Wright State University, 3640 Colonel Glenn Highway, 45435 Dayton, Ohio, USA.*

Abstract. We studied the dynamical response of cylindrical and spherical double quantum dots to an external time-dependent electric field pulse. The density matrix evolution is calculated in the constant dissipation operator approach, considering electron-phonon and electron-electron interaction. This dynamics is evaluated in the high delocalization regime, where the process of decoherence is dominated by relaxation rates. Such rates and their related decay times are obtained from a Fermi golden rule treatment of the interactions. We found convenient conditions for coherent emission in the cylindrical dots case, while for spherical dots the fast relaxation from excited levels destroys the coherence in a time shorter than the period of any of the involved quantum beat oscillations.

Keywords: Coupled Quantum Dots, Relaxation, Coherent Emission.
PACS: 71.38.-k; 72.15.Lh; 73.21.La; 78.45.+h

INTRODUCTION

Double quantum dots arrays are good candidates to be useful in the implementation of nano-devices both for optoelectronics and quantum computation. Tunability of states and long coherence times are the main advantages of such systems[1,2]. In a previous work, we introduced a model to evaluate numerically the dynamics of a single carrier in a rectangular double quantum dot, focusing in the first three levels[3]. Here we basically use the same treatment but extended to five levels because of the geometry of the considered dots. In the first section, we found the electronic levels for the studied geometries. After that, we use the density matrix formalism to evaluate the evolution of the system after the application of an external pulse. Finally, using our computed decay rates, we calculate the total dipole moment looking for the viability of coherent emission from the double dot-arrays.

ENERGY STATES AND COUPLING

The systems we focus in are pairs of quantum dots close enough to be electronically coupled, which is equivalent to having their individual states hybridized. They are chosen as islands of GaAs embedded in a $Al_{0.4}Ga_{0.6}As$ matrix. Experimental parameters are as in reference 3. The confinement potential is modeled as a finite potential step. We consider spherical and cylindrical geometries. The case with cylindrical shape has two options; stacked or lateral coupling. These two configurations are expected to have different behavior since in the latter one, the axial symmetry is broken. We found the energy levels by solving numerically the modified Schrödinger equation

$$\left[\frac{-\hbar^2}{2} \nabla \cdot \left(\frac{1}{m^*(x,y,z)} \nabla \right) + V(x,y,z) - eFx \right]$$
$$\cdot \Psi(x,y,z) = E \ \Psi(x,y,z) \quad , \qquad (1)$$

where m^* is the electron effective mass, V the offset in the conduction band of the two materials, e is the elemental charge, F is the bias electric field applied in the x direction (the coupling direction), Ψ is the one-electron envelope function and E the proper energy. The bias field is used as coupling parameter to tune the High Delocalization Regime (HDR). A volume ratio of ~4.3 between the dots of the pair was established as suitable to reach the HDR when the smaller dots are around 300nm³.

TEMPORAL RESPONSE

We focus on the first two energy values of individual spherical dots and at the first three of cylindrical dots. The spherical dots have non-degenerate ground eigenenergy and a three-fold degenerate first excited eigenenergy. The cylindrical

CP893, *Physics of Semiconductors, 28th International Conference*
edited by W. Jantsch and F. Schäffler
© 2007 American Institute of Physics 978-0-7354-0397-0/07/$23.00

dots also have a non-degenerate ground level and first excited eigenenergy, but a two-fold degenerate second excited energy value close to the former one. So, in both cases, to work with coupled dots with these levels hybridized it is necessary to consider a five-level system: one associated with the smaller dot and four with the bigger one.

The occupation probability of energy levels and the coherence between states for the reduced five-level system after the application of an ultrafast electric field pulse (amplitude 50 mV/nm, duration 4 fs, in our calculations), can be obtained from the density matrix, whose evolution is given by the Liouville equation, which in the Lindblad form in the constant dissipation operator approximation is [4]

$$ i\hbar \frac{d\rho_{ij}}{dt} = [H_{ij}^{U}(t), \rho_{ij}(t)] - i\hbar\Gamma_{ij} \qquad (2) $$

where ρ_{ij} is the ij density matrix component, H^{U}_{ij} the matrix element of the hamiltonian including the exciting electric field, and Γ_{ij} are the relaxation rates to be mentioned at the next section.

RELAXATION RATES

Since we are tuning the system to the HDR, we neglect the pure dephasing rates and link the decoherence process only to the relaxation times[2,5]. We consider interactions of the confined electron with no confined ones present in the matrix as conduction carriers, and with the lattice through acoustic phonons. Their respective scattering rates are evaluated by the Fermi golden rule approximation

$$ \Gamma^{I}_{if} = \frac{2\pi}{\hbar}\left|H^{I}_{if}\right|^{2}\delta(E), \qquad (3) $$

where H^{I}_{if} is the hamiltonian of the correspondent interaction and $\delta(E)$ guarantees energy conservation.

RESULTS AND CONCLUSION

Figure 1 shows the Total Dipole Moment from the excited levels of the density matrix for the three considered geometries. An oscillating dipole moment means coherent emission and for cylindrically shaped dots, especially for the ones coupled vertically, the observation of such emission is feasible since many cycles are completed before the inhibition by scattering by phonons and conduction electrons. The spherical geometry was found not to be suitable to observe coherent emission since the attenuation rate is bigger than the emission frequencies.

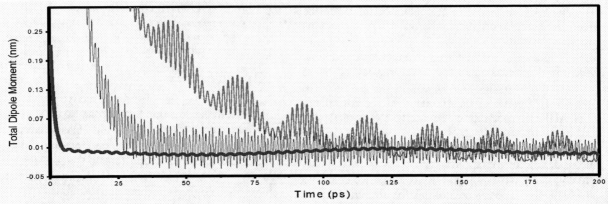

FIGURE 1. Total dipole moment at the HDR of spherical quantum dots (red, ultra bold), vertically-stacked coupled cylindrical quantum dots (green, bold) and laterally-coupled cylindrical quantum dots (grey, solid).

ACKNOWLEDGMENTS

We would like to thank the Comite de Investigaciones y Posgrado, y Departamento de Física of Universidad de Los Andes, Colciencias Colombia (Project No: 1204-05-46852), Banco de La Republica Colombia (Project No. 1857), and Wright State University and the Ohio Board of Regents (Research Challenge Grant) for financial support.

REFERENCES

1. J. M. Villas-Boˆas, A. O. Govorov, and Sergio E. Ulloa. *Phys. Rev. B.* **69**, 125342-125345 (2004)
2. V. N. Stavrou and Hu Xuedong. *Phys. Rev. B*, **72**, 0753621-0753628 (2005)
3. H. Y. Ramirez, A. S. Camacho and L. C. Lew Yan Voon. Nanotechnology. **17**, 1286-1291 (2006)
4. J. M. Villas-Boˆas, S. E. Ulloa and A. O. Govorov. *Phys. Rev. Lett.* **94**, 0574041-0574044 (2005)
5. L. Fedichkin and A. Fedorov Phys. Rev. A. **69**, 0323111-0323114 (2004)

Direct Observation of Electronic Couplings between 1.5 μm Emitting InGaAs/InGaAsP Quantum Dots on InP

Y. D. Jang[1], J. Park[1], D. Lee[1], S. H. Pyun[2], W. G. Jeong[2], and J. W. Jang[3]

[1]Department of Physics, Chungnam National University, Daejeon 305-764, Korea
[2]Department of Materials Engineering, Sungkyunkwan University, Suwon, Korea
[3]NanoEpi Technologies, Gyonggi Technopark, Ansan, Korea

Abstract. We have estimated the vertical and lateral electronic couplings between 1.5 μm emitting InGaAs/InGaAsP quantum dots (QDs) by the carrier lifetime dependence on energy position over the ground state photoluminescence (PL) band. The areal dot density is over 10^{11}/cm^2. For a QD sample with 40 nm barrier spacing, the measured carrier lifetimes are almost the same across the entire PL band, indicating the negligible lateral and vertical electronic couplings between QDs at this high dot density. However, for a QD sample with the 15 nm barrier spacing between QD layers the lifetime increases with increasing wavelength, clearly indicating the significant vertical electronic coupling between QDs.

Keywords: quantum dot, electronic coupling, carrier dynamics.
PACS: 78.66.–w, 78.67.–n, 78.67.Hc

INTRODUCTION

Since a typical quantum dot (QD) sample has a relatively low fill factor, the vertical stacking of QD layers and growth of QDs of higher dot density are very important for many QD devices, such as laser diodes, to increase the modal gain. [1]

In this work, we propose a simple experimental method to directly estimate the electronic coupling and present results on the vertical and lateral electronic couplings from high quality In(Ga)As/InGaAsP QDs on InP (100) substrate.

EXPERIMENTS AND DISCUSSIONS

InGaAs/InGaAsP QD samples were grown on nominally exact (100) InP substrate by metal-organic chemical vapor deposition at 76 torr. The details of the growth were reported elsewhere. [2] According to the obtained atomic force microscopy images, the dot shape is round and dome-shaped with the average diameter of 32 nm and height of 3.4 nm. The dot density is high, about 1.1×10^{11} cm^{-2}. [3] QD1, QD2, and QD3, grown in slightly different conditions, have five stacks of InGaAs QD layers with the InGaAsP spacer layer of 40 nm. QD4 was grown under a similar condition with QD1, except that the spacing is 15 nm-thick.

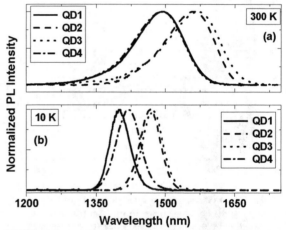

FIGURE 1. (a) PL spectra taken at room temperature from a series of QD samples. The peak positions cover the 1.55 μm band. (b) Low temperature PL spectra from the QD samples. The FWHM of the PL spectrum is between 29 and 31 meV, indicating the uniform dot size.

Figure 1(a) shows photoluminescence (PL) spectra taken at 300 K from four different QD samples. Emission wavelengths are controlled well around 1.55 μm and full widths at half maximum (FWHMs) are between 64 and 69 meV. This consistency in optical properties from several QDs attests the stable QD growth. Integrated PL intensities at RT are about 20% of the 10 K values and comparable to that of a typical InGaAs quantum well of a similar geometry at 1.5 μm.

CP893, *Physics of Semiconductors, 28th International Conference*
edited by W. Jantsch and F. Schäffler
© 2007 American Institute of Physics 978-0-7354-0397-0/07/$23.00

The mole fraction of gallium in the InGaAs QD is chosen to be about 0.6% to match the emission wavelength of ~ 1.55 μm. [3]

Fig. 1(b) shows PL spectra taken at 10 K from the four QD samples. The measured FWHMs are between 29 and 31 meV, attesting the growth of uniform QDs. In addition, no other PL signals from the wetting layer or InGaAsP barrier are observed, implying the very efficient capture of photo-generated carriers in QDs.

The PL spectrum for QD4 with the spacer layer of 15 nm is comparable to that of QD1 with the 40 nm spacing at both 10 K and 300 K. This observation implies that either there is no vertical electronic coupling or the coupling cannot be examined just by the PL spectrum.

In order to check the above mentioned possibilities, time resolved PL measurements were carried out with a picosecond streak camera and 2 ps mode-locked pulses from a Ti:sapphire laser. The PL decay curves are measured with bandpass filters of 30 nm bandwidth. The excitation wavelength was 750 nm.

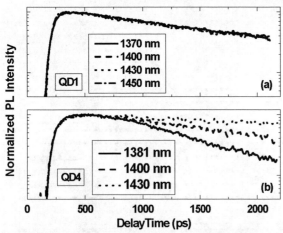

FIGURE 2. (a) Carrier decay characteristics of QD1 of 40 nm spacing at 10 K. The carrier lifetime is the same, 1.8 ns, over the entire PL band. (b) Carrier decay characteristics of QD4 of 15 nm spacing at 10 K. The carrier lifetime varies significantly from 0.8 to 4.4 ns inside the PL band.

The carrier lifetimes are almost the same (~ 1.8 ns) across the whole PL band (110 nm) of QD1 as shown in Fig. 2(a). This observation attests the negligible lateral electronic coupling between dots even at a very high dot density over 10^{11}/cm^2, at which the lateral dot separation (~ 30 nm) becomes comparable to the dot size (~30 nm).

When the InGaAsP spacing is 15 nm between dot layers (QD4) the shorter carrier lifetime at the higher energy side is observed, as shown in Fig. 2(b). The shorter carrier lifetime is most likely due to the relaxation to lower lying energy states in addition to the radiative recombination at that energy state. If QDs are well-isolated there will be no carrier relaxation to lower lying energy states from the ground state of the QD and no lifetime differences across the PL band at a low excitation. Consequently, the lifetime variation inside the PL band is due to the vertical wave function overlap between QDs in adjacent layers. This electronic coupling is related to the large penetration of electron wave function into the barrier caused by the small dot height. [4] In contrast, the same lifetime is observed across the entire PL band for QD1 with the 40 nm layer spacing, suggesting that the 40 nm spacing is enough to get the independent quantum dot behavior.

SUMMARY

We have estimated the vertical and lateral electronic couplings between QDs qualitatively, by measuring the carrier lifetimes at various energy positions inside the ground state PL band. The measured carrier lifetimes from QDs with the 40 nm barrier spacing between QD layers are almost the same across the entire PL band, indicating the negligible lateral electronic coupling between QDs even at this high dot density over 10^{11}/cm^2. However, for a QD sample with the 15 nm spacing the lifetime increases with increasing wavelength, clearly indicating the significant vertical electronic coupling between QDs at this spacing. The proposed method is an excellent method to estimate the coupling between quantum dots since the measurements are simple and the interpretation is direct.

ACKNOWLEDGMENTS

The authors are grateful for fruitful discussions with N. J. Kim. This work was supported by the Basic Research Program (Grant No. R01-2003-000-10268-0) of the Korea Science and Engineering Foundation and, in part, the National Research Laboratory Program (Grant No. 2004-02403).

REFERENCES

1. Y. Qiu, P. Gogna, S. Forouhar, A. Stintz, and L. F. Lester, *Appl. Phys. Lett.* **79**, 3570 (2001).
2. S. H. Pyun, S. H. Lee, I. C. Lee, H. D. Kim, Weon G. Jeong, J. W. Jang, N. J. Kim, M. S. Hwang, D. Lee, J. H. Lee, and D. K. Oh , *J. Appl. Phys.* **96**, 5766 (2004)
3. J. W. Jang, S. H. Pyun, S. H. Lee, I. C. Lee, Weon G. Jeong, R. Stevenson, P. Daniel Dapkus, N. J. Kim, M. S. Hwang, and D. Lee, *Appl. Phys. Lett.* **85**, 3675 (2004)
4. Y. D. Jang, H. Lee, D. Lee, J. S. Kim, J. Y. Leem, and S. K. Noh, *J. Appl. Phys.* **99**, 096101 (2006)

Resonant Amplification And Relaxation Process Of Transient Current In Nano-contact Systems

Hiroyuki Ishii[1,2], Yoko Tomita[3], and Takashi Nakayama[3]

[1] *CREST, Japan Science and Technology (JST) Agency*
[2] *Institute of Applied Physics, University of Tsukuba, 1-1-1 Tennoudai, Tsukuba, Ibaraki 305-8573, Japan*
[3] *Department of Physics, Faculty of Science, Chiba University, 1-33 Yayoi, Inage, Chiba 263-8522, Japan*

Abstract. In order to investigate the transient-current behavior in nano-contact systems, we developed a new calculation method of time-dependent current based on the Liouville equation of density matrix. Using this method, we found the oscillation of transient current originating from quantum-phase interference just after the connection of nano-systems to electrodes. It is shown that the oscillation period is determined by the energy difference between the Fermi energy of electrode and the electronic levels of nano-system, while the relaxation speed of the transient current is determined by the coupling magnitude between electrodes and nano-systems.

Keywords: transient current, density matrix method, relaxation process
PACS: 73.63.-b, 85.35.-p

INTRODUCTION

Recently, quantum electron transport in nano-contact systems, which are often made of molecules and semiconductors, has been studied intensively, and the unique transport properties such as persistent and anisotropic currents, which originate from the quantum interference of electron wavefunctions, have been revealed [1,2]. All these studies are concerned with steady-state currents. However, in order to employ these systems as devices, it is essential to understand the transient-current behavior responding to the sudden switching of circuit and the applied pulse voltage. In practice, recent real-time measurement of electron conductivity found that an input voltage pulse is distorted while the pulse passes through the nano-systems [3].

The purpose of this work is to clarify such current dynamics in nano-systems caused by the sudden connection to the electrode and the application of pulse voltages, by using the theoretical calculations. To investigate the current dynamics, we developed a new calculation method of time-dependent current based on the Liouville equation of density matrix. The merit of this formulation is that one can separately derive the relaxation and memory effects from the time-evolution equation.

RESULTS AND DISCUSSIONS

In this paper, we investigate the joint system consisting of two bulk electrodes and a nano-system. The Hamiltonian is written as follows,

$$H = H_0 + H_1, \qquad (1)$$

$$H_0 = \varepsilon_C a^\dagger a + \sum_{k,\alpha} \varepsilon_{k\alpha} b_{k\alpha}^\dagger b_{k\alpha}, \qquad (2)$$

$$H_1 = \sum_{k,\alpha} -t_\alpha (a^\dagger b_{k\alpha} + h.c.), \qquad (3)$$

where $b^+_{k\alpha}$ is a creation operator of electron with momentum k in the left (α=L) or right (α=R) electrode, and a^+ is that in a nano-system (designated as C). t_α represents the transfer energy between the α electrode and the nano-system.

Since the electrode has macroscopic freedom, we can reasonably assume that the electronic states in electrode obey the grand-canonical ensembles regardless of the connection to the nano-system. This assumption is realized by adopting the Liouville equation for the projected density matrix. The time-dependent current between the α electrode and the nano-system, $I_\alpha(t)$, is evaluated as

CP893, *Physics of Semiconductors, 28th International Conference*
edited by W. Jantsch and F. Schäffler

$$I_\alpha(t) = \frac{e}{\hbar} t_\alpha^2 2\pi D \left\{ -\rho_C(t) + \Gamma(\mu_\alpha - \varepsilon_C; t) \right\} \quad (4)$$

$$\Gamma(\mu_\alpha - \varepsilon_C; t) = \frac{1}{2} + \int_0^t \frac{\sin\{(\mu_\alpha - \varepsilon_C)s/\hbar\}}{\pi s} ds$$

Here, $\rho_C(t)$ is the electron number in the nano-system. μ_α is the Fermi energy of the α electrode. To simplify, we assume that both the left and right electrodes have the infinite-wide bandwidth and their density of states has a constant value, D.

First, we investigate the transient current when the sudden contact is realized at $t=0$ between the nano-system and electrodes. Figure 1 shows the calculated current feature as a function of time. We found that the relaxation speed of transient current to a steady-state value is mainly determined by the effective coupling magnitude between electrodes and the nano-system. This is because, as seen in the first term of Eq.(4), the electron transfer between electrodes and the nano-system or the density of states in electrodes becomes large, the electron transfer probability increases and the transient current rapidly approaches to the steady current. On the other hand, during the relaxation, one can see the oscillation of transient current. This oscillation occurs originating from the quantum-phase interference between the current from the electrode to the nano-system and the current from the nano-system to the electrode. As seen in the second term of Eq.(4), the oscillation period is determined by the energy difference between the Fermi energy of electrode and the discrete electronic levels in nano-system, thus clearly indicating the Fermi's edge effect. It is noteworthy that such oscillation is particularly amplified just after the contact time and we can see the excessive current flow, compared to the steady current.

Next, we investigate the transient current responding to the pulse voltage. The pulse voltage is realized by adopting the time-dependent Fermi energy, $\mu_L(t)$, in Eq.(4) for the left electrode. Figure 2 shows the calculated transient current responding to the rectangular pulse voltage, which has a magnitude of V and is applied from $t=30$ to 50. The relaxation speed and the oscillation period of transient current in the case of Fig.2 are determined by the similar origins to the case of Fig.1. Moreover, one can see the negative amplification of the current from the left electrode, $I_L(t)$, just after the switch-off of voltage pulse. This occurs because electrons stacked in the nano-system run back to the left electrode.

In summary, we developed a new calculation method of time-dependent current and studied the transient current in nano-contact systems. We found the oscillation and relaxation of transient current. It was shown that the oscillation originates from the quantum interference between the electrode and nano-system and reflects the Fermi energy of the electrode. On the other hand, the relaxation reflects the effective coupling between the electrode and the nano-system, such as the density of states and the contact energy.

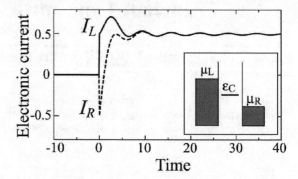

FIGURE 1. Calculated time dependence of transient currents by the sudden contact to electrode at $t=0$. $t_L=t_R=0.2$, $\varepsilon_C=0$, $\mu_L=-\mu_R=1$ and $D=1$ are adopted. The units of current and time are $(2\pi t_L)^2 De/h$ and $h/(\mu_L-\varepsilon_C)$, respectively. The inset is the schematic energy diagram.

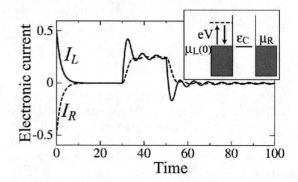

FIGURE 2. Calculated time dependence of transient currents caused by the pulse voltage between $t=30$ to 50. $t_L=t_R=0.2$, $\varepsilon_C=0$, $V=1$ and $D=1$ are adopted. The units of current and time are $(2\pi t_L)^2 De/h$ and $h/(eV-\varepsilon_C)$, respectively. The inset is the schematic energy diagram.

ACKNOWLEDGMENTS

This work was supported by the CREST-JST, Japan, and the 21COE program of Chiba University. We thank the Super Computer Centers, ISSP, University of Tokyo for the use of facilities.

REFERENCES

1. K. Tagami and M. Tsukada, Current Applied Physics **3** (2003) 439.
2. H. Ishii and T. Nakayama, Physical Review B **73** (2006) 235311.
3. B. Naser, J. Heeren, D. K. Ferry and J. P. Bird, Review of scientific instruments **96** (2005) 113905.

Cooling of radiative quantum dot excitons by THz-radiation

Fredrik Boxberg*, Jukka Tulkki*, Go Yusa†,** and Hiroyuki Sakaki†

*Lab. of Computational Engineering, Helsinki University of Technology,P.O.Box 9203, 02015 HUT, Finland
†Institute of Industrial Science, The University of Tokyo,4-6-1 Komaba, Meguro-Ku, Tokyo 153-8505, Japan
**NTT Basic Research Laboratories, NTT Corporation, 3-1 Morinosato-Wakamiya, Atsugi 243-0198, Japan

Abstract. Yusa *et al.* reported an anomalous cooling of radiative quantum dot (QD) excitons by THz-radiation in [Proc. 24th ICPS, 1083 (1998)] We have analyzed this experiment using continuum elasticity, multi-band **k · p** and spin-resolved Monte-Carlo methods. We show that the unexpected discovery is related to hole relaxation via piezo-electric potential minima, induced in the QD sample by InP stressor islands. The THz-radiation gives rise to a drift of dark excitons from the piezo-electric minima to radiative states in the deformation potential minimum. This increases the QD ground state luminescence at the expense of the luminescence from higher QD states. We reproduce also the delayed flash of QD ground state luminescence when a THz-radiation pulse hits the sample even ~ 1 s after switching off the carrier generation.

Keywords: quantum dot, intra-band, relaxation, photoluminescence, cooling
PACS: 73.21.La, 73.43.Cd, 78.47.+p, 78.67.Hc

Semiconductor quantum dots (QD's) are commonly called artificial atoms, due to their man-made single-atom like spectrum, consisting of well separated spectral lines.[1] Nevertheless, time-resolved spectroscopy of intra-band relaxation has proved to be much more difficult with QD's than with free atoms. It is, in distinction to free atoms, not possible to observe QD intra-band relaxation as a sequence of well resolved intermediate steps.

Recently Yusa *et al.* used visible light and near infrared radiation in combination with terahertz (THz) radiation to study intra-band relaxation of carriers in strain-induced quantum dots (SIQD's).[2] The charge carriers were generated in the GaAs barrier with an Ar-ion laser (2.54 eV) or in the InGaAs QW with a Ti-Sap laser (1.3 ~ 1.343 eV). Low-energy THz-radiation (0.44 ~ 16.1 meV) was used together with either one of these two radiation sources to induce intra-band transitions between QD electron and (or) hole levels. The sample contained QD's, induced in an $In_{0.25}Ga_{0.75}As$ quantum well (QW) by InP stressor islands. During continuous wave Ar-ion excitation, the PL consisted of several evenly spaced peaks, in good agreement with earlier reports.[3, 4] When introduced during continuous Ar-ion laser pumping, the THz-radiation drastically enhanced the ground state PL peak and quenched the peaks of recombination between excited QD and QW states. This indicates cooling of carriers and is in striking contrast with previously observed heating of QW excitons during THz-irradiation.[5] Yusa *et al.* reported also that a pulse of THz-radiation gives rise to delayed ground state flash-luminescence even ~ 1 s after turning off the pump laser.

Electro-elasticity and band structure - We have computed electronic structure, relaxation and recombination rates of the QD's using continuum elasticity and the eight-band **k · p** method.[6] The inset of Fig. 1 shows our SIQD model geometry. The calculations showed a large piezo-electric potential (PEP) outside the deformation potential (DP) minimum, near the edges of the InP island. It gives rise to potential minima for holes (+65 meV), which are even deeper and wider than the valence band DP minimum (+24 meV). These PEP minima contain a large number of hole states and their ground-state confinement energy exceeds the confinement of the DP hole ground-state by tens of meV. The electrons are, on the other hand, only confined in the DP minimum (-108 meV) as their DP minimum is much larger than the shallow PEP minima of electrons (-15 meV). The resulting, spatially separated electron (located in DP-minimum) and hole (in the PEP-minimum) pair has a several decades smaller probability of recombining radiatively than one located in the DP-minimum only.

Dynamical model - The presence of the PEP minima makes the relaxation pathways decisively different from the conventional QD carrier dynamics, especially for holes, which sense clear piezo-electric side barriers, blocking the relaxation to the DP-minimum along the y-axis. The relaxation of holes along the x-axis to the DP-minimum is hindered as well, but by the PEP-minima which capture the holes before they can enter the DP-minima. The inefficient hole relaxation was also observed in the experiments as weak QD luminescence during Ti-Sap pumping (generation directly to the QW).

In our analysis we asummed (i) charge neutrality and (ii) included an equal number of electron and hole states. (iii) We excluded non-radiative recombination channels. (iv) We combined groups of nearly degenerate electron and hole states to several degenerate levels and (v) accounted for the spin of the carriers, in the relaxation and

CP893, *Physics of Semiconductors, 28ᵗʰ International Conference*
edited by W. Jantsch and F. Schäffler

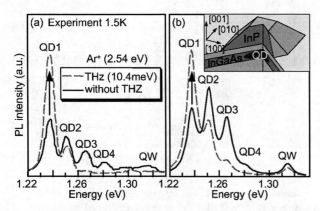

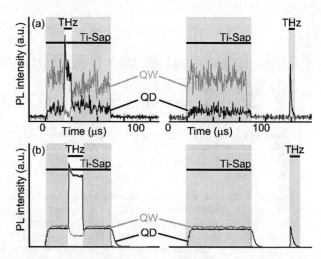

FIGURE 1. Experimental (a) and theoretical (b) photo luminescence during only Ar-ion laser pumping (solid lines) and during simultaneous Ar-ion pumping and THz-irradiation (dashed line).

FIGURE 2. Experimental (a) and simulated (b) time-resolved PL of the QD ground state (black) and the QW (gray), for $T = 15$ K. The time of Ti-Sap laser excitation (to the QW) and THz-radiation ($\hbar\omega_{THz} = 2.5$ meV) are indicated by horizontal bars.

recombination processes. (vi) The same intra-band relaxation time τ_0 was used for all confined hole and electron states and the relaxation was assumed to take place only between consecutive DP or PEP states. The equal relaxation time is motivated at high electron and hole populations for which the carrier relaxation is dominated by the Auger process.[4] (vii) The tunneling rate between the PEP and the DP minima was assumed zero, since it is small in comparison with the prevailing relaxation and recombination rates. The radiative lifetimes τ_{ri} were calculated from the band structure in the electric dipole approximation. However, the relative radiative lifetimes of the three hole minima, were determined by fitting the simulated PL to the experimental one. The model was solved by time-dependent Monte-Carlo simulations of a large ensemble of independent QD's.

Influence of THz-radiation on the luminescence - The enhancement of the QD1 luminescence is due to a THz-radiation induced net-drift of carriers from the deepest PEP levels p_1 to the DP ground state level h_1. Under steady-state condition the total PL intensity is in the first approximation conserved. The PL of higher QD2-QD4 and QW peaks is accordingly reduced. Our calculations predict furthermore that the THz-radiation enhancement of the QD1 peak disappears at high Ar$^+$ pumping intensities due to a saturation of the hole population in the DP minimum. The simulated effect of the THz-radiation on the QW luminescence was smaller than in the experiment, although, Fig. 1 and 2 show a clear decrease of the QW PL. We argue that the large decrease of the experimental QW PL is, related to the conventional heating and ionization of the QW excitons.[5]

Figure 2 (a) and (b) show experimental and simulated time-resolved PL. The black and gray (red) curves correspond to integrated PL of the QD1 (QW) peak. The left panels show results obtained for overlapping time windows of Ti-Sap pumping and THz-radiation excitation. The QW peak is decreased and the QD1 PL is increased during the THz-radiation with both PL peaks returning to their initial value after turning off the THz-radiation. Note the saturation of both the experimental and theoretical PL, during THz-radiation. The right panels show PL with a delayed THz-radiation pulse, appearing after turning off the pump laser. The rise of the QD1 peak by the delayed THz-radiation pulse is due to the excitation and drift of trapped holes from the PEP minima to the DP minimum, where they recombine with the electrons localized in the DP-minimum.

In conclusion - we have shown that the anomalous cooling of radiative QD excitons by THz-radiation[2] is due to a THz-radiation induced drift of holes from piezo-electric potential minima to the lowest radiative states of the QD. Our Monte-Carlo model merits also from being able to reproduce the delayed flash of QD ground state luminescence observed by Yusa *et al.*[2]

REFERENCES

1. M. A. Kastner, *Physics Today* **46**, 24 (1993).
2. G. Yusa *et al.*, in *the 24th ICPS*, 1998, p. 1083. G. Yusa, *Modulation of Zero-Dimensional Carrier Distributions in Quantum Dots by DC-Fields, THz-Fields, and Photons*, Ph.D. thesis, The University of Tokyo (1999).
3. H. Lipsanen, M. Sopanen, and J. Ahopelto, *Phys. Rev B* **51**, 13868 (1995).
4. J. Tulkki, and A. Heinämäki, *Phys. Rev B* **52**, 8239 (1995). Braskén *et al.*, *Phys. Rev B* **58**, R15993 (1998).
5. J. Cerne *et al.*, *Phys. Rev Lett.* **77**, 1131 (1996).
6. S. v Alfthan *et al.*, *Phys. Rev B* **72**, 045329 (2005).

Temperature Dependent Photoluminescence Measurements of Single InP Quantum Dots

Matthias Reischle, Gareth J. Beirne, Robert Rossbach, Michael Jetter and Peter Michler

Institut für Strahlenphysik, Universität Stuttgart, Allmandring 3. 70569 Stuttgart, Germany

Abstract. In this work, we have investigated single InP quantum dots by way of photoluminescence measurements. The lower energy dots show emission from excited states at moderate excitation powers while those emitting at higher energies do not even at high power densities. Temperature dependent measurements were carried out with the objective of understanding this difference and to develop a better understanding of the carrier escape from the dots at elevated temperatures. We observed a strong correlation between the electronic level spacings and the activation energies obtained using an arrhenius model, which thereby indicates that the carriers escape via higher lying levels.

Keywords: Quantum dot, Temperature behavior, Carrier dynamics
PACS: 73.21.La, 78.67.Hc

InP quantum dots (QDs) are very promising candidates for many applications, such as, triggered single photon sources and laser devices. The InP dots under investigation in his work emit in the visible spectral range at the detection maximum of Si-based avalanche photodiodes and charge-coupled devices (CCD) and therefore allow for the efficient detection of single photons. This advantage is important for many future applications, such as, quantum cryptography. It is therefore somewhat surprising that InP QDs have not been studied in more detail. Many properties of these QDs require further detailed investigation, especially the high temperature behavior, as it would be highly advantageous to operate QD devices at room temperature.

The sample was grown by metal-organic vapor phase epitaxy (MOVPE) using the Stranski-Krastanow growth mode. The dots were grown between a 430 nm GaInP barrier layer and a 30 nm GaInP capping layer. After the growth the sample was structured into mesas with a diameter of 200 nm to enable single dot investigations.

For investigations at 4 K the sample was mounted in a He-flow cryostat, capable of variable temperature control, that could be scanned horizontally and vertically using two stepper motors. The QDs were excited using a frequency doubled Ti-Sapphire laser emitting 100 fs wide pulses at 410 nm with a repetition rate of 76 MHz. The light was focused on the sample using a 50x microscope objective which allowed for a spot size below 1 μm in diameter. The laser light was then collected by the same objective and dispersed in a 0.75 m spectrometer and detected by a LN_2 cooled CCD or sent to a Hanbury Brown and Twiss (HBT) type setup [1].

The InP QDs have a height of approximately 3 nm and a diameter of around 20 to 60 nm and emit between

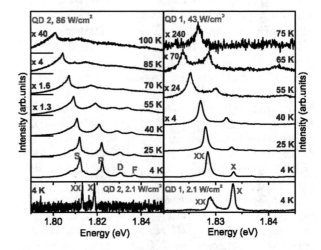

FIGURE 1. Temperature dependent PL-spectra from $QD2$ (left graph) and $QD1$ (right graph). Bottom panels: PL from the dots at 4 k and low excitation power.

1.78 eV and 1.85 eV depending on their height. Some dots (see Fig. 1, labeled $QD2$) show emission from excited states while others, which are named $QD1$ and emit at higher energies, do not exhibit this behaviour even at high PD. The underlying reasons for this difference are still under investigation but it is thought to originate from different carrier relaxation rates in $QD1$ and $QD2$ [2].

At low excitation power densitiy (PD) and a temperature of 4 K (see Fig. 1 bottom panel) the dots exhibit two emission lines one from an exciton and one from a biexciton, that are identified by their linear and superlinear power behavior, respectively (not shown). Please note that even at moderate PD the biexciton dominates

CP893, *Physics of Semiconductors, 28th International Conference*
edited by W. Jantsch and F. Schäffler

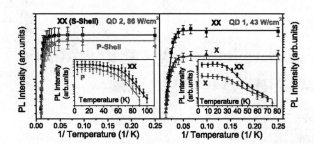 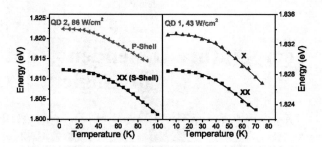

FIGURE 2. Change of the integrated PL intensity with inverse temperature for $QD2$: XX and P-shell (left graph) and for $QD1$: X and XX (right graph). The solid lines are fits to the experimental data obtained using an Arrhenius model.

FIGURE 3. Change of the peak position with temperature for $QD2$: XX and P-shell (left graph) and for $QD1$: X and XX (right graph). The solid lines are fits to the experimental data (see text for explanations).

the spectrum.

The zero dimensional nature of the QDs under investigation was confirmed by second-order autocorrelation measurements. Besides the exciton from $QD2$ that could not be measured due to its low intensity, all emission lines from the ground state showed a strong suppression of multiple photon events by more than a factor of two (not shown) as compared to a Poissonian source of same average intensity, an observation that is regarded as the signature of a single emitter.

For $QD1$ increasing the temperature leads to an increase in the intensity of the exciton relative to that of the biexciton. This may be due to biexciton dissociation and the subsequent escape of one exciton from the dot at elevated temperatures. In the case of $QD2$ a filling of the excited states with increasing temperature is apparent and appears to indicate that carriers escape from the dots via excited states.

The integrated PL intensities of the investigated peaks drop by over two orders of magnitude across the investigated temperature range. The measurement data were fitted using an Arrhenius model (see Fig. 2) from which we obtained activation energies of 13.6 ± 1.3 meV for the exciton transition and 19.7 ± 2.9 meV for the biexciton transition of $QD1$. The difference approximately fits with the biexciton binding energy of 4.2 meV in this case.

For $QD2$ we derived values of 10.4 ± 1.0 meV for the biexciton and 10.5 ± 0.8 meV for the P-shell which both fit to the observed level spacing of approximately 10 meV. These findings indicate that the major loss mechanism is due to the escape of carriers via excited states. In $QD2$ two activation energies are needed. The second is approximately half the offset to the barrier, indicating the escape of excitons directly to the barrier [7].

The dominant phonon energy of the system can be estimated by fitting the temperature dependent redshift of the emission lines with a model which assumes an energy shift due to the increased influence of phonon scattering at elevated temperatures [3]:

$$E_g(T) = E_g(0) - S(\hbar\omega)\left[\coth((\hbar\omega)/(2kT)) - 1\right],$$

where $E_g(0)$ is the band gap at absolute zero, S is a dimensionless coupling constant, and $\hbar\omega$ is the average phonon energy. This model closely fits the data (see Fig. 3) with phonon energies of 10.6 ± 0.8 meV for the XX of $QD1$, 9.9 ± 0.8 meV for the X of $QD1$ and 12.4 ± 0.6 meV for the XX (S-shell) and 9.0 ± 0.3 meV for the P-shell of $QD2$. Higher phonon energies as discussed in literature [4] were not observed over the investigated temperature range. From these values we conclude that the dominant phonon in this system at low temperatures is the transverse acoustic phonon with an energy of approximately 10 meV [5], [6].

In conclusion, we have examined 16 InP QDs. Some showed emission from excited states ($QD2$) while others exhibited emission only from the ground state ($QD1$). Detailed investigations of their temperature characteristics showed the dominant phonon energy in these QDs to be around 10 meV. Furthermore the dominant loss mechanism of carriers at elevated temperatures may be attributed to carrier escape via excited states.

The authors acknowledge financial support from the Alexander von Humbold foundation.

REFERENCES

1. R. Hanbury Brown, and R. Q. Twiss, *Nature* **177**, 27 (1956).
2. G. J. Beirne, M. Reischle, R. Rossbach, M. Jetter, and P. Michler, *to be published*.
3. K. P. O'Donnel, and X. Chen, *Appl. Phys. Lett.* **58**, 2924 (1991).
4. G. Ortner, M. Schwab, M. Bayer, R. Pässler, S. Farfard, Z. Wasilewski, P. Hawrylak, and A. Forchel, *Phys. Rev. B* **72**, 85328 (2005).
5. A. A. Sirenko, M. K. Zundel, T. Ruf, K. Eberl, and M. Cardona, *Phys. Rev. B* **58**, 12633 (1998).
6. I. V. Ignatiev, I. E. Kozin, V. G. Davydov, S. V. Nair, J.-S. Lee, H.-W. Ren, S. Sugou, and Y. Masumoto, *Phys. Rev. B* **63**, 75316 (2001).
7. P. Michler, A. Hangleiter, M. Moser, M. Geiger, and F. Scholz, *Phys. Rev. B* **46**, 7280 (1992).

Characterization of Tunneling and Free-Carrier Screening in Coupled Asymmetric GaN/AlGaN Quantum Discs

Kwan H Lee[1], Jong H Na[1], Stefan Birner[2], Sam N Yi[1], Robert A Taylor[1], Young S Park[3], Chang M Park[3], and Tae W Kang[3]

[1]*Department of Physics, University of Oxford, Parks Road, Oxford, OX1 3PU, United Kingdom* [2]*Walter Schottky Institute and Physics Department, Technical University of Munich, D-85748 Garching, Germany* [3]*Quantum-functional Semiconductor Research Center, Dongguk University, Seoul 100-715, South Korea*

Abstract. We present a systematic investigation of free-carrier screening in coupled asymmetric GaN quantum discs with embedded AlGaN barriers using time-integrated and time-resolved micro-photoluminescence measurements, supported by three-dimensional multi-band **k.p** computational modeling. Free-carrier screening effects decreased with the barrier thickness, which indicates that the source of the free-carriers were carriers tunneling through the barrier.

Keywords: GaN, nanocolumns, time-resolved luminescence, quantum discs
PACS: 78.67.Bf, 78.47.+p, 78.30.Fs

INTRODUCTION

Self-organized GaN nanocolumns have gained interest in application for blue/ultra-violet wavelength optoelectronic devices. They possess desirable properties such as low defect density, good reproducibility, quantum confinement effects and can be produced using conventional growth techniques. These properties make nanocolumns an attractive basis for novel quantum optoelectronic devices (e.g. for quantum information processing [1]) and significant advancement has been made towards practical devices [2].

Quantum well (QW) like structures grown at the tip of GaN nanocolumns are known as quantum discs (Q-discs) and demonstrate lateral confinement. Using a combination of time-resolved (TR-) and time-integrated (TI-) photoluminescence (PL) spectroscopy and multi-band **k.p** computational modeling with next**nano**[3] [3], we have performed a systematic study of carrier tunneling and free-carrier screening in coupled asymmetric GaN Q-discs separated by AlGaN barriers. Carrier tunneling in such structures has been suggested previously [4] and could play an important role in future devices.

SAMPLE DETAILS

GaN/AlGaN Q-discs samples studied were grown at the tip of a 2.7-μm-high GaN nanocolumn, with the nanocolumn and Q-disc grown by plasma assisted MBE on a Si (111) substrate without any buffer layer [5]. The GaN nanocolumns exhibited an average diameter of 100 nm and a density of 1×10^9 cm^{-2}. The samples consisted of ten periods of two alternating GaN Q-disc thicknesses (4nm – DA and 3 nm – DB) separated by Al$_{0.5}$Ga$_{0.5}$N barrier (2, 4 and 8nm).

RESULTS

Details of the apparatus used for TI-PL and TR-PL measurements can be found in our earlier work [4]. The only changes being that excitation was performed at 266 nm and the rise time of the photomultiplier tube was 150 ps.

Spectra as a function of excitation power ranging from 20 μW to 1.4 mW (at the focus) are presented in Fig. 1. Two peaks were observed at 351 and 341 nm, labeled DA and DB in the spectra. As the excitation power increased the DA peak grew more rapidly, relative to DB peak, and it eventually dominated the spectra. This is reflected in the peak intensity versus excitation power plot (Fig. 1), which showed that the DB peak intensity was proportional to the excitation

CP893, Physics of Semiconductors, 28th International Conference
edited by W. Jantsch and F. Schäffler
© 2007 American Institute of Physics 978-0-7354-0397-0/07/$23.00

power, while the DA peak intensity displayed a nonlinear dependence with excitation power, with the effect is weaker in 8 nm barrier sample. This observation is consistent with earlier studies involving GaAs/AlGaAs asymmetric QWs, which demonstrated nonlinear PL dependence with excitation power, due to carrier tunneling [6]. Lastly, results from next**nano³** computer modeling [7] demonstrate that carriers in DB are energetic enough to tunnel into DA, whilst carriers in DB are highly localized.

Through TR-PL measurements, the effects of free-carrier screening were studied. Figure 2 shows the TR-PL trace collected from the DA and DB peaks, at high (1.4 mW) and low (20 μW) excitation power for both 2 and 8 nm barrier samples. In the 2 nm barrier sample DA lifetime decreased from 530 to 240 ps (20 μW to 1.4 mW) while for the sample with the 8nm barrier, DA lifetime decreased from 510 to 400 ps (20 μW to 1.4 mW). Over this range DB lifetime only varied from 480 to 380 ps in both the 2 and 8 nm samples. A series of TR-PL measurements (taken at 2nm intervals, with 1.4 mW excitation) in Fig. 2 indicate that the majority of interactions occur in the first 500 ps [7]. Here the DA peak blue-shifted (gain of free-carriers)

The decrease in lifetime with increasing optical excitation could be explained by free-carrier screening [8,9], which compensates the built-in piezo- and pyroelectric field (responsible for the QCSE). The photo-generated free-carriers screen the built-in fields, which then leads to a reduction in the band structure tilt and consequently the overlap between electron and hole increases (decreased carrier lifetime). However this effect is more significant in DA due to the tunneling, which provides additional free-carriers.

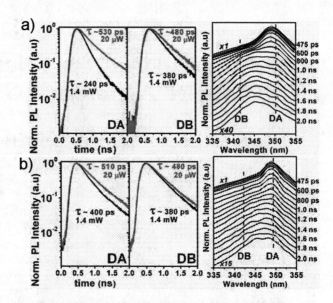

FIGURE 2. TR-PL and reconstruction of the spectrum from TR-PL measurements at an excitation powers for a sample with 2 nm (a) and 8 nm (b) barrier.

CONCLUSION

Using a combination of TR- and TI-PL spectroscopy and multi-band **k.p** computational modeling, we have performed a systematic study of free-carrier screening in coupled asymmetric GaN Q-discs separated by AlGaN barriers. The screening effect is enhanced due to carrier tunneling, which provides additional free-carriers.

ACKNOWLEDGMENTS

This research is part of the QIP IRC supported by EPSRC (GR/S82176/01). KHL thanks the support of the University College old members fund scholarship, Clarendon Fund bursary, Overseas Research Students award and M.A.G. Jones. YSP, CMP and TWK thanks QSRC and AOARD at Dongguk University.

REFERENCES

1. M. Zamfirescu et al., phys. stat. sol. (c) **2**, 822 (2005)
2. A. Kikuchi et al., Jpn. J. Appl. Phys., **43**, L1524 (2004)
3. next**nano³** device simulator: The program is available at www.wsi.tum.de/nextnano3
4. J. H. Na et al., Appl. Phys. Lett., **86**, 083109 (2005)
5. C. M. Park et al., Nanotechnology **17**, 952 (2006)
6. D. J. Leopold, M.M. Leopold, Phys. Rev. B, **42**, 11147 (1990)
7. K. H. Lee et al., Appl. Phys. Lett, **89**, 023103 (2006)
8. F.D. Sala, et al., Appl. Phys. Lett., **74**, 2002 (1999)
9. T. Kuroda, et al., Appl. Phys. Lett., **76**, 3753 (2000)

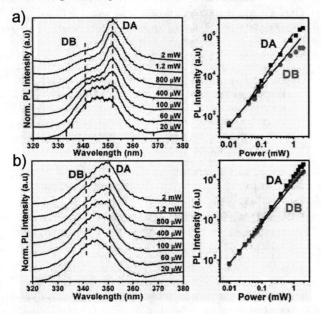

FIGURE 1. TI-PL and peak intensity dependence with power for a sample with 2 nm (a) and 8 nm (b) barrier.

Spatiotemporal dynamics of charge carriers in quantum dot-wire systems following delocalized optical excitations

D. Reiter, V. M. Axt and T. Kuhn

Institut für Festkörpertheorie, Westfälische Wilhelms-Universität, Wilhelm-Klemm-Str.10, 48149 Münster, Germany

Abstract. The density matrix formalism for quantum kinetics is used to model the spatiotemporal dynamics of the carrier density after a spatially homogeneous excitation in a coupled semiconductor quantum wire-dot system. The carrier capture leads to a wave front dynamics in the carrier distribution in the quantum wire region and the formation of a plateau between the fronts. The dynamics are analyzed using different excitation energies.

Keywords: quantum kinetics; carrier capture; ballistic transport
PACS: 73.63.-b, 78.67.-n, 72.20.Jv, 72.10.Di

In quantum mechanics carrier dynamics have to obey basic uncertainty relations, e.g., between momentum and position. In an extended semiconductor the scattering of a carrier with a phonon has a well defined momentum transfer and therefore no well defined position. In contrast, when a transition from a delocalized state into a localized state takes place it acquires a local character. Here we are interested in the spatiotemporal behavior of the carrier dynamics in a semiconductor quantum wire with an embedded dot after a spatially homogeneous excitation. We will show that the capture of the carriers into the localized quantum dot states results in a characteristic inhomogeneous spatial profile of the carrier density in the quantum wire region.

Our calculations are based on the density matrix formalism for quantum kinetics to describe the carrier dynamics in a semiconductor quantum wire with an embedded dot in a two band model. We take periodic boundary conditions and a weakly reflecting quantum dot profile. The carriers are excited by a laser pulse which is spatially homogeneous and Gaussian in time. They couple to longitudinal optical (LO) phonons. The basics variables are given by the single particle density matrix $\rho_{n'n}^{e/h}$ for electron and holes and the interband polarization $p_{n'n}$, where n denotes the n-th eigenstate of the system. While the diagonal elements of the density matrix account for the occupations, the off-diagonal elements contain phase information. In particular, they determine the spatial profile and the spatial dynamics of the carriers. Due to the carrier-phonon interaction the resulting equations of motion for the single particle density matrices are the starting point of an infinite hierarchy of equations, which is truncated on the level of the second Born approximation. A description of the theory can be found in [1, 2].

Here we consider a semiconductor quantum dot with a single bound level at -14.4 meV embedded in a GaAs

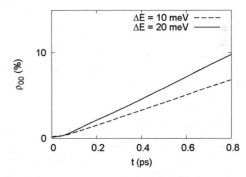

FIGURE 1. Occupation of the electron ground state normalized to the total generated electron density for two different excess energies.

semiconductor quantum wire. The system is spatially homogeneously excited with a laser pulse which has a mean excess energy ΔE of 10 or 20 meV. The duration of the laser pulse is 50 fs and has its maximum at $t = 0$. The LO phonon energy is $E_{LO} = 36.4$ meV. The temperature is sufficiently low such that no phonon absorption processes can take place. Thus, due to the low excess energy no phonon emission processes can occur in the region outside the dot. When the carriers reach the dot region they can be captured by emitting a phonon.

Figure 1 shows the occupation of the bound state in the conduction band as a function of time for the two different mean excess energies. The occupations for both excess energies are rising linearly in time corresponding to a constant effective capture rate. Thus, for the present excitation conditions we observe no saturation neither due to phase space filling of the bound state nor due to depletion of the delocalized states. The absence of phase space filling effects of the bound state is caused by the

CP893, *Physics of Semiconductors, 28th International Conference*
edited by W. Jantsch and F. Schäffler

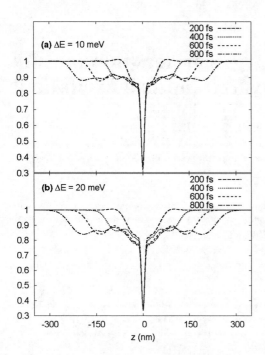

FIGURE 2. Spatial profile of the density of electrons in the delocalized states at different times. The mean excess energy of the laser is (a) 10 meV and (b) 20 meV.

low excitation density. The absence of depletion effects in the continuum states will become clear below.

The capture rate for an excitation at $\Delta E = 20$ meV is considerably higher than for $\Delta E = 10$ meV. For $\Delta E = 20$ meV the peak of the generated electron energy distribution is about one LO phonon energy above the bound state. Therefore, most of the carriers are close to the semiclassically allowed transition. Even if in a quantum kinetic treatment the exact energy conservation in a scattering process is released due to energy-time uncertainty, processes close to the semiclassically allowed ones have the highest probability leading to a rather efficient capture process in this case. For $\Delta E = 10$ meV the peak of the generated electron distribution is below the resonance for capture processes. Thus, only the electrons in the high energy tail of the distribution have a high capture probability leading to a smaller total capture efficiency.

Let us now look at the spatiotemporal electron dynamics. The spatial profile of the density for electrons in the delocalized states is shown in Fig. 2 at different times for both excess energies. During the excitation the carrier density is spatially homogeneous outside the dot. At the dot located at $z = 0$ there is a dip caused by the orthogonality of the continuum states with respect to the bound state. After the excitation we observe the build up of two wave fronts between a low density region adjacent to the quantum dot and regions with the initially generated density. The wave fronts move away from the dot

at a constant velocity which is independent of the excess energy. However the plateau value of the density between the two wave fronts is lower for $\Delta E = 20$ meV.

These findings can be explained as follows: In the wire region, since no phonon absorption or emission processes are possible, the carriers move ballistically. When approaching the dot, the carriers which have an energy resonant for capture, i.e., an energy of about 20 meV, are captured inside the dot, the other carriers are essentially passing the dot. On the other side of the dot the captured carriers are now missing leading to the formation of the lower plateau. The velocity of the fronts is therefore given by the group velocity of the carriers with an energy of E_{LO} above the bound state, independent of the excess energy of the laser pulse. However, the fraction of the carriers which is captured strongly depends on the excess energy. For $\Delta E = 10$ meV less carriers have an energy resonant for the capture process, therefore more carriers pass the dot and give rise to a higher plateau value between the fronts.

The results clearly demonstrate the local character of the carrier capture process. The carriers can only be captured when they are close to the dot. The density far away from the dot remains spatially homogeneous until the wave front reaches it. As long as the wave front has not yet reached the boundary of the system there is a constant flow of electrons towards the dot explaining why we do not observe saturation effects due to the depletion of the continuum states. Finally we want to point out the even if the spatially homogeneous excitation leads only to occupations of states, due to the combination of transport and capture off-diagonal density matrix elements build up. Therefore it is essential to include all elements of the density matrix in the calculations [3].

In conclusion, we have shown that even after a spatially homogeneous excitation the carrier capture leads to the formation of spatially inhomogeneous profiles resulting from the localized character of the capture process. The energy selectivity of the phonon emission process leads to the build up of plateaus and propagating wave fronts between the regions where the carrier distributions are already affected by the capture and regions where they are still unaffected. This behavior can only be obtained when the full non-diagonal character of the single-particle density matrices is taken into account.

REFERENCES

1. M. Herbst, M. Glanemann, V. M. Axt, and T. Kuhn, *Phys. Rev.* B **67**, 195305 (2003).
2. M. Glanemann, V. M. Axt, and T. Kuhn, *Phys. Rev.* B **72**, 045354 (2005).
3. D. Reiter, M. Glanemann, V. M. Axt, and T. Kuhn, to be published.

Electron-Acoustic Phonon Interaction in Semiconductor Nanostructures

Frank Grosse* and Roland Zimmermann*

*Institut für Physik, Humboldt-Universität zu Berlin, Newtonstr. 15, 12489 Berlin, Germany

Abstract. Acoustic phonon modes are investigated in semiconductor nanostructures within continuum elasticity theory. At the example of spherically symmetric quantum dots the influence of the structural confinement and intrinsic strain onto the electron-acoustic phonon interaction compared to bulk phonon modes is discussed. The calculation of effective elastic constants, closely related to the acoustic phonons, is based on first principles calculations and compared to recent analytic theories.

The spatial extension of active regions in semiconductor nanostructures can be reduced down to a few nanometers allowing the localization of electrons and holes with high precision in so called quantum dots. Single dots can experimentally be investigated by optical excitations. A utilization in quantum devices is however only possible if the coherence is not destroyed due to coupling. A crucial role with this respect play acoustic phonons, which contribute significantly to dephasing of optical excitations within semiconductor nanostructures [1].

Embedding a semiconductor material (InAs) in a host crystal (GaAs) pseudomorphically, i.e. without introducing defects, leads to intrinsic strain due to different lattice constants. The strain itself influences the electronic properties as well as the phonon spectrum. The first will be treated here within the deformation potential description whereas the latter is handled employing continuum elasticity theory and treating the strain influence by introducing effective elastic constants.

We will restrict ourselves to the simplest case of a spherical quantum dot embedded in an infinite medium, whereas extensions will be presented elsewhere [2]. In linear continuum elasticity theory the stress tensor σ is proportional to the strain tensor ε related by the fourth order tensor of elastic constants C (Hook's law). For isotropic systems there are only two independent elastic constants, which are related to well-known Lame coefficients by $C_{12} = C_{11} - 2C_{44} = \lambda$ and $C_{44} = \mu$. The strain distribution of the hydrostatic component $\varepsilon_h = tr(\varepsilon)$ within isotropic elasticity is given inside the spherical quantum dot by [3]

$$\varepsilon_h = 4\varepsilon_0 \frac{C_{44}}{C_{11}} \tag{1}$$

and zero outside. For our InAs/GaAs model system $\varepsilon_0 =$

$(a(GaAs) - a(InAs))/a(InAs) = -0.067$ is defined by the equilibrium lattice constants.

The governing equation for the description of acoustic phonons is the equation of motion for the displacement $\mathbf{u}(\mathbf{r})$

$$-\omega^2 \rho(\mathbf{r}) u_i(\mathbf{r}) = \sum_j \frac{\partial}{\partial x_j} \sigma_{ij}(\mathbf{r}), \tag{2}$$

here in Cartesian coordinates $i, j = x, y, z$. The mass density $\rho(\mathbf{r})$ as well as the stress tensor $\sigma_{ij}(\mathbf{r})$ are in general spatially dependent. The stress is given in linear elasticity under the assumption of isotropic elastic constants by

$$\sigma_{jk} = \delta_{jk}(C_{11} - 2C_{44}) \sum_l \frac{\partial u_l}{\partial x_l} + C_{44}\left(\frac{\partial u_j}{\partial x_k} + \frac{\partial u_k}{\partial x_j}\right). \tag{3}$$

It is, however, not sufficient to use the standard numerical values for the elastic constants. Due to the compressive strain present within the quantum dot the elastic constants are modified [4, 5]. The expressions for the effective elastic constants C_{ij}^s can be given analytically for cubic systems [5] under hydrostatic deformation. Transforming from original coordinates ξ to new ones $\mathbf{x}$ with $x_i = \sum_j F_{ij}\xi_j$ and $F_{ij} = (1-\alpha)\delta_{ij}$ the new elastic constants are given by

$$
\begin{aligned}
C_{11}^s &= C_{11} + \eta\,(2C_{11} + 2C_{12} + C_{111} + 2C_{112}) \\
C_{12}^s &= C_{12} + \eta\,(-C_{11} - 2C_{12} + C_{112} + 2C_{123}) \\
C_{44}^s &= C_{44} + \eta\,(C_{11} + 2C_{12} + C_{44} + C_{144} + 2C_{155})
\end{aligned}
\tag{4}
$$

with $\eta = \alpha + \alpha^2/2$ with the numerical value for our model system $\eta = -0.034$. The above equations include contributions up to the third order elastic constants C_{IJK}. Note that the variation of the bulk module $B = (C_{11} + 2C_{12})/3$ under hydrostatic strain contains only contributions from third order elastic constants. The numerical

CP893, *Physics of Semiconductors, 28th International Conference*
edited by W. Jantsch and F. Schäffler

values are given in Fig. 1 for GaAs comparing explicit calculation within DFT [6, 7, 8] and above analytical expressions. Also the mass density $\rho(\mathbf{r})$ is changed due to the hydrostatic pressure.

The electron-phonon interaction is described by

$$H_{def}(\mathbf{r}) = \sum_v D_C [b_v^\dagger \, div \, \mathbf{u}_v(\mathbf{r}) + h.c.] \qquad (5)$$

with the deformation potential coupling constant for the conduction band D_C and the phonon creation operator $b_v^\dagger$. The electron-phonon coupling function, to be used e.g. in the independent Boson model [9], is

$$f(E) = \sum_v \delta(E - \hbar\omega_v) \left| \int d^3\mathbf{r} \, D_C \, \varphi_e^2(\mathbf{r}) \, div \, \mathbf{u}_v(\mathbf{r}) \right|^2, \qquad (6)$$

where we only consider the one-particle ground state electronic wave function $\varphi_e(\mathbf{r})$ of the dot confinement. It is calculated within effective mass approximation including the modified confinement potential due to strain within the deformation potential description. The deformation potential coupling constant is taken as for InAs $D_C = -5.04$ eV. The strain reduces the electronic band-offset significantly form 894 to 380 meV. Due to the spherical symmetry of the electronic ground state wave function there is only coupling to the spheroidal acoustic phonon modes.

The electron-acoustic phonon coupling function is plotted in Fig. 2. Compared to the usual expressions including bulk phonons only, a reduction of the coupling strength for small energies is found. This reduction is due to the change in elastic properties within the nanostructure and additionally to the inherent strain. Also the shape of the coupling function differs from the usual bulk behavior. A nearly linear decay around 1 meV is unexpected but can be explained by the structure in the phonon amplitudes (not shown here).

In summary, calculations are presented which show the significance to include details of the acoustic phonon modes within the electron-phonon interaction. The quantum dot phonons investigated here reduce the overall coupling.

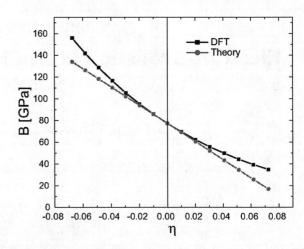

FIGURE 1. Effective bulk modulus under hydrostatic pressure for GaAs. Compared are explicit calculations within DFT with linearized expressions including third order elastic constants.

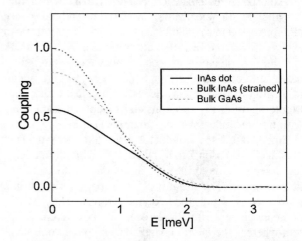

FIGURE 2. Electron-acoustic phonon coupling function for a strained quantum dot. Compared are calculations including bulk phonons either for bulk GaAs (barrier material) or strained InAs (dot).

REFERENCES

1. E. Muljarov, and R. Zimmermann, *Phys. Rev. Lett.* **93**, 237401 (2004).
2. F. Grosse, and R. Zimmermann, unpublished.
3. A. Andreev, J. Downes, D. Faux, and E. O'Reilly, *J. Appl. Phys.* **86**, 297–305 (1999).
4. D. Dunstan, S. Bosher, and J. Downes, *Appl. Phys. Lett.* **80**, 2672–2674 (2002).
5. S. Bosher, and D. Dunstan, *J. Appl. Phys.* **97**, 103505 (2005).
6. X. Gonze, J.-M. Beuken, R. Caracas, F. Detraux, M. Fuchs, G.-M. Rignanese, L. Sindic, M. Verstraete, G. Zerah, F. Jollet, M. Torrent, A. Roy, M. Mikami, P. Ghosez, J.-Y. Raty, and D. Allan., *Computational Materials Science* **25**, 478 (2002).
7. X. Gonze, G.-M. Rignanese, M. Verstraete, J.-M. Beuken, Y. Pouillon, R. Caracas, F. Jollet, M. Torrent, G. Zerah, M. Mikami, P. Ghosez, M. Veithen, J.-Y. Raty, V. Olevano, F. Bruneval, L. Reining, R. Godby, G. Onida, D. Hamann, and D. Allan., *Zeit. Kristallogr.* **220**, 558 (2005).
8. The ABINIT code is a common project of the Université Catholique de Louvain, Corning Incorporated, and other contributors (http://www.abinit.org).
9. G. Mahan, *Many-Particle Physics*, Plenum, New York, 1990.

Temperature dependent photoluminescence from carbon nanotubes

I. B. Mortimer and R. J. Nicholas

Clarendon Laboratory, Physics Department, Oxford University, Parks Road, Oxford OX1 3PU, U.K.

Abstract.
The temperature dependence of the photoluminescence intensity from frozen single walled carbon nanotube solutions is reported. This is modelled assuming that it is dominated by the small energy splitting between the dark and bright states of the singlet excitons which are found to be in the region of 1-5 meV for nanotubes of 0.8-1.2nm. The luminescence is strongly enhanced by a magnetic field along the tube axis due to the mixing of the different valley states of the excitons.

Keywords: carbon nanotubes, excitons, photoluminescence
PACS: 78.67.Ch, 71.35.Ji

The role of excitons in the optical properties of single walled carbon nanotubes (SWCNT) is a matter of considerable debate. Experiments suggest that exciton binding energies are of order several hundred meV [1, 2, 3, 4] in agreement with theory[5, 6] although excitonic interactions due to screening and electron-electron interactions[7, 8] can compensate each other. The two degenerate K valleys, plus the electron and hole spins lead to multiple exciton states with only one predicted to be optically allowed (Bright)[9]. The most strongly bound exciton is an optically forbidden dark (triplet) state[5, 6, 10, 11, 12] which could lead to very strong optical quenching. A second singlet manifold exists at higher energies[12, 13, 14] where the lowest state is again dark, but with a bright exciton state quite close. It has been predicted that the different exciton states will have a strong effect on the radiative lifetime of the excitons[13, 14]. In this paper we give preliminary results from a study of the temperature dependence of the PL efficiency of SWCNT which allow estimates to be made of the singlet dark-bright exciton energy splittings.

Photoluminescence excitation (PLE) maps were taken of quench frozen HiPCO produced SWNT prepared by conventional techniques [15] for each different temperature, to ensure that each species was always measured under resonant excitation[16]. A typical PLE map is shown as the inset to Figure 1. The PL intensities were analysed for each peak from 1.5 to 250K as shown in Figure 1. The intensities show a maximum in the region of 10-40K and a rapid fall-off at lower temperatures. We interpret this as due to the temperature dependence of the radiative decay rate. Calculations have recently been reported[13, 14] which show that the decay rate is dominated by (i) the 1D exciton radiative lifetime where $\tau_r \propto T^{1/2}$[17] and (ii) the thermal distribution of excitons between the bright and dark singlet exciton states. Op-

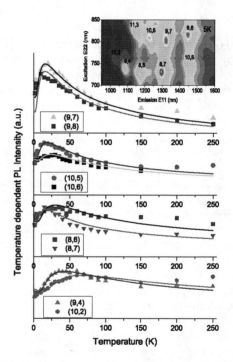

FIGURE 1. Temperature dependence of the PL intensities deduced for specific nanotube species. The inset shows a typical PLE map measured at 5K.

tical excitation creates only spin singlets excitons with odd parity. Scattering into triplet and even parity states is forbidden except for some symmetry breaking processes which are assumed to be weak[13, 14]. The recombination is modelled as taking place entirely within the singlet manifold using the relation for the intensity (I)

$$I \propto \frac{1}{(T^2 + T_0^2)^{\frac{1}{4}}} \times \frac{m + e^{\frac{-\Delta}{kT}}}{1 + e^{\frac{-\Delta}{kT}}} \qquad (1)$$

CP893, *Physics of Semiconductors, 28th International Conference*
edited by W. Jantsch and F. Schäffler
© 2007 American Institute of Physics 978-0-7354-0397-0/07/$23.00

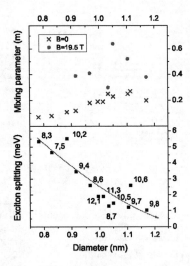

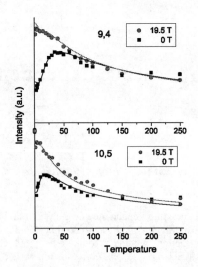

FIGURE 2. Values deduced for Δ and m as a function of nanotube diameter.

FIGURE 3. Temperature dependent PL intensities for selected nanotube species at zero and 19.5T, showing experiment and fits using Equation 1.

based on the simplification that recombination is dominated by radiative emission from two 1-D excitons, one dark and at a lower energy and one bright separated by Δ with a mixing of the even and odd parity states of magnitude m. The $T^{-1/2}$ divergence is removed by the addition of a small broadening term of $T_0 = 1$ meV. This type of analysis has been suggested by the recent work of ref[13, 14]. Figure 1 shows fits to Eq. 1 for the 8 strongest nanotube species observed. Figure 2 shows the values of Δ and m as a function of the nanotube diameter (d). The splitting between the bright and dark exciton states shows a strong dependence on tube diameter. This is consistent with the recently reported calculations from Ando[9], which predict that the relative energies of the bright and dark exciton states are very strongly dependent on the Coulomb interaction strength, which is parameterised in terms of a factor w_1/w_2 which is related to the relative contribution to short range electron-electron interactions from intra- and intervalley processes.

The transition to $T^{-1/2}$ behaviour above 100K in Fig. 1 suggests that optically pumped radiative emission is dominated by the optically active excitons for high temperatures. Scattering into different symmetry and spin states is weak and the optical properties of nanotubes will be dominated by the optically active excitons.

It has been suggested magnetic field could lead to enhanced mixing of the excitonic levels due to the lifting of the degeneracy of the K and K' states[18] which control the symmetry of the excitons[9, 19]. Typical PL results are shown in fig. 3 for the Voigt geometry. At low temperature[20] the magnetic field causes a very significant increase of the PL intensity. The temperature dependence was refitted using eq. 1 as in Fig. 3, which showed that the effect of the magnetic field could be modelled simply by changing the magnitude of the mixing param-

eter. This had the effect of increasing the emission at low temperatures, where the dominant emission processes are from the nominally 'dark' exciton. This behaviour is in good agreement with the results of Ando[9], which predict a rapid rise in intensity for the lower energy state caused by the field induced mixing of the wavefunctions.

REFERENCES

1. Y.Z. Ma, L. Valkunas, S.M. Bachilo and G.R. Fleming, J. Phys. Chem. B **109** 15671(2005)
2. F. Wang et al, Science **308**, 838 (2005)
3. J. Maultzsch et al., Phys. Rev. B **72**, 241402 (2005)
4. L. J. Li et al., Nature. Mat. **4**, 481 (2005).
5. C.D. Spataru et al, Phys. Rev. Lett. **92**, 077402 (2004)
6. V.Perebeinos, J. Tersoff and P. Avouris, Phys. Rev. Lett. **92**, 257402 (2004)
7. T. Ando, J. Phys. Soc. Japan **66**, 1066 (1997)
8. C.L. Kane and E.J. Mele, Phys. Rev. Lett. **93**, 197402 (2004)
9. T. Ando, J. Phys. Soc. Jpn. **75**, 024707 (2006).
10. E. Chang, et al Phys. Rev. Lett.**92**, 196401 (2004)
11. H. Zhao and S. Mazumdar,Phys. Rev. Lett.**93**, 157402 (2004)
12. H. Zhao et al, Phys. Rev. B **73**, 075403 (2006).
13. C.D. Spataru et al, Phys. Rev. Lett. **95**, 247402 (2005)
14. V.Perebeinos, J. Tersoff and P. Avouris, Nano. Lett. **5** 2495 (2005)
15. M. J. O'Connell et al., Science **297**, 593 (2002).
16. L. J. Li, R. J. Nicholas, R. S. Deacon and P. A. Shields, Phys. Rev. Lett. **93**, 156104 (2004).
17. D.S. Citrin, Phys. Rev. Lett. **69**, 3393 (1992).
18. H. Ajiki and T. Ando, J. Phys. Soc. Jpn. **62**, 1255 (1993).
19. S. Zaric et al., Phys. Rev. Lett. **96**, 016406 (2006).
20. L.J. Li and R.J. Nicholas,Int. J. of Modern Physics B **18** 3509 (2004).

One-Dimensional Characteristics of Third-Order Nonlinear Optical Response in Single-Walled Carbon Nanotubes

A. Nakamura[1], Y. Takahashi[1], S. Imamura[1], H. Kishida[1], and Y. Hamanaka[2]

[1]*Department of Applied Physics, Nagoya University, Chikusa-ku, Nagoya 464-8603, Japan*
[2]*Nagoya Institute of Technology, Nagoya 466-8555, Japan*

Abstract. Third-order nonlinear optical susceptibilities have been investigated for individually suspended single walled carbon nanotubes in solution. The imaginary part of susceptibility $\text{Im}\chi^{(3)}$ shows the resonant enhancement at each optical transition of the specific (n,m) tube. We have found that the diameter D dependence of the figure of merit $\text{Im}\chi^{(3)}/\alpha$ (α:absorption coefficient) is $D^{6.1\pm0.9}$.

Keywords: Carbon nanotubes, One-dimensional system, Nonlinear optical response, Femtosecond spectroscopy.
PACS: 78.67Ch, 42.65.-k, 78.67.Ch

INTRODUCTION

The quasi-one-dimensional (1D) electronic states in carbon nanotubes show a van Hove singularity of the density of states and a strong exciton effect[1,2]. These effects are expected to enhance optical nonlinearities in the near-infrared region[3], which have the potential for applications in optical telecommunication systems. However, the contributions of a van Hove singularity and excitons to the nonlinear susceptibility $\chi^{(3)}$ in single-walled carbon nanotubes (SWNTs) are not quantitatively understood. In addition, the dependence of $\chi^{(3)}$ on the diameter and chirality is essential for understanding 1D features of SWNTs.

In this paper, third-order nonlinear optical response in individually suspended SWNTs in solution was investigated using femtosecond pump-probe spectroscopy. We report on the resonance enhancement of $\chi^{(3)}$ and its diameter dependence in semiconducting SWNTs.

EXPERIMENT

HiPco (high-pressure CO conversion)-SWNTs were dispersed in deuterium oxide (D_2O)-sodium dodecyl sulfate (SDS) to obtain individual nanotubes, each encased in a cylindrical micelle. Nanotube bundles were separated and purified by sonification and centrifugation at 85000g for 4 hours. Pump-probe measurements were made using an amplified Ti:sapphire laser system with the pump photon energy of 3.12 eV and the pulse duration of 150 fs[4]. Nonlinear absorption spectra were measured with a white continuum probing beam generated by self-phase modulation in a water cell. Values of $\chi^{(3)}$ in the nondegenerate configuration were measured in the spectral range of 0.85 to 3.0 eV.

RESULTS AND DISCUSSION

Figure 1 (solid curve) shows the absorption spectrum in the photon energy range 0.85–1.45 eV for SWNT-SDS suspensions in D_2O. The spectrum in this energy range indicates sharp structures corresponding to different diameters and chiral angles of semiconducting nanotubes. Each optical transition was assigned to a specific (n,m) nanotube[5]. For example, the peak at 1.110 eV is assigned to the transition between the lowest conduction and valence bands of

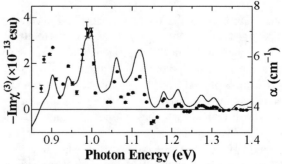

FIGURE 1. Absorption and $\text{Im}\chi^{(3)}$ spectra of SWNTs in D_2O/SDS.

CP893, *Physics of Semiconductors, 28th International Conference*
edited by W. Jantsch and F. Schäffler
© 2007 American Institute of Physics 978-0-7354-0397-0/07/$23.00

the (7,6) tube. The peak at 0.999 eV is ascribed to (9,5), (10,3) and (10,5), which are not separated.

In Fig. 2 we show the linear absorption spectrum and differential absorption spectra with various delay times between the pump and probe pulses. The photon energy of the pump pulse is 3.12 eV, which corresponds to the higher band states of the SWNTs. The differential spectrum $\Delta\alpha$ exhibits absorption bleaching at each peak, and $\Delta\alpha$ slightly decays in the range 0-2.4 ps. The sharp structure corresponding to each optical transition due to the specific (n,m) nanotube suggests the resonance enhancement of the nonlinearities.

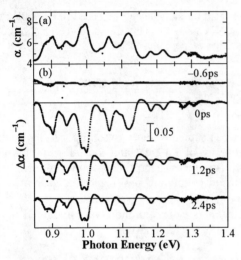

FIGURE 2. (a) Linear absorption spectrum and (b) differential absorption spectra for different delay times.

For a moderate laser intensity of the pump pulse, I, the change in the absorption coefficient $\Delta\alpha$ is described by $\Delta\alpha = \beta I$, where β is a nonlinear absorption coefficient. The imaginary part of $\chi^{(3)}$ ($\mathrm{Im}\chi^{(3)}$) is related to β by

$$\mathrm{Im}\,\chi^{(3)} = \frac{n^2 c^2}{240\pi^2 \omega_{probe}}\beta \qquad (1)$$

where n represents the linear refractive index of the SWNTs at the probe frequency and c is the velocity of light in vacuum. From the dependence of $\Delta\alpha$ on I we can estimate $\mathrm{Im}\chi^{(3)}$ values. The obtained values of $\mathrm{Im}\chi^{(3)}$ are plotted in Fig.1 by closed circles. Comparing the result with the absorption spectrum, we have found that $-\mathrm{Im}\chi^{(3)}$ shows a peak at each optical transition. The figure of merit $\mathrm{Im}\chi^{(3)}/\alpha$ for the E_{11} transition of the (7,6) tube is -1.3×10^{-13} esu cm.

Utilizing the assignment of the optical transitions in the absorption spectrum we investigated the diameter D dependence of $\mathrm{Im}\chi^{(3)}$ in semiconducting

SWNTs. Shown in Fig. 3 is the diameter dependence of the figure of merit. The least-squares fit to the data indicates that $\mathrm{Im}\chi^{(3)}/\alpha$ depends on $D^{6.1\pm0.9}$. As the band gap E_g of the semiconductor nanotubes is proportional to D^{-1}, the dependence of $\mathrm{Im}\chi^{(3)}$ on the band gap is -6.1 ± 0.9. This dependence is comparable to the exciton energy dependence of $E^{-5.5}$ observed in polysilanes[6] in which the 1D exciton effect plays an important role in the resonant enhancement of the nonlinearity. Therefore, we have found that the observed diameter dependence is a feature characteristic of the optical nonlinearity in the 1D exciton system.

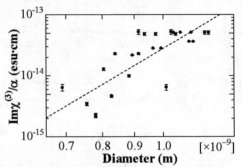

FIGURE 3. Log-log plot of $\mathrm{Im}\chi^{(3)}/\alpha$ vs. diameter for E_{11} transitions of semiconducting nanotubes. The dashed line is the least-squares fit to the data.

CONCLUSIONS

We have investigated third-order nonlinear optical susceptibilities and their dependence on the tube diameter in individual SWNTs. The imaginary part of susceptibility shows the resonant enhancement at each optical transition of the specific (n,m) tube. It is found that the diameter D dependence of $\mathrm{Im}\chi^{(3)}/\alpha$ is $D^{6.1\pm0.9}$.

REFERENCES

1. T. Ando, *J. Phys.Soc. Jpn.* **66**, 1066-1073 (1997).
2. M. Ichida. S. Mizuno, Y. Saito, Y. Tani and A. Nakamura, *J. Phys.Soc. Jpn.* **68**, 3131-3133 (1999).
3. A. Maeda, S. Matsumoto, H. Kishida, T. Takenobu, Y. Iwasa, M. Shiraishi, M. Ata and H. Okamoto, *Phys. Rev. Lett.* **94**, 047404 (2005).
4. M. Ichida, Y. Hamanaka, H. Kataura, Y. Achiba and A. Nakamura, *Physica* B **323**, 237-238 (2002).
5. S. M. Bachilo, M. S. Sreano, C. Kittrell, R. H. Hauge, R. E. Smalley and R. B. Weisman, *Science* **298**, 2361-2365 (2002).
6. T. Hasegawa, Y.Iwasa, T. Koda, H. Kishida, Y. Tokura, S. Wada, H. Tashiro, H. Tachibana and M. Matsumoto, *Phys. Rev.* B **54**, 11365-11374 (1996).

Single electron transport of carbon nanotube quantum dots under THz laser irradiation

T. Fuse[*, †], Y. Kawano[*], T. Yamaguchi[*], Y. Aoyagi[†], and K. Ishibashi[*, ‡]

*) Advanced Device Laboratory, The Institute of Physical and Chemical Research (RIKEN), 2-1, Hirosawa, Wako, Saitama 351-0198, Japan
†) Department of Information Processing, Interdisciplinary Graduate School of Science & Engineering, Tokyo Institute of Technology, 4259, Nagatsuta-cho, Midori-ku, Yokohama 226-8503, Japan.
‡) CREST, Japan Science and Technology (JST), Kawaguchi, Saitama 332-0012, Japan.
E-mail: kishiba@riken.jp

Abstract. Single-electron transport properties have been measured at 1.5K on single-wall carbon nanotube (SWNT) quantum-dots (QDs) under terahertz (THz) laser irradiation with a frequency of 2.5THz. The interesting finding in this study was new side-peaks in Coulomb oscillations, which appeared only under the THz irradiation. From the detailed analysis with energy scales associated with the QD, we conclude that the side-peaks originate from the THz-photon assisted tunneling (PAT) of an electron in the QD to the drain electrode.

Keywords: carbon nanotube, quantum dot, terahertz, photon assisted tunneling.

PACS: 73.63.Fg, 73.63.Kv, 78.90.+t

INTRODUCTION

Carbon nanotubes are attractive building-blocks of nanodevices because of their extremely small diameter[1]. In the previous single-electron transport measurements of single-wall carbon nanotube (SWNT) quantum dots (QDs), the charging energy (E_C) and the energy level spacing of discrete states (ΔE) are found to be typically ~10 meV and a few meV (sub-millimeter ~ terahertz (THz)), respectively[2], which are one or two orders larger than those of lithographically formed QDs in semiconductors[3]. This fact suggests the possibility of the THz-photon assisted tunneling (THz-PAT) in the SWNT QD. In this report, we present, for the first time, experimental observation of the THz-PAT in the SWNT QD at 1.5 K. It may opens the new mechanism of the THz detection with possible single-photon sensitivity by designing the detector combined with a single electron transistor.

EXPERIMENTS AND DISCUSSIONS

The device fabrication procedure is described in Ref. 4. First, current as a function of the source-drain voltage (V_{sd}) and the gate voltage (V_g) were measured and a color scale plot of the differential conductance was plotted in Fig. 1 (a), which corresponds to Coulomb diamond measurement. Then, current at a small fixed V_{sd} was measured as a function of V_g (Fig. 1 (b): Coulomb oscillation measurement) with and without THz irradiation. All measurements were carried out at 1.5 K. From them, E_c and ΔE are estimated as ~ 9.5 meV and ~ 2.1 meV, respectively, which should be compared with the irradiated THz-photon energy (*hf* at 2.5 THz = 10.3 meV). The diamond size, or equivalently, the gate voltage distance between adjacent Coulomb peaks changes alternately, which is a typical behavior of the even-odd effect[2]. In fig. 1 (b), without the THz irradiation, the simple Coulomb oscillations are observed (dotted curve), and the peak current value is ~ 1.5 pA, which gives the average escape rate ($\Gamma = I / e$), roughly about 10 MHz, much smaller than the applied frequency. In the Coulomb oscillations with the THz irradiation (solid curve), there appear many features, all of which are not fully understood. The most important finding here is that the new side-peaks, indicated by "A" and "B", appear under the THz irradiation just at the left-hand side of the main peaks that also appear without the THz irradiation. The side-peaks are observed in another gate voltage range (not shown). From now on, we focus on the side-peaks "A" and "B",

CP893, *Physics of Semiconductors, 28th International Conference*
edited by W. Jantsch and F. Schäffler
© 2007 American Institute of Physics 978-0-7354-0397-0/07/$23.00

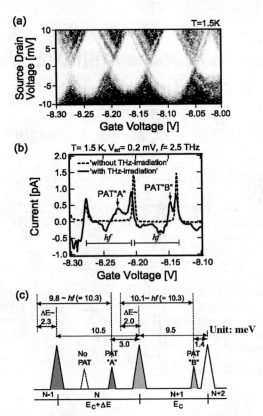

FIGURE 1. (a) Coulomb diamonds without THz irradiation, taken at 1.5K. The darker color indicates the higher conductance. (b) Corresponding Coulomb oscillations with and without THz irradiation (f= 2.5THz). The solid (dotted) curve indicates the oscillations with (without) the THz irradiation. (c) A simple energy diagram of Fig. 1 (b).

and quantitatively analyze them. The energy scale corresponding to the frequency (hf=2.5THz), depicted in Fig.1 (b) as a scale bar, does not seem to correspond to any distances between the side-peaks and the main peaks. The positions of each peak calculated from Fig.1 (a) are shown in Fig. 1 (c). In the V_g condition at "A", the SWNT QD is in the Coulomb blockade state without the THz irradiation. From Fig.1 (c), the side-peak "A" turns out to originate from the PAT of an electron in the (N-1)th state to the bias window at the drain. With a similar analysis, the side-peak "B" is understood as a PAT.

The PAT from the Nth state to the bias window may also occur. But, we should note again that $hf \sim E_c$, so that the side-peak, if any, would overlap with the main peak due to the (N+1)th state coming into the bias window, and would not be distinguished. The PAT from the lower states, such as the (N-2)th state, may be too small to be observed because complicated relaxation processes would occur in the QD. Another possible PAT from the source electrode into the QD (Fig.1 (c)) may not be possible in the present sample, because there are no quantum levels at the energy

higher than the barrier height, $\phi_B \sim 5$meV (estimated from a separate measurement), which is smaller than hf of 2.5 THz (=10.3 meV). As a result, side-peaks due to the PAT are not observed at the left hand side of the main peaks (Fig.1 (b) and (c)). In Fig.1 (b), one can see the negative current, a pumped current, but an exact mechanism is not known yet.

Finally, we discuss about the time and energy scales for the THz-PAT to be observed. First, the average escape time is much longer than the period of the THz wave, as mentioned before, which indicates that the THz wave oscillates many cycles before an electron escape from the QD. Second, the photon energy, hf (= 10.3 meV for 2.5 THz) is much larger than the measurement temperature (~ 0.1meV at 1.5K). The level broadening estimated by Γ (~10^{-5}meV) is much smaller than hf. These conditions have made the THz-PAT observable in the SWNT QD. With the above parameter consideration, it may be possible to observe it even at the liquid nitrogen temperature.

CONCLUSION

In conclusion, we have measured single electron transport in the SWNT QD under THz irradiation at 1.5K. PAT in the THz regime was, for the first time, observed in the SWNT QD. The analysis based on the energy diagram of the QD has shown that the THz-PAT occurred from the dot to the bias window at the electrode. The parameter consideration indicates that the THz-PAT may be possible in more elevated temperatures, and the present results may lead to an ultra-sensitive THz detector. The SWNT QD equipped with an antenna for the THz wave would increase the coupling efficiency and make a broad band response possible, which is the next step of our experiment.

We thank Mr. M. Mihara for his technical assistance, and Dr. S. Moriyama of RIKEN for valuable discussions.

REFERENCES

1. K. Ishibashi, S. Moriyama, D. Tsuya, T. Fuse, M. Suzuki, "Quantum-Dot Nanodevices with Carbon Nanotubes", J. Vac. Sci. Technol. A**24**, 1349 (2006)
2. S. Moriyama, T. Fuse, M. Suzuki, Y. Aoyagi, K. Ishibashi, Phys. Rev. Lett. **94**, 186806 (2005)
3. L. L. Sohn, L. P. Kouwenhoven and G. Schon: *Proc. of the NATO Advanced Study Institute on Mesoscopic Electron Transport*, 1996 (Kluwer Academic Publishers, Dordrecht, Netherlands, 1997)
4. M. Suzuki, K. Ishibashi, T. Ida, D. Tsuya, K. Toratani, Y. Aoyagi, J. Vac. Sci. Technol. B**19**, 2770 (2001)

Electronic Properties of Carbon Nanoribbons and Peculiar Width Dependence

Motohiko Ezawa

Department of Physics, University of Tokyo, Hongo 7-3-1, 113-0033, Japan

Abstract. We make a systematic analysis of the electronic properties of a wide class of carbon nanoribbons, characterizing them by edge shape and width. Carbon nanoribbons are one-dimensional aromatic compounds akin to nanotubes. They exhibit a rich variety of band gaps, from metals to typical semiconductors. The band gaps of several nanoribbons form a valley structure with stream-like sequences of metallic or almost metallic nanoribbons. We find that the band gaps of armchair and chiral nanoribbons oscillate as a function of the width, and take local minima almost at the same values of the width w for any q. Furthermore a possible application of nanoribbons to nanoelectronics is discussed.

Keywords: Carbon nanoribbon, Graphene, electronic property
PACS: 73.22.-f,78.67.Pt,78.66.Sq

Carbon nanoribbons are one-dimensional graphene-related materials with finite width. Recent experimental developments enable us to isolate a graphene, which is a monolayer graphite. Carbon nanoribbons have a higher variety than carbon nanotubes because of the existence of edges.

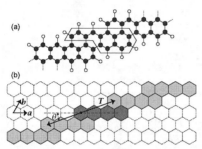

FIGURE 1. (a) A typical structure of nanoribbons. A solid (open) circle stands for a carbon (hydrogen) atom. (b) A nanoribon is constructed from a chain of m connected carbon hexagons, and by translating this chain by the translational vector many times, where $q < m$. A nanoribbon is indexed by a set of two integers $\langle p,q \rangle$ with $p = m - q$. Here we have taken $m = 4$, $q = 2$, $p = 2$.

We characterize a wide class of nanoribbons by a set of two integers $\langle p,q \rangle$ representing edge shape and width, as we illustrate in Fig.1. We use the tight-binding Hamiltonian,

$$H = \sum_i \varepsilon_i c_i^\dagger c_i + \sum_{\langle i,j \rangle} t_{ij} c_i^\dagger c_j, \qquad (1)$$

where ε_i is the site energy, t_{ij} is the transfer energy, and $c_i^\dagger$ is the creation operator of the π electron at the site i. The summation is taken over the nearest neighbor sites $\langle i,j \rangle$. Carbon nanotubes are regarded as a periodic-boudary-condition problem, while carbon nanoribbons are as a fixed-boudary-condition problem.

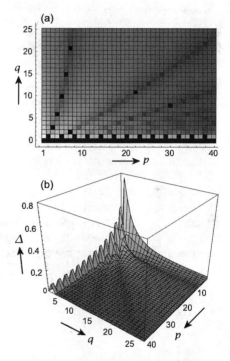

FIGURE 2. The band gap structure of nanoribbons. (a) Magnitudes of band gaps are represented by gray squares. Dark (light) gray squares represent small (large) gap semiconductors. Especially, metallic states are represented by black squares. (b) A bird's eye view.

Based on this Hamiltonian we carry out a systematic analysis of the electronic property of nanoribbons in parallel to that of nanotubes. We calculate the band gap of nanotubes for each point $\langle p,q \rangle$. Collecting all these results, we display the band gap structure in Fig.2. They exhibit a rich variety of band gaps, from metals to typ-

CP893, *Physics of Semiconductors, 28th International Conference*
edited by W. Jantsch and F. Schäffler

ical semiconductors. It is remarkable that they make a valley structure with stream-like sequences of metallic or almost metallic nanoribbons (Fig.2). It is observed that nanoribbons indexed by $\langle p,0 \rangle$ are metallic for all p, which are in the polyacene series with zigzag edges. Nanoribbons indexed by $\langle p,1 \rangle$ with $p = 2,5,8,11,\cdots$ are found to be also metallic, which have armchair edges. This series has period 3, as is a reminiscence of the classification rules familiar for nanotubes.

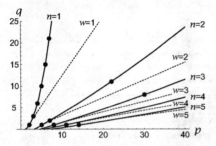

FIGURE 3. Illustration of metallic points, sequences and equi-width curves. Metallic points are denoted by solid circles. Solid curves represent sequences of metallic or almost metallic points, while dotted curves represent the points $\langle p,q \rangle$ possessing the same width.

We point out a peculiar dependence of the electronic property of nanoribbons on the width w, where

$$w = 2(p+q)/\sqrt{3(2q+1)^2 + 9}. \quad (2)$$

We extract the stream curves out of Fig.2, and draw them in Fig.3. On this figure we also present equi-width curves. It is remarkable that these sequences and equi-width curves become almost identical for wide nanoribbons, as is clear in Fig.3. We have depicted the band gap as a function of the width w for each fixed of q in Fig.4. The band gaps oscillate and the envelope of the band gap decreases inversely against w.

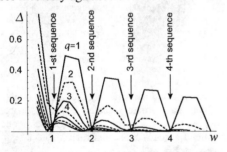

FIGURE 4. The band gaps Δ in unit of $|t|=3.033\text{eV}$ as a function of the width w.

We calculate the energies ε of van-Hove singularities for various $\langle p,q \rangle$ nanoribbons [Fig.5(a)]. On the other hand the width w is determined by p and q as in (2). We show the energy ε of this peak as a function of w in Fig.5. A peculiar stripe pattern is manifest there. In particular, the maximum and minimum values take

almost the same values $\pm 3|t|$, reflecting the electronic property of a graphite. The fact that there are on smooth curves present another justification to call w the width of nanoribbon.

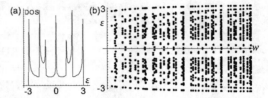

FIGURE 5. (a) The density of state of the $\langle 1,0 \rangle$ nanoribbon. (b) Plot of van-Hove singularities in the w-ε plane. For a given $\langle p,q \rangle$ nanoribbon, we calculate the width w and the energies ε at which van-Hove singularities develop. We have plotted the points (w,ε) for $q = 0,1,2,3,4$ and for all p in the region $w < 3$.

We have revealed a rich variety of band gaps in carbon nanoribbons. They are either one-dimensional metals or semiconductors depending on their edge shape and width. Carbon nanoribbons could be a promising candidate of molecule devices, similarly to nanotubes, because of ballistic transport at room temperature.

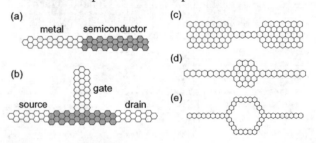

FIGURE 6. Several possible nanoribbon devices. (a) Schottky diode. (b) Schottky-gate field-effect transistor. (c) Point contact. (d) Quantum dot. (e) Aharonov-Bohm ring.

We mention the merits of nanoribbons in comparison to nanotubes. Two nanoribbon segments with different atomic and electronic structures can be seamlessly fused together to create intramolecular metal-metal, metal-semiconductor, or semiconductor-semiconductor junctions without introducing a pentagon and a heptagon into the hexagonal carbon lattice. Several devices could be made of nanoribbons, as illustrated in Fig.6. For instance, a metal-semiconductor junction makes a Schottky barrier and may behave like a Schottky diode. Similarly a Schottky-gate field-effect transistor, a point contact, a quantum dot and an Aharonov-Bohm ring may be realized. We might even design a complex of electronic circuits by etching a monolayer graphite in future.

Reference: M. Ezawa, Phys. Rev. B **73**, 045432 (2006).

Aharonov-Bohm effects on optical phonons in carbon nanotubes

Kohta Ishikawa and Tsuneya Ando

Department of Physics, Tokyo Institute of Technology, 2–12–1 Ookayama, Meguro-ku, Tokyo 152-8551, Japan

Abstract. Effects of electron-phonon interaction on optical phonons are studied in carbon nanotubes. In metallic nanotubes, the gap due to an Aharonov-Bohm magnetic flux oriented in the tube axis causes a singular behavior in the broadening. In particular, the broadening appears in the transverse mode and diverges when the gap reaches the phonon energy. This Aharonov-Bohm effect can be used for the determination of a narrow gap present in chiral nanotubes or in strained nanotubes.

Keywords: carbon nanotube, Aharonov-Bohm effect, optical phonon, broadening
PACS: 73.63.Fg, 72.45.Kc, 78.67,Ch

In this paper Aharonov-Bohm effects on long-wavelength optical phonons through electron-phonon interactions are studied theoretically. In a graphite sheet the conduction and valence bands consisting of π orbitals cross at K and K' points of the Brillouin zone, where the Fermi level is located. Electronic states near a K point are described by the **k·p** equation

$$\mathcal{H}_0\mathbf{F}(\mathbf{r}) = \varepsilon\mathbf{F}(\mathbf{r}), \quad \mathcal{H}_0 = \gamma\vec{\sigma}\cdot\hat{\mathbf{k}}, \qquad (1)$$

where γ is a band parameter, σ_x and σ_y are the Pauli spin matrices, and $\hat{\mathbf{k}} = (\hat{k}_x, \hat{k}_y) = -i\vec{\nabla}$.

The structure of a nanotube is specified by a chiral vector **L** corresponding to the circumference. Electronic states of a nanotube with a sufficiently large diameter are obtained by imposing the boundary conditions around the circumference direction $\mathbf{F}(\mathbf{r}+\mathbf{L}) = \mathbf{F}(\mathbf{r})\exp[2\pi i(\varphi - \nu/3)]$, where $\varphi = \phi/\phi_0$ with ϕ being a magnetic flux passing through the cross section and ϕ_0 the flux quantum given by $\phi_0 = ch/e$, and ν is an integer ($\nu = 0$ or ± 1). Metallic and semiconducting nanotubes correspond to $\nu = 0$ and ± 1, respectively [1].

The energy bands are specified by $s = \pm 1$ ($s = -1$ and $+1$ for the valence and conduction band, respectively), integer n corresponding to the discrete wave vector along the circumference direction chosen along the x axis, and the wave vector k in the axis direction chosen along the y axis. We have

$$\varepsilon_{\nu\varphi}^s(n,k) = s\gamma\sqrt{\kappa_{\nu\varphi}(n)^2+k^2}, \qquad (2)$$

$$\kappa_{\nu\varphi}(n) = \frac{2\pi}{L}\left(n+\varphi-\frac{\nu}{3}\right). \qquad (3)$$

An equation of motion for optical phonons of the two-dimensional graphite in the long-wavelength limit has been derived based on a valence-force-field model [2]. In nanotubes the wave vector becomes discrete in the circumference direction $q_x = 2\pi j/L$ with integer j and remains continuous in the axis direction (q). In the following we shall confine ourselves to the long wavelength limit, $j = 0$ and $qL \ll 1$. Then, the phonon Hamiltonian is written as

$$\mathcal{H}_{\text{ph}} = \sum_{q,\mu}\hbar\omega_0\left(b_{q\mu}^\dagger b_{q\mu} + \frac{1}{2}\right), \qquad (4)$$

where μ denotes the mode ($\mu = l$ for the longitudinal mode with the displacement in the axis direction and $\mu = t$ for the transverse mode with the displacement in the circumference direction), and $b_{q\mu}^\dagger$ and $b_{q\mu}$ are the creation and destruction operators, respectively.

The lattice displacement can be expanded as

$$\mathbf{u}(\mathbf{r}) = \sum_{q\mu}\sqrt{\frac{\hbar}{2NM\omega_0}}(b_{q\mu}+b_{-q\mu}^\dagger)\mathbf{e}_{q\mu}e^{iqy}, \qquad (5)$$

where N is the number of unit cells, M is the mass of a carbon atom, and

$$\mathbf{e}_{ql} = i(0, q/|q|), \quad \mathbf{e}_{qt} = i(q/|q|, 0). \qquad (6)$$

The interaction between optical phonons and electrons is described by the Hamiltonian

$$\mathcal{H}_{\text{int}} = -\sqrt{2}\frac{\beta\gamma}{b^2}\vec{\sigma}\times\mathbf{u}(\mathbf{r}), \qquad (7)$$

where $b = a/\sqrt{3}$ is the equilibrium bond length and $\beta = -d\ln\gamma_0/d\ln b$ with γ_0 being the resonance integral between nearest neighbor carbon atoms appearing in a tight-binding model related to γ through $\gamma = (\sqrt{3}a/2)\gamma_0$ with $a = 2.46$ Å being the lattice constant [3]. The corresponding results for the K' point are obtained by replacing $\vec{\sigma}$ by $\vec{\sigma}^*$ and ν by $-\nu$.

Because the interaction is weak, the shift and the broadening of the phonon frequency are given by the

CP893, *Physics of Semiconductors, 28th International Conference*
edited by W. Jantsch and F. Schäffler
© 2007 American Institute of Physics 978-0-7354-0397-0/07/$23.00

1017

lowest order perturbation. The frequency shift $\Delta\omega$ and the broadening Γ are given by

$$\Delta\omega = \mathrm{Re}\,\Pi(q\mu, \omega_0), \quad \Gamma = -\mathrm{Im}\,\Pi(q\mu, \omega_0), \quad (8)$$

where $\Pi(q\mu, \omega)$ is the self-energy of the phonon Green's function. For the contribution of the K point, for example, we have

$$
\begin{aligned}
\Pi(q\mu, \omega) = -2 \sum_{s,s'} \sum_n \int \frac{dk}{2\pi} \left(\frac{\beta\gamma}{b^2}\right)^2 \frac{\hbar}{NM\omega_0} \\
\times \frac{1}{2}\left(1 \pm \frac{ss'[\kappa_{v\varphi}(n)^2 - k(k-q)]}{\sqrt{\kappa_{v\varphi}(n)^2 + k^2}\sqrt{\kappa_{v\varphi}(n)^2 + (k-q)^2}}\right) \\
\times \frac{f[\varepsilon_{v\varphi}^s(n,k)] - f[\varepsilon_{v\varphi}^{s'}(n,k-q)]}{\hbar\omega - \varepsilon_{v\varphi}^s(n,k) + \varepsilon_{v\varphi}^{s'}(n,k-q) + i0}, \quad (9)
\end{aligned}
$$

where $f(\varepsilon)$ is the Fermi distribution function and the upper and lower sign correspond to $\mu = l$ and t, respectively. The factor two comes from the electron spin. The correct self-energy is obtained by subtracting from the above the contribution in the two-dimensional graphite, which is obtained by the sum over discrete wave vector in the circumference direction $\kappa_{v\varphi}(n)$ replaced with a continuous integration.

The self-energy shows that a singular behavior occurs when the denominator vanishes. Because the phonon frequency is usually much smaller than band gaps in semiconducting nanotubes, this occurs in metallic nanotubes with an Aharonov-Bohm magnetic flux and strain or in narrow-gap semiconductors with a small gap due to curvature. In fact, the most notable feature appears in the broadening.

$$\Gamma_t = \alpha(L)\omega_0 \frac{4\pi\varphi^2}{\tilde{\omega}\sqrt{\tilde{\omega}^2 - 4\varphi^2}}, \quad (10)$$

$$\Gamma_l = \alpha(L)\omega_0 \pi \sqrt{1 - \left(\frac{2\varphi}{\tilde{\omega}}\right)^2}, \quad (11)$$

with $\tilde{\omega} = \hbar\omega_0(2\pi\gamma/L)^{-1}$ and $\alpha(L) = \lambda(a/L)$, where λ is the dimensionless parameter

$$\lambda = \frac{27}{\pi}\beta^2\gamma_0\frac{\hbar^2}{2Ma^2}\left(\frac{1}{\hbar\omega_0}\right)^2. \quad (12)$$

For the parameter $\hbar\omega_0 = 0.196$ eV, $\gamma_0 = 2.63$ eV, and $\beta = 2$, the parameter becomes $\lambda = 0.08$, but can be larger depending of β.

Figure 1 shows this broadening as a function of the Aharonov-Bohm gap $4\pi\gamma|\varphi|/L$. For the transverse mode, with the increase of the gap, the broadening increases in proportion to φ^2, diverges when the gap reaches the optical-phonon energy $\hbar\omega_0$, and vanishes when the gap exceeds the phonon energy. For the longitudinal mode, on the other hand, the broadening gradually

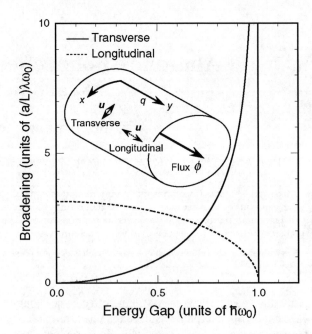

FIGURE 1. The broadening of optical phonons in metallic nanotubes as a function of the band gap induced by an Aharonov-Bohm flux. When the gap reaches the optical-phonon energy $\hbar\omega_0$, the broadening disappears for the longitudinal mode and becomes infinite for the transverse mode.

decreases with the magnetic flux and vanishes when the gap reaches the phonon energy $\hbar\omega_0$.

The magnetic field required for the observation of this anomaly is about 200 T for typical single-wall nanotubes with diameter ~ 1.5 nm. This Aharonov-Bohm effect can be used for the determination of a narrow gap present in chiral nanotubes or in strained nanotubes, because this gap is also a result of an effective flux [4]. Further, this effect can be quite sensitive to carrier doping.

ACKNOWLEDGMENTS

This work was supported in part by a 21st Century COE Program at Tokyo Tech "Nanometer-Scale Quantum Physics" and by Grant-in-Aid for Scientific Research from Ministry of Education, Culture, Sports, Science and Technology Japan.

REFERENCES

1. H. Ajiki and T. Ando, J. Phys. Soc. Jpn. **62**, 1255 (1993).
2. H. Suzuura and T. Ando, Phys. Rev. B **65**, 235412 (2002).
3. K. Ishikawa and T. Ando, J. Phys. Soc. Jpn. **75**, No. 8 (2006).
4. T. Ando, J. Phys. Soc. Jpn. **74**, 777 (2005) and references cited therein.

Transition level dependence of Raman intensities in carbon nanotubes: Role of exciton decay.

S V Goupalov[*], B C Satishkumar[†] and S K Doorn[†]

[*]A.F. Ioffe Physico-Technical Institute, 194021 St. Petersburg, Russia
[†]Los Alamos National Laboratory, Los Alamos, NM 87545 USA

Abstract. We present the first direct comparison of intensities of Raman scattering from the radial breathing mode of semiconducting single-walled carbon nanotubes under excitations resonant with different electronic transitions.

Keywords: carbon nanotubes, Raman spectroscopy, exciton-phonon coupling
PACS: 78.67.Ch, 78.30.Na

Recent advances in nanotube (NT) research have allowed for the fabrication of well-separated single-walled (SW) carbon NTs produced out of aggregated bulk assemblies and isolated in micelles [1]. As a result, it has become possible to assign the radial breathing mode (RBM) features observed in Raman spectroscopy to specific (n,m) semiconducting NTs. Recently it was shown [2] – [4] that the intensity of resonant Raman signal significantly varies with the NT chirality, and quite distinctive behavior is demonstrated by semiconducting NTs with $\nu \equiv (n-m) \bmod 3 = -1$ as compared to NTs with $\nu = +1$. For technical reasons, all Raman measurements on semiconducting carbon NTs reported so far were performed under excitations resonant with some specific electronic transitions, usually matching the gap, E_{22}, between second singularities in electronic densities of states in the conduction and valence bands. Here we present the first direct comparison of resonance Raman intensities for semiconducting NTs under excitations resonant with E_{11} and E_{22} transitions.

In the present work Raman measurements have been carried out on HipCO SWNTs using laser excitation in the energy range of 700-1000 nm and 565-690 nm using Ti:Sapphire laser and dye lasers, respectively. The samples of solubalized NTs were prepared by shear mixing and ultrasonication of NTs and sodium dodecyl sulphate (SDS) in deuterium, followed by centrifugation at 28000 rpm for 6 hours. Examples of the observed resonance Raman excitation profiles for a (9,1) NT under E_{11} and E_{22} excitations are presented in Fig. 1, a and b, respectively. Experimental data shown as circles has been fit by solid lines using Eq. (1) and the decay rates of $\Gamma_{11} = 22$ meV and $\Gamma_{22} = 78$ meV as fitting parameters.

The peak structure in Fig. 1, a is due to the spectral resolution of the input and output resonances [6]. Fig. 1, b shows no structure which is explained by the larger value of the decay rate for the E_{22} excitation.

Both E_{11} and E_{22} transitions were accessible by the

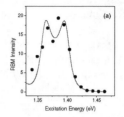 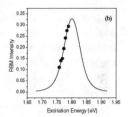

FIGURE 1. Resonance Raman excitation profiles for a (9,1) NT under E_{11} (a) and E_{22} (b) excitations.

TABLE 1. Chiral indices, RBM frequencies, resonant transition energies and Raman intensities for NTs studied.

(n,m)	$\omega_0 (\text{cm}^{-1})$	E_{11} (eV)	E_{22} (eV)	I_{11}/I_{22}
(6,4)	335	1.420	2.146	4.7
(8,3)	296	1.303	1.863	12.2
(9,1)	304	1.359	1.739	38.7
(5,4)	373	1.485	2.566	58
(6,5)	307	1.270	2.190	287
(7,3)	327	1.250	2.457	11700

lasers for the NTs of the following chiralities: (5,4), (6,5), (7,3) [$\nu = +1$], and (6,4), (8,3), (9,1) [$\nu = -1$] present in our samples. The chiral indices and transition energies for these NTs are listed in Table 1 along with the observed peak intensities of the Raman profiles at E_{11} and E_{22} excitations. One can see from Table 1 that for all studied chiralities the peak resonance Raman intensities under E_{11} excitations are larger than those under E_{22} excitation.

The probability of the Raman scattering event is given by

$$P = \frac{2\pi}{\hbar} \left| \sum_{n,m} \frac{\langle 0|\hat{V}_{opt}|n\rangle \langle n, N \pm 1|\hat{V}_{exc-ph}|m,N\rangle \langle m|\hat{V}_{opt}|0\rangle}{(E_m - \hbar\Omega_i - i\Gamma_m)(E_n - \hbar\Omega_i \pm \hbar\omega_0 - i\Gamma_n)} \right|^2$$

$$\times \delta(\hbar\Omega_i \mp \hbar\omega_0 - \hbar\Omega_s). \qquad (1)$$

CP893, *Physics of Semiconductors, 28th International Conference*
edited by W. Jantsch and F. Schäffler
© 2007 American Institute of Physics 978-0-7354-0397-0/07/$23.00

Here $\Omega_s(\Omega_i)$ is the frequency of the scattered (incident) light, ω_0 is the frequency of the emitted or absorbed phonon, indices m and n denote the states of the electron-hole pair (or exciton); E_n and Γ_n are, respectively, the energy and the decay rate of the intermidiate state $|n\rangle$; N is the phonon occupation number for the given phonon mode; $\hat{V}_{opt}$ and $\hat{V}_{exc-ph}$ are the operators of the exciton-photon and exciton-phonon interactions, respectively.

Under resonant excitation conditions, the real part of one of the denominators in Eq. (1) vanishes, and the real part of the other one becomes $\pm\hbar\omega_0$. Two different regimes can be distinguished. For small Γ_n the decay rate can be neglected compared to $\hbar\omega_0$: $|\pm\hbar\omega_0 - i\Gamma_n| \approx \hbar\omega_0$. The NTs studied in our work have similar radii, and the radius dependence of ω_0 in the denominator can be neglected. Thus, the Raman intensity is inversely proportional to Γ_n^2. In the opposite limiting case Γ_n is large compared to $\hbar\omega_0$ and Raman intensity is inversely proportional to Γ_n^4.

The matrix element of the operator of the exciton interaction with the RBM on the electronic states has different form for the electron-hole pairs excited by E_{11} and E_{22} transitions. For the E_{11} transition in the nearest neighbor tight binding model we have [4, 5]

$$V_{exc-ph}^{11} \propto \{0.5 - A\}/R^2 \qquad (2)$$

where R is the NT radius and

$$A = -\frac{\sqrt{6}\sqrt{3}}{5}\frac{R}{a}\cos 3\theta = -\frac{\sqrt{3}\sqrt{3}}{10\pi}\frac{(2n+m)(n^2-2m^2+nm)}{n^2+m^2+nm}. \qquad (3)$$

Here θ is the chiral angle, a is the lattice constant of graphene. For the E_{22} transition we have [4, 5]

$$V_{exc-ph}^{22} \propto \{1 + A\}/R^2 \qquad (4)$$

One can see that Eq. (2) and Eq. (4) differ only by the terms in the curly brackets.

Further difference in the expression for the Raman intensity under different excitations comes from the chirality dependence of the optical matrix element [7]. However, this dependence is rather weak [7] and will be neglected here.

Let I_{11} and I_{22} be the experimentally measured resonant Raman peak intensities under E_{11} and E_{22} excitations. Assuming that the chirality dependence of the decay rates in Eq. (1) is negligible compared to those of the matrix elements (2) – (4), one can see that chirality dependence of $I_{ii}R^4$ will be determined by the square of the curly brackets in Eqs. (2) or (4). Thus, we have

$$I_{11}R^4 = C_{11}\{A-0.5\}^2, \qquad I_{22}R^4 = C_{22}\{A+1\}^2, \qquad (5)$$

where C_{11} and C_{22} are the coefficients of proportionality. If Γ_n is small compared to $\hbar\omega_0$ then from Eqs. (1) – (5) it follows that, under resonant excitation conditions, the ratio of these coefficients gives the square of the ratio of

the decay rates: $C_{11}/C_{22} = (\Gamma_{22}/\Gamma_{11})^2$. In the opposite limiting case of large Γ_n, the right hand part of this relation should be further squared.

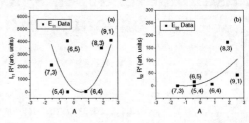

FIGURE 2. A-dependencies of $I_{11}R^4$ (a) and $I_{22}R^4$ (b).

In Fig. 2, a by squares is shown experimental data corresponding to the left-hand part of the first of Eqs. (5) as a function of the parameter A. By the solid line is shown the fit with the parabola given by the right-hand side of the first of Eqs. (5). In a similar fashion, both parts of the second of Eqs. (5) are shown in Fig. 2, b. The coefficients C_{11} and C_{22} are obtained by the best parabolic fits to the experimental data. We thus obtain $C_{22} \approx 8.5$ and $C_{11} \approx 916$. Therefore, taking into account both the limits of small and large Γ_n, we obtain the following estimate for the ratio of the decay rates $3 \lesssim \Gamma_{22}/\Gamma_{11} \lesssim 10$. This result is in agreement with the ratio of decay rates that one can obtain from the fitting of excitation profiles of Fig. 1.

In summary, we have performed the first direct comparison of intensities of Raman scattering from the RBM of semiconducting single-walled carbon NTs under excitations resonant with different electronic transitions. We found that the difference in measured Raman intensities varies from one to several orders of magnitudes depending on the NT chiralities. We showed that explanation of observed results requires addressing the difference in decay rates for exciton states involved in Raman process under different excitations.

This work was supported by the US DOE. NT samples were provided by Prof. R.E. Smalley's group at Rice University.

REFERENCES

1. M.J. O'Connell *et al.*, Science, **297**, 593, (2002).
2. S.K. Doorn *et al.*, Appl. Phys. A, **78**, 1147, (2004).
3. H. Telg *et al.*, Phys. Rev. Lett. **93**, 177401, (2004).
4. S.V. Goupalov, Satishkumar B.C., and S.K. Doorn, Phys. Rev. B **73**, 115401 (2006).
5. S.V. Goupalov, Phys. Rev. B **71**, 153404 (2005); **72**, 159901(E) (2005).
6. J. Jiang *et al.*, Phys. Rev. B **71**, 205420 (2005).
7. S.V. Goupalov, Phys. Rev. B **72**, 195403 (2005).

Carbon nanotubes as terahertz emitters and detectors

O.V. Kibis[*,†], M. Rosenau da Costa[†] and M.E. Portnoi[**,†]

[*]Dept. of Applied and Theoretical Physics, Novosibirsk State Technical University, Novosibirsk 630092, Russia
[†]International Center for Condensed Matter Physics, University of Brasilia, 70904-970 Brasilia DF, Brazil
[**]School of Physics, University of Exeter, Stocker Road, Exeter EX4 4QL, United Kingdom

Abstract. We formulate and justify several proposals utilizing the unique electronic properties of different types of carbon nanotubes in a broad range of applications to THz optoelectronics, including THz generation by hot electrons in quasi-metallic nanotubes, frequency multiplication in chiral-nanotube-based superlattices controlled by a transverse electric field, and THz radiation detection by armchair nanotubes in strong magnetic fields.

Keywords: Carbon nanotubes, terahertz radiation
PACS: 73.63.Fg,78.67.Ch

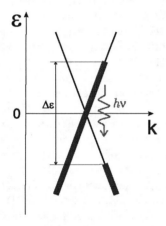

FIGURE 1. The scheme of THz photon generation by hot carriers in metallic carbon nanotubes.

Creating compact reliable sources and detectors of terahertz (THz) radiation is one of the most formidable tasks of the contemporary applied physics [1]. One of the latest trends in THz technology [2] is to use carbon nanotubes — cylindrical molecules with nanometer diameter and micrometer length [3] — as building blocks of novel high-frequency devices. Below we will discuss several novel schemes to utilize physical properties of single-wall carbon nanotubes (SWNTs) for generation and detection of THz radiation.

The first proposed scheme of THz generation is based on the electric-field induced heating of electron gas resulting in the inversion of population of optically active states, with the energy difference within the THz spectrum range. The electron energy spectrum of metallic SWNTs, $\varepsilon(k)$, linearly depends on the electron wave vector k close to the Fermi energy [3]. In the Fig.1 the zero of energy is defined as the Fermi energy position in the absence of an external field. When the voltage is applied

along the SWNT axis, the electron distribution is shifted in the way shown by the blue lines in Fig.1 corresponding to the filled electron states in the presence of the applied voltage. It results in the inversion of population and, correspondingly, in optical transitions between filled states in the conduction band and empty states in the valence band.

It is well-known that the major scattering mechanism in SWNTs is due to electron-phonon interaction [3]. Since the scattering processes erode the inversion of electron population, an optimal condition for observing the discussed optical transitions takes place when the length of the SWNT $L < l_{ac}$, where $l_{ac} \approx 2.4\ \mu$m is the electron mean-free path for acoustic phonon scattering. Below we consider such short SWNTs only. If the electron heating energy $\Delta\varepsilon$ is less than the optical phonon energy $\hbar\Omega \approx 0.16$ eV, the electronic transport is ballistic and $\Delta\varepsilon = eV$, where V is the potential difference between the SWNT's ends. At higher applied voltages, $V \geq \hbar\Omega/e$, the heating energy is $\Delta\varepsilon \approx \hbar\Omega$. The heating results in the spontaneous photon emission with the peak frequency $\nu \approx \Delta\varepsilon/h$ controlled by applied voltage and restricted by the SWNT optical phonon energy corresponding to the frequency of about 40 THz.

Let us select a SWNT with the crystal structure most suitable for observation of the discussed effect. Firstly, the required nanotube should have metallic conductivity and, secondly, the optical transitions between the lowest conduction subband and the top valence subband should be allowed. It is well-known that he crystal structure of SWNTs is described by two integers (n,m), which completely define their physical properties [3]. The SWNTs with true metallic energy band structure, for which the energy gap is absent for any SWNT radius, are the armchair (n,n) SWNTs only [4]. However, for armchair SWNTs the optical transitions between the lowest con-

CP893, *Physics of Semiconductors, 28th International Conference*
edited by W. Jantsch and F. Schäffler
© 2007 American Institute of Physics 978-0-7354-0397-0/07/$23.00

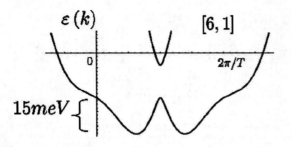

FIGURE 2. Energy spectrum of the $(6,1)$ SWNT in a transverse electric field, $E_\perp = 4$ V/nm.

duction and top valence subbands are forbidden [5]. So we propose to use for the observation of THz generation the so-called quasi-metallic (n,m) SWNTs with $n - m = 3p$, where p is an integer. These nanotubes, which are gapless within the frame of a simple zone-folding model of the π-electron graphene spectrum [3], are in fact narrow-gap semiconductors due to curvature effects. However, their bandgap is decreasing rapidly with increasing the nanotube radius [4]. Therefore for large values of R this gap can be neglected even in the case of moderate applied voltages due to the Zener tunneling of electrons across the gap [6]. For example, for a zigzag $(30,0)$ SWNT the gap is $\varepsilon_g \approx 6$meV and the Zener breakdown takes place for the electric field $E \sim 10^{-1}$V/μm, which corresponds to a typical voltage of 0.1V between the nanotube ends. As a consequence, $(3p,0)$ zigzag SWNTs of large enough radius R and for applied voltages exceeding the Zener breakdown are most suitable for the proposed THz generation by hot carriers.

Chiral nanotubes are natural superlattices. For example, a $(10,9)$ single-wall nanotube has a radius which differs from the radius of the most commonly studied $(10,10)$ nanotube by less than five per cent, whereas a translational period along the axis of the $(10,9)$ SWNT is almost thirty times larger than the period of the $(10,10)$ nanotube. Correspondingly, the first Brillouin zone of the $(10,9)$ nanotube is almost thirty times smaller than the first zone for the $(10,10)$ tube. However such a Brillouin zone reduction cannot influence electronic transport unless there is a gap opening between the energy subbands resulting from the folding of graphene spectrum. In our research we show how an electric field normal to the nanotube axis opens noticeable gaps at the edge of the reduced Brillouin zone, thus turning a long-period nanotube of certain chirality into a 'real' superlattice. The field-induced gaps are most pronounced in $(n,1)$ SWNTs [7]. Fig.2 shows the opening of electric-field induced gap near the edge of the Brillouin zone of a $(6,1)$ SWNT. One can see that this gap opening results in the appearance of a negative effective-mass region in

the nanotube energy spectrum. The typical electron energy in this part of the spectrum of 15 meV is well below the optical phonon energy $\hbar\Omega \approx 160$ meV, so that it can be easily accessed in moderate heating electric fields. The negative effective mass results in the negative differential conductivity in a wide range of applied voltages. We show [6] that this effect also leads to an efficient frequency multiplication in the THz range.

The problem of detecting THz radiation is known to be at least as challenging as creating reliable THz sources. Our proposal of a novel detector is based on several features of the truly gapless (armchair) SWNTs. The main property to be utilized is the opening of the gap in these SWNTs in a magnetic field along the nanotube axis [3]. For a $(10,10)$ SWNT this gap is approximately 1 THz in the field of 10 T. The gap grows linearly with increasing both magnetic field and the nanotube radius. It can be shown [6] that the same magnetic field also allows dipole optical transitions between the top valence subband and the lowest conduction subband, which are strictly forbidden in armchair SWNTs without the field [5]. The electronic (hole) energy spectrum near the bottom (top) of the gap produced by magnetic field is parabolic as a function of a carrier momentum along the nanotube axis. This dispersion results in the van-Hove singularity in the reduced density of states, which in turn leads to a very sharp absorption maximum near the band edge and, correspondingly, to a very high sensitivity of the photocurrent to the photon frequency.

The work was supported by the EU Foundation INTAS (Grants 03-50-4409 and 05-1000008-7801), the Russian Foundation for Basic Research (Grants 06-02-16005 and 06-02-81012), the Russian Ministry for Education and Science (Grant RNP.2.1.1.1604), and MCT and FINEP (Brazil). MEP and OVK are grateful to the ICCMP staff for hospitality.

REFERENCES

1. B. Ferguson and X. C. Zhang, Nature Materials **1**, 26–33 (2002).
2. D. Dragoman and M. Dragoman, *Progress in Quantum Electronics* **28**, 1–66 (2004).
3. R. Saito, G. Dresselhaus, and M. S. Dresselhaus, *Physical Properties of Carbon Nanotubes*, Imperial College Press, London, 1998.
4. C. L. Kane and E. J. Mele, *Phys. Rev. Letters* **78**, 1932–1935 (1997).
5. I. Milošević, T. Vuković, S. Dmitrović, and M. Damnjanović, *Phys. Rev. B* **67**, 165418 (2003).
6. O. V. Kibis, M. Rosenau da Costa, and M. E. Portnoi, *to be published*.
7. O. V. Kibis, D. G. W. Parfitt, and M. E. Portnoi, *Phys. Rev. B* **71**, 035411 (2005).

Yield And Quality Optimization For MWNT Prepared By Catalytic CVD

M.G.Donato[1], S.Galvagno[2], G.Messina[1], C.Milone[2], A.Pistone[2] and S.Santangelo[1*]

[1] INFM, Dip. di Meccanica e Materiali, Fac. di Ingegneria, Univ. "Mediterranea", 89060 Reggio Calabria, Italy
[2] Dip. di Chimica Industriale e Ingegneria dei Materiali, Fac. di Ingegneria, Univ. di Messina, 98166 Messina, Italy
*Corresponding author: saveria.santangelo@unirc.it

Abstract. Multi-walled nanotubes are grown by chemical vapor deposition (CVD) in ethane+hydrogen mixture over 20%Fe/SiO_2 catalyst, and the influence of ethane and hydrogen space velocities on carbon yield and crystalline quality of the reaction products is systematically investigated. It is found that higher carbon yields are paid with loss of selectivity and consequent worsening of the phase purity of the carbonaceous deposits. The most satisfactory results are achieved by inletting into the reactor a gas mixture, composed by 50% ethane + 50% hydrogen, at ~45 min^{-1} space velocity.

Keywords: Carbon nanotubes; MWNT; Raman spectroscopy; Catalytic processes; Chemical vapor deposition.
PACS: 63.22.+m; 68.37.Hk; 68.37.Lp; 78.67.Ch; 81.16.Hc

INTRODUCTION

Carbon nanotubes (NT) constitute an exciting research field, gathering enormous scientific and technologic interest. A lot of methods [1] are successfully utilized for preparing NT with a large spread of properties, as demanded by the various application fields. Multi-walled nanotubes (MWNT) are preferred when higher rigidity and mechanical strength are required. Catalytic methods have reached the goal of high-yield MWNT production [2,3]. However, high crystalline quality and phase purity remain the crucial tasks to be addressed.

In this work, it is shown that higher yields are achieved at expenses of the growth-process selectivity and of the phase purity of the C deposits. At this purpose, MWNT grown by CVD at 750°C in C_2H_6+H_2 atmosphere over 20%Fe/SiO_2 catalyst are considered, and the influence of the space velocities of the reagents on carbon yield and crystalline quality of the reaction products is investigated. The most satisfactory results are attained by the use of a gas mixture, composed by 50%C_2H_6 + 50%H_2, flowing at ~45 min^{-1} space velocity.

EXPERIMENTAL

The catalyst is prepared by wetting (80–150 μm) SiO_2 support in an aqueous solution of $Fe(NO_3)_3\cdot9H_2O$ (20 wt.% Fe) and drying the wet solid at 100°C. After calcination in air at 450°C for 2 h, the iron catalyst (IC) is placed in a ceramic boat inside the horizontal quartz reactor (length 60 cm, ∅ 3 cm), located in an electrical furnace. It is flushed for 30 min in pure H_2 at RT and reduced at 650°C for 10 min. Then, H_2 flow is replaced by C_2H_6+H_2 mixture (flow rates in Tab.1).

The synthesis is carried out at 750°C for 1.75 h. Two sets of samples are prepared. The first one (#201–204), grown using a constant mixture space velocity (MSV, calculated as ratio of total gas-flow to catalyst-bed volume, using an apparent 0.37 g·cc^{-1} SiO_2 density) is employed to optimizing the mixture composition. The second set (#202 and #205–206), grown with optimal composition, is utilized for MSV optimization. Carbon yield, calculated in agreement with [3,4], is $CY(wt.\%) = 100 \cdot (m/m_{IC} - 1)$, where m is the total mass after synthesis and m_{IC} is the mass of catalyst after reduction. After synthesis, the SiO_2 support and the remaining Fe-particles are removed with (1 M) KOH and (1 M) HCl solutions, respectively.

SEM and HRTEM analyses are carried out on a 20 kV JEOL JSM 5600LV instrument and on a 200 kV JEOL JEM 2010 analytical electron microscope (LaB6 electron gun) both equipped with EDX analyzer. Raman scattering is measured by using an Instruments S.A. Ramanor U-1000 double monochromator equipped with an Olympus BX40 microscope and an electrically cooled Hamamatsu R943-02 photomultiplier. A X100 objective focuses the laser spot to a diameter of ~1 μm. A Coherent Innova 70 Ar^+ laser provides excitation.

CP893, *Physics of Semiconductors, 28th International Conference*
edited by W. Jantsch and F. Schäffler

TABLE 1. Average growth rate (AGR) of carbonaceous species and average crystallite size (ACS), as estimated from Raman analysis via the Tuinstra-Koenig relationship [5], as a function of the growth conditions. Φ_E, Φ_H and x_E denote flow rates of ethane and hydrogen and ethane content of the gas-mixture, while m_{IC} standing for the amount of IC utilized.

Sample	AGR, mg·min^{-1}	ACS, nm	Φ_E, cc·min^{-1}	Φ_H, cc·min^{-1}	x_E, %	m_{IC}, g
#201	2.0	4.6	30	90	25	1.00
#202	3.3	4.5	60	60	50	1.00
#203	6.5	3.7	90	30	75	1.00
#204	7.9	3.0	120	0	100	1.01
#205	1.8	4.8	50	50	50	1.00
#206	3.5	3.3	75	75	50	1.01

RESULTS AND DISCUSSION

Under the above conditions 10–50 nm thick hollow (inner channels ≥ 5 nm) MWNT are grown with bamboo-like structure only at the lowest ethane content (x_E).

All the spectra exhibit similar first- and second-order (SO) features (Fig.1). The main parameters obtained by the spectra fitting are plotted, together with CY, as a function of ethane space velocity (ESV) for samples grown at 44.4 min^{-1} MSV (Fig.2a–c), and of hydrogen space velocity (HSV) for samples grown at 22.2 min^{-1} ESV (Fig.2d–f).

At a given MSV, CY increases linearly with ESV, which scales as x_E. However, this improvement is accompanied by quality deterioration: the average defectiveness- and smoothness-degree of C deposits, as respectively measured by D/G and SO/G intensity ratios, both worsen. The best compromise is found for $x_E = 50\%$ (i.e. ESV=22.2 min^{-1}). At this mixture composition, CY saturates as (MSV) HSV exceeds (44.4) 22.2 min^{-1}. Beyond this value, defectiveness raises abruptly, while smoothness improving.

SEM and HRTEM observations confirm the picture drawn by Raman analysis. The increase of ESV produces a gradual selectivity loss, leading to the appearance of an amorphous carbon (AC) layer of increasing thickness on the external tube-walls. The enhanced co-production of amorphous phases, due to the higher average growth rate (AGR) of carbonaceous species [6], further reflects (Tab.1) onto the smaller average crystallite size (ACS). Conversely, the rise of HSV results in the faster abstraction of hydrogen from hydrocarbons chemisorbed onto the Fe-particle surface [6] and, hence, in reduced formation of AC and enhanced NT smoothness. However, due to the higher AGR, increasingly bended and twisted NT are formed, with smaller ACS.

CONCLUSION

By studying MWNT grown by Fe-catalyzed CVD in $C_2H_6+H_2$ atmosphere, it is shown that better yields, achieved at higher gas space velocities, involve loss of selectivity and of phase purity. Simultaneous yield and crystalline-quality optimization is attained by the use of gas mixture, composed by $50\% C_2H_6 + 50\% H_2$, flowing into the reactor at ~45 min^{-1} space velocity.

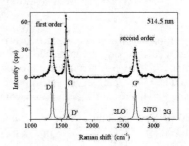

FIGURE 1. Decomposition results of typical Raman spectrum. Spectral features are fitted to Lorentzian curves. The best fit (solid line) to the experimental points is shown.

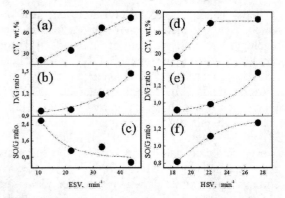

FIGURE 2. Carbon yield CY (a,d) and average defectiveness- and smoothness-degree of C deposits, as respectively measured by (b,e) D/G and (c,f) SO/G intensity ratios, as a function of ethane space velocity ESV for samples grown with constant ethane+hydrogen mixture space velocity, MSV = 44.4 min^{-1}, and different ethane contents (a–c) and of hydrogen space velocity HSV for samples grown with constant ethane content, x_E = 50%, and different MSV (d–f).

REFERENCES

1. M.S.Bell et al., *"Carbon: the future material for advanced technology applications"*, G.Messina, S.Santangelo Eds., Springer, Top. Appl. Phys. **100**, Heidelberg (2006), pp. 77-93
2. H.J.Jeong et al., *J. Phys. Chem.* B**108**, 17695-8 (2004)
3. B.Louis et al., *Catalysis Today* **102-103**, 23-28 (2005)
4. M.M.Shaijumon et al., *Int. J.Hydr.En.* **30**, 311-317 (2005)
5. F.Tuinstra, J.L.Koenig, *J. Comp. Mater.* **4** 492-9 (1970)
6. M.Grujinic et al., *Appl. Surf. Sci.* **191**, 223-239 (2002)

Zitterbewegung of electrons and holes in carbon nanotubes

Wlodek Zawadzki

Institute of Physics, Polish Academy of Sciences, Al.Lotnikow 32/46, 02-668 Warsaw, Poland

Abstract. It is shown that the band structure of single-wall semiconducting carbon nanotubes (CNT) is analogous to relativistic description of electrons in vacuum, with the maximum velocity $u = 10^8$ cm/s replacing the light velocity. One-dimensional semirelativistic kinematics and dynamics of electrons in CNT is formulated. In particular, a relation between the effective mass and the energy is derived that is in direct analogy to the Einstein relation for electrons in vacuum. Two-band kp Hamiltonian is employed to demonstrate that electrons in CNT experience a Zitterbewegung (trembling motion) in absence of external fields. An effect of an external magnetic field parallel to the CNT axis is considered. The amplitude of ZB in CNT can be as large as tens of nanometers.

Keywords: Zitterbewegung, carbon nanotubes
PACS: 73.22.-f 73.63.Fg 78.67.Ch

INTRODUCTION

Zitterbewegung (ZB, the trembling motion) was theoretically devised by Schroedinger [1] after Dirac had proposed his equation describing free relativistic electrons in vacuum. It was pointed out that the ZB also may occur in non-relativistic two-band systems in solids [2]. Recently, an analogy between the Dirac description of electrons in vacuum and the coupled-band $k \cdot p$ formalism for electrons in narrow-gap semiconductors (NGS) was used to demonstrate that the ZB should occur in this system [3]. In agreement with the 'semi-relativistic' analogy [4], the ZB frequency is always $\omega \approx E_g/\hbar$, where E_g is the energy gap between the conduction and valence bands. The amplitude of ZB in NGS was estimated to be $\lambda_Z = \hbar/m_0^* u$, where m_0^* is the effective electron mass and $u \approx 10^8$ cm/s is the maximum electron velocity in the system. The ZB length in NGS turns out to be $10 - 100$Å, i.e. $10^4 - 10^5$ times larger than in vacuum. The ZB was also recently proposed in two-dimensional systems exhibiting spin splitting due to structure and bulk inversion asymmetry [5] in 2D graphite [6] and for nearly free electrons [7]. A unified description of the ZB of electrons in different solid state systems was attempted [8].

Here we use a similarity of the band structure of CNT to the relativistic description of free electrons in vacuum. In particular, we predict that the "semirelativistic" band structure of semiconducting CNT should result in a Zitterbewegung of nonrelativistic electrons in absence of external fields. We will be interested in the simplest single-wall semiconducting and metallic CNT. Such tubes are obtained from a slice of graphene wrapped into a seamless cylinder, so that the 1D band structure of CNT can be constructed by using the 2D band structure of graphene.

Complete results of this work can be found in [9].

SEMIRELATIVITY AND ZITTERBEWEGUNG

We use the $\mathbf{k \cdot p}$ band structure of CNT at the K point of the Brillouin zone [10]. The Hamiltonian is

$$\hat{H} = \alpha \begin{bmatrix} 0 & a_n - i\hat{p} \\ a_n + i\hat{p} & 0 \end{bmatrix}, \qquad (1)$$

where α is a coefficient, $\hat{p}$ is the operator of pseudomomentum in the y direction and a_n is given by the quantization of the wave vector k_x. There is $a_n = \hbar k_x(n) = \hbar(2\pi/L)(n - v/3)$ for $n = 0, \pm 1, \pm 2...$. Here L is the length of circumference. The semiconducting CNT are obtained for $v = \pm 1$. In absence of external fields the resulting energy is $\mathscr{E} = \pm E(p)$, where $E(p) = \alpha(a_n^2 + p^2)^{1/2}$. The upper sign is for the conduction and the lower for the valence band. The above relation is analogous to the dispersion $E(p)$ for free relativistic electrons in vacuum. The energy gap is $\varepsilon_g = 2\alpha a_n$ and $m_0^* = a_n/\alpha$ is the effective mass at the band edge. The electron velocity is $v = dE/dp = \alpha^2 p/E$. For large momenta the velocity reaches a saturation value $u = \alpha = (\varepsilon_g/2m_0^*)^{1/2}$. Using u we can write the energy in equivalent form

$$E(p) = [(m_0^* u^2)^2 + u^2 p^2]^{1/2}, \qquad (2)$$

which is directly reminiscent of the relativistic $E(p)$ relation. We define an energy-dependent effective mass relating velocity to momentum: $m^* v = p$. We calculate $m^* = p/v = E/u^2$. This gives

$$E = m^* u^2, \qquad (3)$$

which is in one-to-one correspondence to the Einstein relation $E = mc^2$ (the maximum velocity u replacing c).

Estimating the introduced quantities, we use $\alpha\hbar = 6.46$ eVÅ[10]. This gives for the maximum velocity $u =$

CP893, *Physics of Semiconductors, 28th International Conference*
edited by W. Jantsch and F. Schäffler

$\alpha = 0.98 \times 10^8$ cm/s, which shows explicitly that we deal with nonrelativistic electrons. The lowest energy gap is $\varepsilon_g(0) = 2\alpha a_0$, where $a_0 = \hbar 2\pi/3L$. For circumference $L = 60$ we get $\varepsilon_g(0) = 0.45$eV. The effective mass is $m_0^*/m_0 = a_0/\alpha m_0 = 0.041$ for the same conditions. The quoted parameters are close to those of InAs, but CNT of higher diameter have smaller ε_g and m_0^*.

Next we consider quantum effects related to the Hamiltonian (1). We introduce an important quantity [3]

$$\lambda_Z = \frac{\hbar}{m_0^* u} = \frac{\hbar}{a_n}, \qquad (4)$$

which we call the length of Zitterbewegung. It corresponds to the Compton wavelength λ_c for electrons in vacuum and it plays for the semirelativistic band structure (1) the role that λ_c does for the Dirac equation. Using $m_0^* = 0.041 m_0$ and $u = 0.98 \times 10^8$ cm/s we calculate $\lambda_Z = 28.6$Å.

Consider the operator of electron velocity $\hat{v} = d\hat{H}/d\hat{p}$. We have $\hat{v}\hat{H} + \hat{H}\hat{v} = 2\alpha^2\hat{p} = 2u^2\hat{p}$. Hence the time derivative of $\hat{v}$ is

$$\frac{d\hat{v}}{dt} = \frac{i}{\hbar} 2u^2\hat{p} - \frac{2i}{\hbar}\hat{v}\hat{H}. \qquad (5)$$

This represents a simple differential equation for $\hat{v}$. Its solution is

$$\hat{v}(t) = \frac{u^2}{\hat{H}}\hat{p} + \left(\hat{v}_0 - \frac{u^2\hat{p}}{\hat{H}}\right)exp\left(-2i\frac{\hat{H}t}{\hbar}\right), \qquad (6)$$

where $1/\hat{H} = E^{-2}\hat{H}$. Equation (6) can be integrated with respect to time to give the position operator $\hat{y}$ in the Heisenberg picture

$$\hat{y}(t) = \hat{y}(0) + \frac{u^2\hat{p}}{\hat{H}}t + \frac{i\hbar u}{2\hat{H}}\hat{A}_0\left[exp\left(\frac{-2i\hat{H}t}{\hbar}\right) - 1\right], \qquad (7)$$

where $\hat{A}_0 = (\hat{v}_0/u) - (u\hat{p}/\hat{H})$. The first two terms of Eq. (7) represent the classical electron motion. The third term describes time dependent oscillations with the frequency $\omega_Z = \varepsilon_g/\hbar$. Since $\hat{A}_0 \approx 1$ the amplitude of oscillations is $2\hbar u/2\hat{H} \approx \hbar/m_0^* u = \lambda_Z$. Thus the third term describes the Zitterbewegung.

However, in our case, for each $k_x(v,n)$ there exists $k_x(-v,-n) = -k_x(v,n)$, resulting in two degenerate subbands, and the ZBs related to these subbands will cancel each other. The easiest way to break this symmetry is to apply an external magnetic field parallel to the tube axis. Such a field changes the phase factor in the wave function leading to $k_x = (2\pi/L)(n - v/3 + \phi/\phi_0)$, where ϕ is the magnetic flux and $\phi_0 = ch/e$ is the flux quantum, see [10]. The magnetic term breaks the above symmetry and the cancellation of the two trembling motions will not occur.

Finally, we briefly consider the case of metallic CNT. In our notation of Eq.(1) the metallic CNT are characterized by the quantum number $v = 0$, which gives $a_0 = 0$ for $n = 0$. This leads to $\mathscr{E} = \pm E(p)$, where $E(p) = \alpha|p|$. This means that for the lowest subband there is no energy gap. The maximum velocity u can still be defined, there is, as before, $u = \alpha$. In fact, the classical velocity is always u. The rest effective mass vanishes: $m_0^* = a_n/\alpha = 0$. Still, the effective mass of Eq. (4), relating velocity to momentum, exists: $m^* = E/u^2$. The equivalence between the energy and the mass, as given by Eq.(3), remains unchanged. An electron (hole) can not be accelerated since its velocity is constant: $v = u$. The above features describe "massless" electrons (holes) which acquire their mass due to motion. According to Eq. (4) the length of Zitterbewegung is $\lambda_Z = \infty$. Using the initial Hamiltonian (1) with $a_n = 0$ and the definition of the quantum velocity $\hat{v}$ it can be easily verified that $d\hat{v}/dt = 0$. Thus, also the quantum velocity is constant, from which we conclude that in metallic CNT the carriers in the lowest subband do not experience the Zitterbewegung.

The ZB described above can be observed with the use of scanning probe microscopy (SPM), which is able to image coherent electron flow [11,12]. The SPM uses a movable tip that, properly biased, probes the electron density below it. As the Zitterbewegung changes the electron density along the tube's circumference, it will induce oscillations of the tube's conductance when the tip is moved along the circumference.

This work was supported in part by The Polish Ministry of Sciences, Grant No PBZ-MIN-008/PO3/2003.

REFERENCES

1. E. Schroedinger, Sitzungsber. Preuss. Akad. Wiss. Phys. Math. Kl. **24**, 418 (1930).
2. F. Cannata, L. Ferrari and G. Russo, Solid State Commun. **74**, 309 (1990); L. Ferrari and G. Russo, Phys. Rev. B **42**, 7454 (1990).
3. W. Zawadzki, Phys. Rev. B **72**, 085217 (2005).
4. W. Zawadzki, in *High Magnetic Fields in the Physics of Semiconductors II*, edited by G. Landwehr and W. Ossau (World Scientific, Singapore, 1997), p.755.
5. J. Schliemann, D. Loss and R.M. Westervelt, Phys. Rev. Lett. **94**, 206801 (2005); Phys. Rev. B **73**, 085323 (2006).
6. M.I. Katsnelson, cond-mat/0512337 (2005).
7. T. M. Rusin and W. Zawadzki, cond-mat/0605384.
8. J. Cserti and G. David, cond-mat/0604526 (2006).
9. W. Zawadzki, cond-mat/0510184 (2005).
10. H. Ajiki and T.Ando, J. Phys. Soc. Jpn **62**, 1255 (1993); H. Ajiki and T. Ando, *ibid* **64**, 4382 (1995); T. Ando and T. Nakanishi, *ibid* **67**, 1704 (1998); T. Ando and H. Suzuura, *ibid* **71**, 2753 (2002).
11. M.A. Topinka et al. Science **289**, 2323 (2000).
12. B.J. LeRoy, J. Phys.: Condens. Matter **15**, R1835 (2003).

Encapsulation of Metallocenes in Single-Wall Carbon Nanotubes: an Ab Initio Study

Solange B. Fagan[1]*, D. L. Azevedo[2], J.Mendes Filho[3], A. G. Souza Filho[3]

[1]*Área de Ciências Naturais e Tecnológicas, UNIFRA, Andradas, 1614, 97010-032, Santa Maria- RS, Brazil*
[2]*Departamento de Física,Universidade Federal do Maranhão, São Luis, MA, Brazil*
[3]*Departamento de Física,Universidade Federal do Ceará, CP. 6030, Fortaleza, CE, Brazil*

Abstract. In this work we study the electronic, magnetic and structural properties of cobaltocene molecule (bis-cyclopentadienyl cobalt) interacting with (13,0) semiconductor single-wall carbon nanotubes through *ab initio* simulations. The calculations are based on the first principles spin-polarized density functional theory, using numerical atomic orbitals as basis set implemented in the SIESTA code. Our calculations indicated that the cobaltocene molecule inside the SWNT behave as electron donor thus charging the electronic bands of the nanotube and increasing its Fermi energy due to the molecule-nanotube interaction.

Keywords: carbon nanotubes, cobaltocene, *ab initio* simulations, electronic properties.
PACS: 71.15.Mb, 71.20.Tx, 73.22.-f, 78.67.Ch

INTRODUCTION

Carbon nanotubes present very interesting electronic, optical and mechanic properties[1] and they have been extensively studied to be building blocks of nanoelectronic devices such as gas sensors, biological sensors, etc.[2] When the nanotubes are combined with other foreign atoms or molecules, their electronic and structural properties can change dramatically thus opening up a new range of technological applications.

Encapsulated molecules in semiconducting single-wall carbon nanotubes (SWNTs) have been reported as very promising systems for modifying the optical and electronic properties of the tubes and are expected as innovative approaches to produce hybrid nanostructures.[3-5] Recent studies of scanning tunneling spectroscopy (STS) have shown that fullerenes or metallocenes encapsulated in semiconductor SWNTs change significantly the electronic properties of the original systems.[3]

In this work we study, through *ab initio* simulations with the density functional theory, the behavior of the cobaltocene molecule encapsulated in the semiconductor (13,0) SWNT. It can be observed that the electronic properties due to the charge transfer and confinement effects modify the electronic properties of the original SWNT.

CALCULATIONS PROCEDURE

The theoretical investigation of the cobaltocene@(13,0) SWNT was based on the spin-polarized first principles density–functional calculations using numerical atomic orbitals as basis set. The simulations were performed with the SIESTA code,[6] which solves the Kohn–Sham (KS) equations using for the exchange and correlation term the Generalized Gradient Approximation, GGA, as parameterized by Perdew et al.,[7] and replacing the core electrons by the standard norm–conserving Troullier–Martins pseudopotentials.[8] The KS orbitals were expanded with a linear combination of numerical pseudoatomic orbitals, similar to those proposed by Sankey and Niklewski.[9] In all procedures, a split–valence double–zeta basis set was used with a polarization function with an energy shift of 0.05 eV to represent the pseudoatomic confinement for all the atom.[6] A cutoff of 150 Ry for the grid integration was utilized to represent the electronic charge density and, for the Brillouin zone sampling, 15 special k–points in Monkhorst–Pack scheme were used.

Our study was performed with a (13,0) semiconductor SWNT with 156 atoms and the

---

* Corresponding author: Solange B. Fagan, UNIFRA, Rua dos Andradas, 1614, 97010-032, Santa Maria – RS, Brazil, Phone: +55-55-32201200, Fax: +55-55-32226484, E-mail: solange.fagan@gmail.com

CP893, *Physics of Semiconductors, 28th International Conference*
edited by W. Jantsch and F. Schäffler
© 2007 American Institute of Physics 978-0-7354-0397-0/07/$23.00

cobaltocene molecule in a bis-cyclopentadienyl cobalt configuration with 21 atoms. The atoms were disposed in a supercell with sides (30 x 30 x 8.52) Å^3 that guarantees axial periodicity and avoids interaction with neighboring tubes. The relaxed atomic structures of the tubes were obtained by a minimization of the total energy using Hellmann–Feynman forces including Pullay–like corrections. Structural optimizations were performed using the conjugate gradient algorithm up to the point of the residual forces to fall bellow 0.05 eV/Å.

RESULTS AND CONCLUSIONS

Fig. 1 (a) shows the structural configuration for the bis-cyclopentadienyl cobalt encapsulated in the (13,0) SWNT. After the relaxation the encapsulated molecules stays in the center of the carbon nanotubes.

The magnetic momentum decreases from 1.0 μ_B (free molecule) to around 0.3 μ_B when they are encapsulated. The magnetization contour plots (Fig. 1(b)) confirmed that the cobaltocene molecules are responsible for the magnetization of the system and it decreases due to the charge transfer.

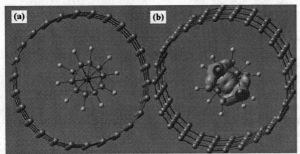

FIGURE 1. (a) Structural configuration and (b) the magnetization contour plot for the cobaltocene@(13,0) SWNT.

Fig. 2 (a) shows the electronic band structures for the pristine (13,0) SWNT. The electronic band structure of the cobaltocene@SWNT for majority and minority spin, are shown in Fig. 2(b) and (c), respectively.

The electronic properties of the encapsulated SWNTs change with an upshift in the Fermi energy with the system initially semiconductor becoming metallic as a consequence of the electron acceptor behavior of the tube in both minority and majority electronic states (Figs. 2(b) and (c), respectively). These calculations are in agreement with a recent experimental work that shown that the SWNTs have an electron acceptor behavior.[3] Electron transfer from the cobalt ions to the nanotubes has been experimentally observed through a change in the charge state of the encapsulated molecules.[3]

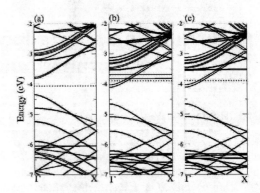

FIGURE 2. Electronic band structure for the (a) pristine (13,0) SWNT and cobaltocene@(13,0)SWNT for (b) majority and (c) minority spins carriers. The horizontal dashed lines correspond to the Fermi energy.

In summary, it is interesting to point out that these cobaltocene-encapsulated SWNTs might offers great promise for interesting applications in molecular devices as highly selective hybrid systems using the cobaltocene encapsulated magnetic properties.

ACKNOWLEDGMENTS

We thank CENAPAD–SP for computational facilities, CAPES, CNPq (Grants 452374/2006-5, 307417/2004-2 and 55.6549/2005-8), FUNCAP (PPP-985/03), FAPERGS (Grant 05/2096.2), and FAPEMA for financial support.

REFERENCES

1. M.S. Dresselhaus, G. Dresselhaus, P. Avouris, *Carbon Nanotubes: Synthesis, Structure, Properties, and Applications (Topics in Applied Physics Vol. 80)* (Springer-Verlag, New York, 2001).M. P. Brown and K. Austin, *The New Physique*, Publisher City: Publisher Name, 2005, pp. 25-30.
2. H. Dai, *Surf. Sci.* **500**, 56 (1991).
3. Lain-Jong Li, et al., *Nature Materials*, **4**, 481 (2005).
4. A. Khlobystov, D. Britz, and G.A.D. Briggs, *Acc.Chem. Res.* **38**, 901 (2005).
5. D. J. Hornbaker, et al. *Science* **295**, 828 (2002).
6. P. Ordejón, E. Artacho, Soler J M *Phys. Rev. B* **53** 10441,1996; D. Sánchez-Portal, E. Artacho, J. M. Soler, *Int. J. Quantum Chem.* **65** 453 (1997).
7. J. P. Perdew, K. Burke, M. Ernzerhof, *Phys. Rev. Lett.* **77** 3865 (1996).
8. N. Troullier , J.L.Martins, *Phys. Rev. B* **43** 1993 (1991).
9. O.F.Sankey, D.J.Niklewski, *Phys. Rev. B* **40** 3979 (1989).

Dynamical response of the perfect conducting channel in carbon nanotubes

Yoichi Asada and Tsuneya Ando

Department of Physics, Tokyo Institute of Technology, 2-12-1 Ookayama, Meguro-ku, Tokyo 152-8551, Japan

Abstract. The dynamical conductivity in metallic carbon nanotubes with impurities is studied based on an exact numerical diagonalization. The results show clearly that the conductivity deviates considerably from the usual Drude behavior due to the absence of backward scattering and the presence of a perfect conducting channel in the low-frequency region.

Keywords: carbon nanotube, effective-mass theory, dynamical conductivity, symplectic symmetry
PACS: 73.63.Fg,78.67.Ch

The electronic transport in carbon nanotubes has been a subject of extensive experimental and theoretical studies [1]. In metallic nanotubes, the backward scattering is absent even in the presence of scatterers unless their potential range is smaller than a few angstroms [2, 3] and there is a perfect conducting channel when there are several bands present at the Fermi level [4]. This unique property can be ascribed to the symplectic symmetry of the effective Hamiltonian in the $\mathbf{k} \cdot \mathbf{p}$ scheme and the presence of odd channel numbers [1, 4]. The dynamical conductivity was calculated in the self-consistent Born approximation (SCBA) [5]. The weak localization correction was calculated also [6]. In this paper, we calculate the dynamical conductivity based on an exact numerical diagonalization in order to clarify the importance of the perfect conducting channel.

We consider a metallic carbon nanotube with circumference L and length A ($A \gg L$). The metallic nanotube has conduction and valence bands crossing at the points corresponding to the K and K$'$ points of the Brillouin zone in the two-dimensional graphite. In the effective mass approximation, electronic states near the K point (or K$'$ point) are described by the $\mathbf{k} \cdot \mathbf{p}$ equation [1, 7]. We consider impurities whose range of scattering potential is larger than the lattice constant but shorter than the electron wave length, typically $2\pi/L$. Most of scatterers present in actual nanotubes are expected to satisfy this condition. For such scatterers, we can neglect the scattering between K and K$'$ points and these two points can be treated independently [2].

The Hamiltonian for the K point is given by

$$H = \gamma(\vec{\sigma} \cdot \hat{\mathbf{k}}) + \sum_i u_i \delta(\mathbf{r} - \mathbf{r}_i). \qquad (1)$$

Here γ is a band parameter, $\hat{\mathbf{k}} = (\hat{k}_x, \hat{k}_y)$ the wave-vector operator defined by $\hat{\mathbf{k}} = -\mathrm{i}\vec{\nabla} + e\mathbf{A}/c\hbar$ with $\mathbf{A}$ being a vector potential, $\vec{\sigma} = (\sigma_x, \sigma_y)$ the Pauli spin matrices

(two sites in a unit cell play a role of quasi-spin). We suppose that a magnetic flux ϕ_x is passing through the cross section of the nanotube. The positions $\mathbf{r}_i$ of impurities are distributed randomly and independently in the system and we assume equal amount of attractive and repulsive scatterers, $u_i = \pm u$. The strength of disorder is characterized by the dimensionless parameter $W = n_i u^2 / 4\pi\gamma^2$ [5], with n_i being the impurity density. We impose periodic boundary conditions in the axis direction. For the purpose of numerical calculations, we restrict the basis by a cutoff energy $\varepsilon_c = 3(2\pi\gamma/L)$. We use $|\sigma, \mathbf{k}\rangle$ ($\sigma = \uparrow, \downarrow$ and $\gamma|\mathbf{k}| < \varepsilon_c$) as a basis.

The number of conducting channels at the Fermi energy N_c can be varied without breaking symplectic symmetry by controlling the Fermi energy and the magnetic flux. When ϕ_x is an integer multiple of the flux quantum $\phi_0 = ch/e$, N_c is odd irrespective of the value of the Fermi energy. When $\phi_x = \phi_0/2$, N_c becomes even, for which the perfect channel disappears and states are localized in spite of the symplectic symmetry [8].

We use the Kubo formula to calculate the dynamical conductivity in the tube axis direction (y-direction),

$$\sigma_{yy}(\omega) = \frac{\pi\hbar}{LA}\Big\langle \sum_{n,m} [f(\varepsilon_m) - f(\varepsilon_n)]$$
$$\times \frac{|\langle n|\hat{j}_y|m\rangle|^2}{\varepsilon_n - \varepsilon_m}\delta(\hbar\omega - \varepsilon_n + \varepsilon_m)\Big\rangle. \qquad (2)$$

Here, $f(\varepsilon)$ is the Fermi distribution function, ε_n and $|n\rangle$ represent nth eigenvalue and eigenvector, respectively, $\hat{j}_y = -(e\gamma/\hbar)\sigma_y$ is the current operator, and $\langle \cdots \rangle$ means the sample average. In practice, we calculate the conductivity averaged in a small frequency window $[\omega - \delta_\omega/2, \omega + \delta_\omega/2]$ to avoid the delta function in the Kubo formula, and the frequency dependence of the conductivity is shown like a histogram.

We present numerical results for $N_c = 1$ and 3. It is known that the backward scattering is absent in the case

CP893, *Physics of Semiconductors, 28th International Conference*
edited by W. Jantsch and F. Schäffler
© 2007 American Institute of Physics 978-0-7354-0397-0/07/$23.00

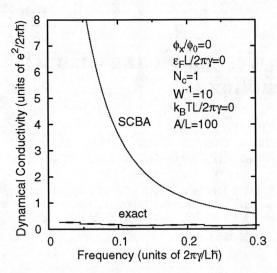

FIGURE 1. Dynamical conductivity for $A/L = 100$, $W^{-1} = 10$, $k_B TL/2\pi\gamma = 0$, $\phi_x/\phi_0 = 0$, $\varepsilon_F L/2\pi\gamma = 0$, and $N_c = 1$ obtained in the SCBA and by exact numerical diagonalization.

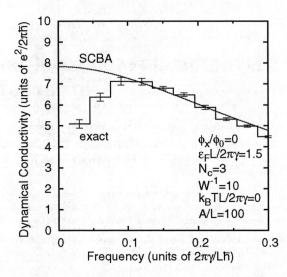

FIGURE 2. Dynamical conductivity for $A/L = 100$, $W^{-1} = 10$, $k_B TL/2\pi\gamma = 0$, $\phi_x/\phi_0 = 0$, $\varepsilon_F L/2\pi\gamma = 1.5$, and $N_c = 3$ obtained in the SCBA and by exact numerical diagonalization.

of $N_c = 1$, i.e., the transmission is perfect [2]. In the case of $N_c = 3$, there is one perfect conducting channel and the conductance of a finite-length nanotube decreases from the ideal value corresponding to $N_c = 3$ to that in the single channel case as the length of nanotube increases [4]. The similar conclusions can be obtained in different methods [9].

A numerical result of the dynamical conductivity for $N_c = 1$ in a small-frequency region is shown in Fig. 1. The result indicates that the Drude behavior cannot be seen in contrast to that in SCBA. It is likely that the conductivity in the vicinity of $\omega = 0$ is not broadened and there is a delta function at zero frequency.

Figure 2 shows a result for $N_c = 3$. When the frequency is larger than $\omega_c \approx 0.1 \times (2\pi\gamma/L\hbar)$, the dynamical conductivity obtained by exact diagonalization is nearly the same as that in SCBA, i.e., the Drude behavior is observed. On the other hand, in a small frequency region, the exact dynamical conductivity deviates from that in the SCBA and decreases with the decrease of the frequency.

The numerical result indicates that a crossover occurs at $\omega_c \approx 0.1 \times (2\pi\gamma/L\hbar)$ in the case of $\phi_x/\phi_0 = 0$, $\varepsilon_F L/2\pi\gamma = 1.5$, $N_c = 3$, and $W^{-1} = 10$. This corresponds to the crossover from the Drude transport regime to the "single-channel" transport regime. The result suggests again that there is a delta-function conductivity at zero frequency even in the case of $N_c = 3$ related to the perfect conducting channel.

More detailed results and discussions, including the case of $N_c = 2$ where the Anderson localization takes place, are reported elsewhere [10]. Further, a detailed study on the presence of a delta function at zero fre-

quency is desirable but left for the future.

ACKNOWLEDGMENTS

One of the authors (Y.A.) acknowledges the support of Research Fellowships of the Japan Society for the Promotion of Science for Young Scientists. This work was supported in part by a 21st Century COE Program at Tokyo Tech "Nanometer-Scale Quantum Physics" and by Grant-in-Aid for Scientific Research from the Ministry of Education, Culture, Sports, Science and Technology, Japan.

REFERENCES

1. T. Ando, J. Phys. Soc. Jpn. **74**, 777 (2005).
2. T. Ando and T. Nakanishi, J. Phys. Soc. Jpn. **67**, 1704 (1998).
3. T. Ando, T. Nakanishi, and R. Saito, J. Phys. Soc. Jpn. **67**, 2857 (1998).
4. T. Ando and H. Suzuura, J. Phys. Soc. Jpn. **71**, 2753 (2002).
5. T. Ando, J. Phys. Soc. Jpn. **71**, 2505 (2002).
6. H. Suzuura and T. Ando, J. Phys. Soc. Jpn. **75**, 024703 (2006).
7. H. Ajiki and T. Ando, J. Phys. Soc. Jpn. **62**, 1255 (1993).
8. T. Ando, J. Phys. Soc. Jpn. **75**, 054701 (2006).
9. Y. Takane and K. Wakabayashi, J. Phys. Soc. Jpn. **72**, 2710 (2003). Y. Takane, J. Phys. Soc. Jpn. **73**, 9 (2004); **73**, 1430 (2004); **73**, 2366 (2004).
10. Y. Asada and T. Ando, J. Phys. Soc. Jpn. (submitted for publication).

Electronic states of single-walled carbon nanotubes with substitutional impurities

Koichi Inoue[*][†], Yasuhide Ohno[*][†], Kenzo Maehashi[*][†] and Kazuhiko Matsumoto[*][†]

[*] *The Institute of Scientific and Industrial Research, Osaka University, 8-1 Mihogaoka, Ibaraki, Osaka 567-0047, Japan.*
[†] *CREST, Japan Science and Technology Agency, 4-1-8 Honcho Kawaguchi, Saitama 332-0012, Japan.*

Abstract. Electronic states and optical transition probabilities between them in oxygen-doped single-walled carbon nanotubes (SWNTs) are studied by tight-binding model calculation with coherent potential approximation. It is found that notable splitting of degenerated bands occurs owing to the breaking of the rotational symmetry even by the diluted impurity potentials which consist of one oxygen atom per 500 carbon sites in (15,0) SWNTs. According to the changes of electronic states, additional peaks relating to the impurity states appear in the joint density of states from unoccupied to occupied bands. Taking the optical matrix elements into account, it is concluded that the lowest transition energy will be shifted due to the doping.

Keywords: nanotube, impurity state, electronic structure, Raman scattering
PACS: 78.67.Ch

Single-walled carbon nanotubes (SWNTs) have attracted much attention because of their unique structural and electrical properties.[1] Precise controls of carrier concentration as well as the carrier types are important in the applications of semiconducting SWNTs. Recently ultra-low-energy O^+ ions have been implanted into p-type SWNTs to obtain n-type SWNTs successfully.[2] Raman scattering experiments have been carried out for the O^+ implanted SWNTs. As the results, characteristic shifts of resonance energies have been observed, which suggests that the O atoms are doped substitutionally in SWNTs.[3] In the previous paper, it has been known that the substitutional O atoms can be stable by the first-principle calculation with local density approximation for (6,0) SWNT.[3] In this paper, the electronic structure of SWNTs doped with substitutional O atoms is studied by the tight-binding calculation (TB) with coherent potential approximation (CPA) to clarify whether the substitutional doping of O atoms can be explain the shifts of Raman resonance energies, or not.

Figure 1 shows the band structures of (a) pure and (b) O-doped (15,0) SWNTs calculated by TB in the region near Fermi levels. The adopted parameters are on-site energy $E_c = 0$ at C sites, $E_o = -5.16$ eV at O sites, and transfer energy $T = 3.12$ eV between the nearest-neighbor O–C and C–C bonds. Strain induced by O impurities is ignored. Fermi level in the pure SWNT is located at the origin of ordinate, and typical unoccupied bands are labeled as C_1 (dashed line) and C_2 (solid line), while occupied bands as V_1 (dashed line) and V_2 (solid line) in Fig 1 (a). It should be noted that these four

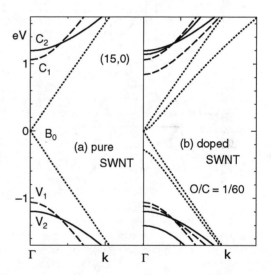

FIGURE 1. Band structures in pure (a) and O-doped SWNT (b).

bands are two-fold degenerated owing to the rotational symmetry of SWNTs. Bands B_0 (dotted lines) are the half-filled bands of metalic (15,0) SWNT.

In the doped SWNT, the breaking of rotational symmetry causes splitting of the bands as shown in Fig 1 (b) where one of 60 C atoms in a unit cell is replaced by an O atom: this impurity concentration is expressed by O/C=1/60 in this paper. The splitting is remarkable near the Γ point, where the bands are nearly flat, and therefore, their density of states (DOS) exhibits sharp peak struc-

CP893, *Physics of Semiconductors, 28th International Conference*
edited by W. Jantsch and F. Schäffler
© 2007 American Institute of Physics 978-0-7354-0397-0/07/$23.00

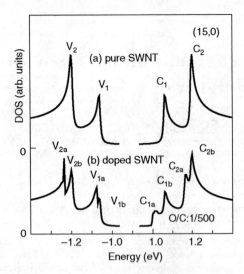

FIGURE 2. Density of states in pure (a) and O-doped SWNT (b). A broadening factor about 5 meV is assumed.

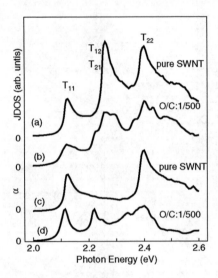

FIGURE 3. Joint density of states in pure (a) and O-doped SWNT (b), and the absorption coefficient in pure (c) and O-doped SWNT (d).

tures as shown in Fig. 2. The spectrum in Fig. 2 (b) shows the DOS in the SWNT randomly doped by O atoms with the concentration of O/C=1/500, which is calculated by CPA where the correlation and the interaction between O atoms are ignored.[4] It should be stressed that the recognizable splitting of DOS peaks are caused by such a diluted impurity potential.

Electronic transition can take place from occupied to unoccupied bands at the singularities especially. Figures 3 (a) and (b) show joint density of states (JDOS) between the occupied and the unoccupied bands. In the spectra of pure SWNT in fig. 3 (a), there are three peaks labeled as

T_{11} which corresponds to the transition from V_1 to C_1 in Fig. 1 (a), T_{12} from V_1 to C_2 T_{21} from V_2 to C_1, and T_{22} from V_2 to C_2. The transition energies of T_{12} and T_{21} coincide to the each other in the present TB model. In the JDOS of the doped SWNT in Fig. 3 (b), several structures are observed correspondingly to the band splitting due to the O impurities. However all of the transitions are not allowed in the optical transition.

Optical transition probabilities are estimated by the evaluation of the matrix elements between two band wavefunctions. Obtained absorption coefficients are shown in Figs. 3 (c) and (d), where polarization directions are averaged. As for the pure SWNT, the peak T_{12} and T_{21} around 2.26 eV in Fig. 3 (a) disappear in Fig. 3 (c) since the optical transition is forbidden. However some structures remain in the region near 2.26 eV in the doped spectra in Fig 3 (d). These transitions are partially allowed owing to the symmetry breaking induced by the doped O atoms locally. Another notable point of the doped spectra is that the lowest peak at about 2.11 eV in Fig. 3 (d) becomes sharp as compared with the peak in Fig 3 (b), and it is located slightly below the position of the peak at about 2.12 eV in Fig. 3 (c). It is due to the suppression of higher component of splitting T_{11} transitions in Fig 3 (b) by optical selection rules. This explains the recent results of resonant Raman scattering experiments where the resonance energies are shifted by the oxygen implantation.

In summary, electronic states and optical transition probabilities between them in O-doped (15,0) SWNTs are studied by TB-CPA model. It is found that some transitions are partially allowed by local symmetry breaking, and the lowest transition energy will be shifted due to the doping. This explains well the recent results of resonant Raman scattering experiments where the resonance energies are much affected by the oxygen implantation.

ACKNOWLEDGMENTS – The one of the authors (K.I.) is partially supported by a Grant-in-Aid for Scientific Research from Japan Society for the Promotion of Science.

REFERENCES

1. R. Saito, G. Dresselhaus, M.S. Dresselhaus, *Physical Properties of Carbon Nanotubes*, Imperial College Press, London, 1998.
2. T. Kawai, K. Yamamoto, T. Kamimura, C.-K. Hyon, A. Kojima, K. Kurachi, M. Maeda, M. Torigoe, T. Nemoto and K. Matsumoto, *Proc. of 46th TMS Electronic Materials Conf.*, 2004, Y3.
3. Y. Ohno, K. Inoue, T. Kamimura, K. Maehashi, K. Yamamoto and K. Matsumoto, *Jpn. J. Appl. Phys.* **44**, 1615 (2005).
4. Y. Toyozawa, *Optical Processes in Solids*, Cambridge University Press, UK, 2003.

Prominent exciton absorption of perpendicularly polarized light in carbon nanotubes

Seiji Uryu and Tsuneya Ando

Department of Physics, Tokyo Institute of Technology, 2-12-1 Ookayama, Meguro-ku, Tokyo 152-8551, Japan

Abstract. Optical absorption in carbon nanotubes for polarization perpendicular to the tube axis is studied taking account of exciton effects. Although a strong depolarization effect tends to shift the position to the higher energy side and suppress the intensity, excitons manifest themselves as prominent peaks because of their large binding energy.

Keywords: carbon nanotube, exciton, depolarization effect, optical absorption, effective-mass approximation
PACS: 78.67.Ch, 73.22.Lp

A carbon nanotube has characteristic optical properties. For example, the absorption of light polarized perpendicular to the axis is known to be suppressed considerably because of strong depolarization effect in comparison with that of light polarized parallel to the axis [1, 2]. Further, exciton effects play a crucial role for light polarization parallel to the axis [3, 4, 5]. In this paper we present preliminary results of exciton effects for perpendicularly polarized light in semiconducting single-wall carbon nanotubes.

In the effective-mass approximation [6, 7] we shall use a screened Hartree-Fock approximation to calculate interaction effect on the band structure and introduce an attractive interaction between a photo-excited electron and a remaining hole using the Coulomb interaction screened by a static dielectric function. Actual calculations can be performed by solving equation of motion for an electron-hole pair [3, 4, 5].

Dynamical conductivity characterizing light absorption is calculated in the linear response theory. The conductivity without depolarization effects is written as

$$\sigma_{xx}^l(\omega) = \frac{2\bar{h}e^2}{AL} \sum_{KK'} \sum_u \frac{-2i\bar{h}\omega|\langle u,l|\hat{v}_x^l|g\rangle|^2}{\varepsilon_u[\varepsilon_u^2 - (\bar{h}\omega)^2 - 2i\bar{h}\omega\Gamma]}, \quad (1)$$

where ε_u and $|u, l\rangle$ are an eigen energy and eigen function of an electron-hole pair without depolarization effects, respectively, $|g\rangle$ the ground state, $\hat{v}_x^l$ a Fourier transform of the velocity in the circumferential direction for the wave number $2\pi l/L$ with L being the circumference length and $l = \pm 1$, and Γ a phenomenological energy broadening.

Depolarization effects are taken into account by considering a self-consistent electric field[1, 2]. Then, the conductivity is given by

$$\tilde{\sigma}_{xx}^l(\omega) = \frac{\sigma_{xx}^l(\omega)}{\varepsilon_{xx}^l(\omega)}, \quad (2)$$

with a dielectric function defined as

$$\varepsilon_{xx}^l(\omega) = 1 + \frac{4\pi^2 i|l|}{\kappa L \omega} \sigma_{xx}^l(\omega), \quad (3)$$

where κ is an effective dielectric constant describing screening by electrons in σ bands, core states, and the π bands away from the K and K' points, and by surrounding materials if any. Excitation energy $\bar{h}\omega_0$ with depolarization effects is given by zero points of the dielectric function, that is,

$$\varepsilon_{xx}^l(\omega_0) = 1 + \frac{4\pi^2 i}{\kappa L \omega_0} \sigma_{xx}^l(\omega_0) = 0. \quad (4)$$

The strength of the Coulomb interaction in nanotubes is characterized by the dimensionless quantity given by the ratio of the typical Coulomb energy $e^2/\kappa L$ and the typical kinetic energy $2\pi\gamma/L$ with γ being the band parameter, i.e.,

$$\frac{e^2}{\kappa L} \frac{L}{2\pi\gamma} \approx \frac{0.35}{\kappa}. \quad (5)$$

Since κ is considered to be of the order of unity, for example, $\kappa = 2.4$ for graphite, the typical strength of the Coulomb interaction is of the order of 0.1∼0.2.

The summation over states must be cut off by a cutoff energy ε_c in the effective-mass approximation. It should be of the order of the half of the π-band width $3\gamma_0$, where γ_0 is the resonance integral between nearest neighbor sites and related to the band parameter through $\gamma = \sqrt{3}a\gamma_0/2$ with a being the lattice constant. Therefore, $\varepsilon_c(2\pi\gamma/L)^{-1} \approx (\sqrt{3}/\pi)(L/a) = \sqrt{3}d/a$, with d being the diameter of the nanotube. In the following, $\varepsilon_c(2\pi\gamma/L)^{-1} = 10$ is used which corresponds to a diameter of typical single-wall nanotubes ∼ 1.4 nm.

Figures 1(a) and (b) show energy dependence of dynamical conductivity for typical Coulomb interaction $(e^2/\kappa L) (2\pi\gamma/L)^{-1} = 0.05$ and 0.2, respectively. The

CP893, *Physics of Semiconductors, 28ᵗʰ International Conference*
edited by W. Jantsch and F. Schäffler
© 2007 American Institute of Physics 978-0-7354-0397-0/07/$23.00

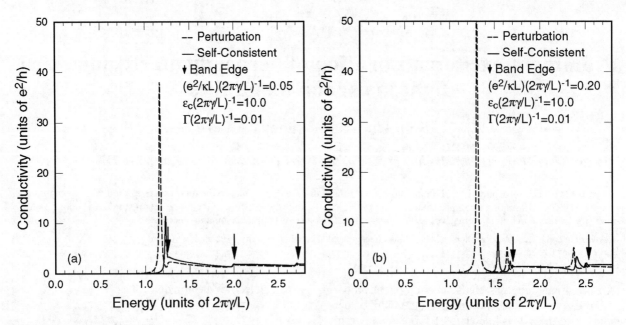

FIGURE 1. Calculated $\tilde{\sigma}_{xx}(\omega)$ and $\sigma_{xx}(\omega)$ for (a) $(e^2/\kappa L)\,(2\pi\gamma/L)^{-1} = 0.05$ and (b) $(e^2/\kappa L)\,(2\pi\gamma/L)^{-1} = 0.2$. Solid and dashed lines denote $\tilde{\sigma}_{xx}(\omega)$ and $\sigma_{xx}(\omega)$, respectively. The vertical arrows indicate band edges. The energy broadening $\Gamma(2\pi\gamma/L)^{-1} = 0.01$ is used.

dashed lines show conductivity without depolarization effect which is denoted by 'Perturbation' and solid lines that with depolarization effect which is denoted by 'Self-Consistent'. The vertical arrows indicate band edges. When the depolarization effect is not considered, the largest peak appears below the lowest band edge. When the depolarization effect is taken into account, the peak is shifted toward the higher energy side and its intensity is reduced. For the stronger interaction $(e^2/\kappa L)\,(2\pi\gamma/L)^{-1} = 0.2$ shown in Fig. 1(b) there is another small peak below the higher band edge and another peak appears below the lowest band edge, corresponding to an excited exciton state.

The results clearly show that exciton effects are important to optical absorption in single-wall nanotubes. In the case of inter-band optical absorption, there are no peaks in the spectra because of depolarization effects [1, 2].

Recently, photoluminescence spectra of single-wall nanotubes were decomposed into those associated with absorption of parallel and perpendicular light [8, 9]. The obtained spectra for perpendicular polarization showed that a peak with intensity about an order-of-magnitude smaller than that for parallel polarization appears at a position closer to that of the second lowest peak for parallel polarization. This result seems to be consistent with our theoretical prediction of the exciton absorption and emission of perpendicularly polarized light.

ACKNOWLEDGMENTS

This work was supported in part by a 21st Century COE Program at Tokyo Tech "Nanometer-Scale Quantum Physics" and by Grant-in-Aid for Scientific Research from the Ministry of Education, Culture, Sports, Science and Technology, Japan.

REFERENCES

1. H. Ajiki and T. Ando, Physica B **201**, 349 (1994).
2. H. Ajiki and T. Ando, Jpn. J. Appl. Phys. Suppl.**34-1**, 107 (1995).
3. T. Ando, J. Phys. Soc. Jpn. **66**, 1066 (1997).
4. T. Ando, J. Phys. Soc. Jpn. **73**, 3351 (2004).
5. T. Ando, J. Phys. Soc. Jpn. **75**, 024707 (2006).
6. H. Ajiki and T. Ando, J. Phys. Soc. Jpn.**62** 1255 (1993).
7. T. Ando, J. Phys. Soc. Jpn.**74**,777 (2005).
8. S. Maruyama, *Proc. 20th Internat. Winterschool on Electronic Properties of Novel Materials*, Phys. Stat. Sol. (to be published).
9. Y. Miyauchi, M. Oba, and S. Maruyama, *Proc. 20th Internat. Winterschool on Electronic Properties of Novel Materials*, Phys. Stat. Sol. (to be published).

Strong inter-tube coupling induced by disorder in double-wall carbon nanotubes

Seiji Uryu and Tsuneya Ando

Department of Physics, Tokyo Institute of Technology, 2-12-1 Ookayama, Meguro-ku, Tokyo 152-8551, Japan

Abstract. The inter-tube conductance in finite-length double-wall carbon nanotubes with impurities is numerically studied. The conductance remains negligibly small in incommensurate tubes due to cancellation of inter-tube coupling at different sites in the absence of disorder. In the presence of impurities, this cancellation becomes incomplete and the conductance increases with increase of the length.

Keywords: double-wall carbon nanotube, incommensurate tube, inter-tube transfer, conductance, impurity
PACS: 73.63.Fg, 73.23.Ad, 72.80.Rj

In double-wall carbon nanotubes the lattice of an outer tube and that of the inner tube is incommensurate [1, 2] and distance between two tubes is about 3.6 Å almost independent of the tube radius [3]. The situation is same in multi-wall nanotubes. Experiments on the electrical transport of an individual multi-wall tube reported ballistic [4] and diffusive transport [5, 6]. Experiments on inter-tube conduction were reported also [7, 8]. Theoretically, negligibly small inter-tube conductance was reported for clean tubes [9, 10]. However, there are few reports on effects of disorders in multi-wall nanotubes [11]. In this paper it is shown that inter-tube transfer of double-wall carbon nanotubes is induced by impurities.

A tight-binding model including only π orbital is used [10]. Intra-tube resonance integral γ_0 between nearest neighbor sites is taken into account. An inter-tube resonance integral is modeled by two hopping integrals V_{pp}^{π} and V_{pp}^{σ} which decay exponentially with distance. Short range impurities are modeled as randomly distributed on-site potentials with density n_i. Each potential takes a value $+v$ or $-v$ in the same probability.

Figure 1 shows illustration of four-terminal double-wall tubes considered in the following. Inter-tube transfer is present only in hatched double-wall regions with length A, while tubes are independent outside the region and connected to reservoirs. The inter-tube conductance for transmission from the left outer tube to the right inner tube, denoted by arrows in Fig. 1, is considered.

In the followings, results for (2,17)/(8,2) and (4,16)/(4,7) tube where outer tubes are (2,17) and (4,16) and inner ones (8,2) and (4,7) are shown as typical results. Impurities are distributed on outer tubes. Qualitative features of the conductance are independent of the tube structure and impurity parameters.

Figure 2 shows length dependence of conductance of (2,17)/(8,2) tube in the absence of impurities. Circles are conductance for tubes with sharp tube edges de-

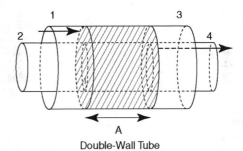

FIGURE 1. Schematic illustration of a four-terminal double-wall tube. Arrows indicate a current for which the conductance is calculated.

noted by $\Delta/a = 0$ with a being the lattice constant for which inter-tube transfer suddenly appears or disappears at tube edges. First, we note that the conductance is much smaller than the conductance quantum $e^2/\pi\hbar$. For such sharp edges, the conductance drastically changes with slight change of the length. Its average and fluctuation which are not shown here are independent of the length. In order to demonstrate roles of sharp boundaries, inter-tube transfer near edges is gradually increased or decreased in a range Δ. A result for $\Delta/a = 1.5$ is denoted by squares in Fig. 2. The conductance is reduced by several order-of-magnitude keeping the qualitative feature unchanged.

This behavior can be understood as follows [10]. The phase of the wave function at K and K' points jumps by an amount $\pm 2\pi/3$ when the position changes by a primitive lattice vector. Because of this rapid phase jump and the quasi-periodic nature due to the incommensurate lattice structure, almost all inter-tube transfers cancel out and remain nonzero only because of an incomplete cancellation due to the presence of sharp edges. The situation is analogous to a series of numbers with alternating

CP893, *Physics of Semiconductors, 28th International Conference*
edited by W. Jantsch and F. Schäffler
© 2007 American Institute of Physics 978-0-7354-0397-0/07/$23.00

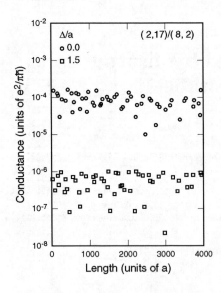

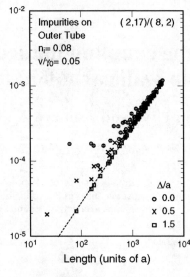

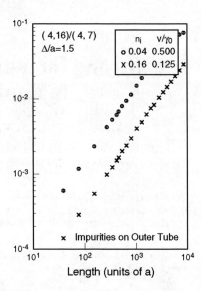

FIGURE 2. Length dependence of inter-tube conductance for a (2,17)/(8,2) tube without impurities.

FIGURE 3. Length dependence of the conductance for a (2,17)/(8,2) tube with impurities of $n_i = 0.08$ and $v/\gamma_0 = 0.05$ on the outer tube. A dotted line is the conductance for sufficiently large Δ.

FIGURE 4. Length dependence of the conductance for a (4,16)/(4,7) tube with $\Delta/a = 1.5$. Circles are a result for $n_i = 0.04$ and $v/\gamma_0 = 0.5$ and crosses for $n_i = 0.16$ and $v/\gamma_0 = 0.125$.

signature with an equal absolute value $(+1, -1, +1, \cdots,$ for example). When the number of terms in the summation increases, such a series does not converge but oscillates with an average and fluctuation independent of the number of the terms.

Figure 3 shows the length dependence of ensemble average of conductance for the same tube with impurities. Results for three edges, i.e., $\Delta/a = 0$, 0.5, and 1.5 are shown by circles, crosses, and squares, respectively. For sharp edges, the conductance oscillates around $10^{-4} e^2/\pi\hbar$ in nanotubes with length $A/a < 10^3$ similar to the case in the absence of impurities in Fig. 2, and starts to increase almost linearly with length for $A/a \approx 10^3$. As edges are smoothed, the conductance for $A/a < 10^3$ is reduced but that for $A/a > 10^3$ remains almost the same. It converges to a linear dependence shown by a dotted line for sufficiently large Δ. This conductance arises from inter-tube transfer induced by impurities in the bulk region of the double-wall nanotube.

Figure 4 shows the length dependence of averaged conductance for (4,16)/(4,7) tube with smooth edges for two kinds of impurities. Qualitative feature is same as that of the previous case. The two results collapse into a single line when the tube length A/a is measured in units of a dimensionless quantity $[n_i(v/\gamma_0)^2]^{-1}$ characterizing the effective strength of scattering as expected. Preliminary results for long nanotubes show that the inter-tube conductance becomes maximum when the length exceeds the mean free path.

This work was supported in part by a 21st Century COE Program at Tokyo Tech "Nanometer-Scale Quantum Physics" and by Grant-in-Aid for Scientific Research from the Ministry of Education, Culture, Sports, Science and Technology, Japan.

REFERENCES

1. M. Kociak, K. Suenaga, K. Hirahara, Y. Saito, T. Nakahira, and S. Iijima, Phys. Rev. Lett. **89**, 155501 (2002).
2. J. M. Zuo, I. Vartanyants, M. Gao, R. Zhang, and L. A. Nagahara, Science **300**, 1419 (2003).
3. S. Bandow, M. Takizawa, K. Hirahara, M. Yudasaka, and S. Iijima, Chem. Phys. Lett. **337**, 48 (2001).
4. A. Urbina, I. Echeverría, A. Pérez-Garrido, A. Díaz-Sánchez, and J. Abellán, Phys. Rev. Lett. **90**, 106603 (2003).
5. L. Langer, V. Bayot, E. Grivei, J. -P. Issi, J. P. Heremans, C. H. Olk, L. Stockman, C. Van Haesendonck, and Y. Bruynseraede, Phys. Rev. Lett. **76**, 479 (1996).
6. A. Bachtold, C. Strunk, J. P. Salvetat, J. M. Bonard, L. Forro, T. Nussbaumer, and C. Schönenberger, Nature (London) **397**, 673 (1999).
7. J. Cumings and A. Zettl, Phys. Rev. Lett. **93**, 086801 (2004).
8. B. Bourlon, C. Miko, L. Forró, D.C. Glattli, and A. Bachtold, Phys. Rev. Lett. **93**, 176806 (2004).
9. Y. -G. Yoon, P. Delaney, and S. G. Louie, Phys. Rev. B **66**, 073407 (2002).
10. S. Uryu and T. Ando, Phys. Rev. B **72**, 245403 (2005).
11. F. Triozon, S. Roche, A. Rubio, and D. Mayou, Phys. Rev. B, 69, 121410(R) (2004).

Strain-induced localization in metallic carbon nanotubes

Norifumi Yonezawa and Hidekatsu Suzuura

Division of Applied Physics, Graduate School of Engineering, Hokkaido University, Sapporo 060-8628, Japan

Abstract. We have calculated the conductance of finite-length carbon nanotubes with randomly distributed long-range impurities under external strain. Without strain, the backward scattering is quite suppressed, but the non-zero strain turns the system into a usual random one-dimensional system, where the Anderson localization takes place.

Keywords: carbon nanotube, band gap, conductance, localization, strain
PACS: 73.63.Fg, 73.22.-f

INTRODUCTION

Electronic states in carbon nanotubes (CNs) are described by massless Dirac particles giving their unusual transport properties[1]. The complete suppression of backward scattering is one of the most prominent features in metallic CNs[2, 3]. Electron-lattice interaction is also unique in this system. For instance, we can modify the electronic states by uniform external strain. That is, twisting or stretching deformation generates the energy gap in metallic CNs or changes the gap in semiconducting ones[4, 5]. Recently, there are several experimental reports on the transport measurement in stretched CNs and the result is consistent with the theoretical prediction for the modification of the gap[6]. In this paper, we have theoretically studied electronic transport in metallic CNs containing many scatterers under external strain.

MODEL

Consider finite-length metallic CNs containing many long-range impurities giving little inter-valley scattering[1, 2] and introduce external strain generating the energy gap. As a matter of course, the conductance is suppressed when the Fermi energy stays in the induced gap. In this study, we assume that the Fermi energy is shifted apart from the crossing point of the two linear bands described by massless Dirac particles so that the strain apparently causes only a small change to the dispersion around the shifted Fermi energy.

We have made intensive calculations of the conductance of stretched metallic zigzag CNs to clarify the dependence on the magnitude of strain as well as that on the carrier density. The conductance is calculated with the recursive Green's function method based on the Landauer-Buttiker formula and the configuration average is taken over about 1000 samples for each data point. Throughout following calculations, we use a (21,0) CN

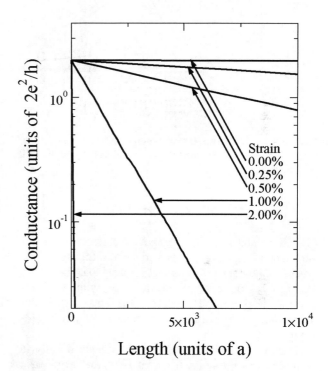

FIGURE 1. The tube length dependence of a stretched metallic zigzag CN. The unit of length is a lattice constant a. The c% strain shows that the tube length A becomes $(1 + c/100)A$ as a result from the streching deformation.

and take the geometric mean of calculated conductances.

Electronic states are given by the simplest tight-binding model with only one parameter: a hopping integral between nearest-neighbor sites. The strain is taken into account through the modification of the hopping integral due to the lattice distortion under uniform strain. The coupling constant between electrons and lattice strain is now adopted so that the energy gap (shift) which is induced by the strain causing one percent extension grows up to 4.8 percents of the energy gap between the Fermi point and the bottom of the next subband[5].

CP893, *Physics of Semiconductors, 28th International Conference*
edited by W. Jantsch and F. Schäffler
© 2007 American Institute of Physics 978-0-7354-0397-0/07/$23.00

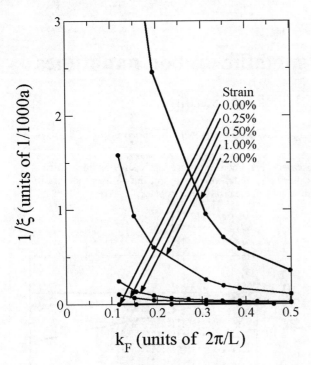

FIGURE 2. The inverse localization length, $1/\xi$, as a function of the Fermi wave number, k_F. Closed dots show the calculated data.

NUMERICAL RESULTS

FIGURE 1 shows the tube-length dependence of the averaged conductance of a stretched metallic zigzag CN for several magnitudes of strain. It is clear that the lattice strain makes the conductance decrease, while the conductance is almost independent of the tube length under no strain regardless of many scatterers taken into consideration.

Here, it should be noted that the charge density is constant while the strain increases. Here, the Fermi wave number, k_F, was fixed to be $0.32 \times 2\pi/L$ with L the circumference length. Apparently, the induced gap is so small that the strain hardly affected the dispersion relation except around the crossing point. However, the strain causes slight modification of wavefunctions so as to break the destructive interference which suppresses the impurity scattering. In normal one-dimensional (1D) systems, Anderson localization takes place no matter how weak the impurity scattering is. This is the reason why the weak modification of electronic states due to external strain can give rise to the significant decrease of the conductance.

The averaged conductance clearly shows exponential decay as the tube length increases as

$$G = G_0 \exp(-A/\xi) \qquad (1)$$

where G_0 is a constant with the dimension of the conductance and A denotes the tube length. The effects of strain exists in ξ which is called the localization length. Namely, we can see from Fig.1 that ξ decreases as the strain increases.

FIGURE 2 shows the inverse localization length for various strains as a function of the Fermi wave number, k_F, which is proportional to the charge density. In 1D systems, the localization length is of the same order of the mean free path. So, we can think of what this figure shows as the inverse of conductivity, or resistivity of the CN in the diffusive regime.

The Drude conductivity for a 1D metal with a certain effective mass gives a simple explanation for the results. The conductivity increases as the charge density does. In contrast, the enhanced effective mass due to the strain reduces the conductivity. Therefore, a metallic CN with strain-induced energy gap behaves as a usual quantum wire, while the conductivity is sensitive to the external strain because the effective-mass purely originates from it.

For larger k_F (or charge density), we have to consider the mixing between subbands caused by the level broadening due to the impurity scattering even when there exists only one conducting channel at the Fermi energy. In that case, the strain dependence of conductances shows so complicated behavior that we will discuss the results elsewhere.

CONCLUSIONS

In conclusion, we have studied the impurity scattering in metallic CNS under external strain. Without strain, the impurity scattering is quite suppressed, leading to the conductance quantization. The strain inducing the energy gap drastically changes the situation, where the metallic CNs becomes a usual dirty one-dimensional quantum wire. It is worth noting that the conductivity is sensitive to the strain because the massless Dirac particles purely acquire the effective mass from the external strain.

This work was supported in part by Grant-in-Aid for Young Scientists(B) 17710184 from The Ministry of Education, Culture, Sports, Science and Technology in Japan.

REFERENCES

1. T. Ando, *J. Phys. Soc. Jpn.* **74**, 777 (2005).
2. T. Ando and T. Nakanishi, *J. Phys. Soc. Jpn.* **67**, 1704 (1998).
3. P.L. McEuen et al., *Phys. Rev. Lett.* **83**, 5098 (1999).
4. L. Yang et al., *Phys. Rev. B* **60**, 13874 (1999).
5. H. Suzuura and T. Ando, *Phys. Rev. B* **65**, 235412 (2002).
6. E.D. Minot et al., *Phys. Rev. Lett.* **90**, 156401 (2003).

Fabrication and transport property of artificial structure of CNTs using SPM nano-manipulation

K. Maejima, M. Kida, Y. Yaguchi, K. Sudo, T. Kawamura, T. Morimoto, N. Aoki, and Y. Ochiai

Department of Electronics and Mechanical Engineering, Chiba University, 1-33 Yayoi-cho, Inage-ku, Chiba 263-8522, Japan

Abstract. We have established a novel manipulation technique using a glass-micro capillary under a high-resolution CCD microscope so far. Two isolated multi-wall carbon nanotubes (MWNTs) are settled to form a well-aligned cross structure. Recently, we have tried to develop a fine manipulation system using a scanning probe microscope with a silicon cantilever. Therefore, thinner high-quality MWNTs (~10 nm in diameter) can be utilized in this system. At the junction, we have observed weak localization and Fano-like-effect, zero bias anomaly whose traces were visible even at room temperature with thick MWNTs (~100 nm in diameter). On the other hand, with thinner high-quality MWNTs (~10 nm in diameter), we have observed also anomalous I-V characteristic and Altshuler-Aronov-Spivak-like magneto-oscillations at low temperature in the nano-space transport.

Keywords Junction; Multiwall carbon nanotube; Weak localization; Manipulation; Fano-effect; Altshuler-Aronov-Spivak
PACS: 73.23.-b, 73.63.Fg, 75.75.+a, 85.35.Kt,

INTRODUCTION

In future nanoscale circuits, carbon nanotube (CNT) are expected to be one of the candidates for a wiring material because of the high conductivity and the high current density, and for a channel material of a field effect transistor because of the high mobility due to the ballistic transport. In order to realize such CNT devices, a study of the transport property at the junction of CNT must be very important not only to know the contact characteristic but also make clear physics of the transport between the CNTs. Moreover, if a peculiar quantum effect was observed at the nano-space of the junctions, it would be applicable for quantum devices operated even at room temperature. So far, we have established a novel manipulation technique using a glass-micro capillary under a high-resolution CCD microscope and two isolated multi-wall carbon nanotube (MWNT) are settled to form a well-aligned crossing structure. At the junction, we have observed weak localization [1] and Fano-like-effect, zero bias anomaly [2,3]. In this study, we have tried to develop a fine manipulation system using a scanning probe microscope (SPM) with a silicon cantilever. Therefore thinner high-quality MWNT (~10 nm in diameter) can be utilized in this system. Artificial structures such a loop of a single MWNT

and a cross-junction combined two MWNT have been skillfully fabricated and measured

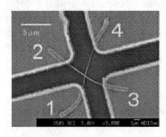

FIGURE 1. A scanning electron micrograph of the crossroads sample with thick MWNTs.

EXPERIMENTS

We have established manipulating the system under a high resolution CCD microscope. Two isolated MWNT were settled to form a well-aligned cross-structure. Thick MWNT (~100 nm in diameter) were necessary to be used in the fabrication method because it was performed under the optical CCD microscope. Recently, we have tried to develop a fine manipulation system using SPM with a silicon cantilever. In order to achieve nano-scale alignment, three-dimensional closed-feedback loop is installed in the scanner of the SPM. Therefore, thinner high-quality MWNT (~10 nm in diameter) can be utilized in this system. Artificial

CP893, *Physics of Semiconductors, 28th International Conference*
edited by W. Jantsch and F. Schäffler
© 2007 American Institute of Physics 978-0-7354-0397-0/07/$23.00

structures such a loop of a single MWNT and a cross-junction combined two MWNT have been skillfully fabricated. Electrical contacts were made by a lithography method and lift-off process with the depositing of Ti and Au shown in Fig. 1. In order to reduce the contact resistance between the MWNT and the metal pads, the sample was subjected to rapid thermal annealing at 600°C for 30 s. We named 2-terminal (2-t) resistance measurement of individual MWNT using electrodes 1-4 and 2-3 for straight resistance (SR). As for other 2-t resistance measurements at the junction using electrodes 1-2, 1-3, 2-4 and 3-4, we also named curve resistance (CR). As for 4-t resistance measurement at the junction using staggered current flow is named for junction resistance (JR). JR must be measuring resistance at the just contacting nano-space.

RESULTS AND DISCUSSIONS

With thick MWNT, we have observed weak localization in all SR, CR and JR at 0.4K. And also, Fano-like-effect, zero bias anomaly, was observed in CR and JR whose anomaly were visible even at room temperature shown in Fig. 2 [4]. These were appeared only in conduction path including junction. Therefore, we thought such an anomaly to be occurred at the nano-space of the junction. On the other hand, at 5K, we have observed Altshuler-Aronov-Spivak (AAS)-like magneto-oscillations in CR at thinner MWNT manipulated by SPM shown in Fig. 3. We can estimate coherent area, S, from relation $\Delta B' S \cong h/2e$, then, $S \cong 600$ nm^2, which almost corresponds to the cross-section of MWNTs. Therefore, we assumed that the quantum interference would be occurred at the nano-space. Furthermore, we have observed a similar magneto-oscillation in the case of the junction in the loop structure of thinner MWNT.

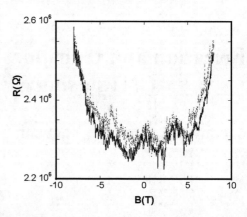

FIGURE 3. In $B(T)$ magneto-resistance at thinner MWNTs, a periodical peak, $1/\Delta B' = 0.3$, is observed in back and forth sweeps.

SUMMARY

We have fabricated cross-junction device of MWNT by glass capillary manipulation and investigated the transport at nano-space of junction between two thick MWNTs. At the junction, we have observed weak localization and Fano-like-effect (zero bias anomaly). In order to utilize thinner high-quality MWNT, we have tried to develop a fine manipulation system using SPM with a silicon cantilever. We also fabricated cross-junction and loop structure devices with thinner MWNT. In the transport at the nano-space, we have observed another anomalous I-V characteristic and AAS-like magneto-oscillation at low temperature. Also, we can determine the coherent area based on the quantum interference of electron-waves.

ACKNOWLEDGMENTS

This work was supported in part by a Grant-in-Aid for Scientific Research from the Japan Society for the Promotion of Science (16656007 & 16206001).

REFERENCES

1. T. Mihara, K. Miyamoto, M. Kida, T. Sasaki, N. Aoki, and Y. Ochiai, Superlattices and Microstructures **34** 383 (2003).
2. J.Kim, J.R. Kim, J.O. Lee, J.W. Park, H. M. So, N. Kim, K. Kang, K.H. Yoo, and J.J. Kim, Phys.Rev.Lett. **90** 166403 (2003)
3. U. Fano, Phys. Rev. **124** 1866 (1961)
4. M. Kida, S. Harada, T. Mihara, T. Morimoto, T. Sasaki, N.Aoki, and Y. Ochiai, AIP Conference Proceedings **772** 1035 (2005)

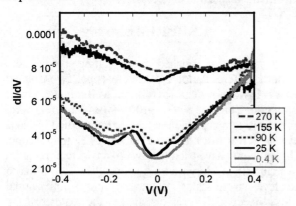

FIGURE 2. The differential conductance dI/dV–V in JR with thick MWNTs. Fano-like-effect, zero bias anomaly, was observed whose traces were visible even at room temperature.

Carbon Nanotube Based Transistors:
A Computational Study

M. Pourfath, H. Kosina, and S. Selberherr

Institute for Microelectronics, TU Wien, Gußhausstraße 27–29, 1040 Wien, Austria
{pourfath\kosina\selberherr}@iue.tuwien.ac.at

Abstract. In this work the non-equilibrium Green's function formalism is used to study the role of the electron-phonon interaction on carbon nanotube based transistors. Electron-phonon interaction parameters depend on the chirality and the diameter of the nanotube. The device response is studied for a wide range of electron-phonon interaction parameters. Results indicate the importance of the effect of phonon absorption on the device characteristics.

Keywords: Carbon nanotube transistors, Non equilibrium Green's function formalism, Electron-phonon interaction
PACS: 61.46.Fg, 85.35.Kt, 63.20.Kr

INTRODUCTION

Carbon nanotube (CNT) based transistors have been studied in recent years as potential alternatives to CMOS devices because of their capability of near ballistic transport [1]. In this work the non-equilibrium Green's function (NEGF) formalism is used to investigate the effect of the electron-phonon interaction parameters on the ballisticity of CNT based transistors. It is explained, why both ballistic and diffusive carrier transport in CNTs have been observed.

THEORY

The NEGF formalism applied to CNTs is discussed in [2]. The total self-energy is due to the coupling of the device to the source contact, drain contact, and electron-phonon interaction, $\Sigma = \Sigma_s + \Sigma_d + \Sigma_{e-ph}$. The self-energy due to electron-phonon interaction comprises contributions of elastic and inelastic scattering mechanisms $\Sigma_{e-ph}^{<,>} = \Sigma_{el}^{<,>} + \Sigma_{inel}^{<,>}$. Assuming local scattering ($\Sigma_{\mathbf{r},\mathbf{r}'} = 0$ for $\mathbf{r} \neq \mathbf{r}'$) the self-energies due to electron-phonon interaction for a single sub-band are given by:

$$\Sigma_{el,(\mathbf{r},\mathbf{r})}^{<,>}(E) = D_{el} G_{\mathbf{r},\mathbf{r}}^{<,>}(E) \qquad (1)$$

$$\Sigma_{inel,(\mathbf{r},\mathbf{r})}^{<}(E) = \sum_v D_{inel}^v$$
$$\times [(n_B(\hbar\omega_v)+1)G_{\mathbf{r},\mathbf{r}}^{<}(E+\hbar\omega_v) \qquad (2)$$
$$+ n_B(\hbar\omega_v)G_{\mathbf{r},\mathbf{r}}^{<}(E-\hbar\omega_v)]$$

$$\Im m[\Sigma_{e-ph,(\mathbf{r},\mathbf{r})}^{R}(E)] = \frac{1}{2i}[\Sigma_{e-ph,(\mathbf{r},\mathbf{r})}^{>} - \Sigma_{e-ph,(\mathbf{r},\mathbf{r})}^{<}] \qquad (3)$$

where v is the phonon mode. $\Sigma_{inel}^{>}$ is calculated similar to (2) [2]. The first term in (3) is due to phonon emission

and the second term due to phonon absorption. Assuming thermal equilibrium for phonons, their occupation number is given by the Bose-Einstein distribution function:

$$n_B(\hbar\omega_v) = \frac{1}{\exp(\hbar\omega_v/k_B T)-1} \qquad (4)$$

THE EFFECT OF ELECTRON-PHONON INTERACTION PARAMETERS

To compare the effect of different scattering mechanisms, we define the ballisticity as the ratio of the current in the presence of electron-phonon interaction to the current in the ballistic case (I_{Sc}/I_{Bl}).

With increasing coupling coefficients (D_v) the self-energies, (1) to (3), increase which adds dissipation to the Hamiltonian and decreases the total current. Fig. 1-a shows the ballisticity as a function of D_v. Elastic scattering conserves the energy of carriers, but decreases the current due to elastic back-scattering. On the other hand, with inelastic scattering the energy of carriers is not conserved. Carriers acquiring enough kinetic energy can emit phonons and scatter into lower energy states.

With the increase of phonon energy (ω_v) scattered carriers lose more kinetic energy and the probability for back-scattering decreases, such that the current is less reduced. As ω_v decreases the phonon occupation number increases (4), as a result the contribution due to phonon absorption (the second term in (3)) increases. In this case carriers gain kinetic energy and the probability of back-scattering increases. As a consequence, the ballisticity decreases, see Fig. 1-b. For a better comparison, Fig. 1-c shows regions of ballistic and diffusive transport for inelastic scattering. These results are for a device of 50 nm length. Ballisticity is inversely proportional to the device length [3].

CP893, *Physics of Semiconductors, 28th International Conference*
edited by W. Jantsch and F. Schäffler
© 2007 American Institute of Physics 978-0-7354-0397-0/07/$23.00

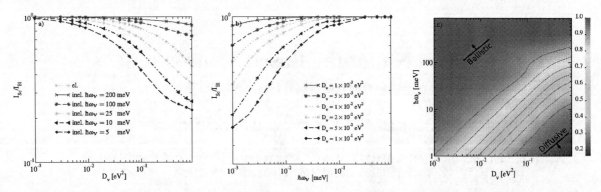

FIGURE 1. a) The ballisticity versus the strength of electron-phonon coupling for a CNT of 50 nm length. The ballisticity is defined as the ratio of the current in the presence of electron-phonon interaction to the current in the ballistic case I_{Sc}/I_{Bl}. b) The ballisticity versus the phonon energy. c) Ballisticity versus both the strength of electron-phonon coupling and phonon energy.

DISCUSSIONS

In general electron-phonon interaction parameters depend on the diameter and the chirality of the CNT. The calculation of these parameters is presented in [4]. We limit our study to semiconducting CNTs with diameters in the range of $d_{CNT} = 1 - 2$ nm corresponding to a band gap in the range of $E_g = 0.8 - 0.4$ eV, which is suitable for nanoelectronic applications.

In CNTs elastic scattering is caused by acoustic phonons (AP) and inelastic scattering by zone boundary (ZB), optical (OP), and radial breathing (RBM) phonon modes. Considering the parameter range discussed above, the energies of the these phonon modes are $\hbar\omega_{ZB} \approx 160$ and 180 meV, $\hbar\omega_{OP} \approx 200$ meV, and $\hbar\omega_{RBM} \approx 30$ meV [5]. The corresponding coupling coefficients are $D_{inel}^{ZB} \approx 10^{-4}$ and 50×10^{-3} eV^2, $D_{inel}^{OP} \approx 40 \times 10^{-3}$ eV^2, and $D_{inel}^{RBM} \approx 10^{-3}$ eV^2 [6]. As discussed in the previous section high energy phonons, such as OP and ZB phonon modes, degrade the performance only weakly, whereas the RBM phonon mode can have a detrimental effect. However, due to weak electron-phonon coupling the RBM mode has a negligible effect at room temperature. The electron-phonon coupling is also weak for AP modes ($D_{el}^{AP} < 10^{-3}$ eV^2), which implies weak elastic backscattering of carriers. Therefore, CNT based transistors can operate close to the ballistic limit [1]. However, increasing the applied voltage increases phonon generation rate. If this rate becomes greater than the rate at which they can be thermalized, the assumption of equilibrium phonons (4) does not hold any longer [7]. For an accurate analysis coupled electron and phonon transport equations should be solved. Reference [8] has shown that, phonon occupation number can increase considerably, especially close to the contacts. The increase of phonon occupation number increases the phonon absorption rate (3). As a result, at high biases (> 0.2 V) ballisticity can reduce considerably.

CONCLUSIONS

Based on the NEGF formalism we investigated the effect of electron-phonon interaction parameters on the performance of CNT based transistors. For elastic scattering, the electron-phonon coupling strength plays an important role. For inelastic scattering not only the coupling strength, but also the phonon energy is an important factor. In CNTs either the electron-phonon coupling is weak or the phonon energies are high. Therefore, CNT based transistors have the potential to operate close to the ballistic limit. However, at high biases phonon occupation number increases above its equilibrium value. In this case, the phonon absorption rate increases, and ballisticity decreases. As a result, short CNT based transistors at low biases can operate close to the ballistic limit.

ACKNOWLEDGMENTS

This work has been partly supported by the Austrian Science Fund, contract I79-N16.

REFERENCES

1. A. Javey, J. Guo, D. Farmer, Q. Wang, E. Yenilmez, R. Gordon, M. Lundstrom, and H. Dai, *Nano Lett.* **4**, 1319–1322 (2004).
2. A. Svizhenko, and M. Anantram, *Phys.Rev.B* **72**, 085430–085440 (2005).
3. M. Lundstrom, *IEEE Electron Device Lett.* **18**, 361–363 (1997).
4. G. Mahan, *Phys.Rev.B* **68**, 125409 (2003).
5. J. Park, S. Rosenblatt, Y. Yaish, V. Sazonova, H. Ustunel, S. Braig, T. Arias, P. Brouwer, and P. McEuen, *Nano Lett.* **4**, 517–520 (2004).
6. S. Koswatta, S. Hasan, M. Lundstrom, M. Anantram, and D. Nikonov, *cond-mat/0511723* (2005).
7. M. Lazzeri, S. Piscanec, F. Mauri, A. Ferrari, and J. Robertson, *Phys.Rev.Lett.* **95**, 236802 (2005).
8. M. Lazzeri, and F. Mauri, *Phys.Rev.B* **74**, 165419 (2006).

Terahertz electrical and optical properties of doublewalled carbon nanotubes

Inhee Maeng, Chul Kang, Seung Jae Oh, Ui Whan Kim, and Joo-Hiuk Son

Department of Physics
University of Seoul, Seoul 130-743, Korea

Abstract. The electrical and optical properties of double-walled carbon nanotubes (DWNTs) were measured utilizing terahertz time-domain spectroscopy (THz-TDS), and were compared with those of single-walled carbon nanotubes (SWNTs). The conductivity of DWNTs was consequently observed as being smaller than that of SWNTs. The plasma frequency, damping rate, etc. were obtained through Bruggman effective medium approximation.

Keywords: doublewalled carbon nanotubes, terahertz, Bruggman effective medium approximation.
PACS: 78.20.Ci

INTRODUCTION

Since the discovery of carbon nanotubes (CNTs), researchers have been inspired by their unique structures and properties [1]. They have long and hollow cylindrical structures, and have good mechanical and electrical properties. Moreover, their characteristics have numerous application potentials for field emission displays, AFM/STM tips, nano-electronics, fuel cells, and secondary batteries [2]. They have been classified according to their shell structure, as single-walled and multi-walled carbon nanotubes, and there are differences between their physical and electrical characteristics [2]. The optimized properties of both kinds of carbon nanotubes have advantages for many applications. To be able to utilize their intermediate properties, DWNTs were studied recently [3].

In general, the electrical properties of CNTs can be obtained using I-V techniques. A study of CNTs' AC electrical properties, however, is required to apply them to high-speed electronics. Terahertz time-domain spectroscopy (THz-TDS) is a good method for studying CNTs' frequency-dependent electrical properties because it has a good signal-to-noise ratio (over 5000:1) and it directly yields the magnitude and phase information of signals [4]. Besides these advantages, the transport parameters of semiconductors are easily extracted by because they reside in the THz region.

In this paper, the electrical and optical properties of DWNTs were studied and compared with those of SWNTs using THz-TDS in the 0.2- to 2.3-THz range. The experimental results were fitted using Bruggman effective medium approximation (BEMA) [5]. Through BEMA, the transport parameters, such as the CNTs' plasma frequency and damping rate, were obtained.

EXPERIMENT

For the measurement of CNTs, the general photoconductive THz-TDS was used [4]. The samples were located between the paraboloidal mirrors, and they were held on an 8-mm pinhole. To eliminate water vapor absorption during the experiment, the THz-TDS system was covered in an airtight acrylic box, and dry air was blown to keep the humidity below 6%.

For the experiment, DWNT and SWNT powders were prepared. The CNTs bundled easily but hardly turned into pellets. As such, the CNT powder was mixed with the KBr powder because KBr had good transparency and a good homogenous index of refraction in the far-infrared region. The total weight of the mixtures was 0.1 g; with the CNT powders, they weigh 0.5 wt% and 1 wt%, respectively. Both samples were pressed with 3000 psi for 10 minutes, by compressor. The samples had a diameter of 0.9 cm and a thickness of 0.6 mm.

CP893, *Physics of Semiconductors, 28th International Conference*
edited by W. Jantsch and F. Schäffler
© 2007 American Institute of Physics 978-0-7354-0397-0/07/$23.00

TABLE 1. The fitting parameters of the Bruggman effective medium approximation

		f	$\omega_p/2\pi$	$\Gamma/2\pi$	$\omega_{p,j}/2\pi$	$\omega_j/2\pi$	$\Gamma_j/2\pi$	ε_∞
Doublewalled CNTs	0.5 wt%	4.1	10.5	24.3	32.2	5.5	23.3	2.4^2
	1.0 wt%	10.5						
Singlewalled CNTs	0.5 wt%	5.6	23.0	24.5	38.9	5.9	29.6	2.9^2
	1.0 wt%	9.1						

NOTE : N : geometrical factor,   f : filling factor (volume), ε_∞ : Dielectric constant of infinity; ω_p : plasma frequency,

Γ : damping rate, $\omega_{p,j}$: oscillator strength of the Lorentz oscillator, ω_j : phonon frequency, Γ_j : spectral width.

RESULTS AND DISCUSSION

The power absorption and the real conductivity of DWNTs, SWNTs, and KBr are shown in Fig. 1. The power absorption and the real conductivities of DWNT composites are smaller than those of SWNT composites. Therefore, the carrier density of DWNT is smaller than that of SWNT because conductivity is dependent on carrier density.

To extract the carrier transport parameters from the experimental results, BEMA fits were utilized [4]. BEMA is a good analytical model to describe the composite system, which is made up of either metallic or semiconducting particles dispersed in the insulating host. The dielectric function of CNT is regarded as a combination of the Drude and Lorentz harmonic oscillator models because CNTs consist of semiconductors and metals.

Fits are shown in Fig. 1, and the fitting parameters in Table 1. In Fig. 1, the fitting lines coincide with the experimental data. As shown in Table 1, the filling factors are different, almost twice both samples, though the other parameters do not change. The plasma frequency of DWNTs is 10.5 THz, less than half of the plasma frequency of SWNTs (23.0 THz), because plasma frequency depends on the square root of carrier density, which can explain the lower conductivity of DWNTs compared to that of SWNTs.

In conclusion, the electrical and optical properties of DWNTs were measured within the 0.2-2.3 THz range using THz-TDS. The power absorption and real conductivity of DWNT were observed to be smaller than those of SWNT. By fitting the experimental results those of BEMA, the plasma frequency and damping rate were obtained, and it was confirmed that DWNTs have lower conductivity.

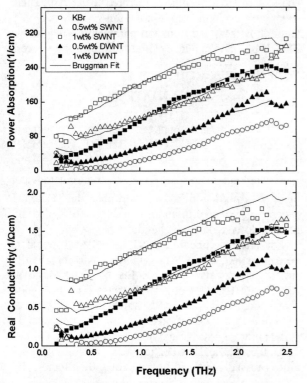

FIGURE 1. The power absorption and real conductivity with the fitted data, using Bruggman effective medium approximation (BEMA).

REFERENCES

1. S. Iijima, *Nature (London)* **354**, 56 (1991)
2. M. S. Dresselhaus, G. Dresselhaus, Ph. Avouris, in *carbon nanotubes systhesis, structure and applications*, Springer (2000).
3. T. Sugai, H. Yoshida, T. Shimada, T. Okazaki, S. Bandow and H. Shinohara, *Nano Letts* **3**, 769 (2003)
4. C. Kang, I-. H. Maeng, S. -J. Oh, J. -H. Son, T. -I. Jeon, K. H. An, S.C. Lim, Y. H. Lee, *Appl. Phys. Letts* **87**, 41908 (2005).
5. A. Ugawa, A. G. Rinzler, and D. B. Tanner, *Phys.Rev. B* **61**, R5129 (1994).

Phonon-drag thermopower of a ballistic semiconducting single-wall carbon nanotube

M. Tsaousidou and K. Papagelis

Materials Science Department, School of Natural Sciences, University of Patras, Patras 265 04, Greece

Abstract. We calculate the phonon-drag thermopower, S^g, in a 'collision free' semiconducting single-wall carbon nanotube with the two ends attached to two electron reservoirs. In the presence of a small voltage difference ΔV between the reservoirs we calculate the produced phonon heat flux, Q, along the axis of the nanotube. Then, S^g is simply obtained from the ratio $Q/\Delta V$ by making use of the Onsager relation. Numerical calculations of S^g as a function of temperature for various values of the Fermi level in the reservoirs are presented.

Keywords: Carbon nanotubes, thermoelectric properties, ballistic transport, electron-phonon coupling
PACS: 73.63.Fg, 73.23.Ad, 72.20.Pa, 63.22.+m

In the last few years, the electron transport properties of carbon nanotubes have received remarkable experimental and theoretical interest. Recently, thermopower measurements on p-doped single-wall carbon nanotubes (SWCNTs) revealed the importance of the phonon-drag contribution, S^g, to the thermopower [1]. Scarola and Mahan have developed a model for the calculation of S^g within the semiclassical Boltzmann framework [2]. Experiments, however, give evidence that the low-field transport of short SWCNTs exhibits a ballistic character (see for example Ref. [3]). For this reason here we present a different theoretical approach for the calculation of S^g which can be applied in the ballistic regime. Our interest is restricted in semiconducting SWCNTs with length smaller than the electron mean free path related to electron-phonon scattering, l_{ep}. At low energies l_{ep} can be over a micron even at $T = 300$ K [4]. The elastic scattering due to defects is also negligible for nanotubes with length smaller than a micron [5].

The SWCNT is considered as an infinitesimally thin cylinder of radius R and his axis along the z-direction. The electrons are free to move along the z-direction while their motion in the plane perpendicular to the axis of the nanotube is quantized. The energy eigenvalues are $E_{nk} = \frac{\hbar^2 k^2}{2m^*} + E_n$ where k is the electron wave vector along the z-direction, n labels 1D orbital sub-bands of the SWCNT electronic structure and m^* is the effective mass.

We assume that the nanotube is an ideal waveguide connecting two electron reservoirs. Electrons can propagate in the channel n when their energy is larger than E_n. Here, we consider transmission through a single channel. The Fermi level, E_F, in the reservoirs lies between the first two sub-band minima. Moreover, E_F is assumed to be close to the ground sub-band minimum, E_1, so effects due to the non-parabolicity are ignored.

The lattice displacement at the point **r** is written as $\mathbf{u}(\mathbf{r}) = \eta_{mq}\exp(im\theta + iqz)$ [6] where η_{mq} is the polarization vector, θ is an angle along the nanotube circumference, q is the phonon wave vector along the z-direction, and $m = 0, \pm 1, \pm 2, ...$ specifies the phonon modes associated with the phonon wave vector along the circumference. It can be shown that when electrons are scattered in a single orbital sub-band only modes with $m = 0$ contribute to the electron-phonon (e-p) scattering. Three modes correspond to $m = 0$, the so-called twisting, stretching and breathing modes [6]. The e-p coupling is described via a deformation potential $V_d = D(u_{xx} + u_{zz})$ where D is the deformation potential constant, $x = R\theta$, and u_{xx}, u_{zz} are the diagonal components of the strain tensor. The nonzero curvature of the nanotube has been taken into account [6]. The twisting mode does not contribute to the e-p deformation potential coupling. We confine our interest in the long-wavelength region where $qR < 1$ and we ignore the breathing mode due to the absence of dispersion for low q. Thus, in what follows, we consider only the stretching phonon mode.

In equilibrium the reservoirs have the same temperature T and the same chemical potential $\mu = E_F$. The occupation probability of the incident waves is given by the Fermi-Dirac distribution function $f^0(E_{1k}) = \{\exp[(E_{1k} - E_F)/k_B T] + 1\}^{-1}$. The phonon distribution in equilibrium is $N^0(q) = [\exp(\hbar\omega_q/k_B T) - 1]^{-1}$, where $\hbar\omega_q$ is the energy of a phonon with wave vector q. We assume that the chemical potential in one of the reservoirs (e.g., the one on the left) is raised by $\Delta\mu$ resulting to a small voltage difference $\Delta V(= -\Delta\mu/|e|)$ across the nanotube. Then more electrons are injected into the nanotube from the left (with positive k) while the number of electrons injected from the right remains the same. The distribution function for electrons with positive k is $f^0(E_{1k}) + f^1(E_{1k})$ where $f^1(E_{1k}) = -\Delta\mu\frac{\partial f^0(E_{1k})}{\partial E_{1k}}$ [7, 8],

CP893, *Physics of Semiconductors, 28th International Conference*
edited by W. Jantsch and F. Schäffler
© 2007 American Institute of Physics 978-0-7354-0397-0/07/$23.00

while for electrons with $k < 0$ the distribution function is $f^0(E_{1k})$. Due to the electron net flux from the left to the right a part of the electron momentum is transferred to the 1D phonons through the e-p interaction. The produced phonon heat flux along the axis of the nanotube is

$$Q = \frac{1}{L_z} \sum_q \hbar \omega_q v_p N^1(q) \tag{1}$$

where L_z is the length of the nanotube, $v_p = v_s q / |q|$ is the phonon group velocity (v_s is the sound velocity for the stretching mode) and $N^1(q)$ is the first-order perturbation of the phonon distribution function. $N^1(q)$ is obtained from the steady-state Boltzmann equation for phonons when $\Delta T = 0$ [8]

$$N^1(q) = -\frac{2 l_p}{v_s k_B T} \Delta \mu \left\{ \sum_{k>0} \sum_{k'<0} \Gamma(k',k) - \sum_{k<0} \sum_{k'>0} \Gamma(k',k) \right\} \tag{2}$$

where l_p is the phonon mean free path limited by collisions with the boundaries and lattice imperfections and $\Gamma(k',k) = f^0(E_{1k})[1 - f^0(E_{1k'})] P_q^a(k,k')$. Here, $P_q^a(k,k')$ is the transition rate at which an electron in a state k is promoted to a state k' by absorbing one phonon with wave vector q. For 1D electrons that are coupled to 1D stretching phonons via a deformation potential coupling $P_q^a(k,k')$ is given by

$$\begin{aligned} P_q^a(k,k') &= \frac{D^2 (1-v)^2}{2 R \rho L_z v_s} |q| N^0(q) \\ &\times \delta(E_{1k'} - E_{1k} - \hbar \omega_q) \delta_{k',k+q} \end{aligned} \tag{3}$$

where ρ is the mass density (carbon mass per unit area) and $v = (B - \mu_s)/(B + \mu_s)$ where B and μ_s are the bulk modulus and the shear modulus for a graphite sheet.

Now, by using the standard relation $Q = -M^g \Delta \mu / |e|$ we readily obtain M^g. According to Onsager's symmetry relation the phonon-drag thermopower is

$$S^g = M^g / TG \tag{4}$$

where $G = 2e^2/h$ is the electron conductance for a single-channel.

In Fig. 1 we show numerical calculations of $-S^g$, obtained from Eqs. (1)-(4), in a nanotube of radius 1 nm as a function of T. The parameters we used for the calculations are: $m^* = 0.04 m_e$ [9], $l_p = 0.5 \ \mu m$, $D(1 - v) = 10$ eV, $\rho = 3.8 \times 10^{-7}$ Kgr/m^2 and $v_s = 19.9$ km/s [6]. We consider four different values of the Fermi level. The solid, dashed, dashed-dotted and dotted lines show the results for $E_F - E_1 = 70$, 80, 100 and 150 meV, respectively.

In the present work we have ignored screening effects. The incorporation of screening will reduce significantly the magnitude of S^g. For GaAs the screening of the

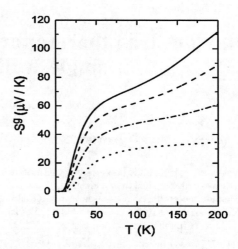

FIGURE 1. The calculated phonon-drag thermopower, $-S^g$, as a function of temperature in a ballistic semiconducting SWCNT of radius 1 nm. The solid line shows the results for $E_F - E_1 = 70$ meV; the dashed line for 80 meV; the dashed-dotted line for 100 meV and the dotted line for 150 meV.

coupling of 1D electrons with 3D phonons reduces the magnitude of S^g by a factor of 0.4 [10].

At low temperatures, assuming that $\hbar \omega_q$ is a small quantity compared to $E_F - E_1$, S^g is approximated by a simple expression according to which

$$S^g \propto \frac{1}{k_F R} \left(\frac{\hbar v_s 2 k_F}{k_B T} \right)^2 \exp \left(-\frac{\hbar v_s 2 k_F}{k_B T} \right), \tag{5}$$

where $k_F = \sqrt{2 m^* (E_F - E_1)} / \hbar$. Good agreement with the numerical results is found when $\hbar v_s k_F > 2 k_B T$ and $E_F - E_1 >> k_B T$.

In conclusion, we have described a theoretical model for the calculation of S^g in ballistic semiconducting SWCNTs. Numerical results of S^g as a function of T are presented for various values of the Fermi level.

REFERENCES

1. J. Vavro et al., *Phys. Rev. Lett.* **90**, 065503 (2003).
2. V. W. Scarola and G. D. Mahan, *Phys. Rev. B* **66**, 205405 (2002).
3. A. Javey et al., *Nature* **424**, 654 (2003).
4. V. Perebeinos et al., *Phys. Rev. Lett.* **94**, 086802 (2005).
5. D. Mann et al., *Nano Lett.* **3**, 1541 (2003).
6. H. Suzuura and T. Ando, *Phys. Rev. B* **65**, 235412 (2002).
7. P. N. Butcher, *J. Phys.:Condens. Matter* **2**, 4869 (1990).
8. M. Tsaousidou and P. N. Butcher *Phys. Rev. B* **56**, R10 044 (1997).
9. G. Pennington and N. Goldsman *Phys. Rev. B* **71**, 205318 (2005).
10. S. S. Kubakaddi and P. N. Butcher, *J. Phys.:Condens. Matter* **1**, 3939 (1989).

Band Structure Changes in Carbon Nanotubes Caused By MnTe₂ Crystal Encapsulation

Lain-Jong Li*, Tsung-Wu Lin†, J. Doig**, I. B. Mortimer**, J. G. Wiltshire**, R. A. Taylor**, J. Sloan†, M. L. H. Green† and R. J. Nicholas**

*School of Materials Science and Engineering, Nanyang Technological University, 639798, Singapore
†Inorganic Chemistry Labratory, University of Oxford, Parks Road, Oxford OX1 3QR, U.K.
**Clarendon Laboratory, Physics Department, Oxford University, Parks Road, Oxford OX1 3PU, U.K.

Abstract. Modification of the band structure of single-walled carbon nanotubes (SWNTs) through encapsulation of the inorganic material manganese ditelluride (MnTe₂) is reported. We show that this leads to a global reduction of their 1st (E_{11}^S) and 2nd (E_{22}^S) band gap energies by a similar percentage (up to 3.8%) and interpret this as due to a lowering of the carbon-carbon transfer integrals.

Keywords: nanotubes, crystal filling, photoluminescence
PACS: 81.05.Tp, 81.05.Ys

The encapsulation of molecules or crystals inside carbon nanotubes is opening up new routes for engineering the electronic properties of carbon nanotubes [1, 2, 3]. Recently we have shown that the encapsulation of cobaltocenes can induce a down-shift in the emission energy of semiconducting tubes due to the formation of localized impurity states below the conduction band [4]. These reports attribute the causes for band gap modulation to an effect of charge transfer or electronic doping. In addition, several experiments have been reported which adjust the band gap of SWNTs by environmental strain (AFM tip manipulation [5, 6], freezing in water [7], drying in polymer [7] and pressurizing the tubes [8]) or by applying a magnetic field [9, 10]. In this report, we show that by using an inorganic compound, MnTe₂, large densities of magnetic ions can be efficiently encapsulated into SWNTs and that these have a significant effect on the entire band structure of the tubes.

The SWNTs were synthesized using a standard catalytic arc process and directly used for filling [11]. SWNTs were mixed with the MnTe₂ compounds in a 1:1 volumetric ratio and heated to 835°C for six hours. The unfilled or crystal-encapsulated nanotubes were then dispersed in aqueous sodium N-lauroyl sarcosinate (Sarkosyl) or sodium dodecylbenzene sulphate (SDBS) suspensions. TEM imaging and Energy Dispersive X-ray (EDX) spectroscopies clearly demonstrated the presence of MnTe₂ crystals inside the nanotubes.

Figure 1 shows a PLE map for MnTe₂ filled arc-SWNTs with arrows clearly indicating a systematic series of diagonal shifts of the peak positions from unfilled tubes caused by MnTe₂-filling. The diagonal peak shifts observed in the PLE maps clearly demonstrate a quantum number q independent [7] red-shift for both E_{11}^S and E_{22}^S

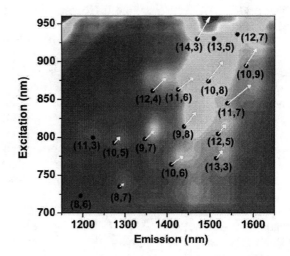

FIGURE 1. PLE map for unfilled (solid circles) and MnTe₂ filled (false color scale image) arc-SWNTs with a very high filling ratio dispersed using Sarkosyl. The arrows indicate the diagonal shifts of the peak positions for identified nanotubes with MnTe₂-filling.

energies. This tells us that the energy shift is unlikely to result from the effects of uniaxial or torsional strains [12] which are known to be strongly dependent on the chiral indices of the tubes and which affect the E_{11}^S and E_{22}^S transitions in the opposite sense due to the strain induced changes in symmetry.

Figure 2 shows selected Raman spectra for the MnTe₂ crystallites, unfilled arc and the MnTe₂-filled tubes. The peaks for MnTe₂ at 122 and 141 cm⁻¹ in Fig. 2a are from the crystalline elementary tellurium formed by decomposition of MnTe₂ due to laser exposure [13] and the weak

CP893, *Physics of Semiconductors, 28th International Conference*
edited by W. Jantsch and F. Schäffler
© 2007 American Institute of Physics 978-0-7354-0397-0/07/$23.00

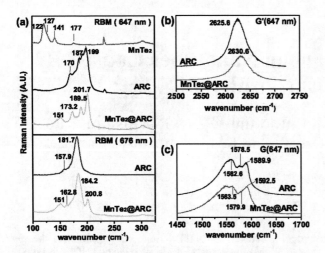

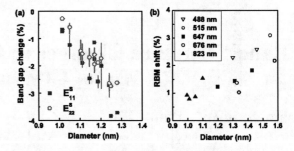

FIGURE 2. Selected Raman spectra for MnTe$_2$, unfilled tubes, and MnTe$_2$-filled tubes. (a) radial breathing modes (b) G'-bands and (c) G-bands.

FIGURE 3. (a) The proportional filling induced energy shifts from E_{11}^S and E_{22}^S of semiconducting SWNTs. (b) The frequency shift of Raman RBM with filling.

peaks at 127 and 177 cm^{-1} are the Te-Te stretching (Ag) and libration (Eg) modes of the MnTe$_2$ [13]. The filled tubes reveal a new broad peak at around 151 cm^{-1} which is characteristic of amorphous Te [14]. This suggests that the structure of MnTe$_2$ inside the tubes is less ordered than that in the original crystallite form. The second consequence of the filling is that the frequencies of the radial breathing modes (RBM) for the filled-tubes (160 - 200 cm^{-1}) in Fig. 2a show a significant up-shift (1-3%) and increase in resolution relative to that of their corresponding unfilled tubes. The graphitic G-modes (Fig. 2c), show a small upshift of order 2 cm^{-1} and the disordered bands (D and G' bands) show upshifts of 4-6 cm^{-1}. The shifts in the D and G' bands can be used to infer a C-C bond length decrease of of order 0.2-0.3% from $-\Delta a_{C-C}/a_{C-C} = \Delta\omega/\omega$, where a_{C-C} and ω represent the bond length and mode frequency [15].

Fig. 3 shows the proportional reduction in the energy gaps for E_{11}^S and E_{22}^S as a function of tube diameter, together with the proportional increase in the RBM frequencies. This shows that there is a threshold for filling in the region of 0.9-1.0 nm. Using the simplest tight binding (TB) model the gaps are related directly to the C-C transfer integral $|\gamma_0|$ as: $E_{11}^S = 2|\gamma_0|a_{C-C}/D$ and $E_{22}^S = 4|\gamma_0|a_{C-C}/D$, where D is the nanotube diameter. Any change in a_{C-C} (which the above discussion suggests is <0.3%) will be accompanied by a similar proportional change in D and to a first approximation will not result in any change in the band gaps. This therefore suggests that changes in γ_0 are the dominant factor responsible for the energy gap shifts.

We would expect that the small reduction in bond length would lead to an increase in the hopping integral γ_0 which is assumed [12, 16] to scale with bond length as

$\gamma_0' = \gamma_0(a_{C-C}/a_{C-C}')^2$ where γ_0' and a_{C-C}' are the hopping integral and bond distance of the strained graphene sheeting [16]. Therefore we conclude that the presence of the filling material produces a strong modification of the bonding orbitals rather than a simple bond distortion. The origin of the changes to the bonding orbitals must be related to the bonding between the tubes and the filling crystals, which increase proportionately as the quantity of material inside the tube increases.

REFERENCES

1. S. C. Tsang, Y. K. Chen, P. J. F. Harris and M. L. H. Green, Nature **372** 159 (1994)
2. B. W. Smith, M. Monthioux, and D. E. Luzzi, Nature **396**, 323-324 (1998)
3. J. Sloan, J. Hammer, M. Zweifka-Sibley and M. L. H. Green, Chem. Comm. **3**, 347(1998)
4. L. J. Li et al., Nature. Mat. **4**, 481 (2005)
5. E. D. Minot et al., Phys. Rev. Lett. **90**, 156401 (2004)
6. J. Cao, Q. Wang and H. Dai, Phys. Rev. Lett. **90**, 157601 (2004)
7. L. J. Li, R. J. Nicholas, R. S. Deacon and P. A. Shields, Phys. Rev. Lett. **93**, 156104 (2004)
8. J. Wu et al., Phys. Rev. Lett. **93**, 017404 (2004)
9. S. Zaric et al., Science **1304**, 1129 (2004)
10. L. J. Li and R. J. Nicholas, Int. J. Mod. Phys. B **18**, 3509 (2004)
11. C. Journet et al., Nature **388**, 756 (1997)
12. L. Yang, M. P. Anantram, J. Han, and J. P. Lu, Phys. Rev. B **60**, 13874 (1999)
13. B. Muller and H. D. Lutz, Solid States Comm. **78**, 469 (1991)
14. M. H. Brodsky et al., Phys. Stat. Sol.(b) **52**, 609 (1972)
15. O. Lourie and H. D. Wanger, J. Mat. Res. **13**, 2418 (1998)
16. Y. N. Gartstein, A. A. Zakhidov and R. H. Baughman, Phys. Rev. Lett. **89**, 045503 (2002)

Probing nanotube-based ambipolar FET by magnetic field

Georgy Fedorov*, Dmitry Smirnov*, Alexander Tselev[†], Paola Barbara[†], Nikolai Kalugin**, David Jimenez[‡], Sylvain Latil[§] and Stephan Roche[¶]

*National High Magnetic Field Laboratory, Tallahassee, Florida, 32310, USA
[†]Department of Physics, Georgetown University, Washington, DC 20057, USA
**Department of Physics, Texas A&M University, College Station, Texas 77843-4242
[‡]Departament d'Enginyeria Electronica, ETSE, UAB, 08193-Bellaterra, Barcelona, Spain
[§]Department of Physics, Facultes Universitaires Notre-Dame de la Paix, B 5000 Namur, Belgium
[¶] CEA, DSM/DRFMC/SPSMS and DRT/LETI/D2NT/LSCP, 38054 Grenoble, Cedex 9 France

Abstract.

We have studied magneto-transport properties of individual quasi metallic single-walled carbon nanotube (CNT) in high magnetic fields. As the Fermi level position, controlled by the gate voltage, is kept close to the charge neutrality point, an exponential magnetoresistance was observed for the magnetic field applied parallel to the CNT axis. Also, the conductance dependence on gate voltage reveals a gap opening with the increasing magnetic field. The experimental results supported by numerical simulations evidence a modification of the band structure in metallic CNTs caused by Aharonov-Bohm effect.

Keywords: carbon nanotubes; electronic transport; magnetoresistance
PACS: 73.63.Fg,73.50.Jt, 72.20.My

Remarkable modifications of the electronic structure due to the Aharonov-Bohm (AB) effect have been predicted for carbon nanotubes (CNTs) subjected to a parallel magnetic field [1]. In particular, an increasing magnetic flux through the cross-section of a nanotube leads to an opening of the gap at the Fermi energy in metallic CNTs and a splitting of van Hove singularities of density of states (DOS) in semiconducting CNTs. Recently, such predictions of AB effects on the DOS were challenged experimentally on both large multiwalled nanotubes (MWNTs) in the Coulomb blockade regime [2] and on semiconducting SWNTs by magneto-optical spectroscopy [3]. AB features resulting in a shift of the 1D energy bands have been observed in transport through very clean, ballistic SWNTs [4, 5].

In this paper, we report on the high magnetic field transport properties of gated small diameter quasi-metallic SWNT at fields up to 30T. An observed exponential magnetoresistance and gap-like features in the conductance dependence on the gate voltage are discussed in relation with the field-induced gap opening in the electronic structure of CNTs with Schottky barriers.

We studied a sample of gated quasimetallic CNT. A detailed description of the sample preparation technique is provided in [6]. The nanotube was contacted with two 50 nm thick Pd electrodes. Length of the nanotube bewteen the electrodes was 2 μm, while diameter of the nanotube was 1.5 ± 0.5 nm as determined by AFM.

First, we measured the DC conductance as a function of the gate voltage $G(V_g)$ at the small constant bias voltage (1mV) and at temperatures from 1.5K up to

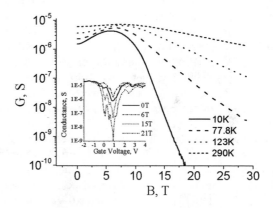

FIGURE 1. Magnetoconductance curves of obtained at temperatures form 10K to 290K. The inset shows the evolution of $G(V_g)$ with parallel magnetic field at 35K.

290K. Typical $G(V_g)$ curves obtained at several values of the magnetic field applied parallel to the CNT axis, are displayed in the inset of Fig. 1. Supression of the conductance around $V_g \approx 1V$ indicates a small gap (of the order of 10meV) in the electronic spectrum [7, 8] that is characteristic for non-armchair metallic nanotubes [9, 10]. Evolution of $G(V_g)$ curves with parallel magnetic field clearly shows a decrease of such a gap until B reaches $\approx$ 6T and increase with magnetic field above that point.

Magnetoconductance curves, shown in Fig. 1, were

CP893, *Physics of Semiconductors, 28th International Conference*
edited by W. Jantsch and F. Schäffler
© 2007 American Institute of Physics 978-0-7354-0397-0/07/$23.00

obtained at the gate voltage corresponding to the conductance minimum on the $G(V_g)$ curves. Position of this minimum was changing with temperature, but not with magnetic field. For the magnetic fields above approximately 10T, a strong exponential magnetoresistance is observed. At temperatures below 80K, the conductance drops by more than three orders of magnitude while the magnetic field is changed by 20T. To our knowledge, such a large magnetoresistance in CNT has never been reported before.

The experimentally obtained dependence of conductance on magnetic field $G(B)$ when B > 10T can be well fitted by $G(B) = G_0 exp(-\Delta/kT)$, where $\Delta = \Delta_0 + \alpha B$. The values of α deduced from the slope of the $logG(B)$ are: $28 \pm 1K/T$ at $T \geq 80K$ and $12 \pm 2K/T$ at $T = 10K$.

According to the theory of the AB effect in CNT [1], the band gap change in a magnetic field can be written as $E_g = E_{g0} + \lambda B$, where E_{g0} depends on the chirality, while λ depends only on the diameter. It is of interest to compare the values of α and the parameter λ of the theory. We note that our transport measurements do not probe directly the energy gap. The measured activation energy can be larger or smaller than E_g. For the reported sample, we obtain $\lambda = 7 \pm 3K/T$, that is close to low temperatures value of α. However, the high temperature values differ significantly.

To interpret the experimental $G(V_g)$ and $G(B)$ characteristics, we first note that the magnetic field lifts degeneracy between the K and K' bands of electron spectrum [1]. Thus the energy gaps are described by $E_{gK,K'} = \lambda |B \pm B_0|$, where + and - signs correspond to different bands. In our case $\lambda = 7K/T = 0.64 meV/T$ and $B_0 \approx 6T$ (see inset on Fig. 2).

Next, we simulate the electrical behavior of a Schottky-Barriered CNT-based field effect transistor (FET) using a model that computes thermionic and tunneling currents, based on a frozen potential energy profile. The latter had been obtained via analitical modeling of a simplified CNT-FET with a back-gate structure [11]. The simulations indicate that the left branch of the $G(V_g)$ curve is due to thermionic emission of holes, and the right branch is due to tunneling emission of electrons through V_g-modulated source and drain Schottky barriers. Both branches cross at the ambipolar conduction point (the hole and electron currents are equal at this point) where the conductance presents a minimum. A Schottky barrier height for electrons of 50 meV is assumed at both drain and source contacts (this parameter produces a parallel shift of the $G(V_g)$ characteristics) for capturing the experimental $V_g(G_{min})$ value.

With an increase of the magnetic field above 6T, the gap is progressively opened increasing the Schottky barrier height for electrons and producing a thicker depletion region. This leads to a reduction in the tunneling

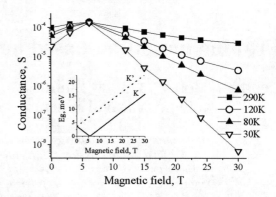

FIGURE 2. Calculated dependence of conductance on magnetic field parallel to the CNT axis. The inset shows the bandgaps of K and K' bands as function of magnetic field.

current, which in turn results in a pronounced reduction of conductance minimum G_{min}.

Typical simulation results are presented in Fig. 2. The calculations reproduce principal experimental findings. For example, for $T = 80K$, the simulations predict exponential magnetoconductance $G(B) = G_0 exp(-\alpha |B - B_0|/kT)$ with $B_0 = 6T$ and $\alpha = 20K/T$. As we see, the predicted value of α is much larger than λ used in the simulations. For lower temperatures simulations predict a lower value of α and in the limit $T \rightarrow 0$ we get $\alpha \rightarrow \lambda$. We therefore conclude that observed strong exponential magnetoresistance in a quasi-metallic CNT occurs due to the field induced opening of the semiconducting gap.

We gratefully acknowledge an assistance of A.Wade. This is work is partially supported by the grant from NHMFL In House Research Program. The NHMFL is supported by NSF Cooperative Agreement No. DMR-0084173, by the State of Florida, and by the DOE.

REFERENCES

1. H. Ajiki and T. Ando, J. Phys. Soc. Jpn. **62**, 1255 (1993).
2. U. C. Coskun et al., Science 304, 1132 (2004).
3. S. Zaric et al., Science 304, 1129 (2004).
4. J. Cao et al., Phys. Rev. Lett. **93**, 216803 (2004).
5. J. Cao et al., Nature Materials, **4**, 745 (2005)
6. A. Tselev et al., Nanotechnology **15**, 1475 (2004)
7. C. Zhou et al., Phys Rev Lett, **84**, 5604 (2000)
8. M. Ouyang et al., Science, **292**, 702 (2001)
9. X. Blase et al., Phys Rev Lett **72**, 1878 (1994)
10. C. L. Kane and E. J. Mele Phys Rev Lett **78**, 1932 (1997)
11. D. Jimenez et al, submitted to Journ. Appl. Phys.

Nanocrystal Plasma Polymerization

Ludovico Cademartiri[1], Reihaneh Malakooti[1], Georg von Freymann[2], Yasemin Akçakir[1], André C. Arsenault[1], Srebri Petrov[1], Andrea Migliori[3], Jacopo Bertolotti[4], Diederik S. Wiersma[4], Vladimir Kitaev[5], Geoffrey A. Ozin[1,*]

1 Lash Miller Chemical Laboratories, Department of Chemistry, University of Toronto, 80, St. George Stree, Toronto, Ontario, M5S 3H6, Canada
2 Institut für Nanotechnologie, Forschungszentrum Karlsruhe in der Helmholtz-Gemeinschaft, 76021 Karlsruhe, Germany
3 Consiglio Nazionale delle Ricerche, CNR-IMM, Area della Ricerca di Bologna, Via Gobetti 101, I-40126 Bologna, Italy
4 European Laboratory for Non-linear Spectroscopy and INFM-Matis, via Nello Carrara 1, 50019 Sesto Fiorentino, Firenze, Italy
5 Department of Chemistry, Wilfred Laurier University, 75 University Avenue West, Waterloo N2L 3C5, Canada

Abstract. We here report on a general strategy for the formation of all-inorganic flexible functional films based on nanocrystal building blocks. Results are reported for PbS and Bi_2S_3 nanocrystals.

Keywords: PbS, Bi2S3, nanocrystals, films
PACS: 73.21.La, 73.63.Bd, 78.55.-m

INTRODUCTION

The development of solution-processable nanocomposite films with properties designed at the nanoscale is of great premise. Colloidal nanocrystals are a natural candidate for this sort of materials as they can be casted on a variety of substrates and their property can be tailored. Nanocrystal solids though possess an inherent mechanical fragility and chemical instability, thus preventing their use on flexible substrates and in real devices. We here present a strategy that overcomes these limits and preserve the inherent properties of the nanocrystals.

SYNTHESIS AND CHARACTERIZATION

PbS and Bi_2S_3 nanocrystals are synthesized according to reported procedures[1,2]. The nanocrystals are casted on a substrate and subsequently exposed to a 5W air plasma[3]. The time of exposure is strictly dependent on the film thickness. The films can be prepared on flexible substrates and retain flexibility. In Figure 1 are shown SEM images of the obtained films.

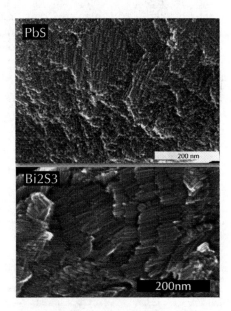

Figure 1. SEM images of plasma-polymerized nanocrystal assemblies.

An in-detail XRD and XPS characterization has been performed on both films in order to identify the composition and microstructure of the matrix surrounding the nanocrystals.

CP893, *Physics of Semiconductors, 28th International Conference*
edited by W. Jantsch and F. Schäffler
© 2007 American Institute of Physics 978-0-7354-0397-0/07/$23.00

As shown in Figure 2 the XRD confirms PbS and Bi2S3 to be the only crystalline phases

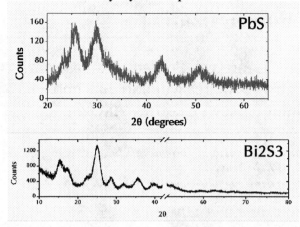

Figure 2. XRD patterns of plasma-polymerized films showing the persistency of the nanocrystalline phase

XPS analysis (not reported here for lack of space) instead report the formation of sulfate, and oxide species, both for PbS and Bi2S3. These species are probably attributable to the oxidation of the nanocrystal surfaces as well as to the oxidation of some excess precursors. The analysis also confirms the almost total removal of organics from the films

Even though the nanocrystal surface has been oxidized and the ligands decomposed the inherent luminescence of the PbS quantum dots remain unaltered. This surprising result is shown in Figure 3.

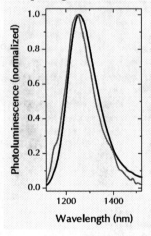

Figure 3. (black) Photoluminescence peak of nanocrystal film before plasma polymerization; (grey) Photoluminescence peak after plasma polymerization. The peaks have been normalized.

Even though the peaks in Figure 3 have been normalized, absolute photoluminescence measurements to account for scattering have demonstrated that the luminescence is unchanged after plasma polymerization, within experimental error.

The chemical stability of the obtained films has been tested by monitoring the photoluminescence intensity during the exposure of the film to harsh chemical and physical processing: 100°C annealing in air, 80°C toluene, 10% H_2SO_4 solution, UV irradiation.

In all cases the luminescence remained virtually unchanged, demonstrating the tremendously enhanced stability of these films when compared to loosely connected nanocrystal solids.

The patterning of such films has also been successfully accomplished. By exposing films obtained from PbS nanocrystals to concentrated HCl, flown through the channels of a PDMS stamp, it was possible to dissolve the nanocrystals without harming the matrix surrounding them, as shown in Figure 4.

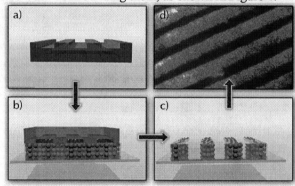

Figure 4. Patterning of plasma-polymerized films by using soft-lithographic techniques.

CONCLUSIONS

In conclusion we have demonstrated the successful fabrication of nanocomposite flexible films with high chemical stability and functionality determined by its building blocks.

ACKNOWLEDGMENTS

G.A.O. is Canada Research Chair in Materials Chemistry. The authors are deeply indebted to NSERC for financial support.

REFERENCES

1. Cademartiri, L.; Bertolotti, J.; Sapienza, R.; Wiersma, D. S.; Kitaev, V.; Ozin, G. A., *J. Phys. Chem. B* 2006, 110, (2), 671-673.
2. Malakooti, R.; Cademartiri, L.; Akçakir, Y.; Petrov, S.; Migliori, A.; Ozin, G. A., *Adv. Mater.*, in press.
3. Cademartiri, L.; von Freymann, G.; Arsenault, A. C.; Bertolotti, J.; Wiersma, D. S.; Kitaev, V.; Ozin, G. A., *Small* 2005, 1, (12), 1184-1187.

Role of a Single Dopant in Binary and Ternary Nanocrystals

Rameshwar N. Bhargava, Vishal Chhabra, Alexei I. Ekimov and Adosh Mehta

Nanocrystals Technology, P.O.Box 820, Briarcliff Manor NY 10510 USA

Abstract. The role of a single dopant in binary and ternary semiconductor nanocrystals has been studied. The changes in the luminescent properties of the dopant brought about by the quantum confinement provided by 2nm to 5nm size host have been studied. Band gap engineering is being sought to develop efficient nanophosphors that are optimized for use for white LEDs and conventional discharge light sources.

Keywords: Doped Nanocrystals, Quantum Confined Atom, Ternary Nanocrystals
PACS: 78.55.-m, 78.67.Bf

INTRODUCTION

An active dopant modulates the property of semiconductor and thereby provides the precise control of device parameters. On the other hand if a dopant is incorporated in a nanocrystal of 2 to 5 nm size, the luminescent properties of the dopant are strongly affected by the quantum confinement provided by the dielectric boundary of the nanocrystal. The dopant in a nanocrystal, henceforth referred as quantum confined atom (QCA), generates high luminous efficiency [1]. This high efficiency suggests that only a single dopant per nanocrystal was incorporated since two or more such dopants per nanocrystal would lead to known phenomena of concentration quenching and drastically reduce the quantum efficiency.

We have been extensively studying the luminescent properties of a single QCA in a nanocrystal. Some of the key observations are summarized: i) The probability of incorporation of a single impurity-ion in a nanocrystal is rather low due to rapid diffusion of the impurity (defect) to the surface. To incorporate a single impurity in a nanosize host, we had to use the molar concentration of the impurity salt at least an order of magnitude higher than what normally is used for doping of bulk semiconductors. This is theoretically studied recently by Delpian and Chelikowsky [2] who conclude that the formation energy of the dopant (defect) increases as the size of the nanocrystal decreases, thereby making incorporation of dopant in small nanocrystals, a very difficult task. ii) The combination of AFM and spectroscopy on the same doped-nanocrystal, showed that the quantum efficiency increases rapidly as the size of the nanocrystal decreases below 10nm [3] when larger molar concentration of dopants were used. The same conclusion was earlier arrived by careful monitoring the efficiency of $ZnS:Mn^{2+}$ agglomerated nanocrystals [1].

Thus, to achieve high-efficiency nanophosphors, we must have the smallest of the nanocrystals that contain only a single activator per nanocrystal. iii) In order to incorporate a single impurity in a nanosize host, (e.g. Mn^{2+} replacing Zn^{2+} in ZnS), its charge state and ionic radius must be compatible with the host-ion it replaces iv) Luminescence experiments performed on QCA nanocrystal of $Y_2O_3:Eu^{3+}$ showed 'on and off' blinking of $^5D_0$-$^7F_2$ transition associated with the single Eu^{3+}-ion, and also this emission is linearly polarized [4]. The linearly polarized emission from Eu^{3+} confirms unequivocally the presence of only one Eu^{3+}ion in the nanocrystal. The polarization property of an impurity in quantum dot is analogous to the recent observation of six-fold splitting of the exciton emission [5] observed in Mn doped quantum dots of CdTe/ZnTe formed during MBE growth of ZnCdTe quantum well structures. The six fold splitting of the exciton was correlated with localized 5/2 spin of single Mn^{2+}.

In order to modify the absorption characteristics of nanophosphors using band gap engineering while retaining the luminescent characteristics of QCA, we have extended the study of doping of nanosize binary host to ternary host. Doping of ZnCdS nanocrystals was carried out with Mn and Ag as dopants. In this case, single dopant-ions of Mn and Ag replace, respectively Zn and Cd cation sites, because of their matched ionic sizes. The combination of band-gap engineering of ternary semiconductors and the right dopant will generate bright and optimized nanophosphors. This is very similar to the modulation doping of quantum well structures. Further enhancements in the luminescent efficiency of ternary nanophosphors can be achieved by fabricating heterostructures of ternary quantum dots containing QCA.

CP893, *Physics of Semiconductors, 28th International Conference*
edited by W. Jantsch and F. Schäffler
© 2007 American Institute of Physics 978-0-7354-0397-0/07/$23.00

RESULTS

In ZnCdS doped with Mn, we observe the characteristic Photoluminescent (PL) spectra associated with an internal $4T_1$-$6A_1$ transition of Mn as shown in fig. 1. On the other hand, the photoluminescent excitation (PLE) spectra shows the characteristic band edge absorption associated with band-gap energy of alloy $Zn_xCd_{1-x}S$ composition. Since Mn^{2+} emission is associated with a localized transition, its PL characteristics do not change with nanocrystal alloy composition.

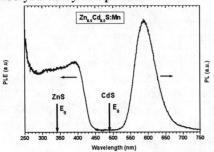

Fig.1 PL and PLE spectra of $Zn_{0.5}Cd_{0.5}S$: Mn^{2+}

When $Zn_xCd_{1-x}S$ is doped with Ag^{2+}, the emission associated with Ag^{2+} was observed as in bulk samples [6]. The peak position of the characteristic Ag^{2+} emission follows the band gap energy as in the case of bulk $Zn_xCd_{1-x}S$ alloys. Based on characteristic PL emission, we suggest that Ag is replacing Cd, as observed in bulk samples. In fig.2, the PLE and PL spectral characteristics of $Zn_{0.5}Cd_{0.5}S$:Ag and CdS:Ag are shown.

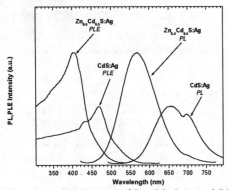

Fig.2 PL and PLE spectra of $Zn_{0.5}Cd_{0.5}S$:Ag and CdS:Ag

Besides ZnCdS ternary nanophosphors, we have also studied the luminescent properties of binary ZnO and ternary ZnOS alloy. In case of binary ZnO doped with Li, we observe the excitonic absorption (PLE) varying from 310nm to 370nm, associated with different sizes of nanocrystals in the range of 3nm to 20nm. At sizes greater than 20 nm, the luminescent characteristics are similar to the bulk materials. The PL emission in nanocrystals is efficient and broad with peak emission ranging from 490nm to 550nm. In case of ternary ZnOS alloy system, we are studying the bowing of the energy band gap as observed recently by Meyer et.al. [7]. Our goal is to grow nanocrystals of $Zn\,O_x\,S_{1-x}$ with varying value of x. In this ternary nanosystem, the peak absorption varies from 310nm to 480 nm, a property very desirable for white LEDs and other conventional discharge lamps.

For practical applications of these nanophosphors, the PL characteristics must remain invariant, hence the choice of the dopants with respect to the host becomes a critical issue. In case of Mn^{2+} the PL characteristics are nearly invariant with the ternary alloy composition while in the case of Ag^{2+} doping the emission characteristics change with alloy composition. The absorption-spectra is optimized by using band-gap engineering of ternary-alloy composition.

One of the biggest advantages of QCA based nanocrystals is that we have the luminescent signal far removed from the band gap of the host (no self absorption), yielding efficient nanophosphors. These non-scattering nanophosphors when properly designed using band gap engineering proposed here, could enhance the performance of products in the field of lighting, displays, biotags etc. For example, the use of efficient nanophosphors with blue/UV LEDs for generating white LEDs could increase the light output by 50% as compared to currently used bulk phosphors.

Under the influence of the confinement, the properties of a single dopant-ion are modified without any change in the property of the host. This is opposite of what we observe in conventional doping of semiconductors. This development of band-gap engineered ternary nanocrystals with QCA as digital-doping, will significantly impact nanotechnology in the near future.

AKNOWLEDEMENTS

This work is partially supported by National Science Foundation SBIR Phase II grant # DMI-0521948.

REFERENCES

1. R.Bhargava et.al. Phys.Rev.Letts. 72, 416 (1994); & R. Bhargava J. Lumin. 70,85 (1996).
2. G.M.Dalpian and J.R.Chelikowsky Phys.Rev.letts 96, 226802, (2006)
3. A. Mehta et. al. Applied Optics 42, 2132 (2003).
4. M. Barnes et.al. J. Phys. Chem. B, 104, 6099 (2000); & A. Bartko et.al Chem. Phys. Lett 358, 459 (2002).
5. L. Besomes et al., Phys.Rev.letts 93, 207403 (2004). & Y. Le´ger, et.al ibid 95, 047403 (2005).
6. Phosphor Handbook, Eds. S Shionoya & W.M.Yen CRC Press 1999
7. B.K.Meyer et.al. Appl. Phys. Letts. 85,4929 (2004)

Stepwise Assembly of Eu_2O_3 Nanocrystals and Nanoneedles

S. V. Mahajan[1,4], M. L. Redigolo[2,4], D. S. Koktysh[3,4] and J. H. Dickerson[2,4]

1. Interdisciplinary Program in Materials Science, Vanderbilt University, Nashville, TN 37235 USA
2. Department of Physics and Astronomy, Vanderbilt University, Nashville, TN 37235 USA
3. Department of Chemistry, Vanderbilt University, Nashville, TN 37235 USA
4. Vanderbilt Institute of Nanoscale Science and Engineering, Vanderbilt University, Nashville, TN 37235 USA

Abstract. We report the stepwise assembly of europium oxide (Eu_2O_3) nanocrystals into one dimensional europium hydroxychloride ($Eu(OH)_2Cl$) nanostructures. Synthesized via a simple colloidal chemistry procedure, the Eu_2O_3 nanocrystals organized into anisotropic nanoneedles and nanospindles via solution-phase heat treatment. Transmission electron microscopy (TEM) revealed the shape and crystalline arrangement of the nanostructures.

Keywords: europium oxide, self assembly, nanocrystals, europium hydroxychloride
PACS: 78.67.Bf, 81.16.Be, 81.16.Dn, 81.07.Bc

INTRODUCTION

The production of rare earth sesquioxide (RE_2O_3) nanostructures has been of interest recently for their use in applications ranging from bioimaging phosphorescent reagents to nanophosphors in electroluminescent displays [1-2]. Zero-dimensional (0D) and one-dimensional (1D) nanomaterials, consisting of europium oxide (Eu_2O_3),[3-5] dysprosium oxide (Dy_2O_3), [6], and Eu^{3+}-doped gadolinium oxide (Gd_2O_3) and yttrium oxide (Y_2O_3),[7-9] have been synthesized through a variety of means, including gas phase condensation, template-assisted sol-gel techniques, and colloidal chemistry. In this paper, we present the synthesis of one dimensional europium hydroxychloride ($Eu(OH)_2Cl$) nanostructures via the stepwise self-assembly of zero dimensional Eu_2O_3 nanocrystals. Dissimilar to other common methods to synthesize 1D nanostructures, our approach involves a heat treatment to facilitate the assembly of 0D Eu_2O_3 nanocrystals into 1D $Eu(OH)_2Cl$ nanostructures.

RESEARCH DETAILS

Eu_2O_3 nanocrystals were produced via a colloidal chemistry procedure, involving europium (III) chloride hexahydrate ($EuCl_3 \cdot 6H_2O$) and trioctylphosphine oxide (TOPO). The details of this can be found elsewhere [3, 10].To synthesize the 1D nanostructures, 100 mL of a methanolic nanocrystal solution were concentrated down to 20 mL. Thereafter, the solution was refluxed at 130 °C for forty-eight hours under vigorous stirring. During this period, the solution grew more opaque. Aliquots of the solution were removed periodically and were washed in methanol for characterization. The nanomaterials were analyzed with a Philips CM20 transmission electron microscope (TEM).

DISCUSSION

TEM and STEM images in Figure 1 chronicled the stepwise self-assembly of the nanostructures. Figure 1a shows a collection of Eu_2O_3 nanocrystals (d_{ave} = 4.0 nm). The observed spacing of the lattice planes was measured to be ~3.1 Å, which matched the {222} lattice spacing of body-centered-cubic Eu_2O_3. As the reaction continued, the nanocrystals aggregated into thin, needle-like objects. Continued heat-treatment caused the nanocrystals to fuse together, producing a single elongated nanostructure, called a nanoneedle (Figure 1b). The nanoneedles were individual crystals, which confirmed that the individual nanocrystals had merged together to form the nanoneedles. As the self-assembly evolved, the individual nanoneedles bundled together (Figure 1c). The aggregated nanoneedles then crystallized in a single structure, called a nanospindle (Figure 1d). The nanospindles continued to grow with additional heat-treatment time. Throughout the assembly, the aspect ratios of the nanospindles and nanoneedles remained between 3:1 and 3.3:1. Occasionally, we observed that the

CP893, *Physics of Semiconductors, 28th International Conference*
edited by W. Jantsch and F. Schäffler
© 2007 American Institute of Physics 978-0-7354-0397-0/07/$23.00

nanospindles aggregated into intriguing flowerlike arrangements, as seen in Figure 2. Interestingly, these collections did not follow the same anisotropic growth that was observed in the nanocrystal assembly. Closer inspection suggests that these spindles fused together at the base of the "flower." Further investigation is warranted on these assemblies.

FIGURE 2. Flowerlike system of $Eu(OH)_2Cl$ nanospindles.

CONCLUSIONS

We observed the stepwise self-assembly of Eu_2O_3 nanocrystals into anisotropic, 1D $Eu(OH)_2Cl$ nanospindles and nanoneedles. We also discovered the subsequent aggregation of the nanospindles into intriguing, intricate flower-like systems. Given the well documented optical properties of rare earth materials, we anticipate that these nanomaterials could be used in a variety of applications, like bioimaging reagents and thin film electroluminescence devices.

ACKNOWLEDGMENTS

One of the authors (JHD) recognizes support from the Ralph E. Powe Junior Faculty Enhancement Award from Oak Ridge Associated Universities.

REFERENCES

[1] W. M. Shionoya, and W. M. Yen, Phosphor Handbook, (CRC Press, Boca Raton, 1999).

[2] J. Feng, *et al*, Anal. Chem. **75**, 5282 (2003).

[3] G. Wakefield, *et al*, J. Colloid Interf. Sci. **215**, 179 (1999).

[4] R. Bazzi, *et al*, J. Lumin. **102**, 445 (2003).

[5] V. G. Pol, *et al*, J. Phys. Chem. B **106**, 9737 (2002).

[6] G. Wang, *et al*, Nanotechnology **15**, 1307 (2004).

[7] C. Louis, *et al*, J. Solid State Chem. **173**, 335 (2003).

[8] H. Z. Wang, *et al*, Adv. Mater. **17**, 2506 (2005).

[9] H. S. Yang, *et al*, Nanotechnology **16**, 2794 (2005).

[10] S. V. Mahajan, *et al*, J. Mater. Sci. **in press**.

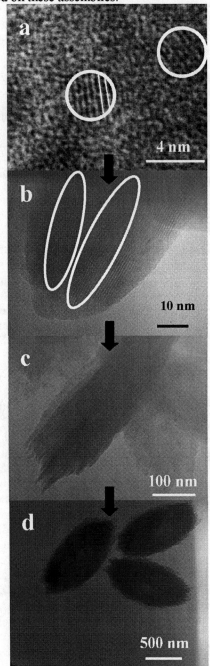

FIGURE 1. The self-assembly process. (a) Eu_2O_3 nanocrystals. (b) A nanoneedle. (c) A bundle of individual nanoneedles. (d) Nanospindles.

Temperature dependence of the whispering gallery effect in ZnO nanoresonators

Thomas Nobis, Andreas Rahm, Michael Lorenz, and Marius Grundmann[*]

Universität Leipzig, Institut für Experimentelle Physik II, Linnéstraße 5, D-04103 Germany
[*]corresponding author e-mail: grundmann@physik.uni-leipzig.de

Abstract. We have investigated the optical modes of zinc oxide (ZnO) nanostructures with hexagonal cross section by temperature-dependent cathodoluminescence spectroscopy. All observed resonance lines show a characteristic red-shift with increasing resonator temperature. From such red-shift we calculate the temperature dependence of the refractive indices of individual ZnO nanopillars on the basis of numerical solutions for the resonant photon energies of hexagonal whispering gallery modes using literature values for the thermal expansion coefficient of ZnO.

Keywords: zinc oxide, hexagon, temperature, refractive index
PACS: 42.55.Sa, 42.60.Da, 78.67.Bf

INTRODUCTION

In recent years, whispering gallery (WG) microresonators with hexagonal cross section have been studied and, e.g., exhibited lasing action [1,2]. Wurtzite zinc oxide (ZnO) and gallium nitride nanostructures, which are now being explored intensively as candidates for novel nanostructured photonic devices, naturally exhibit such hexagonal cross section and therefore form a hexagonal WG nanoresonator [3, 4]. In this article we demonstrate the application of the WG effect in hexagonal resonators for detecting the temperature dependence of the refractive indices of individual ZnO nanocrystals.

EXPERIMENT

The investigated ZnO nanopillars have been grown by high-pressure pulsed laser deposition (PLD). Details about the growth process can be found in [5]. Within the visible spectral range, ZnO exhibits a broad, defect-related luminescence band, the so-called green luminescence of ZnO. Due to the presence of a resonator, the green luminescence of ZnO nanopillars with hexagonal cross section is amplified at resonant photon energies, and the luminescence spectrum is therefore modulated by characteristic resonance lines [3,4,6]. Figure 1a shows resonance spectra of an individual ZnO nanopillar. The spectra have been recorded within temperature-dependent cathodo-luminescence (CL) spectroscopy experiments for temperatures T in a range $10 \text{ K} \leq T \leq 290 \text{ K}$. Five distinct resonance lines are observed. With increasing resonator temperature, all peak positions shift to lower energies as given in Fig. 1b.

THEORY

For hexagonal dielectric resonators, the resonant photon energies $E = h\nu$ are determined by [6]

$$\hbar c a_{m,n}\left[n_r(E)\right] = E \cdot R. \qquad (1)$$

The dimensionless function $a_{m,n}(n_r) = \text{Re}(kR_{m,n})$ is the real part of the complex wave number k of a resonant mode in dependence of the refractive index n_r of the resonator, multiplied with the edge length R of the hexagon. Within $1.9 \leq n_r \leq 2.2$, the functions $a_{m,n}(n_r)$ have been determined by solving a two-dimensional (2D) Helmholtz-equation numerically [6]. For $\text{Re}(kR) < 10$, all solutions are numbered by an angular mode number m and a radial mode number n, similar to the mode numbers for resonant modes of a circular 2D cavity. All resonances can further be separated into transverse electric (TE) and transverse magnetic (TM) polarized modes [7], symbolized by $\text{TE}_{m,n}$ and $\text{TM}_{m,n}$ [6]. In Figs. 1a and b, all peak positions are labeled with their respective mode symbol. Since ZnO is uniaxial and its refractive indices exhibit a spectral dispersion, $n_r(E) = n_{\parallel}(E)$ and $n_r(E) = n_{\perp}(E)$ are used to model TM and TE polarized modes correctly.

CP893, *Physics of Semiconductors, 28th International Conference*
edited by W. Jantsch and F. Schäffler
© 2007 American Institute of Physics 978-0-7354-0397-0/07/$23.00

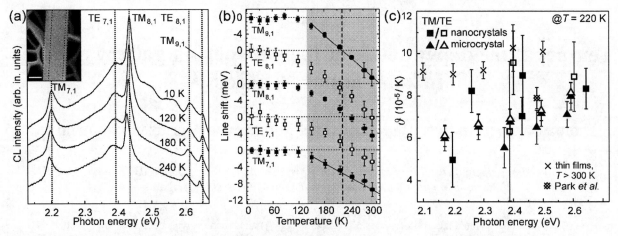

FIGURE 1. (a) Temperature-dependent CL spectra of an individual ZnO nanopillar with edge length $R \approx 460$ nm. Peaks are labeled by the respective mode symbols. Vertical dotted lines guide the eye and indicate temperature-dependent peak shifts. A scanning electron microscopy image of the pillar is given in the inset. The scale bar equals 500 nm. (b) Line shift of the resonant modes in dependence of the resonator temperature. Data for TM (TE) polarized modes are indicated with filled (open) symbols. Within the given representation the ordinate axis overlap for different modes, as line shifts always start at zero for $T = 10$ K. (c) Results for ϑ for individual ZnO micro- and nanostructures within the temperature range 150 K $< T <$ 290 K according to equation (2). Filled and open symbols distinguish between TM and TE polarization. For comparison, values for ϑ of PLD-grown ZnO thin films, determined by spectroscopic ellipsometry at higher temperatures [8] are shown (crosses) together with a literature value for ZnO single crystals [9].

To understand the line shifts observed in Fig. 1a we consider a combination of thermal expansion $\Delta R/R = \alpha_\perp \Delta T$ and simultaneous changings of the refractive index, i.e. $n_r = n_r(E,T)$, with $\vartheta = \partial n_r/\partial T \neq 0$ being the partial derivative of the refractive indices with respect to the temperature. Total differentiation d/dT of equation (1) leads to

$$\vartheta = \frac{\partial n_r}{\partial T} = \frac{a_{m,n}}{a'_{m,n}}\left(\frac{1}{E}\frac{\Delta E}{\Delta T} + \alpha_\perp\right) - \frac{\partial n_r}{\partial E}\frac{\Delta E}{\Delta T}, \quad (2)$$

whereby ϑ is calculated. We use literature values for ZnO bulk material to regard the dispersion of the refractive indices [10, 6]. The linear thermal expansion coefficient perpendicular to the optical axis $\alpha_\perp(T)$ is also known from literature [11]. For temperatures 150 K $< T <$ 290 K (grayed area in Fig. 1b), $\Delta E/\Delta T$ can be determined from the slope of the experimental line shifts.

RESULTS AND CONCLUSION

Results for ϑ according to eqn. (2) are shown in Fig. 1c. Error bars regard Gaussian error propagation. For photon energies between 2.1 eV and 2.7 eV, values for ϑ cover a range of $5\times10^{-5}\mathrm{K}^{-1}$ to $9\times10^{-5}\mathrm{K}^{-1}$. For comparison, results obtained for PLD-grown thin films determined by temperature dependent spectroscopic ellipsometry @$T >$ 300K [8] are shown in Fig. 1c together with a further literature value for

ZnO single crystals [11]. The latter one is in perfect agreement with the data obtained for ZnO micro- and nanocrystals. Due to the detection at elevated temperatures, values for PLD thin films are larger.

In conclusion we used the WG effect to detect optical constants of individal nanocavities by temperature dependent CL spectroscopy.

ACKNOWLEDGMENTS

This work was supported by the Deutsche Forschungsgemeinschaft within FOR 522 (Grant No. Gr1011/12–1 and 12–2).

REFERENCES

1. U. Vietze et al., *Phys. Rev. Lett.* **81**, 4628 (1998).
2. I. Braun et al., *Appl. Phys. B* **70**, 335 (2000).
3. Th. Nobis, E. M. Kaidashev, A. Rahm, M. Lorenz, and M. Grundmann, *Phys. Rev. Lett.* **93**, 103903 (2004).
4. Th. Nobis, M. Grundmann et al., *AIP Conf. Proc.* **772**, 849 (2005).
5. M. Lorenz et al., *Appl. Phys. Lett.* 86, 143113 (2005).
6. Th. Nobis and M. Grundmann, *Phys. Rev. A* **72**, 063806 (2005).
7. J. Wiersig, *Phys. Rev. A* **67**, 023807 (2003).
8. R. Schmidt-Grund et al., *to be published in AIP Conf. Proc. (ICPS)*
9. V. S. Park and J. R. Schneider, *J. Appl. Phys.* **39**, 3049 (1968).
10. R. Schmidt et al., *Appl. Phys. Lett.* **82**, 2260 (2003).
11. H. Ibach, *Phys. Stat. Sol.* **33**, 257 (1969)

Effect of external electric field on photoluminescence of silicon nanocrystals

E.N. Vandyshev, G.A. Kachurin and K.S. Zhuravlev

Institute of Semiconductor Physics SB RAS, Lavrentieva 13, 630090, Novosibirsk, Russia

Abstract. Study of the effect of an external electric field on photoluminescence (PL) of silicon nanocrystals formed in SiO_2 has been carried out. It was found that the electric field results in a red shift of PL band and a decrease of the PL intensity at any temperature in the range of 5-290 K. A decay time of PL intensity after pulse excitation does not depend on the electric field strength. The experimental data are explained in framework of the model of recombination of self-trapped excitons formed at nanocrystal-matrix boundary.

Keywords: exciton, photoluminescence, silicon nanocrystals and electric field
PACS: 61.46.+w, 71.35.-y, 78.55.-m.

INTRODUCTION

Semiconductor nanometer-sized crystals fabricated in dielectric films have physical properties substantially different from the properties of bulk materials due to the presence of three-dimensional confinement effect. This allows one to study new physical phenomena and to create new devices on the basis of such structures.

In spite of variety of publications the mechanism of radiative recombination in silicon nanocrystals (nc-Si) embedded in SiO_2-matrix is still issue. At present two main models of recombination are considered in the literature: recombination through quantum confinement levels in silicon nanocrystals [1] and recombination of self-trapped excitons (STE) formed at the interface between nc-Si and SiO_2 matrix [2, 3].

To obtain arguments in favor of one of the proposed earlier recombination models the effect of an external electric field on the recombination of nonequilibrium charge carriers in the nc-Si has been studied in this work. Moreover, important for practical applications information on behavior of light emitting nc-Si in the external electric field has been obtained.

Previously we had studied the effect of the electric field generated by means of surface acoustic wave on photoluminescence (PL) of nc-Si [4]. However, this technique does not allow us to apply the electric field with a strength higher than 12 kV/cm and study time-resolved PL after pulse excitation. In the present work we proposed another method of application of the electric field to a structure with nc-Si, which permits to increase considerably the electric field strength applied to a sample.

EXPERIMENTAL

The samples present a MOS-structure (metal-oxide-semiconductor) with nc-Si embedded in a 500-nm-thick silicon oxide layer thermally grown on a silicon substrate. The nc-Si were synthesized by Si^+-ions implantation with a dose of 2×10^{17} cm^{-2} at energy of 150 keV. The post-implantation annealing was performed for 3 hours at 1075°C. A 120 nm-thick optically transparent In_2O_3 film with metallic conductivity deposited on the top of the SiO_2 layer was used as metallic contact. A maximum electric field strength within the SiO_2 layer was about 450 kV/cm. Photoluminescence was excited through the In_2O_3 film using a pulsed N_2-laser (λ=337 nm) with a pulse duration of 7 ns and a *cw* He-Cd - laser (λ=325 nm). The PL signal was detected by a double diffraction grating spectrometer with a cooled photomultiplier operating in the photon counting mode. Temperature was varied over 5-290 K range.

RESULTS AND DISCUSSION

Fig. 1 shows the steady-state PL spectra of the nc-Si measured at 90 K with and without application of the external electric field. The PL spectrum presents a broad band with maximum at ~700 nm. Application of

CP893, *Physics of Semiconductors, 28th International Conference*
edited by W. Jantsch and F. Schäffler
© 2007 American Institute of Physics 978-0-7354-0397-0/07/$23.00

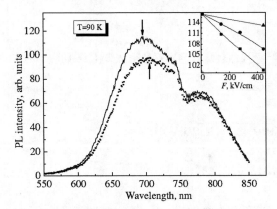

Fig. 1. Spectra of steady-state PL of silicon nanocrystals measured without the electric field (solid line) and with field of 450 kV/cm strength (dotted line). The spectra are not normalized at a spectrum of recording system sensitivity. Inset shows a dependence of the PL intensity on the electric field strength at 5 (circle), 90 (square) and 290 K (triangle), the intensity of PL was normalized at its maximum value.

the electric field with strength of 450 kV/cm causes a decrease of the PL intensity in the maximum of the PL band at 14% and a red shift of the PL maximum at ~20 meV.

Fig. 2 shows temperature dependences of the PL intensity measured with and without application of the external electric field. Tree regions can be distinguished in these curves. The PL intensity is nearly constant in a narrow range of 5-15 K, its increases from 20 K to 90 K and decreases at temperatures higher than 90 K. At any temperature application of the electric field causes PL quenching. Interesting effect was observed at application of the electric field at low temperatures. The PL intensity of the nc-Si measured after switching off the electric field was smaller than the one measured before application of the electric field. This effect was observed at temperatures up to 35 K and disappeared at higher temperatures.

Insert to fig. 2 shows the PL decay curves measured with and without application of the external electric field. These decay curves are identical. This result allows one to choose one model of recombination over another. Indeed, according to the model of recombination via the quantum confinement levels an excitonic lifetime should increase with the electric field strength increasing due to decrease overlapping of the electron and hole wave functions. In the STE model radiative and non-radiative recombination times of self-trapped exciton can be independent on the electric field strength, since a moderate electric field (below 10^6 V/cm) causes approach of the STE and ground excitonic states and does not effect on the wave functions of these states [5]. Thus, the quantum confinement model does not describe all the experimental results, while they can be explained in the STE model.

The PL intensity decrease under the electric field can be caused by two reasons. First, the applied electric

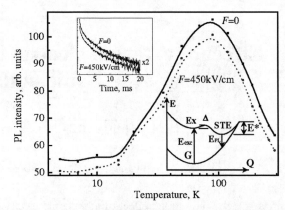

Fig. 2. Temperature dependence of integral intensity of the PL from the nc-Si with and without the electric field with strength of 450 kV/cm. Insets: PL decay curves measured with and without application the electric field at 5 K. Configuration diagram of a nanocrystal with an Si–Si dimer at the interface between the nanocrystal and amorphous matrix. G, Ex, STE – ground, excited and self-trapped excitonic states, accordingly.

field decreases the barrier between the excited and ground excitonic states increasing probability of tunneling of the exciton from the excited state to the ground state. Second, the applied electric field causes injection of carrier (electron or hole) in the nanocrystal. This leads to the Auger-recombination of excitons taking place before its capture in the STE state. At low temperatures the injected carriers can remain in the nanocrystal for a long time leading to decrease of the PL intensity after switching off the electric field. It seems that the carriers escape from the nc-Si at the low temperatures above 35 K at the thermal energy >3.5 meV, which is considerably lower than the barrier height ~4 eV. It is not clear now, which mechanism makes more important contribution in the effect of the PL quenching under the influence the electric field.

The PL red shift under the electric field can be caused by decrease of gap between the ground and excited STE states.

ACKNOWLEDGEMENTS

The work is supported by SB RAS (scientific grant no.53) and the program «Low-dimensional quantum structures» of RAS.

REFERENCES

[1] V. Vinciguerra, G. Franzo, F. Priolo, F. Iacona, C. Spinella. *J. Appl. Phys.*, **87**, p. 8165 (2000).
[2] G. Allan, C. Delerue and M. Lannoo. *Phys. Rev. Lett.*, **76**, p. 2961 (1996).
[3] A.Yu. Kobitsky, K.S. Zhuravlev, H.P. Wagner, and D.R.T. Zahn. *Phys. Rev. (B)*, **63**, p. 115423 (2001).
[4] E.N. Vandyshev, K.S. Zhuravlev, A.M. Gilinsky, V.M. Lisitsyn, W. Skorupa. Thin Solid Films, **493**, p. 297 (2005).
[5] V.N. Abakumov, V.I. Perel, I.N. Yassievich. Nonradiative recombination in semiconductors. *(St. Petersburg)* p. 376 (1997).

Optical excitation and energy transfer of Eu^{3+}-doped CdS nanocrystals in reverse micelles

K. Matsuishi[*], Y. Makita[*], S. Onari[*], T. Orii[†] and A. Seto[¶]

*Institute of Materials Science, University of Tsukuba, Tsukuba, Ibaraki 305-8573, Japan
†RIKEN, 2-1 Hirosawa, Wako, Saitama 351-0198, Japan
¶AIST, Central 2, 1-1-1 Umezono, Tsukuba, Ibaraki 305-8568, Japan

Abstract. The electronic and optical properties of Eu^{3+}-doped CdS nanocrystals in reverse micelles have been investigated by optical absorption, photoluminescence (PL) and PL excitation (PLE) spectra. The PL intensity of f-f transitions of Eu^{3+} exhibits an intriguing nanocrystal size dependence. On the analyses of the PLE spectra and the PL decay of Eu^{3+} f-f transition emission, we have found that the excitation of Eu^{3+} ions is induced by energy transfer from optically excited CdS nanocrystals through their surface states, and follows the f-f transition emissions.

Keywords: Nanocrystal, Optical properties, Quantum dot, Semiconductor, Rare earth ion, Energy transfer
PACS: 78.67.Bf, 78.55.Et, 78.40.Fy

INTRODUCTION

In semiconductor nanocrystals doped with rare-earth (RE) ions, the interaction between the 4f states of RE ions and the electronic states of nanocrystals exhibiting quantum size effects draws much interest in viewpoints of both physics and optical applications[1,2]. However, the properties of RE-doped semiconductor nanocrystals have not been studied extensively due to difficulties in sample preparation, and therefore have not been fully understood. In the present study, we have investigated the electronic and optical properties of Eu^{3+}-doped CdS ($CdS:Eu^{3+}$) nanocrystals surrounded by organic molecules of reverse micelles, and have discussed the electronic interaction among CdS, Eu^{3+} ions and organic molecules.

EXPERIMENTAL

$CdS:Eu^{3+}$ nanocrystals dispersed in heptane were prepared by a reverse micelle method using AOT as surfactant[3]. The mixture of $Cd(ClO_4)_2$ and $Eu(ClO_4)_3$ aqueous solutions, whose molar ratio was $[Eu]/[Cd] = 0.01$, was used for the cation source. The size of the nanocrystals was controlled by changing the molar ratio of surfactant to water in reverse micelles ($D_w = 0.3[H_2O]/[AOT]$ nm)[4] from the nominal diameter $D_w = 1$ to 6 nm. The formation of CdS nanocrystals (zinc blend) was confirmed by TEM images and electron diffraction, and the diameters were found to be larger than the nominal diameter D_w by about 50 %. Photoluminescence (PL), PL excitation (PLE) and time resolved PL measurements were performed at room temperature.

RESULTS AND DISCUSSION

Figure 1 shows the optical absorption and the PL spectra of $CdS:Eu^{3+}$ nanocrystals (D_w=2 nm) surrounded by AOT in heptane. The peak of absorption spectrum at 3.1 eV, the lowest excitation energy, is due to squeezed excitons in CdS nanocrystals. The PL spectrum exhibits three distinct sharp peaks A, B, and C originating from $^5D_0 \rightarrow {}^7F_2$, $^5D_0 \rightarrow {}^7F_4$, and $^5D_0 \rightarrow {}^7F_0$, $^7F_1$ of Eu^{3+} f-f transitions, respectively, besides a relatively broad PL band from the surface states of CdS nanocrystals (the width is 0.7 eV, and the Stokes shift is 1.2 eV). Since the 325 nm line of a He-Cd laser which could not optically excite directly the Eu^{3+} ions was used for excitation for PL, the f-f transition emissions were caused by energy transfer from optically excited CdS nanocrystals to Eu^{3+} ions. In Fig. 1 are shown also the PLE spectra for the peak "A" from Eu^{3+} (open circles) and for the CdS surface emission (solid circles). The PLE spectrum for the Eu^{3+} emission shows a peak corresponding to the lowest excitation energy of CdS nanocrystals, indicating that the energy transfer occurs from the squeezed excitonic states of CdS nanocrystals to Eu^{3+}

CP893, *Physics of Semiconductors, 28th International Conference*
edited by W. Jantsch and F. Schäffler
© 2007 American Institute of Physics 978-0-7354-0397-0/07/$23.00

ions. The PLE spectra for the CdS surface emission and the optical absorption spectra indicate that the lowest excitation energy rises dramatically as D_w decreases, implying a strong confinement regime in the present study. The surface emission also shows blue shifts with decreasing the diameter.

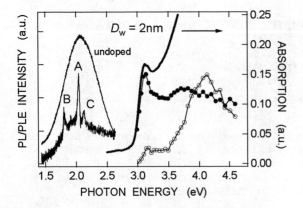

FIGURE 1. PL, PLE and optical absorption spectra of CdS:Eu^{3+} nanocrystals (D_w=2 nm) at room temperature. The PL spectrum was obtained using the 325 nm line from a He-Cd laser. PLE spectra ○ and ● were obtained from the PL peaks of the f-f transition ("A" emission) and of the CdS surface emission, respectively. The PL spectrum of undoped sample (D_w=2 nm) is also shown.

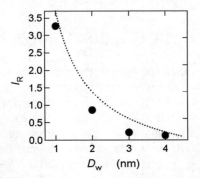

FIGURE 2. I_R, the intensity ratio of Eu^{3+} emission (the peak "A") to CdS surface emission, as a function of D_w. The excitation energy was 3.8 eV. The dotted line denotes a $1/D_w$ dependence.

As the diameter of nanocrystals decreases, the intensity ratio of the f-f emissions to the CdS surface emission increases, as shown in Fig. 2, by following a $1/D_w$ dependence (dotted line). The observation suggests that Eu^{3+} ions are positioned and coordinated to the surface of CdS nanocrystals. This is also supported by the fact that, by surface modification of the nanocrystals using AKYPO and dodecanethiol, the intensity of CdS surface emission increases while the f-f emission intensity decreases.

Figure 3 shows the PL decay curve of the f-f transition ("A" emission) of CdS:Eu^{3+} nanocrystals by

time resolved PL measurements, together with those of Eu^{3+} in AOT micelles and in Eu(ClO$_4$)$_3$ aqueous solution. The results reveal that the decay time of the f-f emission of CdS:Eu^{3+} nanocrystals is prolonged compared with that of Eu^{3+} ions dispersed in water pool in AOT reverse micelles, providing information about the mechanism of energy transfer from CdS to Eu^{3+}. The activation energy of the CdS surface emission determined from its temperature dependence is found different between non-doped CdS (37.3 meV) and Eu^{3+}-doped CdS (280 meV) nanocrystals.

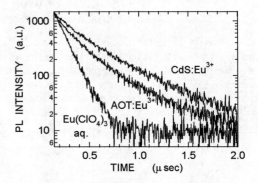

FIGURE 3. PL decay curves of the f-f transition at 2.04 eV for CdS:Eu^{3+} (D_w=2 nm), Eu^{3+} in AOT micelles, and Eu(ClO$_4$)$_3$ aqueous solution. The excitation was provided by the forth harmonic generation of Nd:YAG laser (266 nm).

CONCLUSION

We have investigated the electronic and optical properties of CdS:Eu^{3+} nanocrystals surrounded by organic molecules of reverse micelles by measuring optical absorption, PL, PLE and f-f emission decay. We conclude that the excitation of Eu^{3+} is induced by energy transfer from optically excited CdS nanocrystals through their surface states, and follows the f-f transition emissions.

ACKNOWLEDGMENTS

This work was supported by the Grant-in-Aid for Scientific Research from the Ministry of Education, Culture, Sports, Science and Technology in Japan.

REFERENCES

1. J. S. John *et al.*, *J. Am. Chem. Soc.* **121**, 1888-1892 (1999).
2. A. Kurita *et al.*, *Phys. Rev. Lett.* **83**, 1582-1585 (1999).
3. P. Lianos *et al.*, *Chem. Phys. Lett.* **125**, 299-302 (1986).
4. M. P. Pileni, *J. Phys. Chem.* **97**, 6961-6973 (1993).

Size Dependent Photomodulated Transmission Spectroscopy of CdTe Tetrapod-shaped Nanocrystals

D. Tarì, M. De Giorgi, L.Carbone, S. Kudera, L. Manna and R. Cingolani

National Nanotechnology Laboratory of INFM-CNR c/o Distretto Tecnologico ISUFI, Università di Lecce,Via per Arnesano, 73100 Lecce, Italy

Abstract. We study the excitonic nature of CdTe tetrapod-shaped nanocrystals with different size by photomodulated transmission spectroscopy. The temperature dependence of the obtained spectra evidences two main features: i) the excitonic nature of the optical transitions even at room temperature, resulting in an exciton binding energy higher than 25 meV; ii) the photo-induced Stark Effect as the dominant modulation mechanism.

Keywords: Nanocrystals, CdTe, Photomodulation Transmission Spectroscopy
PACS: 73.22.–f

INTRODUCTION

In the last decade continuous improvements in chemical methods have allowed to synthesize colloidal nanocrystals of different shapes, such as spheres[1], rods[2] and tetrapods[3]. The possibility to tune the absorption and emission properties by changing the dimensions of the nanocrystals, has made both spherical and rod nanocrystals appealing in several fields of the nanoscience. Moreover, the unique morphologic configuration of the tetrapod, which can be sketched by four nanorods branching out at tetrahedral angles from a central core, is actually employed in advanced studies relative to single transistor devices and solar cell applications[4].

Although the study of optical properties of the branched structures is of great interest, a few experimental and theoretical works have exhaustively investigated their complicated band structure. The carriers confinement in CdTe tetrapod as a function of the tetrapod size have been investigated by means of absorption (ABS) and photoluminescence (PL) measurements showing a clear emission from the first two excited states which separation changes with the aspect ratio of the nanocrystals[5].

In this contribution we study the excitonic effects in the tetrapod-shaped nanocrystals by photomodulated transmission spectroscopy (PMT). The temperature dependence of the PMT spectra evidences the excitonic nature of the optical transitions even at room temperature allowing to estimate the exciton binding energy. An accurate lineshape analysis

of the PMT spectra also indicates the photo-induced Stark Effect as the dominant modulation mechanism.

EXPERIMETAL DETAILS

The photomodulation transmittance is a powerful spectroscopic tool used to optically characterize different materials because of its intrinsic high sensitivity. PMT was carried out on two tetrapod samples different in size and synthesized according to the protocol described by Carbone et al [6]. The size of the samples was assessed by transmission electron microscopy (TEM) analysis. The average values of arm diameters (d) and lengths (l) were found to be: d=7.2 nm and l=50 nm for sample T1 and d=5.7 nm and l=30 nm for T2.

For the temperature dependence PMT measurements, the samples were dispersed in a polystyrene film and mounted into a cryostat. A 200 W halogen tungsten lamp was dispersed by a 0.5 m monochromator, producing the probe beam, whereas the blue line of an Ar laser, was used as modulator beam. AC and DC signals, which are proportional to the transmittance changes ΔT and to the transmittance T, respectively, were detected by a Si photodiode using a lock-in amplifier.

Results and Discussion

Figure 1 shows the PMT spectra of the two samples recorded at low temperature. The PMT spectra exhibit several resonances corresponding to different electron-

CP893, *Physics of Semiconductors, 28ᵗʰ International Conference*
edited by W. Jantsch and F. Schäffler

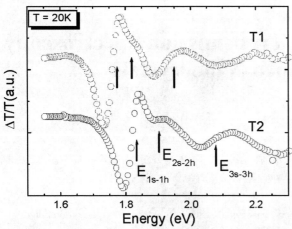

FIGURE 1. PMT spectra for the two samples of tetrapod-shaped nanocrystals.

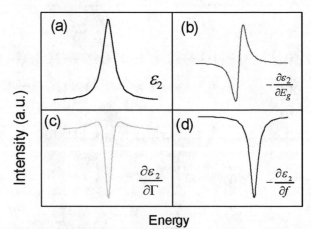

FIGURE 2. Expected PMT line-shapes for the three different modulation mechanisms.

hole transitions. In both samples we could identify three main optical transitions, labelled as E_{1e-1h}, E_{2e-2h}, and E_{3e-3h}, whose spectral features results size-dependent. In the smaller sample (T2), the whole spectrum is blue shifted with respect to the larger tetrapod sample (T1) and the energy spacing between the two lower energy features is remarkably increased, as expected from quantum confinement considerations.

To understand the nature of the optical transitions, we analyze the shape of the PMT spectra induced by an external perturbation field as a function of the parameters that govern the modulation mechanisms. We fit the PMT spectra by using the Aspnes model[7], assuming a Lorentzian broadening:

$$\frac{\Delta T}{T}(E) = \mathrm{Im}\left[\frac{Ae^{i\Theta}}{(E - E_g + i\Gamma)^n}\right]$$

where A the amplitude, Γ the broadening, E_g the transition energy and Θ the phase angle, whereas the exponential coefficient n depends on the type of optical transition. For all temperatures the best fit of our PMT spectra is obtained by using a coefficient n=2 which indicates the occurrence of excitonic resonances up to room temperature. This is attributed to the strong quantum confinement of the carriers that prevents a complete ionization of the exciton, suggesting an exciton binding energy value higher than the thermal energy at room temperature (about 25 meV).

By deconvolution of the PMT spectra, we observe the anti-symmetric line-shape of the first optical transition, whereas the second and third transition are symmetric. Theoretically the PMT line-shape results from three different modulation contribution depending on the energy, broadening and oscillator strength (Fig.2.b-d)) of the transitions. For both samples the dispersive experimental anti- symmetric line-shape of the E_{1e-1h} transition compared

with that expected from Figure 2 indicates that the energy modulation contribution prevails on the other two. As the main effect of the built-in field variation on the lower optical transition is the red-shift of the energy by the photoinduced Stark Effect, which results as the dominant modulation mechanism. For the E_{2e-2h} and the E_{3e-3h} transitions we can assume that both the oscillator strength and the broadening are responsible for the modulation, as they exhibit symmetric spectral forms which are in qualitative agreement with theoretical predictions.

ACKNOWLEDGMENTS

The authors want to thank for useful discussion Dr. G. Rainò and the expert technical help of P. Cazzato. This work has been partially supported by the SA-NANO European project Contract Number STRP013698, and by the MIUR-FIRB project.

REFERENCES

[1] A. L. Efros, M. Rosen, M. Kuno, M. Nirmal, D. J. Norris, and M. Bawendi, *Phys. Rev. B-Condensed Matter* **54** (7), 4843-4856 (1996).

[2] J. T. Hu, L. S. Li, W. D. Yang, L. Manna, L. W. Wang, and A. P. Alivisatos, *Science* **292** (5524), 2060-2063 (2001).

[3] L. Manna, D. J. Milliron, A. Meisel, E. C. Scher, and A. P. Alivisatos, *Nature Materials* **2** (6), 382-385 (2003).

[4] W. U. Huynh, J. J. Dittmer, and A. P. Alivisatos, *Science* **295** (5564), 2425-2427 (2002).

[5] D. Tari, M. De Giorgi, F. Della Sala, L. Carbone, R. Krahne, L. Manna, R. Cingolani, S. Kudera, and W. J. Parak, *App. Phys. Letters* **87** (22) (2005).

[6] L. Carbone, S. Kudera, E. Carlino, W. J. Parak, C. Giannini, R. Cingolani, and L. Manna, *Journal Of The American Chemical Society* **128** (3), 748-755 (2006).

[7] D.E. Aspnes, *Surf. Sci.* **37** (418) (1973).

Electric Field Dependent Photoluminescence Studies of Photorefractive Polymer/Semiconductor Nanoparticle Composites

F. Aslam[a], D. M. Graham[a*], D. J. Binks[a], P. Dawson[a], N. Pickett[b], and P. O'Brien[b]

[a]School of Physics and Astronomy, The University of Manchester, Manchester M60 1QD, UK
[b]School of Chemistry, The University of Manchester, Manchester M13 9PL, UK

Abstract. In this paper we report the electric field dependence of the photoluminescence emission from CdSe and CdSe/ZnS core/shell nanoparticle sensitized photorefractive polymer devices. For the CdSe sensitized device the observed field dependence is attributed to tunneling of holes out of the nanoparticles and their partial recapture, while for the CdSe/ZnS sensitized device the ZnS shell was found to suppress the recapture process.

Keywords: Photorefractive, Photoluminescence, CdSe, ZnS
PACS: 78.55.-m, 78.55.Et, 78.67.Hc

INTRODUCTION

Photorefractivity, the modulation of refractive index due to the redistribution of photogenerated charge, has potential applications in holographic data storage and optical information processing [1]. Polymeric photorefractive materials are of particular interest due to their easy synthesis, large index contrast [2] and fast response times [3].

The spectral response, efficiency and response time of photorefractive polymer composites are largely determined by the sensitizer species, which generates charge in illuminated areas and recaptures charge in dark areas. Semiconductor nanoparticles are promising sensitizers because their optoelectronic properties are size and structure dependent, and thus can be controlled during synthesis. Large electric fields are typically applied to photorefractive polymers to obtain good performance and this has been shown to have a significant effect on the behavior of nanoparticle-sensitized polymers [4,5].

A good understanding of the field-dependence of the optoelectronic properties of polymer-embedded nanoparticles will allow their design to be optimized for the sensitization of photorefractive polymers. In this paper we report on the field-dependent photoluminescence (PL) of nanoparticle sensitized photorefractive polymer composites.

EXPERIMENTAL DETAILS

The composites consist of: the charge transporting matrix poly(N-vinylcarbazole) (PVK); a reorientable dipolar molecule, 1-(2-ethylhexyloxy)-2,5-dimethyl-4-(4-nitrophenylazo) benzene (EHDNPB), which provides the electro-optic response; and CdSe **or** CdSe/ZnS core/shell nanoparticle sensitizers. The sample preparation details have been described in detail elsewhere [6].

For the electric field dependent PL measurements the devices were excited with the 457.9 nm line of a continuous-wave argon-ion laser. The luminescence was dispersed by a single grating spectrometer, detected by a cooled GaAs photomultiplier tube and amplified using a lock-in amplifier. The lock-in amplifier was referenced to either the frequency of a mechanical chopper placed in the laser beam (when $E=0$) or the frequency of a reed switch ($f = 40$ Hz) used to modulate the applied electric field.

RESULTS AND DISCUSSION

Figure 1 shows the PL spectrum of the CdSe sensitized device (PVK:EHDNPB:CdSe 49.5:47.5:3 by %wt) measured without an externally applied electric field. The PL emission peak has previously been attributed to exciton recombination within the

---

* Corresponding author e-mail: Darren.Graham@manchester.ac.uk

CP893, *Physics of Semiconductors, 28th International Conference*
edited by W. Jantsch and F. Schäffler
© 2007 American Institute of Physics 978-0-7354-0397-0/07/$23.00

CdSe quantum dots [7]. Also presented in Fig. 1 are spectra showing both the absolute change and the percentage change of the PL intensity when an electric field of 42 V/μm was applied across the device. As can be seen, the application of the electric field resulted in an increase in intensity of ~1.5 % on the low energy side of the spectrum and a decrease in intensity of ~1.5 % on the high energy side.

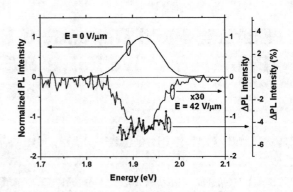

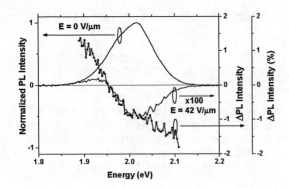

FIGURE 1. Normalized photoluminescence (PL) spectrum of the CdSe sensitized device acquired with $E=0$ and the change in the PL spectrum when $E=42$ V/μm.

A model of electric field dependent photogeneration from polymer-embedded CdSe nanoparticles has been presented [5], where the holes photogenerated within the nanoparticles tunnel through the triangular potential barrier formed by the tilted valence band edge of the polymer. Field-assisted escape of the holes could account for the observed decrease in the photoluminescence intensity. The larger percentage reduction at higher energies can also be partly attributed to an increased tunneling probability, due to the hole energy states lying closer to the top of the triangular potential barrier, hence seeing a smaller effective barrier thickness. The net increase in the PL intensity on the low energy side of the emission peak may be accounted for by the recapture of a small fraction of the librated holes into the lowest energy states (the larger diameter dots).

Figure 2 shows the results of a comparable study into the electric field dependence of the PL emission from a CdSe/ZnS sensitized device (PVK:EHDNPB:CdSe/ZnS 52:47.5:0.4 by %wt). The addition of the ZnS barrier layer resulted in a greater reduction in the PL intensity (4 % at the peak PL emission energy of 1.92 eV). The percentage reduction is approximately constant over the whole PL peak and, in particular, there is no observable intensity increase at lower energies.

FIGURE 2. Normalized photoluminescence (PL) spectrum of the CdSe/ZnS sensitized device acquired with $E=0$ and the change in the PL spectrum when $E=42$ V/μm.

ZnS has a bulk band gap of 3.7 eV which is significantly larger than that of CdSe (1.75 eV), and so the ZnS shell can be expected to act as barrier to charge recapture. Recapture may be by either an ionized nanoparticle encountered by a free hole or by the nanoparticle in which the charge was generated. A reduction in the recapture of photoliberated holes due to the ZnS barrier is consistent with observed absence of an increase in PL with field for the CdSe/ZnS nanoparticle. The greater reduction in PL observed for the shelled nanoparticle in general indicates that immediate recapture of charge by the nanoparticle of origin is also reduced or at least increases less quickly with field than does the escape rate.

In summary, we have studied the field-dependent PL spectra of nanoparticle sensitized photorefractive polymers. The PL intensity was found to be strongly dependent on the applied field; a ZnS shell layer was also found to play a crucial role.

REFERENCES

1. O. Ostroverkhova and W. E. Moerner, *Chem. Rev.* **104**, 3267 (2004).
2. K. Meerholz, B. L. Volodin, B. K. Sandalphon, B. Kippelen, and N. Peyghambarian, *Nature* **371**, 497 (1994).
3. D. Wright, M. A. Diaz-Garcia, J. D. Casperson, M. DeClue, W. E. Moerner, and R. J. Twieg, *Appl. Phys. Lett.* **73**, 1490 (1998).
4. J. G. Winiarz, L. Zhang, M. Lal, C. S. Friend, and P. N. Parsad, *J. Am. Chem. Soc.* **121**, 5287 (1999).
5. D. J. Binks, *IEEE J. Quant. Electron.* **40**, 1140 (2004).
6. F. Aslam, D. J. Binks, M. D. Rahn, D. P. West, P. O'Brien, N. Pickett, and S. Daniels, *J. Chem. Phys.* **122**, 184713 (2005).
7. F. Aslam, D. J. Binks, S. Daniels, N. Pickett, and P. O'Brien, *Chem. Phys.* **316**, 171 (2005).

Size Dependence of Phonon Scattering in CdSe/CdS/ZnS Nanocrystals

Thomas J. Liptay[1], Sonia Rao Pallavi[2], Rajeev J. Ram[1], Moungi G. Bawendi[2]

[1]Research Laboratory of Electronics, Massachusetts Institute of Technology, Cambridge, MA, USA, 02139
[2]Department of Chemistry, Massachusetts Institute of Technology, Cambridge, MA, USA, 02139

Abstract. We extract the room temperature homogeneous linewidth for 5 sizes of CdSe/CdS/ZnS nanocrystals from the temperature dependence of the ensemble emission spectra. We find that the homogeneous linewidth scales as $1/R^2$ for small nanocrystals as is expected for acoustic phonon scattering. We analyze the contributions of an inhomogeneous size distribution, spectral diffusion, and the homogeneous linewidth to the NC ensemble spectrum at room temperature.

INTRODUCTION

We investigate the physical mechanisms that contribute to the emission linewidth of CdSe/CdS/ZnS nanocrystal (NC) ensembles at room temperature with particular attention to the size dependence of the homogeneous linewidth. The room temperature homogeneous linewidth is an important parameter because it sets a fundamental limit on how narrow a NC ensemble photoluminescence (PL) spectra can be made in the relevant temperature regime for most NC applications. The NC ensemble linewidth determines the color saturation for NC-based displays, the number of distinguishable colors in biological imaging, and the number of distinguishable microbead optical barcodes. For all of these applications it is desirable to make the ensemble linewidth as narrow as possible. Our goal is to quantify the ensemble broadening mechanisms at room temperature which include inhomogeneous size/shape distribution, spectral diffusion, and the homogeneous linewidth. We use the temperature dependence of the ensemble PL spectra to infer the homogenous linewidth at T=300K for different sized NCs and find reasonable agreement with the expected magnitude and size dependence of acoustic phonon broadening which is expected to dominate the homogeneous linewidth for small NCs at T=300K.

EXPERIMENT

We embed high quality CdSe/CdS/ZnS NCs from QDot Corp. in a PLMA matrix and measure the emission spectra for T=5-300K for 5 sizes of NC (λ=655nm, 605nm, 585nm, 565nm, 545nm). The samples exhibit ensemble linewidths that are narrow (25-30nm) and have a high quantum yield >50%. We use the temperature dependence of the ensemble PL linewidth to infer the homogeneous linewidth at room temperature. Since the ensemble linewidth is expected to broaden due to an increase in the homogeneous linewidth with temperature, we can infer the room temperature homogeneous linewidth by fitting the room temperature emission spectrum to a convolution of the T=5K spectrum with a Gaussian of variable width. The extracted homogeneous linewidth is the Gaussian width that results in the best least squares fit. This technique allows us to extract the homogeneous linewidth at T=300K, while most experimental data is at cryogenic temperatures. An advantage of this technique is that it is insensitive to the effects of spectral diffusion since spectral diffusion broadening is expected to be temperature independent [1].

RESULTS AND DISCUSSION

Figure 1 shows that the inferred room temperature homogeneous linewidth scales approximately like $1/R^2$ for small R. This size dependence agrees well with calculations of the deformation potential coupling for bare CdSe NCs using bulk material parameters which predict that the homogeneous linewidth is a Gaussian that scales as $\Gamma_{homo}=AT$ where $A\sim1/R^2$ [2]. Our measured value of A is about 60% greater than calculated in ref [2], however this may be due to the ZnS capping layer since the deformation potential coupling is expected to be sensitive to the material surrounding the CdSe core [3]. In bulk CdSe, the room temperature homogeneous linewidth is modeled

CP893, *Physics of Semiconductors, 28th International Conference*
edited by W. Jantsch and F. Schäffler
© 2007 American Institute of Physics 978-0-7354-0397-0/07/$23.00

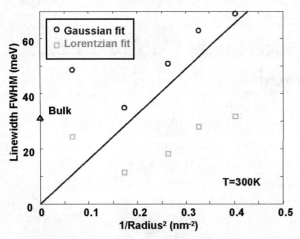

FIGURE 1. Inferred room temperature homogeneous linewidth assuming either a Gaussian (circle) or Lorentzian (square) homogeneous spectra.

as a Lorentzian and determined by optical phonon scattering [4]. Figure 1 shows that as the NCs become larger the inferred homogeneous linewidth assuming a Lorentzian (as opposed to a Gaussian) increases and approaches the bulk value. We interpret our data to indicate that the dominant homogeneous broadening mechanism at room temperature transitions from acoustic phonon scattering to optical phonon scattering when NCs become larger than R~2.5nm. However, NC ensemble spectra are also broadened by an inhomogeneous size distribution and spectral diffusion.

Spectral diffusion refers to the fact that the spectra of single NCs change with time. This effect has been attributed to Stark shifts due to fluctuating local electric fields caused by charges moving in the matrix around the NC. Measurements of the emission spectra of single CdSe/CdS nanorods (R_{core}~3nm) show the broadening due to spectral diffusion is approximately Γ_{SD}=30meV ($\Delta\lambda$=10nm) and is independent of temperature [1]. The size dependence of spectral diffusion broadening can be estimated from measurements of the Stark shift in single NC spectra in ref [5] which infer the average polarizability α and internal electric field ξ_{int} of different sized CdSe NCs when no external electric field is applied. Using the data in ref [5] we infer that the average Stark shift $\Delta E=\alpha\xi_{int}^2/2$ due to fluctuating local electric fields has a weak size dependence (the magnitude can not be inferred without more information about the electric field). We assume that the broadening due to spectral diffusion is 10nm for all NC sizes. If all of the line broadening mechanisms are independent and Gaussian, then their variances add and the broadening due to the inhomogeneous size distribution Γ_{size} can be inferred from $\Gamma_{ensemble}^2 = \Gamma_{homo}^2 + \Gamma_{SD}^2 + \Gamma_{size}^2$. Figure

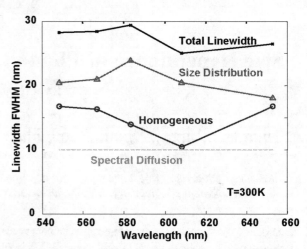

FIGURE 2. Contributions to the room temperature ensemble linewidth. See text for details.

2 indicates that even for our high quality NC samples, the inhomogeneous size distribution is the dominant broadening mechanism at room temperature, but that the homogeneous linewidth is an important contribution. The model in figure 2 agrees well with measurements of single R=2.8nm CdSe/ZnS NC PL spectra at room temperature which show a linewidth of approximately 20nm [6] and should only include the homogeneous linewidth and spectral diffusion effects.

In conclusion, our inferred homogeneous linewidth for CdSe/CdS/ZnS NCs at room temperature scales as $1/R^2$ and is consistent with acoustic phonon broadening. Our analysis indicates that at room temperature the PL linewidth of NC ensembles could be reduced by approximately 50% if size inhomogeneities and spectral diffusion could be eliminated.

ACKNOWLEDGMENTS

This research was funded in part by the Packard Foundation

REFERENCES

1. J. Muller, J.M. Lupton, A.L. Rogach, J. Feldman, D.V. Talapin, and H. Weller, Phys. Rev. Lett., **93**, 167402 (2004).
2. T. Takagahara, *J. Lumin.*, **70**, 129 (1996).
3. S.V. Goupalov, R.A. Suris, P. Lavallard, and D.S. Citrin, *Nanotechnology*, **12**, 518 (2001).
4. J. Voigt, F. Spiegelberg, and M. Senoner, *Phys. Stat. Sol. B*, **91**, 189 (1979).
5. S.A. Empedocles and M.G. Bawendi, *Science*, **278**, 2114 (1997).
6. S.A. Empedocles and M.G. Bawendi, *J. Phys. Chem. B*, **103**, 1826 (1999).

Study of non radiative relaxation and exciton-phonon coupling in colloidal CdTe Quantum Dots

G. Morello, M. De Giorgi, S. Kudera, L. Manna, R. Cingolani and M. Anni

National Nanotechnology Laboratory of INFM-CNR c/o Distretto Tecnologico ISUFI, Università di Lecce, Via per Arnesano, 73100 Lecce, Italy

Abstract. In this contribution we present temperature and size dependence of the non radiative relaxation and exciton-phonon coupling in colloidal CdTe Quantum Dots (QDs). PL measurements as a function of the temperature show that the main non radiative process which limits the quantum efficiency at room temperature is the thermal escape, assisted by multiple LO phonons absorption. The number of phonons involved in the thermal escape and the exciton-phonon coupling strongly depend on the QDs size. In particular, the coupling constant with the acoustical phonons is strongly enhanced in QDs with respect to CdTe quantum well systems and bulk CdTe. On the contrary, the exciton-LO phonon interaction decreases as the degree of quantum confinement increases.

Keywords: Nanocrystals, CdTe, Exciton-phonon couplig, Non radiative relaxation.
PACS: 78.67.Bf, 73.21.La, 78.55.Et

INTRODUCTION

Semiconductor nanocrystals are currently being extensively studied in the context of their size-dependent photophysical properties.

In this work we performed a detailed analysis of the PL temperature dependence of colloidal CdTe core QDs with diameters varying between 4.2 nm and 5.9 nm. The size dependence of both non radiative relaxation and exciton-phonon coupling were studied.

EXPERIMENTAL DETAILS

Following the method described in Ref. 1 we synthesized CdTe QDs having average diameter (estimated by TEM measurements) of 4.2 nm, 4.9 nm, 5.9 nm for samples A1, A2, and A3, respectively. For each sample, we performed PL measurements in the temperature range of 15÷300 K, and absorption measurements at room temperature.

Results and Discussion

A typical absorption spectrum is shown in the inset of Fig. 1. In order to study the size dependence of exciton-phonon coupling, we analized the temperature dependence of the PL broadening. Fig. 1 shows the FWHM for all the three samples as a function of the temperature.

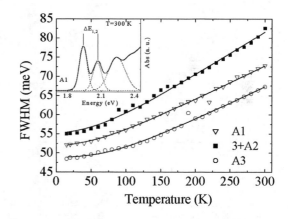

Figure 1. Full Width at Half Maximum (FWHM) of the PL spectra as a function of temperature (symbols) for the three samples, and respective best fit curves (continuous lines). Inset: typical absorption spectrum.

We deduced the role of the acoustical and optical phonons in the PL broadening by fitting the experimental FWHM to the following equation[2]:

$$\Gamma(T) = \Gamma_{inh} + \sigma T + \Gamma_{LO}(e^{E_{LO}/k_B T} - 1)^{-1} \qquad (1)$$

where, Γ_{inh} is the inhomogeneous broadening, which is temperature independent and it is due to fluctuations in size, shape, and composition of the nanocrystals, σ is

CP893, *Physics of Semiconductors, 28th International Conference*
edited by W. Jantsch and F. Schäffler
© 2007 American Institute of Physics 978-0-7354-0397-0/07/$23.00

the exciton-acoustic phonons coupling coefficient, Γ_{LO} represents the exciton-LO phonons coupling coefficient, E_{LO} is the LO phonon energy and k_B is the Boltzmann constant.

We found that the best fit values of the exciton-acoustic phonons coupling constant σ (31, 33, 14 μeV/K for samples A1, A2, A3, respectively) are about three orders of magnitude higher than the theoretical value estimated by Rudin et al[3] (about 0.72 μeV/K) for bulk CdTe. On the contrary, the best fit values of the carrier-LO phonons coupling coefficient, Γ_{LO} (14, 18.3, 21 meV for samples A1, A2, A3, respectively), are smaller than the theoretical bulk value[3] (Γ_{LO} = 24.5 meV) and decreases as the QDs size decreases. These results can be ascribed to quantum confinement and they are consistent with theoretical predictions and experimental observations[4].

Finally, the LO phonon energy (around 20 meV for all the samples) is, within the fitting error, consistent with the bulk value (21.1 meV[5]).

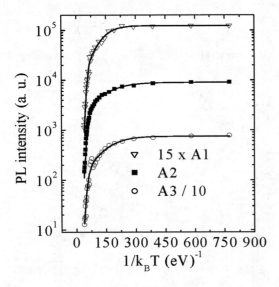

Figure 2. Integrated PL intensity dependence on the samples temperature (symbols), and best fit curves (continuous lines) to Eq.(2). The data are scaled for clarity.

In order to determine the different non radiative processes affecting the carriers relaxation, we studied the PL intensity variations with temperature.

In Fig. 2 we show the PL intensity dependence on $1/k_B T$. For all the samples the photoluminescence intensity is almost constant up to about 40 K, while a first thermally activated PL decrease is visible in the range 40-170 K, followed by a stronger exponential decrease up to 300 K. Usually, the relaxation processes in QDs include radiative relaxation, Auger nonradiative scattering, Förster resonant energy transfer (FRET) between dots of different dimensions,

thermal escape from the dot[6], and carriers localization at surface states.

As we are in the low excitation regime, Auger interaction can be neglected. Moreover, FRET is inefficient because of the large interdot distance ($\geq 1\mu m$). So if we take into account the radiative relaxation, a thermally activated non radiative process (with activation energy E_a), and the thermal escape via LO phonon scattering, the integrated PL intensity $I_{PL}(T)$ as a function of the temperature T is given by the equation[7]:

$$I_{PL}(T) = \frac{I_0}{1 + a \cdot e^{-E_a/k_B T} + b(e^{E_{LO}/k_B T} - 1)^{-m}} \qquad (2)$$

where $I_{PL}(T)$ is the integrated PL intensity at temperature T, I_0 is the 0 K integrated PL intensity, and is the number of LO phonons involved in thermal escape of carriers and E_{LO} is their energy.

The value of E_a is of the order of 10-15 meV and it does not depend on the dot size, suggesting that the process is due to carriers delocalization from surface defect states lying 10-15 meV under the band-edge emission. The average number of LO phonons absorbed in the process increases as the dot diameter decreases (4.0±0.3, 4.9±0.2, 5.6±1.7, for samples A3, A2, A1, respectively). By comparing the total energy absorbed from LO phonons in the thermal escape, given by $E_{LO} \cdot m$ (84±6, 103±4, 118±35 meV for samples A1, A2, A3, respectively) and the energy separation between the first and the second excited states estimated by the absorption spectra analysis $\Delta E_{1,2}$ (82.2, 96.5, 124.5 meV for samples A3, A2, A1, respectively) we observe an overall very good agreement for all the samples, suggesting that the thermal escape is actually the main non radiative process affecting the quantum yeld at high temperature.

REFERENCES

[1] Z. A. Peng and X. G. Peng, *Jour. Am. Chem. Soc* **123**, 183 (2001).

[2] Johnson Lee, Emil S. Koteles and M. O. Vassel, *Phys. Rev. B* **33**, 5512 (1986).

[3] S. Rudin, T. L. Reinecke and B. Segall, *Phys. Rev. B* **42**, 11218 (1990).

[4] F. Gindele, K. Hild, W. Langbein and U. Woggon, *J. Lumin* **87-89**, 381 (2000).

[5] Landolt-Börnstein, *Numerical Data and Functional Relationship in Science and Technology*, edited by K. H. Hellwege (Springer-Verlag Berlin, Germany, 1982), Gp. III, Vol. 17 a.

[6] W. Yang, R. R. Lowe-Webb, H. Lee and P. C. Sercel, *Phys. Rev. B* **56**, 13314 (1997)

[7] D. Valerini, A Creti, M. Lomascolo, L. Manna, R. Cingolani and M. Anni, *Phys. Rev. B* **71**, 235409 (2005).

Self Organized Grown Stranski-Krastanow II-VI Quantum Dots Vs. Colloidal Nanocrystals Integrated In Epitaxial Nanostructures

Ch. Arens[1], O. Schöps[2], M.V. Artemyev[3], U. Woggon[2], K. Lischka[1] and D. Schikora[1]

[1]Dep. Physik, Universität Paderborn, Warburger Str. 100, 33098 Paderborn, Germany
[2]FB Physik, Universität Dortmund, Otto-Hahn-Str. 4, 44227 Dortmund, Germany
[3]Institute for Physico-Chemical Problems of Belarussian State University, Minsk 220080, Belarus

Abstract. We have integrated colloidal CdSe nanocrystals (NC) in MBE-grown ZnSe layers. In this paper we compare their density, size, size distribution and their optical tuning range with that of self-organized grown Stranski-Krastanow (SK) CdSe-QDs which are used as a reference. We find that the density of epitaxially overgrown NCs can be varied in a wider range than the SK-QD density. The size and shape of NCs is variable and this leads to a wide optical tuning range of the NC emission. The size of SK-QD is fixed due to the thermodynamic formation process. Further we found, that the size distribution of overgrown NCs is in the range of the size distribution of SK-QDs or even smaller.

Keywords: Colloidal nanocrystals, Stranski-Krastanow quantum dots
PACS: 78.67.Bf, 78.67.Hc, 81.07.Bc, 81.07.Ta

INTRODUCTION

Semiconductor quantum dots (QDs) find application in optoelectronic devices e.g. QD lasers and single photon sources. They may be produced *either* by an epitaxial growth process (Stranski-Krastanow) or *are prepared* wet-chemically as colloidal nanocrystals (NCs). Recently we have integrated colloidal CdSe NCs in MBE-grown ZnSe layers [1]. In this paper we compare their density, size, size distribution and their optical tuning range with that of self organized grown SK CdSe-QDs [2,3] which are used as a reference.

EXPERIMENTAL RESULTS

For the incorporation of CdSe-NCs into an epitaxial matrix first a ZnSe buffer has been grown by molecular beam epitaxy (MBE) on GaAs. In a second step, the sample has been transferred out of the ultra high vacuum (UHV) and NCs were deposited by spin coating under clean room conditions. Then, the sample was transferred back into the MBE chamber and the epitaxial ZnSe top layer was grown. Figure 1 shows

reflection high energy electron diffraction (RHEED) patterns taken during or after each fabrication step. The pattern shown in Fig. 1a was observed during the growth of the ZnSe buffer revealing a perfect 2-dimensional growth regime. Figure 1b shows the sample surface after ex-situ deposition of CdSe NCs and MBE of a 2.5nm thick ZnSe cap layer. The pattern is spotty due to the presence of NCs. Figure 1c was obtained after epitaxial overgrowth of the NCs with a 22nm thick ZnSe cap layer. The streaky pattern reveals clearly that the surface became 2D again.

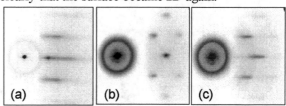

FIGURE 1. RHEED pattern obtained during the preparation of epitaxially overgrown colloidal NCs-QDs. a) ZnSe buffer surface before NC deposition, b) after spin coating with NCs and a caplayer of 2.5nm ZnSe, c) after 22nm ZnSe caplayer.

The SK-QD formation requires continuous UHV conditions. On a ZnSe buffer 2.1 to 3.1 monolayers

CP893, *Physics of Semiconductors, 28th International Conference*
edited by W. Jantsch and F. Schäffler

(ML) of CdSe were deposited. Then CdSe QDs were formed at a temperature of 340°C. In a last step, the CdSe islands were capped by ZnSe. Details of the growth procedure are given in [2,3]. The RHEED patterns observed before and after the SK-QD formation as well as after the cap layer growth are similar to those depicted in Fig. 1. This means the interruption of the growth process and exposure of the ZnSe buffer to air and chemical solutions obviously can be tolerated.

The density of epitaxially overgrown colloidal NCs is mainly influenced by the procedure of NC-deposition on the ZnSe layer before the overgrowth process which allows varying the NC density in a relatively wide range. Especially low densities (in the order of 1 NC/μm^2 may be achieved) [4].

The size and shape of the NC can be influenced during their organometallic synthesis. The monomer concentration in solution determines the NC shape: extremely high monomer concentration leads to highly anisotropic growth of wurtzite NCs. The growth along the c-axis is faster and this leads to the formation of nanorods (NR) instead of nanodots (ND). The diameter of the NCs can be influenced by the growth time [5].

The density and the size of SK-QDs are correlated and cannot be varied independently. They are related to the amount of CdSe deposited before the QD formation. Therefore, the density of CdSe SK-QDs can be varied only in a range between about $10^9 cm^{-2}$ and $10^{11} cm^{-2}$ [2], and the size variation is rather small. This can be inferred from PL measurements since the PL peak energy is correlated with the QD size.

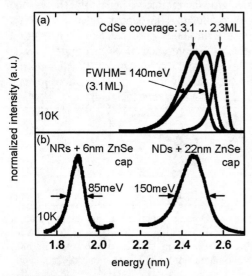

FIGURE 2. Low temperature photoluminescence spectra of a) SK-QDs with different coverages of CdSe (E_{exc}=3.81eV) and b) of overgrown nanorods (NRs) and nanodots (NDs) (E_{exc}=2.87eV).

Figure 2 shows low temperature PL spectra of SK-QD samples and overgrown NCs, respectively. With increasing CdSe coverage the peak emission of the SK-QDs shifts to lower energies, but can only be varied between 2.6eV (2.3ML CdSe) and 2.4eV (3.1ML CdSe) [3]. In contrast, the depicted luminescence spectra of overgrown colloidal NCs span a wide spectral range, due to the variation of size (and shape) of the NCs. Additionally some samples with a cap layer thickness larger than the NC diameter show ZnSe-related trap emission centered around 2.25 eV which is not observed in SK-QD samples and might be suppressed by post growth annealing processes.

The full width at half maximum (FWHM) of the photoluminescence is determined by the size distribution of the nano-objects. As can be seen in Fig. 2 the FWHM of the emission from overgrown NC is about 85meV to 150meV and similar or even smaller than the FWHM of 140meV of SK-QDs, indicating a similar size distribution of the nano-objects.

CONCLUSIONS

Our studies reveal that both growth procedures (the SK-QD formation and the epitaxial overgrowth of colloidal NCs), though fundamentally different, have some advantages. The epitaxial overgrowth of NCs allows efficient tuning of the density and the emission wavelength of the QDs. This is advantageous for their application in optoelectronic devices which can cover a broad spectral range. However, in the production process of these devices the epitaxial process must be interrupted by spin coating of the epilayers with NCs, while the self-organized formation of SK-QDs is fully compatible with monolithic semiconductor structures, but does not allow an independent influence of the physical properties of the QDs.

ACKNOWLEDGMENTS

We acknowledge financial support by DFG (Graduiertenkolleg GRK 726, project Schi 345 and Wo 477) and the EU project HPRN-CT-2002-00298.

REFERENCES

1. U. Woggon et al., *Nano Letters* **5**, 483-490 (2005).
2. D. Schikora et al., *Appl. Phys. Lett.* **76**, 418-420 (2000).
3. M.Strassburg et al., *Appl. Phys. Let.* **76**, 685-687 (2000).
4. U. Woggon, "II-VI Semiconductor Quantum Dots – Self –organized, epitaxially grown nanostructures" in Landolt-Börnstein New Series III/34C2, Optical properties of Semiconductor Nanostructures, edited by C. Klingshirn, Springer-Verlag 2004, pp. 348-393
5. X. Peng, et al., *Nature* **404**, 59-61 (2000)

Controlled Growth of CdSe Tetrapod Nanocrystals

L. J. Zhao[1], Q. Pang[1], N. Regnault[2], S. H. Yang[3], W. K. Ge[1], R. Ferreira[2], G. Bastard[2], and J. N. Wang[1*]

[1]*Physics Department, Hong Kong University of Science and Technology, Clear Water Bay, Hong Kong, China*
[2]*Laboratoire Pierre Aigrain, Ecole Normale Supérieure, 24 rue Lhomond F75005, Paris, France*
[3]*Chemistry Department, Hong Kong University of Science and Technology, Clear Water Bay, Hong Kong, China*

Abstract. Almost pure tetrapod-shaped CdSe nanocrystals were successfully synthesized using a simple method by controlling the protonic acidity of the cadmium OA-TOP precursor. A detailed investigation on the growth mechanism of CdSe tetrapod nanocrystals has been carried out. The results indicate that the proton (H^+) present not only induce the surface modification but also may affect the growth speed and the special morphology of tetrapods can affect the ripening speed. The field induced emission from CdSe tetrapods was also observed.

Keywords: tetrapod, mechanism, proton, emission
PACS: 61. 46. Hk, 73. 63. Bd, 78. 55. Et

INTRODUCTION

The tetrapod-shaped nanocrystals can potentially lead to a variety of interesting mechanical, electrical, and optical properties [1]. Tetrapods can also serve as a very interesting building block to prepare superstructures, especially three-dimensional ones. We have successfully synthesized almost pure tetrapod-shaped CdSe nanocrystals using a simple method by controlling the protonic acidity of the cadmium OA (oleic acid)-TOP (trioctylphosphine) precursor [2]. Here, as a continuation of our previous work, we have carried out a detailed investigation on the growth mechanism of CdSe tetrapod nanocrystals. The TEM results show that the growth time is about 10 min for CdSe tetrapods. The absorption spectra for samples with different reaction time show that the growth and Ostwald ripening of the core of tetrapod is slower than that of dot. The field induced emission from CdSe tetrapods was also observed.

EXPERIMENTS

Detailed syntheses of CdSe nanocrystals can be found elsewhere [2]. When HCl was added to the cadmium OA-TOP precursor, tetrapod-shaped CdSe nanocrystals can be obtained. During the reaction, an aliquot at a given reaction time was taken out from the reaction flask and quickly transferred into a vial with chloroform. The product was washed with methanol three times, and redissolved in chloroform. The size, shape, and crystal structures of CdSe nanocrystals were examined using a JEOL 2010F high-resolution transmission electron microscopy. UV/vis absorption spectra were obtained using a Milton Roy Spectronic 300 spectrometer and samples in solution were used. The field emission measurements were carried out in all metal UHV chamber evacuated at a pressure 1×10^{-7} Torr; CdSe tetrapod nanocrystals deposited on n-type silicon substrate was used as cathode.

RESULTS AND DISCUSSIONS

TEM analyses of the tetrapod samples with different reaction times show that tetrapod -shaped nanocrystals cannot be observed if the reaction time is shorter than 10 minutes. This indicates that the first 10 minutes of the reaction is the core's growth time. When the reaction is beyond 20 minutes, high yields of tetrapod-shaped CdSe nanocrystals are observed. The absorption spectra of the tetrapod samples with different reaction time are shown in Fig. 1 together with that of dot samples. During the core growth time (Fig. 1(a)), the absorption peaks of the dot samples are red shifted in comparison with that of tetrapods. This implies that the dots grow faster than the tetrapods' cores. In our experiments, the only difference between

---

* Corresponding author email: phjwang@ust.hk

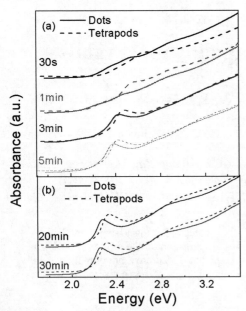

FIGURE 1. Absorption spectra of CdSe tetrapods with different reaction time (a) during core growth stage and (b) during arm growth stage

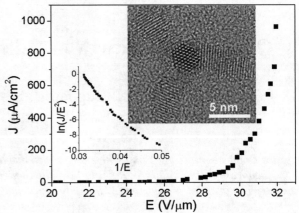

FIGURE 2. Field emission characteristic of CdSe tetrapod samples

the synthesis of dot-shaped and tetrapod-shaped CdSe nanocrystals is the addition of HCl into the cadmium precursor before heating. As a result, we believe it is the proton (H^+) that slows down the growth of tetrapod cores. At the beginning of the reaction, the proton (H^+) influences mainly the yield of zinc blende nuclei and passivates those crystal facets such as {110}, except the four {111} facets. The passivation of some facets slows down the growth of the tetrapod cores. However, for longer reaction times, the four arms are grown out along the four nonpassivated {111} facets. As can be seen from Fig. 1b, the absorption spectra of CdSe tetrapods during arm growth stage show no qualitative difference from that of CdSe dots except the dot spectra are red shifted. These are expected from the theoretical calculation [2] which indicated that the first four states for our tetrapods only depend on the core size. Since the H^+ slows down the growth speed of CdSe tetrapod cores, the dot size is larger than the core size. The quantum confinement effect results in a lower energy states for larger dots.

Figure 2 shows the field emission characteristic of the 30min sample whose HRTEM image was shown in the inset of Fig. 2. The J –E curve in Fig. 2 shows a turn on field, i.e. the field for which J is 0.1 $\mu A\ cm^{-2}$ is 21.5 V μm^{-1}. The J–E data were also analyzed by applying the Fowler–Nordheim (F-N) equation:

$$J = \frac{aE^2}{\beta^2\phi}\exp(\frac{b\phi^{3/2}}{\beta E})$$ where J is the current density,

E is the applied field, ϕ is the work function, β is the field enhancement factor, a and b are constants. The F-

N emission behavior can be examined from the linearity of curves by plotting ln (J/E −2) versus 1/E. The F-N plot is also shown in the inset of Fig. 2 which exhibits a linear behavior in the low field region but deviates from F-N behavior in high field region. We attribute the deviation of F-N plot in the high field region to the emission current contribution from additional emitters and the varied field enhancements for different tetrapods.

CONCLUSIONS

Almost pure tetrapod-shaped CdSe nanocrystals were successfully synthesized using a simple method by controlling the protonic acidity of the cadmium OA-TOP precursor. Results indicate that the proton (H^+) present induce the surface modification and affect the reaction rate of the tetrapods. Field emission characteristic of the sample shows the tetrapods have a turn on field of 21.5 V μm^{-1}. The nonlinear FN plot was attributed to the emission current contribution from additional emitters and the varied field enhancements for different tetrapods.

ACKNOWLEDGMENTS

The authors would like to thank the Research Grant Council of Hong Kong for the financial support via Grant Nos. HKUST6069/02P and F-HK18/03T.

REFERENCES

1. L. Manna, D. J. Milliron, A. Meisel, E. C. Scher and A. P. Alivisatos, *Nat. Mater.* **2**, 382 (2003)
2. Q. Pang, L.J. Zhao, Y. Cai, D. P. Nguyen, N. Regnault, N.Wang, S.H. Yang, W.K. Ge, R. Ferreira, G. Bastard, and J.N. Wang, *Chem. Mater.* **17**, 5263 (2005)

CHAPTER 9

SEMICONDUCTOR QUANTUM ELECTRODYNAMICS, STRONG COUPLING

Cavity quantum electrodynamics for two quantum dots

Elena del Valle, Filippo Troiani and Carlos Tejedor

Dep. de Física Teórica de la Materia Condensada, Universidad Autónoma de Madrid, 28049 Madrid, Spain

Abstract. We analyse the decay rate of one and two quantum dots coupled to a cavity mode in all coupling regimes. In the weak coupling regime, the system undergoes a superradiant cascade in case of identical detunings with the cavity. We study how adding inhomogeneous detuning induces oscillations which can enhace or destroy the cooperative effect.

Keywords: Cavity quantum electrodynamics, Superradiance, Quantum dots
PACS: 78.67.Hc, 42.50.Fx, 42.50.Pq

Semiconductor quantum dots (QD) are artificial atoms with interesting quantum optical properties. In realistic systems, one usually works with several QD embedded in a semiconductor cavity implying situations without counterpart in atoms: QD are not exactly equal in size and spectrum. This disorder effect opens new possibilities in cavity quantum-electrodynamics. As the simplest case, we consider two QD which are not directly coupled to each other. Neglecting spin effects (for instance for charged QD), QD are two level systems with detunings d_1 and d_2 with respect to the cavity mode of frequency ω. The QD–cavity system is described in terms of spin operators by Jaynes Cummings Hamiltonian [1]:

$$\hat{H} = \hbar\omega\hat{a}^\dagger\hat{a} + \hbar\sum_{i=1,2}\left[(\omega - d_i)\hat{s}_i^z + g(\hat{a}\hat{s}_i^+ + \hat{a}^\dagger\hat{s}_i^-)\right] \quad (1)$$

We solved numerically [2] a master equation where both pure dephasing and leaky mode emission can be neglected and photon emission is only from the cavity mode (with rate κ). For identical emitters, we can express the Hamiltonian in terms of the total collective angular momentum $\hat{J} \equiv \sum_{i=1,2}\hat{s}_i$, symmetric under QD exchange. Hence, it is convenient to express all magnitudes in the the Dicke state basis, which in our case consists of the triplet and singlet states $\{|T_1\rangle, |T_0\rangle, |S_0\rangle, |T_{-1}\rangle\}$.

We are interested in the total intensity emitted into the cavity mode starting from the initial state $|T_1, 0 \text{ photon}\rangle$. However, since the only decay process in the system is the emission of cavity photons, we can study the intensity of the emission through QD deexcitation [3]: $I(t) = E_0\Gamma_1\langle\hat{J}_+\hat{J}_-\rangle = 2\rho_{T_1} + 2\rho_{T_0}$. This magnitude can be separated into two contributions, one which is the sum of the independent emissions of the QD ($\langle\hat{s}_+^1\hat{s}_-^1\rangle + \langle\hat{s}_+^2\hat{s}_-^2\rangle$) and the other representing the correlations between them, ($\langle\hat{s}_+^1\hat{s}_-^2\rangle + \langle\hat{s}_+^2\hat{s}_-^1\rangle$). In Fig. 1 we plot the decay rate of the dots, fixing the coupling strengh at a reasonable value $g = 0.05$meV and varying κ (from strong to weak coupling regime). In the *strong coupling* regime ($\kappa \ll 4g$), the main feature are the Rabi oscillations, the exchange

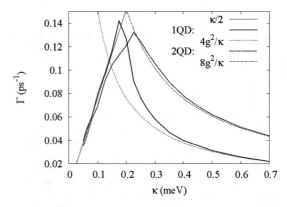

FIGURE 1. Decay rates of two and one QD with $g = 0.05$meV and $d_1 = d_2 = 0$ as a function of κ.

of cavity photons between the two QD and the cavity. Since the photon has finite probability to escape the cavity, the oscillations are exponentially damped with the photon decay rate $\Gamma = \frac{\kappa}{2}$.

In the *weak coupling* regime ($\kappa \gg 4g$), there is little time for Rabi oscillations and stimulated processes before the irreversible photon escape, shortly after being emitted by the QD. Basically (in d_1, $d_2 \ll \kappa$) each QD spontaneously emits cavity photons with a rate which is enhanced by the *Purcell Effect* ($\Gamma_1 = \frac{4g}{\kappa} \sim Q\Gamma_{\text{vac}}$). Time evolution of two identical QD in this regime can be described as a Dicke superradiant cascade, where the emission speed is increased by a factor two [4]. If the initial state is one of the triplet states, as a result of the high symmetry of the system, the singlet remains uncoupled and the time evolution takes place inside the subspace of completely symmetrical states. In a more general case ($d_1 \neq d_2$), the singlet enters the dynamics and the evolution diverges from the ideal radiative cascade. In all cases, the density matrix diagonal elements follow the rate equations [5] with two decay channels (Γ_T, Γ_S) and the total emitted intensity can be found\

CP893, *Physics of Semiconductors, 28th International Conference*
edited by W. Jantsch and F. Schäffler
© 2007 American Institute of Physics 978-0-7354-0397-0/07/$23.00

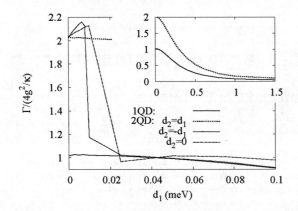

FIGURE 2. Decay rates of two and one QD with $g = 0.05$ *meV* and $\kappa = 0.6$ *meV* $= 12g$, for different detunings

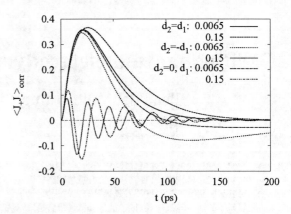

FIGURE 3. $\langle \hat{J}_+ \hat{J}_- \rangle_{\text{corr}}$ as a function of time, for $g = 0.05$meV and $\kappa = 0.6$meV and varying detuning d_1(meV).

as $I(t) = E_0 \big((\Gamma_T + \Gamma_S)\rho_{T_1} + \Gamma_T \rho_{T_0} + \Gamma_S \rho_{S_0} \big)$. There are three possibilities to obtain the decay rate Γ from our numerical results, depending on the configurations of detunings and the number of dots:

1. For one QD, $\langle \hat{J}_+ \hat{J}_- \rangle = e^{-\Gamma_1 t}$. $\Gamma \equiv \Gamma_1$ can be found by fitting this magnitude to an exponential.

2. For two identical QD, $\Gamma_T = 2\Gamma_1$ while $\Gamma_S = 0$ and the intensity reads $\langle \hat{J}_+ \hat{J}_- \rangle = 2e^{-\Gamma_T t}(1 + \Gamma_T t)$. From this expression we can extract $\Gamma \equiv \Gamma_T = 2\Gamma_1$.

3. When the QD are so distinguishable that both channels are equally relevant ($\Gamma \equiv \Gamma_T = \Gamma_S = \Gamma_1$), the intensity is the sum of the independent emission of two isolated QD: $\langle \hat{J}_+ \hat{J}_- \rangle = 2e^{-\Gamma_1 t}$.

In Fig. 1 is seen the resonant case of one and two QD. The weak coupling regime is lost when both Purcell effect ($\Gamma_1 = \frac{4g}{\kappa}$) and the superradiant factor ($\Gamma/\Gamma_1 = 2$) disappear. In Fig. 2 we vary the detuning in the three possible configurations: $d_2 = \pm d_1$ and $d_2 = 0$.

In the case of identical detunings, the Purcell Effect is also lost when d_1 is increased, while the superradiance factor remains as a proof of QD indistinguishability. On the other hand, if the detunings are different, we find a more complex dependence on the detuning. To better understand it, we plot the correlation contribution to the intensity in Fig. 3 and note that it oscillates with increasing frequency. The origin of such oscillations is the inhomogeneous detuning and the opening of the singlet decay channel. Expressing this quantity in the localized excitation basis and in the interaction picture (isolating detuning effects), we analyse the oscillations separately:

$$\langle \hat{J}_+ \hat{J}_- \rangle_{\text{corr}} = \rho_{T_0} - \rho_{S_0} = 2Re[\rho^I_{(1e2g, 1g2e)} e^{i(d_2 - d_1)t}] \quad (2)$$

This shows a new timescale: the semi-period of one of this oscillations, given by $\tau_{\text{corr}} = \big(2(d_2 - d_1) \big)^{-1}$, which is aproximately when $\langle \hat{J}_+ \hat{J}_- \rangle_{\text{corr}}$ becomes negative for

the first time. In our case we have: $\tau_{\text{corr}} = \infty$ if $d_1 = d_2$, $\tau_{\text{corr}} = (4d_1)^{-1}$ if $d_1 = -d_2$ and $\tau_{\text{corr}} = (2d_1)^{-1}$ if $d_2 = 0$. On the other hand, the decay rate at resonance gives us another timescale $\tau_{\text{sup}} = (2\frac{4g^2}{\kappa})^{-1} \sim 19$ps corresponding to the following "critical" detunings: $d_{\text{sup}} = 0.008$meV if $d_1 = -d_2$ and $d_{\text{sup}} = 0.02$meV if $d_2 = 0$. Comparing these two timescales, we find three regions (Fig. 3):

a) $\tau_{\text{corr}} \gg \tau_{\text{sup}}$ ($d_1 \ll d_{\text{sup}}$)—The QD can still be regarded as identical so the triplet decay channel dominates. $\langle \hat{J}_+ \hat{J}_- \rangle_{\text{corr}}$ remains positive during the decay and so adds to the emission. $\langle \hat{J}_+ \hat{J}_- \rangle$ displays only one exponential behaviour fitted with the two identical QD rate equation. The decay rate is enhanced by the incipient oscillations arising from the detuning, reaching a value greater than two.

b) $\tau_{\text{sup}} \sim \tau_{\text{corr}}$ ($d_1 \sim d_{\text{sup}}$)—This region shows a mixed behaviour where $\langle \hat{J}_+ \hat{J}_- \rangle$ undergoes small undulations due to $\langle \hat{J}_+ \hat{J}_- \rangle_{\text{corr}}$ becoming negative. As a consequence appear two different behaviours: The first one occurs before $\langle \hat{J}_+ \hat{J}_- \rangle_{\text{corr}}$ becomes negative and it is still superradiant. The second exponential decay corresponds to the independent emission of the QD.

c) $\tau_{\text{sup}} \gg \tau_{\text{corr}}$ ($d_1 \gg d_{\text{sup}}$)—The decay time is sufficient for many more rapid oscillations. Contribution of correlations is very small in amplitude as both triplet and singlet channels are equally possible and occupation numbers cancel. The emitted intensity is only that of a sum of independent emitters.

REFERENCES

1. E. T. Jaynes and F. W. Cummings, *Proc.IEEE* **51**, 89 (1963)
2. J. I. Perea *et al.*, *Phys. Rev. B* **70**, 115304 (2004)
3. V. V. Temmov *et al.*, *Phys. Rev. Lett.* **95**, 243602 (2005)
4. R. H. Dicke, *Phys. Rev.* **93**, 99 (1954)
5. Y. N. Chen *et al.*, *cond-mat/0401312* (2005)\

Optimized Coherent Control in Semiconductor Nano–Structures: Direct and Indirect Approaches

M. Wenin, H. Jirari and W. Pötz

Institut für Physik (Abt. Theorie), Universität Graz, A-8010, Graz, Austria

Abstract. An electron in a semiconductor double–dot (qubit) is modelled by a driven spin–boson model. Its dissipative dynamics is controlled by various optimization strategies: direct analytical inversion, indirect optimization and genetic optimization. We present results for state trapping as well as electron transfer between wells for both Markovian dynamics within the Lindblad equation and non–Markovian evolution.

Keywords: quantum dot, qubit, coherent control, inverse problem, non–Markovian dynamics
PACS: 78.67.Hc, 03.65.Yz, 73.21.La

Quantum mechanical two–level systems in solid–state materials are realized in various nanostructures, such as quantum dots or SQUIDS.[1, 2] The goal of optimal control theory (OCT) is to identify a (time–dependent) Hamiltonian $H(t)$ to drive the system from a given initial state $\rho(0)$ to a given final state ρ_f in a target time t_f, or more generally, along a prescribed quantum trajectory. [3, 4]

The time–evolution of the density matrix $\rho(t)$ of an open quantum system is governed, in general, by a non–Markovian kinetic equation,[5]

$$i\hbar \frac{\partial \rho}{\partial t} = [H(t), \rho(t)] + \int_0^t dt' K(t, t'; \rho(t'), H(t')). \quad (1)$$

Here the integral contribution accounts for the interaction of the system with the environment, whereas the commutator contains the purely unitary evolution of the system under the time–dependent Hamiltonian $H(t)$. The specific structure of the integrand $K(t, t'; \rho(t'), H(t'))$ depends on both system and environment. Sometimes it is sufficient to incorporate the system–bath interaction within a Lindblad equation.[5]

$$i\hbar \dot{\rho}(t) = [H(t), \rho(t)] + L_D[\rho(t)], \quad \rho(0) = \rho_0. \quad (2)$$

Here we choose

$$L_D[\rho(t)] = i\hbar \begin{pmatrix} \gamma_0(\rho_{11}^e - \rho_{11}(t)) & -\frac{\gamma_0}{2}\rho_{12}(t) \\ -\frac{\gamma_0}{2}\rho_{21}(t) & -\gamma_0(\rho_{11}^e - \rho_{11}(t)) \end{pmatrix}, \quad (3)$$

with ρ_{11}^e denoting the equilibrium population of level 1. γ_0 a constant decay rate. The optimization problem is formulated by a cost functional $J(\varepsilon, \rho)$. As an example we define

$$J(\varepsilon, \rho) = \frac{w_1}{2}\|\rho(t_f) - \rho_T\|^2 + \frac{w_2}{2t_f}\int_0^{t_f} dt \|\rho(t) - \rho_o(t)\|^2$$
$$+ \frac{1}{2}\int_0^{t_f} \alpha(t)\varepsilon^2(t)\,dt. \quad (4)$$

Here $\rho(t_f)$ is the density matrix at target time t_f and ρ_T corresponds to the desired target density matrix, $\rho_o(t)$ is the desired trajectory with $\rho_o(t_f) = \rho_T$. ε is the external control. $w_1 + w_2 = 1$ and $\alpha(t)$ are real weight factors. One has to minimize $J(\varepsilon, \rho)$ whereby the kinetic equation (1) acts as a constraint.

An analytic inversion of the von Neumann equation with Lindbad dissipation is numerically demonstrated for the example of control (minimization) of dissipation (decay of the diagonal elements of the density matrix). The electron Hamiltonian in the basis of left-well/right-well ground state of a double dot is $H(t) = H_0 + H_c(t)$, with $H_0 = (\Omega/2)\sigma_z$, $H_c(t) = \varepsilon_x(t)\sigma_x + \varepsilon_y(t)\sigma_y$ (using Pauli matrices). The goal posed is to trap the electron in a state with $\rho_{11} = \rho_{22} = 1/2$ ($\alpha(t) = 0$).

The fields selected for solving this problem are $\varepsilon_x(t) = -\gamma_0(\rho_{11}^e - 1/2)e^{\gamma_0 t/2}\sin(\Omega t)$, $\varepsilon_y(t) = \gamma_0(\rho_{11}^e - 1/2)e^{\gamma_0 t/2}\cos(\Omega t)$.[4] In Fig. (1) we show in part (a) the motion of the Bloch vector $\vec{r} = (x, y, z) = \text{Tr}(\vec{\sigma}\rho)$ and in part (b) the control fields. The Bloch vector moves in the $z = 0$ plane, which is equivalent to $\rho_{11} = \rho_{22} = 1/2$.

As a second example we consider control of the electron "position" z in the double dot within a spin-boson model. The relevant kinetic equation is given by[8]

$$\dot{z}(t) = -\Delta^2 \int_0^t d\tau\, e^{-Q_2(\tau)}\cos[f(t, t - \tau)]\cos[Q_1(\tau)]z(t - \tau)$$
$$+ \Delta^2 \int_0^t d\tau\, e^{-Q_2(\tau)}\sin[f(t, t - \tau)]\sin[Q_1(\tau)], \quad (5)$$

where Q_1 and Q_2 characterize the system bath correlations and are evaluated for an Ohmic bath.[6, 7] $f(t, t') = \Omega(t - t') + \int_{t'}^t dt'' \varepsilon_z(t'')$ contains the control–dependence of the effective inter–dot coupling. Δ is the intrinsic coupling between the left and right quantum dot eigenstate, respectively. $\varepsilon_z(t)$ can be implemented by one electrode attached to each of the two quantum dots. Here, $\varepsilon_y = 0$.

CP893, *Physics of Semiconductors, 28th International Conference*
edited by W. Jantsch and F. Schäffler
© 2007 American Institute of Physics 978-0-7354-0397-0/07/$23.00

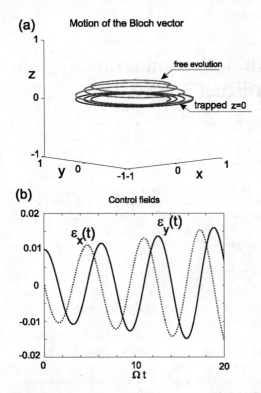

FIGURE 1. (a) Motion of the Bloch vector. Shown are the cases with and without control. In the latter case the Bloch vector moves in the $z = 0$ plane. In (b) we show the time–dependence of the control fields $\varepsilon_x(t)$ and $\varepsilon_z(t)$. Parameters: $\gamma = 0.05\Omega$, $\rho_{11}^e = 0.7$.

The parameters chosen are as follows ($k_B = \hbar = 1$):[6] $\Omega = -2$, $\Delta = 0.25$, $T = 0.5$, system–bath coupling $\eta = 0.5$, and bath cut–off frequency $\omega_c = 2$. Fig. (2) shows the electron transfer from thermal equilibrium at (0,0,-0.96), essentially corresponding to the electron residing in the left well into target state (0,0,1) ("purification"), corresponding to the electron residing in the right well. Since the intrinsic inter–well coupling Δ is constant there is only partial control over the electron and for the small value of $\Delta = 0.25$ the chosen target time of $t_f = 500$ it is challenging to complete the transfer.

For optimizing the transfer rate into the state (0,0,1) with subsequent trapping without restriction on intensity or shape of the control ($w_2 = 1$) and starting from a constant value for the control, the indirect algorithm gives the results shown as solid lines in Fig. (2).[8] We also employed a genetic algorithm (GA).[9] A spline–fit to the control field at 20 equidistant mesh points was optimized and gives the result shown by the dotted lines in Fig. (2). It is clearly visible that different control fields lead to different transfer rates. Finally, we pose the objective of the transfer to be completed at $t = t_f$ ($w_1 = 1$) for a control which is zero at $t = 0$. Results for

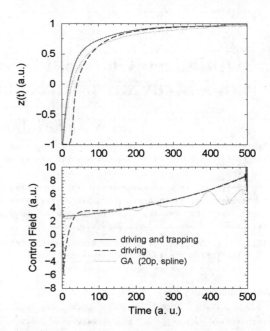

FIGURE 2. Driving the electron from the left well (thermal equilibrium at $z = -0.96$ to the right well $z = 1$. Solid line: indirect optimization (unconstrained) for driving and trapping; dashed line: indirect optimization ($\varepsilon_z(0) = 0$) for driving; dotted line: GA (unconstrained) for driving. Top figure shows relative population, bottom figure shows control field.

the indirect method using the optimal control field from the first case (solid lines) as starting point are shown by the dashed lines in Fig. (2). It can be seen that, while the transfer now is delayed, subsequently it occurs very rapidly towards the target state.

Acknowledgement-We wish to acknowledge financial support by FWF project P16317–N08.

REFERENCES

1. David P. DiVicenzo and D. Loss, Phys. Rev. B, Vol.**71**, 035318 (2005).
2. Y. Makhlin, G. Schön, and A. Shnirman, *Rev. mod. Phys.* **73**, (2001).
3. H. Jirari and W. Pötz, Phys. Rev. A. **72**, 013409 (2005).
4. M. Wenin, and W. Pötz, Phys.Rev A, **74**, 022319 (2006).
5. H. P. Breuer and F. Petruccione, *The Theory of Open Quantum Systems* (University Press, Oxford, 2002).
6. A. J. Leggett, S. Chakravarty, A. T. Dorsey, M. P. A. Fisher, A. Garg and W. Zwerger, Rev. Mod. Phy **59**, 1 (1987).
7. H. Jirari and W. Pötz, Phys. Rev. A., **74** 022306 (2006).
8. A. Goritschnig, H. Jirari, and W. Pötz, Mathmod 2006, Vienna, Feb. 2006, unpublished.
9. See: http://cuaerospace.com/carroll/ga.html

A non-Markovian optical signature for detecting entanglement in coupled excitonic qubits

F. J. Rodríguez*, L. Quiroga* and N.F. Johnson[†]

*Departamento de Física, Universidad de los Andes, A.A. 4976, Bogotá D.C., Colombia
[†]Physics Department, Clarendon Laboratory, Oxford University, Oxford OX1 3PU, U.K.

Abstract. We identify an optical signature for detecting entanglement in experimental nanostructure systems comprising coupled excitonic qubits. This signature owes its strength to *non-Markovian* dynamical effects in the second-order temporal coherence function of the emitted radiation. We calculate autocorrelation and cross-correlation functions for collective light excitation, and prove that the coherence properties of the emitted light do indeed carry information about the entanglement of the initial multi-qubit state. We also show that this signature can survive in the presence of a noisy environment.

Keywords: Semiconductors Quantum Dots Quantum Electrodynamics
PACS: 03.65.Yz, 73.21.La, 78.67.Hc, 85.35.Be

Many physical implementations of qubits have been proposed, and even built, in systems ranging from artificial nanostructures through to naturally-occurring molecules and even biological systems. However the following common problem faces *all* such systems: Having gone through the effort of forming a set of $N \geq 2$ qubits with the intention of undertaking some form of quantum information processing, *how can we be sure that entangled states are indeed being generated experimentally*? More specifically, are there any signatures for two-qubit systems that can distinguish between states such as mixed or product states (which exhibit at most classical correlations) and the crucially important entangled states which carry purely quantum correlations? This question provides the first motivation for the present work. The second motivation stems from the fact that the preparation and detection of highly-correlated quantum states are difficult to perform in a controlled way due to the interaction of the quantum system with the noisy environment – after all, this is still one of the main practical hurdles facing quantum computation. There is, therefore, a general need for detailed quantitative theory concerning the time-evolution of different initial quantum states, including their decoherence properties.

In the present work, we propose such a signature, whose experimental implementation can be achieved using current ultrafast optical spectroscopy(picoseconds scale). In addition to this important practical finding, our work provides a fundamental example of a quantum system where the Markov approximation, which is invariably employed in such calculations, yields incorrect results. Indeed, our results suggest that any such optical probe of entangled states can *only* be correctly interpreted using non-Markovian theories.

For the sake of concreteness, the qubit-matter systems we are addressing can be realized using localized excitons in semiconductor quantum dots (QDs)[1, 2, 3]. We are especially interested in the short time dynamics of such correlations where the coupled system-environment could show some unusual behaviour such as recoherence, among others. Therefore, a proper description of the dynamics must be undertaken including non-Markovian effects.

We consider the concrete example of two optically-driven, dipole-dipole interacting qubits in contact with a boson bath. The reduced density-operator in Lindblad form, is:

$$i\frac{\partial \hat{\rho}}{\partial t} = \sum_{i=1}^{2} \Delta_i [S_i^z, \hat{\rho}] + \sum_{i=1}^{2} \beta_i [S_i^{\dagger} + S_i^-, \hat{\rho}] + \sum_{i \neq j}^{2} V_{i,j} [S_i^{\dagger} S_j^-, \hat{\rho}]$$
$$- i \sum_{i,j=1}^{2} \gamma_{i,j} (S_i^{\dagger} S_j^- \hat{\rho} - 2 S_j^- \hat{\rho} S_i^{\dagger} + \hat{\rho} S_i^{\dagger} S_j^-) \qquad (1)$$

where $S_i^{\dagger}$ is a qubit raising operator, β_i is the Rabi frequency and $\Delta_i = \omega_L - \omega_i$ the laser detuning for the ith-qubit. $\gamma_{i,j}$ and $V_{i,j}$ ($i \neq j$) represent the collective decay and the dipole-dipole interaction[4] between qubits, respectively. The non-Markovian effects are thereby included by employing a time-dependent spontaneous decay $\gamma_{i,i}(t) = \gamma_i(t)$[5]. There are three control parameters: the laser field strength β_i, the driving laser detuning with the qubits, and the inter-qubit separation r_{12} which affects $V_{i,j}$. Note that although our theory employs a generalization of Markovian decay-rates to non-Markovian situations, i.e. $\gamma_{ij}(t) = \gamma_i(t)$, the strong resulting enhancement of photon-photon correlation effects which we observe is a *highly non-trivial* consequence of this generalized decay rate. The second order time correlation

CP893, *Physics of Semiconductors, 28*[th] *International Conference*
edited by W. Jantsch and F. Schäffler
© 2007 American Institute of Physics 978-0-7354-0397-0/07/$23.00

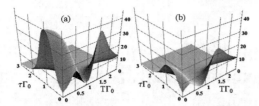

FIGURE 1. The full correlation function $g^2(T, \tau)$ for a separable initial state ($|\Psi_{QQ}\rangle$) with $\beta_1 = \beta_2 = 1.25\Gamma_0$. (a) Non-Markovian case with $\gamma_r = 2\Gamma_0$ and (b) Markovian case ($kr_{12} = \pi$). $\Gamma_0 = 2\mu eV$. The central laser frequency is detuned $\Delta_1 = -0.5\Gamma_0 = -\Delta$ and $\Delta_2 = 0.5\Gamma_0 = \Delta$, from each qubit.

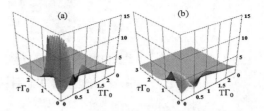

FIGURE 2. $g^2(T, \tau)$ for an initial Bell state and the same parameters as Fig. (1) but $\beta = 2.25\Gamma_0$. (a) Non-Markovian case and (b) Markovian case.

function $g^{(2)}(T, T + \tau)$ gives information about the conditional probability of detecting one photon at time $T + \tau$ provided a previous photon was found at time T. We focus on the full photon correlation is given by $g^{(2)}(T, T +$

$$\tau) = \frac{\Sigma_{i,j,l,m}\langle S_i^\dagger(T)S_j^\dagger(T+\tau)S_l^-(T+\tau)S_m^-(T)\rangle e^{i\vec{k}.\vec{r}_{i,j}}e^{-i\vec{k}.\vec{r}_{l,m}}}{\Sigma_{i,j}\langle S_i^\dagger(T)S_j^-(T)\rangle e^{i\vec{k}.\vec{r}_{i,j}}\Sigma_{l,m}\langle S_l^\dagger(T+\tau)S_m^-(T+\tau)\rangle e^{i\vec{k}.\vec{r}_{l,m}}},$$ where

$\vec{k}$ has magnitude $k = (\omega_1 + \omega_2)/2c$ and its direction coincides with the far-field observation direction ($i, j, l, m = 1, 2$). and for a collective excitation ($\beta_1 = \beta_2 = \beta$) where both qubits are simultaneously illuminated with the same non-resonant laser intensity, Additionally, different initial qubit states are analyzed: (i) A separate (non-entangled) state formed by the product of identical superposition states for each qubit, $|\Psi_{QQ}\rangle = \frac{1}{2}(|0_1\rangle + |1_1\rangle) \otimes (|0_2\rangle + |1_2\rangle)$, where the subscripts indicate the $i = 1, 2$ qubit. (ii) A maximally entangled Bell state $|\Psi_B\rangle = \frac{1}{\sqrt{2}}(|0_1 0_2\rangle + |1_1 1_2\rangle)$.

In Fig. 1, the full correlation function $g^2(T, \tau)$ is plotted for an initial separate state $|\Psi_{QQ}\rangle$. A strong antibunching of the emitted radiation is evident at very short times. Note that, for $0 < T < \Gamma_0^{-1}$, the second-order correlation function is rather immune to decoherence effects in the non-Markovian case (Fig. 1.(a)) as compared with the Markovian case (Fig. 1.(b)). This is a consequence of the *recoherence* processes between the environment and the two qubits. The system decoheres, interacting with the bath, and at $\tau\Gamma_0 \approx 1$ a correlation revival arises. This strong antibunching effect is a non-Markovian process. Thus, the quantum correlations at time $T + \tau$ (a first photon detected at T) are affected by the type of initial state at time $T = 0$. This can be understood by analyzing the initial state as: $|\Psi_{QQ}\rangle = \frac{1}{2}(|1_1, 1_2\rangle + |0_1, 0_2\rangle + |0_1, 1_2\rangle + |1_1, 0_2\rangle)$. This state comprises the superposition of one exciton in each qubit, one non-radiative state (zero excitons) and the triplet state (which is associated to a superradiant state). The contribution from the triplet state provides a distinctive signature which is significantly enhanced by non-Markovian effects.

In order to stress the quite different optical signatures

for different possible initial states, Fig. 2(a) focuses on an initial Bell state: $|\Psi_B\rangle$. This state does not contain the contribution of the triplet state which explains why the intensity of the corresponding correlation function is about three times smaller than the one corresponding to the separate state $|\Psi_{QQ}\rangle$. However, the non-Markovian effects can still be observed, when compared with the results of Fig. 2(b) for the Markovian case. At very short times the slope of $g^2(T, \tau)$ is positive indicating an antibunching behaviour, which is enhanced by non-Markovian effects in the range of $0 < \tau\Gamma_0 < 1$ and $0 < T\Gamma_0 < 1$, allowing the distinguishability among the $|\Psi_{QQ}\rangle$, and $|\Psi_B\rangle$. For $T\Gamma_0 > 2$ the non-Markovian results tend toward the Markovian ones, emphasizing that in this long time regime the time-correlation is stationary and independent of the initial states.

To summarize, we have shown that for an optically-driven coupled qubit system, differently prepared initial states – for example, separate superpositions, Bell and triplet (symmetric) states – can be clearly distinguished as a direct result of non-Markovian effects. Our study exposes new phenomena that can be observable at ultrafast scales of time for which non-Markovian dynamics should be dominant. To our knowledge, the proposed signature is the first of its kind and should act as a powerful tool for experimental groups attempting to realize quantum information processing in a wide range of optically-driven, coupled-qubit systems.

The authors acknowledge partial support from COLCIENCIAS (Colombia) projects No. 1204-05-11408, 1204-05-13614, Banco de la República (Colombia) and Facultad de Ciencias, UNIANDES.

REFERENCES

1. L.Quiroga and N.F.Johnson, Phys. Rev. Lett. **83**, 2270 (1999).
2. D. V. Regelman *et al.*, Phys. Rev. Lett. **87**, 257401 (2001).
3. T. Unold *et al.*, Phys. Rev. Lett. **94**, 137404 (2005).
4. G. V. Varada and G. S. Agarwal, Phys. Rev. A. **45**. 6721 (1992)
5. R. Zwanzig, J. Chem. Phys. **33**, 1338 (1960).

Triplets in the emission spectra of a semiconductor quantum dot in the cavity QED regime

F.P. Laussy, D. Sanvitto and D.M. Whittaker

The University of Sheffield, Department of Physics & Astronomy, S10 2TN, United Kingdom

Abstract. We describe the strong-coupling of a small Quantum Dot (QD) with a pillar microcavity in the nonlinear regime where the number of photons matters. We consider the case where the QD is weakly coupled to one photon, but strongly coupled to two. We show how the emitted spectra then display both a doublet at resonance and a triplet in its vicinity.

Keywords: Strong coupling, microcavity.
PACS: 42.50.Ct, 42.50.Pq, 78.67.Hc

The recent observations of strong coupling (SC) between photons and material excitations of a semiconductor quantum dot (QD) [1, 2] or the more recent observation with nanocrystals [3] have shown that cavity quantum electrodynamics (CQED) is achievable not only with large atomic cavities but also with solid state microcavities. Such observations are particularly interesting for quantum information processing (QIP) where there is need for quantum logical gates and strongly efficient sources of entangled states. However, these applications are mainly based on the principle that in real CQED systems, a single particle, e.g., a photon, can strongly affect some physical properties of the quantum device. In other words, a "genuine" strongly coupled QD (that is, one useful for QIP) should display considerable nonlinear effects with as little as two photons in the system. Unfortunately, to date there is scarce evidence that a single quantum of excitation can perturb the system in such a way. In fact, in most cases where SC has been observed in semiconductors, the photon capture efficiency had been improved by selecting QDs with a very low confinement potential[1, 2]. Clearly, in this case, there is a risk to be in a regime more similar to what is already observed in ordinary quantum wells, for which the saturation of the photon absorption happens at very high number of photons. Recently, triplets have been observed at high pumping of very small QDs embedded in a pillar microcavity, while at low pumping the usual anticrossing of the QD line with the cavity mode was observed [4]. We claim that this is a proof of a genuine nonlinear strong coupling with a small dot that can accumulate a single excitation. We model this single excitation dot in a cavity with the Jaynes-Cummings hamiltonian [5] including lifetime phenomenologically by adding an imaginary part to the oscillators energies, $H = (\hbar\omega_X + i\gamma_X/2)\sigma^\dagger\sigma + (\hbar\omega_C + i\gamma_C/2)a^\dagger a + \hbar g(\sigma a^\dagger + \sigma^\dagger a)$, with a the annihilation operator for a Bose field describing destruction of a photon of the cavity mode with bare energy $\hbar\omega_C$, and σ the pro-

jector of the excited state of the exciton to its ground state with transition energy $\hbar\omega_X$. As this hamiltonian conserves the total number of excitations $N \equiv a^\dagger a + \sigma^\dagger\sigma$, its dynamics can be decoupled in the two-dimensional manifolds of states $\{|g,n\rangle, |e,n-1\rangle\}$ with n photons and ground-excitonic state on the one hand and $n-1$ photons and excited state on the other hand, $n > 0$. The manifold $n = 0$ reduces to the system ground state $|g,0\rangle$. Singling out the nth stair, the eigenenergies read:

$$E_\pm^{(n)} = \hbar\frac{(2n-1)\omega_C + \omega_X}{2} + i\hbar\frac{(2n-1)\gamma_C + \gamma_X}{4}$$
$$\pm \frac{1}{2}\sqrt{4n(\hbar g)^2 + \Delta^2 - \frac{1}{4}\delta^2 + i\delta\Delta} \quad (1)$$

as a function of detuning $\Delta \equiv \hbar\omega_X - \hbar\omega_C$ and $\delta \equiv \hbar\gamma_X - \hbar\gamma_C$. The sign of the expression below the square root splits either the energies (real parts) or their broadening (imaginary part). A splitting of energies indicates *strong coupling* and is reached for the nth step of the energy diagram when

$$g > \frac{1}{\sqrt{n}}\frac{|\gamma_X - \gamma_C|}{4} \quad (2)$$

If Eq. (2) is fulfilled already for $n = 1$, one speaks of *Vacuum Rabi doublet* to describe the two energy peaks which follow from Eq. (1). What happens for higher values of n is the issue we address now. We remind, though, that experimentally a crossing of the lines is observed at low pumping, and parameters estimated in Ref. [4] place g about 40μeV and cavity lifetime about a few ps with γ_C around 200μeV. In this case Eq. (2) is satisfied for $n = 2$ with the right hand side falling to 35μeV. At low pumping when no more than one excitation is present in the cavity at all time, $n = 1$ and the system is weakly coupled. The energies given by Eq. (1) are plotted on Fig. 1 for manifolds $n = 1$ and $n = 2$. On the lower manifold the bare states energies are only

CP893, *Physics of Semiconductors, 28th International Conference*
edited by W. Jantsch and F. Schäffler
© 2007 American Institute of Physics 978-0-7354-0397-0/07/$23.00

perturbed by the interaction with the dot. On the upper manifold the anticrossing splits the energies. Eigenstates associated to Eq. (1) read, in the basis of bare states

$$\left| E_\pm^{(n)} \right\rangle = \frac{1}{\sqrt{|\alpha_{n,\pm}|^2 + |\beta_n|^2}} (\alpha_{n,\pm} |g,n\rangle + \beta_n |e,n-1\rangle)$$

with $\alpha_{n,\pm} = ((\Delta/2) + i(\delta/4)) \pm \frac{1}{2}((4n(\bar{h}g)^2 + \Delta^2 - \delta^2/4) + \delta^2\Delta^2)^{1/4}(C + iS)$ and $\beta_n = \sqrt{n}\bar{h}g$, where we noted C (resp. S) the cosine (resp. sine) of $\arctan(\delta\Delta/4n(\bar{h}g)^2 + \Delta^2 - \delta^2/4)/2$. We calculated the emitted spectrum using Fermi's golden rule neglecting for simplicity perturbations for the first manifold (including them numerically does not affect much the picture). The transitions rates (or strength) for cavity emission with the initial state in strong coupling—Eq. (2) being satisfied for n excitations—and final state in weak coupling—Eq. (2) *not* being satisfied with $(n-1)$—are:

$$\left| \langle n-2,e|a| E_\pm^{(n)} \rangle \right|^2 = \frac{|\sqrt{n-1}\beta_n|^2}{|\alpha_{n,\pm}|^2 + |\beta_n|^2} \qquad (3)$$

$$\left| \langle n-1,g|a| E_\pm^{(n)} \rangle \right|^2 = \frac{|\sqrt{n}\alpha_{n,\pm}|^2}{|\alpha_{n,\pm}|^2 + |\beta_n|^2} \qquad (4)$$

with emitted energies $\Re(E_\pm^{(n)}) - (n-1)\bar{h}\omega_C + \Delta$ and $\Re(E_\pm^{(n)}) - (n-1)\bar{h}\omega_C$ respectively. Transitions rates through σ—the dot annihilation operator—can be computed in the same way to account for lateral emission. The lines are homogeneously broadened with width given by imaginary part of Eq. (1). This procedure which reproduces the usual case $n = 1$ gives, for $n = 2$, the spectra displayed in Fig. 2 (as function of detuning): at resonance the Rabi doublet is observed, but when detuned four lines appear out of which only three are resolvable following from the interplay of the transitions strengths and energy spacing.

In conclusion, we investigated theoretically intensity dependent strong-coupling based on Jaynes–Cummings hamiltonian where lifetime was introduced phenomenologically. Strong coupling is aided by intensity of the optical field resulting in pumping dependent spectra: crossing at low pumping and resonance fluorescence triplet at high pumping. In the intermediate region, we predict a triplet of other nature, arising from transition from strong to weak coupling. At resonance, the Rabi doublet is recovered.

REFERENCES

1. J. P. Reithmaier *et al*. Nature, **432**, 197 (2004).
2. E. Peter *et al*. Phys. Rev. Lett., **95**, 067401 (2005).
3. N. Le Thomas *et al*. Nano. Lett., **6**, 557 (2006).
4. D. Sanvitto *et al*. unpublished.
5. E.T. Jaynes and F.W. Cummings. Proc. IEEE, **51**, 89 (1963).

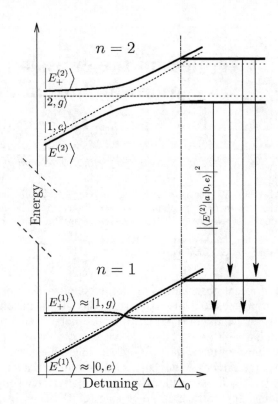

FIGURE 1. Energies of the states dressed by the strong interaction (thick solid) and of the bare states (photon and exciton) as function of detuning Δ, for $n = 1, 2$, with parameters given in the text. The system undergoes transitions from strong to weak coupling. The transition strength of one of the possible channel of decay is indicated.

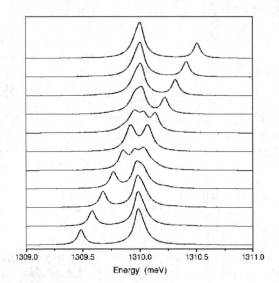

FIGURE 2. Spectra for various detunings emitted by the cavity reconstructed from the energy diagram and energy broadenings of our model. We predict successive observation of a doublet and triplet at high pumping and no spectral features at low pumping (not shown).

Spin mixing of two electrons in a quantum dot

Ş. C. Bădescu* and T. L. Reinecke*

*Naval Research Laboratory, Washington, DC 20375, USA

Abstract. The optical initialization and readout of an electron spin in a quantum dot involves often the lowest excited states of two electrons in a negative trion. The dynamics involves mixing of electron triplets and excited singlets. Typically, the mixing mechanism invoked has been electron-hole exchange in the presence of dot lateral asymmetries, but this has not been always consistent with the observed dephasing rates. We describe here a more general and stronger singlet-triplet mixing mechanism that does not require dot asymmetry.

Keywords: Quantum Dot, Spin, Exchange, Trion
PACS: 71.35.Pq, 71.55.Eq, 71.70.Ej, 71.70.Gm

The electron spin in a semiconductor quantum dot is an attractive qubit for quantum information. Spin qubits in neighboring dots can be coupled by exchange interaction. A spin qubit can be written and read optically [1, 2], when an optically-generated electron-hole pair forms a negative trion with the resident electron. The trion dynamics is initiated by the mixing of electron triplets and excited singlets. Recent experiments [2] observed large triplet-singlet mixings that pointed to the need for new asymmetric exchange mechanisms.

It was commonly assumed that the triplet-singlet mixing is generated by the electron-hole exchange. This requires asymmetries, and it mixes only x (y)-symmetry singlets to x (y)-symmetry triples. We describe here a strong electron triplet-excited singlet mixing independent of the dot asymmetries, generated by a coupling between x-states and y-states.

Here we take the hole to be always in its lowest orbital. The trion ground state involves a singlet of two electrons S_1 [Fig.1(a)], with a dominant s component. The lowest two-electron triplets T_1 (T_2) contain one excited electron, are antisymmetric in orbital coordinates, and have a dominant x (y) component. The excited singlets S_2 (S_3) contain one excited electron, are symmetric in orbital coordinates, and have a dominant x (y) component.

The electrons are described in the effective mass approximation. The parameters are the band gap E_g, the split-off energy Δ, and the matrix element P of $\hbar \hat{p}_x/m_0$ between the conduction and valence bands. We use adiabatic decoupling between lateral and vertical motion. The lateral confining potential V has a symmetric part V_s, and can include a small asymmetric part V_a odd in x, with coefficient C_x. The singlet (triplet) energies ε_s (ε_t) are eigenvalues of the Hamiltonian H_0 with the Coulomb interaction. The symmetric exchange between a triplet and a singlet is given by $J^{ij} = \varepsilon_t^i - \varepsilon_s^j$.

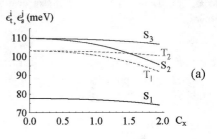

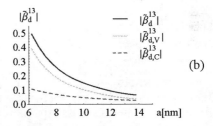

FIGURE 1. (a) Energies of the lowest triplets $i=1,2$ and of the lowest singlets $j=1,3$ vs the lateral asymmetry parameter C_x. The dot is cylindrical for $C_x=0$. (b) Cylindrical dots of different radii a: the lowest triplet T_1 (x-symmetry) and the singlet S_3 (y symmetry) are coupled only by $\beta_d^{13} e_z$. The ratio $\tilde{\beta}_d^{13} = \beta_d^{13}/J^{13}$ contains: $\tilde{\beta}_{d,C}^{13}$ from the spin-relative orbit coupling $\hat{h}_r$, and $\tilde{\beta}_{d,V}^{13}$ from the spin-orbit interaction $\hat{h}$ [Eq.(1)].

Spin-orbit couplings added to H_0 give an asymmetric exchange $\boldsymbol{\beta}^{ij} \cdot (\hat{\boldsymbol{s}}_1 - \hat{\boldsymbol{s}}_2)$. This does not conserve the total spin $\hat{\boldsymbol{S}} = \hat{\boldsymbol{s}}_1 + \hat{\boldsymbol{s}}_2$; the degree of singlet-triplet mixing is determined by the ratio $\tilde{\beta}^{ij} = \beta^{ij}/J^{ij}$. The component β_d^{ij} along the growth axis $\boldsymbol{e}_z$ does not change the spin projection S_z, generating only triplet-singlet dephasing. The

CP893, *Physics of Semiconductors, 28th International Conference*
edited by W. Jantsch and F. Schäffler

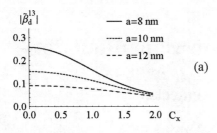

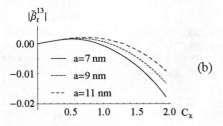

FIGURE 2. The effect of lateral asymmetry C_x on the coupling between the lowest triplet T_1 (with a dominant x component) and the triplet S_3 (with a dominant y component): (a) the ratio $\tilde{\beta}_d^{13}=\beta_z^{13}/J^{13}$ that determines the precession rate of $\hat{\boldsymbol{S}}$ around $\boldsymbol{e}_z$. (b) the ratio $\tilde{\beta}_r^{13}=\beta_\perp^{13}/J^{13}$ that determines the change of S_z.

in-plane component $\boldsymbol{\beta}_r^{ij}=\boldsymbol{\beta}_\perp^{ij}$ flips one spin ($\Delta S_z=\pm\hbar$). Here we consider the spin-orbit coupling $\hat{\boldsymbol{h}}_k$ of electron $k=1,2$, and the spin-relative orbit couplings $\hat{\boldsymbol{h}}_{r,k}$ [3]:

$$H = H_0 + \sum_{k=1,2}\left(\hat{\boldsymbol{h}}_k + \hat{\boldsymbol{h}}_{r,k}\right)\cdot\hat{\boldsymbol{s}}_k. \quad (1)$$

In Eq.(1), $\hat{\boldsymbol{h}}_k$ contains the coupling from the bulk inversion asymmetry, $\hat{\boldsymbol{h}}^D\cdot\hat{\boldsymbol{s}}=\gamma_b^D\varepsilon^{\alpha\beta\delta}\hat{p}_\alpha(\hat{p}_\beta^2-\hat{p}_\delta^2)\hat{\sigma}_\alpha$; this does not couple the orbitals p_x and p_y, but only the s and $p_{x,y}$ orbitals. $\hat{\boldsymbol{h}}_k$ contains also the term $\hat{\boldsymbol{h}}^R=\gamma_s\nabla V^h\times\hat{\boldsymbol{p}}$ that arises from a combination of the confinement potential with $\boldsymbol{k}\cdot\hat{\boldsymbol{p}}$ terms in the effective-mass expansion. V^h is the potential for holes. The main effect of $\hat{\boldsymbol{h}}^R$ is the p_x-p_y mixing. A secondary effect is the Rashba spin-orbit coupling if the potential has a gradient along $\boldsymbol{e}_z$. In Eq.(1), $\hat{\boldsymbol{h}}_{r,k}$ arise from a combination of the Coulomb interaction with $\boldsymbol{k}\cdot\hat{\boldsymbol{p}}$ terms. It has the form $\hat{\boldsymbol{h}}_{r,k}=(-1)^k\gamma_s\nabla_r U_C\times\hat{\boldsymbol{p}}_k$ and it mixes the p_x and p_y orbitals. $\gamma_s\propto P^2/E_g^2$ is derived in the Kane model [3].

The spin-antisymmetric part of H [Eq.(1)] is:

$$H_{ts} = \frac{1}{2}\left(\hat{\boldsymbol{h}}_1 - \hat{\boldsymbol{h}}_2 + 2\gamma_s\partial_{\boldsymbol{\rho}_r}U_C\times\hat{\boldsymbol{p}}_{c\perp}\right)\cdot(\hat{\boldsymbol{s}}_1-\hat{\boldsymbol{s}}_2). \quad (2)$$

The operator $\hat{\boldsymbol{s}}_1-\hat{\boldsymbol{s}}_2$ mixes the triplets with the singlets:

$$H_{ts} = \sum_{i,j}\boldsymbol{\beta}^{ij}\cdot(\hat{\boldsymbol{s}}_1-\hat{\boldsymbol{s}}_2)|T_i\rangle\langle S_j| + h.c.,$$

$$\boldsymbol{\beta}^{ij} = \langle T_i|\hat{\boldsymbol{h}}_1 + \gamma_s\partial_{\boldsymbol{\rho}_r}U_C\times\hat{\boldsymbol{p}}_{c\perp}|S_j\rangle. \quad (3)$$

In Eqs.(3), $\hat{\boldsymbol{p}}_{c\perp}=(\hat{\boldsymbol{p}}_{1\perp}+\hat{\boldsymbol{p}}_{2\perp})/2$. The axial vector $\boldsymbol{\beta}^{ij}$ is determined by the wave functions components of T_i, S_j and by the spin-orbit vector operators. It has two parts:

$$\boldsymbol{A}^{ij} = 2\langle T_i|\left(\tilde{\gamma}_s\partial_{\boldsymbol{\rho}_1}V_s\times\hat{\partial}_{\boldsymbol{\rho}_1} - \gamma_s\partial_{\boldsymbol{\rho}_r}U_C\times\hat{\partial}_{\boldsymbol{\rho}_c}\right)|S_j\rangle,$$

$$\boldsymbol{P}^{ij} = 2\langle T_i|\left(\tilde{\gamma}_s\partial_{\boldsymbol{\rho}_1}V_a\times\hat{\partial}_{\boldsymbol{\rho}_1} - \gamma^R\boldsymbol{e}_z\times\hat{\partial}_{\boldsymbol{\rho}_1}\right) + \quad (4)$$

$$-\gamma^D\left(-\hat{\partial}_x\boldsymbol{e}_x+\hat{\partial}_y\boldsymbol{e}_y\right)|S_j\rangle.$$

In Eq.(4), $\hat{\boldsymbol{A}}$ is a pseudovector operator (odd both in x and in y). Thus the vector $\boldsymbol{A}^{ij}$ is nonzero if one of the states T_i, S_j has x symmetry and the other has y symmetry, e.g. the T_1 singlet and the S_3 triplet in Fig.1. This vector is determined by the symmetric part of the potential, that is dominant. It has only z component, thus generates only spin dephasing, β_d^{ij}. For cylindrical dots [Fig.1(b)] $\beta_d^{24}=-\beta_d^{13}$, giving a mixing only between $T_\pm=\frac{1}{\sqrt{2}}(T_1\pm iT_2)$ and $S_\pm=\frac{1}{\sqrt{2}}(S_2\pm iS_3)$, eigenstates of $\hat{L}_z$.

In Eq.(4), $\hat{\boldsymbol{P}}$ is a polar vector operator (odd either in x or in y). The vector $\boldsymbol{P}^{ij}$ is nonzero if one of T_i, S_j has a x or y component and the other has an s component. For $T_{1,2}$ and $S_{2,3}$, this is possible only with a lateral inversion asymmetry (e.g. $C_x\neq 0$). The first part of $\hat{\boldsymbol{P}}$ (vanishing for $V_a=0$) is along $\boldsymbol{e}_z$; it contributes only to the dephasing (S_z=const). It gives a second order perturbation in parameter C_x [Fig.2(a)] to the main part determined by $\hat{\boldsymbol{A}}$. The last two parts of $\hat{\boldsymbol{P}}$ are the in-plane components of the Dresselhaus and Rashba terms; they can flip one spin, mixing the triplets with the singlets via the vector β_r^{ij}. The dependence on lateral asymmetry is shown in Fig.2(b). Accompanied by phonon transitions between singlets S_3 and S_1, β_r^{13} leads to spin relaxation.

Fig.1(b) and Fig.2 show that there is significant spin mixing without lateral asymmetry. The mixing is strong for small dots, where the magnetic field of the circular orbital motion is strong. Deviations from cylindrical symmetry lead to a decrease in the precession rate of the total spin (singlet-triplet dephasing): for strong lateral asymmetry the electrons cannot move into circular orbits. The ratio of the electron-electron asymmetric exchange to symmetric exchange can be as large as ≈ 0.4, so the mechanism presented here can account for the strong triplet-singlet mixing in negative trions.

We acknowledge discussions with Y. Lyanda-Geller, B. V. Shanabrook, D. Gammon, M. E. Ware, and the support of DARPA and ONR.

REFERENCES

1. S. Cortez *et al.* Phys. Rev. Lett. **89** (20), 207401 (2002)
2. M. E. Ware *et al.* Phys. Rev. Lett. **95**(17), 177403 (2005)
3. Ş. C. Bădescu, Y. B. Lyanda-Geller, T. L. Reinecke, Phys. Rev. B **72**, 161304(R) (2005)

CHAPTER 10

QUANTUM INFORMATION AND PROCESSING

Polarization Dependent Correlations of Single Photons from CdTe/ZnTe Quantum Dots

J. Suffczyński[1], K. Kowalik[1], A. Trajnerowicz[1], T. Kazimierczuk[1], M. Goryca[1], P. Kossacki[1], A. Golnik[1], M. Nawrocki[1], J. A. Gaj[1], and G. Karczewski[2]

[1] *Institute of Experimental Physics, Warsaw University, Hoża 69, 00-681 Warsaw, Poland*
[2] *Institute of Physics, Polish Academy of Sciences, Al. Lotników 32/64, 02-668 Warsaw, Poland*

Abstract. Temporal and polarization correlations between single photons emitted from different excitonic states confined in the same CdTe/ZnTe quantum dot (QD) were measured. Experiment was carried out at low temperature (T = 1.7 K) with nonresonant excitation and in an external magnetic field ranging from 0 to 5 T. The collinear polarization correlation of photons emitted in biexciton (XX) – exciton (X) cascade in the anisotropic QD is converted in magnetic field to counter-circular polarization correlation. Measurements of charged exciton – neutral exciton crosscorrelations revealed that spin orientation of a single carrier left in the dot after charged exciton recombination is preserved in magnetic field over the laser pulse repetition period of more than ten nanoseconds. The spin memory is not destroyed by capture of a next carrier.

Keywords: quantum dot, anisotropy, exciton, photon correlation
PACS: 78.55.Et, 73.21.La, 78.67.-n, 78.47.+p

INTRODUCTION

Determination of polarization properties of single semiconductor quantum dot (QD) emission is an important issue for development of sources of single photons with controllable polarization. Such sources can be useful for applications in quantum cryptography [1]. In this work, we present a study of polarization correlation of single photons emitted consecutively from different excitonic states confined in the same anisotropic QD in magnetic field. We wish to study the symmetry of excitons in a dot and single carrier spin memory effects.

SAMPLE AND EXPERIMENTAL SETUP

The sample, containing self assembled CdTe QDs embedded in ZnTe barriers, was mounted on a mirror type microscope objective and placed inside a cryostat at T = 1.7 K. Vertically polarized, frequency doubled pulsed beam of Ti:Al$_2$O$_3$ laser was used for nonresonant excitation of photoluminescence (PL) from individual QDs with repetition period 6.6 ns. PL signal was split by a polarizing beamsplitter (BS) and spectrally filtered with use of grating monochromators.

Two avalanche photodiodes mounted on exits of monochromators served as single photon counters. Coincidence counting electronics receiving electronic signal from diodes generated histograms of time delays separating detection of photons on the first and the second diode. Insertion of polarization optics in front of the BS, involving combinations of halfwaveplate, quarterwaveplate and linear polarizer, enabled polarization resolved detection. Magnetic field in range from 0 to 5 T was applied in Faraday configuration. PL spectra were recorded using a CCD camera.

RESULTS AND DISSCUSSION

Analysis of relative energy positions in PL spectrum, Zeeman splittings in external magnetic field, fine structure of emission and a dependence of PL intensity on excitation power intensity allowed us to identify emission lines of neutral (X), charged (CX) exciton, and biexciton (XX) originating from the same QD. Excitonic g-factor extracted from the Zeeman splitting measurement was determined as g = -3.51 for all the three lines. Anisotropy measurements revealed the same absolute value of Anisotropic Exchange

CP893, *Physics of Semiconductors, 28th International Conference*
edited by W. Jantsch and F. Schäffler
© 2007 American Institute of Physics 978-0-7354-0397-0/07/$23.00

Splitting (AES = 182 μeV) for X and XX, and no AES for CX.

Correlation measurements for a biexciton-exciton cascade in the absence of the magnetic field (Fig. 1(a-b)) revealed strong polarization correlation in a linear H-V basis, corresponding to the QD symmetry axes. No polarization dependence was found in a linear +45/-45 or a circular basis. These results indicate that photons emitted in the XX-X cascade are polarization correlated, but not entangled, as expected for an anisotropic QD [2].

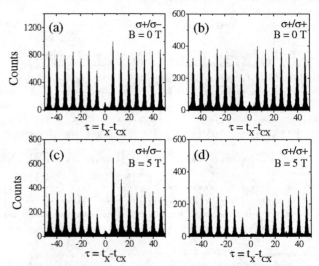

FIGURE 2. CX-X crosscorrelations measured for two (indicated in CX/X order) combinations of circular polarization of the photon pair: (a, b) – at B = 0 T and (c, d) – at B = 5T. The first peak at positive delay represents events of X emission in the pulse subsequent to CX emission.

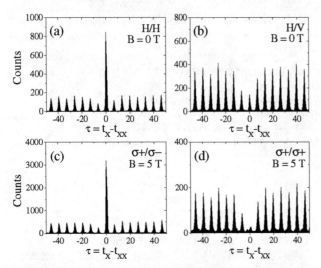

FIGURE 1. XX-X crosscorrelations measured for different combinations of polarization of the photon pair (indicated in XX/X order): (a-b) – linear H-V at B = 0 T, (c-d) – circular at B = 5 T.

With increasing magnetic field, a linearly polarized excitonic doublet is converted into two circularly polarized lines [3]. Application of the magnetic field reduces the influence of the QD anisotropy responsible for coupling of excitonic states with angular momentum M = +1 and -1. In sufficiently high magnetic field pure M = ± 1 exciton eigenstates are observed. This was demonstrated by measurements at B = 5T showing a significant polarization correlation for spin split XX and X lines registered in the orthogonal circular polarizations (Fig. 1(c-d)). Unlike the central peak, the other ones exhibit no polarization effects, witnessing no polarization memory extending over the repetition period.

A different behavior is visible in CX-X correlation histograms (Fig. 2(a-d)), where the strong suppression of the central peak shows an antibunching of X and CX photons following the same pulse. Moreover, correlation of polarizations of CX and X photons emitted in consecutive pulses (first peak at positive delay), absent at B = 0 T (Fig. 2(a-b)), appears clearly at a magnetic field B = 5 T (Fig. 2(c-d)).

We observe a correlation enhancement (suppression) for opposite (equal) combinations of circular polarizations respectively. This observation means that the spin orientation of X is strongly influenced by the spin orientation of CX emitting in the preceding pulse, encoded in the spin state of the carrier left in the QD after recombination. Our experiments show that this polarization memory remains unchanged when the repetition period is doubled from 6.6 ns to 13.2 ns. Thus, the spin orientation of the carrier left in the QD after the CX emission is frozen over the repetition period, indicating that the spin relaxation time in the QD is much longer than 10 ns. Furthermore, it is not perturbed by the capture of an opposite carrier to form an exciton.

ACKNOWLEDGMENTS

This work was supported by the Polish Committee for Scientific Research (grants 2P03B 002 25 and 2P03B 015 25), and the Polonium program.

REFERENCES

1. C. H. Brassard, G. Bennet, *Proceedings of IEEE Int. Conf. on Computers, Systems and Signal processing, Bangalore, India, pp.175-179, (1984)*
2. C. Santori, D. Fattal, M. Pelton, G. S. Solomon, and Y. Yamamoto, Phys. Rev. B **66**, 045308 (2002), S. M. Ulrich, S. Strauf, P. Michler, G. Bacher and A. Forchel, Appl. Phys. Lett. **83**, 1848 (2003)
3. L. Besombes, K. Kheng, and D. Martrou, Phys. Rev. Lett. **85**, 425 (2000)

The Radiative Lifetime of Charged Excitons in a Single Self-Assembled Quantum Dot

Paul A. Dalgarno*, Patrick Gillies*, Jamie McFarlane*, Brian D. Gerardot*, Khaled Karrai[†], Pierre M. Petroff[‡], Ian Galbraith* and Richard J. Warburton*

*School of Engineering and Physical Sciences, Heriot-Watt University, Edinburgh, EH14 4AS, UK
[†]Center for Nanoscience and Sektion Physik, Ludwig-Maximilians-Universität, Geschwister-Scholl-Platz 1, 80539 München, Germany
[‡]Materials Department, University of California, Santa Barbara, California 93106, USA

Abstract. The small physical size of self assembled quantum dots gives rise to pronounced Coulomb interactions within the dots. By studying different excitons in the same quantum dot we show that the Coulomb interactions significantly alter the radiative recombination lifetime. The lifetime changes are larger upon charging from the neutral exciton to the positively charged exciton than from charging from the neutral exciton to the negatively charged exciton. This is attributed to a frozen electron wavefunction and a non-frozen hole wavefunction, leading to a non-perturbative hole-hole Coulomb interaction. Theoretical calculations based on a path integral quantum Monte-Carlo approach show good agreement between experiment and theory.

Keywords: Quantum dot, lifetime, Coulomb interactions, Path integral Monte-Carlo
PACS: 73.21.La

INTRODUCTION

Quantum dots are often referred to as artificial atoms due to their 0D density of states. A quantum dot is therefore a system which is strongly quantized. However, only in the strong confinement limit does quantization dominate. Away from strong confinement, Coulomb interactions between carriers in the dot have significant effects on the dot properties. Such interactions are important as they dictate the spectral shifts between excitons. This allows for the spectral selection of separate excitons photoluminescence (PL), an important feature for the development of a true single photon source, entangled photon production and quantum information processing. An understanding of the Coulomb interactions therefore not only furthers the understanding of quantum dot structures but opens up possibilities in the manipulation and control over the dots environment.

We present here experimental data that demonstrate the significance of Coulomb interactions in the decay dynamics of charged excitons. Theoretical calculations based on a non-perturbative path integral Monte-Carlo method agree well the experiment and allow for a quantitative treatment of the Coulomb interactions.

EXPERIMENTAL

The dots studied in this paper are InAs/GaAs self assembled quantum dots embedded in an n-type field effect diode [1]. The dots are separated from a heavily doped back contact by a 25 nm GaAs tunnel barrier. Either a 30 nm (sample A) or 10 nm (sample B) GaAs capping layer separates the dots from an AlAs/GaAs blocking barrier. By applying a d.c. bias between the back contact and a semi-transparent Schotkky gate electron tunneling into the dots can be controlled. The Coulomb blockade allows for single electron control over the charging. Hole population in the dots is controlled via excitation laser power. It is therefore possible to study both positively and negatively charged excitons in the same single dot, Fig 1.

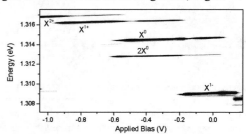

FIGURE 1. Contour plot showing the PL spectra from a single dot from sample B at 4.2 K as a function of applied bias. White corresponds to 0 counts and black to 500 counts.

CP893, *Physics of Semiconductors, 28th International Conference*
edited by W. Jantsch and F. Schäffler
© 2007 American Institute of Physics 978-0-7354-0397-0/07/$23.00

Single dots are studied at 4.2 K using a diffraction limited confocal microscope and low dot density samples, < 1 dot per μm^2. An n = 2.0 solid immersion lens is used to increase collection efficiency by a factor of ~5. Non resonant excitation is via an 826 nm pulsed diode laser. Lifetime measurements are performed using time correlated single photon counting (TCSPC) and reconvolution techniques are used to extrapolate lifetimes with a timing resolution of 100 ps.

RESULTS AND DISCUSSION

Previous work has shown that the decay dynamics of the neutral exciton, X^0, are bi-exponential [2]. The two decay process are attributed to a bias independent radiative lifetime of the bright exciton and a bias dependent electron spin-swap process of the dark exciton. On the other hand the decay dynamics of the negatively charged exciton, X^{1-}, show a single bias independent decay component, attributed to radiative recombination. For sample A the decay dynamics of the positively charged exciton, X^{1+}, is dominated by hole tunneling. Holes tunnel from the dot to 2D valence states formed at the interface between the dots capping layer and the blocking barrier [3]. Reducing the capping layer in Sample B decreases the energy levels of the 2D valence states such that they are no longer resonant with the hole energies in the dot. This effectively turns off the hole tunneling. It is therefore possible to probe the radiative lifetime of X^{1+} from Sample B. The change in sample design allows, for the first time, the possibility to compare the radiative recombination lifetime for X^{1+}, X^{1-} and X^0 from the same dot.

Fig 2. shows lifetime data for X^0, X^{1-} and X^{1+} for the dot shown in Fig 1. The data is taken at the centre of the gate voltage plateau of each exciton. A clear result is that the radiative lifetime increases upon charging. This increase is far more substantial upon charging with a hole than an electron. To verify this

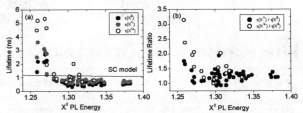

FIGURE 3. (a) $\tau(X^0)$, $\tau(X^{1-})$ and $\tau(X^{1+})$ plotted against X^0 PL energy. The solid line shows the predicted lifetime of an exciton in the strong confinement regime. (b) $\tau(X^{1-})$ / $\tau(X^0)$ and $\tau(X^{1+})$ / $\tau(X^0)$ plotted against X^0 PL energy. Data from both sample A and sample B are included in both (a) and (b).

behavior is representative we have recorded radiative lifetime data for over 50 dots, Fig 3a. The radiative lifetime of all three excitons decreases first rapidly and then gradually as dot energy increases. Fig 3b shows that in most cases $\tau(X^{1-})$ / $\tau(X^0)$ is less than $\tau(X^{1+})$ / $\tau(X^0)$, verifying the hierarchy that $\tau(X^{1+}) > \tau(X^{1-}) > \tau(X^0)$. For an exciton in the strong confinement regime the radiative lifetime would be independent of charge and only slightly dependent on PL energy, Fig 3a. We therefore conclude that the excitons studied here are not in the strong confinement regime. The lifetime hierarchy implies that the electron wavefunctions are frozen and that the hole wavefunctions are free to admix. The electrons are therefore in the strong confinement regime whereas the holes confinement is significantly softer. This conclusion is consistent with a larger hole effective mass over the electron effective mass and consequently a smaller wavefunction extent for the hole when compared to the electron [4].

In order to model the dot behavior a non-perturbative path integral quantum Monte-Carlo model, accurate in all confinement regimes, has been developed. The model determines to a good agreement the exciton lifetime ratios brought about by charging the dot. The results from the model are also consistent with a frozen electron wavefunction and a deviation from strong confinement for the holes.

REFERENCES

1. R.J. Warburton, C. Schaflein, D. Haft, et al. Nature, 2000. **405**(6789): p. 926-929.
2. J.M. Smith, P.A. Dalgarno, R.J. Warburton, et al. Physical Review Letters, 2005. **94**(19): p. 197402-4.
3. P.A. Dalgarno, J. McFarlane, B.D. Gerardot, et al. Applied Physics Letters, 2006. **89**(4).
4. R.J. Warburton, B.T. Miller, C.S. Dürr, et al. Physical Review B, 1998. **58**(24): p. 16221-16231.

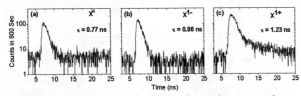

FIGURE 2. TCSPC data from (a) X^0 (b) X^{1-} and (c) X^{1+} for the dot shown in Figure 1. The decays are taken at the centre of the gate voltage plateau for each exciton. The lifetimes are determined using reconvolution fits (not shown). The origin of the process giving rise to the large secondary lifetime of X^{1+} is currently unknown.

Stark Tuning of Donor Electron Spins in Silicon

F. R. Bradbury[1], Alexei M. Tyryshkin[1], Guillaume Sabouret[1], Jeff Bokor[2,3], Thomas Schenkel[2], S. A. Lyon[1]

[1]Department of Electrical Engineering, Princeton University, Princeton, NJ 08544
[2]E. O. Lawrence Berkeley National Laboratory, Berkeley, CA 94720
[3]Department of Electrical Engineering and Computer Science, University of California Berkeley, CA 94720

Abstract. We report Stark shift measurements for ^{121}Sb donor electron spins in silicon using pulse electron spin resonance. Interdigitated metal gates on a Sb-implanted ^{28}Si epi-layer are used to apply the electric fields. Two quadratic Stark effects are resolved: a decrease of the hyperfine coupling between electron and nuclear spins of the donor and a decrease in electron Zeeman g-factor. A significant linear Stark effect is also observed, which we suggest arises from strain. We discuss the results in the context of the Kane model quantum computer.

Keywords: Electron spin resonance, silicon, donors, quantum computing, Stark effect
PACS: 71.79.Ej, 76.30.-v, 03.67.Lx, 71.55.Cn

INTRODUCTION

In the Kane architecture [1] of quantum computation (QC) qubits are envisioned to be encoded in spin states of donor impurities in a silicon lattice. This architecture is attractive because of the proven scalability of silicon devices and the long decoherence times measured for electron spins in silicon [2, 3]. While some aspects of the Kane architecture lie in the realm of existing silicon technologies, the scheme for single qubit operation was based on a theoretical estimate. To perform operations on single qubits, Kane proposed shifting the spin resonance with externally applied electric fields (Stark tuning). In this work, we present experimental proof of concept for Stark tuning the electron spin resonance (ESR) by resolving two quadratic Stark terms: a decrease in the hyperfine interaction and a decrease in the electron g-factor.

The donor electron spin-Hamiltonian is given by

$$\hat{H} = g\beta B_0 S_z + a \cdot S_z I_z \qquad (1)$$

where the first term is the Zeeman interaction in applied field B_0, with g the electron g-factor and β the Bohr magneton, and the second term is the hyperfine interaction between electron (S) and nuclear (I) spins with hyperfine coupling constant, a. A Stark shift in the spin resonance energy may change the hyperfine coupling constant, a, or the electron g-factor.

METHODS

The sample used in this experiment is a ^{28}Si epi-wafer implanted with ^{121}Sb [4] (giving $S = 1/2$ and $I = 5/2$) and patterned with interdigitated metal top gates for the application of electric fields. Because the Stark shift of the donor ESR is smaller than the resonance linewidth (previously measured to be 0.2 MHz in isotopically-purified ^{28}Si [3]), this work extends a pulse ESR technique developed by Mims [5] which is sensitive to small changes in the ESR frequency. In our experiments, two X-band microwave pulses generate a Hahn echo signal from the donor spins. Electric field pulses applied to the donor spins using the interdigitated gates alter the resonance (precession) frequencies of the electrons spins, via the Stark effect, and thus produce a phase shift in the echo signal.

We extend Mims's experiment by introducing bipolar electrical pulse sequences to separate linear and quadratic Stark terms [6]. By flipping the sign of the applied electric field midway through the defocusing period of the Hahn experiment, precession phase shifts that depend asymmetrically on the field are refocused and only symmetric (quadratic to lowest order) Stark shifts are accumulated. Alternatively, pulses of opposite polarity and equal duration applied during the defocusing and refocusing periods will selectively detect only asymmetric (linear to lowest order) Stark shifts.

CP893, *Physics of Semiconductors, 28th International Conference*
edited by W. Jantsch and F. Schäffler
© 2007 American Institute of Physics 978-0-7354-0397-0/07/$23.00

RESULTS AND DISCUSSION

Figures 1a and 1b display the echo phase shift in experiments designed to detect symmetric Stark effects. Measurements were taken on four hyperfine lines of the ^{121}Sb ESR spectrum corresponding to nuclear spin projections, $M_I = \pm 1/2$ and $\pm 5/2$. Fitting the echo phase shift with quadratic Stark terms required integrating over the ensemble of donor electron spins. The calculated curves for all plots were fit with the parameters $\eta_a = -3.7 \cdot 10^{-3}$ and $\eta_g = -1 \cdot 10^{-5}$ (in $\mu m^2/V^2$) where $\Delta g(E) = \eta_g \cdot g \cdot E^2$ and $\Delta a(E) = \eta_a \cdot a \cdot E^2$. Detailed discussions of these symmetric Stark experiments can be found elsewhere [6].

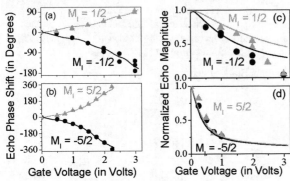

FIGURE 1. (a, b) Phase shift of the echo signal in symmetric Stark experiments and (c, d) decay of the echo magnitude in asymmetric Stark experiments as a function of the applied voltage across interdigitated gates for ^{28}Si:^{121}Sb at 6.2K and interpulse delay $\tau = 40\mu s$. Data (points) and numerical fits (lines) are shown.

In experiments designed to measure asymmetric Stark effects we observed no phase shift of the echo signal and only a reduction of its magnitude as shown in Figures 1c and 1d. In principle, tetrahedral symmetry at the donor site should prohibit the observed asymmetric Stark effects; however, interfacial strain and random defects can break this symmetry. Lattice mismatch strain in ^{28}Si epi-wafers similar to those used in this work has been evidenced in recent photoluminescence experiments [7] and strain in the silicon is known to shift the donor ESR [8]. Thinking of these intrinsic asymmetries as "effective" electric fields to which the real, applied field adds to (or subtracts from) we can fit the data in Figure 1c and 1d using the quadratic Stark terms. These fits assumed a Gaussian distribution of effective electric fields centered at zero with a standard deviation, $\sigma = 0.07$ V/μm.

It is interesting to compare the measured ESR linewidth with that calculated from the distribution of effective electric fields. The calculated linewidth is ~20kHz, an order of magnitude less than the measured

resonance lines. Qualitatively, this supports the local strain explanation of the linear Stark effect. One effect of strain is to admix p-like hydrogenic donor states into the ground state wave function. This effect is analogous to that of an electric field and will give rise to the linear Stark term. More importantly, however, local strains also break the valley degeneracy in silicon and change the admixture of valley states, reducing the hyperfine interaction with the ^{121}Sb nucleus [8]. This term will not be affected by a long wavelength electric field and thus introduces broadening into the ESR line without contributing to the linear Stark effect.

CONCLUSIONS

The ability to Stark tune the spin resonance is an integral and previously unmeasured parameter for Kane model donor spin QC architectures. This study resolves quadratic hyperfine and g-factor Stark effects for ^{121}Sb donors in silicon. Spin resonance shifts are found to be small at the moderate electric fields used in this work; a maximum shift of 25 kHz was observed when average electric fields of ~0.1 V/μm were applied with $M_I = \pm 5/2$. This study also finds a significant linear Stark effect, which is consistent with strain-induced local asymmetries. Consequently, we suggest the importance of controlling strains for precise spin resonance tuning via the Stark effect.

ACKNOWLEDGMENTS

The authors would like to thank Igor Trofimov, Shyam Shankar, Rogerio de Sousa, Mark Friesen, Lloyd Hollenberg, and Cameron Wellard for helpful discussions. This research was supported at Princeton by the Army Research Office and the Advanced Research and Development Activity under Contract No. DAAD19-02-1-0040, and at Lawrence Berkeley National Labs by the National Security Agency under Army Research Office Contract No. MOD707501, the Department of Energy under Contract No. DE-AC02-05CH11231, and the National Science Foundation under Grant No. 0404208.

REFERENCES

1. B. E. Kane, Nature **393**, 133 (1998).
2. J. P. Gordon & K. D. Bowers, Phys. Rev. Lett. **1**, 368 (1958).
3. A. M. Tyryshkin *et al.*, Phys. Rev. B **68**, 193207 (2003).
4. T. Schenkel *et al.*, Appl. Phys. Lett. **88**, 112101 (2006).
5. W. B. Mims, Rev. Sci. Inst. **45**, 1583 (1974); W. B. Mims, Phys. Rev. A **133**, A835 (1964).
6. F. R. Bradbury *et al.*, cond-mat/0603324 (2006).
7. A. Yang *et al.*, Physica B **376-377**, 54 (2006).
8. D. K. Wilson & G. Feher, Phys. Rev. **124**, 1068 (1961).

Quantum control of donor-bound electrons at the Si-SiO$_2$ interface

Belita Koiller*,†, M.J. Calderón†, Xuedong Hu** and S. Das Sarma†

*Instituto de Física, Universidade Federal do Rio de Janeiro, Cx. P. 68528, 21941-972 Rio de Janeiro, Brazil
†Condensed Matter Theory Center, Department of Physics, University of Maryland, MD 20742-4111, USA
**Department of Physics, University at Buffalo, SUNY, Buffalo, NY 14260-1500, USA

Abstract. Prospects for the quantum control of electrons in the silicon quantum computer architecture are considered theoretically. We focus here on the ability to move or "shuttle" electrons between the donors and the Si surface using an external electric field. This is an essential element of donor-based quantum computer architectures. In particular, this shuttling time must be much shorter than the spin dephasing time ~ 1 ms in bulk Si. Application of suitable electrostatic potentials at surface electrodes would drag the electron from and to the donor allowing the manipulation of the electron-donor coupling. We investigate the precise extent to which a donor bound electron in the bulk (a few tens of nanometers from the interface) can be manipulated between the donor-bound state and a surface-bound state (within a few nanometers of the interface) by suitably tuning an external electric field applied perpendicular to the interface.

Keywords: Kane's quantum computer; donor electrons; spin manipulation
PACS: 03.67.Lx, 85.30.-z, 73.20.Hb, 85.35.Gv, 71.55.Cn

Silicon-based structures are among the most promising candidates for developing a quantum computer [1]. We consider theoretically the problem of quantum control of a donor-bound electron near a Si/SiO$_2$ interface, addressing two key issues in this context: (i) How fast can this electron shuttling between the donor and the interface be done in realistic Si structures? (ii) Is the shuttled electron at the surface still localized in all 3 dimensions (which will allow to take it back to the donor) or is it a delocalized 2-dimensional electron?

The potential produced by a donor (in particular, P) in Si a distance d from a Si/SiO$_2$ (001) interface under a perpendicular electric field is schematically represented in the inset of Fig. 1. We solve the problem of the donor electron in this double-well potential in the basis formed by the ground states Ψ_A and Ψ_B of the two wells A and B [2]. The A well is formed, in the z-direction, by the electric field and the electron image and, in the xy-plane, by the sum of the donor and its image Coulomb potentials. The barrier at the oxide interface is assumed to be infinite, so $\Psi_i = 0$ for $z < -d$ ($i = A, B$). For $z > -d$ we adopt the variational forms $\Psi_A = \frac{\alpha^{5/2}}{\sqrt{4!}}(z+d)^2 e^{-\alpha(z+d)/2} \times \frac{\beta}{\sqrt{\pi}} e^{-\beta^2\rho^2/2}$, and $\Psi_B \propto (z+d)e^{-\sqrt{\rho^2/a^2+z^2/b^2}}$, where α, β, a and b are variational parameters chosen to minimize each well's ground state energy, and $\rho = (x,y)$. In Fig. 1 we show the ground and the first excited state energies corresponding to the xy-plane part of the A well. This potential keeps the electron from forming a 2-dimensional electron gas parallel to the interface. The variational parameter β, characterizing the radial confinement of the ground state paral-

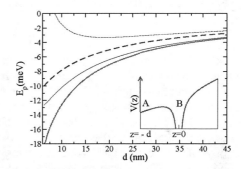

FIGURE 1. The broad lines, solid and dashed respectively, give the ground and first excited state energy terms for the potential at the interface in the xy plane (given by the donor and its image Coulomb potentials $\propto -1/\sqrt{\rho^2+d^2}$) obtained variationally as a function of the donor-to-interface distance. The narrow lines give the same energies calculated within a parabolic approximation of the potential. The inset displays an outline of the double-well potential in the z-direction.

lel to the interface, is given in Fig. 2(a). For the coherent manipulation of electrons in quantum devices, it is crucial that the entanglement of the electronic states occurs in a completely controlled and reversible manner. This requires that the ionized state near the barrier remains laterally bound to its respective donor site, setting an upper bound for the operating temperature as well as for the donor planar density [$n < (\beta/2)^2$] to avoid significant wavefunction overlap among electrons bound to neighboring donors. For $d = 30$ nm, we get an excitation gap ~ 1 meV, and donor electron wavefunction confinement within a ~ 40 nm diameter region parallel to

CP893, *Physics of Semiconductors, 28th International Conference*
edited by W. Jantsch and F. Schäffler
© 2007 American Institute of Physics 978-0-7354-0397-0/07/$23.00

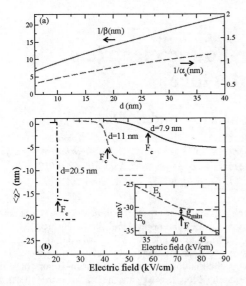

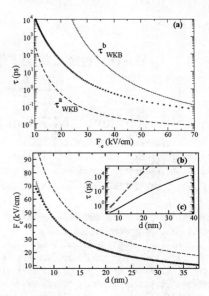

FIGURE 2. (a) Confinement lengths $1/\beta$ and $1/\alpha_c$ (for α calculated at $F = F_c$) obtained variationally. (b) Expectation value of the electron z-coordinate versus electric field intensity F for three values of the donor distance to the barrier d. The horizontal lines indicate the barrier position in each case. The inset shows the eigenvalues E_0 and E_1 as a function of F for $d = 11$ nm.

FIGURE 3. (a) The data points give our estimate for the characteristic donor ionization time, defined here as $\tau = \hbar/g_{min}$, versus F_c. For comparison, we present the inverse ionization rates obtained from the semiclassical approximation (WKB) for the isotropic hydrogenic model with effective Bohr radii equal to each of the variational KL parameters a and b: $\tau^{a_{\mathrm{eff}}}_{\mathrm{WKB}}(F) = \frac{\varepsilon_1 \hbar}{4 e^3} a_{\mathrm{eff}}^3 F \exp\left(\frac{2e}{3\varepsilon_1 a_{\mathrm{eff}} F}\right)$. (b) Critical field versus distance of the donor to the interface. The solid line gives a phenomenological fit $F_c \propto 1/|z_0|$ with $z_0 = d - 5/\alpha$ being the center of mass of the electron at the interface. The dashed line is a fitting to tight-binding results in Ref. [3] of the form $F_c \propto 1/d$. (c) Donor ionization tunneling (solid line) and adiabatic passage (dashed) times versus d.

the interface. These parameters yield an upper bound of $n \sim 10^{10} \mathrm{cm}^{-2}$ for planar donor densities, and limits the operating temperature to a few K.

Direct diagonalization of the problem in the non-orthogonal basis $\{\Psi_A, \Psi_B\}$ leads to the two lowest energy eigenstates Ψ_0 and Ψ_1 and eigenvalues E_0 and E_1. The response of the electron to an applied electric field is depicted in Fig. 2(b), where the expectation value $\langle \Psi_0 |z| \Psi_0 \rangle$ is given for three values of d. We define a critical field F_c as the field value at which the gap is minimized, $(E_1 - E_0)_{\min} = g_{min}$, characterizing the anticrossing point in a (E_0, E_1) vs F diagram [inset in Fig. 2(b)].

The key parameter for general device applications is the tunneling time for donor ionization under an applied field. We present a fully quantum-mechanical estimate for the tunneling time, which we relate here to the anticrossing energy gap through the uncertainty relation. Fig. 3(a) shows the results for the tunneling times versus F_c and compare them with a WKB estimate. Fig. 3(b) gives the critical field versus d results. Fig. 3(c) gives the tunneling times vs d, showing that τ increases by 5 orders of magnitude (from sub-picoseconds to nanoseconds) as the donor distance to the interface increases by a factor of 5 (e.g. $\tau \sim 3$ ps for $d \simeq 15$ nm). Typical adiabatic passage times $\tau_a = \hbar|e|F_c d/g_{\min}^2$ are orders of magnitude larger than the tunneling time (e.g. $\tau_a \sim 0.4$ ns for $d \simeq 15$ nm). In the case of spin qubits, tunneling times define the limiting time scales, since electron tunneling does not affect spin coherence. Spin coherence times in

bulk Si ($T_2 \sim 1$ms) are at least 5 orders of magnitude longer than the tunneling times reported here. Charge relaxation times are much shorter than spin coherence times, of the order of 200ns for Si quantum dots surrounded by oxide layers, but still longer than the adiabatic passage times for $d < 20$nm. Our results [2] indicate that quantum control consistent with Si quantum computer architectures could be achieved.

This work is supported by CNPq and FAPERJ (Brazil) and by LPS and NSA (USA).

REFERENCES

1. B.E. Kane, *Nature* (London) **393**, 133 (1998).
2. M.J. Calderón, B. Koiller, X. Hu and S. Das Sarma, *Phys. Rev. Lett.* **96**, 096802 (2006).
3. A. S. Martins, R. B. Capaz and B. Koiller, *Phys. Rev. B* **69**, 085320 (2004).

Applications of Single Photons from a Single Quantum Dot in Quantum Information Processing

M. Scholz, T. Aichele, S. Ramelow and O. Benson

Humboldt-Universität zu Berlin, AG Nanooptik, Hausvogteiplatz 5-7, 10117 Berlin, Germany

Abstract. We present a two-qubit quantum algorithm and multiplexed quantum cryptography as examples for quantum information processing using single photons generated in a single InP(GaInP) quantum dot. In the first part, a Deutsch-Jozsa algorithm is executed with linear optics obtaining a fidelity of up to 79%, and noise-resistant encoding is implemented by appropriate superpositions of spatial modes. In the second part, multiplexing enhances the bandwidth of quantum key distribution in a BB84 protocol.

Keywords: quantum dots, single photons, quantum information
PACS: 03.67.Lx, 03.67.Pp, 42.50.Dv, 78.67.Hc

DEUTSCH-JOZSA ALGORITHM

Linear optics offers an appealing approach to implement quantum algorithms [1, 2] since only standard optical components like beam splitters and phase shifters are required. However, most approaches suffer from an exponential increase of resources in terms of optical elements. The seminal proposal by Knill, Laflamme, and Milburn [3] suggests a solution by using single-photon states and photon number resolving detectors to enable the efficient generation of a non-linear fundamental two-photon gate. This proposal requires a reliable *on demand* source for indistinguishable single photons that can be triggered and an interferometrically stable optical setup that operates on the single-photon level. We have demonstrated the on demand operation of such a quantum algorithm using a triggered single-photon source, and we choose the two-qubit Deutsch-Jozsa algorithm [4] which often served in the past to demonstrate the applicability of a certain physical system to a particular quantum computational task. Previous all-optical experiments were restricted to emulate the Deutsch-Jozsa algorithm with attenuated classical laser pulses [5, 6].

In our implementation [7], the first qubit is encoded in a dual-rail representation (figure 1). The logical state $|0\rangle_L$ ($|1\rangle_L$) is associated with the physical state $|a\rangle$ ($|b\rangle$) which corresponds to the situation "one photon in mode a (b)". The second qubit is implemented via the photon's polarization state $|H\rangle$ ($|V\rangle$). The initial state is realized by sending a photon into a linear superposition of the two spatial modes using a non-polarizing 50:50 beam splitter after preparing it in a superposition of horizontal and vertical polarization. In a next step, a unitary transformation is realized by selectively adding a half-wave plate to each mode. The four possible setups represent the functions $f(a) = f(b)$ (constant functions) and $f(a) \neq f(b)$

(balanced functions). Recombining the two interferometer arms on a second non-polarizing 50:50 beam splitter implements a final Hadamard gate on the first qubit.

Our experiment resembles a classical Mach-Zehnder interferometer: Constructive (destructive) interference in the extension of mode a indicates a balanced (constant) function, i.e. one and only one wave plate (two or none wave plates) in the beam paths. The single photons are generated by an exciton transition in a single quantum dot [8]. They enter the Mach-Zehnder interferometer (figure 1) that is actively stabilized to the interference signal of a He-Ne laser which propagates about 1 cm above the single photons. The two interferometer outputs are monitored with one avalanche photo detector (APD) each. The same setup is used for intensity correlation measurements. We define the visibility $|I_{APD1/2,bal} - I_{APD1/2,const}|/(I_{APD1/2,bal} + I_{APD1/2,const})$ as a measure for the success probability of our computation. Mean values of 79% and 71% have been obtained for APD 1 and APD 2, respectively.

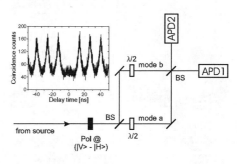

FIGURE 1. Experimental setup: The two balanced and two constant functions are realized via half-wave plates in the arms, a second BS performs a final Hadamard gate. Two photon detectors evaluate the algorithm output and are also used to confirm single-photon emission (inset).

CP893, *Physics of Semiconductors, 28th International Conference*
edited by W. Jantsch and F. Schäffler
© 2007 American Institute of Physics 978-0-7354-0397-0/07/$23.00

The concept of decoherence-free subspaces [9, 10] opens a way to make quantum computation stable by encoding information in certain parts of a Hilbert space that are not affected by the noise operators. A variation of our experimental setup enables us to implement these ideas in a triggered quantum algorithm on the single-photon level.

MULTIPLEXED QUANTUM CRYPTOGRAPHY

For quantum communication protocols, a single-photon source with high repetition rate is desired. A well-established technique from classical communications is *multiplexing*. Each signal is marked with a physical label and identified at the receiver using filters tuned to the carrier frequencies. For single photons, their wavelength can be used as their distinguishing label and polarization to encode quantum information [11]. If the two photons from a biexciton-exciton cascade pass a Michelson interferometer, constructive and destructive interference will be observed at the two output ports by proper choice of the relative path difference (figure 2). These photons are fed into an optical fiber each, and one of them is delayed by half the repetition rate of the excitation laser. Recombination at a beam splitter then leads to a photon stream with a doubled count rate. This is also reflected by auto-correlation measurements with a spacing of only 6.6 ns in the peak structure (see figure 2d).

Multiplexing can enhance the bandwidth of quantum communication systems which use single-photon sources based on spontaneous emission. In our experiment, we implement the BB84 protocol [12, 13]

where the photon wavelength is unimportant. Quantum cryptography has been realized with single-photon states from diamond defect centers [14] and quantum dots [15]. Interferometric multiplexing can be implemented in the BB84 protocol using a cascaded photon source. Behind an exciton-biexciton add/drop filter, Alice randomly prepares the photons' polarization. Bob's detection consists of a second EOM, an analyzing polarizer, and an APD. After key distribution, Alice encrypts her data by applying an XOR operation between every image bit and the sequence of random bits (the secret key) which she has previously shared with Bob by performing the BB84 protocol. The encoded image is transmitted over a distance of 1 m with 30 bits/s with an error rate of 5.5%.

ACKNOWLEDGMENTS

The authors want to thank W. Seifert for providing the quantum dot sample and V. Zwiller and J. Persson for valuable assistance. This work was supported by Deutsche Forschungsgemeinschaft (SFB 296) and the European Union (EFRE). M. Scholz acknowledges financial support from Ev. Studienwerk Villigst and T. Aichele by DAAD.

REFERENCES

1. N. J. Cerf, C. Adami, and P. G. Kwiat, *Phys. Rev. A* **57**, 1477 (1998).
2. M. Fiorentino and F. N. C. Wong, *Phys. Rev. Lett.* **93**, 070502 (2004).
3. E. Knill, R. Laflamme, and G. J. Milburn, *Nature* **409**, 46 (2001).
4. D. Deutsch and R. Jozsa, *Proc. R. Soc. Lond. A* **439**, 553 (1992).
5. S. Takeuchi, *Phys. Rev. A* **62**, 032301 (2000).
6. M. Mohseni, J. S. Lundeen, J. J. Resch, and A. M. Steinberg, *Phys. Rev. Lett.* **91**, 187903 (2003).
7. M. Scholz, T. Aichele, S. Ramelow, and O. Benson, *Phys. Rev. Lett.* **96**, 180501 (2006).
8. V. Zwiller, T. Aichele, J. Persson, L. Samuelson, and O. Benson, *Appl. Phys. Lett.* **82**, 1509 (2003).
9. P. Zanardi and M. Rasetti, *Phys. Rev. Lett.* **79**, 3306 (1997).
10. D. A. Lidar, I. L. Chuang, and K. B. Whaley, *Phys. Rev. Lett.* **81**, 2594 (1998).
11. T. Aichele, G. Reinaudi, and O. Benson, *Phys. Rev. B* **70**, 235329 (2004).
12. C. M. Bennett and G. Brassard, in *Proc. IEEE Conference on Computers, Systems, and Signal Processing in Bangalore, India* (IEEE, New York, 1984), p. 175.
13. N. Gisin, G. Ribordy, W. Tittel, and H. Zbinden, *Rev. Mod. Phys.* **74**, 145 (2002).
14. A. Beveratos, R. Brouri, T. Gacoin, A. Villing, J.-P. Poizat, and P. Grangier, *Phys. Rev. Lett.* **89**, 187901 (2002).
15. E. Waks, K. Inoue, C. Santori, D. Fattal, J. Vučković, G. S. Solomon, and Y. Yamamoto, *Nature* **420**, 762 (2002).

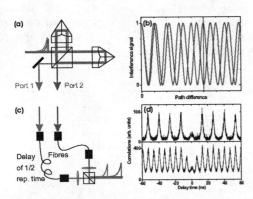

FIGURE 2. (a) Michelson interferometer with two output ports as a single-photon add/drop filter. (b) Interference pattern for two distinct wavelengths versus the relative arm length. (c) Merging the separated photons with one path delayed by half the excitation repetition rate. (d) Intensity correlation of the exciton spectral line and the multiplexed signal.

A quantum device interfacing photons and spins for quantum repeaters

H. Kosaka[1,2], T. Kutsuwa[2], K. Arai[2,3], Y. Rikitake[2,5], K. Ono[4,2], H. Imamura[5,2], T. Takagahara[6,2], Y. Mitsumori[1,2], K. Edamatsu[1]

[1]Research Institute of Electrical Communication, Tohoku University, Sendai 980-8577, Japan
[2]CREST-JST, Saitama 332-0012, Japan, [3]ERATO- JST, Saitama 332-0012, Japan
[4]Low Temperature Physics Laboratory, RIKEN, 2-1 Hirosawa Wako, Saitama 351-0198, Japan
[5] Nanotechnology Research Institute, AIST, Tsukuba 305-8568, Japan
[6]Kyoto Institute of Technology, Kyoto 606-8585, Japan

Abstract. We present experimental and theoretical approach for building a quantum repeater. Device structure for quantum state transfer from a photon to an electron spin was designed, fabricated and evaluated. Light-hole exciton excitation in GaAs/AlGaAs-quantum well with near-zero electron g-factor showed "negative polarization", which indicates polarization transfer from a photon to an electron spin. We have also observed dynamic nuclear polarization implying polarization transfer from a photon to a nuclear spin intermediated by an electron spin.

Keywords: Quantum information, single photon, electron spin, nuclear spin
PACS: 03.67.-a, 85.35.Ds, 72.25.Fe, 85.35.Be

Quantum repeaters [1-5] are required for extending the distance of quantum communication. One of key devices for building quantum repeaters is a quantum interface that enables quantum state transfer (QST) [6-9] from a messenger photonic qubit onto a processor electron-spin qubit [10,11]. QST is unitary transformation from Poincare sphere, describing photon polarization state, to Bloch sphere, describing electron spin polarization state (Fig. 1). This unitarity is satisfied when both spheres are mathematically equivalent by tuning electron in-plane g-factor to zero [12,13] in order to satisfy the energy conservation

condition. Under in-plane magnetic field, spin degeneracy of only light hole is lifted to make bonding and anti-banding states distinguishable, which permits selective excitation of one eigen state of light-hole spin together with either up or down electron spin by σ^+ or σ^- photon absorption (Fig. 1). If this polarization transfer occurred coherently, the V-shaped transition of light-hole exciton enables QST, which is guaranteed by angular momentum conservation between photon and electron-hole system as shown in this paper.

We have prepared GaAs/Al$_x$Ga$_{1-x}$As quantum well

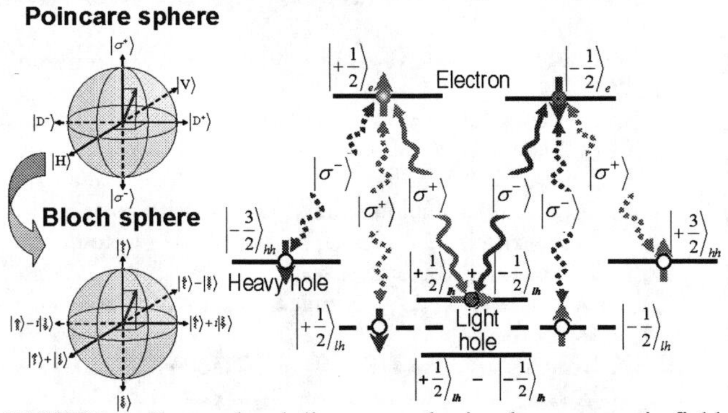

FIGURE 1. Energy band diagram under in-plane magnetic field for QST. A photon should create a light hole in its eigen state together with an electron in up/down-spin state mapped by the photon spin state.

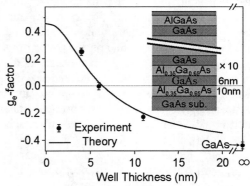

FIGURE 2. Electron g-factor measured for GaAs /Al$_{0.35}$Ga$_{0.65}$As quantum well structure (solid circles) and simulation (solid line). Inset shows layer structure of 6-nm quantum well, which showed nearly zero g-factor.

CP893, *Physics of Semiconductors, 28th International Conference*
edited by W. Jantsch and F. Schäffler
© 2007 American Institute of Physics 978-0-7354-0397-0/07/$23.00

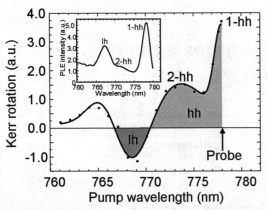

FIGURE 3. Negative polarization with light-hole exciton excitation measured by time-resolved two-color Kerr rotation using GaAs/AlGaAs quantum well with g_e-factor<0.01 probed at 778nm (1st-heavy-hole exciton). Inset: excitation spectrum detected at 1-hh exciton.

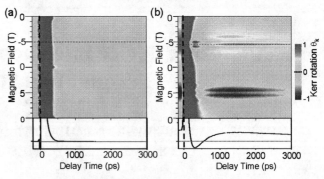

FIGURE 4. Magnetic-field dependence of spin precession dynamics measured by Kerr rotation for GaAs/AlGaAs g-zeroed QW. (a) Pump light helicity was alternated at 42 KHz and the difference was plotted. No precession indicates zero g-factor. (b) Pump helicity was fixed. Spin precession starts around 1T.

structure with various well thicknesses and measured electron in-plane g-factor by using time-resolved Kerr rotation technique. Measured g-factors showed good agreements with simulation as shown in Fig. 2. One of the devices, which has 10 pairs of 6nm-thick multiple quantum wells (x=0.35), showed no spin precession, that indicates electron g-factor to be less than 0.02. By using this structure, we have measured optically injected electron spin polarization by two-color time-resolved Kerr rotation (Fig. 3). Spin polarization projected to the surface normal was measured by Kerr rotation angle as a function of pump wavelength at fixed probe wavelength. Pump light polarization was fixed to σ^+ and probe wavelength was fixed to heavy-hole exciton. Only when light-hole exciton was excited, electron spin showed negative spin polarization opposing to the case of heavy-hole excitation. This negativity comes from the negative sign in orbital and spin angular momentum of light-hole state. We have checked that spin flips when pump polarization was altered to σ^-. These phenomena are the consequence of angular momentum conservation and hence polarization transfer from a photon to an electron spin during the process of light-hole exciton creation. We have also observed photon helicity dependence of spin precession (Fig. 4). Only when pump helicity was fixed, strong spin precession was observed under a magnetic field over a few T. This phenomenon indicates polarization transfer from a photon to a nuclear spin induced by dynamic nuclear spin polarization intermediated by an electron spin. This transfer will be controlled by g-factor tuning.

The QST process is completed by erasing the hole state in one eigen state and remaining electron spin state whose superposition is transferred from that of photonic state. To clarify QST conditions for high efficiency and high fidelity, we have quantum mechanically simulated the process by using input-output theory in bad cavity regime. Ideal QST condition was found to be $\omega_J \ll \Delta\omega_{ph} \ll \Gamma_d \sim \gamma_h$, where ω_J, $\Delta\omega_p$ Γ_d, and γ_h denote electron-hole exchange interaction, photon bandwidth, dipole relaxation rate, and hole extraction rate, respectively. If we assume ω_J to be 20μeV, we obtain conditions for g-factors: $g_e < 0.04$ and $g_h > 1$ for hole. The structure we have examined above will satisfy these conditions.

In conclusion, we have demonstrated the possibility of QST by showing polarization transfer from a photon to an electron spin by selectively exciting light-hole exciton whose electron g-factor was tuned to zero. To prove coherent quantum state transfer, we have to examine superposition states in Poincare sphere to be mapped to the corresponding electron spin states in Bloch sphere.

REFERENCES

1. C.H. Bennett et al., Phys. Rev. Lett. **70**, 1895 (1993).
2. L.M. Duan, M. D. Lukin, J. I. Cirac and P. Zoller, Nature **414**, 413 (2001).
3. L. Childress, J.M. Taylor, A.S. Sørensen and M.D. Lukin, Phys. Rev. A **72**, 052330 (2005).
4. L. Childress, J.M. Taylor, A.S. Sørensen and M.D. Lukin, Phys. Rev. Lett. **96**, 070504 (2006).
5. P. van Loock et al., Phys. Rev. Lett. **96**, 240501 (2006).
6. R. Vrijen and E. Yablonovitch, Physica E **10**, 569 (2001).
7. E. Yablonovitch, H.W. Jiang, H. Kosaka, H.D. Robinson, D.S. Rao and T. Szkopek: Proc. of IEEE, **91**, 761 (2003).
8. A. Matsukevich and A. Kuzmich, Science **306**, 663 (2004).
9. H. Kosaka et at., Phys. Rev. B, **67**, 045104 (2003).
10. D. Loss and D. P. DiVincenzo, Phys. Rev. A **57**, 120 (1998).
11. J.R. Petta et al., Science **309**, 2180 (2005).
12. H. Kosaka et al,, Electron. Lett., **37**, 464 (2001).
13. A.A. Kiselev, K.W. Kim, and E. Yablonovitch, Appl. Phys. Lett. **80**, 2857 (2002).

Spin qubit and its decoherence in QD in a diluted magnetic semiconductor medium

Witold Jacak[1], Jurij Krasnyj[2], Janusz Jacak[1]

[1]*Institute of Physics, Wrocław University of Technology, Wyb. Wyspiańskiego 27, 50-370 Wrocław, Poland*
[2]*Institute of Mathematics, University of Opole, Oleska 48, 45-051 Opole, Poland*

Abstract. The spin degrees of freedom in quantum dots (QDs) of He-type embedded in diluted magnetic semiconductor (DMS) medium are considered for modelling of qubit and gate for quantum information processing (QIP). The qubit is defined as a singlet and triplet pair of states of two electrons in He QD. Methods of qubit rotations and two-qubit operations are considered. Decoherence due to spin waves in magnetically ordered phase of DMS is however recognized as the the source of unavoidable dephasing with inconvenient, from point of view of the DiVincenzo conditions, time-scale.

Keywords: quantum dot, diluted magnetic semiconductor, spin waves, decoherence
PACS: 68.65.Hb, 03.65.Yz

INTRODUCTION: Feasibility of QIP within the solid state technology employing orbital (charge) degrees of freedom is strongly limited by charge-excitations dephasing due to phonons (mostly acoustical) [1], which does not allow for scaling of only-by-light driven gates. Thus spin degrees of freedom in QDs, robust against phonon-induced decoherence, seem to be more promising [2]. Steering of spin in semiconductor QDs is however relatively slow due to a small value of the gyromagnetic factor (e.g. Zeeman splitting in GaAs ~0.03 meV/T). Possible acceleration of spin operations in QDs embedded in a diluted magnetic semiconductor (DMS) medium, due to Weiss-type field, would be thus of particular significance. In a magnetically ordered phase of DMS exist however spin waves (magnons) and via the hybridization with spin in QD cause its decoherence (dephasing), similarly as phonons for local charge. Estimation of relevant time-scale of magnon-induced dephasing of QD spin is thus essential and it is presented below.

SINGLET-TRIPLET QUBIT IN QD IN DMS: In He-type QD (dot with two electrons) one can consider a qubit spanned by singlet and triplet states of the electron pair [3]. The singlet state is the ground state in the absence of the magnetic field, but with growing magnetic field the triplet state is more favorable—the crossing of both levels occurs at $B \approx \hbar\omega_0 / 1.6$ (for parabolic QD model [3,4]). In vicinity of this crossing point the spin singlet-triplet qubit is well defined, with additional possibility of tuning of energy-level separation (Fig.1), which opens a new occasion for organization of quantum gate, i.e. on demand switching on/off interaction between two He QDs. We suppose to change the energy separation ΔE in qubits (by magnetic field shift) and in that manner to control the role of real inter-qubit interaction W—important is

only the ratio $W/\Delta E$[1]. For energy separation ΔE much greater than direct inter-qubit interaction W, this interaction is negligible with accuracy $W/\Delta E \ll 1$. And oppositely, for $\Delta E \sim W$, inter-qubit interaction is active.

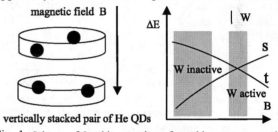

Fig. 1. Scheme of 2-qubit operations: for qubit energy separation much greater than inter-qubit interaction (bar) this interaction is inactive (singlet-s $|0,0\rangle$, triplet-t $|1,-1\rangle$).

The single qubit operations (Rabi rotations) one can achieve by applying an *unhomogeneous* lateral magnetic field—only unhomogeneous field gives nonzero matrix element between singlet and triplet. Out of degeneracy point it is needed the dynamical field with frequency accommodated to ΔE, while for degeneracy point the static field is sufficient [3,5]. This static unhomogeneous field would be created by magnetic admixtures close to QD.

MAGNON-INDUCED DEPHASING OF QD SPIN IN DMS: The effective enhancement of gyromagnetic factor in magnetically ordered phase of DMS can accelerate spin operations in QDs. In that phase occur however collective spin fluctuations—spin waves. To account for energy dispersion of these excitations we have performed: 1) averaging over random distributions of magnetic admixtures (Mn in III(Mn)V or II(Mn)VI)—this procedure allows for effective restitution of translational invariance [8] (the type of admixture distribution can be modelled by appropriate formfactor, which does not however influence results

---

[1]One can verify it within Heitler-London-type calculus for two interacting He QDs

CP893, *Physics of Semiconductors, 28th International Conference*
edited by W. Jantsch and F. Schäffler

significantly), 2) simultaneous diagonalization of spin Hamiltonian of two magnetic interacting subsystems in DMS—spins of Mn and spins of band holes mediating exchange interaction [1]. As the result of this diagonalization (in Holstein-Primakoff representation for both type of spin) we arrive with two branches of spin waves (magnons) with dispersion given by the formulae [1]:

$$\varepsilon_1(\vec{k}) = D_0 - Dk^2, \; \varepsilon_2 = Dk^2, \; D \approx \frac{2Sxx_p}{x_p + 2Sx}.$$

Both this dispersions are of quadratic type, similarly as for optical phonons, and thus give the similar type of dressing of spin as it was for charge due to optical phonons. The kinetics of dressing of QD spin with magnons is displayed by the exciton correlation function [1]. The Fourier transform of this function is the spectral intensity (imaginary part of retarded Green function). It should be underlined that for temporal characteristics important is out-of-pole behaviour of corresponding spectral intensity, which can be accounted for via a mass operator (within the Matsubara-Green function formalism) corresponding to exchange interaction of QD exciton spin structure with magnons (the explicit form of this interaction it follows from the exchange interaction of e-h pair in QD with Mn spins after the diagonalization transformation of magnetic subsystem in DMS). Similarly as for dressing of charge with phonons the characteristic time of formation of magneto-polaron in QD appears to be governed only by two factors: 1) the group velocity of magnons, v_g, and 2) the dimension of QD, d. Behind this statement is the simple physical argument: the formation of magneto-polaron in QD (i.e. hybridization of local exciton spin with magnons) corresponds to transfer of excess interaction energy outside QD region (magneto-polaron state has lower energy than the rapidly created in QD bare exciton). This excess energy is transferred to the rest of the crystal by magnos—thus the characteristic time for this process is: $\tau \approx d / v_g$. The dressing of QD spin one can consider as time-evolution of nonstationary state (the bare exciton in the initial moment) which displays the time-dependent redisrtibution of mean-energy between QD and rest of the system (magnons in DMS).

The data for magneto-polaron formation are available for Zn(Mn)Se/CdSn [6]. In II(Mn)VI pure exchange interaction between Mn ions is of antiferromagnetic type [7] and for ferromagnetic transition additional doping is needed (resulting in 1-2K critical temperature, smaller than for III(Mn)V [7,9]). However the data [6] suggest that the formation of magneto-polaron maintains up to 20K, which can be connected with the fact that QD e-h pair interacts only with Mn subsystem, despite that its magnetization could be screened by band hole spins (an evidence of such 'hidden' transition—cf. fig.12 in [9]). To support this statement in Tab.1 the comparison of measured temperature-blue-shift of exciton energy and the shift due to magnons (theory) is given.

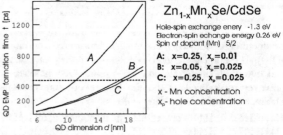

Fig.2. Dephasing time for QD spin in DMS—from correlation function behaviour (quadratic dependence on dot dimension)

TABLE 1. X-QD blue-shift in Zn(Mn)Se/CdSe [meV]

Temperature [K]	Experiment [6]	Theory
5	2.0925	2.0923
12	2.097	2.095
21	2.099	2.1

For Mn and hole concentrations in DMS and dot dimension as in experimental samples we obtain the similar as observed [6] dephasing time of order of 500ps (cf. Fig. 2). Note that dephasing time scales with dot dimension as d^2, which is the consequence of quadratic dispersion of magnons ($v_g \propto k$) and bottle-neck for QD $(k \propto 1/d)$, thus $\tau \propto d^2$. Relatively long time of magnon-induced spin dephasing in DMS is as much inconvenient as ps-scale dephasing time for charge—it is located in the center of available 6-orders DiVincenzo window for spin operation /decoherence[2].

ACKNOWLEDGEMENTS: Supported by Polish Ministry of S.H.E. under the grants 2 PO3B 085 25 and PBZ-MIN-008/PO3/03.

REFERENCES
1. L. Jacak et al., Phys. Rev. B **72**, 245309-1 (2005).
2. D. Loss, D. P. DiVincenzo, Phys.Rev. A **57**, 120 (1998); T. Calarco et al. Phys. Rev. A **68**, 12310 (2003); A. Imamoglu, Phys. Rev. Lett. **83**, 4204 (1999).
3. L. Jacak et al., Acta Phys. Pol. A **99**, 277 (2001).
4. M. Wagner, U. Merkt, A. Chaplik, Phys. Rev. B, **45**, 1951 (1992).
5. L. Landau, E. Lifshic, *Quantum Mechanics* (§39, exs.3), PWN Warsaw 1976.
6. J. Seufert et al., Phys. Rev. Lett. **88**, 27402 (2002); H. Schoning et al, Physica E **13**, 512 (2002).
7. T. Dietl, K. Ohno, F. Matsukura, Phys. Rev. B **63**, 195205 (2001).
8. N. Kovalenko, J. Krasnyj, U. Krey, *Physics of Amorphous Metals*, Wiley-VCH 1999.
9. J. Furdyna, J.Appl.Phys. **64**, R29 (1988).

---

[2] here - decoherence of spin due to nuclear spins and spin-orbit

Effect of the electron-hole exchange interaction on the photon-spin quantum state transfer

Y. Rikitake*,†, H. Imamura*,† and H.Kosaka*,**

*CREST-JST, Saitama 332-00122, Japan
†Nanotechnology Research Institute, AIST, Tsukuba 305-8568, Japan
**Research Institute of Electrical Communication, Tohoku University, Sendai 980-8577, Japan

Abstract. We theoretically analyze the yield and fidelity of the quantum state transfer (QST) from a photon polarization qubit to an electron spin qubit using a spin-coherent photo-detector consisting of a semiconductor quantum dot. We use the modified one-dimensional light-atom interaction model which includes parameters such as photon-dot interaction, the tunneling rate of the created hole, the bandwidth of the input photon, and the electron-hole exchange interaction. The electron-hole exchange interaction disturbs the electron spin state and thus decreases the fidelity of the QST. We find the optimal conditions in which both a high-yield and high-fidelity QST is realized.

Keywords: Quantum information, Single photon, Electron spin
PACS: 03.67.-a, 72.25.Fe, 68.65.Hb

A quantum repeater is a promising technology[1, 2, 3]which enables us to dramatically expand the distance of quantum key distribution as well as realize scalable quantum networks. The quantum repeater requires not only messenger qubits but also processing qubits. A photon is, of course, the most convenient candidate for messenger qubits [4, 5]; however, it is not suitable for use as processing qubits because of the difficulty involved in quantum information storage and two-qubit quantum operations. On the other hand, an electron spin in a semiconductor quantum dot is one of the most convenient candidates for use as processing qubits since the one- and two-bit quantum gate operations are now available by applying electric or/and magnetic fields [6, 7, 8]. Therefore, it is important to investigate a photon-spin quantum state transfer (QST) [9, 10] which transfers the quantum information from a photon-polarization (photon qubit) to an electron-spin (spin qubit), as an interface device for quantum repeaters.

Such a photon-spin quantum state transfer can be performed using the spin-coherent semiconductor photo-detector proposed by Vrijen and Yablonovitch[9]. They showed that the well-known optical orientation in a semiconductor hetero-structure can be used for QST with the help of g-factor engineering[11, 12] and strain engineering[13, 14]. According to the selection rule shown in Figure1 (a), the up (down) spin electron $|\uparrow\rangle$ $(|\downarrow\rangle)$ is excited by the right-handed (left-handed) circularly polarized photon $|\sigma^+\rangle$ $(|\sigma^-\rangle)$ from the $|lh+\rangle$ state. After elimination of the hole in the $|lh+\rangle$ state, the quantum state of photon qubit $\alpha_+|\sigma^+\rangle + \alpha_-|\sigma^-\rangle$ is transferred to the state of the spin qubit $\alpha_+|\uparrow\rangle + \alpha_-|\downarrow\rangle$.

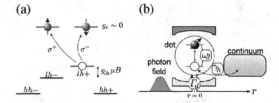

FIGURE 1. (a)Energy levels of the quantum dot. From [the] $|lh+\rangle$ state, the electron with the $|\uparrow\rangle$($|\downarrow\rangle$) spin state is optically excited by the right-handed (left-handed) circularly polarized photon $|\sigma^+\rangle$($|\sigma^-\rangle$). (b)The theoretical model we consider. The model includes the photon-dot interaction Γ_d, the electron-hole exchange interaction in the dot ω_J, and the tunneling rate of the hole γ_h.

We analyze the dynamics of the QST process by using the modified one-dimensional light-atom interaction model[15] shown in Figure1(b). This model contains the photon field, the quantum dot, and the continuum of the hole. The wave function of the system is given by

$$|\Psi(t)\rangle = \sum_{\sigma=\pm} \int dr \phi_\sigma(r;t)|r\sigma\rangle + \sum_{s=\uparrow\downarrow} \varphi_{Es}(t)|Es\rangle + \sum_{s=\uparrow\downarrow} \sum_l \psi_{ls}(t)|ls\rangle. \quad (1)$$

The first term represents the photon field. The polarization of the photon is denoted by $\sigma = \pm$. The input photon propagates along the r-axis in the positive direction and interacts with the quantum dot (in a cavity) located at the origin $r = 0$. The coupling strength between the input photon and the quantum dot is denoted by Γ_d, called the dipole relaxation rate. The second term represents the electron-hole pair (exciton) in the quantum dot excited

CP893, *Physics of Semiconductors, 28th International Conference*
edited by W. Jantsch and F. Schäffler

by the input photon. The index $s = \uparrow, \downarrow$ represents the electron spin state of the exciton. While the electron and the hole form the exciton in the dot, the electron-hole exchange interaction acts between them[16], and rotates the electron spin state. The strength of the electron-hole exchange interaction is denoted by ω_J. Once the electron-hole pair is created in the quantum dot, the hole escapes to the continuum via the tunneling barrier, and only the electron spin remains in the dot. We denote the tunneling rate of the hole as γ_h. The last term represents the state in which the electron spin (s) is in the dot and the hole is in the state l of the continuum.

The time evolution of the quantum state $|\Psi(t)\rangle$ can be calculated by solving the Schrodinger equation with a proper initial state. In our analysis, we assume that the Gaussian wave packet of a photon enters the dot at the initial time $t = t_i$. The incident wave packet is written as $\phi_\sigma(r; t_i) = \alpha_\sigma e^{-i\omega_{ph}r/c - (r-r_0)^2/2L^2}/\pi^{1/4}\sqrt{L}$, where r_0 (< 0) is the center position of the Gaussian wave packet at $t = t_i$, and L is the coherence length of the packet ($L \ll |r_0|$). The center frequency of the photon is denoted by ω_{ph}, and we assume that ω_{ph} corresponds to the excitation energy of the electron-hole pair in the quantum dot. The bandwidth of the input photon is given by $\Delta\omega_{ph} = c/L$. The polarization of the input photon is characterized by the probability amplitudes α_+ and α_- ($|\alpha_+|^2 + |\alpha_-|^2 = 1$).

After solving the Schrodinger equation, we can calculate the yield and the fidelity of the QST within the limit of $t \to \infty$. The yield is defined as the number of generated spins in the quantum dot per single QST process. The fidelity is defined as an inner product between the spin state actually transferred after QST and the ideal spin state. Figure 2 (a) shows a contour plot of the yield as a function of $\Gamma_d/\Delta\omega_{ph}$ and $\gamma_h/\Delta\omega_{ph}$. The incident photon polarization is $|\sigma^+\rangle$ ($\alpha_+ = 1, \alpha_- = 0$) and the strength of the electron-hole exchange interaction is $\omega_J = 0.5\Delta\omega_{ph}$. The plot shows that the dipole relaxation rate Γ_d and the tunneling rate of the hole γ_h should be much larger than the bandwidth of the input photon $\Delta\omega_{ph}$, and the matching condition $\Gamma_d \sim \gamma_h$ should also be satisfied in order to obtain a high yield. Figure 2 (b) shows a contour plot of the fidelity. One can see that the fidelity becomes low for $\Gamma_d, \gamma_h < \omega_J$. When the electron-hole exchange interaction is dominant, the electron spin precesses and changes its states during the period in which the hole is present in the dot. Therefore the condition $\omega_J \ll \Delta\omega_{ph} \ll \Gamma_d \sim \gamma_h$ is required for the ideal QST.

In conclusion, we have studied the yield and fidelity of the photon- electron spin QST in the spin-coherent semiconductor photo-detector. Using the modified one-dimensional light-atom interaction model, we analyzed the quantum dynamics of the QST process and found the conditions necessary for the high-yield and high-fidelity

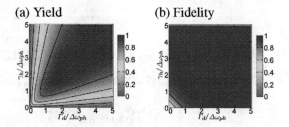

(a) Yield   **(b) Fidelity**

FIGURE 2. Contour plots of (a)yield and (b)fidelity. The horizontal axes represents the dipole relaxation rate Γ_d and vertical axes represents the tunneling rate of the hole γ_h. Both axes are normalized by the bandwidth of input photon $\Delta\omega_{ph}$. The strength of the exchange interaction is taken to be $\omega_J = 0.5\Delta\omega_{ph}$.

QST. It is shown that the condition $\omega_J \ll \Delta\omega_{ph} \ll \Gamma_d \sim \gamma_h$ should be satisfied for the ideal QST.

This work was supported by CREST, MEXT.KAKENHI (14076204 and 16710061), NEDO, and NAREGI Nanoscience project.

REFERENCES

1. H. Briegel, W. Dur, J. Cirac, and P. Zoller, *Phys. Rev. Lett.* **81**, 5932–5935 (1998).
2. L. Duan, M. Lukin, J. Cirac, and P. Zoller, *Nature* **414**, 413–418 (2001).
3. L. Childress, J. Taylor, A. Sorensen, and M. Lukin, *Phys. Rev. A* **72**, 052330 (2005).
4. N. Gisin, G. Ribordy, W. Tittel, and H. Zbinden, *Rev. Mod. Phys.* **74**, 145–195 (2002).
5. C. Gobby, Z. L. Yuan, and A. J. Shields, *Appl. Phys. Lett.* **84**, 3762–3764 (2004).
6. J. Taylor, C. Marcus, and M. Lukin, *Phys. Rev. Lett.* **90**, 206803 (2003).
7. J. R. Petta, A. C. Johnson, J. M. Taylor, E. A. Laird, A. Yacoby, M. D. Lukin, C. M. Marcus, M. P. Hanson, and A. C. Gossord, *Science* **309**, 2180 (2005).
8. F. H. L. Koppens, C. Buizert, K. J. Tielrooij, I. T. Vink, K. C. Nowack, T. Meunier, L. P. Kouwenhoven, and L. M. K. Vandersypen, *Nature* **442**, 766–771 (2006).
9. R. Vrijen, and E. Yablonovitch, *Physica E* **10**, 569–575 (2001).
10. H. Kosaka, D. Rao, H. Robinson, P. Bandaru, K. Makita, and E. Yablonovitch, *Phys. Rev. B* **67**, 045104 (2003).
11. A. Kiselev, E. Ivchenko, and U. Rossler, *Phys. Rev. B* **58**, 16353–16359 (1998).
12. J. Nitta, Y. Lin, T. Koga, and T. Akazaki, *Physica E* **20**, 429–432 (2004).
13. S. Lin, H. Wei, D. Tsui, J. Klem, and S. Allen, *Phys. Rev. B* **43**, 12110–12113 (1991).
14. T. Nakaoka, T. Saito, J. Tatebayashi, S. Hirose, T. Usuki, N. Yokoyama, and Y. Arakawa, *Phys. Rev. B* **71**, 205301 (2005).
15. K. Kojima, H. Hofmann, S. Takeuchi, and K. Sasaki, *Phys. Rev. A* **68**, 013803 (2003).
16. E. L. Ivchenko, and G. E. Pikus, *Superlattices and Other Heterostructures*, Springer-Verlag, Berlin, 1997, 2nd edn.

Cluster states in charge qubits based on coupled quantum dots

T. Tanamoto*, S. Fujita*, X. Hu[†], Y.-x. Liu[**] and F. Nori[**,‡]

*Corporate R & D center, Toshiba Corporation, Saiwai-ku, Kawasaki 212-8582, Japan
[†]Department of Physics, University at Buffalo, SUNY, Buffalo, New York 14260-1500,USA
[**]The Institute of Physical and Chemical Research (RIKEN), Wako-shi, Saitama 351-0198, Japan
[‡]Physics Department, MCTP, The University of Michigan, Ann Arbor, Michigan 48109-1040, USA

Abstract. We propose a method to efficiently generate cluster states in solid-state charge qubits. We show that highly-entangled cluster states can be realized by a 'one-touch' entanglement operation using the gate bias. We also investigate the robustness of these cluster states for non-uniform qubits, which are unavoidable in solid-state systems. We find that quantum computation based on cluster states is a promising approach for solid-state qubits.

Keywords: cluster state, charge qubit, quantum dot
PACS: 03.67.Lx, 03.67.Mn, 73.21.La

INTRODUCTION

One-way computing [1] is a promising approach for measurement-based quantum computation. In this method, quantum computations are carried out by a series of one-qubit measurements starting from cluster states, *instead of* using a series of unitary operations. Cluster states are fixed highly-entangled states that involve all qubits and can be conveniently used for many quantum computing operations.

Here, we theoretically show a method to efficiently create scalable cluster states in solid-state charge qubits based on quantum dots (QDs) [2, 3], In particular, we show that *cluster states in charge qubits can be created by applying a gate bias only once*, right after preparing the initial product state $|\Psi_0\rangle \equiv |\Psi(t=0)\rangle = \Pi_i |+\rangle_i$, where $|+\rangle_i = (|0\rangle_i + |1\rangle_i)/\sqrt{2}$. We also calculate the time-dependent fidelity of the cluster states, under the measurement back-action decoherence, and explore the effect of non-uniformities among qubits, which is realistic for all solid-state qubits.

CLUSTER STATES IN CHARGE QUBITS

The Hamiltonian for an array of charge qubits with nearest-neighbor interactions is described by $H_{\mathrm{cq}} = \sum_i (\Omega_i \sigma_{ix} + \varepsilon_i \sigma_{iz}) + \sum_{i<j} J_{ij} \sigma_{iz} \sigma_{jz}$ with Pauli matrices σ_{ix} and σ_{iz} for the i-th qubit. Ω_i is either the inter-QD tunnel coupling for coupled QD systems [3]. ε_i is the charging energy, and corresponds to the energy difference between $|0\rangle$ and $|1\rangle$ for each qubit. The coupling constants J_{ij} are derived from the capacitance couplings. In one-way computing [1], the σ_{ix} term should be switched off during the

creation of the cluster state (H_{cs}), and switched on when measurements are carried out. In this sense, charge qubits with tunable Ω_i [4, 5] are desirable. However, for most qubit systems, once the qubit array is made, Ω_i and J_{ij} are fixed, and only ε_i is controllable via the gate voltage bias (we call these "simple-design qubits"). Our goal here is to generate cluster states for simple-design qubits.

Typically, cluster states are generated by an Ising-like Hamiltonian $H_{\mathrm{cs}} = (g/4)\sum_{i<j}(1-\sigma_{iz})(1-\sigma_{jz})$ where i and j are nearest-neighbor sites. Preparing an unitary evolution $U_{\mathrm{cs}}(t) = \exp(itH_{\mathrm{cs}})$ at $gt = \pi$ is the first step for one-way computing (we set $\hbar = 1$). Cluster states of charge qubits can be generated in the large bias region $\varepsilon_i \gg \Omega_i > J_{ij}$. Applying a canonical transformation to H_{cq} we have [6]:

$$H_{\mathrm{cq}}^{(\mathrm{eff})} \approx H_{\mathrm{cq}} + [S, H_{\mathrm{cq}}] = \sum_i E_i \sigma_{iz} + \sum_{i<j} J_{ij} \sigma_{iz} \sigma_{jz} + H_{\mathrm{uw}}$$

(1)

where $S = -i\sum_i [\Omega_i/(2\varepsilon_i)]\sigma_{iy}$, with $\Omega/(2\varepsilon) \ll 1$. Also, $E_i \equiv \varepsilon_i + \Omega_i^2/\varepsilon_i$, neglecting terms of higher-order than $(\Omega_i/\varepsilon_i)^2$. H_{uw} is an unwanted interaction term given by $H_{\mathrm{uw}} = -\sum_{i=1}^{N}\sum_{\vec{\gamma}_d}(\Omega_i/\varepsilon_i)J_{i,i+\vec{\gamma}_d}\sigma_{ix}\sigma_{i+\vec{\gamma}_d,z}$ for a d-dimensional qubit array. Here $\vec{\gamma}_1 = \pm 1$, $\vec{\gamma}_2 = \{(\pm 1, 0), (0, \pm 1)\}$ and $\vec{\gamma}_3 = \{(\pm 1, 0, 0), (0, \pm 1, 0), (0, 0, \pm 1)\}$ are nearest neighbor indices for one-, two- and three-dimensional qubit arrays, respectively. As long as H_{uw} is sufficiently small and can be neglected, we can periodically generate cluster states in the tilted frame $|\tilde{\Psi}(t)\rangle = e^{-S}|\Psi(t)\rangle$ after a time t_{cs}, if both $Jt_{\mathrm{cs}} = \pi/4 + 2n_J\pi$ and $E_i t_{\mathrm{cs}} = -(\pi/4)\bar{n}_i + 2n_E\pi$ are satisfied ($\bar{n}_i$ is the number of qubits connected to the i-th qubit; n_J (≥ 0) and n_E are arbitrary integers, and J_{ij} should be uniform:

CP893, *Physics of Semiconductors, 28th International Conference*
edited by W. Jantsch and F. Schäffler
© 2007 American Institute of Physics 978-0-7354-0397-0/07/$23.00

$J_{ij} = J$). These two equalities lead to the relation $J(8n_E - \bar{n}_i)/(8n_J + 1) = E_i \equiv E_{i,t_{cs}}$. Thus, to generate a cluster state, gate bias voltage ε_i for the i-th qubit needs to be set at

$$\varepsilon_i = \varepsilon_i^{cs} = E_{i,t_{cs}}/2 + \sqrt{((E_{i,t_{cs}}/2)^2 - \Omega_i^2)} \quad (2)$$

during $t_{cs} = \pi(8n_J + 1)/(4J)$. To ensure a solution for ε_i^{cs} exists, we require $n_E - (2\Omega_i/J)n_J > (2\Omega_i/J + \bar{n}_i)/8$. An initial product state $|\tilde{\Psi}(0)\rangle = |\Psi_0\rangle$ has to be prepared for qubits other than the input qubits[1]. $|\Psi(0)\rangle = \Pi_i(\cos[(\Omega_i/(2\varepsilon_i) + \pi/4]|0\rangle + \sin[(\Omega_i/(2\varepsilon_i) + \pi/4]|1\rangle)$ is the corresponding state in the original $\{|0\rangle, |1\rangle\}$ basis, which can also be adjusted by the gate bias on each qubit.

We can estimate a lifetime by calculating the *fidelity*, defined by $F(t) = \langle\Psi_0|e^{iH_{cs}t}e^{-i(H_{cs}+H_{uw})t}|\Psi_0\rangle \approx 1 - it\langle\Psi_0|H_{uw}|\Psi_0\rangle + \frac{1}{2}(it)^2\langle\Psi_0|[H_{uw},H_{cs}]+H_{uw}^2|\Psi_0\rangle$. For a d-dimensional N-qubit array, we have

$$F(t) \approx 1 - (\Omega/\varepsilon)^2(Jt)^2 4dN \quad (3)$$

Thus, the lifetime of the cluster state is limited by $t < t_{uw} \equiv (2J(\Omega/\varepsilon)\sqrt{dN})^{-1}$. The constraint $t_{cs} < t_{uw}$ imposes a limitation on the number of clustered qubits: $N_{max} < (2\varepsilon/(\pi\Omega))^2/d$.

To avoid decoherence problems, the number of operations should be as few as possible. Thus, our proposal for producing cluster states by 'one-touch' biasing every qubit has a significant advantage over multiple-step approaches. The one-touch cluster state generation method should work well with charge qubits, which have shorter decoherence times compared with the spin qubit case, where several steps are required to generate cluster states [7, 8].

ROBUSTNESS OF CLUSTER STATES

Cluster states are highly entangled states involving all qubits, and used by a series of measurements on selected qubits. Thus, cluster states are generally expected to be robust against decoherence, because the measurement of qubit states can produce decoherence and back-action. For charge qubits, a capacitively coupled detector, such as a QPC, should be a good detector, but induces shot-noise. Here we investigate the robustness of cluster states on QDs, for up to four qubits (inset of Fig.1), by using density matrix (DM) equations [9].

Figure 1 shows the time-dependent fidelities of both the cluster states and the decoherence-free (DF) states [10], for non-uniform qubits. There, we show the case where the Ω_i, ε_i and Γ_i for the third and fourth qubits deviate from those of other qubits by 10%. Note that the fidelities of $|\Psi\rangle_{C4}$ show almost the same behavior irrespective of the distribution of the non-uniformity.

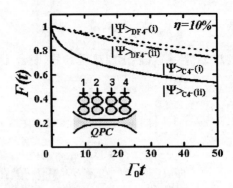

FIGURE 1. Time-dependent fidelities of cluster states $|\Psi\rangle_{C4} = (|+\rangle_1|0\rangle_2|+\rangle_3|0\rangle_4 + |+\rangle_1|0\rangle_2|-\rangle_3|1\rangle_4 + |-\rangle_1|1\rangle_2|-\rangle_3|0\rangle_4 + |-\rangle_1|1\rangle_2|+\rangle_3|1\rangle_4)/2$ and four-qubit DF states $|\Psi\rangle_{DF4} = (|1100\rangle - |1001\rangle - |0110\rangle + |0011\rangle)/2$, for $\Gamma_0 = J$ and $\Delta\Gamma = 0.6J$. $\Omega = 4J, n_J = 0$ and $n_E = 2$ in Eq. (2), thus $\varepsilon_2 = \varepsilon_3 \sim 12.7J$, $\varepsilon_1 = \varepsilon_4 \sim 13.8J$. The case when non-uniformity in the qubit parameters is introduced as $\Omega_i = (1-\eta)\Omega$, $\varepsilon_i = \varepsilon + \eta J$ and $\Gamma_i^{(\pm)} = (1-\eta)\Gamma^{(\pm)}$, with i indicating the i-th qubit. (i) η=0.1 only for the 3rd qubit and (ii) only for the 4th qubit. The fidelities of $|\Psi\rangle_{C4}$ for (i) and (ii) mostly overlap. (inset) Four qubits that use double dot charged states are capacitively coupled to a QPC detector.

In Ref. [9], we showed that the robustness of the DF states strongly depends on the non-uniformity. Thus, although cluster states are much more fragile than DF states, they are stronger against non-uniformities among qubits than DF states.

CONCLUSION

We describe how to efficiently generate cluster states in charge qubits. Using the gate voltage bias, we show how to generate 'one-touch' entanglement via cluster states in charge qubits. We also find that one-way quantum computing would be effective for solid-state qubits.

REFERENCES

1. H. J. Briegel and R. Raussendorf, *Phys. Rev. Lett.* **86**, 910 (2001).
2. J. Gorman *et al*, *Phys. Rev. Lett.* **95**, 090502 (2005).
3. T. Tanamoto, *Phys. Rev. A* **64**, 062306 (2001).
4. J. Q. You and F. Nori, *Phys. Today* **58** (11), 42 (2005).
5. T. Yamamoto *et al.*, *Nature (London)* **425**, 941 (2003).
6. We take the first order of the expansion $e^{-S}H_{cq}e^S = H_{cq} + [S, H_{cq}] + [S, [S, H_{cq}]]/(2!)...$; T. Tanamoto *et al.*, comd-mat/0602613.
7. M. Borhani and D. Loss, *Phys. Rev. A* **71**, 034308 (2005).
8. Y. S. Weinstein *et al.*, *Phys. Rev. A* **72**, 02304 (2005).
9. T. Tanamoto and S. Fujita, *Phys. Rev. B* **72**, 085335 (2005).
10. P. Zanardi and M. Rasetti, *Phys. Rev. Lett.* **79**, 3306 (1997); D. A. Lidar *et al.*, *ibid* **82**, 4556 (1999).

Spin Dynamics of Electron Nuclei Coupled System in a Double Quantum Dot

Ö. Çakır [*,†] and T. Takagahara [*,†]

*Department of Electronics and Information Science, Kyoto Institute of Technology, Matsugasaki, Kyoto
606-8585 JAPAN
†CREST, Japan Science and Technology Agency, 4-1-8 Honcho, Kawaguchi, Saitama 332-0012, JAPAN

Abstract. Electron-nuclei coupled system in a double quantum dot is studied. As a manifestation of quantum nature of nuclear spins, bunching of results of electron spin measurements, and revivals in the conditional probabilities are predicted. The underlying mechanism is the correlations between successive measurements induced via the nuclear spins. The electron spin coherence time can be extended via conditional measurements.

Keywords: Spins in quantum information and processing, nuclear spins in semiconductors
PACS: 73.21.La,71.70.Jp,76.70.-r,03.67.Pb

A qubit encoded in singlet and triplet spin states of a pair of electrons, located in a double quantum dot proves to be a promising candidate for quantum information processingLoss and DiVincenzo [1], Petta et al. [2], Taylor et al. [3]. Further double quantum dots allow a detailed study of various aspects of hyperfine interaction(HF) and electron spin decoherenceJohnson et al. [4].

We consider an electrically gated double quantum dot(QD) occupied by two electrons. Under a high magnetic field, s.t. the electron Zeeman splitting is much greater than the hyperfine fields and the exchange energy, dynamics takes place in the spin singlet ground state $|S\rangle$ and triplet state of zero magnetic quantum number $|T\rangle$,

$$H_e = JS_z + r\delta h_z S_x, \qquad (1)$$

where $\mathbf{S}$ is the pseudospin operator with $|T\rangle$ and $|S\rangle$ forming the S_z basis. $\delta h_z = h_{1z} - h_{2z}$, where h_{1z} and h_{2z} are the components of nuclear HF field along the external magnetic field in the first and second dot, respectivelyCoish and Loss [5], Merkulov et al. [6]. $r = t/\sqrt{t^2 + (\delta/2 + \sqrt{\delta^2/4 + t^2})^2}$ is the amplitude of the hyperfine coupling, which is determined by the gate voltages. δ is the detuning which is a linear function of gate voltage differences, and t is the tunneling coefficient. When $\delta \gg t$, the ground state singlet state corresponds to the case where both electrons are localized in the same dot and HF coupling is switched off, $r \to 0$. The opposite limit $\delta \ll -t$ corresponds to the singlet state where electrons are located in different dots, and HF coupling is maximized $r \to 1$.

Now we show that by electron spin measurements the coherent behavior of nuclear spins can be demonstrated. Electron spins are initialized in the singlet state and the nuclear spin states are initially in a mixture of δh_z

eigenstates, $\rho(t=0) = \sum_n p_n \rho_n |S\rangle\langle S|$, where ρ_n is a nuclear state with an eigenvalue of $\delta h_z = h_n$ and satisfies $Tr(\rho_n) = 1$. p_n is the probability of the hyperfine field δh_z having the value h_n.

In the unbiased regime $\delta \ll -t$, the nuclear spins and the electron spins interact for a time span of τ. Then the gate voltage is swept adiabatically to a high value(s.t. $\delta \gg t$), in a time scale much shorter than HF interaction time, leading to the state, $\rho = \sum_n p_n \rho_n |\Psi_n\rangle\langle\Psi_n|$, where $|\Psi_n\rangle = \alpha_n |S\rangle + \beta_n |T\rangle$, with $\alpha_n = \cos(\Omega_n \tau/2) + iJ/\Omega_n \sin(\Omega_n \tau/2)$, $\beta_n = -ih_n/\Omega_n \sin(\Omega_n \tau/2)$ and $\Omega_n = \sqrt{J^2 + h_n^2}$ is the Rabi frequency.

Next a charge state measurement is performed which detects a singlet or triplet state[2]. Probability to detect the singlet state is $\sum_n p_n |\alpha_n|^2$, and the triplet state is $\sum_n p_n |\beta_n|^2$. Subsequently one can again initialize the system in the singlet state of electron spins, and turn on the hyperfine interaction for a time span of τ, and perform a second measurement. In general over N measurements, the probability of k times singlet outcomes is

$$P_{N,k} = \binom{N}{k} \langle |\alpha|^{2k} |\beta|^{2(N-k)} \rangle. \qquad (2)$$

where $\langle \ldots \rangle$ is the ensemble averaging over the hyperfine field h_n[6]. Here the key assumption is that nuclear states preserve their coherence over N measurements, thus the measurements are not independent due to nuclear memory. One can easily contrast this result with the semiclassical(SC) result for which nuclear spins are assumed to be purely classical, whereas electron spins are taken to obey quantum mechanics[6]. In SC case results of successive measurements are independent and the probability for obtaining k times singlet results over N measurements is given by,

$$P'_{N,k} = \binom{N}{k} \langle |\alpha|^2 \rangle^k \langle |\beta|^2 \rangle^{(N-k)}. \qquad (3)$$

CP893, *Physics of Semiconductors, 28th International Conference*
edited by W. Jantsch and F. Schäffler
© 2007 American Institute of Physics 978-0-7354-0397-0/07/$23.00

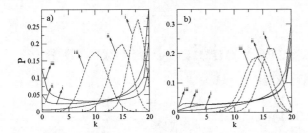

FIGURE 1. Probability distribution at $N = 20$ measurements for $k = 0, 1, \ldots, 20$ times singlet detections, for QM(solid lines), SC(dashed lines). Two cases of the exchange energy are considered a) $J = 0$ b) $J/\sigma = 0.5$ for HF interaction times $\sigma\tau =$ i)0.5, ii)1.5, iii)∞.

In the SC case the probability distribution (3) obeys simply a Gaussian distribution with mean $k = N\langle|\alpha|^2\rangle$, and variance $N\langle|\alpha|^2\rangle\langle|\beta|^2\rangle$, as $N \to \infty$. However, in quantum mechanical(QM) treatment of nuclear spins, the probability distribution (2) may exhibit different statistics depending on the initial nuclear state. If the SC distribution of h_n is characterized by the same distribution as in QM case, the two probability distributions (2) and (3) yield the same mean value, $\bar{k} = N\langle|\alpha|^2\rangle$, however with distinct higher order moments. If the distribution of initial nuclear state p_n has a width Δ, then for HF interaction time $\tau \geq 1/\Delta$, the SC and QM distributions start to deviate from each other. They yield the same distribution only when the initial nuclear state is in a well defined eigenstate of δh_z, i.e. when $\Delta = 0$.

In particular we are going to consider the case when the nuclear spins are initially randomly oriented; probability distribution for hyperfine fields obeying a Gaussian distribution $p_n \to p[h] = 1/\sqrt{2\pi\sigma^2}\exp[-h^2/2\sigma^2]$. In Fig. 1, for $N = 20$ measurements, $P_{N,k}$ is shown for HF interaction times $\sigma\tau = 0.5, 1.5, \infty$. For $\tau = 0$, the probability for both SC and QM cases is peaked at $k = 20$. However, immediately after the HF interaction is introduced, the probability distributions show distinct behavior. The SC distribution converges to a Gaussian distribution. In QM case the probabilities bunch at $k = 0, 20$ for $J = 0$, and when $J/\sigma = 0.5$ those bunch at $k = 20$ only. As J is increased above some critical value, no bunching takes place at $k = 0$ singlet measurement.

The modified nuclear spectrum leads to correlations between the successive electron spin measurements. Depending on the results of previous measurement, one may decrease the singlet-triplet mixing. As a particular example consider the case: Starting from a random spin configuration, N successive electron spin measurements are performed, each following initialization of electron spins in the spin singlet state and a HF interaction of duration τ and all outcomes turn out to be singlet. Then again HF interaction is switched on for a time t, and the $(N+1)$th measurement is carried out. The conditional probability

to detect the singlet state is given by

$$P = \frac{1}{2} + \frac{\sum_{s=0}^{2N}\binom{2N}{s}\left(e^{-\frac{\sigma^2}{2}(t-(N-s)\tau)^2} + e^{-\frac{\sigma^2}{2}(t+(N-s)\tau)^2}\right)}{4\sum_{s=0}^{2N}\binom{2N}{s}e^{-\frac{\sigma^2}{2}(N-s)^2\tau^2}}.$$

(4)

The initial state is revived at $t = n\tau$, $(n = 1, 2, \ldots, N)$ with a decreasing amplitude as it can be seen from (4). In Fig. 2 the conditional probabilities(4) are shown for $\sigma\tau = 1.0, 3.0, 6.0$ subject to $N = 0, 1, 2, 5, 10$ prior singlet measurements in each. Revivals are observable only for $\sigma\tau > 1$, because the modulation period of the nuclear state spectrum characterized by $1/\tau$ should be smaller than the variance σ.

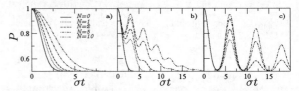

FIGURE 2. Conditional probability for singlet state detection as a function of HF interaction time σt, subject to $N = 0, 1, 2, 5, 10$ times prior singlet state measurements and for HF interaction times a)$\sigma\tau = 1.0$, b)$\sigma\tau = 3.0$, c)$\sigma\tau = 6.0$.

In summary, the bunching of results of the electron spin measurements and the revival in the conditional probabilities are emerging features of quantum nature of nuclear spins. The underlying mechanism is the correlations between successive measurements induced via the nuclear spins and increase in the purity of the nuclear spin state through the electron spin measurements. These correlations are expected to lead to the extension of the electron spin coherence time because the fluctuations in the nuclear magnetic field would be reduced.

REFERENCES

1. D. Loss, and D. P. DiVincenzo, *Phys. Rev. A* **57**, 120 (1998).
2. J. R. Petta, A. C. Johnson, J. M. Taylor, E. Laird, A. Yacoby, M. D. Lukin, and C. M. Marcus, *Science* **309**, 2180 (2005).
3. J. M. Taylor, H. A. Engel, W. Dür, A. Yacoby, C. M. Marcus, P. Zoller, and M. D. Lukin, *Nature Physics* **1**, 177 (2005).
4. A. Johnson, J. R. Petta, J. M. Taylor, A. Yacoby, M. D. Lukin, C. M. Marcus, M. P. Hanson, and A. C. Gossard, *Nature* **435**, 925 (2005).
5. W. A. Coish, and D. Loss, *Phys. Rev. B* **72**, 125337 (2005).
6. I. A. Merkulov, A. L. Efros, and M. Rosen, *Phys. Rev. B* **65**, 205309 (2002).

State Tomography of Layered Qubits via Spin Blockade Measurements on the Edge Qubit in a Spin Field-Effect Transistor Structure Embedded with Quantum Dots

K. Yuasa*, K. Okano†, H. Nakazato†, S. Kashiwada** and K. Yoh**,‡

*RCIS, National Institute of Advanced Industrial Science and Technology (AIST), Tokyo 101-0021, Japan
†Department of Physics, Waseda University, Tokyo 169-8555, Japan
**Research Center for Integrated Quantum Electronics, Hokkaido University, Sapporo 060-8628, Japan
‡CREST-JST, Kawaguchi-shi, Saitama 332-0012, Japan

Abstract. As a promising physical realization of a quantum computer, we discuss a system with stacked quantum dots buried in adjacent to the channel of a spin field-effect transistor. In this scheme, one can measure only the *edge* qubit (nearest to the channel) via the spin-blockade measurement, but still it is possible to know the state of the *whole* qubits.

Keywords: quantum state tomography, spin transistor, Coulomb blockade, spin injection, quantum computer
PACS: 03.65.Wj, 85.75.Hh, 73.23.Hk, 72.25.Hg, 85.35.Gv, 03.67.Lx

As a promising physical realization of a quantum computer, we are investigating, from both experimental and theoretical aspects, a system with stacked self-assembled InAs dots buried in GaAs in adjacent to the channel of a spin field-effect transistor (FET) [1, 2]. As briefly recalled in the following, we have an idea to measure the spin state of the electron in the *edge* quantum dot nearest to the spin-polarized channel of the FET through Coulomb blockade of the channel conductance (spin-blockade measurement) [1, 2]. The purpose of the present work is to show that, although only the edge qubit is measurable, we are still able to know the state of the *whole* qubits, including all the other unmeasurable ones.

The proposed device is illustrated in Fig. 1. Suppose that a single electron is confined in each dot and quantum information is encoded on its spin states, $|\uparrow\rangle$ and $|\downarrow\rangle$. Each qubit (or all qubits at once) may be rotated via the electric spin resonance. The FET structure aims at measuring the spin state of the electron confined in the edge quantum dot X. Notice first that one can detect the injection of another electron from the channel into the edge dot X by looking at the channel (source-drain) current I_D as a function of the gate voltage V_G. As the gate voltage V_G is increased, the channel current I_D increases. But if an electron tunnels from the channel into the edge dot in the meanwhile, the edge dot is charged and the channel current is suppressed. As a result, the channel current I_D drops down and exhibits a peak as a function of the gate voltage V_G (Coulomb blockade). Note that the impurity level of the GaAs and related materials grown by the molecular beam epitaxy are known to be extremely low ($\lesssim 10^{14}\,\mathrm{cm}^{-3}$) [3] and the injection of an electron trapped in an impurity in the insulator is unlikely. Sup-

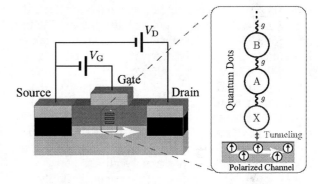

FIGURE 1. Spin FET embedded with quantum dots.

pose now that the channel electrons are spin polarized in a definite state, say $|\uparrow\rangle$. When the edge electron is in the $|\downarrow\rangle$ state, a channel electron in $|\uparrow\rangle$ may enter the edge dot at a certain gate voltage V_G, but when the edge electron is in $|\uparrow\rangle$, the channel electron is not allowed to enter there due to Pauli's exclusion principle. Therefore, a peak of the polarized channel current I_D as a function of the gate voltage V_G reveals that the edge electron is in $|\downarrow\rangle_X$, while the growth of I_D indicates that the edge electron is in $|\uparrow\rangle_X$. We can thus measure the state of the edge qubit X and we call it "spin-blockade measurement" [1, 2].

The important feature of the spin-blockade measurement is that one can repeatedly measure $|\uparrow\rangle_X$. Although one is allowed to measure only the edge qubit X, this feature enables one to do several things. The initialization of multiple qubits and an entanglement generation are discussed in Ref. [2, 4]. Furthermore, the present work clarifies that the *tomography* of the state of the *whole* qubits X+A+B+⋯ is also possible via the spin-blockade mea-

CP893, *Physics of Semiconductors, 28th International Conference*
edited by W. Jantsch and F. Schäffler

surements only on the *edge* qubit X.

The idea is to make use of the entangling dynamics of the coupled qubits X+A+B+$\cdots$, through which the measurable qubit X bears information on the others A+B+$\cdots$, which is extracted through the measurements of the former. We let the qubits X+A+B+$\cdots$ evolve from a given state ρ to be reconstructed, and in the meanwhile, we repeat rotations and measurements on the qubit(s) a few times. The probability of finding qubit X in certain states during such a process reads, for example,

$$p = \mathrm{Tr}\{P_\downarrow \cdots e^{-iH\tau} P_\uparrow R_x(\theta)\rho R_x^\dagger(\theta) P_\uparrow e^{iH\tau} \cdots P_\downarrow\}$$
$$= \mathrm{Tr}\{\rho [R_x^\dagger(\theta) P_\uparrow e^{iH\tau} \cdots P_\downarrow \cdots e^{-iH\tau} P_\uparrow R_x(\theta)]\}, \quad (1)$$

where $P_{\uparrow(\downarrow)} = |\uparrow(\downarrow)\rangle_X\langle\uparrow(\downarrow)|$ represents the spin-blockade measurement of $|\uparrow(\downarrow)\rangle_X$, $R_i(\theta)$ ($i = x, y$) the rotation of a specific qubit (or all qubits) by the angle θ around the i axis, and $H = g_{XA}\boldsymbol{\sigma}^{(X)} \cdot \boldsymbol{\sigma}^{(A)} + g_{AB}\boldsymbol{\sigma}^{(A)} \cdot \boldsymbol{\sigma}^{(B)} + \cdots$ the Hamiltonian of the whole qubits. Note that we are allowed to measure only the $|\uparrow\rangle_X$ state during the process except for the final measurement, since finding X in the state $|\downarrow\rangle_X$ means that two electrons have occupied the edge qubit and we cannot proceed any further. The key observation for the state tomography is that the probability p is regarded as the expectation value of the quantity in the square bracket in (1) over the given state ρ. Therefore, provided that $4^M - 1$ independent sequences of the rotations and the measurements are arranged for an M-qubit system so as for the probabilities p to give the expectation values of $4^M - 1$ independent observables of the whole qubits, one can reconstruct the given density operator ρ from the set of the probabilities.

For example, for a two-qubit system X+A, the sequence of operations (measurement $P_\uparrow$) → (evolution $e^{-iH\tau}$ for time $\tau = \pi/4g_{XA}$) → (measurement $P_\uparrow$) yields an element of the density operator ρ,

$$p_\uparrow^{(1)} = \mathrm{Tr}\{P_\uparrow e^{-iH\tau} P_\uparrow \rho P_\uparrow e^{iH\tau} P_\uparrow\}$$
$$= \mathrm{Tr}\{\rho |\uparrow\uparrow\rangle_{XA}\langle\uparrow\uparrow|\} = {}_{XA}\langle\uparrow\uparrow|\rho|\uparrow\uparrow\rangle_{XA}, \quad (2)$$

another sequence (evolution $e^{-iH\tau}$ for time τ) → (measurement $P_\uparrow$) → (evolution $e^{-iH\tau}$ for time τ) → (measurement $P_\downarrow$) provides us with another element

$$p_\downarrow^{(2)} = \mathrm{Tr}\{P_\downarrow e^{-iH\tau} P_\uparrow e^{-iH\tau} \rho e^{iH\tau} P_\uparrow e^{iH\tau} P_\downarrow\}$$
$$= \mathrm{Tr}\{\rho |\downarrow\uparrow\rangle_{XA}\langle\downarrow\uparrow|\} = {}_{XA}\langle\downarrow\uparrow|\rho|\downarrow\uparrow\rangle_{XA}, \quad (3)$$

and so on. It is possible to construct 15 independent sequences of operations to know all the elements of the density operator ρ.

Several points should be clarified to confirm the feasibility of the present scheme. First, if the channel spins are not perfectly polarized, the above recipe may fail to reconstruct the density operator accurately. Figure 2 shows

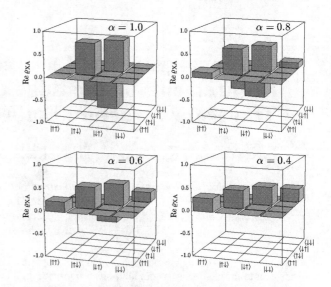

FIGURE 2. State tomography of $|\Psi^-\rangle = [|\uparrow\downarrow\rangle_{XA} - |\downarrow\uparrow\rangle_{XA}]/\sqrt{2}$ with partially polarized spin channel. The polarization is defined by $\alpha = (N_\uparrow - N_\downarrow)/(N_\uparrow + N_\downarrow)$ with $N_{\uparrow(\downarrow)}$ the number of spins in the $|\uparrow(\downarrow)\rangle$ state in the channel.

the effect of the polarizability α of the channel: we can see that $\alpha \gtrsim 0.6$ would give a reasonable performance. Another feature to be investigated is the effect of decoherence and is an important future subject.

ACKNOWLEDGMENTS

This work is partly supported by the bilateral Italian–Japanese Projects II04C1AF4E of the Italian Ministry of Instruction, University and Research, and 15C1 of the Italian Ministry for Foreign Affairs, by the Grants-in-Aid for The 21st Century COE Program at Waseda University, for Scientific Research on Priority Areas (No. 13135221), and for Young Scientists (B) (No. 18740250) from MEXT, and by the Grants-in-Aid for Scientific Research (C) (Nos. 14540280 and 18540292) from JSPS.

REFERENCES

1. K. Yoh and H. Kazama, *Physica E* **6**, 490 (2000); **7**, 440 (2000); K. Yoh, M. Ferhat, A. Riposan, and J. M. Millunchick, *AIP Conf. Proc.* **772**, 1315 (2005).
2. K. Yoh, K. Yuasa, and H. Nakazato, *Physica E* **29**, 674 (2005).
3. See, for example, R. F. C. Farrow Ed., *Molecular Beam Epitaxy*, Noyes Publications, New Jersey, 1995, p. 185, and references therein.
4. H. Nakazato, T. Takazawa, and K. Yuasa, *Phys. Rev. Lett.* **90**, 060401 (2003); H. Nakazato, M. Unoki, and K. Yuasa, *Phys. Rev. A* **70**, 012303 (2004).

Acoustic Charge Transport In Lateral n-i-p InSb/Al$_x$In$_{1-x}$Sb Quantum Well Diodes

S. J. Smith[1], G. R. Nash[2], M. F. Lewis[3], C.J. Bartlett[2], L. Buckle[2], M. T. Emeny[2] and T. Ashley[2]

[1]University of Bristol, Department of Electrical and Electronic Engineering, Merchant Venturers Building, Bristol, BS8 1UB, UK – [2]QinetiQ, St Andrews Road, Malvern, WR14 3PS, UK – [3] 5 Church Down Rd, Malvern, WR14 3JX

Abstract. Light emitting diodes have been fabricated in InSb/Al$_x$In$_{1-x}$Sb quantum wells using a simple bevel etching technique. Charge has been transported across the diodes at zero bias, proving that bevel etching can be used to fabricate lateral n-i-p diodes suitable for use as the basis of a surface acoustic wave driven single photon source.

Keywords: Surface acoustic waves, Lateral Diode, Single Photon Source
PACS: 77.65.Dq

INTRODUCTION

There have been many recent developments in the field of InSb/Al$_x$In$_{1-x}$Sb quantum well (QW) heterostructures grown on GaAs substrates, including the fabrication of high speed low power dissipation transistors [1], mid-infrared (IR) QW well LEDs [2], and devices exhibiting quantum transport effects such as quantized conductance [3,4].The low electron mass (0.014m$_e$) and large g-factor (-51) make InSb/Al$_x$In$_{1-x}$Sb QWs an ideal material system for spintronic and quantum information applications, such as the surface acoustic wave (SAW) driven single photon source [5]. In this proposed device, single electrons are injected into the p-type region of a lateral n-i-p QW diode. The development of a suitable lateral junction, with sufficiently a shallow electric potential gradient to allow acoustic charge transport, has been a major obstacle to the fabrication of the SAW driven single photon source.

DEVICE DESIGN AND FABRICATION

Samples were grown by molecular beam epitaxy on semi insulating GaAs at QinetiQ in Malvern and consisted of a 20nm undoped InSb quantum well with doped and undoped Al$_{0.15}$In$_{0.85}$Sb barriers above and below, as shown schematically (after bevel etching) in Figure 1a. As material is etched from the surface the Fermi level in the quantum well moves from the valance band through the band gap into the conduction

band. Hence by bevel etching it is possible to produce a lateral n-i-p diode [6]. Samples were etched a maximum depth of 100nm with a bevel angle of 5×10^5 radians. Metallic contacts were deposited in n-type and p-type regions. Interdigital transducers fabricated on the semi insulating GaAs at either end of the mesa allowed a surface acoustic wave (SAW) to be propagated across the diode.

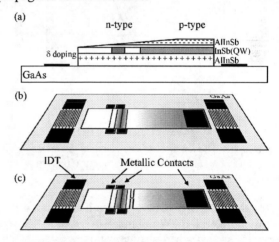

FIGURE 1. (a) The bevelled layer structure in profile, showing the quantum well marked as QW. The + signs represent Be acceptors and the – signs Te donors (b) Plan view of the device layout with metallic contacts and interdigital transducers. (c) Plan view of a device with a constriction in the intrinsic region of the n-i-p diode.

CP893, *Physics of Semiconductors, 28th International Conference*
edited by W. Jantsch and F. Schäffler
© 2007 American Institute of Physics 978-0-7354-0397-0/07/$23.00

Two devices were tested one with a wide (200μm) mesa, and one with a 12μm constriction in the intrinsic region, as shown in figure 1b and 1c respectively.

ACOUSTIC CHARGE TRANSPORT

By applying a 350MHz RF voltage, across the interdigital transducer SAWs were propagated across the bevel. SAWs travelled from n-type to p-type regions of the quantum well Because InSb is a piezoelectric material the wave has an electrical component which interacts with free carriers in the quantum well. When the free carrier density is high the SAW electric potential is screened by the mobile charge. However as the carrier concentration drops to zero near the intrinsic this cannot happen and charge is dragged in the SAW minima toward the p-type region.

Varying the RF amplitude applied to the interdigital transducer it was possible vary the potential of the SAW. By doing this and measuring the current at zero bias it was shown that it it possible to move in excess of 125 electrons per SAW minima, as shown in figure 2.

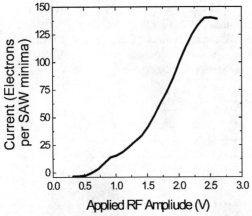

FIGURE 2. The charge driven using a 350MHz SAW transporting charge from an n-type to a p-type region in a 200μm mesa.

To create a single photon source it is required that the current in each SAW minima is reduced to a single charge [5] so that when recombination occurs a single photon per period is produced.

The first step to producing this quantised current is to reduce the width of the mesa. This was done in the device shown in figure 1c to a width of 12μm. When the current was measured against power in these devices a significant reduction was observed. The maximum current observed was under 7 electrons per SAW minima as shown in figure 3.

In conclusion we have used bevel etching to fabricate a lateral n-i-p diode from InSb/Al$_x$In$_{1-x}$Sb

quantum well heterostructures, and shown that it is possible to transport charge across the diode at zero bias. By restricting the width of the mesa it was possible to reduce the charge transported. This represents a significant step towards the development of a surface acoustic wave driven mid IR single photon source.

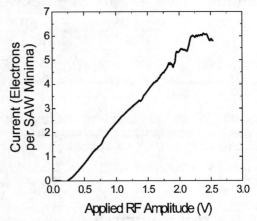

FIGURE 3. The charge driven using a 350MHz SAW transporting charge from an n-type to a p-type region in a 12μm mesa.

ACKNOWLEDGMENTS

QinetiQ acknowledges support for this work from the UK Department of Trade and Industry's Technology Programme. One of the authors (GN) acknowledges the support of The Royal Society through an Industrial Research Fellowship.

REFERENCES

1. Ashley T., Barnes A. R., Buckle L., Datta S., Dean A. B., Emeny M. T., Fearn M., Hayes D. G., Hilton K. P., Jefferies R., Martin T., Nash K. J., Phillips T. J., Tang W. H. A., Wilding P. J. and Chau R., Proceedings of the 7th International Conference on Solid-State and Integrated Circuit Technology, 2004, p2253
2. Nash G. R., Haigh M. K., Hardaway H. R., Buckle L., Andreev A. D., Gordon N.T., Smith S. J., Emeny M. T. and Ashley T., *Appl. Phys. Lett.* **88**, 051107 (2006)
3. Goel N., Graham J., Keay J. C., Suzuki K., Miyashita S., Santos M. B., Hirayama Y., *Physica E* **26**, p455 (2005)
4. Orr J.M.S., Buckle P.D., Fearn M., Bartlett C.J., Buckle L., and Ashley T. To be published in proceedings of ICPS 2006
5. Foden C. L., Talyanskii V. I., Milburn G. J., Leadbeater M. L. and Pepper M., *Phys. Rev. A* **62**, 011803 1 (2000)
6. Nash G. R., Nash K. J., Smith S. J., Bartlett C. J., Jefferson J. H., Buckle L., Emeny M. T., Buckle P. D. and Ashley T., Semicond. Sci. Technol. 20, p144 (2005)

A Radio Frequency Quantum Point Contact Charge Read-Out

Thomas Müller*, Kilian Vollenweider*, Thomas Ihn*, Roland Schleser*, Martin Sigrist*, Klaus Ensslin*, Matthias Reinwald† and Werner Wegscheider†

*Solid State Physics Laboratory, ETH Zürich, 8093 Zürich, Switzerland
†Institut für experimentelle und angewandte Physik, Universität Regensburg, Germany

Abstract.
A quantum point contact, capacitively coupled to a quantum dot, has been used to detect single electron charging inside the dot. Embedding the quantum point contact in a radio frequency matching circuit and measuring the reflection coefficient of the circuit, rather than the conductance of the point contact, allowed for real time measurements with a time resolution of 50 ns.

Keywords: Quantum Point Contact, Coulomb Blockade, Radio Frequency, Quantum Computing
PACS: 03.67.Lx

1. INTRODUCTION

For reading out the charge state of a quantum dot (QD), capacitively coupled quantum devices are considered most promising. This includes single-electron transistors (SETs) [1] and quantum point contacts (QPCs) [2, 3, 4]. Both can be tuned to a regime in which they are highly sensitive to changes in local potentials - for instance electrons tunneling into and off a QD in close proximity.

In our setup, the QPC, capacitively coupled to a QD, was embedded in a radio frequency (RF) matching circuit and the reflection of an applied signal was measured. We demonstrate how the reflection measurement can be calibrated to give a direct measure of the QPC conductance. This is achieved by measuring the low frequency conductance simultaneously to the RF response. We demonstrate the functionality of our setup by time-resolved measurements of defect charging with a bandwidth of 10 MHz.

Measurements probing the QPC at low frequencies suffer from large $1/f$ noise. Additionally, the RC constant of the I/V-converters has so far limited the measurement bandwidth to 40 kHz [5]. With the RF technique, we can avoid these restrictions. In this case we are only limited by the bandwidth f_{res}/Q of the matching circuit, where Q is the so-called quality factor. This limit can be higher than 10 GHz [6].

2. SETUP

A parallel LCR circuit in series to a capacitance was used as a matching circuit, as shown in Fig. 1. It was realized on a printed circuit board which was soldered to the chip

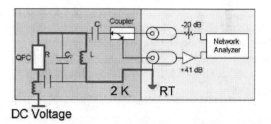

FIGURE 1. Schematic representation of the circuitry used for the experiment. The thick line indicates the possibility of simultaneous low frequency (lock-in) measurement.

carrier containing the sample. The QPC takes the place of the parallel resistance. A change in QPC resistance, due to single electron charging in the dot, leads to a mismatch of the circuit and hence to a change in the reflection of an applied RF signal.

Additionally, components for simultaneous lock-in measurement were included. The thick line in Fig. 1 indicates the path an applied low frequency current can take.

The measurements were performed with two samples, identical in structure. They consist of a QD with a diameter of approximately 200 nm at a distance of 250 nm to a QPC, both patterned by AFM lithography [7].

3. MEASUREMENT

The ability to measure the RF reflection simultaneously to the low frequency QPC conductance gives us the possibility to convert the reflection coefficient directly to a conductance value. Figure 2 a) shows the two terminal conductance of the QPC at 1.7 K, measured with the

CP893, *Physics of Semiconductors, 28th International Conference*
edited by W. Jantsch and F. Schäffler

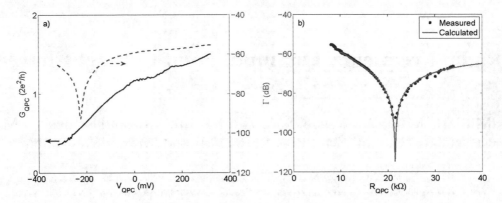

FIGURE 2. a) Two terminal QPC conductance as a function of gate voltage at 1.7 K measured simultaneously with lock-in and RF reflection techniques. b) Plotting the relation of the RF reflection coefficient and QPC resistance allows for direct conversion from Γ to R_QPC. A calculated curve for realistic values of $C_1 = 1.5$ pF, $C_2 = 5.5$ pF, $L = 100$ nH, and an attenuation of 42 dB due to an attenuator and the directional coupler has been included. The dip in this calculation is much deeper than our current equipment allows us to detect.

lock-in technique (50 μV applied; solid line) and the reflection coefficient Γ (-40 dBm applied; dashed line).

It can be clearly seen that Γ strongly depends on the applied gate voltage. Hence it is sensitive to local potentials such as electrons entering/leaving the dot nearby. This provides a proof of principle for the method of detecting changes in QPC conductance by measuring RF reflection.

For a certain QPC conductance value the reflection takes a distinct dip. Here, the resonant circuit matches the input impedance of 50 Ω. In figure 2 b), the RF reflection coefficient is shown as a function of QPC resistance. This plot allows for a direct calibration between Γ and a resistance or conductance value.

Additionally, we measured time-dependent switching of a charge trap near the QPC. Figure 3 shows a 500 μs time trace of this two level system. It was recorded with a bandwidth of 10 MHz, corresponding to a time resolution of 50 ns. However, we have not yet been able to detect single electron charging inside the dot with such high bandwidths. The main problem is that, so far, we could not close the dot enough and at the same time stay in the QPCs sensitive regime. We have estimated the maximal bandwidth for measurements on the dot to be of the order of 1 MHz, corresponding to a time resolution of 0.5 μs.

4. CONCLUSION

In conclusion, we have demonstrated our ability to detect single electron charging on time scales of 50 ns measuring the RF reflection of a resonant circuit containing a QPC.

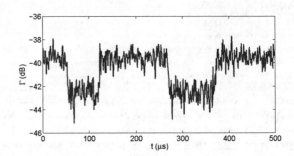

FIGURE 3. 500 μs time trace of a charge trap near the QPC, recorded with a bandwidth of 10 MHz. The timescale of a switching event is of the order of, or below, 50 ns.

REFERENCES

1. W. Lu, J. Zhongqing, L. Pfeiffer, K. W. West, and A. J. Rimberg, *Nature* **423**, 422 (2003).
2. M. Field, C. G. Smith, M. Pepper, D. A. Ritchie, J. E. F. Frost, G. A. C. Jones, and D. G. Hasko, *Phys. Rev. Lett.* **70**, 1311 (1993).
3. R. Schleser, E. Ruh, T. Ihn, K. Ensslin, D. C. Driscoll, and A. C. Gossard, *Appl. Phys. Lett.* **85**, 2005 (2004).
4. S. Gustavsson, R. Leturq, B. Simovic, R. Schleser, T. Ihn, P. Studerus, K. Ensslin, D. C. Driscoll, and A. C. Gossard, *Phys. Rev. Lett.* **96**, 076605 (2006).
5. L. M. K. Vandersypen, J. M. Elzermann, R. N. Schouten, L. H. Willems van Beveren, R. Hanson, and L. P. Kouwenhoven, *Appl. Phys. Lett.* **85**, 4394 (2004).
6. R. J. Schoelkopf, P. Wahlgren, A. A. Kozhenikov, P. Delsing, and D. E. Prober, *Science* **280**, 1238 (1998).
7. A. Fuhrer, A. Dorn, S. Lüscher, T. Heinzel, K. Ensslin, W. Wegscheider, and M. Bichler, *Superlattices and Microstructures* **31**, 19 (2002).

Spin Rotations and Non-Abelian Phases in Quantum Wire Networks

A.W. Cummings, R. Akis, and D.K. Ferry

Center for Solid State Electronics Research and Department of Electrical Engineering
Arizona State University, Tempe, AZ 85287-5706 USA

Abstract. We study quantum transport under the influence of both external magnetic fields and Rashba spin-orbit coupling. We consider two geometries—a straight wire and a ring structure. Our results reveal the precession of spin-polarized modes in the straight wire, and conductance resonances in the ring due to phase shifts from the magnetic field and from the Rashba effect. The conductance resonances arising from the Rashba effect are due to the non-Abelian nature of the phase shifts acquired by electrons propagating around the ring.

Keywords: quantum transport, Rashba effect, spin operations.
PACS: 72.25.Dc, 73.23.-b

INTRODUCTION

The study of the phase acquired by propagation in a mesoscopic device is important for determining the presence of phase interference in re-entrant geometries. While the study of the Aharonov-Bohm phase, due to a magnetic flux, has been known for some time, it recently has been realized that additional geometric phase can be introduced through the presence of the Rashba spin-orbit interaction in a heterostructure [1,2]. In the presence of both fields, a more complicated behavior can be present [3]. It is still controversial as to whether the spin dynamics follows the orbital motion adiabatically or even whether the geometrical phase can be detected in interference experiments. Nevertheless, the phase shifts introduced by these interactions produce non-Abelian phases in the network, and the general use of such statistics is of interest in quantum computation [4,5].

Here we report on simulations of quantum wire networks at the interface of a GaAs/AlGaAs heterostructure. The transport problem is solved with a recursive scattering matrix formulation for the total wave function that includes the spin variable and the effects of external magnetic fields and Rashba spin-orbit coupling [6]. In our simulations, we consider transport through a straight wire under the influence of the Rashba effect, and transport through a ring structure under the influence of both the Rashba effect and an external magnetic field.

RESULTS AND DISCUSSION

The straight quantum wire structure we consider has a width of 100 nm and a length of 3000 nm. The polarization of the electrons entering the wire is assumed to be spin-up (in the $+z$-direction), and we assume an external electric field applied in the $+z$-direction, perpendicular to the 2D electron gas. The precession of the spin-resolved electron density is shown in Fig. 1 as the electron propagates along the wire under the effect of Rashba spin-orbit coupling. The z-component of the electric field couples via the y-component of momentum to the σ_x spin matrix, giving spin precession around the S_x axis.

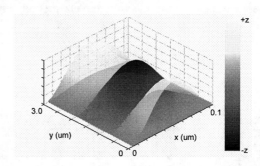

FIGURE 1. Spin precession in a single quantum wire. The spin orientation is in the z-direction. Lighter shades refer to spin up and darker shades refer to spin down.

In the ring structure, the wire width is 100 nm and the radius of the ring (from the center of the structure

CP893, *Physics of Semiconductors, 28ᵗʰ International Conference*
edited by W. Jantsch and F. Schäffler
© 2007 American Institute of Physics 978-0-7354-0397-0/07/$23.00

to the center of the wires) is also 100 nm. In this structure we consider the effects of an external magnetic field and an external electric field, both applied in the $+z$-direction.

The magneto-conductance of the ring structure is shown in Fig. 2, with no Rashba term present. Here we see normal Aharonov-Bohm interference for transport around the ring. The sharp drops in conductance near $|B| = 0.3$ T are due to localization resonances where the wire meets the ring. As the magnetic field increases, the conductance minima also increase. This is because the presence of edge states causes a larger proportion of the wave function to pass through one side of the ring, which in turn reduces the magnitude of destructive interference.

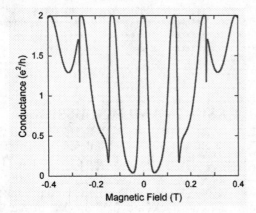

FIGURE 2. Ring conductance as a function of the magnetic field, with no Rashba electric field applied.

In Fig. 3, we plot the variation of the conductance through the ring as the electric field, and thus the Rashba coupling strength, is varied. Now we observe resonances in the transmission due to the non-Abelian phases acquired as the electron travels around both sides of the ring.

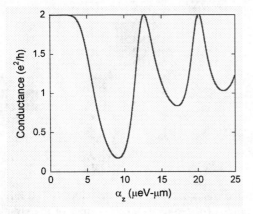

FIGURE 3. Ring conductance as a function of the Rashba coupling term, with no magnetic field.

In Fig. 4 we plot the magneto-conductance for the case in which a Rashba field, giving $\alpha_z = 1.0$ µeV-µm, is present. The conductance is more complicated due to the interplay of both phase factors. In particular we see that at low magnetic fields the conductance profile qualitatively follows that of Fig. 2, but loses that pattern at higher fields. This is due to a term in the spin-orbit Hamiltonian that is proportional to the product of the magnetic field strength and the spin-orbit strength. At low magnetic fields this term does not contribute much to the overall phase. However, this term becomes significant at larger magnetic fields, even when the spin-orbit coupling strength is relatively small.

In conclusion, we see the expected Rashba phase shifts and spin rotations when finite wire widths are used. Furthermore, we see that the effect of including magnetic and Rashba phases is not merely additive, due to a cross term in the Hamiltonian.

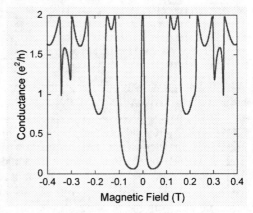

FIGURE 4. Ring conductance as a function of magnetic field for the Rashba coupling term equal to 1.0 µeV-µm.

ACKNOWLEDGMENTS

AWC acknowledges the support of the DOE Computational Science Graduate Fellowship; grant number DE-FG02-97ER25308.

REFERENCES

1. Y. Aharonov and A. Casher, *Phys. Rev. Lett.* **53**, 319 (1984).
2. D. Bercioux, M. Governale, V. Cataudella, and V. M. Ragaglia, *Phys. Rev. B* **72**, 075305 (2005).
3. R. Capozza, D. Giulianno, P. Lucignano, and A. Tagliacozzo, *Phys. Rev. Lett.* **95**, 226803 (2005).
4. M. H. Freedman, M. Larsen, and Z. Wang, *Commun. Math. Phys.* **227**, 605 (2002).
5. S. Das Sarma, M. Freedman, and C. Nayak, *Phys. Rev. Lett.* **94**, 166802 (2005).
6. A.W. Cummings, R. Akis, and D.K. Ferry, to appear in *J. Comp. Elect.*

CHAPTER 11

MICROCAVITIES AND PHOTONIC CRYSTAL STRUCTURES

Optical Parametric Oscillation In A Vertical Triple Microcavity

C. Diederichs, J. Tignon, G. Dasbach, C. Ciuti, Ph. Roussignol and C. Delalande

Laboratoire Pierre Aigrain, Ecole Normale Supérieure, 24 rue Lhomond, F-75005 Paris, France

A. Lemaître and J. Bloch

Laboratoire Photonique et Nanostructures, CNRS, Route de Nozay, F-91460 Marcoussis, France

Abstract. We report the first realization of a monolithic vertical-cavity, surface emitting micro-optical parametric oscillator, triply resonant with the parametric frequencies, allowing parametric oscillation with an ultra-low pump power threshold.

Keywords: Nanostructure, Microcavity, Optical Parametric Oscillation
PACS: 78.67.Pt, 42.65.Yj

INTRODUCTION

Optical parametric oscillation (OPO) is a nonlinear process that enables coherent generation of signal and idler waves, shifted in frequency from the pump wave. Efficient parametric conversion is the paradigm for the generation of twin or entangled photons for quantum optics applications such as quantum cryptography [1]. Rapid development in the field of quantum information requires monolithic sources allowing for efficient coupling into optical fibers and possibly electrical injection. To date OPOs typically rely on crystals with $\chi^{(2)}$ nonlinearities placed into complex external cavities and pumped by external lasers. Long interaction lengths are typically required and the phase mismatch between the parametric waves propagating at different velocities results in poor parametric conversion efficiencies. Recently [2-4], it has been shown that very large $\chi^{(3)}$ polaritonic nonlinearities in semiconductor microcavities can be used to achieve low-threshold optical parametric oscillation.

Here, we report the realization of a monolithic vertical-cavity, surface emitting micro-optical parametric conversion structure, triply resonant with the parametric frequencies, allowing parametric oscillation or amplification with ultra-low pump power threshold [5-7]. The OPO geometry and threshold is low enough to envision the realization of an all-semiconductor electrically-pumped micro-optical parametric oscillator.

SAMPLE DESCRIPTION

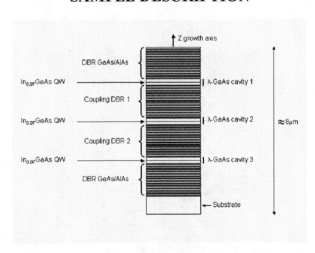

FIGURE 1. Triply resonant semiconductor microcavity consisting of: a GaAs substrate, three λ-GaAs cavities coupled through Bragg mirrors DBR1 and DBR2 and enclosed by a bottom and a top DBR. The mirrors are made of pairs of λ/4 layers of GaAs and AlAs. Each cavity contains one or several InGaAs QWs.

The scheme of the MBE grown triply resonant microcavity nanostructure is display in Figure 1. It

CP893, *Physics of Semiconductors, 28th International Conference*
edited by W. Jantsch and F. Schäffler
© 2007 American Institute of Physics 978-0-7354-0397-0/07/$23.00

consists of three λ-GaAs microcavities (840 nm), coupled via two intermediate Bragg mirrors (DBRs). The ensemble is enclosed between a bottom and a top DBR. The active medium consists of a set of quantum wells (QWs) at the anti-nodes of the electromagnetic field. In the following, we refer to two samples showing distinct thresholds. Sample A (resp. sample B) consists of 13 pairs of AlAs/GaAs in each Bragg mirror (resp. 15, 11, 11 and 18 pairs) and one $In_{0.05}Ga_{0.95}As$ QW in each cavity (resp. 9 QWs). A slight wedged has been voluntarily introduced in all three resonators so that the cavity-mode energies can be independently adjusted by moving the laser spot position on the sample surface.

EXPERIMENT

Figure 2 displays the measured angular resolved emission at 6 K (sample A) under continuous-wave resonant pumping of the middle energy mode (pump mode) at normal incidence when all cavities are resonant. The strong optical coupling through DBR 1 and 2 results in lifting the degeneracy and the resulting normal optical modes are split by the same energy (as can be seen from the three cavity-like background emission with upward dispersions). Above a threshold power, one observes the apparition of a strong, spectrally narrow emission at the lower energy (signal) as well higher energy (idler). The emission shows the characteristic signature or parametric oscillation with energy and momentum conservation.

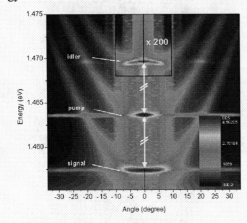

FIGURE 2. Angle-resolved emission measured in transmission geometry (sample A). T = 6K. Parametric oscillation under resonant excitation of the second mode above OPO threshold (pump power 28 kW/cm^{-2}). The detuning of the pump mode with respect to the QW exciton energy is + 10 meV. The idler emission is multiplied by 200.

Figure 3 shows the signal and idler intensity versus pump power (sample B). The pump-power dependence shows the OPO threshold at 2.4 kWcm^{-2}. The idler

mode saturates above threshold partly because this mode is quasi-degenerate with the QW absorption continuum, inducing losses and fast dephasing [6]. Figure 3 also shows the emission for a laser spot position on the sample for which all three cavities are not resonant, precluding energy conservation and parametric conversion. Nevertheless, above a higher pump power threshold of 6 kW/cm^{-2}, the structure then behaves as a conventional VCSEL (vertical cavity surface emitting laser) with a strong emission at the low energy mode (but no idler emission nor energy conservation requirement).

We remark that contrary to polariton-OPOs, this micro-OPO does not rely on the strong exciton-photon coupling. In particular, we observed OPO up to 150 K (compared to 50 K for polariton-OPO using similar materials).

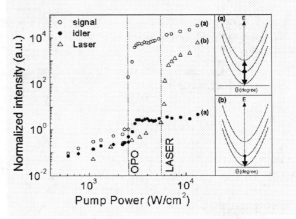

FIGURE 3. (a) Pump-power dependence of the optical parametric oscillator (sample B). Emitted intensity for the signal mode (open circles) and idler (closed circles). (b) The open triangles indicate the emission at the lowest-energy mode for an excitation of the middle mode and for a position on the sample surface for which energy conservation does not allow parametric conversion. In this case, the system behaves as a regular VCSEL laser with a higher threshold.

REFERENCES

1. N. Gisin, G. Ribordy, W. Tittel and H. Zbinden, *Rev. Mod. Phys.* **74**, 145-195 (2002).
2. P. G. Savvidis, J.J. Baumberg, R.M. Stevenson, M.S. Skolnick, D.M. Whittaker and J.S. Roberts, *Phys. Rev. Lett.* **84**, 1547-1550 (2000).
3. M. Saba *et al.*, *Nature* **414**, 731-735 (2001)
4. G. Dasbach *et al. Phys. Rev. B* **71**, 161308(R) (2005)
5. C. Diederichs and J. Tignon, *App. Phys. Lett.* **87**, 251107 (2005).
6. C. Diederichs, J. Tignon, G. Dasbach, C. Ciuti, A. Lemaître, J. Bloch, Ph. Roussignol and C. Delalande, *Nature* **440**, 904-907 (2006).
7. J. Tignon, C. Ciuti, G. Dasbach and C. Diederichs, French Patent Application No 05/05 708 (06 June 2004).

Coherent modulation of microcavity-polaritons by acoustic phonons

Maurício M. de Lima, Jr.*, Mike van der Poel†, Paulo V. Santos* and Jørn M. Hvam†

*Paul-Drude-Institut für Festkörperelektronik, Hausvogteiplatz 5–7, 10117 Berlin, Germany
†COM•DTU, NanoDTU, Technical University of Denmark, DK-2800 Kgs. Lyngby, Denmark

Abstract. We show that the coherent interaction between microcavity polaritons and externally stimulated acoustic phonons forms a tunable polariton superlattice with a folded energy dispersion determined by the phonon population and wavelength. The results are in good agreement with model calculations.

Keywords: polaritons, acoustic phonons, surface acoustic waves
PACS: 42.50.-p, 71.35.-y, 63.20.Ls, 73.21.Cd

The strong coupling between photons and excitons in a quantum well (QW) inserted in a semiconductor microcavity leads to the formation of new quasi-particles known as cavity-polaritons [1]. Their investigation has attracted great interest in recent years motivated, among other reasons, by the possibility of achieving Bose-Einstein condensation as well as lasers with very low threshold. Recently, Ivanov and Littlewood have proposed the use of acoustic fields for the coherent modulation of microcavity-polaritons [2]. In this contribution, we investigate the interaction of cavity-polaritons with coherent acoustic phonons in the form of surface acoustic waves (SAWs) with a wavelength of $\lambda_{SAW} = 5.6\ \mu m$. We observe additional resonances in reflection experiments under acoustic excitation, which are attributed to the folding of the polariton dispersion within a mini-Brillouin zone (MBZ) defined by λ_{SAW}. The experimental observation of these features clearly demonstrates that the spatial coherence of the polariton wave function exceeds a few λ_{SAW}.

The studies were performed in a (Al,Ga)As microcavity sample grown by molecular-beam-epitaxy with the structure sketched in Fig. 1(a). Figure 1(b) shows the energy of the lower (LP) and upper polariton (UP) branches measured by photoluminescence at 20 K as a function of the energetic detuning [$\hbar\delta \equiv \hbar(\omega_\ell - \omega_\chi)$] between the cavity resonance ($\hbar\omega_\ell$) and electron-heavy hole exciton energy ($\hbar\omega_\chi$). The anti-crossing signalizes the strong coupling regime with a Rabi splitting of 4 meV.

The cavity resonance energy depends on the thickness (d) and refractive index (n) of the cavity layer according to $\hbar\omega_\ell = c\pi/(nd)$, where c is the speed of light. The SAW introduces a modulation $\Delta\hbar\omega_\ell$ in $\hbar\omega_\ell$ by changing simultaneously n and d through the elasto-optic effect and through the strain component in the direction perpendicular to the surface (ε_{zz}), respectively. For large negative detunings, excitonic effects are negligible and

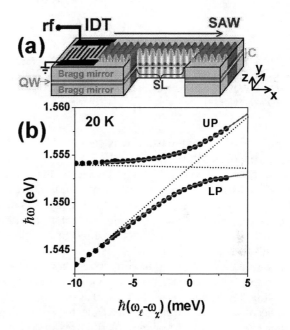

FIGURE 1. (a) Schematic diagram of a microcavity-polariton sample modulated by a SAW excited by interdigital transducers (IDTs) with an acoustic wavelength (λ_{SAW}) of 5.6 μm. The top and bottom mirrors consist, respectively, of Bragg stacks with 15 and 25 $Al_{0.15}Ga_{0.85}As/AlAs$ $\lambda/4$ bilayers. The structure contains a 10 nm GaAs quantum well (QW) surrounded by 5.2 nm $Al_{0.3}Ga_{0.7}As$ barriers, centered in a $Al_{0.07}Ga_{0.93}As$ λ-cavity (C). The latter is wedged in order to taper its resonance energy along the wafer surface. (b) Energy of the upper (UP) and lower polariton (LP) branches measured for different detuning energies by photoluminescence.

the periodic perturbation of the photonic energies by the SAW strain [$\Delta\hbar\omega_\ell/(\hbar\omega_\ell) \approx 10^{-3}$ for linear acoustic power densities (P_ℓ) of approximately 200 W/m] produces a tunable photonic superlattice along the SAW propagation direction ($\hat{x}$) with period λ_{SAW}, as we have

CP893, *Physics of Semiconductors, 28th International Conference*
edited by W. Jantsch and F. Schäffler

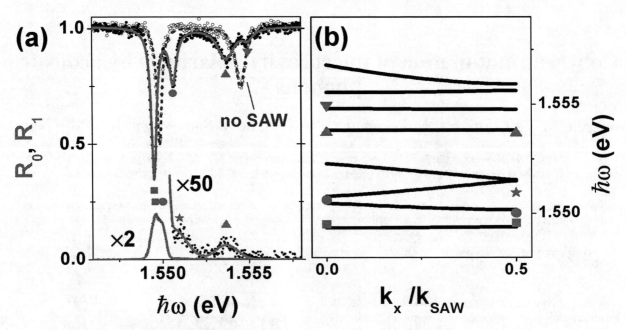

FIGURE 2. (a) Normal incidence reflectivity (R_0) measured in the absence of a SAW and under SAWs as well as first-order diffraction intensity (R_1) from a dynamic superlattice induced by SAWs. The detuning energy was $\hbar\delta = -2.7$ meV and $P_\ell \approx 100$ W/m. (b) Calculated dispersion for the experimental conditions of (a). The symbols represent the energies obtained from fits to the data of (a).

recently demonstrated in bare cavity samples [3]. In the strong coupling regime, the modulation $\Delta\hbar\omega_\chi$ of the excitonic energies, which is primarily due to the SAW strain (*i.e.*, deformation potential interaction), has also to be taken into account. For the experimental conditions employed here, $\Delta\hbar\omega_\chi \sim 2\Delta\hbar\omega_\ell$. Polaritons are expected to be, therefore, much more sensitive to the acoustic fields than bare photons.

The folding of the polariton dispersion, however, requires a spatial coherence length for the polaritons substantially larger than λ_{SAW}. To show that this condition is indeed satisfied, we have probed the modes in the center (*i.e.*, for $k_x = 0$) of the polariton dispersion by reflectivity measurements under normal incidence (R_0) for $P_\ell \approx 100$ W/m and $\hbar\delta = -2.7$ meV. The comparison of R_0 spectra with and without acoustic excitation [Fig. 2(a)] shows that the SAW redshifts the reflection minima associated with LP and UP branches and introduces new additional minima at higher energy. The latter are attributed to the excitation of folded dispersion modes, thus indicating the formation of a polariton superlattice. Further evidence for the folding is obtained by detecting the modes at the edge $k_x = k_{SAW}/2$ of the MBZ, where $k_{SAW} = 2\pi/\lambda_{SAW}$. These modes were probed by illuminating the samples at the Bragg angle $\theta = \tan^{-1}[k_{SAW}/(2k_0)]$, where k_0 is the light wave vector, and measuring the intensity of the back-diffracted beam [R_1, cf. Fig. 2(a)]. The diffraction signal observed for both polariton branches demonstrates again the super-

lattice formation. The experimental energies are in very good agreement with the calculated dispersion curves [solid lines in Fig. 2(b)] that take into account the modulation of the band-gap and of the optical thickness of the microcavity spacer layer by the SAW strain field.

In summary, we present experimental evidence for the formation of a polariton superlattice through the modulation by surface acoustic waves, which also demonstrate that the spatial coherence of the polaritons exceeds several λ_{SAW}.

ACKNOWLEDGMENTS

We thank L. Schrottke for comments and for a critical reading of the manuscript as well as J. R. Jensen, S. Krauß and W. Seidel for the growth and preparation of the samples. Support from ePIXnet is gratefully acknowledged.

REFERENCES

1. C. Weisbuch, M. Nishioka, A. Ishikawa, and Y. Arakawa, *Phys. Rev. Lett.* **69**, 3314–3317 (1992).
2. A. L. Ivanov, and P. B. Littlewood, *Phys. Rev. Lett.* **87**, 136403 (2001).
3. M. M. de Lima, Jr., R. Hey, P. V. Santos, and A. Cantarero, *Phys. Rev. Lett.* **94**, 126805 (2005).

Polaritons composed of 2DEG Fermi-edge transitions in a GaAs/AlGaAs modulation doped quantum well embedded in a microcavity

A. Gabbay*, Yulia Preezant*, E. Cohen*, B. M. Ashkinadze* and L. N. Pfeiffer†

*Solid State Institute, Technion-Israel Institute of Technology, Haifa 32000, Israel
†Bell Laboratories, Lucent Technologies, Murray Hill, NJ 07974, USA

Abstract. The reflection and photoluminescence spectra of a GaAs/Al$_{0.1}$Ga$_{0.9}$As structure consisting of a modulation doped quantum well embedded in a microcavity (MC) were studied under a perpendicularly applied magnetic field (B < 7T) and at T = 2K. The two dimensional electron gas (2DEG) density in the quantum well was 1.8×10^{11} cm^{-2}. Sharp lines are observed, whose energy dependence on the energy of the MC-confined photon identifies them as cavity polaritons, similar to those observed in structures of an undoped quantum well embedded in a MC. We show that they arise from the strong coupling between the MC-confined photons and interband transitions above the Fermi edge or inter-Landau level transitions of the 2DEG.

Keywords: polaritons, microcavity, 2DEG
PACS: 78.67.De, 71.36.+c, 73.21.Fg

Cavity polaritons are observed when there is a strong interaction between the confined photon in a microcavity (MC) and the confined excitons in a semiconductor quantum well (QW) that is embedded in the MC [1, 2]. In high quality, undoped QW/MC structures, particularly those grown of layers of III-V ternary compounds, the exciton and photon linewidths are much smaller than the exciton - MC-confined photon coupling strength [3], and the resulting polariton linewidths are much smaller than their Rabi splitting. However, when either an electron-hole (e-h) plasma or a two dimensional electron gas (2DEG) are photoexcited in a GaAs/AlGaAs QW/MC, and their density reaches the range of $n_e \sim 5 \times 10^{10} cm^{-2}$, the exciton-photon system transforms into the weak coupling regime and the Rabi splitting is washed out [4, 5]. This was explained by a large increase in the exciton linewidth that is caused by efficient exciton-free carrier scattering [4, 5], and by the exciton binding energy reduction due to both phase space filling and screening of the e-h Coulomb interaction [6, 7]. In the present study we demonstrate that a strong coupling is maintained between MC-confined photons and e-h pair excitations above the 2DEG Fermi edge, in GaAs/AlGaAs structures that consist of a MC with an embedded, modulation doped quantum well (MDQW).

We conducted a comparative spectroscopic study of a bare GaAs/Al$_{0.1}$Ga$_{0.9}$As MDQW, having a width of 200Å, and a MDQW, with exactly the same parameters, that is embedded in a λ-wide GaAs/Al$_{0.1}$Ga$_{0.9}$As MC. The 2DEG density was measured by monitoring the magnetic field at which the N_{LL}=1 e-h Landau transition freezes out in the photoluminescence (PL) spectrum,

and was found to be $n_e = 1.8 \times 10^{11}$ cm^{-2}. The Si-doped layers are spaced symmetrically on both sides of the QW, at a large distance of 980Å. This results in a very high 2DEG mobility, that is apparently important in preserving the phase of the e-h pair excitations that produce the cavity polaritons.

Fig. 1a shows a series of reflection spectra of the MDQW/MC measured in normal incidence at T = 2K, with B = 0. They were measured at successive illumination points on the sample surface, corresponding to MC-confined photon energies (E_C) that increase along the radial direction of the grown wafer. The single sharp line observed in the top spectra is the MC-confined photon. It is tuned into resonance with an interband transition of the MDQW. The peak energy of the reflection lines are plotted in Fig. 2a as a function of E_C. The extrapolated energy of the interband transition is E$_{X1}$ = 1.525 eV. It is used to define the detuning energy: $\delta = E_C - E_{X1}$. Fig. 1b shows a series of reflection spectra measured at the illumination point on the MDQW/MC surface corresponding to $\delta = -0.5$ meV. They were measured under a magnetic field that increases from 0 to 6.2T in steps of ΔB = 0.2T, in σ^+ circular polarization. The reflection spectrum of the bare MDQW shows no lines in the same spectral range, without B, and weak interband transitions into depleted Landau levels with increasing B [8].

As Fig. 1a shows, the dependence of the MDQW/MC reflection spectra on E_C is qualitatively similar to that observed for undoped QW/MC's (that have similar structure parameters) [1, 2]. In the latter case, the most prominent feature is the appearance of "level anticrossings" in the resonance spectral range. This is a manifesta-

CP893, *Physics of Semiconductors, 28th International Conference*
edited by W. Jantsch and F. Schäffler
© 2007 American Institute of Physics 978-0-7354-0397-0/07/$23.00

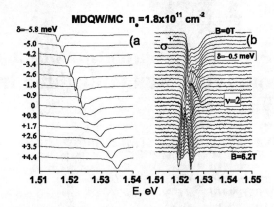

MDQW/MC n₀=1.8x10¹¹ cm⁻²

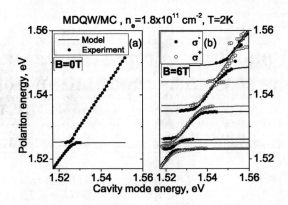

MDQW/MC , n₀=1.8x10¹¹ cm⁻², T=2K

FIGURE 1. Reflection spectra of the MDQW/MC: a) B = 0, observed at various detuning energies. b) Observed at detuning energy δ=-0.5 meV and under a perpendicular magnetic field increasing in steps of ΔB=0.2T.

FIGURE 2. Polariton peak energy dependence on the MC-confined photon energy (level anticrossing diagrams): a) B=0. b) B=6T. The solid lines are coupled oscillators model fittings.

tion of the strong interaction between the MC-confined photon and the QW excitons. We therefore applied the coupled oscillators model [1] to the "anticrossing diagram" of Fig. 2a (solid lines), as a first stage in analyzing the MDQW/MC reflection lines energy dependence on E_C. The coupling strength that is extracted from the fitting is $\Gamma_{X1} = 0.9 \pm 0.2$ meV. The smallest linewidths obtained by lineshape fitting are $\gamma_{X1} = 3 \pm 1$ meV and $\gamma_C = 1 \pm 0.1$ meV. It is noted that the linewidth of the exciton-like transition and MC-confined photon are larger than the coupling strength. In order to further test the validity of the coupled oscillators model, in this case of a MDQW/MC structure with a high n_e, the magneto-reflection spectra were measured at B = 6T as a function of E_C, in both σ^- and σ^+ circular polarizations. The peak energies of the observed reflection lines are plotted in Fig.2b, and the coupled oscillators model fitting is shown in solid lines. Several "level anticrossings" are observed, pointing at strong resonances that correspond to interband transitions between depleted Landau levels (with $N_{LL} = 0, 1, 2$) of the 2DEG and those of the hole. The spin splittings of these Landau transitions are revealed in the circular polarization.

The good fit of the coupled oscillators model and the appearance of strong resonances suggest that the exciton-like transition and the inter-Landau level transitions represent sets of MDQW interband transitions that interact coherently with the MC-confined photon. These transitions do not form excitons since the binding energy due to the e-h Coulomb interaction is screened in bare QW's with a high n_e [6,7]. We thus conclude that the e-h pair transitions that combine to form an exciton-like line, all have the same coupling strength with the MC-confined photons. The resulting cavity polaritons are composed of

these sets of interband transitions.

In summary, the "level anticrossings" and their variations with applied magnetic, as observed in the reflection spectra of a MDQW/MC's containing a high 2DEG density lead to the conclusion that the observed cavity polaritons arise from the strong coupling between the MC-confined photons and e-h pair excitations above the 2DEG Fermi edge and their inter-Landau level transitions. These polaritons can be formed since the coherence between the e-h pair excitations stems from their strong interaction with the same MC-confined photon, and is not due to an e-h Coulomb interaction, since it is screened by the 2DEG. In this respect, these cavity polaritons are fundamentally different from those commonly observed in undoped QW/MC systems.

Acknowledgments: The research at the Technion was done in the Barbara and Norman Seiden Center for Advanced Optoelectronics and was supported by the Israel-US Binational Science Foundation (BSF), Jerusalem.

REFERENCES

1. Y. Yamamoto *et al.*, *"Semiconductor Cavity Quantum Electrodynamics"*, Springer Tracts in Modern Physics, Vol. 169, (2000).
2. M. S. Skolnick *et al.*, *Semicond. Sci. Technol.* **13**, 645 (1998).
3. J. R. Jensen *et al.*, *Appl. Phys. Lett.* **76**, 3262 (2000).
4. R. Houdre *et al.*, *Phys. Rev.* **B52**, 7810 (1995).
5. G. Ramon *et al.*, *Phys. Rev.* **B65**, 085323 (2002).
6. D. A. Kleinman, *Phys. Rev.* **B32**, 3766 (1985).
7. F. G. Pikus, *Sov. Phys. Semicond.* **26**, 26 (1992).
8. B. B. Goldberg *et al.*, *Phys. Rev.* B**38**, 10131 (1988).

A Semiconductor Theory for Quantum-Dot Microcavity Lasers

J. Wiersig, C. Gies, M. Lorke and F. Jahnke

Institute for Theoretical Physics, University of Bremen, P.O. Box 330440, 28334 Bremen, Germany

Abstract. We introduce a semiconductor theory based on a many-body Hamiltonian to describe lasing from quantum dots embedded in optical microcavities. The light intensity and the photon autocorrelation function is calculated including semiconductor-specific effects. Numerical results demonstrate the limitations of the often used atomic models.

Keywords: Microcavity lasers, quantum dots
PACS: 42.55.Sa,78.67.Hc,42.50.Ar

INTRODUCTION

Quantum-dot (QD) microcavity lasers are of strong topical interest because of their potential applications as ultra-low-threshold lasers and single-photon sources in various fields of physics, like quantum information processing or cavity quantum electrodynamics. In these structures the spontaneous emission coupling factor β of the laser mode, which is defined as the ratio of spontaneous emission into that mode divided by the spontaneous emission into all available modes, can become close to 1. This has serious implications on the nature of the emitted light. With increasing β values, the step-like 'threshold' transition, which is observable in the output intensity of conventional $\beta \ll 1$ laser devices, gradually disappears until the so-called thresholdless laser is reached in the limit $\beta = 1$. The degree of coherence of the emitted light of such high-β lasers has been measured recently [1].

In the literature, semiconductor QD-based laser devices are modelled nearly without exception by considering atomic two- or multi-level systems, see e.g. [2]. Using such models, it is, however, not possible to consider intrinsic semiconductor effects, such as a modified source term of spontaneous emission [3, 4], Pauli-blocking effects of the occupied states, and many-body Coulomb effects. In this paper we introduce a microscopic theory to calculate both the light output and the intensity correlation function of QD microcavity lasers including the above mentioned semiconductor effects.

THEORETICAL MODEL

The intensity of the laser light is proportional to the photon number $\langle n \rangle = \langle b^\dagger b \rangle$, expressed via creation and annihilation operators for the laser mode. Statistical fluctuations around this mean value can be described in terms of the second-order autocorrelation function [5]

$$g^{(2)}(\tau = 0) = \frac{\langle n^2 \rangle - \langle n \rangle}{\langle n \rangle^2} = \frac{\langle b^\dagger b^\dagger bb \rangle}{\langle b^\dagger b \rangle^2}. \qquad (1)$$

The goal is to derive equations of motion for the involved expectation values. Starting from a semiconductor Hamiltonian for the interacting carrier-photon system [4], we use Heisenberg's equations of motion to obtain the time evolution of the carrier and photon operators. From this, coupled equations for operator averages, like the carrier population or photon number in the cavity, are determined. Due to the two-particle parts of the Hamiltonian, here the Coulomb and the light-matter interaction, an infinite hierarchy of equations arises. In order to truncate this hierarchy, we use the cluster expansion scheme [6].

To formulate the laser theory, we distinguish between the laser mode and the non-lasing modes. The equation of motion for the non-lasing modes is eliminated adiabatically in order to introduce the β-factor into the theory. We consider self-assembled InGaAs QDs with two confined shells for electrons and holes. The laser transition is the recombination between the s-shells. The pump process is modeled with a constant carrier generation rate in the p-shell, incorporating saturation effects due to Pauli blocking. We consider fast carrier scattering from the p- to the s-shell in relaxation time approximation [7]. Furthermore, rates for cavity losses and dephasing of polarization-like correlations are introduced.

NUMERICAL RESULTS

For our numerical calculations we choose the following realistic set of parameters: total spontaneous emission time 100 ps, relaxation times for electrons 2 ps and holes 1 ps, cavity lifetime 7 ps, emission energy 1.32 eV and

CP893, *Physics of Semiconductors, 28th International Conference*
edited by W. Jantsch and F. Schäffler
© 2007 American Institute of Physics 978-0-7354-0397-0/07/$23.00

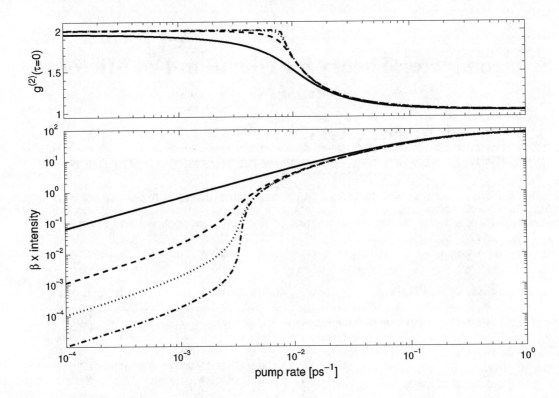

FIGURE 1. Calculated output curves (bottom) and correlation functions $g^{(2)}(0)$ (top) for $\beta = 1$ (solid line), $\beta = 0.1$ (dashed), $\beta = 0.01$ (dotted), and $\beta = 0.001$ (dotted-dashed).

dephasing $250\,\mu\text{eV}$. The number of QDs is 100 in the case of $\beta = 1$. For smaller β we choose $100/\beta$ to compensate the reduced emission into the laser mode.

The bottom panel of Fig. 1 shows the calculated input-output curves for different values of β in a double-logarithmic scale. As in the case of atomistic models [2] we find that the threshold disappears in the limit $\beta = 1$. There are, however, two important features which are not predicted by the atomistic models: (i) the s-shaped intensity jump with $\beta < 1$ does *not* scale with $1/\beta$. This is a direct result of the fact that our semiconductor model does not assume full population inversion. (ii) The intensity saturates for large pump rates due to Pauli blocking.

The correlation function $g^{(2)}(0)$ is shown in the top panel of Fig. 1. It has the value of two for thermal light below the threshold. In the threshold region, the correlation function decreases to unity, which is the expected value for coherent laser light. For large values of β, this transition becomes broader, but still showing a clear transition from spontaneous to stimulated emission. In contrast to atomistic models, our semiconductor model shows that the regime of coherent light emission is reached well above the conventional laser threshold

visible in the input-output curves. An experimental indication of this interesting effect is discussed in Ref. [1].

ACKNOWLEDGMENTS

We acknowledge financial support from the DFG research group "Quantum optics in semiconductor nanostructures" and a grant for CPU time at the Forschungszentrum Jülich (Germany).

REFERENCES

1. S. M. Ulrich *et al.*, *submitted* (2006).
2. P. R. Rice, and H. J. Carmichael, *Phys. Rev. A* **50**, 4318 (1994).
3. M. Schwab *et al.*, *cond-mat/0605728, to appear in Phys. Rev. B* (2006).
4. N. Baer, C. Gies, J. Wiersig, and F. Jahnke, *Eur. Phys. J. B* **50**, 411–418 (2006).
5. P. Meystre, and M. Sargent III, *Elements of Quantum Optics*, Springer, Berlin, 1999.
6. J. Fricke, *Ann. Phys.* **252**, 479–498 (1996).
7. T. R. Nielsen, P. Gartner, and F. Jahnke, *Phys. Rev. B* **69**, 235314 (2004).

Optical Microtube Ring Resonators

T. Kipp*, Ch. Strelow*, H. Welsch*, Ch. Heyn* and D. Heitmann*

*Institut für Angewandte Physik und Zentrum für Mikrostrukturforschung, Universität Hamburg,
Jungiusstraße 11, 20355 Hamburg, Germany

Abstract. In this work, we demonstrate that semiconductor microtubes fabricated by utilizing the self-rolling mechanism of epitaxially grown strained bilayers can act as optical ring resonators. The mode structure is probed by the photoluminescence of an optically active material, i.e. self-assembled quantum dots, embedded inside the microtube wall. We find a spectrum of sharp modes, which is in very good agreement with the result of a theoretical modelling of the microtube as a closed thin dielectric waveguide. This novel kind of microcavity, in which the optically active material is intrinsically located close to the optical field maximum, is a good candidate for both, new optoelectronic devices and cavity quantum electrodynamic experiments.

Optical microcavities confine light on a micrometer length scale. The integration of optically active material like quantum dots (QDs) or quantum wells inside semiconductor microcavities makes them very interesting both for applications like low-threshold lasers and for fundamental research on light-matter interaction. For example, recently, Rabi-splitting has been observed in three different microcavity systems, i. e. micropillars, photonic-crystal microcavities, and microdisks [1, 2, 3].

Semiconductor microtubes can be fabricated by exploiting the self-rolling mechanism of a thin pseudomorphically strained bilayer [4, 5]. Their diameter, length, position on the sample, and number of walls can be precisely controlled [6, 7, 8].

Very recently we could show that semiconductor microtubes can act as a new kind of ring resonator [9]. The starting point for the fabrication of these microtube ring resonators is a MBE-grown sample consisting of a GaAs substrate, an AlAs sacrificial layer, a strained InGaAs layer (20 nm), and a GaAs layer (30 nm), in which one layer of self-assembled InAs quantum dots (QDs) is embedded. By use of optical lithography and wet-chemical etching processes [7, 8], a U-shaped strained mesa is defined and lifted off the substrate. Strain relaxation then leads to the formation of self-supporting microtube "bridges," where the middle part of the microtube is raised from the substrate. Details on the fabrication process are described in Ref. [9]. Figure 1 (a) shows a scanning electron microscope (SEM) picture of the microtube. Apparently, beginning at the starting edge, the strained mesa has rolled up over the full width of the mesa. After a distinct distance defined by the dimension of the mesa, only the side pieces of the tube have continued to roll. The diameter of the center part is measured

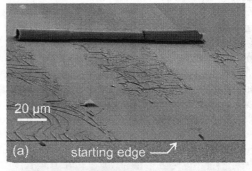

FIGURE 1. SEM pictures of a microtube ring resonator. (a) The U-shaped part has rolled-up beginning at the starting edge. (b) Magnified topview on microtube bridge and its bearing.

to be 5.25 μm. The number of revolutions at the center part is of about 3.8, leading to an overall tube wall tube wall thickness of 150 to 200 nm. The side pieces have rolled up for approx. 6 more revolutions [see Fig. 1 (b)]. This has lead to a lifting of the center part of about 300 nm above the substrate [not resolvable in Fig. 1 (a)].

The microtube shown in Fig. 1 has been investigated

CP893, *Physics of Semiconductors, 28th International Conference*
edited by W. Jantsch and F. Schäffler
© 2007 American Institute of Physics 978-0-7354-0397-0/07/$23.00

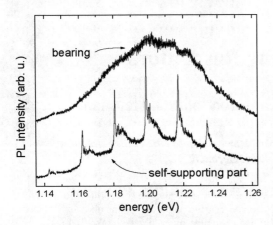

FIGURE 2. Micro-PL spectra of the self-supporting part (lower curve) and of a bearing (upper curve) of the microtube bridge. The spectra a vertically shifted for clarity.

by micro-photoluminescence (PL) spectroscopy at low temperature ($T = 5\,$K). Details on the experimental setup can be found in Ref. [9]. Figure 2 shows PL spectra of the microtube measured on its self-supporting center part (lower curve) and on its bearing (upper curve). The most striking feature of the lower curve is the regular sequence of sharp peaks superimposed on a broad background from the luminescence of the QDs. We measured these peaks to be polarized with its electric field vector parallel to the tube axis. They are optical resonances arising from constructive interference of light with itself. Therefore they proof the microtube to be an optical ring resonator. The peaks do not appear in spectra of the unstructured sample. The spectrum taken on the microtube bearing (upper curve in Fig. 2) only shows much weaker and broader features with a smaller spacing compared to the spectrum taken on the center part of the tube, which is raised from the substrate. The larger outer radius of the microtube bearing leads to an increased cavity length of the resonator resulting in a smaller mode spacing. The broadness of the features can be explained by strong losses into the substrate, on which the bearing of the microtube lies.

We compare the measured mode structure of the center part of the tube with theoretical models. Regarding a dielectric ring as a thin planar waveguide and applying periodic boundary conditions delivers a mode structure which is in very good agreement to the results of an exact calculation by solving Maxwell's equations for a thin dielectric ring. Both theoretical results fit very good with the measured mode spacing and polarization [9]. We assign the sharp peaks in Fig. 2 to modes with field distributions having no node in radial direction and $2m$ nodes in azimuthal direction, with the azimuthal mode number $m \in \mathbb{N}$ and $44 \lesssim m \lesssim 49$.

The measured quality factor $Q = E/\Delta E$ is about

3000 for the investigated microtube. This is magnitudes smaller than the Q factors we calculate in the exact model, where one only takes into account the tunnelling losses. Therefore other loss mechanisms, like absorption, scattering, or coupling to the substrate have to be dominant. In excitation-power dependent PL measurements, no bleaching of the QDs has been observed, which shows that absorption is not the limiting mechanism. Scattering losses on the surface should be low since the surfaces of our microtube should be very smooth because of the highly selective lift-off process during preparation [see Fig. 1 (b)]. Since the microtube has the shape of a rolled carpet, there are discontinuities in both the inner and outer radius which might lead to some losses. Further experiments have to be performed to quantify the different loss mechanisms. Nevertheless, since microtube ring resonators are just at the beginning of their development and their investigation, a further improvement of their Q factors seems to be accomplishable. Further experiments should also allow a complete three dimensional confinement of light, e. g. by laterally structuring the strained bilayer before rolling.

ACKNOWLEDGMENTS

We thank S. Mendach for fruitful discussions and F. Wilde for help with the SEM. We gratefully acknowledge financial support of the Deutsche Forschungsgemeinschaft via the SFB 508 "Quantum Materials" and the Graduiertenkolleg 1286 "Functional Metal-Semiconductor Hybrid Systems".

REFERENCES

1. J. P. Reithmaier, G. Sek, A. Löffler, C. Hofmann, S. Kuhn, S. Reitzenstein, L. V. Keldysh, V. D. Kulakovskii, T. L. Reinecke, and A. Forchel, *Nature* **432**, 197 (2004).
2. T. Yoshie, A. Scherer, J. Hendrickson, G. Khitrova, H. M. Gibbs, G. Rupper, C. Ell, O. B. Shchekin, and D. G. Deppe, *Nature* **432**, 200 (2004).
3. E. Peter, P. Senellart, D. Martrou, A. Lemaître, J. Hours, J. M. Gérard, and J. Bloch, *Phys. Rev. Lett.* **95**, 067401 (2005).
4. V. Y. Prinz, V. A. Seleznev, A. K. Gutakovsky, A. V. Chehovskiy, V. V. Preobrazhenskii, M. A. Putyato, and T. A. Gavrilova, *Physica E* **6**, 828 (2000).
5. O. G. Schmidt and K. Eberl, *Nature* **410**, 168 (2001).
6. A. B. Vorob'ev and V. Y. Prinz, *Semicond. Sci. Technol.* **17**, 614 (2002).
7. S. Mendach, O. Schumacher, Ch. Heyn, S. Schnüll, H. Welsch, and W. Hansen, *Physica E* **23**, 274 (2004).
8. S. Mendach, T. Kipp, H. Welsch, Ch. Heyn, and W. Hansen, *Semicond. Sci. Technol.* **20**, 402 (2005).
9. T. Kipp, H. Welsch, Ch. Strelow, Ch. Heyn, and D. Heitmann, *Phys. Rev. Lett.* **96**, 077403 (2006).

Selective Excitation of a Single Quantum Dot in a Photonic Crystal Nanocavity by using Cavity Resonance

M. Nomura, S. Iwamoto, T. Yang, S. Ishida, and Y. Arakawa

Institute of Industrial Science, Research Center for Advanced Science and Technology, and Nanoelectronics Collaborative Research Center, University of Tokyo, Tokyo 153-8505, Japan

Abstract. We demonstrate enhancement of photon emission from a single InGaAs quantum dot (QD) embedded in a photonic crystal (PhC) nanocavity by using cavity resonant excitation. The cavity resonant excitation selects only a single QD whose δ-function-like density of state of the first excited state exactly coincides with the resonance of a PhC nanocavity, and largely enhances the light emission from the ground state of the QD. This highly efficient single dot selective excitation technique can be useful for investigations in PhC-QD coupled systems and single photon devices.

Keywords: Photonic crystal, Quantum dot, Nanocavity, Selective Excitation, Resonance
PACS: 73.21.La, 42.70.Qs, 78.55.Cr

INTRODUCTION

The physics of the cavity quantum electrodynamics systems can be divided into weak and strong coupling regimes depending on the coupling strength between the optical cavity mode and a single two-level system. In the field of semiconductors, the atomic-like single quantum dot (QD) is the two-level system and semiconductor structures such as micropillars,[1] microdisks,[2] and photonic crystals (PhCs)[3] are the optical cavities. These physical phenomena are very interesting, but also, very delicate. In particular, very low excitation power density is essential to observe strong coupling phenomena in these systems. Therefore, excitation techniques that can efficiently excite a single QD will be useful to observe this delicate physics clearly.

SAMPLE and EXPERIMENTAL SETUP

The sample was grown on a (100)-oriented GaAs substrate by low-pressure MOCVD. A 160-nm-thick GaAs slab layer was grown on a 600-nm-thick $Al_{0.7}Ga_{0.3}As$ sacrificial layer and the InGaAs QD layer was inserted in the middle of the slab layer. The density of QDs is 2×10^{10} cm^{-2}. Postgrowth rapid thermal annealing was performed under N$_2$ flow at 820 °C for 30 s, using GaAs proximity capping. The postgrowth annealing, which resulted in the blue shift of the PL peak shorter than 1 μm from 1.3 μm.

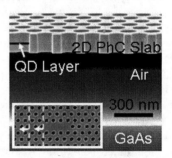

FIGURE 1. Scanning electron micrograph of the cross section of the PhC. The inset is the top view of a nanocavity.

We fabricated the PhC with a triangular lattice in this sample with lattice period of $a = 240$ nm and an air hole radius of $0.27a$. We adopted a defect structure consisting of three missing air holes, called L3 defect, along the Γ-K direction. The first and third nearest air holes at both edges of the cavity were shifted outwards the cavity by $0.15a$ as shown in the inset in Fig. 1. The AlGaAs sacrificial layer was etched off using HF acid solution to form a two-dimensional PhC slab structure as shown in Fig. 1. The cavity quality factor of the investigated cavity was ~ 8,000. Details of the crystal growth and fabrication processes were reported in our previous paper.[4]

RESULTS AND DISCUSSION

Figure 2 shows the PL spectrum with He-Ne laser pumping with an excitation intensity of ~ 100

CP893, *Physics of Semiconductors, 28th International Conference*
edited by W. Jantsch and F. Schäffler
© 2007 American Institute of Physics 978-0-7354-0397-0/07/$23.00

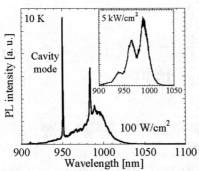

FIGURE 2. μ-PL spectrum of the InGaAs QD ensemble in a PhC structure measured at ~ 100 W/cm² at 10 K. The inset shows the μ-PL spectrum measured at ~ 5 kW/cm².

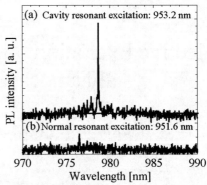

FIGURE 3. PL spectra of (a) a cavity resonant single QD and (b) a normal resonant single QD measured at ~ 30 W/cm² at 10 K.

W/cm² at 10 K. The peak observed around 980 nm is the PL from the InGaAs QD ensemble. The sharper peak observed at around 950 nm is the strong light emission from the lowest-order cavity mode. The inset in Fig. 2 is the PL spectrum measured by cw Ti:sapphire laser pumping with a relatively high excitation intensity of ~ 5 kW/cm² to clearly show the emission wavelengths of the ground and excited states. The PL peaks at 989 and 963 nm are attributed to the transition from the ground and first excited states of QDs, respectively.

We performed PLE measurements by tuning the excitation wavelength of the cw Ti:sapphire laser. The excitation wavelength was tuned with ~ 0.1 nm step size. In this measurement, a PhC cavity with the resonant wavelength of 953.2 nm was investigated. The excitation wavelength was tuned from 950.0 to 956.0 nm at ~ 30 W/cm². The PL spectra at the characteristic excitation wavelengths are shown in Figs. 2(a) and 2(b). Sharp peaks that can be attributed to photon emission from two different single QDs, were observed at 976.5 and 978.8 nm when the excitation wavelengths were tuned at 951.6 and 953.2 nm, respectively. The energy levels of the discrete ground and excited states are different between each QD mainly due to the size fluctuation. We suppose that there are two QDs: one QD, whose energy level of the excited state is slightly above that of the cavity resonance (QD1), and the other QD, whose excited state is resonant with the cavity resonance (QD2). For the PL peak at 976.5 nm in Fig. 3(b), the signal corresponds to the photon emission from the ground state of a non-cavity resonant single QD (QD1). For the higher PL peak at 978.8 nm in Fig. 3(a), the excitation light is resonant with both the cavity mode resonance at 953.2 nm and the excited state of a single QD (QD2). These peaks are observed at the shoulder of the shorter wavelength side of the ground state, while the excitation wavelengths are at the shoulder of the shorter wavelength side of the first excited state. The energy difference of the photon emission

wavelength and excitation wavelength is 35 meV. On the other hand, the energy difference between the first excited and ground state is 37 meV. The quantitative coincidence of the two values supports the cavity resonant excitation. We can see that the photon emission from a single QD, whose excited state couples to the cavity resonance, is enhanced nearly ten times compared with that from a normally resonant single QD. This stronger light emission from the resonant single QD can be attributed to the enhancement of the effective absorption by the cavity resonant effect. In other words, the photon density in the cavity is locally enhanced by the long photon lifetime and small mode-volume. We can spatially select and excite only QDs in a nanocavity, even the excitation spot is larger than the cavity size, by using the local electric field enhancement due to cavity resonant effect. Moreover, we can select only a single QD by adding the spectral selection using the cavity resonant effect.

ACKNOWLEDGMENTS

This work was supported by the Focused Research and Development Project for the Realization of the World's Most Advanced IT Nation, Ministry of Education, Culture, Sports, Science and Technology.

REFERENCES

1. J. P. Reithmaier, G. Sek, A. Loffler, C. Hofmann, S. Kuhn, S. Reizenstein, L. V. Keldysh, V. D. Kulakovskii, T. L. Reinecke, and A. Forchel, *Nature* **432,** 197 (2004).
2. E. Peter, P. Senellart, D. Martrou, A. Lemaitre, J. Hours, J. M. Gerard, and J. Bloch, *Phys. Rev. Lett.* **95,** 067401 (2005).
3. T. Yoshie, A. Scherer, J. Hendrickson, G. Khitrova, H. M. Gibbs, G. Rupper, C. Ell, O. B. Shchekin, and D. G. Deppe, *Nature* **432,** 200 (2004).
4. M. Nomura, S. Iwamoto, T. Nakaoka, S. Ishida, and Y. Arakawa, *Appl. Phys. Lett.* **88**, 141108 (2006).

Sub-terahertz phonon dynamics in acoustic nanocavities

N. D. Lanzillotti-Kimura[1,2], A. Huynh[1], B. Jusserand[1], B. Perrin[1], A. Fainstein[2], M. F. Pascual-Winter[1,2], E. Peronne[1], and A. Lemaître[3]

1- INSP/UPMC,CNRS, Campus Boucicaut, 140 Rue de Lourmel, 75015 Paris, France
2- Centro Atómico Bariloche and Instituto Balseiro, C.N.E.A., 8400 S. C. de Bariloche, R.N., Argentina
3- LPN/CNRS, Route de Nozay, 91460 Marcoussis, France

Abstract. We report a direct determination of the dynamic behavior of confined acoustic phonons in nanocavities by picosecond acoustics. We provide the broadband, high resolution transmission amplitude curve in the sub-terahertz range and we give evidence of resonant transmission peaks in three successive stop bands, in quantitative agreement with transfer matrix simulations. We demonstrate transit times in the nanosecond range at the cavity peaks reflecting the strong phonon confinement within the cavity layer and picosecond times in the stop bands, shorter than in any of the constituting materials, a tunneling effect known in photonic systems as superluminal propagation.

Keywords: acoustic phonons, cavities, pump-probe spectroscopy
PACS: 63.22.+m 78.47.+p 78.67.Pt 43.38.+n

Acoustic phonons manifest themselves practically in all electronic, thermal, and optical phenomena in semiconductors nanostructures. Based on the concept of photon microcavity, it has been recently suggested that confining GHz-THz acoustic phonons in specifically designed resonant multilayers could significantly modify the electron-phonon interaction in nanostructures. GaAs/AlAs acoustic nanocavities have been proposed and phonon confinement demonstrated by Raman scattering[1]. The epitaxial growth of semiconductor multilayers allows the conception of monolithic 1D phononic crystals based on the contrasting acoustic impedances of standard semiconductors such as GaAs and AlAs. Superlattices are well known for their novel optical and electronic properties and much less as high reflectance phonon mirrors in the GHz-THz range, i.e. in the energy range which is important for the performance of several electronic and optoelectronic devices. We present here the first direct measurement of phonon spectral transmission through a phonon nanocavity, based on the picosecond acoustics technique[2]. We demonstrate that inserting a phonon cavity between two identical phonon Bragg mirrors induces a narrow transmission peak within the lowest stop bands and that a narrow phonon wave packet centered at this peak is significantly delayed when transmitted through the device.

GaAs/AlAs phonon devices have been grown by Molecular Beam Epitaxy on (001) oriented two-side polished GaAs substrates. They contain two high reflectance phonon Bragg mirrors centered at 100 GHz, made of 10 periods of ($3\lambda/4$, $\lambda/4$) building blocks, i.e. 35.4 and 14.1 nm thicknesses for GaAs and AlAs, respectively. A GaAs single layer was inserted between these two mirrors and we compare here the results on two different samples, differing only in the thickness of this layer, being $3\lambda/4$ in the standard mirror M and $\lambda/2$ in the phonon cavity C. Broadband acoustic transmission spectroscopy has been performed using thin aluminum layers deposited on both sides of the samples for generation (substrate side) and detection (surface side) of the acoustic pulse. A femtosecond optical pulse is focused on the substrate side and the short absorption length in Al leads to the generation of an acoustic pulse containing frequencies up to 0.25 THz. The sample is cooled down to 15 K so that the acoustic pulse propagates with negligible attenuation over the 325 µm thick GaAs substrate. We finally used a Sagnac interferometer and a lock-in detection to measure the time-variation of the imaginary part of the transient reflectivity at the sample surface.

We show in Fig.1 the Fourier transform amplitude F(ω) of the experimental signals (ME, CE) measured in samples M and C and compare them with the Fourier transform of the deformation of the sample surface normalized with the relevant incoming acoustic spectrum (MT, CT) as deduced from acoustic simulations based on a standard transfer matrix

CP893, *Physics of Semiconductors, 28th International Conference*
edited by W. Jantsch and F. Schäffler
© 2007 American Institute of Physics 978-0-7354-0397-0/07/$23.00

method. The overall correspondence in the transmission structures is remarkable, including the observation of three gaps around 0.05, 0.1 and 0.15 THz in the mirror M. The same gaps are observed in cavity C together with additional narrow cavity modes. Because the building blocks of the mirrors are ($3\lambda/4$, $\lambda/4$), the cavity mode appears at the centre of the second gap while the modes in the first and third stop bands are downshifted (respectively up shifted) with respect to the stop-band centre. The spectral width (FWHM) of the cavity peaks, which reflects the lifetime of phonons in the cavity, amounts to 0.35 GHz in close agreement with the 0.3 GHz value expected from the model.

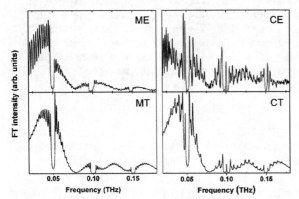

FIGURE 1. Fourier transform amplitudes of the measured surface displacement for the mirror (ME) and the cavity (CE) compared to the corresponding calculated quantities (MT, CT). The energy range of the phonon stop bands are highlighted in red.

A definitive advantage of picosecond acoustics with respect to light transmission spectroscopy is that the full complex transmission is experimentally available, the phase ϕ of which gives access to the group delay time t_G associated to the transit of the sound pulse through the acoustic device. t_G can be alternatively determined either from the basic definition $t_G(\omega)=d\phi(\omega)/d\omega$ or from numerically filtering the data with a Gaussian filter centered at ω provided that the filter is narrow enough for the pulse shape not to be significantly modified after transmission. Because the later method is less affected by experimental noise, we used it to quantify the time evolution in the studied nanocavity. The results of filtering the measured transmission at varying energies with a Gaussian pulse of width 0.01 GHz are shown in Fig.2 and compared with the simulation. Despite of the noise due to low transmission amplitude in this energy range, we clearly demonstrated picosecond transit times in the stop band, shorter than in any of the constituting materials. This is an illustration of what is known as the Hartman effect of electron tunneling through potential barriers[3]. When analyzed in the context of light propagation, the same phenomena

leads to much debated consequences, in view that light velocities above c have been deduced from indirect measurements. Here, in the framework of sub-THz acoustics, we have the advantage that direct observations in the time domain become accessible.

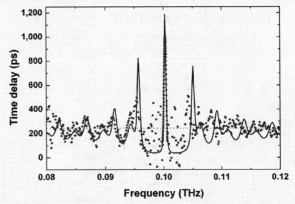

FIGURE 2. Time delay for a Gaussian pulse of width 0.01 GHz to cross the full nanocavity device deduced from the measured time-dependent surface displacement though numerical filtering (blue dots) compared to the simulated one (black line). The red dotted line gives the standard propagation time neglecting any reflection at the layer interfaces.

Long transit times above one nanosecond are measured on the other hand at the cavity peaks reflecting the strong confinement of resonant phonons within the cavity layer. When an acoustic pulse hits the cavity device at this frequency, a significant part of the energy is transferred to the cavity mode, setting on a confined displacement that then decays slowly with time though the acoustic Bragg mirror. This result is similar to what is observed in photonic microcavities, an effect that is at the basis of modifications of the angular distribution of the emitted light, and of the emission rate, for optical emitters such as excitons embedded in the cavities.

To summarize, we demonstrated in this communication new experimental results in the sub-Terahertz acoustic domain opening the possibility of using phonon nanocavities to modify the way in which sound interacts with light, with other phonons, and with electrons. They could, in addition, provide a new useful approach as a the feedback mechanism for phonon "lasing" devices.

REFERENCES

1. M. Trigo, A. Bruchhausen, A. Fainstein, B. Jusserand, and V. Thierry-Mieg, Phys. Rev. Lett. **89**, 227402 (2002)
2. H. Maris, Scientific American **278**, 64-67 (1998); B. Perrin, B. Bonello, J.-C. Jeannet, and E. Romatet, Physica B **219&220**, 681-683 (1996)
3. T. E. Hartman, J. Appl. Phys. **33**, 3427 (1962).

Single and Coupled Microcavities – AlAs/GaAs DBR Pillars and GaAs Pyramids

M. Karl*, W. Löffler*, J. Lupaca-Schomber*, T. Passow*, S. Li*, J. Hawecker†, F. Pérez-Willard†, D. Gerthsen†, H. Kalt*, C. Klingshirn* and M. Hetterich*

*Institut für Angewandte Physik and Center for Functional Nanostructures (CFN), Universität Karlsruhe (TH), Wolfgang-Gaede-Straße 1, 76131 Karlsruhe, Germany
†Laboratorium für Elektronenmikroskopie and CFN, Universität Karlsruhe (TH), Engesserstraße 7, 76131 Karlsruhe, Germany

Abstract. We discuss two different types of GaAs-based microcavities: Single and coupled pillar-type resonators with AlAs/GaAs distributed Bragg reflectors (DBRs) were fabricated by means of molecular-beam epitaxy (MBE) and focussed-ion-beam (FIB) milling. The dependence of the observed cavity modes on the pillar diameter and on the coupling bridge were investigated. Additionally, we present an alternative cavity design consisting of a pyramidal GaAs resonator placed on top of an AlAs/GaAs DBR. Single or even coupled pyramids were achieved by combining electron-beam lithography and wet chemical etching. In(Ga)As quantum dots (QDs) served as a broad-band light source at around 950 nm.

Keywords: Optical resonator, micropillar cavity, pyramidal resonator, coupled resonators.
PACS: 73.61.Ey, 73.21.La, 78.55.Cr, 78.55.-m

INTRODUCTION

Microcavities with QDs are considered to be promising elements for quantum information processing, since they enable strong light-matter interaction which can be used for the entanglement of quantum bits in the QDs and a controlled interaction between locally separated QDs.

Two different approaches of single and coupled microcavities are investigated: conventional pillar-shaped resonators with top and bottom DBRs, similar to those of Bayer et al. [1], and novel pyramidal-type cavities with bottom DBRs. The layer structures for both types have been grown using molecular-beam epitaxy (MBE) and contain In(Ga)As QDs as a broad-band light source in the spectral range from 900 nm to 1000 nm.

MICROPILLARS

The cylindric pillar-like resonators consist of a GaAs one λ-cavity with embedded QDs in the middle of the structure as well as top and bottom AlAs/GaAs DBRs each with 20 mirror pairs. A FIB system allowing a one-step prototyping has been used to etch the desired shapes, i.e., a circle for a single pillar and a dumbbell for two pillars coupled by a bridge (see Figs. 1(a, b)). Different pillar diameters

and coupling bridges could be realized easily.

We study the dependence of the cavity mode spectrum on the resonator geometry (e.g. the pillar diameter ranging from 2.7 to 15 μm and the width of the coupling bridge) in a confocal microphotoluminescence (μ-PL) set-up with a tunable titanium-sapphire laser as the excitation source for the QDs. Figure 1(c) displays the optical resonator modes as peaks in the μ-PL spectra for the single pillars, while the inset shows the achieved Q-factor of the fundamental mode reaching up to 12500.

The measured cavity mode spectra can be modeled quite accurately utilizing a two-dimensional finite-element-method (FEM) simulation, where the resonators are treated as step-index fibers with a GaAs core and a cladding given by the surrounding air. An effective vertical wavevector of the cavity modes is determined by the distance between top and bottom DBR. The simulation returns the wavelengths of cavity modes (marked as vertical lines in Fig. 1(c)) and thus is a viable tool to design any DBR-based microcavity effortlessly, e. g. our coupled pillars.

PYRAMIDS

Pyramidal ZnS resonators selectively grown on GaAs have already reached Q-factors of up to 5000

CP893, *Physics of Semiconductors, 28th International Conference*
edited by W. Jantsch and F. Schäffler
© 2007 American Institute of Physics 978-0-7354-0397-0/07/$23.00

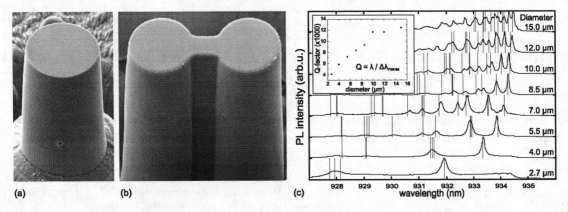

FIGURE 1. (a) Single and (b) coupled pillars with a one λ thick cavity, top and bottom DBRs consist of 20 mirror pairs. (c) Curves show optical resonator modes of pillars with different diameters, vertical lines mark the wavelength positions of calculated modes. Inset with Q-factor of fundamental mode vs diameter.

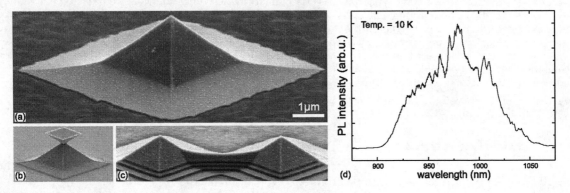

FIGURE 2. (a) Single pyramid, (b) vertically and (c) laterally coupled pyramids. (d) Characteristic μ-PL spectrum of a pyramid with a base length of $2.5\,\mu m$.

[2]. Such pyramidal shapes can also be achieved out of GaAs utilizing a sacrifical AlAs layer in a wet chemical etching process [3]. The etching mask was prepared by electron-beam lithography. We have successfully used this technique to realize not only single but also laterally and vertically coupled cavities (Figs. 2(a–c)). The GaAs pyramids acting like retro-reflectors are placed on top of an AlAs/GaAs DBR.

Pyramids containing QDs were examined with the same μ-PL set-up as the micropillars. PL spectra (Fig. 2(d)) show reproducible structures with peaks of different widths. Temperature and excitation dependent analyses suggest these to be (unresolved) optical modes. Further investigations are currently under way.

ACKNOWLEDGMENTS

This work has been performed within project A2 of the DFG Research Center for Functional Nano-structures (CFN). It has been further supported by a grant from the Ministry of Science, Research and the Arts of Baden-Württemberg (Az: 7713.14-300).

REFERENCES

1. M. Bayer, T. Gutbrod, J. P. Reithmaier, A. Forchel, T. L. Reinecke, P. A. Knipp, A. A. Dremin, and V. D. Kulakovskii, *Phys. Rev. Lett.* **81**, 2582–2585 (1998).
2. I. Suemune, T. Shimozawa, and K. Hoshi, "Demonstration of high-Q three-dimensional optical microcavities with pyramidal structures constructed on lossy substrates," in *Physics of Semiconductors, Proc. 26th Int. Conf. Phys. Semicond. (Edinburgh 2002)*, edited by A. R. Long, and J. H. Davies, Conference Series 171, Institute of Physics, Bristol, Philadelphia, 2003.
3. V. Cambel, D. Gregušová, and R. Kúdela, *J. Appl. Phys.* **94** (2003).

Emission Properties of 6.7 Micron Vertical-Emitting Microcavity Lasers Operating in Continuous-Wave Mode

T. Schwarzl[*], J. Fürst[#], G. Springholz[*], M. Böberl[*], E. Kaufmann[*], J. Roither[*], G. Bauer[*], H. Pascher[#], W. Heiss[*]

[*]Institut für Halbleiter- und Festkörperphysik, Johannes Kepler Universität, A-4040 Linz, Austria
[#]Experimentalphysik I, Universität Bayreuth, Universitätsstrasse 30, D-95447 Bayreuth, Germany

Abstract. The emission properties of lead salt continuous-wave (cw) vertical-cavity surface-emitting lasers for the mid-infrared are presented. The structures, based on high-finesse microcavities containing PbSe as active medium, show optically pumped cw laser emission up to temperatures of 100 K at a long wavelength of 6.7 µm. Stimulated emission with a very narrow beam divergence below 1° and a large temperature tuning range of 70 nm is found. The measured line width of the laser emission is only 0.6 nm limited by the spectrometer resolution with a strong narrowing with respect to the line width of the sub-threshold signal. The sharp laser threshold is at a low pump power of 67 W/cm^2 and the observed cw output power amounts up to 1.2 mW at 85 K with a conversion efficiency of 0.5 %.

Keywords: lead compounds; IV-VI semiconductors; narrow band gap semiconductors; mid-infrared; microcavity lasers; surface emitting lasers; optical pumping; laser tuning; stimulated emission; molecular beam epitaxial growth.
PACS: 81.15.Hi, 42.55.Px, 78.20.Ci, 78.30.Hv

INTRODUCTION

Lasers for the mid-infrared (3-30 µm) are important tools for gas sensing or medical diagnostics [1]. The narrow-gap lead salt materials are commonly used for such lasers, because they exhibit a favorable electronic band structure and low Auger recombination rates. This results in conventional edge-emitting lead salt lasers operating in pulsed mode up to 60°C [2] and in continuous-wave (cw) mode up to 223 K [3].

In contrast to edge-emitters, surface-emitting lead-salt microcavity lasers offer several advantages such as a small beam divergence, single mode operation and the possibility of monolithic integration. Since their first demonstration [4], the performance of optically pumped IV-VI vertical-cavity surface-emitting lasers (VCSELs) was strongly improved with pulsed lasing up to 65°C [5]. In addition, we have demonstrated optically pumped cw lead salt VCSELs for very long wavelengths of 8 µm optimized for 2 K operation [6].

In the present work, we have performed a detailed study of the lasing characteristics of optically excited PbSe cw VCSELs operating up to 100 K.

The high-finesse microcavity structures were grown by molecular beam epitaxy and consist of two EuSe/PbEuSe Bragg mirrors with high reflectivity and a two-wavelength microcavity with a PbEuSe buffer

and the PbSe active layer in-between [6]. Owing to the high refractive index contrast between the mirror materials in excess of 50 %, only five layer pairs are necessary to obtain a reflectivity well above 99 % as required for VCSEL operation. Due to the strong temperature dependence of the band gap energies, IV-VI VCSELs have to be tailored for a certain operation temperature [7]. Here we have chosen 85 K, in contrast to our previous work [6] with 2 K.

RESULTS

First, the VCSEL samples were characterized by transmission measurements revealing three narrow cavity resonances in a broad Bragg mirror stop band. The measured linewidth of the central mode at 190 meV is only 0.17 meV (7 nm). This demonstrates the very high finesse of the microcavity of about 300.

The laser samples were optically excited by a CO laser in cw operation mode at a wavelength of 5.3 µm using the set-up already described in Ref. 6. Figure 1 shows the emission spectra at a temperature of 85 K. At a low pump power of 43 mW, a weak emission line at 6.685 µm with a FWHM of 11 nm is found (open squares). This corresponds to the expected wavelength and linewidth of the central cavity resonance at 85 K. Thus, this signal is attributed to spontaneous emission,

CP893, *Physics of Semiconductors, 28th International Conference*
edited by W. Jantsch and F. Schäffler
© 2007 American Institute of Physics 978-0-7354-0397-0/07/$23.00

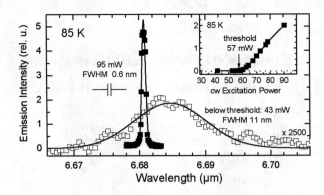

FIGURE 1. Emission spectra at 85 K above (pump power 95 mW, filled squares) and below threshold (pump power 43 mW, open squares, strongly enlarged scale). Inset: Emission intensity versus cw pump power.

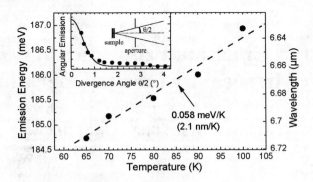

FIGURE 2. Tuning characteristic of the emission wavelength by temperature. The dashed line is a linear fit to the data. The inset shows the angular laser emission with a sketch of the measurement geometry.

filtered out by the cavity mode. In contrast, at an excitation power of only 95 mW (filled squares) the emission is by a factor of 5000 stronger and by a factor of 20 narrower. The linewidth as determined by a Gaussian line fit (solid line) is only 0.6 nm (16 μeV) limited by the resolution of the spectrometer (denoted by −‖− in the figure). Therefore, for pump powers above the threshold, we observe a very strong spectral narrowing not only with respect to the width of the passive cavity mode, but also compared to the spontaneous emission signal. This corresponds exactly to the expected behavior of cw VCSEL emission. The slight shift of the laser line to shorter wavelengths with respect to the sub-threshold signal is due to a slightly decreased cavity refractive index attributed to a band filling effect upon laser operation.

The threshold behavior is shown in the inset of Fig. 1, in which the dependence of the emission intensity on excitation power is plotted. The threshold pump power was evaluated to be 57 mW at 85 K. This corresponds to an internal threshold power density of only 67 W/cm². The observed total cw output power at 85 K was 1.2 mW corresponding to a conversion efficiency of 0.5 %.

For the application of the lasers for gas spectroscopy, the tuning ability and laser beam divergence are of crucial importance. These are shown in detail in Fig. 2 for our current lead salt VCSEL. The total tuning range by temperature variation was found as 70 nm with a linear tuning coefficient of 0.058 meV/K or 2.1 nm/K. This for a VCSEL large tuning range is particularly advantageous for spectroscopy. The angular emission characteristic of the VCSEL is depicted in the inset of Fig. 2. For an emission angle of only 1° off from the surface normal (see sketch in the inset), the emission intensity (filled circles) drops to zero. The solid line shows a Gaussian line fit to the emission profile, which yields a half width at half maximum of only 0.5°. This narrow for-

ward directed emission is a further proof for VCSEL emission and also demonstrates one of the major advantages of VCSELs.

CONCLUSIONS

In summary, we have presented an analysis of cw emission from lead salt mid-infrared VCSELs operating up to 100 K. Optically pumped lasing was observed at a wavelength of 6.7 μm with a large tuning range of 70 nm and a low threshold pump power of 67 W/cm². A very narrow beam divergence below 1° was found. The laser linewidth was only 0.6 nm limited by the spectrometer resolution. Therefore, our vertical emitting IV-VI lasers are well suited for mid-infrared gas sensing applications.

ACKNOWLEDGMENTS

We thank for financial support from FWF, Austria.

REFERENCES

1. M. Tacke, in Long wavelength infrared emitters based on quantum wells and superlattices, edited by M. Helm, Gordon and Breach Science Publishers, Amsterdam, 2000, pp. 347–396.
2. U. P. Schiessl and J. Rohr, Infrared Phys. Technol. **40**, 325-329 (1999).
3. Z. Feit, M. McDonald, R. Woods, V. Archembault, and P. Mak, Appl. Phys. Lett. **68**, 738-740 (1996).
4. T. Schwarzl, W. Heiss, G. Springholz, M. Aigle, and H. Pascher, Electron. Lett. **36**, 322-323 (2000).
5. W. Heiss, T. Schwarzl, G. Springholz, K. Biermann, and K. Reimann, Appl. Phys. Lett. **78**, 862-864 (2001).
6. J. Fürst, H. Pascher, T. Schwarzl, M. Böberl, G. Springholz, G. Bauer, and W. Heiss, Appl. Phys. Lett. **84**, 3268-3270 (2004).
7. W. Heiss, T. Schwarzl, J. Roither, G. Springholz, M. Aigle, H. Pascher, K. Biermann, and K. Reimann, Prog. Quantum Electron. **25**, 193-228 (2001).

ZnO micro-pillar resonators with coaxial Bragg reflectors

R. Schmidt-Grund*, B. Rheinländer*, T. Gühne†, H. Hochmuth*, V. Gottschalch†,
A. Rahm*, J. Lenzner* and M. Grundmann*

*Universität Leipzig, Institut für Experimentelle Physik II, Linnéstr. 5, 04103 Leipzig, Germany
†Universität Leipzig, Institut für Anorganische Chemie, Linnéstr. 3, 04103 Leipzig, Germany

Abstract.
Lateral confinement for cylindrical micro-resonator light emitters improves the ratio of the number of the axial resonant modes to the number of the spontaneous emitting lateral modes. We have observed resonator behaviour of cylindrical micro-structures as ZnO micro-pillars and glass-rods, whose lateral surfaces were coated with coaxial Bragg reflectors.

Keywords: Microcavity; Zinc oxide; Silicon oxide; Magnesium Oxide; Zirconium Oxide; Micropillar; Resonator; Cylindrical; Ellipsometry
PACS: 07.60.Fs; 42.55.Sa; 42.60.Da; 42.79.Dj; 78.55.Et

INTRODUCTOIN

The wurtzite-structure (hexagonal) II-VI-semiconductor ZnO has currently gained substantial interest in research because of its attractive properties for possible applications in optoelectronics and spintronics [1]. Light emission from ZnO has been observed by several groups. Optical pumped lasing from ZnO at cryogenic temperatures was already demonstrated many years ago [2] and recently observed at room temperature from various structures, especially from nano-wires and micro-pillars [3], Besides the near band-gap emission ($E_g \sim 3.37$ eV [4]), ZnO can emit light with photon energies below the fundamental band gap in a broad band, the so called green and orange luminescence [5]-[7], and which have already been used in green LED applications [8].

Coating of the lateral surfaces of such nano-wire and micro-pillar light-emitters with dielectric or metallic single layers or Bragg reflectors (BR) enhances the light confinement due to the improvement of the ratio of the number of the axial resonant modes to the number of the spontaneous emitting lateral modes and which in general improves the emission properties. For example, lateral confinement was demonstrated on free standing micro-resonators, which are surrounded by air or coated with single films [9]-[13], by lateral patterning of planar micro-resonators, and by introducing of annular BR due to etching of concentric air trenches in vertical light emitting devices (c.f. e.g. the Refs. [14]-[18] and Refs. in their). However, coating of free standing cylindrically shaped nano- and micro-structures with coaxial BR was not reported so far.

In this communication, we report on optical properties of hexagonally shaped ZnO micro-pillars (diameters: $0.8 \ldots 10\,\mu$m) and of circularly shaped glass-rods (diameters: $5 \ldots 5000\,\mu$m), whose lateral surfaces were coated with coaxial BR. As BR, stacks of the materials ZrO_2 / MgO and a-Si$/SiO_x$ (a-Si: amorphous Si) were used [19]-[23].

EXPERIMENTAL DETAILS

The ZnO wires were grown using high-pressure pulsed-laser deposition [24] and the micro glass rods were produced by pulling of glass bars.

The a-Si and SiO_x single layers and BR have been prepared by means of plasma-enhanced chemical vapour deposition (PECVD) at 13.56 MHz in a Plasmalab 80 plus equipment. During the deposition, the temperature was held at approximately 90 °C. The ZrO_2 and MgO single layers and BR have been deposited using pulsed-laser deposition (PLD) at approximately 700 °C in 0.002 mbar O_2 atmosphere.

The optical properties of the Bragg reflectors were investigated using confocal micro reflectometry (μR), confocal micro spectroscopic ellipsometry (μE), and cathodoluminescence (CL) measurements. While the μE technique has been applied to cylindrically shaped micro-structures with diameters of the objects not less than $5\,\mu$m, whereas the length of the objects was larger than approximately $50\,\mu$m, the diameters of the objects for the μR technique was small as $0.8\,\mu$m.

The μR and μE measurements were performed with the light beam directed perpendicular to the axis of the glass-rods and ZnO micro-pillars. Therefore, a stack of layers consisting of the front-side BR (at one of the lateral surfaces), the glass or ZnO cavity, and the respective back-side BR (at the opposite lateral surface) contribute to the measured spectra. In the case of the circular-cylindrically shaped glass-rods, the curvature of the cavity and the layers have to be taken into account

CP893, *Physics of Semiconductors, 28th International Conference*
edited by W. Jantsch and F. Schäffler
© 2007 American Institute of Physics 978-0-7354-0397-0/07/$23.00

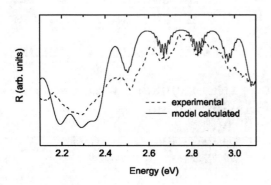

FIGURE 1. Reflectivity of a ZnO micro-pillar coated with a ZrO$_2$ / MgO Bragg reflector.

[15, 21, 22] and the model analysis have to be done, in principle, by means of solutions of the wave equation in cylindrical coordinates. Using a transfer matrix algorithm on the base of cylindrical waves, the electric field distribution within and the reflectivity R from such structures can be calculated [15]. We have found, that for cylinders with diameters larger 10 medium wavelength, that means for the here used materials and wavelength ranges diameters of the cylinders larger then 2 μm, the cylindrical-wave approach converges to the planar-wave approach. Therefore, for all investigated structures stacks of planar layers can be assumed in the model analysis, whereas for the circularly shaped structures the angle of incidence spread have to be taken into account [21].

Detailed information on the deposition properties and the optical techniques can be found in the Refs. [19]-[22].

RESULTS

For a-Si / SiO$_x$ Bragg reflectors deposited on glass-rods we have found that the layer thicknesses, and therefore the spectral position of the Bragg-Stop-Band (BSB), depends on the diameter of the rod and on the azimuthal position with respect to the PECVD plasma stream. The last causes a spectral shift of the BSB as a function of the azimuthal position. However, for each azimuthal direction, a part of each respective BSB lies in a common narrow photon energy range. That means, for this range, high values of the reflectivity are reached for each direction. These properties are promising for resonators with spatial selective emission characteristics.

For the deposition of a-Si / SiO$_x$ and ZrO$_2$ / MgO BRs and single layers on the lateral surfaces of the free standing ZnO micro-pillars, we have found no dependence of the layer thicknesses on the diameter. As an example, in Fig. 1, experimental μR and calculated R spectra of the

light collected from a lateral surface of a ZnO pillar (diameter: 1 μm) coated with a ZrO$_2$ / MgO BR (5.5 pairs), which is designed for the spectral range of the green luminescence, are shown. The modulation of R with varying photon energy between 2.4 eV and 3.1 eV within the BSB is caused by multiple-reflection induced interferences within the ZnO cavity. This indicates the resonator behaviour of the coated ZnO pillar. As it can be seen at the four minima within the BSB, four resonator modes are present. The fine structure modulation in the calculated spectra stems from interferences within the whole layer stack and which cannot be seen in the experimental spectra, mostly caused in inhomogeneities of the layer thicknesses. The reflectivity of the deposited BR seen from inside the wire reaches values larger 0.8. CL measurements confirms the results of the μR experiments. In the luminescence spectra, local enhancement of the luminescence of the coated pillars in the spectral range of the BSB is visible.

ACKNOWLEDGMENTS

This work was supported by the DFG within the projects No. Go 629/5, Rh 28/4-2 (FOR 522).

REFERENCES

1. M. Zamfirescu *et al.*, *Phys. Rev. B* **65**, 161205(R) (2002).
2. F. H. Nicoll, *Appl. Phys. Lett.* **9**, 13 (1966).
3. M. H. Huang *et al.*, *Science* **292**, 1897 (2001).
4. W. Hirschwald *et al.*, in *Current Topics in Materials Science* **7**, edited by E. Kaldis, North-Holland, Amsterdam, 1981, p. 143.
5. E. M. G. Heiland *et al.*, *Solid State Physics* **8**, 191 (1959).
6. R. Dingle, *Phys. Rev. Lett.* **23**, 579 (1969).
7. Y. G. Wang *et al.*, *J. Crystal Growth* **252**, 265 (2003).
8. J. Nause, *Compound Semiconductor* **11**, 29 (2005).
9. G. Björk *et al.*, *Phys. Rev. A* **47**, 4451 (1993).
10. T. Gutbrod *et al.*, *Phys. Rev. B* **57**, 9950 (1998).
11. J. M. Gérard and B. Gayral, *Physica E* **9**, 131 (2001).
12. Y. Yamamoto *et al.*, *Phys. Rev. A* **44**, 657 (1990).
13. M. Bayer, *Physica E* **17**, 393 (2003).
14. M. A. Kaliteevski *et al.*, *J. Mod. Optics* **47**, 677 (2000).
15. W. M. J. Green, *PhD thesis*, California Institute of Technology, Pasadena, California, 2005.
16. J. Scheuer *et al.*, *IEEE J. Sel. Top. Quantum Electron.* **11**, 476 (2005).
17. T. Erdogan *et al.*, *Appl. Phys. Lett.* **60**, 1921 (1992).
18. A. Shaw *et al.*, *Appl. Phys. Lett.* **75**, 3051 (1999).
19. V. Gottschalch *et al.*, *Thin Solid Films* **416**, 224 (2002).
20. M. Lorenz *et al.*, *Ann. Phys.* **13**, 59 (2004).
21. R. Schmidt-Grund *et al.*, *Thin Solid Films* **483**, 257 (2005).
22. R. Schmidt-Grund *et al.*, SPIE **6038**, 489 (2005).
23. R. Schmidt-Grund *et al.*, *J. Appl. Phys.* **99**, 123701 (2006).
24. M. Lorenz *et al.*, *Appl. Phys. Lett.* **86**, 143113 (2005).

Using Phonons to Populate the Bottom of the Polariton Dispersion Relation

M. D. Martín[1], D. Ballarini[1], A. Amo[1], L. Viña[1], R. André[2]

[1] SEMICUAM, Depto. Física de Materiales, Universidad Autónoma de Madrid, E-28049 Madrid, Spain
[2] Laboratoire Spectrométrie Physique (CNRS), Université Joseph Fourier 1, F-38402 Grenoble, France

Abstract. We have studied the dynamics of polariton-LO phonon scattering in a CdTe microcavity at low temperatures under resonant excitation. We have set an exciton-cavity detuning such that the energy difference between the two polariton branches coincides with that of an LO phonon. Our experiments reveal a sub-linear dependence of the integrated emission with pump power. Simultaneously, we have observed that the rise time of the emission does not depend on excitation power. These two facts suggest that the relaxation dynamics after resonant excitation is not governed by polariton-polariton scattering.

Keywords: Microcavities, II-VI semiconductors, polaritons, relaxation dynamics.
PACS: 71.36.+c, 78.47.+p, 78.55.Et

INTRODUCTION

In the last years, the possibility of achieving a polariton condensation in the bottom of the dispersion relation has elicited great interest [1]. In this paper we explore polariton-phonon scattering as a potential candidate to reach a macroscopic occupation of $K \sim 0$ states in the lower polariton branch (LPB). We have set an exciton-cavity detuning such that the energy difference between the upper polariton branch (UPB) and the LPB is close to that of an LO phonon. Then we have resonantly created $K \sim 0$ polaritons into the UPB. Previous reports in III-V microcavities indicate that direct scattering from $K \sim 0$ states in the UPB to $K \sim 0$ states in the LPB is inhibited [2] and show that UPB polaritons are more efficiently scattered to large-K LPB states. One could follow the argument and claim that, from those large-K states, polaritons relax to the bottom of the LPB through polariton-polariton scattering in a similar way as for non-resonant excitation. Our results show that this is not the case and that there are remarkable differences in the polariton relaxation after UPB resonant excitation.

SAMPLE AND EXPERIMENT

The sample under study is a $Cd_{0.4}Mg_{0.6}Te$ λ-microcavity with embedded CdTe quantum wells characterized by a Rabi splitting $\Omega = 10$ meV. The measurements are performed at 5 K and at different points of the sample corresponding to negative detunings, such that the energy difference between UPB and LPB (Δ) is approximately that of an LO phonon ($\hbar\omega_{LO} = 21.2$ meV). The excitation laser pulse is tuned to the UPB and arrives to the sample almost perpendicular to its surface. We have time-resolved the photoluminescence (PL) originating from the bottom of the LPB at $K \sim 0$ by means of a spectrograph coupled to a streak camera.

RESULTS AND DISCUSSION

We have concentrated our analysis on the polariton relaxation dynamics, studying the rise and decay times of the emission and the excitation-power dependence of the integrated intensity of the PL from $K \sim 0$ LPB states. Figure 1 displays the time evolution of the LPB emission obtained for an excitation power of 1 mW. We observe a very fast rise of the PL (≤ 15 ps), which is not modified by the increase of excitation power over two orders of magnitude. This short rise time is related to a fast, but inefficient, relaxation to the LPB [2]. The tuning of Δ to the LO-phonon energy does not increase the efficiency (one could expect a large increase if $\Omega = \hbar\omega_{LO}$ [3]). Only a small acceleration in the recombination dynamics is observed, with a reduction of the decay time from 125 to 110 ps with increasing excitation power (inset Fig. 1). This time is much longer than the photon lifetime inside the cavity (~ 10 ps) and is generally attributed to the relaxation of po-

CP893, *Physics of Semiconductors, 28th International Conference*
edited by W. Jantsch and F. Schäffler
© 2007 American Institute of Physics 978-0-7354-0397-0/07/$23.00

laritons along the LPB via the emission of acoustic phonons and/or polariton parametric scattering.

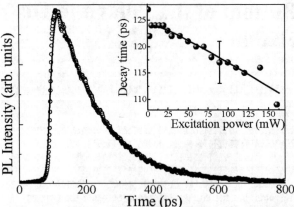

FIGURE 1. Time evolution trace of the emission from K ~ 0 LPB states for an excitation power of 1 mW and Δ = 21.2 meV. The line is a fit to $y = \frac{N_0}{t_r - t_d}(e^{-(x-x_0)/t_r} - e^{-(x-x_0)/t_d})$. Inset: excitation power dependence of the PL decay time. The line is a guide to the eye.

One of our most remarkable findings is a complete absence of non-linear emission from K ~ 0 LPB states, which has been observed in an identical system under non-resonant excitation [4, 5]. In fact we find a sub-linear dependence of the integrated intensity increasing the pump power by more than two orders of magnitude (Figure 2). This fact reveals an inhibition of polariton-polariton final-state stimulated scattering for these energy settings. We have also studied different values of Δ in the vicinity of the LO phonon. We have found that even for an energy difference (Δ = 23.1 meV), which would involve acoustic phonon- and polariton-polariton scattering in the relaxation towards K ~ 0 LPB states, the power dependence of the integrated emission is unaffected (inset Fig. 2). Only after a large reduction of the exciton-cavity detuning (Δ = 17. 6 meV) does the integrated PL approach a linear dependence, recovering the non-linear behaviour of Ref. 5 for even smaller detunings (not shown).

The behaviour described above could be related to two very different causes. The first one is the large reflectivity of the microcavity at the UPB energy for large negative detunings, such as these. This implies that the effective excitation that gets inside the cavity is much smaller than in the non-resonant case and therefore it is not possible to achieve polariton populations large enough to drive the system into the non-linear regime. Yet it would not explain why the dependence is so clearly sub-linear. The second possibility is the fact that K ~ 0 UPB polariton scattering to large-K states in the LPB occurs to a particular region,

further from the bottleneck than in the case of non-resonant excitation, from which polariton-polariton scattering is strongly inhibited, resulting in a weaker emission from K ~ 0 LPB states [6].

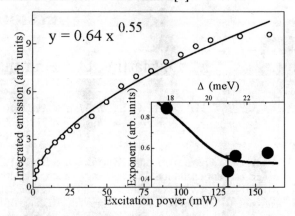

FIGURE 2. Integrated PL from K ~ 0 LPB states as a function of the excitation power. The solid line represents a fit with the equation that appears on the graph. Inset: dependence of the fit's exponent on the energy difference between UPB and LPB. The line is a guide to the eye.

CONCLUSIONS

We have investigated polariton-LO phonon scattering after resonant excitation in the UPB. We have found that the efficiency of the fast relaxation from K ~ 0 UPB to LPB states is not strongly modified by tuning Δ to $\hbar\omega_{LO}$. We have also found a sub-linear dependence of the integrated PL from K ~ 0 LPB states as a consequence of the inhibition of polariton-polariton final-state stimulated scattering. This inhibition could be due to a large reflectivity at the UPB energy or a narrow polariton distribution at large-K LPB states that will result in a very weak emission/small population at K ~ 0.

ACKNOWLEDGMENTS

This work has been partially supported by the Spanish MEC (MAT2005-01388 and NAN2004-09109-C04-04), the CAM (S-0505/ESP-0200) and the "Marie-Curie" MRTN-CT-2003-503677.

REFERENCES

1. Special Issue on Microcavities, *Semic. Sci. & Tech.* **18** (2003) Ed. by J. J. Baumberg and L. Viña.
2. J. Bloch and J. Y. Marzin, *Phys. Rev.* B **56**, 2103-2108 (1997); A. I. Tartakovskii et al, *ibid.* **60**, R11293-11296 (1999).
3. A. Fainstein et al, *Phys. Rev.* B **57**, R9439-9442 (1998).
4. M. D. Martín et al. *Phys. Rev. Lett.* **89**, 077402 (2002).
5. L. Viña et al., *Semic. Sci. & Tech.* **19**, S333-335 (2004).
6. A. I. Tartakovskii et al, *Phys. Rev.* B **67**, 165302 (2003).

Resonant Raman Scattering of Cavity Confined Acoustic Phonons in an Optical Microcavity

N. D. Lanzillotti-Kimura[1], A. Fainstein[1], B. Jusserand[2] and A. Lemaître[3]

[1]*Centro Atómico Bariloche and Instituto Balseiro, C.N.E.A., 8400 S. C. de Bariloche, Río Negro, Argentina*
[2]*INSP/UPMC, C.N.R.S., Campus Boucicaut, 140 Rue de Lourmel, 75015 Paris, France*
[3]*Laboratoire de Photonique et de Nanostructures, C.N.R.S., Route de Nozay, 91460 Marcoussis, France*

Abstract. We describe a device that has a resonant cavity for acoustic phonons embedded inside an optical cavity. This double cavity structure is a resonator for photons and acoustical phonons that can be tuned to an exciton resonance. We present Raman scattering experiments on this structure under double optical resonance, and we study the amplification of the photon-phonon interaction due to the electronic resonance. Besides the confined acoustic mode amplification, we report the presence of features corresponding to the Brillouin zone edge and oscillations related to finite size effects.

Keywords: microcavities, acoustic phonons, acoustic cavities, Raman scattering, phononics.
PACS: 78.67.-n 78.67.Pt 63.22.+m 78.30.-j 78.67.De

Following the concept of optical microcavity, acoustic nanocavities have been demonstrated to confine and amplify the acoustic field both spatially and in the spectral domain [1]. An acoustic cavity consists of two superlattices acting as distributed mirrors enclosing a spacer layer. In addition, a system constituted by an acoustic cavity embedded in an optical microcavity presents an enhancement of the Raman efficiency that can be as high as five orders of magnitude [2], and gives access to forward scattering features of the Raman spectra. In this work we study the possibility of enhancing the sound-light interaction furthermore by resonantly exciting an electronic state confined in the acoustic cavity spacer. The considered system is an acoustic cavity constituted by two GaAs/AlAs ($\lambda_S/4$, $3\lambda_S/4$) superlattices acting as acoustic Bragg reflectors enclosing an acoustic $\lambda_S/2$ cavity spacer. The phonon-cavity structure constitutes the λ_L spacer of an optical microcavity enclosed by 14 and 10 $Al_{0.2}Ga_{0.8}As$/AlAs ($\lambda_L/4$, $\lambda_L/4$) DBR pairs on the bottom and top respectively. Here λ_S (λ_L) refers to the sound (light) wavelength.

Figure 1 shows the measured Raman spectra obtained while detuning the laser energy away from double optical resonance [1] for the first acoustic cavity mode. A tunable Ti-Saph laser was used as excitation source, and the spectra where collected using a triple JY-T6400 spectrometer. The features corresponding to the first and second minigap at the Brillouin zone center can be clearly identified in a single measure due to the relatively low finesse of the optical cavity (~300). These features are indicated with arrows in the plot.

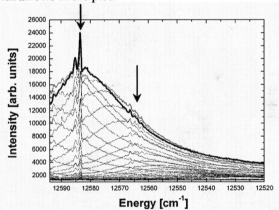

FIGURE 1. Measured Stokes Raman spectra obtained while detuning the laser energy away from double optical resonance for the first acoustic cavity mode.

The electronic level confined in the acoustic cavity was set within the transparency region of the optical microcavity, i.e., below the gap of the $Al_{0.2}Ga_{0.8}As$ layers. By choosing a $\lambda_S/2$ acoustic spacer, the electronic level is also set below the acoustic BRs absorption. By changing the position of the laser spot in the tapered sample and changing the laser energy we can tune the optical cavity mode energy with respect to this electronic level. So the optical

CP893, *Physics of Semiconductors, 28th International Conference*
edited by W. Jantsch and F. Schäffler
© 2007 American Institute of Physics 978-0-7354-0397-0/07/$23.00

excitation in the Raman scattering experiments can be done with the laser tuned both with the optical cavity mode (as shown in fig. 1) and with the confined electronic state. Raman spectra measured with different wavelengths at 80 K can be observed in figure 2. In all cases, the optical resonance is centered approximately at the first minigap of the Brillouin zone center. The experimental spectra show an amplification of the Raman signal (narrow features on top of the luminescence background) as the excitation source approaches the electronic energy level of the acoustic cavity spacer. From 804 nm to 768 nm an amplification factor of 5.5 was measured due to the electronic resonance. At room temperature amplification factors higher than 10 were measured, where the studied energy range was wider.

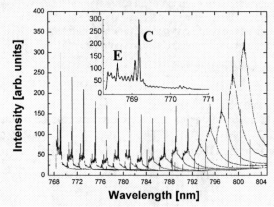

FIGURE 2. Stokes Raman spectra measured with different wavelengths at 80 K. The inset shows a detail of a spectrum where the first zone edge can be observed. The optical resonance is centered approximately at the first minigap of the Brillouin zone center.

The inset in the figure 2 shows a detail of a spectrum where the most intense peak corresponds to the first zone center cavity mode (C). To left of the latter an additional peak related to the zone edge (E) becomes observable as the excitation approaches the electronic resonance. Besides the resonant enhancement of the acoustic cavity mode intensity, clear oscillations related to finite size effects can be discerned in the left side of the spectra.

Figure 3 shows the acoustical reflectivity of the studied structure (top), and the calculated (T) and measured (M) Raman spectra taken at room temperature. The features corresponding to the Brillouin minizone edge are indicated with circles. We have observed that their intensity increases as the resonant condition is approximated. We interpret this as reflecting wavevector nonconservation due to the selective excitation of a single quantum well state. [3,4] The experimental results can be excellently accounted for with simulations performed using a

photoelastic model. The observation of features corresponding to the Brillouin minizone edge was reproduced by increasing the photoelastic constant of the acoustic spacer by a factor of 5. By increasing the photoelastic constant, the side oscillations amplitude also increases as observed in the experiments.

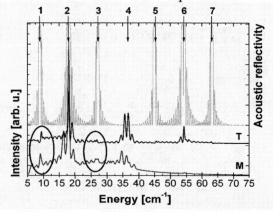

FIGURE 3. Acoustical reflectivity for the acoustic cavity with one confined mode. Theoretical (T) and measured (M) Stokes Raman spectra obtained for the phonon cavity embedded in optical cavities are also shown. The experimental spectrum was taken at room temperature. The arrows indicate the confined phononic modes of the structure. Zone edge features are highlighted with circles.

In conclusion, we report experimental results on resonant Raman scattering of confined phonons in an acoustic nanocavity embedded in an optical microcavity. In addition to the optical resonance amplification, we have observed an amplification of the acoustic cavity mode due to the resonance with the exciton of the cavity spacer. We have observed oscillations and features corresponding to the Brillouin zone edge that are attributed to the resonant regime. The described engineering of acoustic phonons, and of the photonic and electronic states, provide interesting alternatives for the study, and the generation and control of coherent THz hypersound with light.

ACKNOWLEDGMENTS

This work is supported by a SECyT-ECOS(Sud) collaboration. NDLK acknowledges support from Fundación YPF and Sigma Xi grants-in-aid of research.

REFERENCES

1. M. Trigo et al. Phys. Rev. Lett. **89**, 227402 (2002).
2. P. Lacharmoise et al. Appl. Phys. Lett. **84**, 3274 (2004).
3. V. F. Sapega et al. Phys. Rev. B **46**, 16005 (1992).
4. T. Ruf et al. Phys. Rev. Lett. **71**, 3035 (1993).

Parametric polariton scattering in single micropillar microcavities

D. Bajoni, P. Senellart, E. Peter, J. L. Smirr, I. Sagnes, A. Lemaître and J. Bloch

LPN-CNRS, Route de Nozay, 91460 Marcoussis, France

Abstract. Three dimensional microresonators (micropillars) operating in the strong coupling regime were studied by photoluminescence. Parametric oscillations of 0-dimensional polaritons are evidenced on a single micropillar. Signal and idler beam are of comparable intensities, a promising result in the aim of the emission of correlated photon pairs.

Keywords: microcavity, strong coupling, parametric scattering
PACS: 71.36.+c, 78.55.-m, 42.65.-k

Microcavity Polaritons are the mixed exciton-photon states arising form the strong coupling of a Quantum Well (QW) and the mode of an optical microcavity. They have attracted considerable research for their strong non-linear properties. Because of the peculiar shape of the lower polariton dispersion in the $k_\parallel - \omega$ space, polaritons resonantly pumped at the inflection point (the so called "magic angle") scatter toward the energy minimum at $k_\parallel = 0$ (signal) and toward a higher energy state near the excitonic reservoir (idler) in a four-wave mixing process which conserves energy and momentum (polariton parametric scattering) [1, 2, 3]; this process is of particular interest because non-classical correlations exists between the signal and idler beams [4, 5, 6]. Planar microcavities have however an intrinsic drawback: the idler beam, because of scattering toward the excitonic reservoir, is several orders of magnitude less intense than the signal beam, making their quantum correlations difficult to evidence [4].

On the other hand, promising results were obtained on 0-dimensional polaritons [7]. By laterally patterning a planar microcavity in the shape of micropillars (μPs) the fundamental mode is split in several discretized modes [8, 9]. The major advantage over the planar microcavity case is that the energy difference between the exciton and the lowest polariton modes can be large enough to get negligible scattering toward the excitonic reservoir, while still retaining a sufficient excitonic character to assure the non-linear properties. Dasbach and coworkers [7] fabricated square shaped pillars in order to have the energies of the three lowest modes (E_1, E_2 and E_3) equidistant ($E_3 - E_2 = E_2 - E_1$): this is a fundamental requirement because it grants energy conservation in polariton-polariton scattering from the pump state ($2 \cdot E_2 = E_1 + E_3$). Polariton scattering toward the first and the third mode by pumping on the second one was evidenced and the two complementary beams were of comparable intensities [7]. These experiments were performed on an ensemble of μPs, and experimental evidence of polariton parametric scattering on a single μP has not been reported so far. In this paper we report a study by photoluminescence (PL) of round micropillars in the strong coupling regime and we demonstrate parametric scattering on a single μP.

The planar microcavity consists in a 2λ GaAs cavity with a top (bottom) Bragg Mirror of 20 (24) $Al_{0.1}Ga_{0.9}As/AlAs$ pairs on a GaAs substrate. An 8 nm wide $In_{0.05}Ga_{0.95}As$ QW was placed at each of the three antinodes of the cavity mode. The cavity is wedge-shaped so that the energy difference between the cavity mode and the exciton at $k_\parallel = 0$ may be tuned by choosing the investigated position on the sample. Photoluminescence (PL) was performed on the planar cavity: strong coupling with a Rabi splitting of 5.5 meV and a quality factor of 10000 were measured. Round micropillars with diameters ranging from 10 to 1.5 μm were defined by Electron Beam Lithography followed by Reactive Ion Etching. In the PL experiments the sample is kept at low temperature; a tunable cw Ti:Saph laser (pump) is focused on a 2 μm spot on the sample surface and the PL signal is spectrally dispersed and detected by an avalanche photodiode.

PL spectra were taken at 5 K for several μPs at different positions along the cavity wedge so that a map of the energies of the modes versus their position can be drawn: a clear anticrossing of the modes with the exciton line, typical of the strong coupling regime, was evidenced [10].

A typical PL spectrum taken under non-resonant excitation on a pillar of 3 μm diameter is shown in Fig. 1a). The three lowest modes are clearly visible on the low energy side of the exciton emission peak at 1479 meV (E_X). The linewidth of the lowest modes (0.2 meV) corresponds to a quality factor near to that of the planar microcavity. In round pillars the three first photon modes are not equidistant in energy [8], but equally spaced po-

CP893, *Physics of Semiconductors, 28th International Conference*
edited by W. Jantsch and F. Schäffler
© 2007 American Institute of Physics 978-0-7354-0397-0/07/$23.00

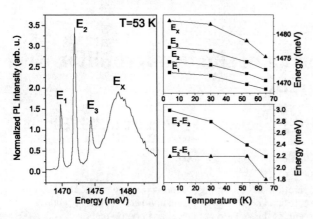

FIGURE 1. **a)** PL spectrum from a 3 μm diameter μP under non-resonant excitation at 53 K. **b)** E_1, E_2, E_3, E_X and **c)** $E_3 - E_2$ and $E_2 - E_1$ plotted as a function of temperature.

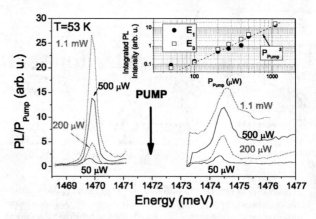

FIGURE 2. Emission spectra from a 3 μm diameter μP under excitation resonant to the second polariton mode at 53 K. **Inset:** Integrated PL intensities for E_1 (round dots) and E_3 (open square dots) as a function of P_{Pump}. The dashed line is parallel to P_{pump}^2.

lariton modes can be obtained by tuning temperature. E_1, E_2, E_3 and E_X are plotted as a function of temperature (T) in Fig. 1b). Reduction of the electronic band gap and increase of the refractive index in the materials lead to a redshift of all the peaks by increasing T; the exciton shift is however stronger that that of the modes. As E_X approaches E_3, the latter is pushed toward E_2 by the anticrossing. $E_3 - E_2$ and $E_2 - E_1$ versus T are plotted in Fig. 1c). They reach a distance of 0.2 meV close to 53 K: at this temperature $2E_2 \simeq E_1 + E_3$. At higher T, because of the anticrossing between E_2 and E_X, equidistance is lost. Spectra taken under excitation resonant to the second polariton mode, for different pumping rates (P_{Pump}) are shown in Fig. 2: each spectrum was divided by P_{Pump}. Two emission lines corresponding to the first (signal) and third (idler) modes are clearly visible. Notice that upon increasing P_{Pump} the modes slightly blueshift, because of renormalization due to coulombian interactions between polaritons: the pump energy was shifted accordingly. The intensities of the signal and idler beams are almost equal, and show a superlinear increase with P_{Pump}. The integrated intensities of the signal and idler beams are plotted as dots in the inset of Fig. 2: their dependence on P_{Pump} is quadratic. This is the expected dependence as the signal and idler states are populated by a two-particle scattering process in the pump state [3], and thus proves the occurrence of parametric polariton scattering in our sample.

In planar microcavities, parametric scattering undergoes a marked threshold when the occupation of signal and/or idler states exceeds unity [2]and the stimulated signal increases exponentially above threshold by several orders of magnitude. In 0-dimensional microcavities (in the present sample or in ref. [7]), no threshold could be observed. Further improvement of the sample quality, in particular the cavity quality factor, needs to be considered in order to reach the regime of stimulated parametric

scattering.

In summary we have studied round micropillars for 0-dimensional polariton confinement by PL experiments and, by tuning temperature, found the suitable conditions to achieve polariton parametric scattering. By pumping resonantly the second polariton mode, emission from the first and third polariton modes with comparable intensities have been measured. The quadratic dependence of the emitted intensities on the pumping rate indicates that the emission is due to polariton parametric scattering. These promising results are a first step toward the achievement of quantum interferences between the signal and idler beams on a single μP, which could lead to applications of polariton-based devices for quantum cryptography.

This work was supported by the European Community through the Marie Curie project "Clermont 2" contract number MRTN-CT-2003-503677.

REFERENCES

1. P. G. Savvidis *et al.*, *Phys. Rev. Letters* **84**, 1547 (2000).
2. R. M. Stevenson *et al.*, *Phys. Rev. Letters* **85**, 3680 (2000).
3. C. Ciuti *et al.*, *Phys. Rev. B* **63**, 041303 (2001).
4. J. P. Karr *et al.*, *Phys. Rev. A* **69**, 063807 (2004).
5. S. Savasta *et al.*, *Phys. Rev. Letters* **94**, 246401 (2005).
6. M. Romanelli *et al.*, cond-mat/0505639 (2005).
7. G. Dasbach *et al.*, *Phys. Rev. B* **64**, 201309(2001).
8. J. M. Gérard *et al.*, *Appl. Phys. Letters* **69**, 449 (1996).
9. T. Gutbrod *et al.*, *Phys. Rev. B* **59**, 2223 (1999).
10. J. Bloch *et al.*, *Superlatt. Microstruct.* **22**, 371 (1997).
11. D. M. Whittaker *et al.*, *Phys. Rev. B* **63**, 193305(2001).

Strong Optical Confinements inside The Wavelength-size Metal Mirror Microcavities: - New Concept for Small Light Emitters using InAsSb QDs Microcavities -

Akio Ueta[1], Sin-ichiro Gozu[1], Kouichi Akahane[1], Naokatsu Yamamoto[1], Masahiro Tsuchiya[1], and Naoki Ohtani[2]

[1]National Institute of Information and Communications Technology, 4-2-1 Nukui-Kitamachi, Koganei, Tokyo 184-8795, Japan
[2]Doshisha-University, 1-3, Tatara-Miyakodani, Kyotanabe-shi, Kyoto 610-0321, Japan

Abstract. We studied optical cavity properties of metal mirror microcavities. The μ-PL spectrum for the metal mirror structure showed a sharp emission at the resonance wavelength obtained by the μ-reflection measurement. Small temperature dependences of the cavity resonance were also observed, and the slope of the cavity resonance wavelengths was about 0.05 meV/K. These metal mirror microcavities might be useful for small, high performance optical devices.

Keywords: microcavity, InAsSb, GaAs, quantum dot
PACS: 78.30.Fs, 78.55.Cr, 78.67.Hc

INTRODUCTION

The combination of quantum dots (QDs) and microcavities is of great interest for understanding the pure interaction of atoms and vacuum fields. It is well known that the radiative properties of the QDs in an optical resonator can be controlled, and these structures may be used in the future in small, high performance optical devices, such as nano-lasers and single photon emitters. Most studies on III-V microcavities, up to now, have focused on planar microcavities with distributed Bragg reflectors (DBRs) based on AlAs/GaAs systems. The drawback is that a large number of pairs of layers must be grown to obtain DBRs with high reflectivity because of the low refractive index contrast. In contrast, gold (Au) metal films show high reflectivity and might be an alternative mirror material for microcavities.

In this work, we have investigated in detail the optical cavity properties of InAsSb QDs/GaAs microcavities with Au metal mirrors on both sides.

EXPERIMENTAL

Microcavity structures consisting of InAsSb QDs and GaAs were grown on (001) GaAs substrates by molecular beam epitaxy (MBE). The InAsSb has a narrowgap and is thus a suitable material for QD-based optical devices operating at optical fiber communication wavelengths.[1] The 300-nm-thick AlAs selectively etched layers were grown on the (001) GaAs substrate prior to growing the microcavity structure. The total thickness of the InAsSb QD/GaAs microcavity structure was about 110 nm, and this corresponded to a cavity length of λ/2, taking into account the phase changes upon reflection from the Au mirrors.[2] The metal mirror microcavity structure was mounted on Si substrates using liftoff techniques. The

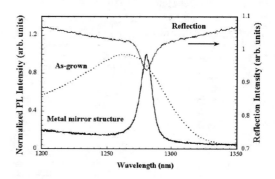

FIGURE 1. μ-PL spectra for metal mirror structure and as-grown InAsSb QDs/GaAs structure at RT. μ-reflection spectrum for metal mirror structure at RT.

CP893, *Physics of Semiconductors, 28th International Conference*
edited by W. Jantsch and F. Schäffler
© 2007 American Institute of Physics 978-0-7354-0397-0/07/$23.00

thickness of the Au mirrors on one side was 150 nm and on the other side was 50 nm. The emission properties of the metal mirror microcavities were characterized by μ-photoluminescence (μ-PL) measurements using a 532-nm laser. The optical cavity properties were characterized by μ-reflection measurements using a halogen lamp.

RESULTS AND DISCUSSIONS

FIGURE 1 shows μ-PL spectra for the metal mirror structure, and the as-grown InAsSb QDs/GaAs structure. It also shows a μ-reflection spectrum for the metal mirror structure. These measurements were performed at room temperature (RT). The beam spot of the laser used to excite the structures was about 3 μm in diameter. The excitation power density, estimated from the total supplied laser power, was about 42.4 kW/cm^2. Strong PL emissions from both the as-grown and metal mirror structures were observed even at RT. The peak wavelength and the full width at half maximum (FWHM) of the emission from the as-grown structure were 1262 nm and 111 nm, respectively. In contrast, a very sharp emission from the metal mirror structure was observed. The peak wavelength and the FWHM from the metal mirror structure were 1280 nm and 11.4 nm, respectively. The cavity resonance of the metal mirror structure at 1280 nm was clearly observed from the μ-reflection spectrum. The quality factor (Q) value of the resonance, estimated as $Q = \lambda/\Delta\lambda$, was about 112. This result clearly indicated that the emission property from the metal mirror structure was modulated by the optical cavity effect.

Optical cavity properties on temperatures are very interesting for understanding pure atom-vacuum interactions. FIGURE 2 shows energy shifts of the peak of the cavity resonances to the temperatures. The positions of the peak cavity resonances were eatimated by μ-reflection measurements. The calculated

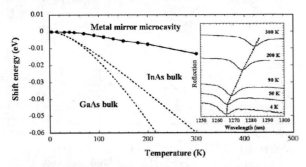

FIGURE 2. Energy shifts of the cavity resonances to the temperatures. Dotted lines are calculated bandgap shifts of InAs and GaAs. The inset shows the μ-reflection spectra of the metal mirror structure at various measurement temperatures.

temperature dependent bandgap shifts of InAs and GaAs are also shown. The inset shows the μ-reflection spectra of the metal mirror structure at various temperatures. The peak wavelengths of optical cavity resonances from the metal mirror structure slightly shifted to longer wavelength at higher temperatures. For the metal mirror structures, the energy shifts were much smaller than that of InAs and GaAs, and the estimated slope around RT was about 0.05 meV/K. This energy shift of the cavity resonances on the temperature is attributed to the temperature dispersion of the refractive index of the GaAs.[3] A high Q value of 209 was obtained from the metal mirror structure at 4 K. This Q value is not a maximum value because the top Au mirror of the metal mirror structure in this study was 50 nm. Making the upper Au mirror thicker will give it higher reflectivity and thus improve the optical cavity properties of the metal mirror microcavity. However, it is necessary to choose certain thickness of the top metal mirror, because the trancemittance of the emission through the thick top metal mirror decreases. These results indicate that this easily fabricated metal mirror structure acts as an effective microcavity and should be a useful structure for small, high performance optical devices.

CONCLUSION

We have studied the optical cavity properties of metal mirror microcavities. The μ-PL spectrum for the metal mirror structure showed a sharp emission at the resonance wavelength. The small temperature dependences of the cavity resonance were also investigated, and the slope of the cavity resonance at around RT was about 0.05 meV/K. We intend to continue these microcavities with regard to developing small, high performance optical devices.

ACKNOWLEDGMENTS

We are grateful to Mr. S. Miyashita at NTT Advanced Technology for his technical support. We also thank Dr. F. Tomita, Dr. T. Itabe, and Dr. M. Izutsu at the National Institute of Information and Communications Technology (NICT) for their encouragement.

REFERENCES

1. A. Ueta, S. Gozu, K. Akahane, N. Yamamoto, and N.Ohtani, *Jpn. J. Appl.* Phys. **44**, L696 (2005).
2. H. Becker, S. E. Burns, N. Tessler, and R. H. Friend, *J. Appl. Phys.* **81**, 2825 (1997).
3. T. Skauli, P. S. Kuo, K. L. Vodokanov, T. J. Pinguet, O. Levi, L. A. Eyres, J. S. Harris, M. M. Fejer, B. Gerard, L. Becouarn, and E. Lallier, *J. Appl. Phys.* **94**, 6447 (2003).

Enhanced Spontaneous Emission of CdSe/ZnSe Quantum Dots in Monolithic II-VI Pillar Microcavities

H. Lohmeyer, K. Sebald, C. Kruse, D. Hommel and J. Gutowski

Institute of Solid State Physics, University of Bremen, P.O. Box 330440, 28334 Bremen, Germany

Abstract. The emission properties of CdSe/ZnSe quantum dots in ZnSe-based pillar microcavities are studied. All-epitaxial cavities made of ZnSSe and MgS/ZnCdSe superlattices with a single quantum-dot sheet embedded have been grown by molecular-beam epitaxy. Pillar structures with diameters down to 500 nm have been realized by focused-ion-beam etching. As evidence for the Purcell effect a pronounced enhancement of the spontaneous emission rate by a factor of up to 3.8 is found for quantum dots coupling to the fundamental mode of the cavities.

Keywords: Pillar microcavity, II-VI, CdSe/ZnSe quantum dot, Purcell effect, focused-ion beam
PACS: 78.67.Hc, 78.55.Et, 42.55.Sa, 78.47.+p

Tailoring the optical emission properties of semiconductor quantum dots (QDs) by embedding them in solid-state microcavities (MCs) [1, 2] is promising for applications in new quantum-optical devices, particularily with regard to efficient solid-state sources of single photons. If QDs couple to discrete modes of a cavity the Purcell effect [3] can yield optimized and polarization controlled photon collection. A remarkably high temperature stability of epitaxial CdSe/ZnSSe QD emission has been demonstrated by of suppressed multiphoton emission up to 200 K in samples without cavity [4]. However, a spontaneous emission enhancement (SEE) has been observed for these QDs only recently after embedding them in hybrid pillar MCs [5].

We report on the observation of the Purcell effect for CdSe/ZnSe QDs coupling to the discrete fundamental mode of high-Q all-epitaxial ZnSe-based pillar MCs. Planar MC samples were grown by molecular beam epitaxy on GaAs at a substrate temperature of 280°C. A ZnSSe λ cavity contains a single sheet of CdSe/ZnSe QDs (QD density $\approx 5 \cdot 10^{10}\,\mathrm{cm}^{-2}$) grown by migration-enhanced epitaxy [6]. This cavity is positioned between an 18-period bottom and a 15-period top distributed-Bragg-reflector (DBR) stack. The high-index material of the DBRs is made of $ZnS_{0.06}Se_{0.94}$ (48 nm) while the low-index material consists of a MgS(1.7 nm)/ZnCdSe(0.6 nm) 25.5-period superlattice (for details see [7]). Completely etched cylindrically shaped pillar MCs with diameters between 500 nm and $2.6\,\mu$m were prepared from the planar cavities by focused-ion-beam etching (FIB) using a FEI NOVA NanoLab system [8]. A scanning electron microscope (SEM) image of one of the resulting structures, i.e. that with 500 nm diameter, is shown in Fig. 1 (a). A microphotoluminescence (μPL) setup has been used to excite individual pillar structures and to collect their

emission at variable temperatures. A frequency doubled Ti:sapphire laser (pulse width 120 fs) excited the QD layer at 2.71 eV, i.e. spectrally below the ZnSSe barrier so that carriers are generated in the surrounding ZnCdSe matrix. The cw-mean excitation density was kept below ≈ 20 W/cm^2 (pulse energy below 5 fJ). Time-correlated single-photon counting was used for lifetime measurements with a spectral/temporal resolution of 1.8 meV/30 ps.

The QD ensemble shows a nearly Gaussian PL emission band (FWHM 9 nm) centered at 496 nm at low temperatures if measured for an unstructured reference sample without cavity (data not shown). The longitudinal cavity resonance was set to 509 nm, i.e., on the low-energy tail of the QD distribution, in order to reduce the number of QDs coupling to the pillar modes. μPL spectra of pillars measured at 5 K exhibit well-separated pronounced resonant modes of the pillars due to the three-dimensional optical confinement, as shown exemplarily for a $1\,\mu$m pillar in the inset of Fig. 1 (b). We reported on these modes in comparable all-epitaxial quantum-well MCs recently [8]. Partly resolution limited lines attributed to emission of individual QDs are observed in the spectra being situated spectrally on and off resonance to the pillar modes. In the latter case QDs are emitting into leaky modes (LM) of the pillars [2]. If QDs couple effectively to pillar modes they show up as enhanced single lines, a fact which reflects the much larger collection efficiency of the PL emitted into the pillar modes. The quality factors $Q = \lambda / \Delta\lambda$ of the fundamental pillar modes (FMs) are determined through their spectral FWHM $\Delta\lambda$ measured at elevated temperatures for which the individual QD lines become broadened due to coupling to acoustic phonons [4]. Typical values of $Q = 2500, 1850, 1550,$ and 700 are obtained for pillars with diameters of $2.0\,\mu$m, $1.0\,\mu$m, $0.7\,\mu$m, and $0.5\,\mu$m,

CP893, *Physics of Semiconductors, 28th International Conference*
edited by W. Jantsch and F. Schäffler
© 2007 American Institute of Physics 978-0-7354-0397-0/07/$23.00

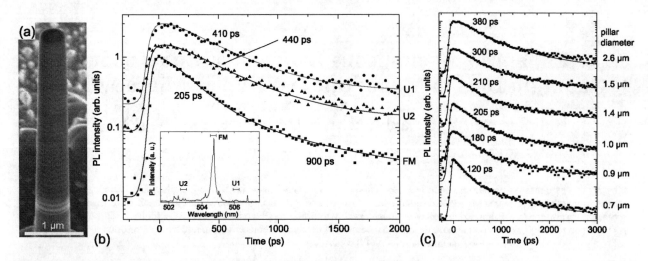

FIGURE 1. (a) SEM image of a pillar structure with 500 nm diameter prepared by FIB. (b) PL decay curves measured resonant (FM) and off-resonant (U1 and U2, shifted for clarity) to the fundamental mode of a 1.0 μm pillar as indicated on the PL spectrum shown in the inset. Solid lines are a fit to the experimental data using a biexponential (monoexponetial) decay for FM (U1, U2). (c) PL decay curves measured resonant to the fundamental mode for different pillar diameters. The fast decay times obtained from the fit (solid lines) are given.

respectively. By further calculating the mode volumes V (see [8]), Purcell factors up to 19.5 can be estimated which increase for smaller pillar diameters due to a larger Q/V ratio. To probe the action of the Purcell effect, time-resolved PL measurements have been performed on a series of pillars with varying diameters. For individual pillars PL transients are compared as obtained for detection at the spectral position of the FM and of LMs. As shown in Fig. 1 (b) for a 1 μm pillar the PL decay characteristics detected on the FM clearly differs from that measured on LMs. For the LMs (spectral positions U1 and U2) the transients can be fitted using a single exponential decay (including an offset for dark counts). The obtained decay times (380 – 500 ps) are comparable to data of the QD ensemble in a ZnSe matrix without cavity at the respective spectral position ($\tau = 460$ ps). Such a behavior is expected for QDs coupling to a continuum of low-Q LMs. On the FM of the 1.0 μm pillar, a clearly faster but non-exponential decay dynamics is observed. A reasonable fit to the measured data can be achieved using a biexponential decay with a fast decay time (205 ± 10) ps and a long decay time (900 ± 50) ps. Comparable PL decay curves are found for pillars with other diameters if detected on resonance to the FM (Fig. 1 (c)). All transients exhibit a fast decay component which becomes systematically *shorter* when going to smaller pillar diameters. This trend together with the clear difference in the decay when measuring off- and on-resonant to the FM on each single pillar is an unambiguous fingerprint of the strong SEE, i.e. the Purcell effect, for QDs coupled to the MC modes. The introduced slow decay component being in the range of 600 – 950 ps (± 50 ps) shows only a weak correlation to the pillar diameter. Whether the assumption of such a second slow decay component is physically meaningful cannot be decided yet, however, this is of no importance for the clear observation of an SEE. In a similar manner as in [3] we quantify an achieved *effective* SEE by a factor of up to 3.8 for a 0.7 μm pillar by the shortening of the extracted fast decay time (Fig. 1 (c)) with respect to the decay time of 460 ps measured on a reference sample. The determined SEE is in good agreement with the value estimated for an average SEE in an ensemble of many QDs with different spectral and spatial matching to the twofold degenerate FM of the pillar with a given Purcell factor [2].

In conclusion, coupling of CdSe/ZnSe quantum dots to modes of high-Q pillar microcavities has been demonstrated in an all-epitaxial sample. The Purcell effect is reflected by an average enhancement of the spontaneous emission rate by a factor of up to 3.8 for quantum dots coupling to the fundamental modes of the pillars.

We acknowlegde financial support by the *Deutsche Forschungsgemeinschaft*.

REFERENCES

1. K. J. Vahala, Nature **424**, 839 (2003).
2. J. M. Gérard, Top. Appl. Phys. **90**, 269 (2003).
3. J. M. Gérard et al., Phys. Rev. Lett. **81**, 1110 (1998).
4. K. Sebald et al., Appl. Phys. Lett. **81**, 2920 (2002).
5. I. C. Robin et al., Appl. Phys. Lett. **87**, 233114 (2005).
6. T. Passow et al., J. Appl. Phys. **92**, 6546 (2002).
7. C. Kruse et al., phys. stat. sol. (b) **241**, 731 (2004).
8. H. Lohmeyer et al., Appl. Phys. Lett. **88**, 051101 (2006).

Quantum dots in a tube as light emitters, waveguides and ring resonators

S. Mendach, R. Songmuang, M. Benyoucef, A. Rastelli, and O.G. Schmidt

Max-Planck-Institut fuer Festkoerperforschung, Heisenbergstrasse 1, D-70569 Stuttgart, Germany

Abstract. We present micro-photoluminescence investigations of InAs quantum dots (QDs) integrated into self-rolling InGaAs/GaAs strained layers. Light, which originates from the QDs at the laser excitation spot and propagates with a component parallel to the tube axis ($k_z \neq 0$), can be detected at the tube ends using a special μ-PL method, which features independent locations of excitation and collection. With light collection in the vicinity of the laser excitation spot we detect sharp peaks in the spectrum, which we attribute to constructive interference of light circulating around the tube axis ($k_z = 0$). The spectral positions and shapes of these whispering gallery mode-like resonances as well as the spatial mode distribution inside the tube are modeled using calculations based on the finite difference time domain method.

Keywords: ring resonator, microtubes, quantum dots, quantum electrodynamics
PACS: 78.30Fs, 78.67Hc, 78.67Ch

Semiconductor micro- and nanotubes fabricated from self-rolling strained epitaxial layers [1, 2] gain increasing interest particularly due to the possibility of transferring initially flat quantum systems to a cylindrical shape [3, 4]. In this paper we demonstrate the fabrication of a cylindrical semiconductor waveguide containing self-assembled InAs-quantum dots as quantum emitters.

Our samples are grown by solid source molecular beam epitaxy (MBE) on GaAs(001) substrates. The sample structure is shown in Fig. 1(a). Growth details can be found in Ref. 5. On top of the AlAs-sacrificial layer we grow a strained layer system which contains self-assembled InAs-quantum dots. After selective etching of the AlAs-layer the strained layer system is released from the substrate and rolls up into cylindrical geometry. In order to prevent radiative losses into the substrate due to direct contact between the cylindrical waveguide and the GaAs-substrate we prepare suspended tubes as shown schematically in Fig. 1(b). Details of the preparation method which is based on the rolling-up of U-shaped strained mesa can be found in Ref. 6. Figure 1(c) shows a false-color photoluminescence image of a freestanding tube with 1.2 rotations and a diameter of 7 μm taken at T = 7K. Optical excitation is performed using a frequency-doubled Nd:YVO$_4$ laser operating at 532 nm. The excitation power is 60 μW for all data shown in this paper. As indicated in Fig. 1(b) the laser excitation spot is located in the middle of the tube.

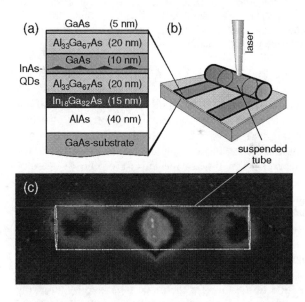

FIGURE 1. (a) MBE-sequence (b) Schematic of a suspended tube rolled up from a U-shaped strained mesa. (c) false-color photoluminescence image of a suspended tube with 1.2 rotations and 7 μm diameter corresponding to (b).

Micro photoluminescence (μPL) investigations with independent location of excitation and collection reveal that the blue spots at the tube ends are due to wave guided light originating from QD emission at the laser excitation spot [5]. Spectra collected in the vicinity of the laser excitation spot exhibit sharp peaks which can be attributed to light circulating around the

CP893, *Physics of Semiconductors, 28th International Conference*
edited by W. Jantsch and F. Schäffler

tube axis resulting in whispering gallery mode-like optical resonances.

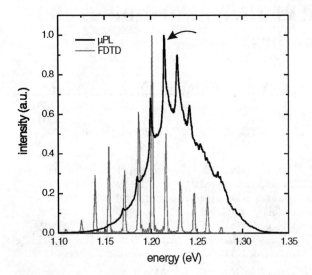

FIGURE 2. µ-photoluminescence from a suspended tube (7 µm diameter, 1.2 rotations) collected in the vicinity of the laser excitation spot (thick black curve) together with the corresponding spectrum calculated with the finite difference time domain method (thin green curve). The arrow points to the mode which is calculated in Figure 3.

Figure 2 shows a typical µPL spectrum (thick black curve) together with a corresponding spectrum calculated based on the finite difference time domain (FDTD, software by Lumerical Solutions Inc.) method (thin green curve). In contrast to theory the mode amplitudes for the measured curves are reduced for lower energies due to the cut-off of the Si-detector used in the experiment. In terms of peak position and quality factor ($Q \sim 500$) we find a good agreement between experiment and theory. A close look at the peak shapes in the experimental data, however, reveals an additional broadening which might be explained by means of the spatial mode distribution in the rolled-up structures. Figure 3 shows the frequency domain cross-section of the tube for the mode indicated by an arrow in Fig. 2. First, the overall thickness of the multilayered tube wall is a crucial factor for the mode leakage into continuum, i.e. the relatively low Q-factor of the investigated structure is due to the small overall wall thickness caused by the small rotation number of only 1.2 (For tube resonators with a smaller diameter of 4.5 µm and 2.5 rotations we found $Q \sim 4000$). Furthermore, there are two different wall-thicknesses in every rolled-up structure. The wall of the investigated tube consists of two layers in the thick fraction of circumference (indicated by *ns* in Fig. 3) and of one layer in the thin fraction of circumference. As illustrated by the inserts in Fig. 3, the thicker double-layered fraction shows a smaller overlap

between mode field and continuum and a smaller mode knot spacing than the thinner single-layered fraction. FDTD-calculations show that already a slight change in the length of *ns* results in a spectral shift of the modes. In the area of the light collection the length fluctuation of the rolled-up mesa, i.e. the length fluctuation of *ns*, is in the order of some microns. This might result in the mode broadening observed in the experiment.

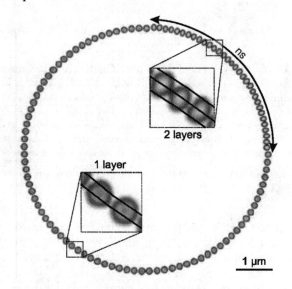

FIGURE 3. Calculated cross-sectional frequency domain image for the mode indicated by an arrow in Fig. 2. *ns* indicates the fraction of circumference with increased tube wall thickness. The inserts illustrate the different mode knot patterns for the two different wall thicknesses.

In conclusion we demonstrated that rolled-up semiconductor layers can be used as waveguides and optical resonators containing quantum emitters. Their mechanical flexibility and the possibility to choose the radial position of the quantum emitters just at the maximum of the mode field makes such structures particularly interesting for novel quantum electrodynamics experiments.

REFERENCES

1. V.Y. Prinz et al., *Physica E (Amsterdam)* **6**, 828 (2000).
2. O.G. Schmidt and K. Eberl, *Nature (London)* **210**, 168 (2001).
3. M. Hosoda et al., *Appl. Phys. Letters* **83**, 1017 (2003).
4. S. Mendach et al., *Appl. Phys. Letters* **88**, 212113 (2006).
5. S. Mendach et al., *Appl. Phys. Letters* **88**, 111120 (2006).
6. T. Kipp et al., *Phyical Review Letters* **96**, 077403 (2006).

Polariton relaxation dynamics in semiconductor microcavities: Non-Markovian effects

F.J.Rodríguez[*], L.Quiroga[*], C.Tejedor[†], M.D.Martín[**] and L. Viña[**]

[*]Departamento de Física, Universidad de los Andes, A.A. 4976, Bogotá D.C., Colombia
[†]Departamento de Física Teórica de la Materia Condensada, Universidad Autónoma de Madrid, Cantoblanco, E-28049, Madrid, Spain
[**]Departamento de Física de Materiales C-IV, Universidad Autónoma de Madrid, Cantoblanco, E-28049, Madrid, Spain

Abstract. We report results on the theoretical study of the ultrafast relaxation of polaritons in semiconductor microcavities. The photoluminescence decay dynamics is found to be controlled by the initial density of excitons. In the high density regime, the parametric conversion of excitons dominates the relaxation with memory (Non-Markov) effects producing a non-monotonous decay of the emission signal. This behavior agrees with recent experimental observations.

Keywords: Polariton dynamics
PACS: 71.36.+c, 78.47.+p, 78.67.-n, 42.50.Md

Semiconductor microcavities have attracted a great deal of attention in recent years due to the possibility of tailoring the matter-radiation interaction in a solid-state environment [1, 2]. Recent results on time-resolved polariton photoluminescence (PL), following a non-resonant pump pulse exciting a quasi-two-dimensional II-VI semiconductor quantum well microcavity, show unusual features challenging conventional theoretical approaches [3, 4]. In particular, it has been reported that a very different emission dynamics is observed when an initial high exciton density is created by a high intensity laser pulse. Unexplained oscillatory/plateaux time behavior in PL decay is clearly present in the high excitation regime [4, 5]. Furthermore, spin effects could manifest themselves in experiments where co- and counter-polarized emissions are analyzed.

Most theoretical models describe the polariton dynamics within the Born-Markov approximation, which is indeed adequate for weak couplings and/or the long-time limit. In the present work we show that oscillations in the time-resolved emission signals that memory (non-Markovian) effects in the polariton evolution from an initially pumped bath of excitons relaxing towards $\vec{k} \sim 0$, the optically active polariton states, are present. The intensity dependent dynamics can be explained by resorting to an effective model where polaritons are coupled to an exciton bath. The coupling strength is determined by the excitation power. Possible spin effects are not included in the present study.

By the parametric down conversion process two excitons are simultaneously scattered: one of them goes to a near $\vec{k} = 0$ polariton state in the lower polariton (LP) branch while the other one (conserving energy and linear momentum) goes to a high $|\vec{k}|$ exciton state, the so-called idler particle. The Hamiltonian can be described as ($\hbar = 1$)[6, 7]

$$H = \sum_{\vec{q}} E(\vec{q})a_{\vec{q}}^{\dagger}a_{\vec{q}} + \sum_{\vec{k}} \omega(\vec{k})b_{\vec{k}}^{\dagger}b_{\vec{k}} + H_{XP} + H_{SI} \qquad (1)$$

where $E(\vec{q})$ describes the LP bare energy while $\omega(\vec{k})$ corresponds to the bare exciton energy (polaritons and excitons are described by boson-like operators a and b, respectively). The polariton-exciton interaction term is given by $H_{XP} = \sum_{\vec{k},\vec{k}',\vec{k}_1,\vec{k}_2} \tilde{V}(\vec{k},\vec{k}',\vec{k}_1,\vec{k}_2)a_{\vec{k}}^{\dagger}b_{\vec{k}'}^{\dagger}b_{\vec{k}_1}b_{\vec{k}_2} + H.C.$ where $\tilde{V}(\vec{k},\vec{k}',\vec{k}_1,\vec{k}_2)$ accounts for the polariton-exciton coupling and $H.C.$ means hermitic conjugate. The self-interaction term associated to the condensed $\vec{k} = 0$ polariton state is given by $H_{SI} = V_0 a_0^{\dagger}a_0^{\dagger}a_0 a_0$.

We consider that excitons optically pumped out of resonance rapidly relax into excited polaritons. At a high intensity pumping the initial density of excited polaritons can be described by classical fields, the so called parametric approximation. This approximation ignores quantum fluctuations in the pump polariton fields. Pump depletion is well accounted for with a pulse shaped classical field as determined by the shape/length of the excitation laser pulse as well as by proper exciton relaxation mechanisms in a quantum well. In H_{XP}, the $b_{\vec{k}_1}b_{\vec{k}_2}$ operator is replaced by the c-number $< b_{\vec{k}_1}b_{\vec{k}_2} > \sim \mathscr{I}_{\vec{k}_1}(t)\delta_{\vec{k}_1,\vec{k}_2}$ with $\mathscr{I}_{\vec{k}}(t)$ the effective pump intensity envelope. Thus, the polariton-exciton interaction term adopts the time-dependent effective form

$$H_{XP}(t) = \sum_{\vec{k},\vec{k}'} V(\vec{k},\vec{k}',t)a_{\vec{k}}^{\dagger}b_{\vec{k}'}^{\dagger} + \sum_{\vec{k},\vec{k}'} V^*(\vec{k},\vec{k}',t)a_{\vec{k}}b_{\vec{k}'} \qquad (2)$$

CP893, *Physics of Semiconductors, 28th International Conference*
edited by W. Jantsch and F. Schäffler
© 2007 American Institute of Physics 978-0-7354-0397-0/07/$23.00

where $V(\vec{k},\vec{k}',t) = \sum_{\vec{k}_1,\vec{k}_2} \tilde{V}(\vec{k},\vec{k}',k_1,k_2)\mathscr{I}_{\vec{k}_1}(t)\delta_{\vec{k}_1,\vec{k}_2}$. Note that in Eq.(2), the Hamiltonian describing the coupling of LP particles ($a_{\vec{k}}$ modes) to a high energy exciton bath ($b_{\vec{k}}$ modes), the coupling strength $V(\vec{k},\vec{k}',t)$ is now dependent on the excitation pulse intensity. This is why a Born-Markov based theoretical approach should fail: (i) even in the weak coupling regime a time-dependent coupling strength yields to a nonexponential decay and (ii) a strongly coupled system-reservoir is achieved beyond a certain excitation power. Furthermore, it is worth noting that the Hamiltonian in Eq.(1), with H_{XP} as given by Eq.(2), corresponds to a nondegenerate parametric amplifier for massive particles, where the parametric gain implies that the LP population, as well as exciton bath population, is amplified at the expenses of pump polaritons depletion. Since we are considering a pulsed situation, no indefinite gain will arise and the validity of the parametric approximation is still guaranteed.

The effective time-dependent polariton-bath coupling is taken as $V(\vec{k},\vec{k}',t) = g(\vec{k},\vec{k}')h(t)$ where the function $h(t)$ describes the time envelope shape of the polariton pump pulse. The Heisenberg equations of motion for $a_{\vec{k}}$ and $b_{\vec{k}}^{\dagger}$ yield finally to

$$
\begin{aligned}
\dot{a}_{\vec{k}}(t) =& -i\left(E(\vec{k}) - i\Gamma_0 + 2V_0 a_0^{\dagger}a_0\delta_{\vec{k},0}\right)a_{\vec{k}} - i\eta_{\vec{k}}(t) \\
& + \int_0^t h(t)h(t-\tau)a_{\vec{k}}(t-\tau)K_{\vec{k}}(\tau)d\tau \quad (3)
\end{aligned}
$$

where the kernel function is $K_{\vec{k}}(\tau) = \sum_{\vec{k}'} | g(\vec{k},\vec{k}') |^2 e^{i\omega(\vec{k}')\tau}$ and the exciton noise term is $\eta_{\vec{k}}(\tau) = \sum_{\vec{k}'} g(\vec{k},\vec{k}')b_{\vec{k}'}(0)e^{i\omega(\vec{k}')\tau}h(\tau)$. A phenomenological damping term Γ_0 has been added in Eq.(3) to account for radiation losses from the microcavity. Since the bare energy dispersion relation for the exciton bath in Eq.(1) is simply $\omega(k) = k^2/2M_X$, where M_X represents the exciton effective mass in the quantum well, a Gaussian form for $g(\vec{k},\vec{k}')$ is adequate [8], $g(\vec{k},\vec{k}') = \frac{\Gamma^{1/2}}{(2\pi\sigma_k^2)^{1/4}}e^{-\frac{(k-\vec{k}')^2}{4\sigma_k^2}}$ where Γ settles the polariton-exciton coupling strength maximum and σ_k its width dispersion.

In the following we focus on the time evolution of the mean number of polaritons in the optically active $\vec{k} = 0$ state, i.e. $< a_0^{\dagger}a_0 > (t)$. We solve numerically Eq.(3). Parameters used correspond to CdTe microcavities. The bottom polariton state corresponds to $E(q=0) = \Omega_0 = 0.1671606ps^{-1}$ and the exciton mass is $M_X = m_e + m_h = (0.11 + 0.35)m_0 = 0.46m_0$. The time evolution of the polariton population in the bottom trap state $\vec{q} = 0$ is depicted in Fig.1. After a high intensity pulse excitation the emission at short times starts growing with a nonlinear slope, as has already been shown experimentally [4, 5]. This behavior is a clear manifestation of non-Markovian

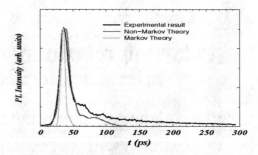

FIGURE 1. Time evolution of the PL: experiment (black line), Non-Markov (red-line)and Markov results (green-line).

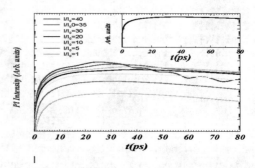

FIGURE 2. Time evolution, on a semi-log scale, of the PL for different pump intensities. The inset shows the pump pulse shape.

effects. For contrast, we also plot the Markov results, i.e. $K(\tau) \sim \delta(\tau)$. Indeed, in the latter case the experimental results cannot be simulated.

In order to show the main differences between the low and high density regimes, we plot in Fig. 2 the results of our model. Clearly, at long times the decays are similar for both high and low intensity pumping, and memory effects are negligible.

In summary, we have demonstrated that observed features in recent polariton PL experiments have their origin in non-Markovian or memory effects, as they are enhanced by a high power excitation. We found that the nonlinear raising and the oscillations/plateaux in the time-resolved polariton PL are well explained by the excitation induced strong coupling between the polariton-exciton systems.

REFERENCES

1. P.G.Savvidis et al., *Semicond.Sci.Technol.* **18**, S311 (2003).
2. J.J.Baumberg et al., *Phys.Stat.Sol.* **(b)242**, 2210 (2005).
3. M.D.Martin et al., *Phys.Rev.Lett.* **89**, 077402 (2002).
4. G.Aichmayr et al., *Semicond.Sci.Technol.* **18**, S368 (2003).
5. L.Viña et al., *Semicond.Sci.Technol.* **19**, S333 (2004).
6. D.Porras et al., *Phys.Rev.* **B67**, 161310 (2003).
7. C.Ciuti et al., *Phys.Rev.* **B62**, 4825 (2000).
8. H.P.Breuer et al., *Phys.Rev.* **A60**, 3188 (1999).

Spin-Dependent Strong- to Weak-Coupling Transition in Semiconductor Microcavities

D. Ballarini[1], A. Amo[1], M.D. Martin[1], L. Viña[1], D. Sanvitto[2], M.S. Skolnick[2] and J.S. Roberts[3]

[1]SEMICUAM, Dept. Física de Materiales, Universidad Autónoma de Madrid, E-28049 Madrid, Spain
[2]Dept. of Physics, University of Sheffield, S3 7RH, Sheffield, U.K.
[3]Dept. of Electronic & Electrical Engineering, University of Sheffield, S1 3JD, Sheffield, U.K.

Abstract. We present a study of the transition from the strong- to the weak-coupling regime in InGaAs microcavities by means of time-resolved photoluminescence. We have found that under circularly-polarized excitation, with increasing excitation power, the co-polarized polaritons undergo a transition to bare modes (exciton + photons) at a power significantly lower than that of the cross-polarized polaritons. This demonstrates that the appearance of the weak coupling depends mainly on the excitonic population of a given spin orientation.

Keywords: microcavities, polaritons, ultrafast spectroscopy, spin, polarization.
PACS: 78.55.Cr, 78.47.+p, 71.36.+c, 72.25.Rb

Semiconductor microcavities are a very suitable systems to investigate the light-matter interaction in confined structures. In a microcavity, a quantum well (QW) excitonic state can be brought into resonance with a discrete Fabry-Perot mode (FP) of the cavity ($\delta = E_{FP} - E_{QW} = 0$). If their interaction energy is greater than any homogeneous or inhomogeneous broadening of the bare photon or exciton mode, the system is in the strong-coupling regime (SC). In the SC regime, the eigenstates of the system are mixed states of light and matter, called polaritons, and the energy eigenvalues are modified with respect to those of the uncoupled particles. The normal-mode splitting breaks the degeneracy of photons and excitons into lower and upper polariton branches (LPB, UPB). The Rabi splitting Ω is a function of the exciton oscillator strength f_{osc}:[1]

$$\Omega \propto \sqrt{(f_{osc} - f_{th})}, \qquad (1)$$

where f_{th} is a threshold oscillator strength.

Saturation of the strong-coupling regime can be achieved, for example, by increasing the density of the electron-hole pairs, leading to a continuous transition to the weak-coupling regime (WC), where the light-matter interaction is well described by a perturbative approach: the energies of the coupled modes are very similar to those of the bare modes and Ω vanishes.

The SC regime has attracted great interest because of its importance from a fundamental point of view as well as for possible applications, in particular when the system is excited by non-resonant optical pumping.

To get a further understanding of the role of the spin in the polariton relaxation process and in the bleaching of the oscillator strength, we have analyzed the polarization properties of InGaAs microcavities under non-resonant optical excitation and have studied the transition from the strong- to the weak-coupling regime as a function of the excitation power.

The studied sample is a $3/2\ \lambda$ GaAs microcavity with two stacks of three $In_{0.06}Ga_{0.94}As$ QWs, characterized by a Rabi splitting of 6 meV. Dielectric Bragg Reflectors confine the electromagnetic field in one dimension and are composed by 17 (top) and 20 (bottom) layers of $Al_{0.1}Ga_{0.9}As$ and AlAs. The photoluminescence (PL) is non-resonantly excited by circularly-polarized, 2 ps-long, pulses and analyzed into its co- (σ^+) and cross- (σ^-) polarized components. Excitation energy is 1.635 eV, just above the cavity stop-band. The PL emission at K~0 is time- and energy-resolved using a spectrograph and a streak camera (energy and time resolution of 0.2 meV and 10 ps, respectively).

Under low excitation power, the system is in the SC regime and at resonance the LPB energy is $\Omega/2$ lower than the energy of the bare cavity modes.

CP893, *Physics of Semiconductors, 28th International Conference*
edited by W. Jantsch and F. Schäffler

Increasing the excitation power, the coupling of the QW excitons and cavity photons reduces, due to many-body effects, and the LPB emission is blue shifted towards the bare cavity mode energy.

Time-resolved PL shows that not-shifted and blue-shifted polaritons coexist (see Fig. 1: the streak at ~1.45 eV together with the comma-shaped image).

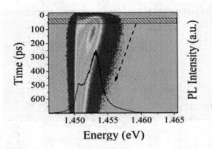

FIGURE 1. Streak-camera image of LPB-PL depicting its spectral and temporal behavior. Black line: PL-intensity spectrum at short time (selected shaded region in the figure) showing the coexistence of low- and high-energy components of the LPB.

The high-energy component, dominating the spectrum at short time, vanishes when a low carrier density is recovered. We have also studied the spatial distribution of the PL scanning the emission area (0.03 mm^2) with a resolution of 80 μm^2. We find that the two components are present on the whole emission area, ruling out inhomogeneities on the excitation spot as the origin of this coexistence.

An analysis of the polarized-PL spectra shows that σ^+ and σ^- polaritons have different energies at excitation powers near the strong- to weak-coupling transition, as shown in Fig. 2. With a direct calibration of our experimental setup it is possible to obtain from the intensity of the PL the number of polaritons, N_p, with momentum K~0. Selecting K~0 states by a pin-hole, a finite number, N_k, of K-states contribute to the PL. The occupation factor, f_p, is $f_p = N_p/N_k$ (see Ref. 2). As shown in Fig. 3, the dependence of the occupation factors with excitation power is very different for σ^+ and σ^- polaritons.

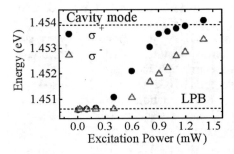

FIGURE 2. LPB-peak energies as a function of the excitation power for the two polarizations σ^+ ($\bullet$) and σ^- ($\triangle$).

Both $f_p^{\sigma+}$ and $f_p^{\sigma-}$ are smaller than one while the strong coupling dominates, hindering the possibility of stimulated polariton-polariton scattering[3, 4]. At an excitation power of ~1 mW, $f_p^{\sigma+}$ approaches unity, but the σ^+ polaritons are in the WC regime, as borne out by the values of their energies that approach the bare-cavity mode energy (see Fig. 2). However, at this excitation power, the σ^- polaritons are still in the SC regime, with $f_p^{\sigma-}$~0.2 and energies well below the bare-mode energy. The WC regime for σ^- polaritons is reached at P~1.4 mW. Cavity laser emission in the WC regime is obtained, for a given polarization, when its occupation factor is greater than one (in the WC regime the occupation factor is evaluated considering a polariton photon fraction of 100%).

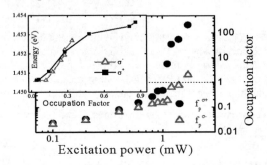

FIGURE 3. Occupation factor as a function of excitation power for the two polarizations σ^+ ($\bullet$) and σ^- ($\triangle$). Inset: LPB energies as a function of f_p.

In the inset of Fig. 3, a plot of the σ^+ and σ^- LPB-peak energies versus the respective occupation factors (while the system is in the SC regime) reveals that the energy shifts depend only on the number of polaritons with a given spin orientation. Therefore the loss of SC for a polariton population of a given spin is determined by the occupation factor of that population and not strongly influenced by the presence of opposite spin polaritons. Our findings suggest that not only screening but also exchange interactions and phase-space filling play a very important role on the strong- to weak-coupling regime transition.

The work was partially supported by the Spanish MEC (MAT2005-01388 and NAN2004-09109-C04-04), the CAM (S-0505/ESP-0200) and the "Marie-Curie" MRTN-CT-2003-503677.

REFERENCES

1. R. Houdré, J. L. Gibernon, P. Pellandini, et al., *Phys. Rev.* B **52**, 7810 (1995).
2. P. Senellart, J. Bloch, B. Sermage, et al., *Phys. Rev.* B **62**, R16263–R16266 (2000).
3. R. Butté, G. Delalleau, A. I. Tartakovskii, et al., *Phys. Rev.* B **65**, 205310 (2002).
4. A. I. Tartakovskii, D. N. Krizhanovskii, and V. D. Kulakovskii, *Phys. Rev.* B **62**, R13298–R13301 (2000).

Is the definition of left-handed materials ($\varepsilon < 0, \mu < 0$) valid ?

Kikuo CHO

Toyota Physical and Chemical Research Institute, Nagakute, Aichi 480-1192, JAPAN

Abstract.

   Model-independent derivation of macroscopic Maxwell equations is made from a general microscopic Lagangian of coupled light-matter system. For both microscopic and macroscopic responses, we need only the susceptibility (χ_{cd}) connecting transverse (T-) current density and T-vector potential, in contrast to the traditional descrition via electric and magnetic susceptibilities, or ε and μ, as independent parameters. The dispersion equation of a plane wave in a uniform macroscopic medium is not $(ck/\omega)^2 = \varepsilon\mu$, but $(ck/\omega)^2 = 1 + (4\pi c/\omega^2)\chi_{cd}$, which may seriously affects the arguments of left-handed materials (LHM). An alternative definition of LHM "materials with negative group velocity" is recommended as a consequence of this theory.

Keywords: macroscopic Maxwell equations, dielectric constant, magnetic permeability, microscopic derivation, left handed materials
PACS: 41.20.Jb, 42.70.Qs, 78.20.Ci

INTRODUCTION

Maxwell equations (M-eqs.) are one of the most fundamental frameworks of physics, dealing with the electromagnetic field produced by the current density of matter. At a microscopic level, we can find a general Lagrangian providing M-eqs. together with the equation of motion of each charged particle under Lorentz force, which gives quite a sound basis for mechanics and electromagnetism, in both non-relativistic and relativistic regimes, and also for classical and quantum mechanical descriptions.

However, the M-eqs. in macroscopic form do not seem well established in spite of the long history of its practical use. This may be due to the general attitude to overlook the close relationship of M-eqs. with the mechanics of matter system. In a microscopic level, the mutual dependence between EM field and matter motion is obvious, but in a macroscopic level, M-eqs. tend to be regarded as the equations for EM field alone, with the understanding that the information of matter is included in ε and μ. This attitude seems to allow certain sloppy ways to ascribe their values, because they are "parameters" anyhow.

In many textbooks, there are "derivations" of the macroscopic M-eqs. from the microscopic ones by using classical or quantum mechanical arguments to derive some typical expressions of ε and/or μ. But the argument is not general enough, and the consideration of the mutual dependence between EM field and matter seems to be lacking, in the sense that there has never been an argument to show (1) the microscopically correct M-eqs. in model-independent way, and then (2) the approximation to make them macroscopic. Because of the lack of such a logic, we do not know when this approximation is valid, and how the susceptibilities should be calculated in a consistent way.

The purpose of this note is to give an outline of the full argument [1] to derive the macroscopic M-eqs. from the microscopic ones, and discuss the consequence in comparison with the traditional theory. For this purpose, we start from the general Lagrangian of coupled EM field and matter (charged particles)

$$L = \sum_{\ell} [\frac{1}{2}m_{\ell}v_{\ell}^2 - e_{\ell}\phi(\vec{r}_{\ell}) + \frac{e_{\ell}}{c}\vec{v}_{\ell}\cdot\vec{A}(\vec{r}_{\ell})] \quad (1)$$

$$+ \int d\vec{r}\,\frac{1}{8\pi}(\vec{E}^2 - \vec{B}^2) .$$

This Lagrangian gives the microscopic M-eqs. (in a relativisically invariant form) and the eq. of motion of each particle driven by Lorentz force, and the Hamiltonian is the sum of the matter part (kinetic energy in EM field plus Coulomb interaction among particles) and that of vacuum EM field. If relativistic correction is necessary for matter, we may add mass velocity term, spin-orbit interaction, spin Zeeman term etc. The light-matter interaction can be written as

$$H_{int} = -\frac{1}{c}\int d\vec{r}\,\vec{J}(\vec{r})\cdot\vec{A}(\vec{r}) \quad (2)$$

where $\vec{J}$ is the current density operator, containing the contributions of both electric and magnetic polarizations. When the relativistic correction is included, $\vec{J}$ contains the effect of spin magnetization, too.

Using this interaction term as perturbation, we obtain the general expression of linear susceptibility

$$\chi_{cd}(\vec{r},\vec{r}') = \frac{1}{c}\sum_{v}\left[\frac{\vec{J}_{0v}(\vec{r})\vec{J}_{v0}(\vec{r}')}{E_{v0}-\hbar\omega-i0^+} + \frac{\vec{J}_{0v}(\vec{r}')\vec{J}_{v0}(\vec{r})}{E_{v0}+\hbar\omega+i0^+}\right]$$

$$(3)$$

CP893, *Physics of Semiconductors, 28th International Conference*
edited by W. Jantsch and F. Schäffler

which describes the induced current density as $\tilde{J}(\vec{r}, \omega) = \int d\vec{r}' \chi_{cd}(\vec{r}, \vec{r}') \cdot \vec{A}(\vec{r}', \omega)$. Solving this equation and the microscopic M-eqs. (for $\vec{A}$) simultaneously, we have a complete solution for linear response [2].

To derive the macroscopic M-eqs., we apply long wavelength approximation (LWA) to $\tilde{J}(\vec{r}, \omega)$, which allows us to bring $\vec{A}$ outside the integral in the lowest order of Taylor expansion, and the remaining matrix element $\vec{J}_{\mu\nu}(\vec{r})$ may, in the spirit of LWA, be replaced by its space average $N \int d\vec{r} \, \vec{J}_{\mu\nu}(\vec{r})(= N < \vec{J}_{\mu\nu} >)$ where N is the density of the relevant quantum states $|\mu\nu >$ in the macroscopic point $\vec{r}$. This procedure straightforwardly gives the well known form of macroscopic susceptibility

$$\bar{\chi}_{cd}(\omega) = \frac{N}{c} \sum_{\nu} \left[\frac{<\vec{I}_{0\nu}><\vec{I}_{\nu 0}>}{E_{\nu 0} - \hbar\omega - i0^+} + \frac{<\vec{I}_{0\nu}><\vec{I}_{\nu 0}>}{E_{\nu 0} + \hbar\omega + i0^+} \right]$$

(4)

together with the relationship $\tilde{J}(\vec{r}, \omega) = \bar{\chi}_{cd}(\omega) \cdot \vec{A}(\vec{r}, \omega)$ at a macroscopic point $\vec{r}$. This serves as a constitutive equation to solve the macroscopic M-eqs. in $\vec{A}$ representation. (Similar argument for the higher order terms leads to the response to the space derivatives of A, which gives wave number dependent terms in the numerator of $\bar{\chi}_{cd}$.) The susceptibility $\bar{\chi}_{cd}$ is just enough to get the complete information about linear response in LWA.

Now there arises a problem whether this scheme mentioned above is equivalent to the traditional M-eqs. in terms of $(\vec{E}, \vec{D}, \vec{B}, \vec{H})$, supplemented by $\vec{D} = \varepsilon\vec{E}$ and $\vec{B} = \mu\vec{H}$. Here ε and μ are regarded as material parameters, which might be calculated by using $-\vec{P} \cdot \vec{E}$ and $-\vec{M} \cdot \vec{H}$ (integrated over space) as interaction Hamiltonian. This perturbation calculation would lead to similar expressions as (4) with the numerators replaced by those of the matrix elements of $\vec{P}$ and $\vec{M}$.

For simple cases, the excited states $\{|\nu >\}$ contributing to electric and magnetic polarizations are different, but, if the symmetry of matter system is low, same excited states can contribute to both polarizations. This means that in the dispersion equation of a plane wave $(ck/\omega)^2 = \varepsilon\mu$, there can occur second order poles, which never occurs in the corresponding equation of the present scheme $(ck/\omega)^2 = 1 + (4\pi c/\omega^2)\bar{\chi}_{cd}$. (The effect arising from the space derivatives of $\vec{A}$ does not change the single pole character of $\bar{\chi}_{cd}(\omega)$.) This clearly shows the inequivalence of the two schemes. In view of the fact that optical response is completely fixed from the selfconsisitent set of $\vec{J}$ and $\vec{A}$, we need only one susceptibility $(\bar{\chi}_{cd}(\omega))$ rather than two (ε and μ).

Using the operator form of $\vec{P}$ and $\vec{M}$ [3] together with the first principles Lagrangian (1), we can calculate their expectation values and the susceptibilities. But the results turns out to be equivalent to the present scheme. The details will be published in the full paper [1].

Agranovich et al. [4] discussed a similar problem, proposing an alternative $(\vec{E}, \vec{D}, \vec{B})$ scheme to discuss the nonlinear processes in left handed materials (LHM). An essential difference from our viewpoint is that they consider the $(\vec{E}, \vec{D}, \vec{B})$ scheme being equivalent to the traditional one by showing the one-to-one correspondence, while we are proposing an inequivalent scheme.

Since the present scheme requires to discuss the plane wave dispersion in a macroscopic medium via $(ck/\omega)^2 = 1 + (4\pi c/\omega^2)\bar{\chi}_{cd}$, we need to reconstruct the argument for the quest of LHM. This is not a serious problem, if we consider that the odd behavior of LHM is based on the different sign of the phase and group velocity of propagating wave in such a medium. We just need to look for materials having dispersion curves with negative group velocity. If time reversal symmetry exists, there is always a corresponding branch with positive group velocity for negative wave number. The boundary condition for light propagation in such a system should guarantee the dissipation of field energy as the light proceeds due to the finite or infinitesimally small damping effect. (In a slab geometry, for example, transmittance of a light should decrease as the slab thickness increases.) This was discussed for exciton polaritons [5], and a general conclusion is that the waves in the medium to be connected with the incident one should be those with positive group velocity or those of analytically continued parts. These waves usually have negative phase velocity and positive group velocity, which is a typical situation in LHM [6].

From this point of view, we already have many examples in (i) the exciton-polaritons in CuI, CuBr, and CdTe, and (ii) photonic crystals. In the former, the observation of LHM character may be difficult due to a significant damping, which does not exist in the latter (ii).

ACKNOWLEDGMENTS

This work was supported in part by by the Grant-in-aid for scientific research (No.18510092) of the Ministry of Education, Culture, Sports, Science and Technology of Japan.

REFERENCES

1. K. Cho, to be published
2. K. Cho, *Optical Response of Nanostructures: Microscopic Nonlocal Theory*, Springer Verlag, Heidelberg, 2003
3. C. Cohen-Tannoudji et al. *Photons and Atoms*, Wiley Interscience, New York 1989, Sec. IV.C
4. V. M. Agranovich et al., Phys. Rev. B*69* (2004) 165112
5. S. Suga et al., Phys. Rev. B*22* (1980) 4931
6. V. G. Veselago, Soviet Phys. Uspekh *10* (1968) 509

A New Criterion for Focusing in Photonic Crystals

Ronald Meisels*, Friedemar Kuchar* and Rados Gajic†

*Institute of Physics, University of Leoben, 8700 Leoben, Austria
†Institute of Physics, Belgrade, Serbia

Abstract. A new criterion for flat-lens focusing by photonic crystals (PhC) is presented, viz. the condition of constant ratio of tangents of incident and refracted angle when varying the incident angle. Focusing is improved by increasing the dielectric constant of the PhC material.

Keywords: Photonic crystals, flat lens, focusing
PACS: 42.70.Qs, 42.79.Bh, 41.20.Jb

INTRODUCTION

The perfect lens is a particularly interesting optical element for basic studies and many applications. Beside meta-materials [1], photonic crystals (PhC) [2] have the potential of realizing the perfect lens. It has to be operated in the regime of negative refraction. Possible PhC materials for the near-infrared and visible are III-V and II-VI semiconductors. Commonly, it is assumed that $n_{eff} = -1$ is the condition for the focussing of all the beams with different incident angles Θ_i (n_{eff} ... effective index of refraction). In this contribution we propose a novel and more general criterion. It considers the ratio of the tangents of the incident and refracted beams which in the ideal case has to be the same for all incident angles Θ_i. This includes the condition "all-angle $n_{eff} = -1$".

THE NEW CRITERION

To fulfill the conventional criterion "all-angle $n_{eff} = -1$" the equi-frequency contours (EFC) of the photonic band structure has to be a circle as in air. While the EFCs of many PhCs become more circular as they approach a point of high symmetry in the Brillouin zone, the radius of the EFC is generally different from that in air. This corresponds to a constant n_{eff} but unequal to -1. In this case perfect focusing does not take place.

The new focusing criterion is developed on the basis of the EFCs. In contrast to the "all-angle $n_{eff} = -1$" criterion, it also works for different sizes of the EFCs in the air and the PhC and for deviations from circular shape. We consider the ratio of the tangents of the angles of the incident and refracted beams, ($R_{tan} = \tan(\Theta_i)/\tan(\Theta_r)$). If the ratio is the same for all incident angles, or at least for all the beams that can propagate in the PhC, a focusing by a flat lens can be achieved. It involves the directions of the group velocities and not of the phase veloc-

ities as in Snell's law (for isotropic media). Under this condition all the beams emanating from the source at a distance g from the first surface will focus within the crystal at a distance $b = gR_{tan}$. They will be refracted by the second surface of the slab and form an image of the source at a distance $b' = d/R_{tan} - g$. Using the ratio of the tangents implies an EFC shaped as an ellipse with the semi-major axis equal to the radius of the air-EFC. This will not generally be the case. However, the EFCs can closely fit the ellipse on an arc corresponding to a limited range of incident angles.

RESULTS

The R_{tan} criterion is tested on the two-dimensional (2D) square-lattice PhC with rods in air (the ratio rod radius r to lattice period a is $r/a = 0.329$). Negative refraction occurs in the upper part of the first TM band (electric field vector parallel to the rods). To find the frequencies where focusing can be achieved, we analyse R_{tan} vs. f curves for varying Θ_i. These curves should cross or be close to each other at an optimal f_{opt}. For the 2D square lattice this is fulfilled for a limited range of Θ_i only (Fig.1). It increases with increasing dielectric constant ε of the rods, being very small for ε about 10, 0° - 15° for $\varepsilon = 13$ and 0° - 60° for $\varepsilon = 90$. The optimal dimensionless frequencies a/λ (*i.e.*, f in units of c/a) lie in the range above 0.18 for $\varepsilon = 16$ and around 0.080 for $\varepsilon = 90$. The latter value is a realistic one for microwave frequencies and ultra-high dielectric constant material only.

The focusing by a flat lens is tested by using FDTD calculations. Focusing improves by increasing the dielectric constant of the rod material. Fig.2 shows the wave pattern for a wave emitted from a point source (lateral extension $\lambda/10$) at $f = 12.90$ GHz and for $a = 1.86$ mm). This is the optimal frequency for fulfilling the

CP893, *Physics of Semiconductors, 28th International Conference*
edited by W. Jantsch and F. Schäffler
© 2007 American Institute of Physics 978-0-7354-0397-0/07/$23.00

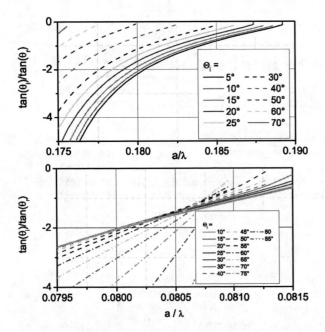

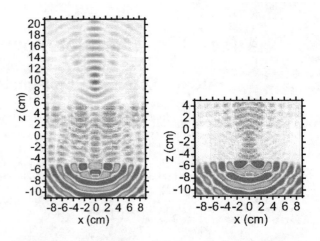

FIGURE 1. Ratio R_{tan} of incident angle Θ_i to refracted angle Θ_r vs. dimensionless frequency a/λ for dielectric constant $\varepsilon = 16$ (upper diagram) and $\varepsilon = 90$ (lower diagram) in the range of negative refraction. The beams are TM polarised. The surface of the PhC slab is parallel to ΓM.

FIGURE 2. Wave pattern (E_y) for a small ($= \lambda/10$) source and propagation (TM polarization) through a PhC slab (surface parallel to ΓM, 79 rows of alternatingly 91 and 90 rods). $\varepsilon = 90$. $\lambda \approx 23$ mm. $f = 12.90$ GHz ($a/\lambda = 0.800$). The position of the source is indicated by a green rectangle (not to scale, color online) at $z = -7$ cm. Right diagram: No reflections at upper surface of PhC.

$R_{tan} = const$ criterion. For obtaining a steady wave pattern a long computation time is necessary. This leads to several internal reflections in the PhC and disturbs the wave pattern in the interior. In order to make the internal focus observable, we performed calculations where reflections by the second surface of the PhC are inhibited by placing an absorptive layer there. The internal foci are clearly visible now (lower figure). Regarding the external focusing, the maximum of the electric field (E_y) is at a distance of 43 mm ($\approx 2\lambda$) from the second surface of the PhC. There the full width at half maximum of the intensity is 0.6λ.

CONCLUSIONS

We define a new criterion for flat-lens focusing by introducing the ratio R_{tan} of the tangents of the incident and refracted angles which is required to be constant when varying the incident angle. The effect of increasing the dielectric contrast from about 10 (representative for semiconductors in the visible to microwave ranges) to 90 (lead salts and ultra-high-dielectric constant ceramics in the microwave range) is to reduce the deviations of R_{tan} from a constant value. Consequently the focusing is significantly improved due to this increase and FDTD simulations show spot sizes below one wavelength at distances several wavelengths behind the PhC.

ACKNOWLEDGMENTS

The authors thank Kurt Hingerl from the Christian Doppler Laboratory for Surface Optical Properties, Univerity of Linz for valuable scientific discussions and Johann Messner from the Linz supercomputer department for technical support. This work is supported by MNA, Micro@Nanofabrication Austria.

REFERENCES

1. J. B. Pendry, *Phys. Rev. Letters* **85**, 3966 (2000).
2. K. Guven, K. Aydin, K. B. Alici, C. M. Soukoulis, and E. Ozbay, *Phys. Rev. B* **70**, 205125 (2004).
3. R. Meisels, R. Gajic, F. Kuchar, and K. Hingerl, *Optics Express (accepted)*.

Stability of Photonic Band Gap in the Presence of Disorder

M.A. Kaliteevski, D.M. Beggs, S. Brand, R.A. Abram,

Department of Physics, Durham University, Durham, DH1 3LE, UK

Abstract. The photonic eigenmodes near a band gap of a type of one-dimensional disordered photonic crystal have been investigated statistically. For the system considered, it is found that the tail of the density of states entering the band gap is characterized by a certain penetration depth, which is proportional to the disorder parameter. A quantitative relation between the relative penetration depth, the relative width of the photonic band gap and the disorder has been found. It is apparent that there is a certain level of disorder below which the probability of the appearance of photonic eigenstates at the centre of the photonic band gap essentially vanishes.

Keywords: Photonic band gap, photonic crystals, disorder.
PACS: 42.70.Qs, 79.60.Ht

INTRODUCTION

Interest in the properties of disordered photonic crystals has arisen for various reasons, including the necessity to produce photonic crystals for technical applications, whose photonic band gap (PBG) will not be significantly degraded (filled with photonic states) due to disorder, and also the possibility of light localization in such structures. The aim of the present work is further investigation of the spectrum of optical eigenmodes in a one-dimensional disordered photonic crystal in the frequency region corresponding to the PBG, and the establishment of a relationship between the transmission properties and the associated modifications to the eigenmode spectrum.

RESULTS AND DISCUSSION

Figure 1 show the eigenfrequencies and lifetimes of the disordered 1D photonic crystal characterized by different level of disorder which we describe by disorder parameter defined as relative fluctuation of the optical length of the period of the structure. When disorder is below certain threshold level of disorder δ_{th} the states does not penetrate into PBG. We have found that threshold disorder to the relative width of PBG by the formula (see [1, 2] for the details)

$$\delta_{th} \approx \sqrt{(\Delta\omega / \omega_0)/3} \qquad (1)$$

When disorder parameter is above the threshold value states fill the PBG.

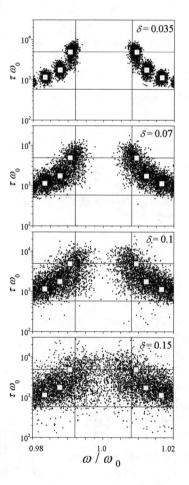

FIGURE 1. Open squares denote the frequencies $\mathrm{Re}(\omega_i)$ and lifetimes $\tau = 1/\mathrm{Im}(\omega_i)$ for an ideal structure ($\delta = 0$). The dots show frequencies and lifetimes for eigenmodes for 10^3 disordered structures with δ =0.035; 0.07; 0.1; and 0.15.

CP893, *Physics of Semiconductors, 28th International Conference*
edited by W. Jantsch and F. Schäffler
© 2007 American Institute of Physics 978-0-7354-0397-0/07/$23.00

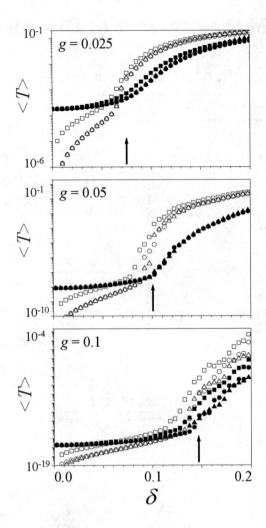

Figure 2. Transmission coefficient averaged over 10^6 structures (solid symbols) and its standard deviation (open symbols) as function of disorder parameter δ for the photonic crystals, $n_0 = 2.0$ and different modulation of the refractive index: $g = 0.025; 0.05;$ and 0.1. Circles and triangles corresponds to the "refractive index" and "thickness" disorder with top-hat distribution of D_i, squares corresponds to "Gaussian" distribution. Vertical arrows indicate threshold level of disorder obtained by formula $\delta_{th} \approx \sqrt{(\Delta\omega/\omega_0)/3}$.

An existence of the threshold value of disorder is illustrated in the figure 2, where the dependencies of the transmission coefficient $< T >$ and its standard deviation for the structures, characterized by different refractive index modulation g (and, consequently, by the different relative gap width $\Delta\omega/\omega_0$) on disorder parameter is shown for three different models of disorder for the centre of the band gap.

For all the cases considered the dependences are characterized by a threshold; when $\delta < \delta_{th}$, $< T >$ grows slowly with increasing δ, and the attenuation length virtually does not change. When δ reaches δ_{th}, a threshold occurs in the dependence of $< T >$ on δ, after which $< T >$ grows much faster with increasing δ. Threshold in the dependence $< T >$ on δ is accompanied by crossing of the dependencies of the $< T >$ and its standard deviation on δ: below threshold $< T >$ is larger than its deviation, above threshold deviation exceeds mean value of $< T >$.

CONCLUSIONS

For the one-dimensional photonic crystals of finite size considered, the states closest to the band gap have frequencies and lifetimes which are defined by the periodic dielectric structure and the length of the structure. The introduction of a small level of disorder results in small perturbations of the frequencies and lifetimes of those states which depend on the particular configuration of the disorder. As the disorder is increased, the fluctuations of the frequencies in an ensemble of systems increases and it is no longer possible to associate a particular state with a counterpart in the crystalline system.

The tail of the density of states in the band gap is characterized by a certain penetration depth. As a result, there is a threshold level of disorder in the one-dimensional photonic crystals considered, below which the probability of the appearance of photonic eigenstates at the centre of photonic band gap essentially vanishes. The relation between the relative penetration depth, relative gap width and the parameter defining the level of disorder has been found.

ACKNOWLEDGMENTS

Research was supported by EPSRC grant.

REFERENCES

1. Kaliteevski et al., *Phys. Rev. B* **73** 033106 (2006)
2. Kaliteevski et al., *Phys. Rev. E* **73** 056616 (2006)

Positional Disorder in the Regime of Negative Refraction in Photonic Crystals

Ronald Meisels*, Friedemar Kuchar* and Rados Gajic†

*Institute of Physics, University of Leoben, 8700 Leoben, Austria
†Institute of Physics, Belgrade, Serbia

Abstract. The effect of positional disorder on the density-of-states and the wave propagation in a two-dimensional square-lattice photonic crystal is calculated. Directed beams and negative refraction persist up to only few percent of disorder. At 5% disorder and above diffusive propagation dominates.

Keywords: Photonic crystals, flat lens, focusing
PACS: 42.70.Qs, 41.20.Jb

INTRODUCTION

Photonic crystal (PhC) structures are used as the basis for novel devices in semiconductor optoelectronics and integrated optics. The quality of these devices is influenced by the presence of disorder, which is unavoidable to some degree, regardless of the technique of fabrication. Particularly when the smallest dimensions are in the sub-micrometer regime [1,2], the fabrication related disorder can play a crucial role. Previous work studied the effect of disorder on transmission through PhC [3] and on the quality of focusing [4] by flat lenses. Since the lensing effect is based on the negative refraction (NR) of beams emanating from a point source, here we concentrate on the effect of disorder on the NR by studying the propagation of beams.

Various kinds of disorder can be present, e.g. positional or radial disorder of the elements of the PhC, i.e. deviations from a perfectly periodic PhC. In Ref. 5 positional and radial disorder was found to be of similar strength for holes in membranes designed for the infrared range. In arrays of dielectric rods used as scale models in the microwave range[2], positional disorder dominates as the radii of the rods are tightly controlled by the manufacturer. As part of a investigation into the effects of disorder in this contribution we address the problem of positional disorder in particular.

Generally, disorder destroys the translational symmetry of a crystal. Therefore, the eigenstates of the system are no longer Bloch waves $u_{nk}(\mathbf{r}) \exp(i\mathbf{kr})$ and therefore $\mathbf{k}$ is no longer a meaningful quantity. However, the frequency f of these states is well defined and it is possible to define a density-of-states $D(f)$. One of the purposes of this work is to find the degree of disorder which can be tolerated in the fabrication process.

CALCULATIONS

As an approximation for the infinite randomly disordered crystal, a supercell approach can be used (as for point defects). Here a $N \times N$ region of the disordered crystal is taken as the unit cell. Each of the N^2 unit cells of the originally perfect crystal contains a single element (rod or hole) whose position varies randomly by $\delta_{x,y}$. The bandstructure is then calculated for the infinite crystal consisting of the periodic arrangement of this supercell. If the supercell is large enough $D(f)$ will approach that of the infinite random crystal. To determine $D(f)$ the frequency range is divided into intervals ("bins") $[f_i, f_{i+1}], i = 0, 1, 2, \ldots$. Due to the finite number of states calculated, the bins must not be made too small or otherwise $D(f)$ will fluctuate strongly. The number of calculated states can be increased by increasing the supercell and by increasing the number N_k of wave vectors $\mathbf{k}$ for which $f(\mathbf{k})$ is calculated. The first method increases calculation time overproportionally. To avoid artefacts due to the second approach, the wave vectors are not spaced in a grid in the Brillouin zone of the supercell but chosen randomly (evenly distributed). As a compromise $N = 10$ and $N_k = 150$ are chosen.

The effect of the disorder on the wave propagation is calculated by using the FDTD method.

RESULTS

The calculations are performed for a two-dimensional (2D) square-lattice PhC with rods in air. Values of the dielectric constant ε of the rod material are chosen between 12 and 16, being representative values for III-V and group IV semiconductors. The effect of weak disorder ($\delta/a < 5\%$) on the $D(f)$ for TM polarization (electric field parallel to the rods) is mainly a narrowing of the

CP893, *Physics of Semiconductors, 28th International Conference*
edited by W. Jantsch and F. Schäffler
© 2007 American Institute of Physics 978-0-7354-0397-0/07/$23.00

gaps. For higher degree of disorder ($\approx$ 5 -10%) additionally sharp DOS peaks appear in the gaps (Fig. 1). In the first gap a peak is located near the second band edge. In the second gap several peaks appear. The modes corresponding to these peaks are localized since their electromagnetic fields are restricted to the area between adjacent rods. They are extremely attenuated over distances of the super cell extension and the relative variation of the frequency of a gap state with wave vector **k** of the super cell is typically only of the order of 10^{-5}.

Regarding the wave propagation in a PhC slab, we consider frequencies of the first TM band and of the second TE band (Fig. 2) of the unperturbed crystal, where NR occurs in the upper parts of the bands. Incidence is on the (11) and (10) surface, resp. (ΓM and ΓX surface, resp. in reciprocal space). At zero disorder a directed beam propagates through the crystal which shows NR[2]. With increasing disorder in the first TM band the directed beam with NR survives up to $\delta/a \approx 5\%$, however, this is accompanied by an increasing amount of scattered waves. Diffusive propagation dominates for $\delta/a \approx 10\%$.

In the second band (TE polarization) additionally to NR, left-handed (LH) behaviour occurs in the undisturbed PhC (for incidence on the (10) surface)[2]. With disorder, NR and LH survive up to $\delta/a \approx 3\%$ with diffusive propagation also present. Diffusive propagation dominates already at $\delta/a \approx 5\%$. A surprising result for $\delta/a \approx 1 - 2\%$ is that the wave pattern contains intensity indicative of a positively refracted wave (see Fig. 2).

CONCLUSIONS

For positional disorder of few percent the density-of-states is only weakly affected (band tails) and directed beams and negative refraction in the PhC persist. Disorder of 5% and above, depending on the band considered, strongly influences the density-of-states, creates localized states in the gap, and deteriorates the propagation of directed beams. Our results presented here, put severe constraints on the fault tolerances of the fabrication process of PhC based devices.

ACKNOWLEDGMENTS

The authors thank Kurt Hingerl from the Christian Doppler Laboratory for Surface Optical Properties, Univerity of Linz for valuable scientific discussions and Johann Messner from the Linz supercomputer department for technical support. This work is supported by MNA, Micro@Nanofabrication Austria.

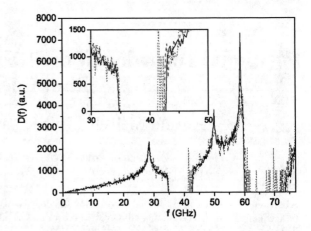

FIGURE 1. Density-of-states of the first two bands and gaps of the 2D square-lattice PhC for different degrees of disorder: $\delta/a = 0\%$ (solid black), 5% (dashed blue), 10% (short dashed red) (color online). $\varepsilon = 13$.

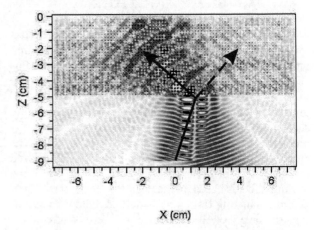

FIGURE 2. Wave pattern for propagation in the second TE band. $\delta/a = 1\%$. Incidence is on the ΓX surface with an angle of 15°. $f = 58.27$ GHz, $\varepsilon = 13$. In the simulation, the source only produces upward waves. Therefore, below its position at $z = -9$ cm only the reflected waves are seen. The main intensity in the PhC is in the negatively refracted beam. Some intensity is also in diffusively scattered waves with indications of a regular wave pattern for positive refraction (dashed arrow). The arrows are guides to the eye for incident and refracted beams (color online).

REFERENCES

1. J.-M. Lourtioz, *Photonic Crystals*, Springer, 2005.
2. R. Gajic, R. Meisels, F. Kuchar, and K. Hingerl, *Optics Express* **13**, 8596 (2005).
3. D.M. Beggs, M.A. Kaliteevski, R.A. Abram, D. Cassagne and J.P. Albert, *J. Phys.: Condens. Matter* **13**, 8596 (2005).
4. B.C. Gupta and Z. Ye, *J. Appl. Phys.* **94**, 2173 (2003).
5. M. Skorobogatiy, G. Begin and A. Talneau, *Optics Express* **13**, 2487 (2005).

Deep Hole InP Photonic Crystals Infiltrated With Solid Polymers And Liquid Crystals

C.F. Carlström[1,2], R. van der Heijden[1,2], B.K.C. Kjellander[2,3], R.W. van der Heijden[1,2], C.W.M. Bastiaansen[3], D.J. Broer[3], F. Karouta[1], R. Nötzel[1,2], E. van der Drift[4], H.W.M. Salemink[1,2,4]

[1] COBRA Inter-University Research Institute and Center for NanoMaterials, Eindhoven University of Technology, PO Box 513, NL-5600 MB Eindhoven, The Netherlands, c.f.c.carlstrom@tue.nl

[2] Department of Applied Physics, Eindhoven University of Technology, PO Box 513, NL-5600 MB Eindhoven The Netherlands

[3] Department of Chemistry and Chemical Engineering, Eindhoven University of Technology, PO Box 513, NL-5600 MB Eindhoven, The Netherlands

[4] Kavli Institute of Nanoscience, Delft University of Technology, P.O. Box 5053, NL-2600 GB Delft, The Netherlands

Abstract. A procedure to etch deep photonic crystal holes in InGaAsP and subsequently fill them with a low index material such as liquid crystal or a solid polymer has been developed. Successful infiltration was proven by optical transmission measurement and in the case of solid polymer also by cross section inspection.

Keywords: Photonic crystal, InP, inductively coupled plasma, etching, infiltration, lithographic tuning.
PACS: 42.70.Qs, 81.05.Ea, 81.05.Lg, 81.07.Pr, 81.65.Cf

INTRODUCTION

Future InP-based optically integrated circuits for operation at infrared wavelengths can be expected to include devices based on photonic crystals. For most practical applications involving optical switching and cavities, the ability to tune the optical properties is required. An attractive route to accomplish this in photonic crystals is to replace the low-index part (air) with a material that has a tunable refractive index such as liquid crystals (LCs) [1]. Solid infills could be of interest as well, if they consist of nonlinear optical material or if they can be applied selectively for new device applications [2]. In this paper we demonstrate a fabrication procedure to both etch and refill the photonic crystals.

RESULTS AND DISCUSSION

The photonic crystal holes were etched into an InP-InGaAsP waveguide hetero-structure employing inductively coupled plasma (ICP) after which infiltration was carried out. Scanning electron microscopy (SEM) and atomic force microscopy (AFM) was used to analyze the cross-section.

The ICP process is based on Cl_2 (14 sccm) with a small (3 sccm) addition of O_2 for sidewall passivation [3]. A typical cross-section of the etched structure is shown in Fig. 1a. The holes are more than 3 μm deep and almost straight in the upper 2 μm, which includes the quaternary layer (visible as light contrast) where most of the electric field is localized. The aspect ratio is larger than 10, which is required for low out-of-plane optical loss. However, care has to be taken when tuning the O_2/Cl_2 ratio since a too high O_2 concentration (4/14) was found to result in tapered sidewalls in the quaternary layer (Fig. 1b), possibly due to preferential passivation of InGaAsP over InP. The AFM inspection of etched structures not only confirmed the depth and hole shape observed in SEM but also provided an estimate of the narrowing in the hole at high O_2-concentration (See example in Fig. 1c), allowing for fine-tuning of the etch process in terms of hole shape.

CP893, *Physics of Semiconductors, 28th International Conference*
edited by W. Jantsch and F. Schäffler
© 2007 American Institute of Physics 978-0-7354-0397-0/07/$23.00

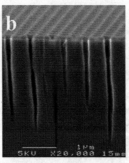
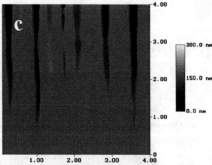

FIGURE 1. (a) Cross section SEM image of photonic crystal structure after ICP etching using 3/14 sccm O_2/Cl_2, (b) same as in (a) but with 4/14 sccm O_2/Cl_2, and (c) cross section AFM image of the surface in (b).

Prior to infiltration, the etched structure went through a surface treatment in HF (10 %) and propanol-2 to promote wetting of the infiltrant, which was either LC or liquid monomer. Contact angle measurements of the infiltrants on plane InP surface showed a reduction from 33° to about 10° by this preparation method. Other acid treatments also improved wetting, pointing towards oxide removal being beneficial for infiltration. The monomer was infiltrated at room temperature either in vacuum (20 mbar) or in ambient atmosphere and subsequently solidified to tri-methylpropane triacrylate (TMP-TA) through thermal polymerization.

Optical end-fire type transmission measurements were carried out on both empty and filled structures, using a tunable laser (1470-1570 nm) in combination with lithographic tuning to cover the whole stop band [4]. Fig. 2 shows the stop band for both empty and filled photonic crystals, infiltrated with either TMP-TA (Fig. 2a) [5] or LC K15 (Fig. 2b) [6]. In both cases the stop-band exhibits narrowing upon filling with a shift of the high frequency air-band to lower frequencies. This is attributed to the localization of the electric field in the hole for the air band and thus being more sensitive to the index change there. Further, the level of transmission after filling is increased, which is

most likely due to reduced refraction at the interface between crystal and dielectric, which reduces the scattering. The observed narrowing of the stop bands after infiltration is in agreement with simulations and indicates a close to complete infiltration. The infiltration of the solid polymer is also clearly visible in SEM (insert fig. 2a) as a plug in the hole. The polymer plug is slightly detached from the sidewall due to polymerization shrinkage, but its surface texture matches that of the hole sidewall, confirming good wetting. Complete filling was observed for several samples in all cases, which highlights the reproducibility and versatility of this method.

ACKNOWLEDGMENTS

The authors would like to thank P.Nouwens, R. van Veldhoven, E.J. Geluk, T. de Vries, M. Sander, and E. Smalbrugge for their contributions to the experimental work and J. van der Tol, A. Kok, S. Oei, J. Haverkort, and A. Silov for helpful discussions. NanoNed, a technology program of the Dutch ministry of Economic Affairs, supports a part of this research.

REFERENCES

1. Busch K., and John S., Phys. Rev. Lett. **83**, 967 (1999)
2. Y. Jiao, S.F. Mingaleev, M. Schillinger, D.A.B. Miller, and K. Busch, Photon. Technol. Lett. **17**, 1875 (2005)
3. C.F. Carlström, R. van der Heijden, F. Karouta, E. van der Drift, R.W. van der Heijden, H.W.M. Salemink, J. Vac. Sci. Technol. B **24**, L6 (2006)
4. D. Labilloy, H. Benisty, C. Weisbuch, C.J.M. Smith, T.F. Krauss, R. Houdré, U. Oesterle, Phys. Rev. B **59**, 1649 (1999).
5. R. van der Heijden, C.F. Carlström, J.A.P. Snijders, R.W. van der Heijden, F. Karouta, R. Nötzel, H.W.M. Salemink, B.K.C. Kjellander, C.W.M. Bastiaansen, D.J. Broer, and E. van der Drift, Appl. Phys. Lett. **88**, 161112 (2006)
6. R. Ferrini, J. Martz, L. Zuppiroli, B. Wild, V. Zabelin, L. A. Dunbar, R. Houdré, M. Mulot, and S. Anand, Optics Lett., **31**, 1238 (2006)

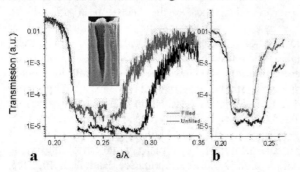

FIGURE 2. Transmission through the photonic crystal as function of normalized frequency (a=lattice constant) before and after infiltration with (a) solid polymer TMP-TA, and (b) LC K15.

Micro-optical Spectroscopy of Stacking Faults in Colloidal Photonic Crystal Films

Evangellos Vekris*, Vladimir Kitaev[‡], J. Stewart Aitchison[†], Doug D. Perovic*, and Geoffrey A. Ozin[§]

* *Department of Materials Science and Engineering, 184 College St.,University of Toronto, Canada, M5S 3E4*
[‡] *Chemistry Department, Wilfrid Laurier University, 75 University Ave. W, Waterloo, Canada, N2L 3C5*
[†] *Department of Electrical and Computer Eng., 10 Kings College Rd., University of Toronto, Canada, M5S 3G4*
[§]*Department of Chemistry, University of Toronto, 80 St. George Street, Toronto, Canada, M5S 3H6*

Abstract. We report on direct measurements of the influence of stacking faults on the optical properties of thin colloidal crystal films. Spatially resolved micro-optical spectroscopy is used to demonstrate that variations in the stacking sequence of close-packed spheres give rise to unique optical spectra, which can be convoluted by large area spatially averaged measurements. FDTD simulations are in excellent agreement with the measured spectra.

Keywords: Photonic crystal, Stacking faults, Colloidal self-assembly, Opal.
PACS: 42.70.Qs 61.72.Nn 81.16.Dn

Self-assembled colloidal crystal films, or "opals", have received great attention over the last decade due to their applicability as photonic crystals. Colloidal crystal films have been shown to serve as inexpensive templates for the infiltration of a material with sufficiently high refractive index (i.e. $n \geq 2.8$), which can give rise to a material possessing a three-dimensional photonic bandgap [1]. However, the self-assembled nature of colloidal crystals creates the possibility for the formation of intrinsic crystalline defects, including point defects, polycrystallinity, and stacking faults.

Stacking faults can be characterized as breaks in the periodicity in the stacking sequence of close-packed crystallographic planes. For opals, which are ideally considered to be face-centered cubic (fcc), this consists of a deviation in the stacking of the {111} planes parallel to the substrate from a periodic *ABC...* to a random *ABACBAB...* sequence. This randomized structure can be regarded as a mixture of fcc and hcp (hexagonally close-packed) structures, the latter possessing an *ABAB...* close-packed plane stacking. The tendency for stacking fault formation in colloidal crystals has been accounted for by the small difference in free energy (i.e. on the order of 10^{-3} RT mol^{-1}) of the fcc and hcp structures, with fcc being marginally more stable [2]. Yet while several experimental [3,4] efforts have been made to study the influence of stacking faults on the optical properties of opal films, a

direct spectroscopic measurement of stacking faults on a structural basis has yet to be carried out. Here, we report on a detailed spatially-resolved spectroscopic study of the influence of stacking faults on the optical properties of colloidal crystal films.

Silica spheres of 850 nm diameter were deposited onto bare glass substrates using an accelerated vertical assembly method [5]. Spatially-averaged UV-vis measurements (Cary 9000) were taken using an aperture of 1.2 mm diameter, while spatially-resolved measurements were taken by coupling a spectrometer (Ocean Optics SD2000) to the ocular port of an optical microscope (Olympus BX-41 20× objective lens, $NA = 0.4$) *via* an optical fiber. All spectroscopic measurements were taken in transmission at normal incidence. Finite-difference-time-domain (FDTD) simulations were calculated using a mesh size of $a/120$ for ϕ=850 nm silica spheres on a semi-infinite glass substrate; the calculated fields were projected into the far-field to simulate measurement through a spatial filter of $NA = 0.4$.

Figure 1(a) shows an optical image of a 3-layer opal film, which can be seen to be composed of areas of two distinct colors. Under an SEM these regions prove to be domains of 3 layers of spheres stacked in the *ABC* and *ABA* sequences (Figs. 1(c,d)). Considering the aperture size (1.2 mm) and the average domain size of ~75 μm, it can be deduced that

CP893, *Physics of Semiconductors, 28th International Conference*
edited by W. Jantsch and F. Schäffler
© 2007 American Institute of Physics 978-0-7354-0397-0/07/$23.00

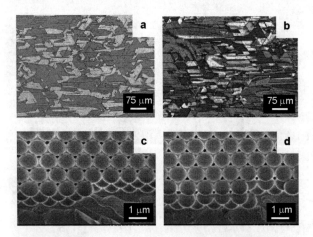

FIGURE 1. Optical transmission micrographs of thin colloidal crystal films consisting of (a) 3 layers and (b) 5 layers of ϕ=850 nm silica spheres. The differently coloured regions correspond to different stacking patterns of close-packed spheres. Top-view SEM images of a 3-layer film showing the (c) *ABC* and the (d) *ABA* stacking patterns, representing the dark and light areas in (a), respectively.

many domains of each stacking sequence are sampled during a single UV-vis measurement. However, through micro-optical spectroscopy the measurement area can be reduced to a size of 8 μm, allowing the differently-stacked domains to be probed individually.

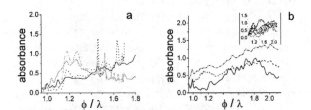

FIGURE 2. Micro-optical spectra of domains in a 3-layer ϕ= 850nm silica colloidal crystal film stacked in an *ABC* (dark) and *ABA* (grey) stacking pattern, showing excellent agreement with FDTD simulations (dotted) of the corresponding structures. b) Micro-optical spectra of a 5-layer ϕ =850nm silica colloidal crystal film showing the case of fcc stacking (i.e. *ABCAB*, solid), and a comparison to the numerical average (dashed) of the 8-possible stacking patterns, each plotted in the inset. The spatially-averaged UV-vis spectrum (dash-dot) closely resembles the numerical average of the micro-optical spectra.

The micro-optical spectra of the 3 layer film are shown in Fig. 2(a). A comparison of the spectra of the *ABC* and *ABA* domains reveals a variance in both the peak intensities and the overall transparencies of the films over the measured range. The combination of these differences gives rise to the two distinct colors of the 3-layer film and, as the thicknesses and filling fractions of the two domains are identical, the color

difference can be ascribed solely to photonic crystal behavior and not to thin film interference.

We have analyzed 5-layer film, imaged in Fig. 1(b), and the micro-optical spectra for the 8 permissible stacking patterns therein are plotted in Fig. 2(b, inset). Similar differences among these 8 spectra exist as for the 3-layer film. In Fig. 2(b), we compare the numerical average of the 8 micro-optical spectra to the spatially-averaged UV-vis spectrum of the 5-layer film, and find strong agreement. Also shown in Fig. 2(b) is the single micro-optical spectrum for the case of fcc stacking, *ABCAB*. A comparison of this spectrum to the numerical average reveals differences in both the overall absorbance and in the relative peak intensities and positions. This highlights a key difference between what can be called a "realistic" material, one containing stacking faults, and the idealized, purely fcc case, which is the crystal structure generally used in the literature to describe and simulate the photonic properties of opal and inverse opal films.

In summary, the influence of stacking faults on the optical properties of thin colloidal crystal films has been directly measured *via* spatially resolved micro-optical spectroscopy. Different stacking sequences give rise to unique optical spectra; the spatially-averaged spectrum represents a composite measurement, and is different from the ideal fcc structure. Certain growth parameters, specifically the growth rate and the impurity sphere concentration, have been found to strongly influence stacking fault formation during colloidal self-assembly, and a full investigation of their influence is the subject of current experimental efforts.

ACKNOWLEDGMENTS

GAO is Canada Research Chair of Materials Chemistry, and he is grateful to the Natural Sciences and Engineering Council for support of this work.

REFERENCES

1. A. Blanco, E. Chomski, S. Grabtchak, M. Ibisate, S. John, S. W. Leonard, C. Lopez, F. Meseguer, H. Miguez, J. P. Mondia, G. A. Ozin, O. Toader, H. M. van Driel, *Nature* **405**, 437-440 (2000).
2. L. V. Woodcock, *Nature* **385**, 141-143 (1997).
3. Yu. A. Vlasov, V. N. Astratov, A.V. Baryshev, A. A. Kaplyanskii, O. Z. Karimov, and M. F. Limonov, *Phys. Rev. E* **61**, 5784-5793 (2000).
4. S. A. Asher, J. M. Weissman, A. Tikhonov, R. D. Coalson, and R. Kesavamoorthy, *Phys. Rev. E* **69**, 066619 (2004).
5. E. Vekris, V. Kitaev, G. von Freymann, D. D. Perovic, J. S. Aitchison, G. A. Ozin, *Adv. Mater.* **17**, 1269-1272 (2005).

CHAPTER 12

SEMICONDUCTOR SPINTRONICS

Ultrafast Spin Relaxation and Dynamics of Carriers in Diluted Magnetic Semiconductor Quantum Wells

K. Saito, K. Nishibayashi, I. Souma, A. Murayama, and Y. Oka

Institute of Multidisciplinary Research for Advanced Materials, Tohoku University,
2-1-1 Katahira, Sendai 980-8577, Japan

Abstract. Spin dynamics of carriers in multiple quantum wells of $Cd_{0.95}Mn_{0.05}Te$ has been studied by the transient pump-probe absorption spectroscopy in magnetic field. The spin-flip relaxation time of electrons in the quantum wells increases from 7 ps to 18 ps with increasing magnetic field up to 2 T due to the suppression of the exchange mechanism for the spin-flip relaxation of electrons interacting with Mn ions. In fields higher than 3 T, the electron spin-flip relaxation time turns to decrease caused by the LO phonon-related relaxation. The spin-flip time of holes is less than 200 fs due to the band-mixing effect in the valence bands.

Keywords: Carriers, Diluted Magnetic Semiconductors, Spins, Dynamics.
PACS: 78.30.Fs, 78.47.+p, 78.67.De, 78.20.Ls

INTRODUCTION

Electrons and holes in a diluted magnetic semiconductor quantum well (DMS-QW) show varieties of spin dynamics due to the s, p-d exchange interaction with localized spins of magnetic ions. These phenomena are highly related to the spintronic applications. However, the polarization and relaxation dynamics of the carrier spins in the DMS-QWs have not been well investigated. We have performed the transient pump-probe absorption spectroscopy on the carrier spin dynamics by using femto-second pulse lasers in magnetic field. The results clarify the ultrafast dynamics of the spin-polarization and relaxation of carriers.

RESULTS AND DISCUSSION

A sample used in this study is multiple QWs (MQWs) of $Cd_{0.95}Mn_{0.05}Te$ with barrier layers of $Cd_{0.75}Mg_{0.25}Te$ (Fig. 1). The thickness of the magnetic well (MW) and the barrier is 4.2 and 10.2 nm, respectively. The heavy-hole (*hh*) exciton transition energy in the MW at 0 T is 1.77 eV. Magnetic-field dependence of the transient differential absorption intensities ($\Delta\alpha d$) after the pump excitation was measured for the QW excitons at 2 K. Spin injection and spin-flip relaxation processes of electrons and holes were directly probed by $\Delta\alpha d$ for right/left circular polarizations (σ^+/σ^-).

Figure 2 shows the spectra of $\Delta\alpha d$ with the σ^+ and σ^- polarizations at magnetic field (B) of 5 T. The top panel displays the absorption spectrum of the Zeeman-split spin levels (down-spin and up-spin states) of the *hh*-excitons. In the lower two panels of Fig. 2, $\Delta\alpha d$ for the down-spin hh-exciton (denoted as (a)) decays with a time constant of 160 ps. On the other hand, the up-spin exciton (denoted as (b)) shows a two-component decay with the decay time of 11 and 150 ps. Furthermore, $\Delta\alpha d$ in (c) with the σ^+ polarization, which corresponds to the light hole (*lh*) exciton transition, decays with ~11 ps. The observed time-variations of $\Delta\alpha d$ for the *hh* and *lh* excitons were analyzed by using rate equations for the dynamical

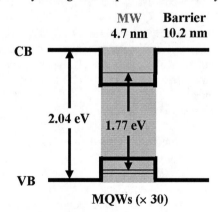

FIGURE 1. Sample structure of the $Cd_{0.95}Mn_{0.05}Te/$ $Cd_{0.75}Mg_{0.25}Te$ MQW.

CP893, *Physics of Semiconductors, 28th International Conference*
edited by W. Jantsch and F. Schäffler
© 2007 American Institute of Physics 978-0-7354-0397-0/07/$23.00

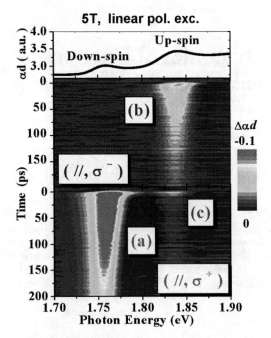

FIGURE 2. Circularly-polarized transient differential absorption spectra of the down- and up-spin excitons in the $Cd_{0.95}Mn_{0.05}Te/$ $Cd_{0.75}Mg_{0.25}Te$ MQWs at 5 T. The pump-excitation (2.1 eV) is made with linearly polarized (//) photons to excite both hh and lh exciton states.

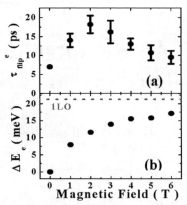

FIGURE 3. Magnetic field dependence of the spin-flip relaxation time of electron (a) and the Zeeman splitting of the electron level in the MW (b).

exciton-spin populations during the injection and relaxation. From the analysis at 5 T, we deduce the radiative recombination time of the hh-exciton (τ_r^{hh-ex}) as 160 ps and the spin-flip relaxation time of the electron in the MW (τ_{flip}^e) as 11 ps. The spin-flip relaxation time of hh and lh (τ_{flip}^{hh}, τ_{flip}^{lh}) are shorter than 200 fs (less than the time resolution of the set-up).

In the present DMS-QW at B=0 T, we obtained τ_s^e = 7 ps and $\tau_{flip}^{hh} < 1$ ps. For a non-magnetic QW of CdTe, the observed values of τ_{flip}^e and τ_{flip}^{hh} were 46 and 1.0 ps, respectively.[1, 2] Similar spin-flip relaxation times in the CdTe QW at 0 T is also reported.[3] Therefore the shorter τ_{flip}^e in the DMS-QW must be caused by the s-d exchange interaction of electrons with Mn spins. Hole spins are always relaxed fast, which is attributed to the band-mixing effect of the valence bands.[1]

In Fig. 3(a), we depict the magnetic field dependence of τ_{flip}^e obtained from the present transient absorption measurement. With increasing B to 2 T, τ_{flip}^e increases from 7 ps to 18 ps. For B>3 T, τ_{flip}^e turns to decrease and reaches to 10 ps at 6 T. Figure 3 (b) shows the Zeeman-splitting energy of the electron sublevel in the MW (ΔE_e) by extracting the electron component from the exciton splitting using the known exchange parameters for the electron and hole. With increasing B, ΔE_e increases and tends to saturate to 18 meV, which is close to the LO phonon energy (21

meV). In the region of 1~3 T, the Mn spins are gradually polarized to the magnetic field direction, which causes the giant Zeeman splitting for the electron and hole sublevels in the MW due to the exchange interaction. On the other hand, for these carriers, the spin-flip relaxation by the exchange mechanism is significantly decreased. This is because the Mn spins are forced to polarize to the field direction and therefore can not any more participate in carrier spin-flips by counter-flipping of their spins. The increase of τ_{flip}^e for B=0~2 T is quantitatively interpreted by the suppression of the s-d exchange mechanism for the electron spin-flip due to the pinning of Mn-spins in magnetic field.

For B>3 T, τ_{flip}^e turns to decrease, while ΔE_e approaches to the LO phonon energy. Therefore the decrease of τ_{flip}^e must be affected by the LO phonon relaxation aided by the spin-orbit coupling. However, an LO phonon cannot participate solely to the electron-spin-flip relaxation, since the Zeeman splitting energy for the electron-spin is still smaller than the LO phonon energy even at 6 T. Nevertheless, the spin-flip relaxation related to the LO phonon can be possible via the second-order process by emission of LO and absorption of acoustic phonons. This spin relaxation mechanism explains the decrease in τ_{flip}^e for B>3 T.

The magnetic-field-dependent spin-flip relaxation of electrons observed in the DMS-QW can be applicable for the control of electron spins in spintronic devices.

This work is supported in part by the Ministry of Education, Science and Culture, Japan, and also the NEDO Nanotechnology Materials Program.

1. A. Murayama, K. Seo, Nishibayashi, I. Souma, and Y. Oka, *Appl. Phys. Lett.* **88**, 261105(1-3) (2006).
2 K. Nishibayashi, I. Souma, A. Murayama, and Y. Oka, *Appl. Phys. Lett.* **88**, 211108(1-3) (2006).
3. R. Akimoto, K. Ando, F. Sasaki, S. Kobayashi, and T. Tani, *Phys. Rev. B* **56**, 9726-9733 (1997).

Quantitative study of the Giant Zeeman Effect in (Zn,Co)O and (Ga,Mn)N

W. Pacuski[1,2], D. Ferrand[2], P. Kossacki[1,2], J. Cibert[3], J. A. Gaj[1], A. Golnik[1], S. Marcet[2], C. Deparis[4], C. Morhain[4], E. Sarigiannidou[2], H. Mariette[2]

[1]*Institute of Experimental Physics, Warsaw University, Warszawa, Hoża 69, PL-00-681, Poland*
[2] *CNRS-CEA-UJF Joint Group "Nanophysique et semiconducteurs", Laboratoire de Spectrométrie Physique, BP 87, F-38402 Saint Martin d'Hères Cedex, France*
[3] *Laboratoire Louis Néel, CNRS, BP 166, F-38042 Grenoble Cedex 9, France*
[4] *Centre de Recherches sur l'Hétéroépitaxie et ses Applications, CNRS, rue Bernard Grégory, Parc Sophia Antipolis, F-06560 Valbonne, France*

Abstract. We report observation of the giant Zeeman splitting of the *A* and *B* excitons in reflectivity and transmission spectra measured on paramagnetic (Zn,Co)O and (Ga,Mn)N layers grown by molecular beam epitaxy. The splitting decreases with increasing temperature, and increases non-linearly with the magnetic field. It shows the same behavior as the magnetization of the magnetic ions. We present description of the giant Zeeman effect in wide gap DMS, which takes into account weak spin-orbit and strong electron-hole exchange interaction. For diluted samples (0.4%Co and 0.5%Mn) we deduce exchange integrals difference for Co^{2+} in ZnO, $N_0|\alpha-\beta| = 0.8$ eV and for Mn^{3+} in GaN $N_0(\alpha-\beta) = -1.2$ eV.

Keywords: wide gap DMS, ZnO:Co, GaN:Mn, giant Zeeman effect
PACS: 75.50.Pp, 75.30.Hx, 78.20.Ls, 71.35.Ji

INTRODUCTION

Making quantitative a study of the giant Zeeman effect is of primary importance for the assessment of new diluted magnetic semiconductors (DMS). Such a study allows to determine the value of spin-carrier exchange integrals, and to reach clear-cut conclusions concerning the origin of the magnetic properties observed by standard magnetometry. It is also a key parameter for applications in magneto-optics. In wide bandgap semiconductors such as GaN and ZnO, the presence of anisotropy and the unusual value of several parameters make the interpretation of giant Zeeman effect less straightforward than in more regular zinc-blende DMS.

SAMPLES AND EXPERIMENT

We studied thin layers grown by molecular beam epitaxy on sapphire substrates, with the *c*-axis of the wurtzite structure perpendicular to the surface. Reflectivity, absorption and photoluminescence were measured in the Faraday configuration, in magnetic field up to 11 T, at temperature down to 1.5 K, using a high pressure Xe lamp and a HeCd laser.

EXCITONS IN WIDE GAP DMS

ZnO and GaN have been extensively studied as hosts for magnetic impurities such as Cobalt and Manganese, respectively. Both are wide bandgap semiconductors with the wurtzite structure (so that three excitons labeled *A*, *B*, and *C* can be detected). They are characterized by a weak spin-orbit coupling and a strong electron-hole exchange interaction. This makes the interpretation of the giant Zeeman effect not straightforward: Excitons anti-cross, and not only the transition energies, but also the oscillator strengths are strongly affected. In addition, the strong exciton-photon coupling affects reflectivity spectra, which are described using the formalism of polaritons.

Giant Zeeman effect in (Zn,Co)O

Magnetoreflectivity spectra of a (Zn,Co)O epilayer with 0.4%Co are shown in Fig. 1. Two excitons split

CP893, *Physics of Semiconductors, 28th International Conference*
edited by W. Jantsch and F. Schäffler
© 2007 American Institute of Physics 978-0-7354-0397-0/07/$23.00

further in σ^+ circular polarization and get closer in σ^- circular polarization upon increasing the magnetic field. Using the polariton formalism, we were able to determine the energy position of both excitons as a function of field and temperature. This dependence follows the magnetization curves of non-interacting Co^{2+} ions, with the c-axis as a hard magnetization axis. This demonstrates s,p-d exchange interactions between the Co ions and the photocarriers. A complete analysis was given in Ref 1.

Note that even the shape of the spectra is changed under magnetic field: the oscillator strength of exciton A decreases while exciton B increases in σ^- polarization, when the two excitons get closer. This is an effect of the electron-hole exchange interaction: at complete anticrossing, the upper exciton forms a bright exciton (maximal oscillator strength) while the lower one is dark. From the minimum distance between A and B, the electron-hole exchange energy is determined to be equal to 3.4 meV. This is a large value, so large that the giant Zeeman shift of the excitons is reduced by a factor of 2. A full description of the giant Zeeman shift allows us to determine the difference of exchange integrals, $N_0|\alpha-\beta| = 0.8$ eV.

Assuming that the valence band ordering in ZnO is the normal one (Γ_9, Γ_7, Γ_7) corresponding to a positive sign of the spin-orbit coupling, we find that the sign of $N_0(\alpha-\beta)$ is positive, as usually observed in II-VI DMS [2].

Giant Zeeman effect in (Ga,Mn)N

Reflectivity spectra showing well resolved A and B excitons have been obtained also in the case of (Ga,Mn)N, with Mn in the d^4 electronic configuration (Mn^{3+}, see Ref 3). This will be analyzed in detail in Ref 4. A striking difference, when compared to (Zn,Co)O, is that exciton A shifts to lower energy in σ^+ circular polarization in GaN:Mn^{3+}. It means that $N_0(\alpha-\beta)$ is negative (-1.2 eV). Assuming an usual value $N_0\alpha=0.2$ eV, we conclude that $N_0\beta = +1.4$ eV. A positive sign means that the p-d interaction is ferromagnetic for Mn^{3+}, as opposed to the antiferromagnetic p-d exchange observed for Mn^{2+} in II-VI DMS.

DISCUSSION

A large, negative value $N_0\beta \approx -3$ eV has been predicted for Co^{2+} in ZnO [2]. Assuming $N_0\alpha \approx 0.2$ eV and the usual valence band ordering, we found that the sign determined for β is in agreement with theory, but the value is much smaller (~0.6 eV). The calculation of the exchange integrals

for Mn^{3+} in GaN is much more complex, because it has the d^4 electronic configuration. In Ref 5, a value $N_0\beta = -1.6$ eV has been obtained, but the analogy with the other realization of the d^4 electronic configuration, Cr^{2+} in II-VI compounds, suggests a positive sign of β. In fact, depending on the values assumed for the energies of donor and acceptor levels of Mn^{3+}, positive and negative signs of β could be deduced from theory. This uncertainty shows the importance of an experimental determination of $N_0\beta = +1.4$ eV.

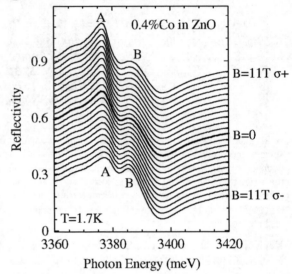

Figure 1. Reflectivity of $Zn_{0.996}Co_{0.004}O$ measured at 1.7K, in two circular polarizations: σ^+ (top) and σ^- (bottom). The two A and B excitonic features are indicated on the graph.

ACKNOWLEDGMENTS

We thank T. Dietl, P. Kacman, and R. Stępniewski for fruitful discussions. This work was partially supported by the Polish Committee for Scientific Research (grant 2P03B 002 25), program Polonium and a grant from the French Ministry of Foreign Affairs.

REFERENCES

1. W. Pacuski, D. Ferrand, J. Cibert, C. Deparis, J. A. Gaj, P. Kossacki, and C. Morhain, *Phys. Rev. B* **73**, 035214 (2006).
2. J. Blinowski, P. Kacman, and T. Dietl, in Spintronics, MRS Symp. Proc. No. 690, paper No. F6.9, (Materials Research Society, Warrendale, PA, 2001).
3. S. Marcet, D. Ferrand, D. Halley, S. Kuroda, H. Mariette, E. Gheeraert, F.J Teran, M.L Sadowski, R. M. Galera, and J. Cibert, cond-mat/0604025 (2006).
4. W. Pacuski *et al.*, to be published.
5. Blinowski and Kacman, *Acta Phys. Pol. A* **100**, 343 (2001)

Intrinsic ferromagnetism in wurtzite (Ga,Mn)N grown by plasma-assisted molecular-beam epitaxy

E. Sarigiannidou*, F. Wilhelm†, E. Monroy*, R.M. Galera**, E. Bellet-Amalric*,
A. Rogalev†, J. Goulon†, J. Cibert** and H. Mariette*

*CEA-CNRS-UJF group "Nanophysique et Semiconducteurs", DRFMC/SP2M/PSC, CEA-Grenoble, 17 rue des
Martyrs, 38054 Grenoble Cedex 9, France
†European Synchrotron Radiation Facility (ESRF), BP 220, 38043 Grenoble, France
**Louis Néel, CNRS, BP 166, 38042 Grenoble, France

Abstract. We report on the *intrinsic* ferromagnetic properties of wurtzite $Ga_{0.937}Mn_{0.063}N$ diluted magnetic semiconductor grown by plasma-assisted molecular beam epitaxy. The growth conditions were carefully optimized to obtain single phase (Ga,Mn)N samples. The high structural quality is confirmed by x-ray diffraction experiments. Ferromagnetism is unambiguously demonstrated by both macroscopic magnetization measurements and x-ray magnetic circular dichroism spectra recorded at the Mn K-edge. The Curie temperature is found ≈ 8 K with a spontaneous magnetic moment of 2.4 μ_B per Mn at 2 K.

Keywords: Diluted magnetic semiconductor, (Ga,Mn)N, x-ray magnetic circular dichroism
PACS: 78.70.Dm, 75.50.Pp, 81.15.Hi, 75.70.Ak

INTRODUCTION

The work of Dietl *et al.* [1] on diluted magnetic semiconductors (DMS), has impelled worldwide research on (Ga,Mn)N due to the prediction of ferromagnetism above room temperature. However, the electronic and magnetic properties of (Ga,Mn)N remain under debate. Moreover, recent *ab-initio* calculations predict a low Curie temperature (T_C) [2]. (Ga,Mn)N films reported to exhibit a ferromagnetic-like state present a T_C which varies from liquid He [3] up to 940 K [4]. The observation of a ferromagnetic-like state at high temperatures might be due to the presence of secondary phases like Mn_4N and $Mn_{3.2}Ga_{0.8}N$. Therefore, single-phase (Ga,Mn)N layers are required to clarify the electronic and magnetic properties of Mn atoms, and to understand the origin of ferromagnetism in this DMS [5].

Here, we report on the optimization of the growth conditions of wurtzite (Ga,Mn)N epilayers grown by plasma-assisted molecular beam epitaxy (PAMBE) in order to obtain intrinsic ferromagnetic behavior.

EXPERIMENTAL DETAILS

The (Ga,Mn)N samples were grown in a PAMBE chamber, with standard effusion cells for Ga and Mn, and a radio-frequency plasma cell to supply active nitrogen. The substrates were 10 μm-thick GaN templates grown on c-sapphire by metalorganic vapor phase epitaxy. Prior to the growth a 20 nm GaN buffer layer was initially deposited. The substrate temperature was fixed at 715°C.

A SEIFERD 3003 PTS diffractometer is used for the x-ray diffraction experiments. Magnetization measurements were performed in a 5 T Quantum Design superconducting quantum interference device (SQUID), with the magnetic field applied perpendicular to the c growth axis. X-ray Magnetic Circular Dichroism (XMCD) measurements at the Mn K-edge were performed at the European Synchrotron Radiation Facility (ESRF) in Grenoble at the ID12 beam line [6].

RESULTS-DISCUSSION

We have previously demonstrated that Mn perturbs the Ga kinetics during growth [7]. Here, we have optimized the growth conditions in order to control the two-dimensional growth mode, maximize Mn incorporation and prevent the appearance of secondary phases (e.g. $GaMn_3N$ or Mn_4N). We have observed that the incorporation of Mn is inhibited under Ga-rich conditions (Ga/N > 1). Under N-rich conditions (Ga/N < 1), Mn favors the two-dimensional growth, is substitutionally incorporated into the wurtzite lattice and inhibits the Stranski-Krastanow transition when growing (Ga,Mn)N on AlN. Note that for extremely N-rich conditions, the surface morphology becomes rough. To maximize the incorporation of Mn, we have performed the growth under N-rich conditions (0.9 < Ga/N < 1) and we have introduced periodic growth interruptions that prevent Mn accumulation at the surface. Under these optimal conditions, we have succeed the growth of 400-nm-thick single-phase (Ga,Mn)N epilayers containing up to 6 at.% of Mn. The

CP893, *Physics of Semiconductors, 28th International Conference*
edited by W. Jantsch and F. Schäffler
© 2007 American Institute of Physics 978-0-7354-0397-0/07/$23.00

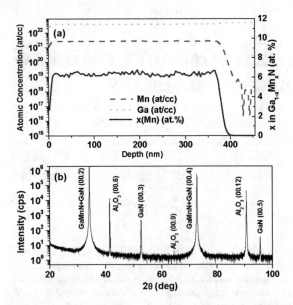

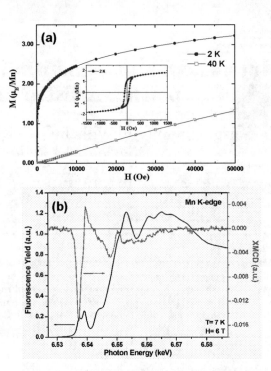

FIGURE 1. (a) SIMS profiles for Mn and Ga of a (Ga,Mn)N epilayer. (b) Corresponding X-ray diffraction $2\theta - \theta$ scan.

Mn incorporation is homogeneous along the layer, as measured by secondary ion mass spectroscopy (Fig. 1 (a)). No secondary phases are observed as shown in the $2\theta - \theta$ scan given in Fig. 1 (b) [5].

SQUID magnetization measurements were performed within a temperature range of 2-300 K. However, no signature of high-temperature ferromagnetic phases has been observed above 20 K. Figure 2 (a)(inset), illustrates the magnetization loop recorded at 2 K for a (Ga,Mn)N sample with 6.3% Mn. We observe a clear opening of the hysteresis cycle which is characteristic of ferromagnetic order. At 2 K, the coercive field is ≈ 100 Oe whereas the remanent magnetization reaches only 44 % of the spontaneous magnetization, $2.4 \pm 0.2\mu_B$ per Mn as deduced from the Arrott plot (not shown) of the isothermal magnetization curve shown in Fig. 2 (a). For the same sample, from the thermal variation of the magnetization measured under an applied field of 500 Oe we determined, from the maximum in the derivative, a T_C equal to ≈ 8 K.

Since SQUID measurements probe the magnetic response of the whole system, to further demonstrate the intrinsic magnetic properties of (Ga,Mn)N, we have performed element selective magnetic studies using XMCD measurements performed at the Mn K-edge. Figure 2 (b) shows the Mn K-edge isotropic XANES and XMCD spectra of a (Ga,Mn)N epilayer with 6.3% Mn recorded at 7 K and under an applied field of 6 T. Knowing that the XMCD signal at the K-edge is proportional to the orbital polarization of the absorbing atom [8], the observed XMCD signal clearly demonstrates that in our (Ga,Mn)N layers the Mn atoms carry an orbital magnetic moment.

FIGURE 2. (a) Isothermal magnetization curves of a (Ga,Mn)N epilayer with 6.3% Mn for 2 and 40 K measured by SQUID. The inset shows the magnetization loops at 2 K for the same sample. (b) Mn K-edge measured isotropic x-ray absorption near edge structure spectrum and its corresponding XMCD signal recorded under 6 T in-plane field and at 7 K.

CONCLUSIONS

We have demonstrated that using PAMBE we can achieve the growth of high structural quality wurtzite (Ga,Mn)N epilayers with Mn homogeneous concentration up to 6.3%. By combining macroscopic and element-selective magnetic measurements, we have determined a spontaneous magnetic moment of 2.4 μ_B per Mn at 2 K and a T_C of ≈ 8 K in a (Ga,Mn)N sample with 6.3% Mn. These results are a strong experimental evidence of the *intrinsic* origin of ferromagnetism in (Ga,Mn)N DMS.

REFERENCES

1. T. Dietl, et al., *Science* **287**, 1019 (2000).
2. G. Bouzerar, et al., *Europhys. Lett.* **69**, 812 (2005).
3. S. Dhar, et al., *Phys. Rev. B* **67**, 165205 (2003).
4. S. Sonoda, et al., *J. Cryst. Growth* **237-239**, 1358 (2002).
5. E. Sarigiannidou, et al., *Phys. Rev. B* p. In press (2006).
6. A. Rogalev, et al., *Magnetism and Synchrotron Radiation*, Springer, Heidelberg, 2001.
7. S. Kuroda, et al., *Appl. Phys. Lett.* **83**, 4580 (2003).
8. H. Ebert, *Rep. Prog. Phys.* **59**, 1665 (1996).

Ultrafast Magneto-Optical Kerr Study of Standing Spin Waves in Ferromagnetic GaMnAs Films

D. M. Wang[*], Y. H. Ren[*,¶], X. Liu[†], Y. J. Cho[†], J. K. Furdyna[†], M. Grimsditch[††] and R. Merlin[*]

[*]Focus Center and Department of Physics, University of Michigan, Ann Arbor, Michigan 48109-1040, USA
[†]Department of Physics, University of Notre Dame, Notre Dame, Indiana 46556, USA
[††]Materials Science Division, Argonne National Laboratory, Argonne, Illinois 60439, USA

Abstract. We report on the observation of standing spin waves in thin films of the ferromagnetic semiconductor GaMnAs in time-resolved magneto-optical Kerr measurements. We observe two modes, one of which is the near-uniform spin excitation. From the magnetic-field dependence of the frequencies and the ratio between the intensities of these modes, we obtain the spin stiffness D as well as the bulk and surface anisotropies. For as-grown samples with ~5–6% concentration of Mn, $D = 6 \pm 1$ T·nm^2 while $D = 18 \pm 3$ (25 ± 4) T·nm^2 for a 3% Mn as-grown (annealed) sample. The surface anisotropy is negative.

Keywords: ferromagnetic semiconductors, GaMnAs, spin waves, spin stiffness
PACS: 78.47.+p, 75.30.Ds, 75.70.-I, 76.70.Hb

INTRODUCTION

Despite the considerable interest in ferromagnetic GaMnAs [1-4], its magnetic constants are still poorly known and there is limited information as to their behavior as a function of growth and annealing parameters. Values of the spin stiffness and magnetic anisotropy reported in recent ferromagnetic (FMR) and spin-wave resonance (SWR) studies were gained under the assumption of free-pinning at the boundaries [5,6]. However, it remains unclear whether alternative pinning conditions might exist and what influence they might have on the accuracy of the measured constants. In this work, we determine the spin stiffness and pinning conditions through a time-domain pump-probe study of standing spin waves in thin films.

MEASUREMENTS AND DISCUSSION

We studied one annealed and three as-grown GaMnAs films grown by low-temperature molecular-beam-epitaxy. Two of the as-grown samples have the same Mn concentration, in the range of 5-6%, and Curie temperature $T_C \sim 65$ K, but different thicknesses: 47 nm and 71 nm. The third as-grown and the single annealed sample are both 120-nm-thick, with a Mn concentration of 3% and $T_C \sim 70$ and 80 K, respectively. Experiments were performed at 4-6 K. The easy

axis of all these films is in-plane, along the $x \equiv$ [100] direction [7]. In the time-domain pump-probe experiments, the pump pulses induce a coherent precession of the magnetization, which we detect by measuring the rotation of the polarization of the delayed probe pulses. We used 70-fs pulses of intensity 2 nJ/mm^2 from a Ti:Sapphire laser operating at 82 MHz and central wavelength of 800 nm.

Figure 1(a) shows data for the 120-nm-thick as-grown sample. Here, $\Delta\theta$ is the pump-induced rotation of the probe polarization. Using linear prediction (LP) methods, and after subtracting the electronic background, the time-domain trace was fitted to a superposition of exponentially damped sinusoidal waves. The Fourier transform, shown in Fig. 1(b), exhibits two modes.

The relationship between $\Delta\theta$ and the spin wave profile is given by [8]

$$\Delta\theta \propto \int M_y dz \cdot \int M_z dz \Big/ \left(\int M_y^2 dz \right) \quad , \quad (1)$$

where M_y and M_z are the components of the precessing magnetization along $y \equiv$ [010] and $z \equiv$ [001]. Based on this expression, the stronger mode in Fig. 1(b), at 10.03 GHz, is assigned to the near-uniform spin wave mode (SW$_0$), and the weaker one, at 11.92 GHz, to the next even mode (SW$_2$). The first odd mode, SW$_1$, is

CP893, *Physics of Semiconductors, 28th International Conference*
edited by W. Jantsch and F. Schäffler
© 2007 American Institute of Physics 978-0-7354-0397-0/07/$23.00

forbidden because the rotation integrated over the whole film vanishes and the absorption length at 800 nm is much larger that the film thickness.

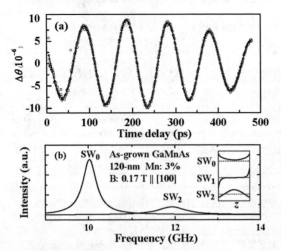

FIGURE 1. Differential magneto-optical Kerr data for the 120-nm-thick as-grown sample. (a) The solid line is the LP fit. (b) Fourier transform. The inset shows M_z vs. z for the first three modes.

Our assignment of the two modes is supported by the results on the two as-grown samples which have the same Curie temperature and Mn concentration, but different thicknesses. As shown in Fig. 2(a), the measured frequencies of the lowest mode nearly overlap for the two samples, thus agreeing well with the expected behavior of the near-uniform mode, SW_0. The high-frequency modes, however, depend strongly on the sample thickness. The magnetic-field dependence of the intensity ratio between SW_0 and SW_2 for the two samples is shown in Fig. 2(b). The measured ratios are larger than the maximum values calculated from Eq. (1) for positive surface anisotropies (~ 0.07 and ~ 0.06 for the 71-nm and 47-nm samples), but they fit well for negative anisotropies [8]. Our calculations assume that the static magnetization is uniform along the growth direction of the film.

With the knowledge that the surface anisotropy is negative, we fit the magnetic field dependence of the spin wave frequencies, as shown by the dashed line in Fig. 2(a). From the fits, we obtain the gyromagnetic factor $g = 2 \pm 0.2$, which is consistent with known values for the $3d$ electrons of Mn^{2+} ions. Values of the magnetic bulk anisotropies for all five samples are in good agreement with those from FMR and SQUID measurements [5]. The spin stiffness inferred from our experiments is $D = 6 \pm 1$ T·nm^2 for the as-grown samples with Mn concentration ~ 5-6%. For the 3% Mn as-grown and annealed samples, $D = 18 \pm 3$ T·nm^2 and $D = 25 \pm 4$ T·nm^2, respectively. The fact that the spin stiffness for the annealed sample is $\sim 40\%$ larger

is likely due to an increase of the ferromagnetic interaction between Mn spins achieved via annealing. Our values of D for as-grown samples are comparable to those obtained from SWR measurements [6], and we also find that the value for 3% Mn is approximately two times greater than for 5-6%.

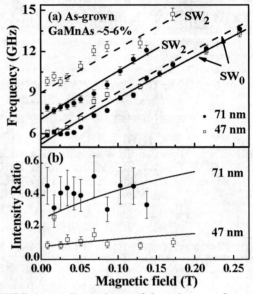

FIGURE 2. (a) Dependence of the spin-wave frequencies on a magnetic field applied along the easy axis for as-grown samples of thickness 47 nm (open square) and 71 nm (solid circle). The dashed and solid lines are theoretical fits. (b) Measured intensity ratio between the SW_0 and SW_2 modes for the two samples. The solid lines are fits using Eq. (1).

ACKNOWLEDGMENTS

This work was supported by the NSF Focus Physics Frontier Center and NSF Grant DMR 0603752.

REFERENCES

[1] Present address: Department of Physics and Astronomy, Hunter College, 695 Park Avenue, New York, NY 10021, USA.
1. H. Ohno, *Science* **281**, 951-956 (1998).
2. J. König, H. H. Lin and A. H. MacDonald, *Phys. Rev. Lett* **84**, 5628-5631 (2000).
3. T. Dietl, H. Ohno and F. Matsukura, *Phys. Rev. B* **63**, 195205 (2001).
4. G. Bouzerar, J. Kudrnovský, L. Bergqvist and P. Bruno, *Phys. Rev. B* **68**, 081203(R) (2003).
5. X. Liu, Y. Sasaki and J. K. Furdyna, *Phys. Rev. B* **67**, 205204 (2003).
6. S. T. B. Goennenwein *et al.*, *Appl. Phys. Letters* **82**, 730-732 (2003).
7. U. Welp, V. K. Vlasko-Vlasov, X. Liu, J. K. Furdyna and T. Wojtowicz, *Phys. Rev. Lett* **90**, 167206 (2003).
8. D. M. Wang, Y. H. Ren, X. Liu, Y. J. Cho, J. K. Furdyna, M. Grimsditch and R. Merlin, unpublished.

Mn $L_{3,2}$ X-ray Absorption Spectroscopy And Magnetic Circular Dichroism In Ferromagnetic Ga$_{1-x}$Mn$_x$P

P.R. Stone[1,2], M.A. Scarpulla[1,2], R. Farshchi[1,2], I.D. Sharp[1,2], J.W. Beeman[2], K.M. Yu[2], E. Arenholz[3], J. Denlinger[3], E.E. Haller[1,2], and O.D. Dubon[1,2]

[1] Department of Materials Science and Engineering, University of California, Berkeley, CA 94720
[2] Lawrence Berkeley National Laboratory, Berkeley, CA 94720
[3] Advanced Light Source, Lawrence Berkeley National Laboratory, Berkeley, CA 94720

Abstract. We have measured the X-ray absorption (XAS) and X-ray magnetic circular dichroism (XMCD) at the Mn $L_{3,2}$ edges in ferromagnetic Ga$_{1-x}$Mn$_x$P films for $0.018 \leq x \leq 0.042$. Large XMCD asymmetries at the L_3 edge indicate significant spin-polarization of the density of states at the Fermi energy. The spectral shapes of the XAS and XMCD are nearly identical with those for Ga$_{1-x}$Mn$_x$As indicating that the hybridization of Mn d states and anion p states is similar in the two materials. Finally, compensation with sulfur donors not only lowers the ferromagnetic Curie temperature but also reduces the spin polarization of the hole states.

Keywords: Ferromagnetic semiconductors, x-ray magnetic circular dichroism (XMCD), Gallium Manganese Phosphide, Gallium Manganese Arsenide
PACS: 75.50.Pp, 71.55.Eq, 78.70.Dm, 61.72.Vv, 78.20.Ls

INTRODUCTION

The discovery that III-V semiconductors exhibit ferromagnetism when doped with a few atomic percent of Mn has led to unique possibilities for combined non-volatile information storage and processing [1]. Inter-Mn exchange is mediated in these ferromagnetic semiconductors (FMSs) by holes provided by substitutional manganese acceptors. We recently demonstrated the synthesis of a carrier-mediated ferromagnetic phase in Ga$_{1-x}$Mn$_x$P using ion implantation and pulsed-laser melting (II-PLM) [2]. Unlike the holes in the prototypical FMS Ga$_{1-x}$Mn$_x$As where ferromagnetism is mediated by itinerant valence band holes, in Ga$_{1-x}$Mn$_x$P these holes are localized in a Mn-derived band. Ga$_{1-x}$Mn$_x$P is thus an important medium for probing the interplay between electronic structure, localization and carrier-mediated exchange. Here we report X-ray absorption spectroscopy (XAS) and X-ray magnetic circular dichroism (XMCD) measurements of ferromagnetic Ga$_{1-x}$Mn$_x$P.

EXPERIMENTAL PROCEDURE

GaP (001) wafers were implanted with 50 keV Mn$^+$ to doses between 4.5×10^{15} and 2.0×10^{16} /cm^2. Samples for compensation studies were subsequently implanted with 60 keV S$^+$ to doses between 1.0×10^{15} and 7.3×10^{15} /cm^2. Samples were irradiated in air with a single 0.44 J/cm^2 pulse from a KrF (λ = 248 nm) excimer laser having FWHM of 18 ns, and subsequently etched in concentrated HCl for 24 hours. The concentrations of substitutional manganese (Mn$_{Ga}$) were determined by the combination of SIMS and ion beam analysis. We define x as the peak Mn$_{Ga}$ concentration as we have shown that the magnetic properties of II-PLM films are dominated by the film region having maximum x [3]. DC magnetization was measured by SQUID magnetometry along <110> in-plane directions. Room temperature XAS was performed at beamline 8.0 at the Advanced Light Source (ALS). Low-temperature XAS and XMCD measurements were carried out at beamline 4.0.2 at the ALS in applied fields of ±5.4 kOe. Data were collected with the field and beam oriented 30° from the plane of the samples along a <110> in-plane direction with 90% circular polarization of the incident X-rays.

RESULTS AND DISCUSSION

The main panel of Fig. 1 presents Mn $L_{3,2}$ TEY XAS spectra taken at 17 K with the field and photon helicity parallel (Γ^+) and antiparallel (Γ^-) for a sample having x=0.034. The XMCD (Γ^+-Γ^-) spectrum is also

CP893, *Physics of Semiconductors, 28th International Conference*
edited by W. Jantsch and F. Schäffler
2007 American Institute of Physics 978-0-7354-0397-0/07/$23.00

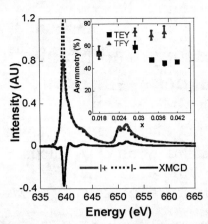

FIGURE 1. (main) Mn $L_{3,2}$ TEY XAS spectra for magnetization and helicity parallel (I^+) and antiparallel (I^-) as well as the difference (XMCD) spectrum for a $Ga_{1-x}Mn_xP$ sample with x=0.034 measured at 17 K. (inset) TEY and TFY asymmetry at the Mn L_3 peak versus x.

shown. Room temperature XAS demonstrated that these spectra arose from well-incorporated Mn_{Ga} and not from surface oxide phases which obscured early XMCD studies of $Ga_{1-x}Mn_xAs$ [4]. Strong XMCD is present at both the L_3 and L_2 edges indicating a large spin polarization of states derived from Mn d levels at E_F. While TEY mode probes depths of under 10 nm the total fluorescence yield (TFY) mode can probe depths on the order of tens of nanometers. Since the Mn_{Ga} peak in these films occurs 20-30 nm from the surface, TFY is a better probe of their bulk magnetic properties. The inset of Fig. 1 compares the magnitude of the asymmetry $((I^+-I^-)/(I^++I^-))$ for the L_3 edge at 17 K as measured in TEY and TFY modes. When corrected for incident angle and photon polarization, the TFY data exhibit a maximum asymmetry value of 0.70±0.04 in all samples except for the one having x=0.018. This is primarily because the T_C of 18 K of this film is very close to the measurement temperature. The TEY data are generally lower than the TFY data, which is consistent with lower Mn concentration and magnetic coupling near the surface of the films.

The similarity between the XAS and XMCD lineshapes for $Ga_{1-x}Mn_xP$ and those reported for $Ga_{1-x}Mn_xAs$ [4,5] is remarkable. Because XAS and XMCD lineshapes are strongly influenced by the hybridization of the t_2-symmetric Mn d orbitals with the neighboring anion p orbitals, this suggests that the bonding and p-d exchange between Mn and As or P in dilute alloys are substantially similar.

The data in Table 1 show a marked decrease in T_c with increasing S concentration. SIMS and channeling RBS yielded $x \approx 0.041$ as well as a Mn substitutionality of 85-90% for all S-doped films, indicating that Mn incorporation is not significantly affected by S

concentration. Indeed it is likely that S enhances Mn incorporation (by as much as 15% in this study). Thus, the decrease in T_c is attributed to a decrease in hole concentration (p) due to the presence of S donors. Furthermore, we find that the XMCD decreases monotonically with S concentration despite the T_c of most films being well above the measurement temperature (Table 1). This result indicates that inter-Mn exchange is intimately related to hole concentration. While changes in Mn_{Ga} and p both affect T_c, only modulation of p significantly affects the spin polarization of carriers for $T>T_c$.

TABLE 1. Properties of $Ga_{0.959}Mn_{0.041}P{:}S$

Sulfur Implant Dose (S^+/cm^2)	T_c(K)	TFY XMCD Asymmetry at 17 K and ±5 kOe(%)
0	56*	70±4$^\$$
1.0×10^{15}	39	55±3
2.5×10^{15}	35	48±3
5.0×10^{15}	29	37±2
7.3×10^{15}	21	21±2

*Interpolated from Ref. 6. $^\$$Interpolated from Fig. 1

CONCLUSION

X-ray absorption studies of ferromagnetic $Ga_{1-x}Mn_xP$ have been reported as a function of Mn_{Ga} and hole concentrations. Large XMCD is observed for $0.018 \le x \le 0.042$, which is consistent with, but not exclusive to, a spin-polarized impurity band. The XMCD and XAS lineshapes are nearly identical to those observed in $Ga_{1-x}Mn_xAs$ suggesting similar electronic environments around Mn_{Ga} in the two systems despite differences in carrier localization. Both T_c and XMCD decrease monotonically with increasing S donor concentration, a hallmark of a hole-mediated ferromagnetic phase.

ACKNOWLEDGMENTS

This work is supported by the Director, Office of Science, Office of Basic Energy Sciences, Division of Materials Sciences and Engineering, of the U.S. Department of Energy under Contract No. DE-AC02-05CH11231. PRS acknowledges support from a NDSEG Fellowship.

REFERENCES

1. Ohno, H., *Science* **281**, 951 (1998).
2. Scarpulla, M.A. *et al.*, *Phys. Rev. Lett.* **95**, 207204 (2005).
3. Dubon, O.D. *et al.*, *Physica B* **376-377**, 630-634 (2006).
4. Stone, P.R. *et al. Appl. Phys. Lett.* **89**, 012504 (2006); Edmonds, K.W. *et al. Appl. Phys. Lett.* **84**, 4065 (2004).
5. Edmonds, K.W. *Phys. Rev. B* **71**, 064418 (2005).
6. Farshchi, R., *et al.* (unpublished)

Optical Spectroscopy On Metastable Zincblende MnS/ZnSe Heterostructures

Limei Chen[1], Peter J. Klar[1], Wolfram Heimbrodt[1], Lorraine David[2], Christine Bradford[2] and Kevin A. Prior[2]

[1]Department of Physics and Material Sciences Center,
Philipps-University Marburg, Germany
[2]School of Engineering and Physical Sciences,
Heriot-Watt University, Edinburgh

Abstract. We have grown MnS/ZnSe heterostructures by molecular beam epitaxy on (100) GaAs substrates. The thickness of the MnS layers ranges from about 1 to 8 nm. We studied the optical properties of the heterostructures using time-resolved photoluminescence spectroscopy with time scales from microseconds to milliseconds at low temperature. The photoluminescence is dominated by the $^4T_1$ to $^6A_1$ internal transition of the Mn^{2+} ($3d^5$) cations at 590 nm. The decay times of the internal luminescence show a weak dependence only on the MnS layer thickness and do not vary when using different excitation energies, i.e. 355 nm (3.49 eV) exciting above the ZnSe band gap or 532 nm (2.33 eV) excitation exciting directly into the Mn $3d^5$ absorption but below the ZnSe and MnS band gaps.

Keywords: photoluminescence, time-resolved spectroscopy, magnetic semiconductors
PACS: 78.66.Hf   78.47.+p   75.50.Pp

INTRODUCTION

The antiferromagnet MnS might occur in three different crystal structures, i.e. rocksalt, wurtzite, and zincblende (ZB), which exhibit different antiferromagnetic orders with slightly different Néel temperatures. Of these crystal structures, the thermodynamically most stable configuration is the rocksalt structure whereas ZB is the less stable phase. So far most magnetic and optical studies of ZB MnS have been performed on powder and polycrystalline specimens only. A fundamental issue in the context of magnetic semiconductors is the change of the magnetic properties at different dimensionality, e.g. going from 3D to 2D. Well characterized MnS layers of controlled thickness are essential for such studies.

EXPERIMENTAL DETAILS

A Vacuum Generators V80H MBE system was used for growing the MnS/ZnSe heterostructures, using Zn, Se, Mn elemental sources and ZnS as sulphur source [1]. The MnS layers of defined thickness of 1.8, 4.3, 6.5, and 8.6 nm, respectively, embedded between ZnSe layers were grown pseudomorphically on GaAs (100) substrates at a growth temperature of 240-270 °C. A thin (20-50 nm) ZnSe buffer layer was deposited prior to the growth of the ZB MnS layer. The MnS was grown using Mn and ZnS sources. Finally, the heterostructure was capped with 20 nm of ZnSe.

Time-resolved photoluminescence spectroscopy (PL) was performed using a pulsed Nd:YAG laser doubled to 532 nm or tripled to 355 nm, respectively. The laser pulse typically has a spectral width of about 5 meV and a duration of about 5 ns. The samples were mounted in a helium cryostat. The PL was focused onto the entrance slit of a 0.25 m grating monochromator and detected by a gated intensified CCD detector system. The PL decay was investigated up to 0.5 ms after the excitation. The maximum temporal resolution was 2 ns.

RESULTS AND DISCUSSION

Fig. 1 shows PL spectra of the four MnS/ZnSe heterostructures obtained at 10 K using 532 nm excitation, i.e. exciting below the ZnSe and MnS band gaps directly into the absorption of the lowest spin-forbidden internal transition of the Mn $3d^5$ shell between the $^6A_1$ ground state and $^4T_1$ excited state.

CP893, *Physics of Semiconductors, 28th International Conference*
edited by W. Jantsch and F. Schäffler
© 2007 American Institute of Physics 978-0-7354-0397-0/07/$23.00

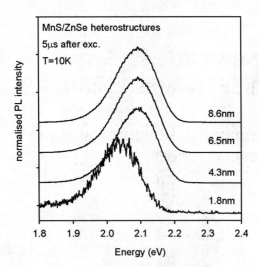

FIGURE 1. PL spectra of the four MnS/ZnSe heterostructures of different MnS thickness. 532 nm excitation.

The spectra of the three wider MnS samples are centered at 2.1 eV (590 nm) and, thus, are typical for ZB MnS [2]. The spectrum of the narrowest sample is shifted to lower energies indicating probably that the Mn ions are in a slightly different crystal field, i.e. a Se-rich tetrahedral environment instead of a four S tetrahedral environment. This may occur assuming interface roughness or intermixing in a region of about 2 monolayers as observed by other authors [3].

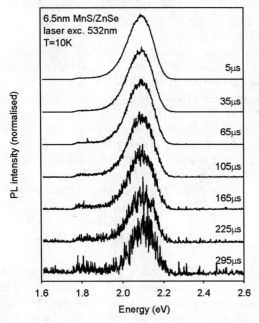

FIGURE 2. Time-evolution of the PL spectrum of the MnS/ZnSe structure with a 6.5 nm MnS layer.

Fig. 2 demonstrates exemplarily for a MnS layer of 6.5 nm thickness that the Mn-related emission is the only emission band in the spectral range under study. At all times after excitation from 5 to 300 μs the spectral shape of the PL remains the same. This holds for both excitation conditions and for all four samples.

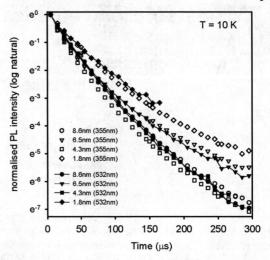

FIGURE 3. PL decay of the MnS/ZnSe samples for two different excitation conditions.

Fig. 3 shows the PL decay curves of all samples for both excitation conditions, exciting into the Mn internal 3d absorption only and exciting above the ZnSe gap. The temporal PL behavior is almost independent of the excitation energy for all specimens indicating that excitation transfer into the Mn system from the ZnSe band states takes place on much shorter time-scales (t < 1 μs) than studied here. This implied that the observed decay behavior is solely determined by processes within the Mn system. The PL decay is non-exponential indicating that the excitation is transferred resonantly between Mn ions and then transferred to other centers. There is no clear dependence on the MnS layer thickness, but tentatively it seems that the overall PL behavior is slower for thinner samples and less mono-exponential. Approximated by a single exponential decay all PL lifetimes are of the order of 50 μs reflecting that the internal transition is largely spin-forbidden.

In summary, the Mn internal PL in MnS/ZnSe heterostructures shows only a weak dependence on the MnS thickness.

REFERENCES

1. L. David, C. Bradford, X. Tang, T.C.M. Graham, K.A. Prior, and B.C. Cavenett, *J. Cryst. Growth* **251**, 591 (2003).
2. O. Goede and W. Heimbrodt, *phys. stat. sol. (b)* **146**, 11 (1988).
3. L. Wang, S. Sivananthan, R. Sporken, and R. Caudano, *Phys. Rev. B* **54**, 2718 (1996).

High Resolution Spin-Flip Raman Spectroscopy in CdZnTe/CdZnMnTe Quantum Wells at ³He Temperatures

Koushiro Arahara[1], Takaaki Koyama[1], Kenichi Oto[2], Kiyofumi Muro[2], Shojiro Takeyama[3],Grzegorz Karczewski[4],Tomasz Wojtowicz[4], and Jacek Kossut[4]

[1]*Graduate School of Science and Technology, Chiba University, Chiba 263-8522, Japan*
[2]*Department of Physics, Faculty of Science, Chiba University, Chiba 263-8522, Japan*
[3]*Institute for Solid State Physics, University of Tokyo, Kashiwa, 277-8581, Japan*
[4]*Institute of Physics, Polish Academy of Sciences, Warsaw, 02-668, Poland*

Abstract. A high resolution spin-flip Raman experiment was carried out in $Cd_{0.93}Zn_{0.07}Te/Cd_{0.48}Zn_{0.04}Mn_{0.48}Te$ quantum wells at 0.4 K in a magnetic field up to 14 T. The spin-flip Raman scatterings strongly depended on the well width. Resonant excitation of the exciton state in a 4 nm quantum well presented two electron-like spin-flip Raman peaks in addition to multiple Mn^{2+} spin-flip Raman scatterings. The spin-flip energies are well described by the modified Brillouin functions and are assigned to the electron spin-flip in the localized excitons and the spin-flip of residual electrons, respectively, although the origin of the large energy difference between the two spin-flip processes is a puzzle. On the other hand, in a 9 nm quantum well, we observed a new type of spin-flip excitation instead of the conventional electron spin-flip excitation. The spin-flip energy seemed to be zero up to 4T and then linearly increased with a magnetic field. Furthermore, the spin-flip energy increased with temperature in the temperature range; 0.4~20 K. These unusual behaviors resemble "softening mode" of spin resonance observed in p-doped ferromagnetic CdMnTe quantum wells.

Keywords: magnetic semiconductor, quantum well, spin-flip Raman scattering
PACS: 71.35.Ji , 73.21.Fg, 75.50.Pp, 78.66.Hf, 78.67.De

INTRODUCTION

In order to investigate the coherent evolution of the spin states and the spin-spin correlations between the carrier and the magnetic ions in the semiconductor nano-structures, a high-resolution resonant spin-flip Raman experiment has been carried out at ultra-low temperature and thermal radiation-free environment.

Excitation light from an etalon-tuned Ti:Sapphire laser or an external-cavity diode laser was coupled into the polarization maintaining fiber and was introduced to the ³He chamber of a home-made cryostat equipped with a 14 T super-conducting magnet. The light was incident on the sample at the angle of ~45 degree through a collimation lens. Scattered light was collected by a pair of miniature lenses into the bundled multi-mode fibers, and then introduced to the slit of a 1.26 m single grating spectrometer equipped with a multi-channel CCD detector. The spectral resolution was 0.02 nm (36 μeV).

The experiment was carried out in the quantum well, composed of non-magnetic well layer, $Cd_{0.93}Zn_{0.07}Te$ and magnetic barrier layers, $Cd_{0.48}Zn_{0.04}Mn_{0.48}Te$.

EXPERIMANTAL RESULTS

Figure 1 shows the Raman/luminescence and PLE spectra of 4 nm quantum well at 0.4 K and 14 T in Voigt configuration for the various excitation energies.

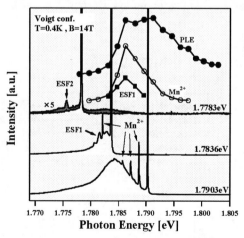

FIGURE 1. Resonant Raman spectra of 4 nm quantum well.

CP893, *Physics of Semiconductors, 28th International Conference*
edited by W. Jantsch and F. Schäffler

A 5 meV deviation between the luminescence and PLE peaks reflects a significant localization of excitons in 4 nm quantum well. At the excitation around the absorption peak of the exciton, multiple Mn^{2+} spin-flip scatterings were observed. With decreasing photon energy, the multiple Mn^{2+} spin-flip scatterings weakened, and a broad spin-flip Raman peak, ESF1 appeared, and reached a maximum intensity at the excitation energy around the luminescence peak.

With further decreasing photon energy, we observed another spin-flip Raman peak, ESF2, only when we illuminated the sample with the light which has the photon energy larger than the band gap of quantum barrier. The spin-flip energies observed in the 4 nm well in Voigt configuration are shown in Fig. 2.

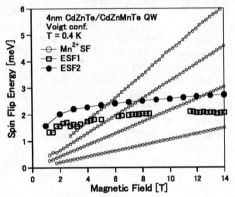

FIGURE 2. Spin-flip energies in 4 nm quantum well.

Heavy-hole spins are considered to be frozen along the growth axis. Multiple Mn^{2+} spin-flip scatterings observed in Voigt configuration are well analyzed by the model by J. Stuhler et. al..[1] The magnetic field dependences of the spin-flip energies of ESF1 and ESF2 are well described by the well-known modified Brillouin function. Evolution of ESF2 spectra is shown in Fig. 3. A similar evolution was observed for ESF1.

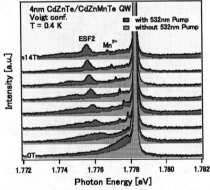

FIGURE 3. Evolution of spin-flip Raman spectra of ESF2

ESF1 and ESF2 are ascribed to the electron spin-flip process since the spin-flip energies are isotropic against the magnetic field direction. Based on the

analysis of 532 nm-illumination effect on the Raman and luminescence spectra we assign that the ESF2 is ascribed to the spin-flip Raman scattering of the electrons injected into the quantum well by the illumination. Consequently, ESF1 is ascribed to the electron spin-flip of the localized exciton in the quantum well.[2] The large energy difference between ESF1 and ESF2 is difficult to ascribe to the exchange interaction between the electron and the hole in an exciton. The origin of the energy difference between ESF2 and ESF1 is still a puzzle.

Both of ESF2 and ESF1 presented non-zero Raman shifts at zero field, as seen in Fig. 3. The shifts disappeared with increasing temperature. These are the evidence for the facts that the bound magnetic polaron [3] and the localized exciton polaron [4] are formed at low temperature even in the weak exchange interaction between the electron in the well and Mn in the barriers.

Figure 4 shows the spin-flip Raman spectra of 9 nm well at 0.4 K in Voigt configuration. In contrast to the 4 nm well, the Mn^{2+} spin-flip scattering was very weak and a low-energy spin-flip excitation was observed instead of the "electron-like" spin-flip scattering. The spin-flip energy was zero up to 4 T and then linearly increased with field, furthermore, the energy increased with temperature. These unusual behaviors rather resemble "softening mode" of spin resonance observed in p-doped ferromagnetic CdMnTe quantum well. [5]

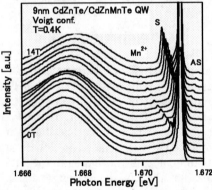

FIGURE 4. Spin-flip Raman spectra of 9 nm quantum well

High resolution Raman spectroscopy at ultra-low temperature revealed some new aspects of the spins in the dilute magnetic semiconductor quantum well.

This work is supported by a Grant-in-Aid for Sci. Res. on priority Areas "High Field Spin Science in 100T" (No.451) from MEXT, Japan.

REFERENCES

1. J. Stuhler et. al., *Phys. Rev. Lett.* 74, 2567-2570 (1995)
2. A. A. Sirenko et. al., *Phys. Rev. B* 56, 2114-2119 (1997)
3. A. Gornik et. al., *J. of Phys. C* 16, 6073-6084 (1983)
4. G. Mackh et. al., *Phys. Rev. B* 49, 10248-10258 (1994)
5. D. Scalbert et. al., Phys. Rev. B 70, 245304-7 (2004)

Photoluminescence and Tunneling of Direct and Indirect Excitons of Semimagnetic Asymmetric Double Quantum Wells CdSe/CdMgSe/CdMnSe

I.I. Reshina, S.V. Ivanov, D.N. Mirlin, I.V. Sedova, and S.V. Sorokin

Ioffe Physical-Technical Institute RAS, Polytecknicheskaya 26, 194021 Sanct-Petersburg, Russia

Abstract. Exciton photoluminescence and reflection spectra of CdSe/CdMgSe/CdMnSe asymmetric double quantum wells with different barriers thickness were studied in strong magnetic fields for the first time. Direct excitons from the nonmagnetic CdSe and semimagnetic CdMnSe quantum wells were observed as well as a spatially indirect exciton formed by the electron in the CdSe quantum well and the heavy-hole in the CdMnSe one. The indirect exciton became observable at magnetic fields around 2 T when it was the lowest energy state of the structure. Its position shifted to lower energies with increasing magnetic field, the intensity increased drastically and the half-width decreased. Up to two LO-phonon replicas of the indirect exciton were observed. The problem of localized magnetic polarons formation is addressed. Polarization properties of the direct and indirect excitons were studied. In case of the effective tunneling of σ^+ - polarized excitons from the CdMnSe well to the CdSe well, a change of circular polarization of the direct CdSe exciton from the negative to positive value was observed under magnetic field. Large anisotropy of the valence band of the CdMnSe quantum well was revealed by comparison of energy shifts in Faraday and Voigt magnetic field configurations. Calculations of exciton energies were performed. Calculated and experimental values were found to be in reasonable accordance.

Keywords: Excitons, semimagnetic double quantum wells
PACS: 78.55.Et; 78.67.De; 71.35.-y; 75.75.+a

INTRODUCTION

Asymmetric double quantum wells (ADQWs) present a possibility to study direct and indirect excitons and their tunneling properties and have received a great deal of attention due both to fundamental scientific significance and device applications. Recently semimagnetic ADQWs gained interest in the growing field of spintronics.

In the present work we have studied spectra of exciton photoluminescence (PL), photoluminescence excitation (PLE) and reflection as well as exciton tunneling in novel ADQW structures CdSe/CdMgSe/CdMnSe grown by molecular beam epitaxy on InAs (100) substrates. The tunneling properties of ADQW's were controlled by the barrier thickness and energy level tuning by applied magnetic field in Faraday configuration. Three samples under study had coupled wells of equal width of 4 nm and different barrier thickness of 1.2, 3 and 5.1 nm. Concentration of Mn was about 7%.

To our knowledge such structures were not grown and studied previously. We have studied recently PL and vertical transport of excitons of CdSe/CdMgSe superlattices with different periods [1].

EXPERIMENTAL RESULTS AND DISCUSSION

Representative PL spectra of the sample 1-307 with 3nm barrier thickness are shown in Fig.1. Three types of excitons were observed: direct excitons (donor-bound and quasi-free E_{11}) of the nonmagnetic quantum well (NQW), direct exciton E_{22} of the MQW and exciton E_{12} which was identified as a spatially indirect exciton formed by the electron in the NQW and the heavy hole in the MQW. Due to large exchange interaction between carriers and Mn^{2+} ions under magnetic field applied in Faraday configuration there is a very large splitting between the spin levels of the conduction and heavy-hole bands. This causes the shift of the E_{22} heavy-hole exciton of the semimagnetic quantum well (MQW) with the ground state $\left|-\frac{1}{2}, \frac{3}{2}\right\rangle$ to lower energies as B is increasing.

CP893, *Physics of Semiconductors, 28th International Conference*
edited by W. Jantsch and F. Schäffler
© 2007 American Institute of Physics 978-0-7354-0397-0/07/$23.00

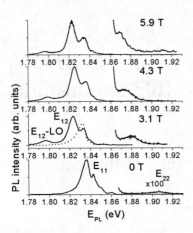

FIGURE 1. Spectra of sample 1-307 (4.2/3/4 nm) at different B in σ^+ polarization. Dotted line corresponds to σ^- polarization.

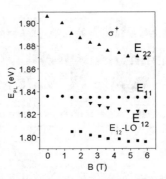

FIGURE 2. Energy of excitons in PL spectrum as a function of magnetic field applied in Faraday configuration.

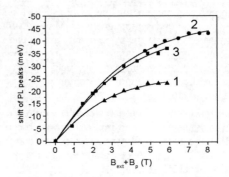

FIGURE 3. Shifts of excitons in the total magnetic field ($B_{ext} + B_p$). 1- E_{12} without account of MP formation ($B_p = 0$ T), 2- shift of MP E_{12} ($B_p = 2.1$ T), 3- shift of E_{22} ($B_p = 0$ T).

The intensity of E_{22} is small due to effective tunneling to the NQW. Exciton E_{12} becomes the lowest energy state and observable in the spectrum around $B = 2$ T. It shifts to lower energy, narrows and enhances markedly in intensity as B increases. It has up to two phonon replicas. The indirect exciton E_{12} was not observed in reflection spectra due to its small oscillator strength. The energy positions of all exciton lines in PL are presented in Fig.2. From the shift of excitons E_{22} and E_{12} effective Mn^{2+} concentration x_{eff} can be obtained [2]. Different values were found from the shifts of E_{22} and E_{12} excitons. This may be explained by formation of localized magnetic polarons (MP). For the indirect exciton with its long lifetime we have indeed measured polaron energy of about 25 meV by the method of selective excitation [3]. If the corresponding exchange field $B_p = 2.1$ T is taken into account, the shift of the E_{12} peak in Fig.3 must be shown not by curve 1, but by curve 2. The shift for the direct exciton E_{22} is shown by curve 3. The process of magnetic polaron formation for E_{22} in samples with small barrier thickness is interrupted due to its small lifetime and tunneling time. Data 2 and 3 are very close and the same values for x_{eff} were obtained from them.

If the magnetic field was applied in the Voigt configuration, the shifts of E_{22} and E_{12} were much smaller revealing large magnetic anisotropy of the heavy-hole band of the semimagnetic quantum well.

Excitons E_{22} and E_{12} are σ^+ polarized already at small B. The peak E_{11} is slightly σ^- polarized at small B. It changes polarization to positive one in the sample 1-309 with the barrier width of 1.2 nm due to tunneling of σ^+ polarized excitons from the MQW and population inversion.

ACKNOWLEDGEMENTS

The authors are very thankful to K.V. Kavokin for helpful discussions. The work was partly supported by the RFBR Grant 06-02-16245.

REFERENCES

1. I I. Reshina, S.V. Ivanov, D.N. Mirlin et al., *Semiconductors* **39,** 432 (2005).
2. J.A. Gaj, R. Planel, and G. Fishman, *Solid State Commun.* **29**, 435 (1979).
3. G. Mackh, W. Ossau, D.R. Yakovlev et al., *Phys. Rev. B* **49**, 10248 (1994).

Exciton and polariton spin beats in a CdMnTe based microcavity

A. Brunetti*, M. Vladimirova*, D. Scalbert* and R. André†

*Groupe d'Etude des Semi-conducteurs, UMR 5650 CNRS-Université Montpellier 2, Place Eugène Bataillon, 34095 Montpellier Cedex, France
†LSP/CNRS, Université J. Fourier, Grenoble, BP 87, 38402 St Martin d'Héres, France

Abstract. Exciton and polariton spin beats are observed in a CdMnTe quantum well embedded in a microcavity using time-resolved Kerr rotation experiments under magnetic field. Photoinduced linear birefringence phenomenon allows to comprehend the polariton spin beats using linear polarized pumping in Faraday geometry. Exciton spin beats can be detected in the standard configuration with circularly polarized pump pulse and under in-plane magnetic field.

Keywords: Polariton, spin beats, time-resolved Kerr rotation
PACS: 71.36.+c, 75.50.Pp, 78.47.+p

Rabi oscillations in microcavities represent quantum beats in a mixed exciton-photon system [1]. Upon excitation by a short laser pulse, a coherent superposition of the upper and lower polariton branches is created. The system then evolves passing from the purely photonic to the purely excitonic state, with the frequency given by the splitting of lower and upper polariton modes. In the presence of the external magnetic field the degeneracy of polariton energy levels is lifted. The coherent excitation of polariton branches leads then to the polariton spin beats at at least two different frequencies, originating from both Rabi and Zeeman polariton splittings [2]. These polariton spin beats persist until the phase correlation between upper and lower polariton branches is lost. The corresponding decay time is expected to be much shorter than the transverse spin relaxation time associated with exciton spin beats in quantum wells. In this paper we study a CdMnTe quantum well in a CdMgTe microcavity using time-resolved Kerr rotation (TRKR) experiments. In the presence of the magnetic field, the excitation by 120 fs laser pulses allows for detection of both exciton and polariton spin beats.

TRKR experiments consist of sending on the sample two optical pulses separated by a time delay Δt. The first pulse (pump) creates a population of circularly or linearly polarized excitons. The second pulse (probe) is always linearly polarized. After reflection from the sample, its polarization plane is rotated due to circular or linear birefringence induced by the pump pulse. The rotation angle oscillates with the frequencies given by exciton (polariton) spin splittings and decays exponentially because of spin depolarization and/or optical polarization decoherence.

Fig. 1a shows an example of the reflectivity spectra measured at zero field, temperature 2 K, detuning $\delta =$

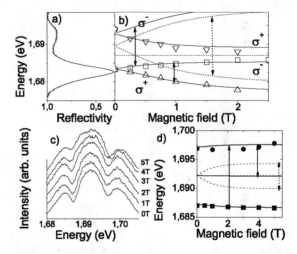

FIGURE 1. (a) Reflectivity at B=0. (b) Polariton energies as a function of the magnetic field in Faraday geometry, extracted from the reflectivity spectra (symbols) and calculated (solid lines). Dashed lines show the corresponding exciton and photon energies in the absence of the coupling. Solid (dashed) arrows show exciton (polariton) splittings. (c) Reflectivity in Voigt geometry, measured using the pump pulse. (d) Same as (b) but in Voigt geometry.

−2.5 meV using a 120 fs pulse. Two polariton modes show up. The magnetic field applied in Faraday geometry splits the σ^+ and σ^- polariton states. The corresponding energies extracted from the reflectivity spectra are shown in Fig. 1b . These energies are described in the framework of the two coupled oscillators model [3], for both circular polarization and taking into account giant exciton Zeeman splitting in the QW [4]. The fitting parameters are Rabi splitting $\Delta_R =10$ meV, zero field detuning of −2.5 meV, exciton splitting at saturation $E_Z^s =10$ meV,

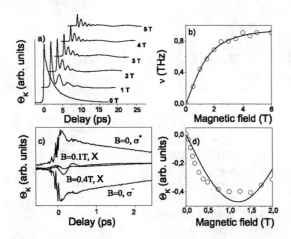

FIGURE 2. (a) Kerr rotation scans under magnetic field in Voigt geometry. (b) Corresponding precession frequencies. (c) TRKR using linearly polarized pump at B=0.1T, B=0.4T applied in Faraday configuration and at B=0, using circularly polarized pump. (d) Amplitude of TRKR at Δt=0.17 ps as a function of magnetic field, fitted by $\sin(\pi B/B_0)$.

effective temperature T =2 K. Dashed lines indicate the exciton and phonon energy levels in the absence of Rabi coupling. One can show that at a given magnetic field the TRKR signal may exhibit the oscillations at the frequencies given by the splittings between the polariton eigen energies [2]. Thus, in the Faraday configuration one expects to detect either exciton spin beats at the frequency given by the Zeeman splitting, or polariton spin beats at both Rabi frequency and the frequency given by the polariton Zeeman splitting. The arrows in Fig. 1b illustrate this argument.

Fig. 1c, d summarizes similar cw magneto-reflectivity experiments realized in Voigt geometry using the circularly polarized light. One can see that polariton energies exhibit almost no shift with magnetic field, because exciton splitting (see dashed lines in Fig. 1 d) is much smaller in this configuration [4]. Solid lines in Fig. 1d) are the polariton energies calculated as described in Ref. [2], using Δ_R=10 meV, zero detuning, electron splitting at saturation E_Z=3.8 meV, T=2 K. Again, the arrows indicate the frequencies of the expected exciton and polariton beats.

Let us now address the results of the TRKR experiments. A waterfall plot of TRKR scans measured under magnetic field up to 5T in Voigt configuration is shown in Fig. 2a. One can see that the rotation angle Θ_K plotted as a function of the pump-probe delay oscillates at a field dependent frequency and exponentially decays at zero field. The decay time is about 3 ps. The frequencies are reported in Fig. 2b as a function of the magnetic field. The observed field dependence of the spin beats frequency corresponds to the conduction band splitting and can be perfectly described by the Brillouin function

at T=3.8 K. The polariton spin beats can not be distinguished in these data, except in B=0 scan, where exciton spin beats do not appear (see also Fig. 2c). In contrast, in Faraday configuration at linear pumping the polariton beats do show up, and their intensity depends on the applied field. Fig. 2c shows the TRKR scans measured at B=0.1 T and B=0.4 T. One can see the oscillations with 0.5 ps period (corresponding to the 10 meV level splitting), with sub-picosecond decay time. This is the manifestation of Rabi beats in the coherently excited polariton system. The second precession frequency, resulting from the polariton Zeeman splitting, is much lower than Rabi frequency. Since the oscillation period is longer then the decay time, these beats are hard to detect. However, the contribution of Zeeman beats can be extracted in a tricky way. This is shown in Fig. 2d, where the amplitude of the TRKR signal at Δt=0.17 ps is shown as a function of magnetic field. The experimental points are fitted with the periodic function, $\sin(\pi B/B_0)$. Such behavior reflects the fact that the TRKR is proportional to the sinus of the angle, by which the pump-induced polarization in the sample is rotated during the pump-probe delay time. $B_0 = hB/(2E_Z\Delta t)$, where E_Z is the polariton Zeeman splitting, h is Planck constant, and it does not depend on the field in the linear regime. From the fit of the data shown in Fig. 2d we obtain B_0=2.4T, in good agreement with polariton Zeeman splitting measured from the reflectivity spectra.

In conclusion, we have studied the spin beats in the CdMnTe QW microcavity in the strong coupling regime using TRKR. Both exciton and polariton beats could be observed. In Voigt configuration the TRKR is dominated by the exciton spin precession, while in Faraday geometry the polariton spin beats are clearly marked. The polariton beats decay on the sub-picosecond time scale, governed by the optical decoherence time. This time is much shorter then the spin decoherence time, which characterize exciton spin relaxation (3 ps).

We acknowledge the support from the Marie-Curie RTN project 503677 "Clermont2".

REFERENCES

1. T.B. Norris, J.K. Rhee, C.Y. Sung, Y. Arakawa, M. Nishioka, C. Weisbuch, Phys. Rev. B **50** 14663 (1994).
2. A. Brunetti, M.R. Vladimirova, D. Scalbert, R. André, D. Solnyshkov, G. Malpuech, I. A. Shelykh, A. V. Kavokin, Phys. Rev. B **73**, 205337 (2006).
3. V. Savona, L.C. Andreani, P. Schwendimann, and A. Quattropani, Solid State Commun. **93**, 733 (1995).
4. Diluted Magnetic Semiconductors, J. K. Furdyna and J. Kossut (eds.), Semiconductors and Semimetals Vol. 25 (Academic, New York, 1988).
5. M. Vladimirova, D. Scalbert, M. Nawrocki Phys. Stat. Sol. (c), **2**, 910-913 (2005).

The magnetotransport properties of Co-doped ZnO films

Qingyu Xu, Lars Hartmann, Heidemarie Schmidt, Holger Hochmuth, Michael Lorenz, Rüdiger Schmidt-Grund, Chris Sturm, Daniel Spemann, and Marius Grundmann

Universität Leipzig, Fakultät für Physik und Geowissenschaften, Institut für Experimentelle Physik II, Linnéstrasse 5, D-04103 Leipzig, Germany

Abstract. Co-doped ZnO films with Co content above 7% have been grown by pulsed laser deposition on a-sapphire substrates. Temperature and magnetic field dependent magnetotransport measurements have been performed on samples with electron concentration n around the critical electron concentration $n_c \approx 4.9 \times 10^{19}$ cm^{-3}, where the metal-insulator transition (MIT) occurs. At 5 K we observed positive magnetoresistance (MR) in the insulating range (n<n_c) and negative MR in the metallic range (n>n_c). The MIT was determined from the MR and Hall effect at 5 K to occur at the electron concentration $n_c \approx 4 \times 10^{19}$ cm^{-3}. In the vicinity of the MIT (n~n_c) we observed negative MR at low field and positive MR at high field. Only for n<n_c we observed clear anomalous Hall effect in the Co-doped ZnO films being of relevance for use in future spintronic devices.

Keywords: magnetic oxide semiconductor, magnetoresistance, anomalous Hall effect, metal-insulator transition.
PACS: 75.50.Pp, 75.47.De, 73.61.Ga, 71.30.+h

INTRODUCTION

ZnO doped with 3d transition metals to form diluted magnetic semiconductor is attracting much attentions due to the theoretical prediction of the realization of room temperature ferromagnetism and potential applications in the future spintronics [1]. The charge carrier type may play essential role in mediating the ferromagnetism in 3d-doped ZnO. Ferromagnetism is favoured in p-type conducting Mn-doped ZnO, and in n-type conducting Co-doped ZnO [2]. However, ZnO is intrinsically n-type conducting. The p-type conducting ZnO is still an open issue. In this paper, we study the magnetotransport properties of n-type conducting Co-doped ZnO films, a critical electron concentration (n_c) has been determined which controls the magnetoresistance (MR) behaviour.

EXPERIMENTAL DETAILS

The Co-doped ZnO films were grown from a $Zn_{0.945}Co_{0.05}Al_{0.005}O$ PLD target on a-plane sapphire substrates by pulsed laser deposition (PLD) using a KrF excimer laser. The PLD target was prepared by mixing and pressing appropriate amounts of ZnO (99.9%), CoO (99.999%), and Al_2O_3 (99.998%) powders. The 0.5 mol% Al was included in the target to fabricate conductive thin films. The resulting composition of the films was determined by combined Rutherford Backscattering Spectrometry (RBS) and Particle Induced X-ray Emission (PIXE) measurements, and varied from ~7% to ~10% with increasing the substrate temperature during growth from 390 °C to 820 °C. Due to the Al_2O_3 substrate, the Al content in the Co-doped ZnO films could not be determined. Only (002) and (004) ZnO peaks were observed without any other impurity phase observed in the X-ray diffraction patterns. The magnetic field was applied perpendicular to the film plane. The resistance was measured in the van der Pauw geometry.

RESULTS AND DISCUSSIONS

Fig. 1 summarizes the electron concentration n dependence of MR measured at 6 T and 5 K. It can be clearly seen that the critical electron concentration amounts to $n_c \sim 4 \times 10^{19}$ cm^{-3}. The samples will show negative MR for n>n_c and positive MR for n<n_c. The positive MR increases dramatically with decreasing n. The electronic properties of n-conducting semiconductors sensitively depend on the ratio between the mean distance of donors $r = (3/4\pi n)^{1/3}$ and their effective Bohr radius a_B [3]. In the diluted case, r>>a_B, electrons are bound to individual impurities,

CP893, *Physics of Semiconductors, 28th International Conference*
edited by W. Jantsch and F. Schäffler
© 2007 American Institute of Physics 978-0-7354-0397-0/07/$23.00

and low-temperature conduction proceeds by means of phonon-assisted tunneling between occupied and empty states. The semiconductor is in the insulating regime. In the opposite limit, $r \ll a_B$, electrons reside in the conduction band, and low temperature mobility is determined by ionized impurity scattering. The critical electron concentration n_c, where the metal insulator transition (MIT) happens, can be estimated from $r = a_B$, thus, $n_c = (0.62/a_B)^3$. With a_B amounting to 1.7 nm for ZnO, n_c is calculated to be 4.9×10^{19} cm^{-3} and agrees well with the experimental determined value [4].

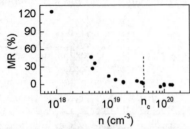

FIGURE 1. The MR value at maximum field 6 T for the Co-doped ZnO films in dependence on electron concentration n at 5 K. The scattered line indicates the critical electron concentration n_c.

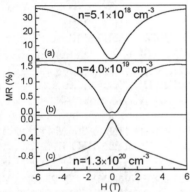

FIGURE 2. The MR as a function of the magnetic field measured on Co-doped ZnO films at 5 K with (a) $n < n_c$ (b) $n \sim n_c$ and (c) $n > n_c$.

Fig. 2 clearly shows the MR behaviour for the Co-doped ZnO films in the insulating range ($n < n_c$), metallic range ($n > n_c$), and transition range ($n \sim n_c$) at 5 K. In the metallic range, only negative MR was observed, which was interpreted to be due to the suppression of the magnetic scattering by the applied magnetic field. In the insulating range, positive MR was observed, which is interpreted to be due to the modified electron-electron interactions by the s-d exchange interaction [5]. For the film in the transition range ($n \sim n_c$), negative MR at low field and positive MR at high field was observed.

Anomalous Hall effect (AHE) is a well-known ferromagnetic response of charge carriers in ferromagnetic semiconductors. AHE can only be clearly observed in the insulating film. Fig. 3 shows the field dependence of ρ_{xy} at 20 K for an insulating Co-doped ZnO film ($n = 6.7 \times 10^{17}$ cm^{-3} at 20 K). The s-shaped curve clearly indicates the AHE.

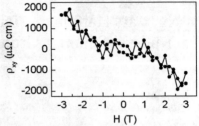

FIGURE 3. Hall resistivity versus magnetic field for Co-doped ZnO with $n = 6.7 \times 10^{17}$ cm^{-3} at 20 K.

The observed positive MR and clear AHE for Co-doped ZnO films with $n < n_c$ indicates the possible realization of ferromagnetism in insulating Co-doped ZnO films, which was further demonstrated by the recent observation of the giant magnetic moment of 6.1 μ_B/Co and high Curie temperature of 790 K in ferromagnetic insulating (4 at.%) Co-doped ZnO [6]. However, more experimental and theoretical work is needed to further clarify the electron-electron interaction in the doped ZnO films and the relation between the magnetic and magnetotransport properties.

ACKNOWLEDGMENTS

This work is partially (Q. X., H. S., and H. H.) supported by BMBF (FKZ03N8708). The authors would like to thank G. Ramm for the target preparation.

REFERENCES

1. T. Dietl, H. Ohno, F. Matsukura, J. Cibert, and D. Ferrand, *Science* **287**, 1019-1022 (2000).
2. K. R. Kittilstved, N. S. Norberg, and D. R. Gamelin, *Phys. Rev. Lett.* **94**, 147209 (2005).
3. T. Dietl, "Transport phenomena in semimagnetic semiconductors," in *Semimagnetic Semiconductors and Diluted Magnetic Semiconductors*, edited by M. Averous and M. Balkanski, New York: Plenum Press, 1991, pp. 83-119.
4. Q. Xu, L. Hartmann, H. Schmidt, H. Hochmth, M. Lorenz, R. Schmidt-Grund, C. Sturm, D. Spemann, and M. Grundmann, *Phys. Rev. B* **73**, 205342 (2006).
5. T. Andrearczyk, J. Jaroszyński, G. Grabecki, T. Dietl, T. Fukumura, and M. Kawasaki, *Phys. Rev. B* **72**, 121309 (2005).
6. C. Song, K. W. Geng, F. Zeng, X. B. Wang, Y. X. Shen, F. Pan, Y. N. Xie, T. Liu, H. T. Zhou, and Z. Fan, *Phys. Rev. B* **73**, 024405 (2006).

Room Temperature Magneto-optics Of Ferromagnetic ZnO Doped With Transition Metals And Aluminum

JR Neal[1], XH Xu[2], AJ Behan[1], RM Ibrahim[1], H J Blythe[1], M Ziese[3], AM Fox[1] and GA Gehring[1]

[1]Department of Physics and Astronomy, The University of Sheffield, Sheffield, S3 7RH. UK
[2]School of Chemistry and Materials Science, Shanxi Normal University, Shanxi, Linfen 041004, P. R. China
[3] Universitaet Leipzig, Fakultaet fuer Physik und Geowissenschaften, Abteilung Supraleitung und Magnetismus, Linnestrasse 5, 04103 Leipzig, Germany

Abstract. Thin film samples of ZnO doped with Co were grown on sapphire substrates by pulsed laser deposition (PLD). The magnetization was measured by SQUID magnetometry and the films were found to be ferromagnetic at room temperature. The transmission and magnetic circular dichroism were measured as a function of energy at room temperature and carrier concentrations were determined from Hall effect measurements. Clear magneto-optical signals that are ferromagnetic in origin were observed at the ZnO band edge and the conditions for optimizing the magnetization are discussed.

Keywords: ZnO, Dilute magnetic semiconductor, Magneto-optic.
PACS: 78.20.Ls; 72.20.–i; 75.50.Pp

INTRODUCTION

Dilute magnetic semiconductors (DMS) are a highly topical due to the possibility of integrating these materials into new or existing electronic and optoelectronic devices in order to provide increased functionality by the provision of an additional electronic state.

The prototypical material system of GaMnAs has received a great deal of attention with clear demonstration of DMS behavior though numerous studies[1,2]. However, the highest T_C obtained so far is still well below room temperature [3], so, whilst providing valuable insight into the physical processes involved within DMS materials and devices, there is still a great need to realize DMS materials with T_C in excess of room temperature.

Transition metal doped ZnO based DMS appear to be a particularly promising group of materials for achieving room temperature ferromagnetism within a semiconductor since the prediction[4], and subsequent observation[5,6] of ferromagnetism within Mn doped ZnO. However, the mechanism behind the observed ferromagnetism has proven to be somewhat controversial since magnetization measurements alone cannot differentiate unambiguously between genuine ferromagnetic semiconductors and semiconductors containing clusters of magnetic dopants.

Despite numerous magneto-optical studies[7,8] of ZnO doped with various transition metals, which are able to directly observe the origin of the ferromagnetism, there has not until recently[6] been any direct observation of a band edge signal at room temperature. The aim of this paper is to demonstrate that the magnetic properties of such samples are optimized for one carrier per two transition ions. We also show that the observed magnetization is due to spin-splitting of the ZnO conduction band as opposed to the presence of a secondary impurity phase.

EXPERIMENT

The samples studied were thin films of $Zn_{1-x-y}Co_xAl_yO$ with x=5% and y=0-2% that were grown from a corresponding target by pulsed laser deposition. The films were deposited upon Al_2O_3 (0001) which was maintained at approximately 725K in an oxygen atmosphere. The oxygen pressure was varied from 10-0.03mTorr in order to change the number of Zn interstitials and oxygen vacancies, and subsequently the carrier concentration.

Hall effect measurements were made in a continuous flow cryostat equipped with an iron bore magnet and allowed the ratio of the number of carriers to the number of transition metal donors (n_c/n_i) to be determined for each sample. SQUID magnetometry measurements were performed to

CP893, *Physics of Semiconductors, 28th International Conference*
edited by W. Jantsch and F. Schäffler
© 2007 American Institute of Physics 978-0-7354-0397-0/07/$23.00

determine the magnetic moments of the samples that exhibited room temperature ferromagnetism.

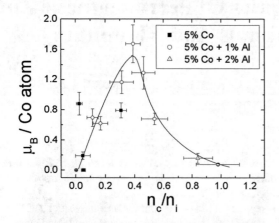

FIGURE 1. Room temperature magnetic moment per Co ion for $Zn_{0.95}Co_{0.05}O$ with and without Al co-dopant as a function of the ratio of the room temperature carrier density to the density of magnetic ions. The curve is a guide to the eye.

From figure 1 it can clearly be seen that irrespective of the means of adding carriers to the Co doped thin film samples, either by introducing zinc interstitials by low pressure growth or by Al co-doping, that the magnetic moment of the samples is optimized for a ratio of the carrier density to the density of magnetic ions, n_c/n_i of 0.5. This ratio corresponds to having one carrier to two transition metal dopant ions[9]. The dependence of the magnetization on the carrier density is shown to vary in a way that is predicted by theory for T_C [10].

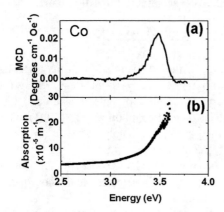

FIGURE 2. (a) MCD spectra and (b) absorption spectra for a 300nm thick $Zn_{0.98}Co_{0.02}O$ thin film measured at room temperature.

Magneto-optical spectra were recorded with a Xenon lamp and monochromator with a photoelastic modulator that allows for the simultaneous recording

of the Faraday rotation and magnetic circular dichroism (MCD) as a function of energy. An electromagnet provided a field of 1T.

Figure 2(a) shows the MCD of a thin film of $Zn_{0.98}Co_{0.02}O$ approximately 300nm thick with n_c/n_i = 0.5. The peak in the MCD centered at approximately 3.4eV, which can be seen from figure 2(b) to correspond to the ZnO band edge, is indicative of the magnetic Co ions hybridizing with the ZnO conduction band resulting in band splitting.

CONCLUSIONS

The inclusion of free electrons can be highly beneficial for the magnetism in ZnO and highlights the importance of electron-mediated exchange. The MCD spectra of a sample with optimal carrier concentration illustrates that the Co ions hybridize with the ZnO conduction band and provide further evidence that the observed magnetism is an intrinsic property of the samples and not due to an impurity phase.

ACKNOWLEDGMENTS

The authors are grateful for support from the Engineering and Physical Sciences Research Council (EPSRC) and Royal Society of UK.

REFERENCES

1. A.H. MacDonald, P.Schiffer, M.Samarth, *Nature Materials* **4**, (2005) p. 195
2. J.Sinova, T. Jungwirth, J.Cerne, *Int. J. of Mod. Phys. B* **18**, (2004) p.1083
3. K.Wang, R.P.Campion, K.W. Edmonds, M. Sawicki, T. Dietl, C.T.Foxon, B.L.Gallagher *Proc. 27th Conf. on Phys. Of Semicon Flagstaff, Az, July 2004*, Eds. J. Menendez and CH. Van de Walle, p333, New York (2005).
4. T. Dietl, H. Ohno, F. Matsukura, J. Ciebert, D. Ferrand, *Science* **287**, (2000) p. 1019
5. P.Sharma, A. Gupta, K.V. Rao, F.J. Owens, R. Sharma, R. Ahuja, J.M.O. Guillen, B. Johansson, G.A.Gehring, *Nature Materials* **2**, (2003) p. 673
6. J.R.Neal, A.J. Behan, R.M. Ibrahim, H.J. Blythe, M. Ziese, A.M. Fox, G.A.Gehring, *Physical Review Letters* **96**, (2006) 197208-1
7. K. Ando, H. Saito, Z. Jin, T. Fukumura, M. Kawasaki, *Applied Physics Letters* **78**, (2001) p. 2700
8. K. Ando, H. Saito, V. Zayets, M.C. Debnath, *Journal of Physics: Condensed Matter* **16**, (2004) p. S5541
9. X.H. Xu, A.J. Behan, M. Ziese, H.J. Blythe, J.R. Neal, A. Mokhtari, M.R. Ibrahim, A.M. Fox and G. A. Gehring, *cond-mat* (2006) 0605654
10. T. Jungwirth, J. Masek, K.Y. Wang, K.W. Edmonds, M. Sawicki, M. Polini, J. Sinova, A.H. MacDonald, R.P. Campion, L.X. Zhao, N.R.S. Farley, T.K. Johal, G. van der Laan, C.T. Foxon, B.L. Gallagher, *Phys. Rev. B*, **73**, 165205 (2006).

Theoretical model of magnetoexcitons in $Zn_{1-x}Co_xO$

Witold Bardyszewski

Institute of Theoretical Physics, Warsaw University, Hoża 69, 00-681 Warsaw, Poland

Abstract. The excitonic spectra of $Zn_{1-x}Co_xO$ in magnetic field are studied theoretically. Our model takes into account the full hexagonal symmetry of electron states, the electron-hole exchange coupling and the *s,p-d* interaction of free carriers with the localized Co^{2+} ions. The absorption curves for various magnetic fields are obtained by diagonalizing the multiband excitonic equation using the Lanczos reduction method.

Keywords: magnetoexcitons, electron-hole exchange
PACS: 78.66.Hf,75.50.Pp

Zinc oxide doped with cobalt has been recently studied as a possible semiconducting ferromagnetic material at room temperature [1]. Due to the *s,p-d* exchange interaction of free carriers and localized spins, the magnetic ordering of the Co^{2+} ions can be studied by means of magneto-optical measurements. However, proper interpretation of the optical spectra of such a system requires a detailed discussion of excitonic effects in the presence of the external magnetic field. The complications associated with the complex structure of the valence band in this wurtzite type material, possible built-in strain in the sample and the s,p-d coupling of the electron and hole with the magnetic ions can be described only using a very advanced theoretical model.

Although the symmetry of the conduction and valence band states in ZnO is determined by the sp^3 hybridization of atomic orbitals, the actual sequence of the valence band levels is still a matter of controversy. In general, taking into account the spin, the twofold conduction band level has Γ_7 symmetry while the sixfold top of the valence band is split by the crystal field and spin-orbit interaction into one twofold Γ_9 level and two Γ_7 levels. It is commonly believed that the topmost valence band level has Γ_9 symmetry [2] although it was shown that in the regime of negative spin-orbit interaction, the sequence $\Gamma_7 + \Gamma_9 + \Gamma_7$ is also possible. This ambiguity is related to the fact that the spin-orbit coupling in ZnO seems to be fairly small. Moreover the strong asymmetry in the intensity between the lowest in exciton line A and the next exciton B seems to indicate that the short range electron-hole interaction in excitons plays a very important role. Adding Co ions into the system at first sight provides an additional degree of freedom which could be used to settle this controversy. Unfortunately it also brings two additional unknowns - the coupling constants of electrons and holes to the magnetic ions.

Recently we have developed a universal computational technique to evaluate excitonic spectra in complex, multiband systems in the presence of the magnetic field of arbitrary strength [3]. Our model which employs the Lanczos reduction method to solve the excitonic eigenvalue problem in the Landau orbital representation provides a rather accurate description of the low energy part of the excitonic spectra. In this report we demonstrate theoretical results of our technique for interband excitonic spectra in $Zn_{1-x}Co_xO$ as function of the magnetic field.

THEORETICAL MODEL

The exciton Hamiltonian is assumed in the form:

$$\mathscr{H}^X = H^c(p_e) - H^v(p_v) + H_{ex} + H_{s,p\text{-}d} \qquad (1)$$

where $H^c(p_e)$ and $H^v(p_v)$ denote free conduction and valence band Hamiltonians depending on respective kinematic momenta of the electron and hole in the magnetic field parallel to the *c*-axis. The electron-hole exchange interaction is given by $H_{ex} = \frac{J}{2}((1 - \sigma_e \cdot \sigma_h)$ where σ_i, $i = e, h$ denote Pauli operators for electrons and holes while the coupling to the localized Co spins is given by $H_{s,p\text{-}d} = N_0 x_{eff} < -\hat{S}_z > (\alpha \hat{s}_{e,z} + \beta \hat{s}_{h,z})$. Here N_0 is equal to the concentration of cations, x_{eff} denotes the effective fraction of Co ions and $< S_z >$ is equal to the mean value of the cobalt spin which can be easily estimated assuming the paramagnetic phase. The exchange constants α and β can be estimated from the experiment by analyzing the enhanced Zeeman splitting of excitonic lines. We solve the excitonic eigen-value problem using the Lanczos reduction technique in the basis set of the Landau orbitals to describe the relative electron-hole motion in the plane perpendicular to the *c*-axis, multiplied by plane waves in the direction of the magnetic field. We have employed Landau orbitals corresponding to the fixed field $B_0 = 18T$ at which the magnetic length is comparable to the characteristic Bohr radius of the

CP893, *Physics of Semiconductors, 28th International Conference*
edited by W. Jantsch and F. Schäffler

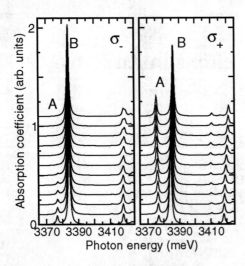

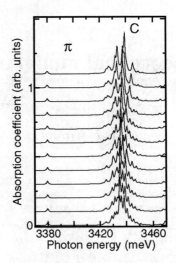

FIGURE 1. Exciton absorption in σ_- and σ_+ polarization for magnetic fields $B = 1, 2, \ldots, 11T$. The curves are shifted vertically for clarity.

FIGURE 2. Exciton absorption in π polarization for magnetic fields $B = 1, 2, \ldots, 11T$. The curves are shifted vertically for clarity.

exciton[3]. In the present calculations we have used 80 Landau orbitals and 31 plane waves.

RESULTS AND DISCUSSION

We have employed the band structure constants for the conduction and valence band such as the conduction band effective mass and $A_1, \ldots, A_6$ parameters obtained from the *ab initio* band structure calculations [4]. The parameters Δ_1, Δ_2 and Δ_3 describing the crystal field and spin-orbit interaction, as well as the electron-hole exchange constant J and the Luttinger parameter κ responsible for the coupling of the exciton angular momentum to the magnetic field are obtained by fitting the Zeeman splitting of the lowest excitons A and B to the experimental data obtained for low cobalt content of 0.4% in ref. [1]. Similarly, as in this reference , a very good agreement with experimental Zeeman splitting can be achieved using two sets of parameters: one with positive spin-orbit coupling yielding the "standard" $\Gamma_9 - \Gamma_7 - \Gamma_7$ ordering of the valence band levels and one with the negative spin-orbit leading to the inversion of the topmost Γ_7 and Γ_9 levels. The parameters obtained in our fitting procedure differ only slightly from those obtained in the reference [1] for a very simple model Hamiltonian. We have noticed that these two sets of parameters lead to very similar dependence of the absorption spectra on the magnetic field. In Fig. 1 we present the absorption curves in $Zn_{1-x}Co_xO$ for $x = 0.004$ for the σ_+ and σ_- polarization of light corresponding to the excitons of symmetry Γ_5. For the sake of presentation the discrete absorption lines are broadened with the Lorentzian line-shape function with FWHM equal to 0.7 meV. We have assumed

$\Delta_1 = 51\text{eV}, \Delta_2 = 3\text{eV}, \Delta_3 = 6.3\text{eV}, \kappa = -0.015, J = 3.2$ meV,$N_0(\alpha - \beta) = 0.8eV$. Strong asymmetry in intensity between the lowest A exciton and the next B exciton line is clearly visible. Fig. 2 shows the absorption spectra in the π polarization with the electric field parallel to the c axis. The visible exciton lines are of Γ_1 symmetry. We can see a characteristic, strong C exciton line at 3437 meV which is broadened due to the coupling to the continuum of states of the other two excitons via $k \cdot p$ interaction. The FWHM of this line is as large as 10meV. Below this strong line we see a weak Γ_1 line at 3380 meV. This low energy Γ_1 line is the only feature which distinguishes the absorption spectra models with positive and negative spin-orbit couplings. In conclusion, we have presented an accurate model of excitonic transitions in $Zn_{1-x}Co_xO$ in the magnetic field taking into account the full symmetry of excitons, the exchange e-h coupling as well as the interaction with localized Co spins. We have analyzed the absorption spectra for the low concentration of Co. We have found that the spectra for positive and negative spin orbit interaction are very similar.

REFERENCES

1. W. Pacuski, D. Ferrand, J. Cibert, C. Deparis, J. A. Gaj, P. Kossacki, and C. Morhain, Phys.Rev. B **73**, 035214 (2006).
2. D.C. Reynolds, D.C.Look, B.Jogai,C.W.Litton, G,Cantwell and W.C. Harsh, Phys.Rev. B **60**, 2340 (1999-II).
3. M. Sobol and W. Bardyszewski, Phys.Rev. B **73**, 075208 (2006).
4. W.R.L. Lambrecht, A.V.Rodina, S.Limpijumnong, B.Segall,and B.Meyer, Phys.Rev. B **65**, 075207 (2002).

Fabrication and characterization of *n*-type modulation-doped (Cd,Cr)Te quantum well

F. Takano[1], T. Nishizawa[1,2], H. Kinjo[2], J.W. Lee[2], S. Kuroda[2], H. Ofuchi[3], Y. Imanaka[4], T. Takamasu[4], G. Kido[4], K. Takita[2] and H. Akinaga[1]

[1]*Nanotechnology Research Institute (NRI), National Institute of Advanced Industrial Science and Technology (AIST), Tsukuba Central 2, 1-1-1 Umezono, Tsukuba, Ibaraki 305-8568, Japan*
[2]*Institute of Materials Science, University of Tsukuba, 1-1-1 Tennodai, Tsukuba, Ibaraki 305-8573, Japan*
[3] *Japan Synchrotron Radiation Research Institute (JASRI), 1-1-1 Kouto, Sayo-cho, Sayo-gun, Hyogo, 679-5198, Japan*
[4]*National Institute for Materials Science (NIMS), 3-13 Sakura, Tsukuba, Ibaraki 305-0003, Japan*

Abstract. A novel ferromagnetic II-VI diluted magnetic semiconductor, (Cd,Cr)Te, has been combined with a two-dimensional electron system. The anomalous Hall effect accompanied by the hysteresis loop was successfully observed in the Hall measurement. This fact shows the ferromagnetic exchange interaction between carrier and magnetic moment was realized in the present system.

Keywords: Ferromagnetic diluted magnetic semiconductor (DMS), (Cd,Cr)Te, modulation-doped quantum well.
PACS: 72.25.Dc, 73.61.Ga

INTRODUCTION

Over the past decade, there has been a growing interest in the two-dimensional electron systems (2DESs) based on II-VI diluted magnetic semiconductors (DMSs) such as (Cd,Mn)Te [1] and (Zn,Cd,Mn)Se [2] having paramagnetic properties. The incorporation of magnetic elements into 2DES made it possible to investigate the spin properties of 2DES emerging prominently due to the exchange interaction with localized magnetic moments [3]. Moreover, the anomalous Hall effect (AHE) successfully observed in (Zn,Cd,Mn)Se-2DES was quite recently reported [4]. On the other hand, the study on ferromagnetic II-VI DMSs, such as (Zn,Cr)Te [5], is now in full flood. As a consequence of coupling of the ferromagnetic DMS with 2DES, one may expect the novel physical phenomena resulting from the 'ferromagnetic' *sp-d* exchange interaction. However, in ZnTe-based structure, the control of *n*-type doping is very difficult because of its strong *p*-type polarity. For CdTe, on the other hand, the polarity type is negative. Actually, (Cd,Cr)Te has been found to be ferromagnetic in our recent study [6]. In this paper, a new class of DMS-based 2DES, a modulation-doped (Cd,Cr)Te quantum well, is shown for the first time to our knowledge. We discuss the transport properties in this system.

EXPERIMENTAL

Our modulation-doped QW (MDQW) structure was fabricated using a molecular-beam epitaxy (MBE) technique on a (001)-oriented semi-insulating GaAs substrate. A (Cd,Cr)Te well layer (~100Å) was sandwiched between the (Cd,Mg)Te barriers, and an *n*-type doped layer (~80Å) was separated by a spacer (~80Å) from the well. Here, the iodine (I) was used for the *n*-type dopant. The Cr was uniformly incorporated into the well. The Cr composition of 1% was estimated by the electron probe micro-analyzer (EPMA) measurement of the thin film prepared under the same condition as the well layer. To investigate the local atomic order around the Cr atoms in the (Cd,Cr)Te film, the extended X-ray absorption fine structure (EXAFS) measurement was performed. A superconducting quantum interference device (SQUID) magnetometer was used to investigate the magnetic property of the (Cd,Cr)Te film. The transport measurements were performed on the MDQW.

RESULTS AND DISCUSSION

We show in FIG. 1(a) the Fourier transforms of the Cr K-edge EXAFS oscillation of the $Cd_{0.99}Cr_{0.01}Te$

CP893, *Physics of Semiconductors, 28th International Conference*
edited by W. Jantsch and F. Schäffler
© 2007 American Institute of Physics 978-0-7354-0397-0/07/$23.00

film. The theoretically calculated EXAFS spectrum for the substitutional Cr atom on the Cd-site in the zinc-blende CdTe lattice is compiled in FIG. 1(b). The experimental result is in good agreement with the theoretical calculation to support that our (Cd,Cr)Te is pure DMS excluding any secondary phases. This is consistent with the result of the X-ray diffraction measurement (not shown). A Curie temperature (T_C) of $Cd_{1-x}Cr_xTe$ film increased with the Cr composition up to ~150K (x ~ 0.224) [6]. For the present case, i.e. x ~ 0.01, the T_C was estimated to be below 5K. FIG. 1(c) shows the magnetic field dependence of magnetization (M-H) of the $Cd_{0.99}Cr_{0.01}Te$ film. A clear hysteresis loop showing ferromagnetism was observed at 2K.

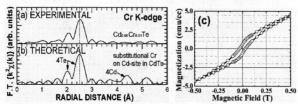

FIGURE 1. (a),(b) Fourier transform of Cr K-edge EXAFS oscillations for the $Cd_{0.99}Cr_{0.01}Te$ thin film and theoretical EXAFS spectrum for the substitutional Cr atom on the Cd-site in the CdTe lattice. 4Te and 4Cd show the coordination number. The theoretical EXAFS spectrum was generated by FEFF8 [7]. (c) M-H curve of the $Cd_{0.99}Cr_{0.01}Te$ film at 2K. The magnetic fields were applied perpendicular to the film.

The temperature dependence of longitudinal resistivity of the MDQW (FIG. 2) shows metallic behavior between room temperature and ~50K to support that 2D electron gas formed. At below 50K, on the other hand, the resistivity was suppressed rapidly with an increase in the temperature. This could be resulting from a carrier capture effect due to the Cr deep level. A detailed mechanism is now controversial.

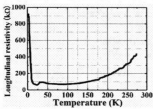

FIGURE 2. Temperature dependence of longitudinal resistivity of the MDQW.

We show in FIG. 3(a) the field dependence of Hall resistivity of the MDQW at 1.6K. The AHE accompanied by hysteresis loop was successfully observed. This fact supports the ferromagnetic exchange interaction between carrier and magnetic moment was realized in the present system. The estimation of 2D carrier density and Hall mobility was unsuccessful because of the AHE dominantly observed in the vicinity of zero magnetic fields. Negative

magneto-resistivity (MR) was observed continuously up to ±7T. (FIG. 3(b)). Here, two possible explanations for the negative MR are considered. One is the effect of magnetic polarons (MPs) formation, that is, the localized carriers due to the MPs formation in a zero magnetic field was released by the magnetic fields [8]. The suppression of 'simple' spin-disorder scattering is considered as the second possible candidate, i.e., the electron scattering due to the randomly oriented *d*-spins in a zero magnetic field was suppressed by applying the magnetic fields.

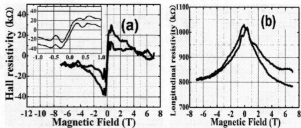

FIGURE 3. (a) Hall resistivity (HR) and (b) magneto-resistivity (MR) of the MDQW measured at 1.6K. Magnetic field was swept between +7T and -7T to obtain the hysteresis loop of HR and MR.

ACKNOWLEDGMENTS

This work was partly supported by Grant-in-Aid for Scientific Research on priority Areas 'High Field Spin Science in 100T' from MEXT. EXAFS study was performed as part of a project (Project No. 2005G181) accepted by the Photon Factory Program Advisory Committee.

REFERENCES

1. S. Scholl, H. Schafer, A. Waag, D. Hommel, K. von Schierstedt and B. Kuhn-Heinrich, Appl. Phys. Lett. **62**, 3010 (1993).
2. I. P. Smorchkova, N. Samarth, J. M. Kikkawa, and D. D. Awschalom, Phys. Rev. Lett. **78**, 3571 (1997).
3. e.g., F. Takano, S. Kuroda, K. Takita, T. Takamasu, Y. Imanaka and G. Kido, Physica E **22**, 615 (2004)., F. Takano, T. Tokizaki, H. Akinaga, S. Kuroda and K. Takita, Phys Rev. B **71**, 125326 (2005).
4. J. Cumings, L. S. Moore, H. T. Chou, K. C. Ku, G. Xiang, S. A. Crooker. N. Samarth, and D. Goldhaber-Gordon, Phys. Rev. Lett. **96**, 196404 (2006).
5. H. Saito, V. Zayets, S. Yamagata and K. Ando, Phys. Rev. Lett. **90**, 207202 (2003).
6. H. Kinjo, S. Kuroda, K. Takita, H. Ofuchi, F. Takano and H. Akinaga, unpublished.
7. A. L. Ankudinov, and J. J. Rehr, Phys. Rev. B **65**, 104107 (2002).
8. D. Ferrand, J. Cibert, A. Wasiela, C. Bourgognon, S. Tatarenko, T. Andrearczyk, J. Jaroszyński, S. Koleśnik, T. Dietl, B. Barbara, and D. Dufeu, Phys. Rev. B **63**, 85201 (2001).

Single Particle Parameters of a Spin Polarized Electron Gas in CdMnTe Quantum Wells: Comparison between Raman Scattering and Photoluminescence

C. Aku-Leh[1,2], F. Perez[1], B. Jusserand[1], D. Richards[2], and G. Karczewski[3]

[1] Institut des Nanosciences de Paris, UMR 7588, CNRS/Université Paris VI et VII, Campus Boucicaut, 140 rue de Lourmel, 75015 PARIS, France
[2] Department of Physics, King's College London, Strand, London WC2R 2LS, United Kingdom
[3] Institute of Physics, Polish Academy of Sciences, al. Lotników 32/46, 02-668 Warszawa, Poland

Abstract. We compare resonant Raman Scattering (RS) and Photoluminescence (PL) measurements on a spin polarized two-dimensional electron gas embedded in a CdMnTe quantum well. RS by single particle excitations furnishes the Fermi energy E_F, which is more than E_F extracted from PL. Spin-flip RS spectra at wavevector $q \sim 0$, show the one electron spin-flip energy, Z^*. Magneto-PL spectra give only Z. If we neglect mass renormalization, the spin polarization degree, ζ obtained from the PL lineshape is different from those derived from spin-flip RS. We attribute the discrepancies in E_F and ζ to the renormalized mass.

Keywords: Optical properties, spin-polarized electron gas, Zeeman splitting, quantum well
PACS: 72.25.Dc, 73.21.-b, 78.30.-j, 78.55.-m

Over the last 30 years, two-dimensional electron gases embedded in quantum wells have provided a means for understanding many-body exchange and correlation effects of the Coulomb interaction energy. Dilute semi-magnetic quantum wells, especially those of II-VI materials are ideal systems to study the spin-polarized case because of the large Zeeman splitting effect they provide [1]. Couple with tools of spectroscopy such as RS and PL, a better understanding of many-body physics can be achieved.

RS is a well-established technique for studying low energy elementary excitations of electron gases in semiconductors. RS probes and determines quantitatively the many-body interaction parameters. PL is also a widely used and popular spectroscopic tool for studying electronic excitations.

Here we perform a quantitative comparative study of fundamental parameters of a spin-polarized electron gas embedded in CdMnTe single quantum well using RS and PL. We will show that an understanding of the renormalized mass is needed to explain the differences we observe in our measurements.

RS and PL measurements were carried out on a 15 nm thick $Cd_{1-x}Mn_xTe$ modulation-doped (Iodine) quantum well with 0.75% Mn. The barriers were made of $Cd_{1-x}Mg_xTe$ with 15% Mg. The sample was mounted in the core of a 5 T superconducting magnet

providing a field in the plane of the quantum well, and all were immersed in superfluid helium. The Voigt configuration was used. A Ti:sapphire laser with incident power densities below 1 W/cm^2 (to avoid heating the Mn^{2+} ions) was tuned to resonate close to 1.65 eV (the E_1H_2 absorption edge: the transition energy between the first conduction band and the second hole level).

To determine E_F, we first obtain the density of electrons in our system using RS. We measured dispersions of the single particle excitation (SPE) in zero magnetic field at various q in the parallel configuration (incident and scattered light have the same polarization), one of which is shown in the insert of Fig. 1 for $q = 5.7\ \mu m^{-1}$. The parallel spectra give the unscreened SPE line. We extract the midpoints of the SPE lines, which is less sensitive to disorder compared to the peak position, and plot it as a function of q. The slope of the resulting line is proportional to the Fermi velocity and hence using the uncorrected mass m^* (= 0.105), the electron density and $E_{F, RS}$ were found to be 4.4 x 10^{11} cm^{-2} and 10 meV, respectively. For comparison, we measured E_F from the PL linewidth at zero magnetic field to obtain $E_{F, PL}$ = 7.2meV. Measurements were made on several samples and an average value for $E_{F, RS}/E_{F, PL}$ = 1.6 was obtained. Kossacki and co-authors also made a similar

CP893, *Physics of Semiconductors, 28th International Conference*
edited by W. Jantsch and F. Schäffler
© 2007 American Institute of Physics 978-0-7354-0397-0/07/$23.00

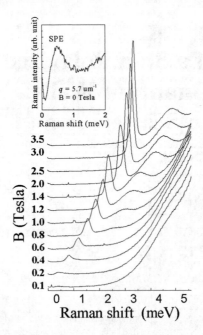

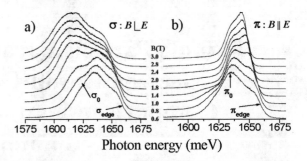

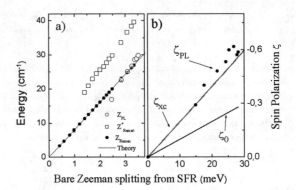

FIGURE 1. Spin-flip RS spectra showing resonances near Z and Z^* in the Voigt configuration at $q \sim 0$. The insert is representative dispersive RS spectrum taken at B = 0 T for $q = 5.7$ μm^{-1}.

FIGURE 2. Photoluminescence spectra in the Voigt configuration at various magnetic fields: a) from the majority spin split subbands and b) from the minority spin-split subbands in the σ and π configurations, respectively.

FIGURE 3. a) Energy values for Z and Z^* from the RS spectra (solid and open squares) and from the PL lineshape (open circle) taken from Figs 1 and 2. b) ζ values obtained from PL and RS. The RS values correspond to ζ_0.

observation in estimating hole densities in p-type CdMnTe quantum well using excitonic Moss-Burstein shift, Hall and filling factor measurements [2]. They found a factor of 1.5 less in the Moss-Burstein shift measurement as compared to theory. The resulting factor may be attributed to excitonic effects, manifesting in the PL lineshape, and mass renormalization.

In an applied magnetic field, spin-flip RS spectra show two lines below 6 meV, Fig 1. At $q = 0$, these lines correspond to the spin-flip wave and the spin-flip single particle excitation which gives Z and Z^*, respectively, due to Larmor's theorem [3, 4, 5]. With a knowledge of E_F and Z^*, ζ can be found using

$$\zeta = -\frac{Z^*}{2E_F}. \qquad (1)$$

Consider the magneto-PL spectra shown in Fig 2. The PL line splits into two lines associated with each spin population: (a) the majority spin-split subband and the b) minority spin split subband. The characteristic energy separation between the two lines, i.e. peak in σ - π, gives Z and not Z^* contrary to our expectation (see Fig. 3a). The PL spectra is therefore not sensitive to Z^* but exhibit collective mediated recombination.

If we neglect mass renormalization, the ratio of the difference in widths of the σ and π spin split subbands to the sum results in ζ. Fig. 3b shows ζ from PL as a function of the bare Zeeman splitting from spin-flip

RS (SFR). This extraction agrees well with our model, which takes into account exchange and correlation effects [4].

The results presented thus far strongly signify that the renormalized mass should be taken into account in our RS determination of ζ. We therefore conclude that the discrepancies in our values for ζ and E_F by the two approaches are due to the mass renormalization.

This work was supported by EPSRC, King's College London and the CNRS.

1. G. Karczewski, J. Jaroszynski, A. Barcz, M. Kutrowski, T. Wojtowicz, J. Kossut, *J. Cryst. Growth* **184/185**, 814 (1998).
2. P. Kossacki *et al.*, *Phys. Rev. B*, **70**, 195337 (2004).
3. B. Jusserand *et al.*, *Phys. Rev. Lett.* **91**, 086802 (2003)
4. F. Perez, B. Jusserand , D. Richards, G. Karczewski, *Physica Status Solidi B*, **243**(4), 873-877 (2006).
5. F. Perez *et al.*, Poster **WeA2n.31**, ICPS conference Vienna, Austria, 2006.

Studies of intrinsic exchange interactions in Zn(Mn)O, Zn(Mn)S and Zn(Mn)Te at 4 kbar by inelastic neutron scattering.

Z. Q. Wiren[*], H. Kepa[*,†], C. M. Brown[**,‡], J. Leao[**], S. Kolesnik[§], B. Dabrowski[§], J. K. Furdyna[¶] and T. M. Giebultowicz[*]

[*]Dept. of Physics, Oregon State University, Corvallis, OR 97331, USA
[†]Dept. of Physics, Warsaw University, Hoza 69 St., 00-681 Warsaw, Poland
[**]NIST Center for Neutron Research, Gaithersburg, MD 20899, USA
[‡]Cyclotron Facility, Indiana University, Bloomington, IN 47405, USA
[§]Dept. of Physics, Northern Illinois University, DeKalb, IL 60115, USA
[¶]Dept. of Physics, University of Notre Dame, Notre Dame, IN 46556, USA

Abstract. The intrinsic antiferromagnetic (AFM) interactions between nearest-neighbor Mn ions in Zn(Mn)O, Zn(Mn)S, Zn(Mn)Te have been studied by inelastic neutron scattering at ambient pressure and at 4 kbar. To find how the J values in a single alloy change when the Mn-Mn distance R decreases we have launched systematic measurements of the nearest-neighbor exchange constants J_1 in these alloys using inelastic neutron scattering spectrometry. We present the J_1 data so far obtained at 4 kbar for the three aforementioned systems, as well as the result of measurements of the pressure dependence of the Mn-Mn distance. We discuss our findings in the context of the analysis presented in the paper by Szuszkiewicz et al. [1]

Keywords: Dilute Magnetic Semiconductors, ZnMnTe, Exchange Constant
PACS: 71.70 Gm, 75.50 Pp, 78.70 Nx

Due to the emergence of spintronics technology there is a renaissance of interest in studying the exchange interactions in magnetic semiconductors. Material technologists in many labs are attempting to "make semiconductors ferromagnetic" (FM) by substituting some part of their non-magnetic atoms by magnetic ions, and to introduce high concentration of carriers into their lattices that would give rise to RKKY-type FM interactions between these ions. However, in addition to the carrier-induced FM exchange, in such alloys there are always intrinsic exchange interactions that exist even in the insulating state, and are virtually insensitive to the presence of carriers. They are produced by a superexchange mechanism mediated by intervening anions, and are almost always AFM. In order to obtain a material that is ferromagnetic, the carrier-induced FM component has to overcome that intrinsic antiferromagnatism. Hence, the characterization of the AFM intrinsic exchange, as well as good understanding of the physical mechanisms underlying this interaction, are certainly of considerable current importance. In a recent paper [1], Szuszkiewicz et al. have presented a thorough analysis of the existing Mn-Mn AFM exchange interactions data from the family of diluted magnetic semiconductors based on the II-VI compounds. The analysis revealed one intriguing fact - namely, when the J values from sulfides, selenides and tellurides are plotted vs. spin-spin distance R in the same figure in log-log scale, all points fall practically on the same line - in other worlds, all those superexchange interactions somehow "ignore" the fact that they are mediated by there different anions.

In zinc-blende and wurtzite $A^{II}_{1-x}Mn_xB^{VI}$ dilute magnetic semiconductor (DMS) alloys the Mn atoms are randomly distributed through the fcc or hcp host lattices. An isolated pair of exchange coupled Mn ions (each having $S = 5/2$) has a simple excitation level scheme of energies $E(S_T) = S_T(S_T + 1)|J|$ where $S_T = 0, 1, 2, \ldots, 5$ and is the total spin of the pair. Due to the selection rules for the transition between levels only transitions to adjacent levels are allowed ($\Delta S_T = \pm 1$). Inelastic neutron scattering from these pairs is a means of directly probing these transitions. This results in peaks in the scattered neutron spectrum containing peaks corresponding to neutron energy gain/loss by $\Delta E = \pm 2J, \pm 4J, \pm 6J, \ldots$ (for details see Refs. [3]).

Neutron diffraction from a zinc-blende material produces Bragg peaks at a position given by:

$$\lambda = 2\sqrt{\frac{a^2}{h^2 + k^2 + l^2}} \sin\theta$$

where a is the lattice constant and $h, k,$ and l are the Miller Indices. Because of the lattice symmetries only certain combinations contribute to the spectra, either all the indices must be even or all must be odd.

CP893, *Physics of Semiconductors, 28th International Conference*
edited by W. Jantsch and F. Schäffler
© 2007 American Institute of Physics 978-0-7354-0397-0/07/$23.00

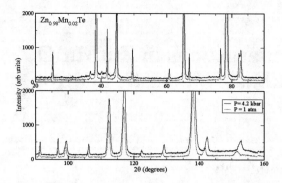

FIGURE 1. Overlay of neutron diffraction spectra at atmospheric pressure and at 4.2 kbar (420 GPa). The spectrum was taken using a Cu(311) monochromator yielding a wavelength of $\lambda = 1.540$ Å

Measurements were made at the National Institute of Standards and Technology (NIST) Center for Neutron Research (NCNR) in Gaithersberg, MD, USA. Inelastic neutron scattering experiments were performed on the Disk-Chopper Time-of-Flight spectrometer (DCS TOF) and neutron diffraction used the Powder Diffractometer. Both used a helium pressure cell allowing approximately 1.5 cm^3 of powdered sample (corresponding to 5-7 g of sample) to be loaded in.

A neutron diffraction spectrum obtained from $Zn_{0.98}Mn_{0.02}Te$ is shown in Figure 1. A shift to higher angles is visible between the atmospheric pressure measurement and the high pressure measurement. These correspond to a lattice constant of $a = 6.103 \pm 0.002$Å (in good agreement with previous measurements) and $a = 6.090 \pm 0.001$Å respectively for a lattice compression of 0.24%.

Just as a shift was clearly visible in the lattice parameter, an even larger shift is seen in the exchange parameter (see Figure 2). Fitting the peaks in the inelastic scattering spectrum yields an exchange constant of $J_1 = 0.795 \pm 0.008$ meV for the atmospheric pressure measurements. This is again in good agreement with previous measurements on the material [2, 5]. At higher pressures, 4.2 kbar, the exchange constant becomes $J_1 = 0.838 \pm 0.007$ meV.

The summary of results is shown in Figure 3. There is good agreement with the common points, of particular interest is the $Zn_{1-x}Mn_xO$ which lies significantly off the trend line, thus corroborating this anomaly. Current speculation is that this is due to oxygen not behaving as a typical B^{IV} element with respect to its valence electrons thus altering its superexchange properties. It seems that compressing the material does not maintain the same trend for J_1 vs. R (see trend-lines in Figure 3) which is peculiar as it seems more benign than chemical alterations. Farther refinement of the data and more material studies

must be done before drawing this conclusion however.

This work was supported by NSF grants No. DMR0509478 and No. DMR-0302617

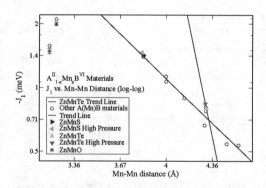

FIGURE 2. Inelastic peaks from the second excited level ($E = 6|J_1|$) to the first excited state ($E = 2|J_1|$) in NN spin pairs. The incident neutron energy was 3.55 meV. The negative sign of the energy transfer represents crystal energy loss. The DAVE software package was used for elements of the data reduction and analysis. [4]

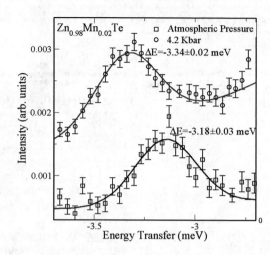

FIGURE 3. Dependence of J_1 on spin-spin distance with our data points shown (ZnMnO high pressure points omitted)

REFERENCES

1. W. Szuszkiewicz, E. Dynowska, B. Witkowska, B. Hennion, Phys. Rev. B **73**, 104403 (2006)
2. H. Kepa, Le Van Khoi, C. M. Brown, M. Sawicki, J. K. Furdyna, T. M. Giebultowicz, T. Dietl, Phys. Rev. Lett. **91** (2003) 087205
3. A. Furrer, H. U. Gudel, J. Magn. Magn. Mater. **14** (1979) 256
4. http://www.ncnr.nist.gov/dave
5. T. M. Giebultowicz, J. J. Rhyne, J. K. Furdyna, J. Appl. Phys. **67** (1990) 5096

Magneto-Optical Properties of Co-doped TiO$_2$ Thin Films Grown by Pulsed Laser Deposition

W.R. Branford[1,2], J.R. Neal[3], C.L. Spencer[3], G.A. Gehring[3], A.M. Fox[3], N. Popovici[4], R.C. da Silva[5], O. Conde[4] and L.F. Cohen[1],

[a]*Blackett Laboratory, Imperial College, Prince Consort Road, London SW7 2AZ, UK*
[b]*Department of Chemistry, UCL, Gordon St. London WC1H 0AJ, UK*
[c]*Department of Physics and Astronomy, The University of Sheffield, Sheffield, S3 7RH, UK.*
[d]*Department of Physics, University of Lisbon, Campo Grande Ed. C8, 1749-016 Lisboa, Portugal*
[e]*Department of Physics, Instituto Tecnologico e Nuclear, Estr. Nac. no. 10, 2685 Sacave'm, Portugal*

Abstract. Co-doped TiO$_2$ thin films on (0001) Al$_2$O$_3$ were grown at 310°C by pulsed laser deposition, using a KrF excimer laser. The ablation of polycrystalline TiO$_2$ rutile - Co$_3$O$_4$ targets was performed in a pure argon or mixed argon-hydrogen atmosphere at total pressure of 10 Pa, with various H$_2$ flow rates. X-ray diffraction analysis showed that the as deposited films consist of TiO$_2$ rutile-based nanocrystallites with preferred orientation along the [101] direction. The chemical composition of the samples was evaluated by Rutherford backscattering measurements, revealing that Ti distribution is homogeneous on the surface and along film depth, and that the Co:Ti ratio is 0.03:0.97 for all the films investigated. In this paper, preliminary magnetic circular dichroism spectroscopy measurements on a 2.1μm film grown in a mixed argon/hydrogen atmosphere is suggestive of spin splitting at the band-edge energy of our films.

.Keywords: Magneto-Optical spectroscopy, dilute magnetic semiconductor, cobalt doped TiO$_2$, band edge.
PACS: 78.20.Ls, 75.50.Pp, 75.70.-i

INTRODUCTION

Titanium dioxide (TiO$_2$) finds many applications due to its remarkable optical, electronic and photocatalytic properties. It naturally occurs in three structural forms, rutile, anatase and brookite, of which rutile is the most thermodynamically stable. Optical band gaps of 3.05 eV, corresponding to an optical absorption threshold of 406 nm, and 3.2 eV (387 nm) have been reported respectively for rutile and anatase[1]. More recently, lightly cobalt-doped TiO$_2$ has generated a great interest as a diluted magnetic semiconductor (DMS) with room-temperature ferromagnetism. Ferromagnetism was first reported for thin films of Co$_x$Ti$_{1-x}$O$_2$ obtained by combinatorial laser molecular beam epitaxy[2]. A major research effort has gone into understanding the origin of room temperature ferromagnetism in this system and the controversy coming from the existence of cobalt clusters is still ongoing. Recently MCD in the spectral region close to the ZnO band edge at ~3eV was used to show that 300K ferromagnetism in doped ZnO films is intimately connected with the ZnO band electrons,

and that the carriers are polarised[3] Hence it is hoped that MCD studies may help resolve the issue in Co-TiO$_2$ films.

Magnetic coupling in DMS materials has been attributed to exchange interaction between the magnetic spins and the free carriers in the semiconductor. Chambers et al.[4] in contrast reported on highly resistive Co:TiO$_2$ films exhibiting very weak magnetism, large magnetization values being measured only for adequately n-type doped films. However, these authors also referred that the n-type doping of the materials is independent of Co-concentration. As far as we know, all the results reported in literature for Co-doped TiO$_2$ thin films have been obtained for growth experiments carried out in vacuum, inert gas and oxygen reactive atmospheres.

Previously, we reported[5] on the growth of Co-doped TiO$_2$ thin films grown by PLD in pure argon and with addition of small amounts of hydrogen. The ferromagnetism in these films showed unusual temperature dependence, so here we report preliminary magneto-optic spectroscopy in the spectral region around the band edge of our films.

CP893, *Physics of Semiconductors, 28th International Conference*
edited by W. Jantsch and F. Schäffler
© 2007 American Institute of Physics 978-0-7354-0397-0/07/$23.00

EXPERIMENT

Co-doped TiO_2 thin films were deposited on (0001) Al_2O_3 substrates by ablating a composite ceramic target prepared from a dry mixture of TiO_2 (rutile) with Co_3O_4 addition, using a pulsed UV laser (KrF, 248 nm wavelength, 30 ns pulse duration). The PLD procedure used to produce these films is described in detail elsewhere[5]. The structural and compositional characterization of $Co_xTi_{1-x}O_2$ films grown by this method is described in the same publication; X-ray diffraction (XRD) was used for phase analysis and crystallinity studies and the chemical composition of the films was determined with Rutherford backscattering spectrometry (RBS). The thickness and the band gap energy of the films were determined from optical transmittance measurements carried out in a UV–Visible–near IR spectrophotometer (300 – 1100 nm) with a bare substrate placed in the reference beam path.

The magneto-optic (M-O) spectroscopy described here were performed on a 2.1 μm thick film of composition $Ti_{0.97}Co_{0.03}O_2$ on an (0001) Al_2O_3 substrate grown at 310°C in an argon/hydrogen atmosphere with an argon flow rate 30 sccm and hydrogen flow of 0.6 sccm. A measurement of the magnetic circular dichroism (MCD) at photon energy E gives the difference in absorption for left and right circularly polarized light at that same energy. Hence it provides a clear indication of the extent to which the states involved in the transition at that particular energy are influenced by the magnetism.

The M-O spectra were taken with a xenon lamp and monochromator with a photoelastic modulator that allows for simultaneous recording of the Faraday rotation and magnetic circular dichroism as a function of frequency. For low temperature measurements the samples were mounted in a cold finger cryostat with a temperature range of 10 K to 300 K. An electromagnet provided a field of 0.45 T with the cryostat and 0.9 T without the cryostat. Figure 1 shows preliminary MCD results of the film at 10 K in a field of 0.45 T. The arrows indicate the Co d-d transitions at 2 eV and the band edge for bulk TiO_2 at 3.05 eV. The broad peak centered at ~2.8 eV, which corresponds to the band edge measured for equivalent thin films,[5] is indicative of the magnetic ions hybridizing with the TiO_2 conduction band causing spin splitting. The width of this peak is attributed to the oxygen vacancy impurity band.

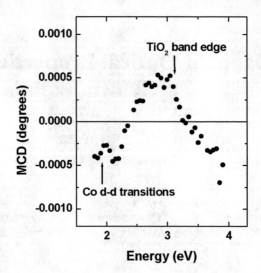

FIGURE 1. MCD of a 2.1 μm $Ti_{0.97}Co_{0.03}O_2$ film on an (0001) Al_2O_3 substrate, at 10 K in a field of 0.45 T. The arrows indicate the Co d-d transitions at 2 eV, the feature near the TiO_2 band edge centered at ~2.8 eV is due to spin splitting of the TiO_2 conduction band. The width is attributed to the oxygen vacancy impurity band broadening the peak.

CONCLUSION

We have successfully grown Co-doped TiO_2 films of single-phase rutile structure onto (0001) Al_2O_3 substrates by PLD at a deposition temperature as low as 310°C, which allows deposition on thermally sensitive semiconductor substrates. Whilst the presence of Co-nanoclusters in the films cannot be eliminated, the presence of a reduced band energy with associated magnetic circular dichroism is consistent with spin splitting of the TiO_2 conduction band indicating that the observed magnetic behaviour is directly associated with the titania lattice.

ACKNOWLEDGMENTS

W.R.B is supported by the Ramsay Memorial Fellowships Trust and N.P. by a PhD scholarship from Fundacao para a Ciencia e Tecnologia.

REFERENCES

1. H. Tang, H. Berger, P. E. Schmid, and F. Levy, Solid State Commun. **92**, 267 (1994).
2. Y. Matsumoto *et al*, Science **291**, 854 (2001).
3. J. R. Neal, A. J. Behan, R. M. Ibrahim, H. J. Blythe, M. Ziese, A. M. Fox, and G. A. Gehring, Phys. Rev. Lett. **96**, 197208 (2006).
4. S. A. Chambers *et al*, Appl. Phys. Lett. **79**, 3467 (2001).
5. N. Popovici, E. Jimenez, R. C. da Silva, W. R. Branford, L. F. Cohen, and O. Conde, J. Non-Cryst. Solids **352**, 1486 (2006).

Diluted Magnetic III-V Semiconductors With Mn For Possible Spintronic Applications

A. Wolos,[a] M. Zajac,[a] J. Gosk,[a] K. Korona,[a] D. Wasik,[a] A. Wysmolek,[a] M. Palczewska,[b] I. Grzegory,[c] M. Bockowski,[c] M. Piersa,[b] G. Strzelecka,[b] A. Hruban,[b] M. Kaminska,[a] and A. Twardowski [a]

[a] Institute of Experimental Physics, Warsaw University, Hoza 69, 00-681 Warsaw, Poland
[b] Institute of Electronic Materials Technology Physics, Wolczynska 133, 01-919 Warsaw, Poland
[c] High Pressure Institute, Polish Academy of Science, Sokolowska 29/37, 01-142 Warsaw, Poland

Abstract. In this paper we present results of comprehensive studies performed on GaN, GaP, InP and GaAs semiconductors containing Mn ions. Electron Paramagnetic Resonance, optical absorption, magnetization and hopping transport measurements performed on the samples with different Mn concentration allowed to determine the nature of neutral Mn acceptor center in the studied crystals. It occurred that for neutral Mn acceptor, configuration of $Mn^{2+}(d^5)$ plus a bound hole was realized. The localization radius of a bound hole changed from 1.1nm for GaAs though 0.7nm for InP to 0.4nm for GaP. The highest localization was reached for Mn doped GaN, in which configuration $Mn^{3+}(d^4)$ was observed.

Keywords: spintronics, diluted magnetic semiconductors, III-V semiconductors, hopping transport, iron group ions
PACS: 75.55.-i, 71.55.Eq, 71.70.Ch, 75.20.-g, 76.30.Fc, 78.55.Cr, 72.20.Ee

INTRODUCTION

Theoretical predictions of possible ferromagnetism at room temperature in some of III-V semiconductors containing high amount of Mn ions triggered extensive studies of such materials in recent years[1]. However, up to now, confirmed ferromagnetism has been observed only in GaMnAs, InMnAs, InMnSb and in GaMnSb, and the highest Curie temperature achieved is still below 200K(see for example[2]). Therefore, it is of high importance to understand behavior of Mn centers in different III-V semiconductors in order to aim for optimal spintronic III-V-based compound.

We performed wide studies of GaN, GaP, InP and GaAs doped with Mn in order to understand Mn behavior in these compounds.

SAMPLES AND EXPERIMENT

GaN samples used in these studies were strain-free bulk crystals of wurzite structure, grown by high pressure technique from the solution of nitrogen in liquid gallium. Crystals were doped with Mn, and in some cases co-doped with Mg acceptor to lower Fermi level to the GaN midgap and achieve substantial part of Mn acceptor in neutral state. Mn concentration was in the range of 2×10^{17} to 4×10^{18} cm^{-3}.

Bulk GaAs, InP and GaP crystals of cubic structure were grown by Czochralski method. Manganese was added to the melt and it incorporated to the crystal during growth with concentration ranged from 10^{16} up to 10^{19} cm^{-3}.

Electron Paramagnetic Resonance (EPR), optical absorption, magnetization and electron transport measurements were performed, using standard equipment with low temperature inlets.

RESULTS AND ANALYSIS

EPR revealed substitutional manganese in $Mn^{2+}(d^5)$ state (singly ionized acceptor), in both n-type and p-type GaAs. Besides, such Mn configuration was detected in all other semiconductors studied, and it decayed with lowering of Fermi level, what indicated transition to neutral Mn acceptor state. In p-type GaAs characteristic EPR signal assigned to neutral Mn acceptor in form of $Mn^{2+}(d^5)$ plus a coulombically

CP893, *Physics of Semiconductors, 28th International Conference*
edited by W. Jantsch and F. Schäffler
© 2007 American Institute of Physics 978-0-7354-0397-0/07/$23.00

bound hole[3] was detected. Such signal was not observed in either of other semiconductors studied.

As already reported by us[4], optical absorption experiments performed on highly resistive GaN:Mn showed clear evidence of neutral Mn acceptor in form of $Mn^{3+}(d^4)$ configuration. The full confirmation of such configuration was obtained by means of magnetic field dependence of Mn intracenter absorption (see Fig.1a) fine structure (in energy range of about 1.4eV and at magnetic field up to 22T), as well as by strong anisotropy of magnetization. Thus, we did not find any evidence of $Mn^{2+}(d^5)$ plus a bound hole center in GaN, but instead $Mn^{3+}(d^4)$ configuration was proved.

On the other hand, in p-type GaP, InP and GaAs, manganese neutral acceptor in form of $Mn^{2+}(d^5)$ plus a bound hole was seen in optical absorption experiments. Characteristic photoionization bands[5] with fine structure at energy starting from about 0.4eV, 0.2eV and 0.1eV, respectively, were observed and their behavior in magnetic field (up to 15T) resembled that of hydrogenic-like acceptors[6]. The observed fine structure was due to Lyman transitions of a bound hole to Mn center (see Fig.1b, for the case of GaAs).

temperature for GaP, InP, as well as GaAs crystals. Transport measurements were impossible for GaN:Mn due to large inhomogenity of the samples. Fitting to the experimental curves of mobility, concentration and conduction temperature dependence for samples with different Mn concentration allowed to determine characteristic radius of bound hole on $Mn^{2+}(d^5)$. This radius decreased from 1.1nm for GaAs through 0.7nm for InP to 0.4nm for GaP. As mentioned above, the highest localization was reached for Mn doped GaN(see Fig.2).

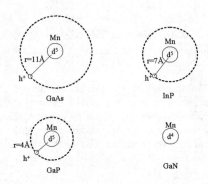

FIGURE 2. Configurations of neutral Mn acceptor in different $A^{III}B^V$ semiconductors studied. Note the increase of bound hole localization within the series.

It seems to us that ferromagnetic ordering of localized Mn spins in $A^{III}B^V$ semiconductors is mediated by the bound holes and the value of the localization radius of hole is critical for the strength of magnetic interaction and, therefore the value of Curie temperature. It needs further calculations to determine the optimal value of the radius leading to efficient magnetic ordering.

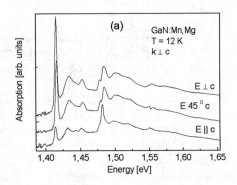

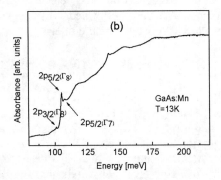

FIGURE 1. Optical absorption spectrum due to intracenter transitions within $Mn^{3+}(d^4)$ in GaN (a) and Lyman transitions of a bound hole on $Mn^{2+}(d^5)$ in GaAs (b).

Temperature characteristics of electron transport revealed regular band transport at high temperatures and hopping conduction via Mn centers at low

REFERENCES

1. T. Dietl, H. Ohno, F. Matsukura, J. Cibert, and D. Ferrand, *Science* **287**, 1019 (2000).
2. K.C. Ku, S.J. Potashnik, R.F. Wang, M.J. Seong, E. Johnston-Halperin, R.C. Meyers, S.H. Chun, A. Mascarenhas, A.C. Gossard, D.D. Awschalom, P. Schiffer, and N. Samarth, *Appl. Phys. Lett.* **82**, 2302 (2003).
3. J. Schneider, U. Kaufmann, W. Wilkening, and M. Baeumer, *Phys. Rev. Lett.* **59**, 240 (1987).
4. A. Wolos, A. Wysmolek, M. Kaminska, A. Twardowski, M. Bockowski, I. Grzegory, S. Porowski, and M. Potemski, *Phys. Rev. B* **70**, 245202 (2004).
5. E. Tarhan, I. Miotkowski, S. Rodriguez, and A.K. Ramdas, *Phys. Rev. B* **67**, 195202 (2003).
6. A. Rutkowska, D. Wasik, A. Witowski, M. Sadowski, W. Orlowski, G. Strzelecka, A. Hruban, M. Kaminska, A. Twardowski, and M. Potemski, *Acta Phys. Pol. A* **108**, 845 (2005).

Low Temperature Transport Properties in Ferromagnetic GaMnAs Films

H.T. He[1], C.L. Yang[1], J.C. Ji[2], Y.Q. Wang[2], W.K. Ge[1], J.N. Wang[1*]

[1]Physics Department, The Hong Kong University of Science and Technology, Clear Water Bay, Kowloon, Hong Kong, China
[2]Institute of Solid State Physics, CAS, Hefei, Anhui, China

Abstract. The temperature dependence of the resistivity of ferromagnetic GaMnAs films with various Mn compositions and film thicknesses is measured. Resistivity minima are observed at low temperatures for all the GaMnAs samples studied. Below the temperature corresponding to the resistivity minimum, a logarithmic temperature dependence of the resistivity is established. It is independent of the external magnetic fields up to 9 T. These phenomena are explained in terms of the Kondo effect arising from the coexistence of the Mn substitutionals and interstitials in the GaMnAs lattice.

Keywords: GaMnAs; Kondo effect
PACS: 75.50.Pp; 75.20.Hr

Ferromagnetic GaMnAs are attracting worldwide attentions due to its potential applications in spintronics. Previous studies[1, 2, 3] have shown that the Mn ions occupying Ga sites (Mn^G) give rise to the hole-mediated ferromagnetism. But some Mn ions take interstitial sites (Mn^I) and they tend to form antiferromagnetically coupled $Mn^G – Mn^I$ pairs. The amount of Mn interstitials can be reduced by low temperature annealing, resulting in a significant increase of Curie temperatures.[1, 4] In this work, we show that the Mn^I ions also play important roles in the low temperature transport properties of ferromagnetic GaMnAs films. Due to the coexistence of Mn^G and Mn^I ions in the GaMnAs lattice, Kondo-related resistivity minima are observed at low temperatures. This Kondo effect is explained in terms of the effective field distribution which takes into account the antiferromagnetic superexchange as well as the dominant hole-mediated ferromagnetism.

Two sets of ferromagnetic GaMnAs samples grown by low-temperature molecular-beam epitaxy (MBE) are investigated in this work. Set I consists of four samples with the same film thickness of 30 nm and the same Mn composition of 5.2%. They are labeled A, B, C, and D, corresponding to the as-grown sample and the samples annealed at 160, 200, and 260 ^0C for 2 hours, respectively. Set II includes Sample E, F, and G. They have the same thickness of 150 nm and the

corresponding Mn composition is 2.1%, 3.3%, and 4.5%, respectively.

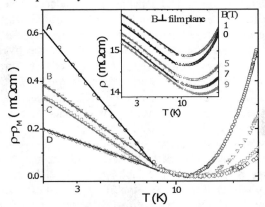

Figure 1. The normalized $\rho(T)$ curve for Sample A, B, C, and D at low temperature region. Inset: The $\rho(T)$ curves for Sample A with a magnetic field up to 9 T applied perpendicularly to the film plane.

Fig. 1 shows the temperature dependence of resistivity [$\rho(T)$] for Sample A, B, C, and D at low temperatures, respectively. The corresponding Curie temperature (T_C) is 71, 83, 104, and 116 K, respectively. Each $\rho(T)$ curve in Fig. 1 clearly exhibits a resistivity minimum around 10 K. Note that the resistivity in Fig. 1 has been normalized by subtracting ρ_M, which is the minimum resistivity. Below the temperature (T_M) where the resistivity minimum

* Corresponding author email: phjwang@ust.hk

CP893, *Physics of Semiconductors, 28th International Conference*
edited by W. Jantsch and F. Schäffler
© 2007 American Institute of Physics 978-0-7354-0397-0/07/$23.00

appears, logarithmic temperature dependence, i.e. $\alpha ln(T)$, is found for each sample. The corresponding slope α is shown to decrease with increasing T_C. In addition, the measurement of the $\rho(T)$ curves for Sample A with an external magnetic field (B) up to 9 T applied perpendicularly to the film plane indicates that the α is independent of B, as shown in the inset of Fig. 1.

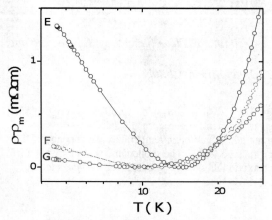

FIGURE 2. The normalized $\rho(T)$ curve for sample E, F, and G at low temperature region.

Such logarithmic temperature dependence below T_M can also be observed for Sample E, F, and G, which have much larger thickness than the samples in Set I. The corresponding T_C is 37, 55, and 68 K, respectively. Fig. 2 shows the normalized $\rho(T)$ curves of these three samples in low temperature region. As one can see, Sample E, F, and G also exhibit $ln(T)$ dependence at low temperatures and α is also found to decrease with increasing T_C.

We ascribe this $ln(T)$ dependence to the Kondo effect,[5] which was first observed in dilute magnetic alloys and shown to exhibit $ln(T)$ dependence of resistivity at low temperatures. Previous studies have shown that the Kondo effect observed in certain amorphous ferromagnets can be analyzed in terms of the effective field distribution function $P(H)$, which represents the probability of a spin staying at a local internal magnetic field H.[6] In the GaMnAs system, if all Mn ions substitute the Ga ions in the lattice and are ferromagnetically coupled via hole mediations, the corresponding $P(H)$ will only have a peak located at high positive H, as illustrated by the dashed curve in Fig. 3. As a result, no free spins exist in the lattice and the Kondo effect is not expected. But it has been shown that besides the Mn^G ions, a certain amount of Mn^I ions are also present in the lattice and tend to form antiferromagnetically coupled Mn^G–Mn^I pairs due to the electrostatic attraction.[1, 2, 3] Taking into account this antiferromagnetism as well as the hole-mediated ferromagnetism, $P(H)$ is expected to have a long flat tail extending to negative H in addition to the peak at high positive H, as shown by the dotted curve in Fig. 3. This implies that some spins will experience zero local fields and be free. The antiferromagnetic coupling between the valence holes and these free spins gives rise to the Kondo effect observed in ferromagnetic GaMnAs films.

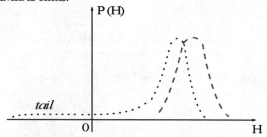

FIGURE 3. Schematic plot of $P(H)$ in a ferromagnetic system when both the dominant ferromagnetism and the antiferromagnetic superexchange are considered (dotted curve) and only the ferromagnetism is considered (dashed curve).

The decrease of α with increasing T_C, as shown in Fig. 1 & 2, can also be explained. The increase of T_C indicates that the corresponding hole-mediated ferromagnetism becomes stronger, i.e. the possibility of finding a spin at positive H increases. Therefore, the tail of $P(H)$ will be less prominent at zero fields, giving rise to less free spins in the lattice. As a result, the Kondo-related scattering is reduced, or the α, which measures the Kondo contribution, decreases. By applying an external magnetic field, the $P(H)$ function will be shifted uniformly toward higher H, but the long flat tail extending to negative H ensures that the number of free spins changes little with the fields. Therefore, the independence of α on B is expected, in agreement with the results shown in the inset of Fig. 1.

ACKNOWLEDGMENTS

This work is supported by the Research Grant Council of Hong Kong SAR, via Grant No. 603704.

REFERENCES

1. K. M. Yu, W. Walukiewicz, T. Wojtowicz, I. Kuryliszyn, X. Liu, Y. Sasaki, and J. K. Furdyna, *Phys. Rev. B* **65**, R201303 (2002).
2. J. Blinowski and P. Kacman, *Phys. Rev. B* **67**, R121204 (2003).
3. K. W. Edmonds, N. R. S. Farley, T. K. Johal, G. van der Laan, R. P. Campion, B. L. Gallagher, and C. T. Foxon, *Phys. Rev. B* **71**, 064418 (2005).
4. T. Hayashi, Y. Hashimoto, S. Katsumoto, and Y. Iye, *Appl. Phys. Lett.* **78**, 1691 (2001).
5. J. Kondo, *Prog. Theor. Phys.* **32**, 37 (1964).
6. G. S. Grest and S. R. Nagel, *Phys. Rev. B* **19**, 3571 (1979).

The optical properties of (Mn,Ga)As and (Be,Ga)As

C. S. Lee[1], C. C. Chang[1], M. F. Shih[1], C. C. Huang[1]. Y. H. Chang[1], H. H. Lin[2], T. C. Ma[2] and J. K. Furdyna[3]

[1]Department of Physics, National Taiwan University, Taipei 106, Taiwan
[2]Department of Electrical Engineering, National Taiwan University, Taipei 106, Taiwan
[3]Department of Physics, University of Notre Dame, IN 46556, U.S.A

Abstract. Infrared spectroscopy was used to study the optical responses of ferromagnetic $Ga_{1-x}Mn_xAs$ samples and heavily p-doped GaAs:Be samples to clarify whether the optical response of the $Ga_{1-x}Mn_xAs$ is related to the presence of the magnetic ions in the sample. Absorption dips are observed for both $Ga_{1-x}Mn_xAs$ and GaAs:Be samples and could be attributed to the intervalence band transition. The temperatures dependence of the absorption spectra for the two samples shows similar behavior and it is concluded that the optical response of the $Ga_{1-x}Mn_xAs$ is not related to the presence of the magnetic ions in the samples.

Keywords: Ferromagnetic semiconductor, Infrared spectroscopy, optical property
PACS:71.33.+I;78.40.Fy;71.30+h;71.35Eq

$Ga_{1-x}Mn_xAs$ is of great interest because of its potential technological application as well as the fundamental novelty that it is a ferromagnetic semiconductor with Tc~100K[1,2]. It is well-known that for $0.01<x<0.07$, $Ga_{1-x}Mn_xAs$ is a ferromagnetic semiconductor and it is also a metal. For x outside the above-mentioned range, $Ga_{1-x}Mn_xAs$ is non-ferromagnetic and is an insulator [3,4]. The ferromagnetism is generally believed to be a RKKY type interation mediated by mediated by the itinerantly doped hole [5]. Optical absorption measurements on the nonmagnetic GaAs which doped with Mn in the very dilute limit show that Mn atom forms a shallow acceptor level at 110 meV above the valence band.[6] But the interpretation of the optical response of the samples at high Mn doping concentration is still not well understood. Previous FTIR measurements of the absorption coefficient on thin films of $Ga_{1-x}Mn_xAs$ has discovered a resonance near 2000cm^{-1}.[7,8], but the origin for this broad IR absorption is controversial. It could be explained either in terms of the inter-valence band transition [8], the transition between impurity band and valence band.[7], or small polaron[9].

The Ferromagnetic (FM) (Mn,Ga)As samples used in this experiment were grown by molecular-beam epitaxy at T=200 ℃, with the concentration of Mn ranging from x =0.014 to 0.068. The high temperature (HT) grown heavily Be doped samples (10^{20}cm^{-3}) were grown at 500℃, and the low temperature (LT) grown samples were growth at 250℃. These films had a

thickness of 400 nm, and had a buffer layer of undoped GaAs which is 200 nm thick. Infrared transmission experiments were measured in the range between 50cm^{-1} and 13000cm^{-1}. Fig.1 is the spectra taken for $Ga_{1-x}Mn_xAs$, and Fig.2 are spectra taken with HT samples, respectively. In the low energy region the spectral response is flat and almost ω independent for the FM samples, the FM sample has very low transmission. This indicate that although the FM sample are metallic and the free holes has very short scattering times in the FM samples On the other hands, for the HT-sample, the responses in the low energy region could be fitted with the Drude-Lorentz model. For the FM samples, broad absorption features with minimum at around 2000 cm^{-1} for all the samples but for the HT samples, the absorption dips were at around 600 cm^{-1}. The difference between the spectra responses of these two sets of samples could be attributed to the difference in the Fermi energy of the samples.

In the near-IR regime, for the LT samples, the absorption starts to appear at 7500 cm^{-1}, and increase quite rapidly toward the band gap (11200 cm^{-1}) of GaAs, indicating there are a lot of band tail states or midgap states and the Fermi-level of the system is pinned inside the forbidden gap. However, although the (Mn,Ga)As samples were also grown at LT, the optical response is flat from 7500 cm^{-1} to 11200 cm^{-1}, indicating that the midgap or bandtail states are filled up by free holes provided by Mn, The large amount of

CP893, *Physics of Semiconductors, 28th International Conference*
edited by W. Jantsch and F. Schäffler
© 2007 American Institute of Physics 978-0-7354-0397-0/07/$23.00

free holes raises the Fermi level of the Ga1-xMnxAs above the band edge of the valence band and makes it possible to observe the intervalence band transition. It is also found that the overall T-dependent spectra of the HT sample and the FM sample are quite similar.

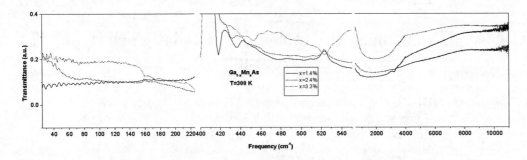

FIGURE 1. (a) The measured transmission for the (Mn,Ga)As sample transmission at T=300 K. Non-Drude like responses were observed in the low energy region.(b) Broad absorptions center around 2000 cm^{-1}.

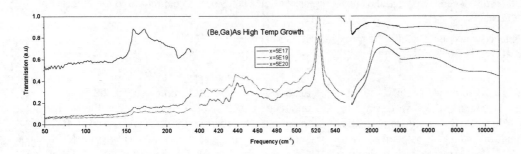

FIGURE 2. In the region between 400cm^{-1} and 550cm^{-1}, the feature of these transmission spectra is very similar with the multiphonon spectrum of GaAs. The absorption dips for HT samples around 600 cm^{-1}.

In conclusions, we have performed complete measurements on the optical responses of the FM, LT and HT GaAs samples. The results show that, the FM samples are metallic, but is a poor conductor as the FIR response is non-Drude like. The observed absorption at 2000 cm^{-1} could be attributed to intrvalence band transition. For the high T grown, heavily doped samples, strong inter-valence band absorption could also be identified. It is found that the temperature-dependence spectra FM sample is quite similar to the high T grown, heavily doped samples. These results indicated that the optical response of the Ga$_{1-x}$Mn$_x$As is not related to the presence of the magnetic ions in the samples.

REFERENCES

1. H.Ohno, Science 281, 251 (2001); H. Ohno, A. Shen, F. Matsukura, A. Oiwa, A. Endo, S. Katsumoto, and Y. Iye, Appl. Phys. Lett. **69**, 363 (1996).
2. S. A. Wolf et al., Science **294**, 1488 (2001).
3. H. Ohno, 1998 Science **281**, 951.
4. A. Shen, F. Matsukura, S.P. Guo, Y. Sugawara, H. Ohno, M. Tani, H. Abe and H.C. Liu, 1999, J. Cryst. Growth **201/202**, 673.
5. T. Dietl, H. Ohno, F. Matsukura, J. Cibert, and D. Ferrand, Science **287**, 1019 (2000); T. Dietl, Semicond. Sci. Technol. **17**,377 (2002).
6. M. Linnarsson, E. Janzen, B. Monemar, M. Kleverman, and A. Thilderkvist, Phys. Rev. B **55**, 6938 (1997).
7. S. Katsumoto, T. Hayashi, Y. Hashimoto, Y. Iye, Y. Ishiwata, M. Watanabe, R. Eguchi, T. Takeuchi, Y. Harada, S. Shin, and K. Hirakawa, Mater. Sci. Eng., B **84**, 88 (2001); K. Hirakawa, S Katsumoto, T. Hayashi, Y. Hashimoto, and Y. Iye, Phys. Rev. B **65**, 193312 (2002).
8. Y. Nagai, T. Kunimoto, K. Nagasaka, H. Nojiri, M. Motokawa, F. Matsukura, T. Dietl, and H. Ohno, Jpn. Soc. Appl. Phys. **11**, 6231 (2001).
9. S. Katsumoto, T. Hayashi, Y. Hashimoto, Y. Iye, Y. Ishiwata, M. Watanabe, R. Eguchi, T. Takeuchi, Y. Harada, S. Shin, and K. Hirakawa, Mater. Sci. Eng., B **84**, 88 ~2001!; K. Hirakawa, S. Katsumoto, T. Hayashi, Y. Hashimoto, and Y. Iye, Phys. Rev. B 65, 193312 (2002).

Carrier Dynamics and Magnetization-induced Nonlinearity in Ferromagnetic GaMnAs

Ji-Hee Kim[1 a)], Kang-Jeon Han[1], Ki-Ju Yee[1], X. Liu[2], J. K. Furdyna[2], Y. S. Lim[3]

[1]*Department of Physics, Chungnam National University, Daejeon, Korea 305-764*
[2]*Department of Physics, University of Notre Dame, IN 46556, USA*
[3]*Department of Applied Physics, Konkuk University, Chungju, Chungbuk 380-701, Korea*

Abstract. Using a femtosecond Ti:sapphire laser, we have performed time-resolved transmission/reflection measurements. Carrier dynamics is studied for a series of GaMnAs layers and the observation of magnetization induced nonlinearity signal is reported.

Keywords: diluted magnetic semiconductor, magnetization, carrier dynamics, GaMnAs
PACS: 78.47.+p, 78.20.Ls, 75.50.Pp, 42.65,-k

INTRODUCTION

Ferromagnetic $Ga_{1-x}Mn_xAs$ has already been investigated by a number of optical techniques, including optical absorption and magnetic circular dichroism (MCD)[1]; and Raman scattering was used to determine the hole concentration in this material. However, in spite of their importance for basic understading of the material as well as for spintronic device applications, studies of $Ga_{1-x}Mn_xAs$ by optical methods are much less fully explored than the investigation of this material by magnetic and transport techniques[2]. In this paper, we report a magnetization-induced nonlinearity and a systematic optical study of carrier dynamics in $Ga_{1-x}Mn_xAs$ specimens.

EXPERIMENT

We have performed degenerate pump-probe measurements on a ferromagnetic $Ga_{1-x}Mn_xAs$ layers with a Kerr-lens mode-locked Ti:sapphire laser. The laser gerates transformed-limited pulses with pulse durations of 50 fs FWHM at a repetition rate of 90 MHz. Center wavelength of the laser was tunable from 760nm to 840nm.We have measured time-resolved transmission/ reflection changes on ferromagnetic GaMnAs layers under magnetic fields. Magnetic field up to a 0.15 tesla was generated by an electro-magnet, and field direction was set to be parallel to the sample growth direction (Faraday geometry). Polarization of pump and probe beams could be independently adjusted to be right-handed (σ^+) or left-handed (σ^-) circular polarization by putting $\lambda/4$ plate insides paths of both pump and probe beams. The sample was put inside a continuous-flow cryostat, and temperature dependence of the signal was measured down to 10 K.

RESULTS

Figure 1 shows the time-resolved transient absorption changes (expressed in terms of the change of the absorption coefficient relative to its value prior to excitation) for LT-GaAs and for the $Ga_{1-x}Mn_xAs$ samples. In the case of LT-GaAs, we see a sharp drop in absorption immediately following the excitation pulse, after which the absorption gradually recovers to its equilibrium (i.e., preexcitation) value. The decrease of absorption through photoexcited carrier generation can be explained by the effect of band filling: i.e., the occupation of the conduction and valence bands generated by the pump pulse induces a decrease in the absorption probability of the probe beam that follows.[3] We suggest that the increase in absorption observed in $Ga_{1-x}Mn_xAs$ originates from reabsorption of probe photons by carriers trapped in defect centers which lie in the middle of the bandgap. As more electrons occupy the defect states, the probability for the probe

CP893, *Physics of Semiconductors, 28th International Conference*
edited by W. Jantsch and F. Schäffler
© 2007 American Institute of Physics 978-0-7354-0397-0/07/$23.00

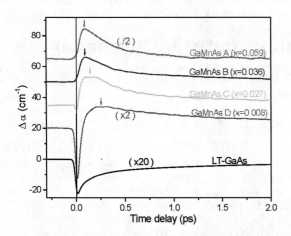

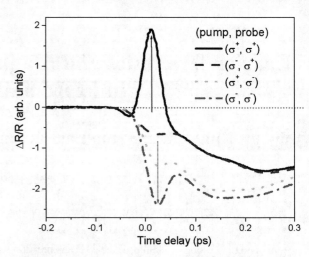

FIGURE 1. Time-resolved absorption changes for LT-GaAs and for $Ga_{1-x}Mn_xAs$ layers with different Mn contents. The arrow indicates the positions of maximum absorption changes.

FIGURE 2. Coherent artifact at zero time delay due to overlap of pump and probe beams at different circular polarization.

photon to reexcite the trapped electrons to conduction bands will increase.

Figure 2 shows transient probe beam intensity changes induced by the pump beam measured in reflection geometry at a center wavelength 810nm. A magnetic field of 1,300 gauss was applied along the sample growth direction, and the measurements were performed at a sample temperature of 10 K with different circular pump and probe beam polarizations. Under the applied magnetic field, positive coherent peak signal is observed near zero time delay at a (pump pol., probe pol.) configuration of (σ^+, σ^+), where σ^+ (σ^-) correspond to right-handed (left-handed) circular polarization, respectively. On the contrary, a negative coherent peak is observed for pump and probe polarizations of (σ^-, σ^-). While the coherent signal peak is smaller at pump and probe configurations of (σ^+, σ^-) or (σ^-, σ^+). The dependence of the coherent artifact signal on both pump and probe polarizations manifests that it is originating from the mutual interaction between pump and probe photons. As we compare the magnetic field dependence of the coherent signal amplitude and the magnetic circular dichroism (MCD) which is a measure of the sample magnetization in diluted magnetic semiconductor (DMS), the amplitude of the coherent artifact signal follows the sample magnetization. From the observed dependences of the coherent artifact signal on the magnetic field, temperature, and the wavelength, it becomes obvious that the signal observed in pump-probe measurements near zero time delay is originated

from magnetization-induced coherent interactions between pump and probe beams. Regarding more detailed analysis on its origin, we need more intensive theoretical studies on nonlinear magneto-optical phenomena.

ACKNOWLEDGMENTS

This work was supported by KOSEF (Grant No. R01-2005-000-10616-0) and Korea Research Foundation Grant (KRF-2004-041-C00117).

REFERENCES

1. K. Ando, T. Hayashi, M. Tanaka, A. Twardowski, Jounal of applied Physics, vol 83, no 11, June 1998.
2. H. Ohno, Science, vol 281, 14, August 1998.
3. K. J. Yee, D. Lee, X. Liu, W. L. Lim, M. Dobrowolska, J. K. Furdyna, Y. S. Lim, K. G. Lee, Y. H. Ahn, D. S. Kim, Jounal of applied Physics, vol 98, No 113509 (2005).

Hot-Electron Photoluminescence of Para- and Ferromagnetic (Ga,Mn)As Layers

V. F. Sapega*,†, M. Ramsteiner*, O. Brandt*, L. Däweritz* and K.H. Ploog*

*Paul-Drude-Institut für Festkörperelektronik, Hausvogteiplatz 5-7, D-10117 Berlin, Germany
†Ioffe Physico- Technical Institute, Russian Academy of Sciences, 194021 St. Petersburg, Russia

abstract
Abstract. We study the spectral shape and the magnetic field induced polarization of hot-electron photoluminescence from the diluted magnetic semiconductor (Ga,Mn)As. It is demonstrated that the holes occupy predominantly the impurity band and not the valence band as required for the Rudermann-Kittel-Kasuya-Yosida-type exchange interaction. The polarization of the impurity band holes in a magnetic field is strongly enhanced by antiferromagnetic exchange interaction with Mn ions and saturates at value much lower than predicted by Rudermann-Kittel-Kasuya-Yosida-like models. The temperature dependence of the hole polarization shows that the ferromagnetic and paramagnetic phases coexist in the whole temperature range below Curie temperature. This observation rather supports percolation based theories of ferromagnetism in (Ga,Mn)As diluted magnetic semiconductor.

Keywords: Hot electron photoluminescence, diluted magnetic semiconductors
PACS: 75.30.Et, 75.50.Pp, 78.55.-m

INTRODUCTION

The discovery of ferromagnetism in (Ga,Mn)As diluted magnetic semiconductors (DMS) opened new prospects for realizing semiconducting spintronics devices. The effect of magnetic Mn ions on the transport of free carriers as well as the reverse effect of spin-polarized photogenerated carriers on ferromagnetically coupled Mn spins have recently been investigated by several groups. Most frequently, the origin of ferromagnetism in this material has been described by a mean-field Zener model based on a Rudermann-Kittel-Kasuya-Yosida (RKKY)-like exchange interaction. In this work, we measure the valence-band hole polarization in quasi-bulk (Ga,Mn)As by means of polarized hot-electron photoluminescence (HPL), which enables us to directly test this model [1, 2].

SAMPLES AND EXPERIMENTAL

The samples for the present study were grown on GaAs (001) substrates by solid-source molecular-beam epitaxy equipped with an As valved cracker cell. Prior to the deposition of (Ga,Mn)As, a GaAs buffer layer was grown at 580°C. Dilute (Ga,Mn)As layers with a Mn content ranging from 1% to 4% were grown at a substrate temperature of 250°C, while doped GaAs:Mn layers (5×10^{17} cm^3) were grown at 560°C.

For excitation of HPL, we used the lines of He-Ne (632.8 nm), Kr (676.4 nm) and Ar (488 nm) ion lasers. The photoluminescence (PL) spectra were dispersed by a DILOR spectrograph and detected by a charge-coupled device (CCD) array. The experiments were carried out in the temperature range 4–300 K in a continuous He-flow cryostat and in magnetic fields up to 12 T, either in the backscattering Faraday or in Voigt geometry.

RESULTS AND DISCUSSION

Figure 1 shows the HPL spectra obtained from doped GaAs:Mn and (Ga,Mn)As layers under above-band-gap excitation and at a temperature of 5 K. The doped layer (D) exhibits a spectrum with a well-defined onset and clear intensity oscillations due to the relaxation of hot electrons by longitudinal optical (LO) phonons [see inset (b) in Fig. 1]. The high Mn concentration in both the paramagnetic and ferromagnetic (Ga,Mn)As layers strongly modifies the HPL shape and shifts its onset to higher energies in comparison to the doping regime. Both changes are caused by impurity band formation. Free holes in the valence band contribute to the HPL only at elevated temperature as seen in inset (a) of Fig. 1. Thus, even for layers with high Mn content, the holes occupy predominantly the impurity band and not the valence band as required for the RKKY-like exchange interaction.

This conclusion is supported by the HPL polarization in a magnetic field. Figure 2 presents the degree of circular polarization [$\rho_c = (I^+ - I^-)/(I^+ + I^-)$, where I^+ and I^- are the HPL intensities being σ^+ and σ^- polarized, respectively] for a GaAs:Mn and two (Ga,Mn)As layers. For the ferromagnetic sample, the polarization degree saturates at low magnetic fields contrary to both the

CP893, *Physics of Semiconductors, 28th International Conference*
edited by W. Jantsch and F. Schäffler
© 2007 American Institute of Physics 978-0-7354-0397-0/07/$23.00

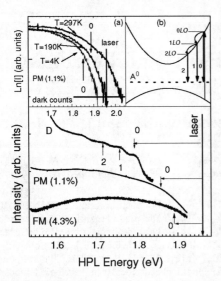

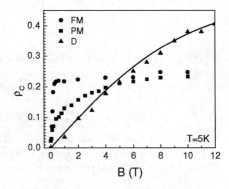

FIGURE 1. HPL spectra obtained from doped GaAs:Mn, paramagnetic (PM) DMS and ferromagnetic (FM) layers under excitation from a He-Ne laser at 1.96 eV and at a temperature of 5 K. Inset (a) shows HPL spectra for different temperatures. Inset (b) explains the origin of the HPL. The arrows in the main figure denote the onset (0) and the first (1) and second (2) LO-phonon oscillations.

FIGURE 2. Magnetic field dependences of the HPL circular polarization measured in backscattering Faraday geometry for a doped GaAs:Mn (solid triangles), and in paramagnetic (solid squares) and ferromagnetic (solid circles) (Ga,Mn)As layers.

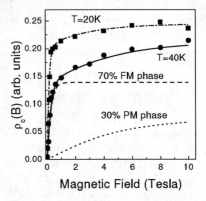

FIGURE 3. Fit of magnetic field dependencies of the HPL circular polarization measured in Faraday geometry in the two-phase model for FM sample. The fits of the data of FM sample for $T = 20$ K (solid squares) and $T = 40$ K are presented by dash-dotted and solid lines, respectively. The fit for $T = 40$ K (solid line) is deconvoluted on paramagnetic and ferromagnetic phases, presented by dotted and dashed lines, respectively.

paramagnetic and Mn-doped layers. The polarization degree for all samples can be explained by a model assuming that the Mn acceptor states experience random stress (or electric) fields, leading to a splitting of the acceptor state into states with angular momentum of 0 and ± 1 with the latter being the ground state. The lower circular polarization for the (Ga,Mn)As layers as compared to the GaAs:Mn layer is to be understood in terms of the much stronger stress for samples with a high Mn content.

A careful analysis of the magnetization curves measured at various temperatures FM samples leads to the important conclusion that the ferromagnetic and the paramagnetic phases coexist below the Curie temperature as they do in the polaron-percolation theory [3]. To support this conclusion we fit the experimental polarization curves using a two-phase model. The result of this fit for $T = 40$ K is shown in Fig. 3 by the solid line. The best fit for this temperature is achieved for a mixture of 30% paramagnetic (dotted line in Fig. 3) and 70% ferromagnetic (dashed line in Fig. 3) phases. The contribution of the FM and PM phases varies with temperature. The best fit for $T = 20$ K (shown by the dash-dotted line in Fig. 3) obtained for contribution of 15% PM and 85% FM phases. The contribution of FM in the HPL polarization dominates only at very low temperatures when the ferromagnetic phase spreads over all the sample. This observation supports percolation based theories of ferromagnetism in (Ga,Mn)As DMS.

ACKNOWLEDGMENTS

We thank C. Herrmann for samples growth, as well as G. Paris for valuable technical assistance. One of us (V.F.S.) acknowledges the financial support from the Paul-Drude-Institute and Russian Foundation for Basic Research Grant No. 06-02-16245.

REFERENCES

1. V. F. Sapega, M. Moreno, M. Ramsteiner, L. Däweritz, and K. Ploog, Phys. Rev. Lett. **94**, 137401 (2005).
2. V. F. Sapega, M. Ramsteiner, O. Brandt, L. Däweritz, and K. Ploog, Phys. Rev. B **73**, 235208 (2006).
3. S. Das Sarma, E.H. Hwang, and A. Kaminski, Phys. Rev. B **67**, 155201 (2003).

Magnetic domain patterns in as-grown and annealed (Ga,Mn)As epilayers with perpendicular easy axis

A. Dourlat*, C. Gourdon*, V. Jeudy*, C. Testelin*, L. Thevenard[†] and A. Lemaître[†]

*Institut des Nanosciences de Paris, Université Pierre et Marie Curie - Paris 6,
Université Denis Diderot - Paris 7, CNRS, UMR 7588, 140 rue de Lourmel, 75015 Paris, France
[†]Laboratoire de Photonique et Nanostructures, CNRS, Route de Nozay, 91460 Marcoussis, France

Abstract. Magnetic properties of ferromagnetic (Ga,Mn)As epilayers grown with tensile strain are investigated using combined experimental techniques including Kerr microscopy, transport measurements, and SQUID magnetometry. We show that post-growth annealing substantially increases the Curie temperature, strengthens the perpendicular anisotropy, weakens the in-plane anisotropy and drastically changes the magnetic domain pattern.

Keywords: magnetic semiconductors, GaMnAs, annealing, magnetic anisotropy, domain effects
PACS: 75.50.Pp, 75,60.-d, 75.30.Gw, 75.60.Nt

INTRODUCTION

The diluted magnetic semiconductor (Ga,Mn)As has received a lot of attention in these past few years as a model for magnetic semiconductor with carrier-mediated ferromagnetism [1]. Depending on the carrier concentration and the layer in-plane strain, the magnetization easy-axis lies in the layer plane or in the perpendicular direction. For (Ga,Mn)As layers with in-plane magnetization, the effect of post-growth annealing on transport and magnetic properties has been thoroughly investigated. The main effect is the out-diffusion of interstitial Mn atoms that electrically compensate the substitutional Mn acceptors [2]. This leads to an increase of the carrier concentration. However little is known about the effect of annealing on the structure of magnetic domains [3]. (Ga,Mn)As layers with perpendicular magnetization easy-axis are much less investigated although they are promising for the study of current-driven magnetization switching by spin transfer. We report here on the effect of annealing on the transport and magnetic properties of (Ga,Mn)As layers with perpendicular magnetization. We concentrate on the effect of annealing on the domain structure at magnetization reversal.

EXPERIMENTAL

Two different samples were investigated in order to know whether the effect of annealing on the magnetic domain pattern depends on the sample composition and on its magnetic and transport properties. The samples were prepared by molecular beam epitaxy. They consist of a (Ga,Mn)As epilayer grown on a (Ga,In)As buffer designed to minimize the amount of threading dislocations emerging in the magnetic layer [4]. The layer thickness, Mn concentration and In concentration of the buffer layer are 50 nm, 7 %, 9.8 % and 200 nm, 5 %, 16 %, for samples 1 and 2, respectively. Annealing was done at T = 250°C during 1 hour for sample 1 and at 190°C during 50 hours for sample 2. The transport properties were investigated by four-point resistivity measurements. The magnetization hysteresis cycles and the temperature dependence of the saturation magnetization were obtained by superconducting quantum interference device (SQUID) magnetometry. The domain pattern was studied using the intrinsic magneto-optical Kerr effect (MOKE) of the (Ga,Mn)As layer. The sample was glued on the cold pillar of a helium flow Oxford Microstat Hires II cryostat. The pillar was inserted in the bore of a standard magnetic coil. The light source was a halogen lamp filtered at 630 nm for sample 1 and 700 nm for sample 2, which correspond in both cases to the maximum of the Kerr rotation angle.

RESULTS AND DISCUSSION

SQUID results and transport measurements show an increase of the Curie temperature T_c from 56 K to 120-130 K for sample 1 and from 55 K to 80 K for sample 2. Upon annealing the resistivity of sample 1 decreases from 13 mΩ cm down to 2.58 mΩ cm at 4 K. Sample 2 has an insulating behavior with a resistivity more than two orders of magnitude larger than for sample 1 at low temperature.

The hysteresis cycles of the as-grown and annealed parts of sample 1 are displayed in Fig. 1. Each data point corresponds to the average signal of a MOKE image. Below 20 K, the as-grown part exhibits a double hysteresis

CP893, *Physics of Semiconductors, 28th International Conference*
edited by W. Jantsch and F. Schäffler
© 2007 American Institute of Physics 978-0-7354-0397-0/07/$23.00

loop (Fig. 1a). Magneto-optical images (not shown here) reveal that the magnetization lies in the sample plane at zero field. With increasing field it is slightly tilted out of the plane. As the magnetization abruptly changes with the field, domains with perpendicular magnetization appear. They first form a series of lines along the <110> directions. These lines then evolve into a grid-pattern until complete saturation [5]. With increasing temperature the hysteresis cycle becomes square and magneto-optical images reveal a perpendicular easy axis (Fig. 1c). For the annealed part of sample 1, the hysteresis cycle is square at all temperatures between 3 K and T_c. The magnetic easy-axis is perpendicular to the plane. Sample 2 exhibits a perpendicular easy axis for the as-grown as well as the annealed parts at all temperatures up to T_c.

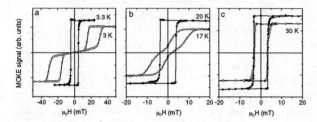

FIGURE 1. MOKE hysteresis cycles for sample 1 as-grown (open circles) and annealed (black circles).

Magneto-optical images of the domain structure close to magnetization reversal are displayed in Fig. 2 for sample 1, as-grown (left column) and annealed (right column). For the as-grown part, magnetization reversal proceeds through multiple nucleation (Fig. 2a left) followed by strongly anisotropic domain wall propagation and dendritic-like domain growth along the [110] and [1$\bar{1}$0] directions (Fig. 2b left). This ends up in a grid-like pattern (Fig. 2c left). For the annealed part of sample 1 the density of nucleation centers is drastically reduced (Fig. 2a right). Two kinds of defects are shown to hinder the domain walls propagation: line-like defects (hundreds of μm long) and point-like defects. The line-like defects have no preferential orientation with respect to the crystallographic axes. In between line-defects, which strongly pin domain walls, propagation is much more isotropic than for the as-grown sample (Fig. 2a and 2b left). During their propagation, domain walls skirt around point-like defects leaving filament domains of non-reversed magnetization (Fig. 2c right). Repetitive cycling of the field shows that the point-like pinning centers observed for successive runs are not always the same, a fraction of 1/3 to 1/2 of them being nevertheless systematically observed. The cartography of those centers shows no preferential alignment along crystallographic directions. It gives a minimum density of point-like pinning centers of about $2.5 \cdot 10^5$ cm^{-2}.

Sample 2 exhibits the same general features: (i) a decrease of the density of nucleation centers upon annealing, (ii) a strongly anisotropic and dendritic-like domain expansion for the as-grown sample, which becomes less anisotropic for the annealed sample, (iii) the presence of line-like defects in the annealed sample. It must be noted that sample-2-as-grown has a much larger resistivity than sample-1-as-grown but they both exhibit very similar domain patterns.

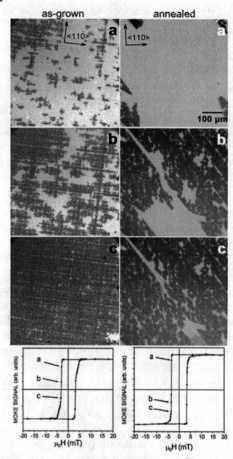

FIGURE 2. Magneto-optical images of the domain structure in sample 1: as-grown (left) and annealed (right). The applied magnetic field for each image is shown by the arrows on the hysteresis cycles. The temperature is 30 K. For both samples, the magnetization easy-axis is perpendicular to the layer plane.

REFERENCES

1. T. Dietl, H. Ohno, and F. Matsukura, Phys. Rev. **63**, 195205 (2001).
2. K.W. Edmonds *et al.*, Phys. Rev. Lett. **92**, 037201 (2004).
3. A. Pross *et al.*, J. Appl. Phys. **95**, 3225 (2004).
4. L. Thevenard, L. Largeau, O. Mauguin, G. Patriache, A Lemaître, N. Vernier and J. Ferré, Phys. Rev. B **73**, 195331 (2006).
5. A. Dourlat *et al.*, to be published.

Ferromagnetic Resonance Study of Ultra-thin Ga$_{1-x}$Mn$_x$As Films as a Function of Layer Thickness

Y. Y. Zhou, Y. J. Cho, Z. Ge, X. Liu, M. Dobrowolska, and J. K. Furdyna

Department of Physics, University of Notre Dame, Notre Dame, Indiana 46556, USA

Abstract. A series of films of the ferromagnetic semiconductor GaMnAs were grown on GaAs substrates by low temperature molecular beam epitaxy, with film thickness ranging from 10nm to 200nm. We measured the angular and temperature dependences of ferromagnetic resonance for each specimen, both as-grown and annealed. Our experiments indicate that the in-plane uniaxial anisotropy field strongly depends on sample thickness. Additionally, spin wave resonances (SWRs) were observed in specimens with thicknesses of 100nm and 200nm. The analysis was carried out using the SW model of Portis as well as the surface SW model of Puszkarski. Our results clearly point to the existence of surface anisotropy in ferromagnetic semiconductor films.

Keywords: Ferromagnetic resonance, Spin waves, Ferromagnetic semiconductors, Magnetic anisotropy, GaMnAs.
PACS: 75.50.Pp, 76.30.-v, 76.50.+g, 75.70.Cn

Recently ferromagnetic (FM) semiconductors (e.g., GaMnAs) have been under intense investigation because of the likelihood of their "spintronic" applications.[1] In order to utilize these new materials in magnetic logic devices, such as magneto-resistive random access memory, understanding of magnetic anisotropy in these materials is of critical importance. Ferromagnetic resonance (FMR) is a powerful tool for investigating magnetic anisotropy in FM films like GaMnAs.[2] In this paper we will focus on the behavior of FMR in GaMnAs films with different thicknesses.

The GaMnAs films used in this study were grown in a Riber 32 R&D molecular beam epitaxy (MBE) machine on semi-insulating GaAs (001) substrates. The GaAs substrates were first overgrown by a GaAs buffer layer at the substrate temperature $T_s \sim 600°C$ to achieve an atomically flat surface. The substrates were then cooled to 250°C for low temperature (LT) MBE growth. After depositing a thin layer of LT-GaAs (2 nm), GaMnAs layers with a series of thicknesses (10nm, 15nm, 20nm, 50nm, 100nm and 200nm) were grown. All specimens have a Mn concentration of 0.05 as determined by x-ray diffraction measurements of the lattice constant. The specimens were then annealed in N$_2$ gas for one hour at 290°C, and were then cooled by rapid quench to room temperature. The Curie temperature T_C of the six as-grown specimens is around 60 K. The LT-annealing has increased the T_C of all specimens to a range from 80K to 130K, the thinner specimens reaching the higher T_C values.

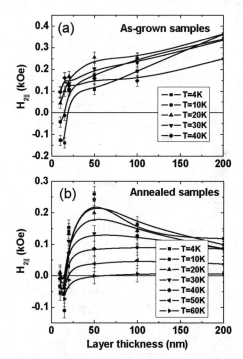

FIGURE 1. Thickness dependence of in-plane uniaxial anisotropy at different temperatures: (a) in as-grown samples (b) in annealed samples. The curves are guides for the eye.

FMR measurements were carried out at 9.46GHz using a Bruker EPR spectrometer.[3] We measured the angular and temperature dependences of FMR for each specimen. The angular dependence of the FMR position was then fitted by a nonlinear least squares

CP893, *Physics of Semiconductors, 28th International Conference*
edited by W. Jantsch and F. Schäffler
© 2007 American Institute of Physics 978-0-7354-0397-0/07/$23.00

method in order to obtain the magnetic anisotropies.[2,4] The quality of the theoretical fits clearly indicates that the FMR data can be reliably used for determining the uniaxial and the cubic anisotropies of GaMnAs.

Our experiments indicate that the in-plane uniaxial magnetic anisotropy field $H_{2\parallel}$ strongly depends on the sample thickness. For as-grown specimens, the in-plane uniaxial anisotropy field increases rapidly with thickness for film thicknesses below 20nm, and much more slowly for thicknesses above 20nm, as shown in Fig. 1(a). For annealed samples the in-plane uniaxial anisotropy field shows a slight decrease below 15nm, then increases rapidly with thickness between 15nm to 50nm and finally decreases slightly or keeps constant above 50nm, as shown in Fig. 1(b). We have observed that when the thickness is equal or greater than 20nm, the resonance field for $\mathbf{H}\|[110]$ slightly exceeds that for $\mathbf{H}\|[\bar{1}10]$. In contrast, for thicknesses below 20nm the resonance for $\mathbf{H}\|[110]$ occurs at lower fields than for $\mathbf{H}\|[\bar{1}10]$. Combining the present data with the earlier results[5] on GaMnAs with thicknesses from 0.2 to 6.8μm, we attribute this behavior to the existence of surface anisotropy in GaMnAs.

However, other magnetic properties, i.e., the in-plane cubic and the perpendicular uniaxial anisotropies all depend on the hole concentration, but show little if any dependence on the film thickness. To understand our results, we turn to the details of the FMR spectra observed on GaMnAs films, including strong SWRs[6] in films with thicknesses of 100nm and 200nm.

It is well established that SWRs provide valuable information on magnetic interactions at or near the surfaces of the film.[7] In the specimens under this study, SWRs and their angular dependence have been observed in films with thicknesses of 100nm and 200nm. We illustrate this by the angular dependence of SWRs in the as-grown 200nm specimen when the external magnetic field is in the (110) plane. In Fig. 2(a), the derivative of SWR absorption as a function of $\mathbf{H}$ is shown for different angles from 0° to 90°. There is a critical angle at which a transition occurs from one type of SW modes to another. Between 0° and 24° several linear SW harmonics are present, while only 2 SWs are seen from 24° to 90°. In Fig. 2(b), we plot the positions of all observed SWRs. Clearly, when $\mathbf{H}$ is normal or nearly normal to the film, the observation of Portis-type linear SWRs[8] suggests a volume inhomogeneity of the magnetic anisotropy.[9] However, when the external magnetic field is in an orientation away from the normal, two SWR lines are typically observed due to the surface inhomogeneity of magnetic anisotropy, as discussed by Puszkarski.[7] The critical angle, where only the uniform mode of the FMR is observed, suggests that surface pinning depends on the orientation of the magnetization.

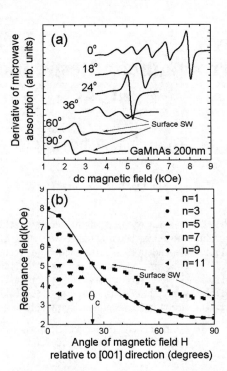

FIGURE 2. (a) SWR spectra from perpendicular (0°) to parallel (90°) configurations observed for the 200nm as-grown GaMnAs sample at 4K when $\mathbf{H}$ is in the (110) plane. (b) SWR positions from (0°) to (90°) configurations for the same sample. The arrow indicates the critical angle $\theta_c \approx 24°$. The black curve is a theoretical fit for the uniform mode.

In summary, FMR measurements presented above show unambiguously that the in-plane uniaxial anisotropy strongly depends on the sample thickness, and the surface anisotropy plays an important role in thin GaMnAs samples. In specimens with thicknesses of 100nm and 200nm, we found that Portis-type linear SWRs are excited when $\mathbf{H}$ is normal (or nearly normal) to the layers; while surface SWR modes are observed for off-perpendicular orientations of $\mathbf{H}$. The study of SWRs provides valuable new information on the nature of surface pinning (surface anisotropy) and on exchange energy between Mn ions in GaMnAs.

This work was supported by NSF Grant DMR06-03752 and NSF-NIRT Program DMR02-10519.

REFERENCES

[1] H. Ohno, Science 281, 951 (1998).
[2] X. Liu and J. K. Furdyna, J. Phys.: Condens. Matter 18, R245 (2006).
[3] X. Liu et al., Phys. Rev. B 67, 205204 (2003).
[4] X. Liu et al., J. Appl. Phys. 98, 63904 (2005).
[5] U. Welp et al., Appl. Phys. Lett. 85, 260 (2004).
[6] Y. Sasaki et al., J. Supercond. 16, 143 (2003).
[7] H. Puszkarski, Prog. Surf. Sci., 9, 191 (1979).
[8] A. M. Portis, Appl. Phys. Lett., 2, 69 (1963).
[9] T. G. Rappoport et al., Phys. Rev. B 69, 125213 (2004).

Photoluminescence and ultrafast spectroscopy on GaAs quantum wells close to a Ga(Mn)As layer

R. Schulz, T. Korn, A. Maurer, D. Schuh, W. Wegscheider and C. Schüller

Institut für Experimentelle und Angewandte Physik, Universität Regensburg, 93040 Regensburg, Germany

Abstract. We present a study of nonmagnetic GaAs quantum wells (QWs) embedded in AlGaAs barriers close to a Ga(Mn)As layer. The photoluminescence (PL) spectra of QWs close (3 - 10 nm) to the Ga(Mn)As layer show a pronounced broadening and quenching of the PL. This may be due to diffusion of Mn ions into the QW during growth. Employing time-resolved Faraday rotation measurements, we observe that the spin lifetime in the QW, separated by 10 nm from the Ga(Mn)As layer, is increased by a factor of 3, as compared to a control well, at a distance of 122 nm. However, in the measured g factors we see no influence of the Mn.

Keywords: Ga(Mn)As, photoluminescence, time-resolved Faraday rotation, spin lifetime
PACS: 61.72.Vv,78.47.+p,78.55.-m,78.67.De

The ferromagnetic semiconductor Ga(Mn)As [1] is very interesting for spintronics applications, where it may serve as an injector of spin-polarized carriers into nonmagnetic semiconductors. For future devices, it is important to know the properties of nonmagnetic semiconductor structures close to ferromagnetic Ga(Mn)As. Novel effects have, e.g., recently been observed for semiconductor layers in close proximity to a ferromagnetic metal [2].

We have investigated MBE samples from 3 different wafers. The following layer sequence is common to all 3 samples: after a standard 150 period GaAs/$Al_{0.3}Ga_{0.7}As$ superlattice, a 10 nm wide GaAs well is grown (in the following referred to as *lower well*). After a 100 nm $Al_{0.3}Ga_{0.7}As$ barrier, a second well with 12 nm width follows (*upper well*). The upper well is separated either by a 3 nm (sample A) or a 10 nm (sample B) $Al_{0.3}Ga_{0.7}As$ barrier from a 50 nm wide ferromagnetic $Ga_{0.95}Mn_{0.05}As$ top layer. A reference sample is grown, which is identical to sample B (10 nm barrier), except that the top layer consists of low-temperature GaAs, grown under the same conditions (T ∼ 250°C) as the GaMnAs layer. For optical measurements, the substrate was removed by selective chemical etching to provide optically-transparent samples.

Photoluminescence (PL) measurements (Fig. 1) were performed in a split-coil magnet cryostat at ∼ 4 K, using a 532 nm cw laser at typical excitation densities of ∼ 100 W/cm². the PL spectra of the reference sample without Mn in the top layer show two peaks, as expected for the QW widths. Sample B (10 nm barrier) exhibits a noticable broadening of the upper QW PL, whereas in sample A (3 nm barrier) the PL from the upper QW is totally quenched. We attribute the quenching and broadening to Mn diffusion through the barrier [4] during and

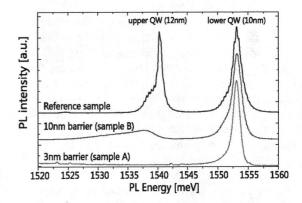

FIGURE 1. Photoluminescence signal of three different samples at low temperature. The spectrum of the reference is shifted by 5 meV to lower energies for better comparability.

after growth. In addition, the PL of the reference sample, as well as of the lower QW's in samples A and B have low-energy shoulders, which may be attributed to donor-bound excitons [3] due to Mn background doping in the growth chamber.

A modelocked Ti:Sa laser with laser pulses of about 100 fs length and 20 meV spectral width is used for the time-resolved Faraday rotation (TRFR) measurements. A circularly-polarized pump, and a weaker, linearly-polarized probe beam are focused onto the sample. A magnetic field of up to 6 Tesla is applied in the sample plane (Voigt geometry). The polarization rotation of the transmitted probe beam induced by the spin polarization in the sample is measured. Figure 2 shows TRFR measurements performed at zero magnetic field on sample B (10 nm barrier). The laser energy is tuned to be in resonance with either the upper, 12 nm wide QW or the lower, 10 nm wide QW. Both measurements show a

CP893, *Physics of Semiconductors, 28th International Conference*
edited by W. Jantsch and F. Schäffler
© 2007 American Institute of Physics 978-0-7354-0397-0/07/$23.00

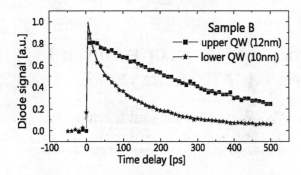

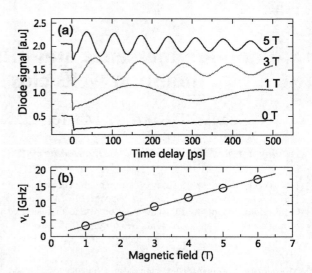

FIGURE 2. TRFR measurements at zero magnetic field for the upper (squares) and lower (stars) QW in sample B. The solid lines represent (bi-)exponential fits to the data points.

FIGURE 3. (a) TRFR measurements on the upper QW in sample B for different magnetic fields applied in the QW plane. (b) Larmor frequency dispersion determined from (a). The solid line represents a linear fit to the data points.

decay of the optically-induced spin polarization that is analyzed by fitting a monoexponential (upper QW) and biexponential (lower QW) function, respectively. For the upper QW, we find a decay time of $\tau = (411 \pm 22)$ ps. For the lower QW, we observe a two-component decay with $\tau_{fast} = (15 \pm 1)$ ps, and $\tau_{slow} = (128 \pm 3)$ ps. These two decay constants may correspond to the spin lifetimes of holes (τ_{fast}) and electrons (τ_{slow}). Comparing the decay times for the two QWs, we find that the spin lifetime in the upper QW is about 3 times longer than that of the lower QW. This is an indication for the D'Yakonov-Perel [5, 6] mechanism, where the spin lifetime is inversely proportional to the momentum scattering time. The Mn ions within the upper QW act as scattering centers and thus increase the spin lifetime.

Figure 3a shows TRFR measurements performed on the upper QW in sample B at different in-plane magnetic fields. In this field configuration, the optically excited spins precess about the external field, B, with the Larmor frequency $\nu_L = g_L \mu_B / h \cdot B$, where g_L is the Landé factor and μ_B the Bohr magneton. An exponentially damped sine function is used to fit these measurements. The Larmor frequency extracted from these fits is shown in Figure 3b versus magnetic field. From this, we extract $|g_L| = 0.206 \pm 0.01$, which is in good agreement with literature data [7] for GaAs QWs of similar width. From this and from the linear dependence of ν_L on B we conclude that the Mn concentration, even in the upper QW, is very low, since otherwise one would expect an increased g_L due to antiferromagnetic coupling [3, 4]. An upper limit to the concentration may be given by figure 8 in reference [4], where a nonlinear dependence of ν_L on B is observed for a Mn concentration of $x \geq 0.05\%$.

In summary, we have performed both PL and TRFR measurements on GaAs QWs, close to a Ga(Mn)As top layer. We observe broadening and quenching of the PL signal as the distance between the QW and the Ga(Mn)As layer is 10 nm or below. We attribute this to Mn diffusion into the QW. The TRFR measurements

show for this case a threefold increase of the spin lifetime, which may be due to the D'yakonov-Perel mechanism caused by the Mn ions in the QW acting as scattering centers. However, the observed g factor is as expected for a nonmagnetic QW, indicating that the Mn concentration within the QW is still small ($< 0.05\%$). Furthermore, a low-energy shoulder is seen in the PL peaks even for the QWs in a control sample without nominal Mn content. These structures may arise from donor-bound excitons within the QWs, indicating that there is an unintentional background Mn doping in the growth chamber.

We acknowledge support by the Deutsche Forschungsgemeinschaft via project SCHU1171/1, GK 638 and SFB 689 TP B4.

REFERENCES

1. H. Ohno, A. Shen and F. Matsukura, A. Oiwa, A. Endo, S. Katsumoto, and Y. Iye, *Appl. Phys. Lett.* **69**, 363 (1996)
2. R. J. Epstein, I. Malajovich, R. K. Kawakami, Y. Chye, M. Hanson, P. M. Petroff, A. C. Gossard, and D. D. Awschalom, *Phys. Rev. B* **65**, 121202(R) (2002)
3. R.C. Myers, M. Poggio, N. P. Stern, A. C. Gossard, and D. D. Awschalom, *Phys. Rev. Lett.* **95**, 017204 (2005)
4. M. Poggio, R. C. Myers, N. P. Stern, A. C. Gossard, and D. D. Awschalom, *Phys. Rev. B* **72**, 235313 (2005)
5. M.I. D'yakonov, and V.I. Perel, *Sov. Phys. Solid State* **13**, 3023 (1972)
6. J. Fabian, and S. Das Sarma, *J. Vac. Sci. Technol. B*, **17**, 1708 (1999)
7. M.J. Snelling, G.P. Finn, A.S. Plaut, R.T. Harvey, A.C. Tropper, R. Eccleston, and C.C. Phillips, *Phys. Rev. B* **44**, 11345 (1991)

Infrared Magneto-Optical Studies in Ga$_{1-x}$Mn$_x$As Films

G.Acbas[*], J. Cerne[*], M.Cukr[¶], V. Novak[¶] and J. Sinova[†]

[*]*Physics Dept., Univ. at Buffalo, SUNY, Buffalo, NY*
[¶]*Institute of Physics, Acad. of Sciences of the Czech Republic, Prague, Czech Republic*
[†]*Physics Dept., Texas A\&M Univ., College Station, TX*

Abstract. The mid and near infrared (115-1165meV) complex Faraday and Kerr effects are studied in a Ga$_{1-x}$Mn$_x$As random alloy film (x=0.05 and Curie temperature of 100 K) as a function of frequency and temperature. The strong infrared magneto-optical response shows clear ferromagnetic behavior that is consistent with dc magnetization measurements. The real and imaginary parts of the measured Faraday and Kerr angles are in qualitative and quantitative agreement with the values predicted by effective Hamiltonian models within a mean field treatment.[1] Strong features in the Kerr and Faraday effects, with a peak rotation angle at around 5.5μm (220 meV) is observed consistent with theoretical predictions

Keywords: Faraday Effect, Kerr Effect, Diluted Magnetic Semiconductors, infrared, magneto-optics, GaMnAs.
PACS: 75.50.Pp, 78.20.Ls, 78.30.Fs, 78.66.Fd, 78.20.Jq

The interplay between the magnetic and semiconducting properties of III-Mn-V diluted magnetic semiconductors has been intensely studied in the last few years since it is believed that this will shed light on ways to reach room temperature ferromagnetism in these materials.[2] In particular magneto-optical measurements have been used to obtain information on the hole mediated exchange interaction between Mn ions, the spin-split bands, the magnetic anisotropies, and the presence of segregated second phases, for example.[3]

However, magneto-optical measurements in the 1-11 μm (1165-115 meV) range, which characterizes the energy scale of the valence band electronic structure, are limited. In this paper we extend these types of measurements to this critical wavelength range. Mid-infrared free carrier Faraday-rotation is well known as a technique to determine the effective mass of semiconductors[4] and metals[5] with simple band structures. These measurements can probe a wide range of temperatures and impurity concentrations. Faraday effect experiments have revealed, for example, in p-type GaAs features associated with the transitions between Zeeman split valence sub-bands.[6] For GaMnAs, theoretical calculations based on effective Hamiltonian models predict strong features due to free holes and transitions between spin-split valence sub-bands in this wavelength range.[1]

The Faraday and Kerr effects are measured with a modulation technique using laser sources.[7] Linearly polarized laser light is incident parallel to the magnetic field and normal to the sample surface. The refracted and reflected beams become elliptically polarized with the major axis rotated by an angle. The real (imaginary) part of the Faraday angle θ_F characterizes the rotation (ellipticity) of the transmitted polarization. The rotation angle of the ellipse is due to a difference in the index of refraction for left and right circular polarized light while the ellipticity is due to a difference in absorption. Similarly, the complex Kerr angle θ_K describes the polarization of reflected light. θ_F and θ_K in turn can be used to determine the complex magneto-conductivity tensor.[8] The sample studied in this experiment is a 50 nm GaMnAs film grown by low temperature molecular beam epitaxy on a GaAs substrate with 5 % Mn. After growth the sample was annealed for one hour at 200 °C. The hole concentration of 2.5·10^{20} cm^{-3} is determined through dc Hall effect measurements at fields up to 9 T and at a temperature of 4K. The hole density is estimated to be within 30% of the high field (~30 T) value.[9] The Curie temperature is approximately 100 K.

Both θ_F and θ_K show hysteretic and non-linear behavior up to 110 K (see inset Fig. 1). The linear magnetic field dependence is subtracted to obtain θ_F and θ_K as functions of temperature and wavelength. The temperature dependence of Re(θ_F) and Im(θ_F) is shown in Fig. 1 for a wavelength of 10.22 μm Notice that the ellipticity changes sign at about 80K. In magnetic circular dichroism experiments the sign of the signal, which depends on the difference between

CP893, *Physics of Semiconductors, 28th International Conference*
edited by W. Jantsch and F. Schäffler
© 2007 American Institute of Physics 978-0-7354-0397-0/07/$23.00

absorption coefficients for left and right circularly polarized light was shown to be influenced by population effects. At this energy (120 meV) transitions between light hole and heavy hole bands dominate together with a tail contribution from the transition between the split-off band and the heavy and light hole bands. Transitions to an impurity band could have the same characteristic energy, but there is no qualitative or quantitative theory to compare with the experimental results.

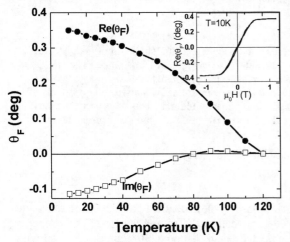

Figure 1. Temperature dependence of the $\text{Re}(\theta_F)$ and $\text{Im}(\theta_F)$ at 10.22 μm wavelength. Inset shows hysteresis loop at 10 K.

The wavlength dependence of the $\text{Re}(\theta_K)$ is shown in Fig. 2. The solid and dotted lines correspond to theoretical calculations using a 8 band $\vec{k}\cdot\vec{p}$ effective Hamiltonian model,[1] for hole density of $2.2\cdot10^{20}$ cm^{-3} and $3.3\cdot10^{20}$ cm^{-3}, respectively. Disorder effects have been taken into account by the introduction of a fixed hole lifetime dominated by impurity scattering. The points correspond to Kerr angle measurements at 10 K.

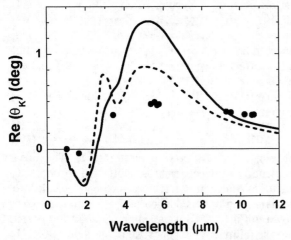

Figure 2. $\text{Re}(\theta_K)$ as function of the wavelength. Theoretical lines[1] at T=0K, solid line for p=$2.2\cdot10^{20}$ cm^{-3}, dotted line for p=$3.3\cdot10^{20}$ cm^{-3}; the experimental points are taken at 10 K.

The Kerr rotation peak in the 5-6μm (200-300 meV) range, and the change of sign in the 2-3μm range are consistent with predictions from the model. Additional laser lines in the 2-5μm range are needed in order to differentiate between contributions due to transitions from the light hole to split-off band, and transitions from the heavy hole to split-off band. The spectral dependence appears broader than the 100 meV value used in the theory. Some broadening is due to the thermal fluctuations which are not taken into account in the theoretical calculations.

Our data show resonance behavior in all components of the complex Faraday and Kerr angles, and provide information on the carrier mediated magnetism. Systematic analysis as a function of hole density is under way to provide a more complete understanding of the electronic band structure of GaMnAs.

Acknowledgments: This work was supported by DARPA/ONR N0001400-1-0951 (Buffalo), Research Corporation Cottrell Scholar Award (Buffalo), NSF-CAREER-DMR0449899 (Buffalo), NSF-CAREER-DMR-0547875 (Texas A&M). and GACR-202/04/1519 (Prague).

REFERENCES

1. E. M. Hankiewicz , J. Sinova et al., Phys. Rev. B **70**, 245211 (2004).
2. T. Jungwirth, J. Sinova, J. Mašek, J. Kučera, and A. H. MacDonald, Rev. Mod. Phys. **78**, 809-864 (2006).
3. K. Ando, T. Hayashi, M. Tanaka, and A. Twardowski. Appl. Phys. **83**, 6548 (1998); B. Beschoten, P.A. Crowell, I. Malajovich, D.D. Awschalom, F. Matsukura, A. Shen, and H. Ohno, J. Szczytko, W. Mac, A. Twardowski, F. Matsukura and H. Ohno, Phys. Rev. B **59**, 12935 (1999); D. Hrabovsky, E. Vanelle, A. R. Fert, D. S. Yee, J. P. Redoules, J. Sadowski, J. Kanski and L. Ilver, Appl. Phys. Lett. **81**, 2806 (2002); R. Lang, A. Winter, H. Pascher, H. Krenn, X. Liu, J.K. Furdyna, Phys. Rev. B **72**, 024430 (2005).
4. I.M. Boswarva, R.E. Howard, A.B. Lidiard, Proc. Royal Soc. London A **269**, 125 (1962).
5. J. Cerne, D.C. Schmadel, M. Grayson, G.S. Jenkins, J. R. Simpson, and H., D. Drew,Phys. Rev. B **61**, 8133 (2000).
6. T. H. Lee, H.Y Fan, Phys. Rev. **165**, 927 (1968).
7. J. Cerne, D.C. Schmadel, L. Rigal, and H.D. Drew, Rev. Sci. Instr. **74**, 4755-4767 (2003).
8. M.-H. Kim, G. Acbas, M.-H. Yang, I. Ohkubo, H. Christen, M.Cukr, V. Novak, Z. Schlesinger, and J. Cerne, in preparation (2006).
9. G.B. Kim, M. Na, G. Acbas, B.D. McCombe, S. Wang, M. Cheon, H. Luo, X. Liu, Y. Sasaki, and J.K. Furdyna, Proc. Int. Conf. High Mag. Fields Semicond. Phys. 16, 285-293 (2005).

GaMnAs annealing under various conditions: air vs. As cap

Kamil Olejník*, Vít Novák*, Miroslav Cukr*, Oliva Pacherová*, Zdeněk Matěj[†],
Václav Holý,[†] and Miroslav Maryško*

*Institute of Physics AS CR, Cukrovarnická 10, 162 53 Prague, Czech Republic
[†]Department of Electronic Structures, Charles University, Ke Karlovu 2, 121 16 Praha, Czech Republic

Abstract. The presence of As-capping layer on GaMnAs sample during its post-growth annealing is shown to affect the annealing kinetics: it accelerates the increase of the Curie temperature and conductivity. The effect is explained in terms of an enhanced surface recombination of the Mn interstitial atoms, and simulated by a one-dimensional numerical model.

Keywords: diluted magnetic semiconductors, annealing
PACS: 71.55.Eq,75.50.Pp

Introduction

For thin GaMnAs layers an optimal low temperature annealing is known to improve the magnetic properties and to increase the critical temperature from less than 100 K of an as-grown sample to the current maximum of about 170 K. It is commonly accepted that the improving effect stems from the outdiffusion of Mn interstitials, which act as antiferromagnetically coupled double donors compensating the itinerant holes in the as-grown GaMnAs.

The details of the outdiffusion of the Mn interstitials and the mechanism of their surface passivation are still matter of controversy. Whereas some experimental data can be interpreted in terms of a diffusion dynamics only [1], other authors emphasize the role of surface reactions in the annealing process [2, 3]. In the latter case, surface nitridation [4], oxydation [5], and/or MnAs formation appear to be the relevant processes.

In this work we present the results of a simple annealing experiment and propose a relevant one-dimensional model.

Experiment

Two nominally identical, 100 nm thick $Ga_{1-x}Mn_xAs$ layers with $x \approx 0.035$ were grown by the low-temperature MBE. After cooling down to room temperature one of the samples was in-situ covered by an amorphous arsenic capping layer. The samples cut from each of the layers were subjected to several annealing steps in air at temperature $200\,°C$. Between the steps the Curie temperature T_C of the ferromagnetic transition was measured by the SQUID magnetometer.

As shown in Fig.1 the as grown samples started at the same Curie temperature. During the annealing the Curie

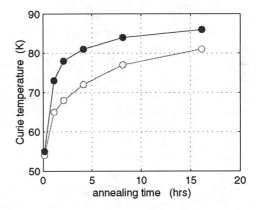

FIGURE 1. Curie temperature vs. annealing time for the As-capped sample (full circles) and the bare sample (empty circles).

temperature monotonously rised, showing a significantly faster increase in the sample with the As-cap.

Model

In the one-dimensional case the transport of the interstitial Mn atoms can be described in terms of their diffusion and drift as follows:

$$j_n = -D_n \frac{dn}{dx} - 2\mu_n n \frac{d\Psi}{dx} \quad (1)$$

where n is the density of the Mn interstitials, D_n and μ_n are their diffusion constant and mobility, respectively, Ψ is the electrical potential; factor 2 in the drift term reflects the charge of the Mn interstitial. Introducing the Einstein relation $D_n = k_B T / e \cdot \mu_n$, and normalizing properly all

CP893, *Physics of Semiconductors, 28th International Conference*
edited by W. Jantsch and F. Schäffler
© 2007 American Institute of Physics 978-0-7354-0397-0/07/$23.00

quantities one can write the continuity equation

$$\frac{dn}{dt} = \frac{d}{dx}\left(\frac{dn}{dx} + 2n\frac{d\Psi}{dx}\right) \qquad (2)$$

An analogous equation can be written for free holes with density p, except for the single charge and sign in the drift term. The system is closed by the Gauss law

$$\frac{d^2\Psi}{dx^2} = 1 - p - 2n \qquad (3)$$

where both p and n are normalized to density of substitutional Mn atoms. The system can be solved numerically assuming proper boundary conditions. While in the bulk the vanishing gradients are assumed, on the surface the flux j_n is set equal to a surface recombination rate

$$j_{ns} = S_0\left[1 - N_s(t)/N_{smax}\right]n_s(t) \qquad (4)$$

where $N_s(t)$ is the number of Mn interstitial atoms currently trapped in a surface container, N_{smax} is the container capacity, S_0 is the recombination rate of the empty container, n_s is the Mn interstitial density on the surface. In order to maintain the charge neutrality, each Mn interstitial atom vanishing in the surface container causes two free holes being injected to the system from the surface.

An example of the temporal evolution of the Mn interstitial profile is shown in Fig.2. Initial n profile (not shown in the figure) corresponds to zero surface flux, i.e. to the flat stationary state at the surface. When the diffusion and surface recombination are enabled at time $t = 0$, Mn interstitial density drops steeply in the surface vicinity, Fig.2a. The depletion layer spreads into the bulk and the interstitial atoms are sucked out of the volume. Flux towards the surface gradually decreases as the surface container is filling, Fig.2b–e. Once it is completely full, the diffusion process continues to flatten the profile, without, however, changing the number of interstititials in the volume any more, Fig.2f–h. Finally, homogeneous steady state profile is reached in the whole Mn-doped part of the structure, Fig.2i.

The time evolution of the free holes p is roughly complementary (not shown here). Thus, an average value of the product $(1 - n) \cdot p^{1/3}$ can be computed, representing approximately the Curie temperature T_c and its temporal evolution during the transient process. The T_c evolution corresponding to Fig.2 is shown in Fig.3 by the red line. With a reduced recombination rate of the surface container the increase in T_C is slower, approaching the same saturation value as long as the container capacity N_{smax} is the same. Reduced capacity leads, of course, to a reduced Curie temperature, see Fig.3.

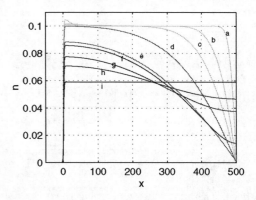

FIGURE 2. Profiles of Mn interstitials in successive time periods (from a to i). The sample has constant density of substitutional Mn atoms (normalized to unity) between $x = 0$ and $x = 500$. Recombination surface is at $x = 500$.

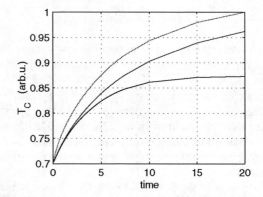

FIGURE 3. Simulated Curie temperature (normalized to maximum T_C) vs. annealing time. The parameters are as follows: $S_0 = 0.1, N_{smax} = 100$ (red/upper line), $S_0 = 0.02, N_{smax} = 100$ (blue/middle line), $S_0 = 0.02, N_{smax} = 50$ (black/lower line).

ACKNOWLEDGMENTS

The work was supported by AVOZ10100521 and GACR-202/04/1519.

REFERENCES

1. K.W. Edmonds, et al., *Phys. Rev. Lett.* **92**, 037201 (2004).
2. M. Adell, et al., *Phys. Rev. Lett.* **94**, 139701 (2005).
3. J. Sadowski, et al., *cond-mat/0601623* (2006).
4. K.C. Ku, et al., *Appl. Phys. Lett.* **82**, 2302 (2003).
5. M. Malfait, et al., *Appl. Phys. Lett.* **86**, 132501 (2005).

Magnetic cluster phases of Mn-interstitial-free (Ga,Mn)As

Y. J. Cho,[1] M. A. Scarpulla,[2] X. Liu,[1] Y. Y. Zhou,[1]
O. D. Dubon,[2] and J. K. Furdyna[1]

[1]*Department of Physics, University of Notre Dame, Notre Dame, Indiana 46556, USA*
[2]*Department of Materials Science and Engineering, University of California, Berkeley,
California 94720, USA*

Abstract. We report an investigation of magnetic cluster phases of (Ga,Mn)As of varying dosages formed by Mn ion implantation followed by pulsed-laser melting (II-PLM). A systematic study of zero-field-cooled and field-cooled magnetization along several high-symmetry crystallographic directions reveals the presence of magnetic cluster-like phases, and manifests an unambiguous in-plane uniaxial anisotropy in all samples. Since such anisotropy has been previously seen in (Ga,Mn)As grown by molecular beam epitaxy, its observation in (Ga,Mn)As prepared by II-PLM suggests that it is an intrinsic property of (Ga,Mn)As rather than a consequence of a specific growth method. Our results also indicate a unique uniaxial component along $[\bar{1}10]$ for the magnetic cluster phase at intermediate Mn dosage indicating that composition as well as processing may determine the details of the magnetic anisotropy in (Ga,Mn)As.

Keywords: ferromagnetic semiconductors; magnetic anisotropy; implantation; pulsed-laser melting; magnetic phases.
PACS: 75.50.Pp, 75.50.Dd , 75.30.Gw, 75.70.Ak, 68.55.Ln, 61.72.Vv, 75.60.Ej, 75.30.Kz

Although extensive efforts have been made to understand the magnetic anisotropy of (Ga,Mn)As, principally based on models involving hole-mediated ferromagnetism,[1,2] the mechanism of in-plane uniaxial anisotropy observed in (Ga,Mn)As grown by low temperature molecular beam epitaxy (MBE) remains unclear. Hamaya *et al.* have recently suggested that the in-plane uniaxial anisotropy may originate from spin-glass-like cluster phases existing within the cubic (Ga,Mn)As matrix.[3,4] Herein, this issue is explored using zero-field-cooled (ZFC) and field-cooled (FC) magnetization (M_{ZFC} and M_{FC}) along several high-symmetry crystallographic directions on a series of Mn-interstitial-free (Ga,Mn)As specimens prepared by Mn ion implantation and subsequent pulsed laser melting (II-PLM).[5,6]

Semi-insulating GaAs (001) wafers were implanted with 80 keV Mn ions to one dose of 5×10^{15} cm^{-2} Mn ions (Sample #1); two doses (Sample #2); and four doses (Sample #3). The implanted samples were irradiated in air with a single pulse from a KrF excimer laser (248 nm, ~30 ns), causing the implanted layer to first melt and then re-crystallize upon solidification. This process leads to high levels of Mn incorporation in the re-crystallized (Ga,Mn)As layer, while suppressing the formation of Mn interstitials.[7] The Curie temperatures (T_Cs) are near 30 K, 60 K, and 80 K for Samples #1, #2, and #3, respectively. Using

ferromagnetic resonance and magnetization hysteresis loop measurements, all three samples show the unambiguous presence of an in-plane uniaxial anisotropy similar to that observed in MBE-grown (Ga,Mn)As film.[8] Since the samples were produced by an entirely different process, this result supports the hypothesis that the breaking of in-plane cubic symmetry is an intrinsic property of (Ga,Mn)As films.

Figure 1 shows the temperature dependences of M_{ZFC} and M_{FC} for Samples #1 (a), #2 (b), and #3 (c). M_{ZFC} was obtained by first cooling the sample in zero magnetic field from $T > T_C$ to 4 K. A dc magnetic field of 35 Oe was then applied along [110], $[\bar{1}10]$, [001], or in-plane <100> directions, and the magnetization was measured as the temperature was increased. M_{FC} was obtained in a similar way, except that the sample was cooled in 35 Oe. Except for the results on Sample #2 along $[\bar{1}10]$, there are clear differences between M_{ZFC} and M_{FC} in all cases. Such dependence on thermal history is usually attributed to the existence of spin glass and/or magnetic cluster phases.

The ferromagnetic ordering in the lowest-dosed sample (#1) is believed to be local based on its rapidly increasing resistivity with decreasing temperature. We thus expect phenomena associated with magnetic clusters to dominate the magnetization for all directions. Interestingly, for this sample the easy

CP893, *Physics of Semiconductors, 28th International Conference*
edited by W. Jantsch and F. Schäffler
© 2007 American Institute of Physics 978-0-7354-0397-0/07/$23.00

magnetization axis is the perpendicular [001], rather than the in-plane <100> found for the other samples.

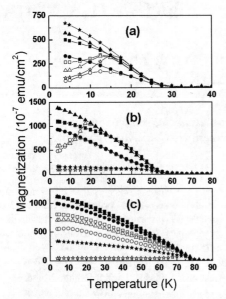

FIGURE 1. M_{ZFC} and M_{FC} as a function of temperature for Samples #1 (a), #2 (b), and #3 (c). An external magnetic field of 35 Oe is applied parallel to either [110] (circles), [$\bar{1}$10] (squares), [001] (stars), or to the in-plane <100> directions (triangles). M_{ZFC} data are denoted by open symbols; M_{FC} by full symbols.

As for Sample #2, magnetic cluster-like behavior along [$\bar{1}$10] is ruled out because there is no difference between M_{ZFC} and M_{FC} along that direction. Temperature dependence of magnetization induced by a minute residual field ($\sim1.5 \pm 1.0$ Oe) in Sample #2 is plotted in Fig. 2. Note that such minute field exists also during the process of ZFC. For this sample, temperature dependent M_{ZFC} and M_{FC} obtained for **H**(35 Oe)$\|$[$\bar{1}$10] is also plotted in Fig. 2. The three conditions along [$\bar{1}$10] give almost identical results. Importantly (and in contrast with Fig. 1(b)) the magnetization along [$\bar{1}$10] for Sample #2 is the highest for the vanishingly small cooling field. By applying a stronger cooling field (~35 Oe), however, we obtain the largest magnetization in the <100>.

For Sample #3, magnetic cluster-like behavior is again dominant along all directions, similar to Sample #1. Although twice the Mn dosage of Sample #2 was implanted in Sample #3, the values of its magnetization at low temperature are lower than those observed in Sample #2, as shown in Fig. 1. Therefore, we postulate that the fraction of non-substitutional of Mn ions (possibly in the form of Mn clusters or MnAs precipitates (but not as interstitials in tetrahedral or hexagonal sites) increases with increasing Mn dosage. These Mn complexes may obstruct ferromagnetic interaction among substitutional Mn ions, thus decreasing the magnetization and enhancing the cluster-like magnetic behavior in this specimen.

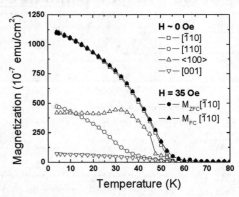

FIGURE 2. Temperature dependence of magnetization induced by a small residual field ($\sim1.5 \pm 1.0$ Oe) in Sample #2 along either [110], [$\bar{1}$10], [001], or in-plane <100> axes. For comparison, temperature dependences of M_{ZFC} and M_{FC} obtained at **H**(35 Oe)$\|$[$\bar{1}$10] for Sample #2 are also plotted. Note the striking fact that the three conditions give almost identical result for [$\bar{1}$10].

To sum up, direct magnetization was used to study magnetic cluster behavior in II-PLM (Ga,Mn)As. Based on obvious differences between the observed M_{ZFC} and M_{FC}, we conclude that magnetic cluster-like phases exist in all samples studied in this series. It is also observed that every specimen in the series has a [$\bar{1}$10] uniaxial anisotropy; and that both M_{ZFC} and M_{FC} measured along that direction are highly sensitive to the Mn dosage. It is interesting that the magnetic cluster anisotropy in Sample #2 (with an intermediate Mn implantation dosage) is different from that in Samples #1 and #3. The present results suggest that further investigation of the cluster-like phases in III-Mn-V alloys should shed important light on the magnetism in these materials.

Supported by NSF Grant DMR06-03752 and NSF-NIRT Program DMR02-10519 and by the U.S. Department of Energy under Contract No. DEAC02-05CH11231.

REFERENCES

[1] T. Dietl, J. Phys.: Condens. Matter **16**, S5471 (2004).
[2] X. Liu and J. K. Furdyna, J. Phys.: Condens. Matter **18**, R245 (2006).
[3] K. Hamaya *et al.*, Phys. Rev. Lett. **94**, 147203 (2005).
[4] K. Hamaya *et al.*, Phys. Rev. B **73**, 155204 (2006).
[5] M. A. Scarpulla *et al.*, Appl. Phys. Lett. **82**, 1251 (2003).
[6] M. A. Scarpulla *et al.*, AIP Conf. Proc. **772**, 1367 (2005).
[7] M. A. Scarpulla *et al.*, Phys. Rev. Lett.**95** 207204 (2005).
[8] Y. J. Cho *et al.*, (unpublished).

Kerr Rotation and Magnetic Circular Dichroism in Ferromagnetic InMnSb and InMnAs

A. Winter[*], H. Pascher[*], H. Krenn[**], T. Wojtowicz[†,††], X. Liu[†] and J. K. Furdyna[†]

[*]Experimentalphysik I, Universität Bayreuth, D-95440 Bayreuth, Germany
[**]Institut für Experimentalphysik, Karl-Franzens-Universität, A-8010 Graz, Austria
[†]Department of Physics, University of Notre Dame, Notre Dame, Indiana 46556, USA
[††]Institute of Physics, Polish Academy of Sciences, 02-668 Warsaw, Poland

Abstract. Kerr rotation and magnetic circular dichroism (MCD) were measured in thin epitaxial layers of the narrow gap ferromagnetic semiconductors InMnSb and InMnAs grown by low-temperature molecular beam epitaxy. The measurements were carried out in the wavelength range from 400 to 7000 nm at saturated magnetization conditions. The wavelength dependence of Kerr rotation and MCD have been successfully modeled using the same set of parameters. To calculate the Landau level energies for the above systems we have employed the Pidgeon-Brown model combined with an exchange matrix, as described by Rigaux [1]. Taking into account transition energies corresponding to the selection rules for right- and left hand circularly polarized light enabled us to calculate both the Kerr rotation and MCD using procedures described by Lang et al.[2] The fits give reliable values for the sign and magnitude of the exchange parameters $N_0\alpha$ and $N_0\beta$.

Keywords: Ferromagnetic Semiconductors, Magnetooptics.
PACS: 71.55.Eq, 75.50.Pp, 78.20.Ls

INTRODUCTION

The discovery of ferromagnetism in the dilute magnetic semiconductor GaMnAs [3] has promoted intense research on the exchange interaction mechanisms in III-V semiconductors alloyed with Mn [4]. In contrast to the widely investigated system GaMnAs, in the case of InMnSb and InMnAs the large effective g-factors of the narrow gap host material have to be considered in band structure models for these alloys in an external magnetic field.

Thin layers of InMnSb (Mn-content x=2%) and InMnAs (x=7%) were grown by low temperature molecular beam epitaxy and investigated by polar magneto-optical Kerr effect (MOKE) and reflectance magneto-circular dichroism (MCD).

BAND STRUCTURE MODEL AND CALCULATION OF THE DIELECTRIC FUNCTION

Landau-level-energies are obtained by diagonalization of two 4x4 Pidgeon-Brown matrices [5] for the a- and b-sets, with the exchange interaction between free carriers and Mn ions taken into account by adding exchange matrices, as described by Rigeaux [1]:

$$EX_a = \begin{pmatrix} 3A\dfrac{\alpha}{\beta} & 0 & 0 & 0 \\ 0 & -A & 0 & -2A\sqrt{2} \\ 0 & 0 & 3A & 0 \\ 0 & -2A\sqrt{2} & 0 & A \end{pmatrix} \quad \text{(1a)}$$

$$EX_b = \begin{pmatrix} -3A\dfrac{\alpha}{\beta} & 0 & 0 & 0 \\ 0 & -3A & 0 & 0 \\ 0 & 0 & A & 2A\sqrt{2} \\ 0 & 0 & 2A\sqrt{2} & -A \end{pmatrix} \quad \text{(1b)}$$

$$A = \frac{1}{6}N_0\beta x\langle S_z \rangle \quad \text{(1c)}$$

$$\langle S_z \rangle = -\frac{5}{2}B_{5/2}\left(\frac{g_{Mn}\mu_B B}{k_B T}\right) \quad \text{(1d)}$$

$$M = -g\mu_B x\langle S_z \rangle . \quad \text{(1d)}$$

Here $\langle S_z \rangle$ is the mean value of the magnetic moment parallel to the applied magnetic field, $B_{5/2}$ is the Brillouin function, $N_0\beta$ ($N_0\alpha$) the exchange integral for the valence band (conduction band), and M is the magnetization.

The imaginary part of the dielectric function is deduced by summing up the contributions of the allowed interband transitions (including the occupation of the

CP893, *Physics of Semiconductors, 28th International Conference*
edited by W. Jantsch and F. Schäffler
© 2007 American Institute of Physics 978-0-7354-0397-0/07/$23.00

levels being considered) for right and left hand circularly polarized light to the absorption coefficient:

$$\varepsilon_2(E) = \frac{f}{E^2}\sqrt{E - E_k} \ , \qquad (2)$$

where f is the oscillator strength, E is the photon energy, and E_k the interband transition energy.

The real part $\varepsilon_1(E)$ of the dielectric function is obtained by Kramers-Kronig transformation. Then:

$$\varepsilon(E) = \sum_k \varepsilon_{1,k}(E + i\Gamma) + \varepsilon_{fc}(E) \ , \qquad (3)$$

where Γ is the linewidth-parameter and $\varepsilon_{fc}(E)$ the free carrier contribution (in the Drude model framework). From the dielectric function the Kerr rotation angle and MCD are obtained, with multiple reflections taken into account by the transfer matrix method [6].

RESULTS

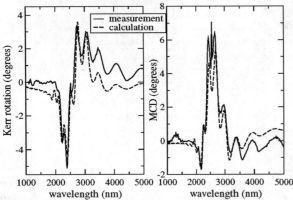

FIGURE 1. Polar Kerr effect and MCD spectra for InMnSb, x=2%, T=1.6K, magnetization saturated, experimental trace and fit with parameters according to Table1.

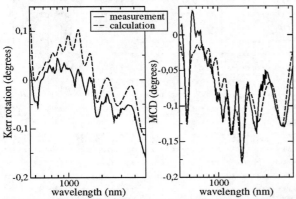

FIGURE 2. Polar Kerr effect and MCD spectra for InMnAs, x=7%, T=1.6K, magnetization saturated, experimental trace and fit with parameters according to Table 2.

TABLE 1. Fitting parameters for InMnSb

ε_∞	p cm^{-3}	E_g eV	$N_0\alpha$ eV	$N_0\beta$ eV	f_{HH} (eV)$^{3/2}$	f_{LH} (eV)$^{3/2}$
18.9	$2.3\cdot10^{20}$	0.235	2.4	3.3	1.1	0.7

TABLE 2. Fitting parameters for InMnAs

ε_∞	p cm^{-3}	E_g eV	$N_0\alpha$ eV	$N_0\beta$ eV	f_{HH} (eV)$^{3/2}$	f_{LH} (eV)$^{3/2}$
13.7	$2.1\cdot10^{19}$	0.41	0.24	2.5	0.9	0.6

DISCUSSION

Ferromagnetic ordering in narrow gap semiconductors modifies substantially the effective band gap due to a field-induced splitting, which is enhanced by the smaller effective masses and strong band-band interaction. Using the static mean-field approximation (MFA), a RKKY-driven ferromagnetic spin-spin exchange predicts for p-doped samples a transition temperature of [7]

$$T_c = \left[S(S+1)/3k_B\right]s^2\left(N_0\beta\Omega\right)^2 D(E_F)N_{Mn} \ , \qquad (4)$$

where $S = 5/2$, $s = 1/2$, and $D(E_F)$ is the density of states in the heavy hole valence band at the (degenerate) Fermi level E_F. Clearly for our two cases MFA overestimates the ordering temperatures: $T_c =$ 137K for InMnSb, $T_c = 96$K for InMnAs. The measured values $T_c = 12$K (InMnSb) and $T_c = 40$K (InMnAs), respectively, are not only lower, but also in reversed order. The main reason for this latter effect is that the spin-flip relaxation of polarized holes is more efficient in InMnSb than in InMnAs [8], since spin-orbit interaction is stronger in the narrower gap InSb host than in InAs. For InMnAs we observe a smaller Kerr rotation and MCD than for InMnSb, in contradiction to its higher T_c. The reduction of magneto-optical response arises from the initiation of transitions from the more proximate split-off band (Δ = 0.38 eV) in InAs, which is more or less excluded for InSb due to its larger spin-orbit spitting $\Delta = 0.85$ eV.

In summary, our results on narrow gap dilute ferromagnetic semiconductors elucidate the interesting interferences between the exchange and Landau band splitting when the Lande-factor of itinerant carriers becomes comparable to the giant g-factor arising from the $s,p\text{-}d$ Mn-free-carrier exchange in these materials.

REFERENCES

1. C. Rigaux, in *Semiconductors and Semimetals*, Vol. 25, ed. by J. K. Furdyna and J. Kossut (Academic, Boston, 1988), p. 235
2. R. Lang *et al.*, Phys. Rev. B **72**, 024430 (2005)
3. H. Ohno *et al.*, Appl. Phys. Lett. **87**, 026602 (2001).
4. T. Dietl, Semicond. Sci. Technol. **17**, 377 (2002).
5. C. R. Pidgeon, R. N. Brown, Phys. Rev. **146**, 575 (1966)
6. P. Yeh, Surf. Sci. **96**, 41 (1980); P. Yeh, *Optical Waves in Layered Media* (Wiley, New York, 1988).
7. J. Schliemann *et al.*, Appl. Phys. Lett. **78**, 1550 (2001).
8. M. Csontos *et al.*, Phys. Rev. Lett. **95**, 227203 (2005).

Depth profile study using x-ray photoemission spectroscopy of Mn-doped GaN prepared by thermal diffusion of Mn

J. I. Hwang[1], Y. Osafune[2], M. Kobayashi[2], K. Ebata[1], Y. Ooki[1], Y. Ishida[2],
A. Fujimori[1], A. Tanaka[3], Y. Takeda[4], T. Okane[4], Y. Saitoh[4] and K. Kobayashi[4]

[1]*Department of Complexity Science and Engineering, University of Tokyo, Kashiwa-shi, Chiba 277-8561, Japan*
[2]*Department of Physics, University of Tokyo, Kashiwa-shi, Chiba 277-8561, Japan*
[3]*Deperment of Quantum Matter, ADSM, Hiroshima University, Highashi-Hiroshima739-8530, Japan*
[4]*Synchrotron Radiation Research Center, JAEA, SPring-8, Sayo-gun, Hyogo 679-5148, Japan*

Abstract. We have performed an *in-situ* depth profile photoemission study of Mn-doped GaN prepared by a low temperature thermal diffusion method. It was revealed from core-level photoemission spectra that Mn atoms are doped as Mn^{2+} ions in deep regions of the GaN substrates. In magnetization measurements, weak hysteresis was detected in samples using *p*-type GaN substrates while samples using *n*-type GaN substrates showed only paramagnetism.

Keywords: diluted magnetic semiconductor, photoemission spectroscopy, thermal diffusion.
PACS: 75.50.Pp, 71.55.Eq, 79.60.-i, 85.40.Ry

INTRODUCTION

Diluted magnetic semiconductors (DMSs) have attracted much interest because of novel functions and potential applications to spintronics. One of the important issues is to synthesize DMSs with Curie temperatures (T_C) exceeding the room temperature. Recent theoretical studies have predicted that Mn-doped GaN shows ferromagnetism at room temperature [1, 2, 3]. So far, most of Mn-doped GaN thin films have been grown by molecular beam epitaxy (MBE). On the other hands, it has been reported that $Ga_{1-x}Mn_xN$ prepared by thermal diffusion method shows ferromagnetic behavior at room temperature [4, 5]. The growth procedure of this method consists of Mn deposition on the sample surface followed by annealing. However, the details of the electronic structures and the profile of atomic diffusion have not been studied so far. In the present study, therefore, we have performed an *in-situ* depth profile studies of Mn-doped GaN prepared by the low temperature thermal diffusion method using photoemission spectroscopy.

EXPERIMENTAL

GaN substrates used in this study were high-quality 2 μm-thick Mg-doped epitaxial layers grown by metal-organic chemical vapor deposition (MOCVD) (POWDEC Co. Ltd.). The epitaxial layers were grown on a 1μm-thick undoped GaN layer, which had been grown on a 30 nm-thick buffer layer on a sapphire (0001) substrate. Solid Mn of 99.9995 at % purity was used as the evaporant. Before the Mn deposition, surface contaminations and oxidized layer of the substrate were removed by N_2^+-ion sputtering followed by 500 °C annealing. Then 3 nm-thick Mn was deposited on the GaN surface at room temperature. After the Mn deposition, the samples were post-annealed at 500 °C for 6 hours.

Depth profile analysis was achieved by repeated Ar^+-ion sputtering (rate: 0.2 Å/min) and photoemission measurement. As a reference, GaN without Mn was also measured. The *in-situ* depth profile experiments were performed using core-level x-ray photoemission spectroscopy (XPS). In the XPS measurements, photoelectrons were collected using a VSW multi channel analyzer. The total energy resolution including the temperature broadening was ~900 meV. The photoemission spectra were referenced to the Fermi edge of a metal in electrical contact with the sample.

DEPTH PROFILE ANALYSIS

Figure 1 shows the core-level photoemission spectra recorded in the depth profile series. Sputtering time t is indicated in the figure. In Fig. 1 (a) and (b), Ga $2p_{3/2}$ and N $1s$ signals were observed for the as-annealed surface (0 min), indicating the occurrence of diffusion of Ga and N atoms to the surface. Near the sample surface (0 - 100 min sputtering), the Ga $2p_{3/2}$ and

CP893, *Physics of Semiconductors, 28th International Conference*
edited by W. Jantsch and F. Schäffler

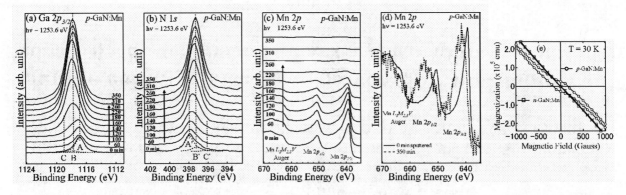

FIGURE 1. Core-level photoemission spectra of *p*-GaN:Mn recorded in the sputter-etching series. Raw data of the Ga 2$p_{3/2}$ (a), N 1s (b) and Mn 2p (c) core levels. 0 min corresponds to the as-annealed surface. The sputtering rate is 0.2 Å/min. (d) Mn 2p photoemission spectra at 0 min (solid line) and 350 min sputtering (dashed line). (e) Magnetization curve at 30 K of *p*- and *n*-GaN:Mn.

the N 1s spectra consisted of three components indicated by dashed vertical lines, which are at 1116.9 (A), 1117.8 (B) and 1119.0 eV (C) for Ga 2$p_{3/2}$ and 396.1 (C'), 397.2 (B') and 398.0 eV (A') for N 1s, while Mn metal was dominant in Mn 2p spectra as shown in Fig. 1 (c). After 120 min sputtering, the intensities of Ga 2$p_{3/2}$ (B) and N 1s (B') rapidly increased while that of Mn 2p and other components of Ga 2$p_{3/2}$ and N 1s were rapidly reduced. After 200 min sputtering, Ga 2$p_{3/2}$ (B) and N 1s (B') became dominant and these intensities remained nearly unchanged for further sputtering. These peaks are attributed to GaN because these line shapes and the energy difference between Ga 2$p_{3/2}$ and N 1s in this region agreed with the sample of reference GaN. This indicates the other components near the surface region (A, C, A', C') were due to metallic Mn compounds. The Mn 2p spectra near the sample surface and that in the deep region are compared in Fig. 1 (d). The spectrum in the deep region was shifted toward higher binding energies compared to the metallic one near the sample surface. The peak position was 641.5 ± 0.1 eV which was close to that of Mn^{2+} in Ga$_{1-x}$Mn$_x$N grown by MBE (641.4 eV) [6] and Zn$_{1-x}$Mn$_x$O grown by pulsed-laser deposition (641.0 eV) [7]. This clearly indicates that the valence state of Mn in this region was different to that of metallic Mn. These results imply that dilute Mn ions were doped into GaN.

The magnetization measured using a super-conducting quantum interference device (SQUID) showed weak hysteresis at 30 K, as shown in Fig. 1 (e). The diamagnetic component in the data came from the sapphire substrate and the GaN layer without Mn ions. Hysteresis was not observed in the sample using a Si-doped *n*-type GaN substrate. Although it has been reported that intentionally hole doped Ga$_{1-x}$Mn$_x$N shows ferromagnetism [8, 9] while conventional Ga$_{1-x}$Mn$_x$N show paramagnetism, it is not clear at present whether the ferromagnetic component was intrinsic or

that came from an undetectably small amount of precipitates in this study. Further systematic studies are necessary to clarify whether the ferromagnetism in the *p*-type GaN:Mn is intrinsic or not.

ACKNOWLEDGMENTS

This work was supported by a Grant-in-Aid for Scientific Research in Priority Area "Semiconductor Nano-Spintronics (14076209)". We thank the Material Design and Characterization Laboratory, Institute for Solid State Physics, University of Tokyo, for the use of the SQUID magnetometer.

REFERENCES

1. T. Dietl, H. Ohno, F. Matsukura, J. Cibert and D. Ferrand, Science **287**, 1019 (2000).
2. K. Sato and H. Katayama-Yoshida, Jpn. J. Appl. Phys. **40**, L485 (2001).
3. P. Mahadevan and A. Zunger, Appl. Phys. Lett. **85**, 2860 (2004).
4. M. L. Reed, N. A. El-Masry, H. H. Stadelmaier, M. K. Ritums, M. J. Reed, C. A. Parker, J. C. Roberts and S. M. Bedair, Appl. Phys. Lett. **79**, 3473 (2001). :
5. X. M. Cai, A. B. Djurišić, M. H. Xie, H. Liu, X. X. Zhang, J. J. Zhu and H. Yang, Mater. Sci. Engineer. B, **117**, 292 (2005).
6. J. I. Hwang, Y. Ishida, M. Kobayashi, H. Hirata, K. Takubo, T. Mizokawa, A. Fujimori, J. Okamoto, K. Mamiya, Y. Saito, Y. Muramatsu, H. Ott, A. Tanaka, T. Kondo and H. Munekata, Phys. Rev. B. **72**, 085216 (2005).
7. T. Mizokawa, T. Nambu, A. Fujimori, T. Fukumura and M. Kawasaki, Phys. Rev. B. **65**, 085209 (2002).
8. K. H. Kim, K. J. Lee, D. J. Kim, H. J. Kim, Y. E. Ihm, C. G. Kim, S. H. Yoo and C. S. Kim, Appl. Phys. Lett. **82**, 4755 (2003).
9. F. E. Arkun, M. J. Reed, E. A. Berkman, N. A. El-Masry, J. M. Zavada, M. L. Reed and S. M. Bedair, Appl. Phys. Lett. **85**, 3809 (2004)

Theoretical Study of Magnetic Properties of VN, CrN, MnN, FeN and CoN under strain

M. Ribeiro Jr.*, M. Marques*, L. M. R. Scolfaro*, L. K. Teles† and L. G. Ferreira**

*Instituto de Física, Universidade de São Paulo, CP66318, 05315-970 São Paulo, SP, Brazil
†Departamento de Física, Instituto Tecnológico de Aeronáutica, Centro Técnico Aeroespacial, 12228-900 São José dos Campos, SP, Brazil
**Instituto de Física Gleb Wataghin, Universidade Estadual de Campinas, Caixa Postal 6165, 13083-970 Campinas, SP, Brazil

Abstract.
We present an *ab initio* tooled study on magnetic and electronic properties of 3d transition metals mononitrides under hydrostatic and biaxial strain, in *wurtzite* (*w*) and *zincblende* (*zb*) structure, and find all of them to become half-metallic (HM) under lattice expansion in the *zb* structure. The first compound to become HM under lattice expansion is MnN, followed by CrN, VN, FeN and CoN, with integer magnetic moments of 4, 3, 2, 5 and 6 μ_B, respectively. We investigate the possibility of MBE growing of *zb*-CrN on cubic GaN.

Keywords: Spintronics, DMS, Transition Metals Nitrides, Ab initio
PACS: 71.20.Be

INTRODUCTION

Transition metals nitrides (TMN) show technologically superior characteristics, as high Curie temperature (T_C), high bulk modulus (for surface coating and thin films), superconductivity (in the case of VN), sharp interface with III-N semiconductors, among others. Nowadays, by the emerging field of **spintronics** and the diluted magnetic semiconductors (DMS) principle, we turned out our efforts to produce new ferromagnetic (FM) materials for spin injection. However, it is not clear yet how homogeneous can those alloys be, and there is the possibility that the observed FM behaviour is due to the formation of clusters and other phases inside the material, like MnN separated phases inside GaMnN, for example[1]. The same can occur when doping with other TM, such as CrN[2]. As such TMN inside the compound material can differ very much from their bulk equilibrium properties (many of them become (HM) under lattice expansion, that means 100% spin polarization at the Fermi level), a better understanding of the volume dependence of their magnetic trends is important to understand the properties of these TMN compounds in film (for MBE growing on semiconductor substrates) or small clusters form [3, 4]. The calculations performed here are based on an *ab-initio* pseudopotential projected augmented wave method as implemented in "Vienna Ab-initio Simulation Package" (VASP-PAW) code[5]. The Brillouin zone was sampled using Monkhorst and Pack method, and Perdew-Wang GGA as the exchange-correlation functional [6].

RESULTS

The results are summarized in Table 1 for VN, CrN, FeN and CoN. The table shows the full optimizations for *zb* and *w* phases. The calculations emphasize the great structural sensitivity of CrN due to magnetism. This is clearly seen in total energy differences for *zb* phases and for the very different c/a ratios for *w* phases - also different from the "ideal" $\sqrt{8/3}$ value.

The highest total magnetic moments correspond to CrN *w* and *zb*, respectively. As the hydrostatic strain is applied, the magnetic properties change, according to Figure 1. We can see a transition to the integer magnetic moment platform, that corresponds to the HM state. The transition occurs for MnN, CrN, VN, FeN and CoN, in this sequence, with magnetic moments of 4, 3, 2, 5 and 6 μ_B, respectively. The magnetic moments of CrN and MnN show themselves more sensible to lattice expansion than CoN and FeN do.

As FM *zb*-CrN (a=4.40Å) showed a tendence to stabilize its ferromagnetism under lattice expansion, we investigate the applicability of this material to thin film fabrication under MBE conditions. As a first analysis the calculations show a FM ground state with total magnetic moment 1.9μ_B *per* Cr atom, under biaxial strain and over c-GaN (a=4.54Å) (Figure 2).

CP893, *Physics of Semiconductors, 28th International Conference*
edited by W. Jantsch and F. Schäffler
© 2007 American Institute of Physics 978-0-7354-0397-0/07/$23.00

TABLE 1. Results for TMN, structure, magnetic ordering, equilibrium lattice constant, c/a for *wurtzite*, total magnetic moment per atom and total energy per pair TM-N.

Struc.	Mag. order	a(Å)	c/a	$\mu(\mu_B)$	E(eV)
zb-VN	NM	4.44			-18.983
	FM	4.45		0.636	-18.982
	AFM[100]	4.44			-18.983
	AFM[111]	4.45			-18.998
w-VN	NM	3.02	1.82		-18.926
	FM	3.02	1.82	0.000	-18.926
	AFM	3.02	1.82		-18.926
zb-CrN	NM	4.34			-18.530
	FM	4.40		1.873	-18.765
	AFM[100]	4.39			-18.701
	AFM[111]	4.40			-18.708
w-CrN	NM	2.96	1.81		-18.418
	FM	3.11	1.65	1.941	-18.532
	AFM	3.06	1.71		-18.546
zb-FeN	NM	4.24			-16.805
	FM	4.24		0.030	-16.805
	AFM[100]	4.24			-16.805
	AFM[111]	4.24			-16.805
w-FeN	NM	2.96	1.71		-16.584
	FM	2.96	1.71	0.000	-16.584
	AFM	2.96	1.71		-16.584
zb-CoN	NM	4.26			-15.175
	FM	4.26		0.001	-15.175
	AFM[100]	4.26			-15.175
	AFM[111]	4.26			-15.175
w-CoN	NM	2.94	1.77		-15.058
	FM	2.94	1.77	0.000	-15.059
	AFM	2.94	1.77		-14.809

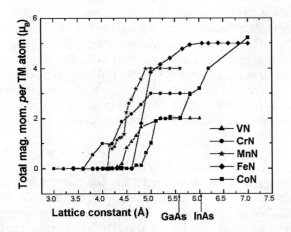

FIGURE 1. Transition to the half-metallic state of the set of TMN. For comparison we indicate the lattice constant of two common semiconductors GaAs and InAs.

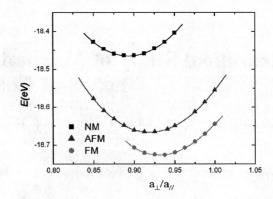

FIGURE 2. Biaxial strain of *zb*-CrN, with $a_\parallel = a_{GaN}$, showing a FM ground state, suitable for applications in spintronics device structures.

CONCLUSIONS

The main conclusions are summarized below. The FM *w*-CrN presents a high magnetic moment, and seems to have a magnetic driven structural parameter c/a. The *zb*-CrN and *zb*-MnN magnetism are more sensible to lattice expansion than the other *zb*-TMN. The *zb*-CrN is FM in ground state, and becomes more stable in FM order under lattice expansion. For growth on c-GaN, *zb*-CrN is FM. We achieve the HM state for all *zb*-TMN investigated.

ACKNOWLEDGMENTS

We acknowledge the support provided by brazilian agencies CNPq and FAPESP.

REFERENCES

1. B. K. Rao, and P. Jena, *Phys. Rev. Lett.* **89**, 185504–1 (2002).
2. G. P. Das, B. K. Rao, and P. Jena, *Phys. Rev. B* **69**, 214422 (2004).
3. M. S. Miao, and W. R. L. Lambrecht, *Phys. Rev. B* **71**, 214405 (2005).
4. M. Marques, L. K. Teles, L. M. R. Scolfaro, J. Furthmüller, F. Bechstedt, and L. G. Ferreira, *Appl. Phys. Lett.* **86**, 164105 (2005).
5. G. Kresse, and D. Joubert, *Phys. Rev. B* **59**, 1758 (1999).
6. Y. Wang, and J. P. Perdew, *Phys. Rev. B* **43**, 8911 (1991).

Above Room Temperature Ferromagnetism in Mn-ion Implanted $Si_{0.75}Ge_{0.25}$

V. Ko[*], K.L. Teo[†], T. Liew[¶] and T.C. Chong[¶]

[*]NUS Graduate School for Integrative Sciences and Engineering, National University of S'pore, S'pore 117597
[†]Information Storage Materials Laboratory, Electrical & Computer Engineering Department, National University of S'pore, S'pore 1175763
[¶]Data Storage Institute, 5 Engineering Drive 1, S'pore 1176081

Abstract. Ferromagnetic behaviour above room temperature has been observed in Mn-ions implanted $Si_{0.75}Ge_{0.25}$. The 900°C annealed sample with Mn dosage of $2x10^{16}$ cm^{-2} exhibit saturation magnetization, saturation field and coercive field of ~9 emu/cm^3 and ~1500 Oe and ~60 Oe respectively at 300K.

Keywords: Magnetic semiconductor, Manganese, Silicon
PACS: 75.50.Pp

INTRODUCTION

"Spintronic" is an emerging technology, where not only the electron charge but the electron spin as well are exploited. This could offer opportunities of a new generation of devices that are nonvolatile, with high data processing speed, large integration capabilities and low power consumption. In order to realize "spintronic" applications in current semiconductor technology, there is a need to develop Si-based magnetic semiconductors that is ferromagnetic (FM) above room temperature. Recently, it has been predicted [1] and experimentally [2] shown that Si can be made FM with Mn-doping. The reported Curie temperature above 400 K is encouraging. Since $Si_{1-x}Ge_x$ is a promising material for future CMOS technology, this aroused our curiosity whether Mn-doped $Si_{1-x}Ge_x$ can be made FM above room temperature as well. It has also been shown theoretically that for $x \geq 0.16$ in $Si_{1-x}Ge_x$, substitutional Mn in Ge-rich neighborhoods is more stable than interstitial Mn, and that Mn-doped $Si_{1-x}Ge_x$ can be a potential FM semiconductor. [3]

EXPERIMENTAL PROCEDURES

Ion implantation is known to be useful to screen particular combinations of magnetic dopants and host semiconductors for their FM properties, and may have applications in forming selected area contact regions for spin-polarized carrier injection in device structures. Thus, we employed this method to synthesis Mn-doped $Si_{1-x}Ge_x$. Two different dosages of Mn-ions (W1: $1x10^{16}$ and W2: $2x10^{16}$ $/cm^2$) were implanted at 100 keV into the relaxed $Si_{0.75}Ge_{0.25}$ layers that were grown by chemical vapour deposition on SiGe graded buffer layer on Si(100) substrates. Rapid thermal annealing (RTA) were performed at temperatures ranged from 700 °C to 900 °C for 20s. Characterizations were carried out with the use of x-ray photoelectron spectroscopy (XPS), x-ray diffraction (XRD), Raman spectroscopy, superconducting quantum interference device (SQUID), and Hall measurements.

EXPERIMENTAL RESULTS

Mn peaks concentrations (determined from XPS sputter depth profiles) of the as-implanted W1 and W2 are, ~8 % and ~12 %, respectively. The Raman spectrum of the RTA sample W2, as shown in Fig. 1 shows the characteristic phonon frequencies of Si-Si, Ge-Ge and Si-Ge modes. The as-implanted sample shows a curve characteristic of an amorphous material, with all the characteristic peaks being smeared out. After annealing, the crystalline quality has been recovered.

Field dependent magnetization (*M-H*) curves in Fig. 2 show hysteresis for all of the samples, evidence of FM behaviour. The magnetization strength

CP893, *Physics of Semiconductors, 28th International Conference*
edited by W. Jantsch and F. Schäffler
© 2007 American Institute of Physics 978-0-7354-0397-0/07/$23.00

increases with increasing annealing temperature, which can be related to improved crystal quality (Raman peak intensity). After RTA900 °C, sample W2 exhibits saturation magnetization, saturation field and coercive field of ~9 emu/cm³ and ~1500 Oe and ~60 Oe respectively at 300K.

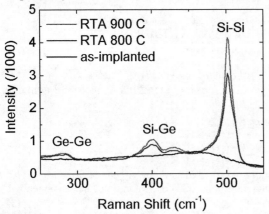

FIGURE 1. Raman spectra of as-implanted and RTA sample W2

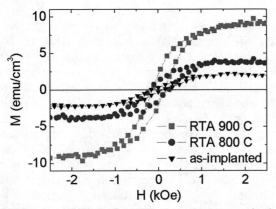

FIGURE 2. Magnetic-field (H) dependent magnetization (M) curves of the as-implanted and RTA sample W2

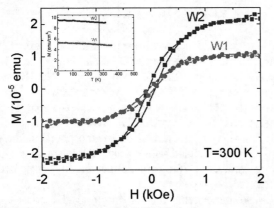

FIGURE 3. Magnetic-field (H) dependent magnetization (M) curves of W1 and W2 after RTA900°C. Inset shows their temperature (T) dependent magnetization (M) curves

It can be seen from Fig. 3 that clear FM behaviours are observed at 300 K, and the magnetization strength is increased by 2X as the implantation dosage doubled. The temperature-dependent magnetization curves (M-T) show that the magnetization persists up to 350 K and the critical temperature can be well above 400 K. The measured coercive field decreases with increasing temperature, as shown in Fig. 4.

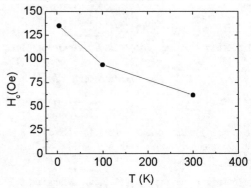

FIGURE 4. Coercive field (H_c) vs temperature (T) of W2 after RTA900 °C

CONCLUSION

FM behaviour above device operating temperature has been observed in Mn-implanted $Si_{0.75}Ge_{0.25}$ alloys, and the magnetizations strength increases with increasing Mn-dosage and annealing temperature. This material can be suitable candidates for spintronic applications, due to the presence of Si which guarantees the desired integrability with the well-assessed Si technology.

ACKNOWLEDGMENTS

This work is supported by Singapore Agency for Science, Technology and Research (A*STAR), under Grant No. 022 105 0053.

REFERENCES

1. H. Weng and J. Dong, *Phys. Rev. B* **71**, 035201 (2005)
2. M. Bolduc, C. Awo-Affouda, A. Stollenwerk, M.B. Huang, F.G. Ramos, G. Agnello and V.P. LaBella, *Phys. Rev. B* **71**, 033302 (2005)
3. Antonio J.R. da Silva, A. Fazzio and Alex Antonelli, *Phys. Rev. B* **70**, 193205 (2004)

Magnetic Properties of Ge$_{1-x-y}$Mn$_x$Eu$_y$Te Mixed Crystals

W. Dobrowolski[1], B. Brodowska[1], M. Arciszewska[1], I. Kuryliszyn-Kudelska[1],
V. Domukhovski[1], M. Wójcik[1], V.E. Slynko[2], E.I. Slynko[2], and V.K. Dugaev[2,3]

[1]*Institute of Physics, Polish Academy of Sciences, Al. Lotników 32/46, PL-02-668 Warsaw, Poland*
[2]*Chernivtsy Department of the Institute of Materials Science Problems, Ukrainian Academy of Sciences*
[3]*Department of Physics and CFIF, Instituto Superior Tecnico, Av. Rovisco Pais, 1049-001 Lisbon, Portugal*

Abstract. Interesting possibilities of application gives co-occurrence of ferroelectric and ferromagnetic properties. GeMnTe is known to possess such unique properties. Here, we report preliminary AC magnetic susceptibility and magnetization studies of GeMnTe co-doped with another magnetic ion - Europium, aimed at investigating of Eu ions influence on the magnetic properties of the resulting quaternary compound. We found that the Curie temperature of GeMnEuTe substantially (about 3 times) exceeds the values of T_C reported in GeMnTe crystals and layers with similar Mn composition, equal ~40 K. The origin of this substantial Curie temperature enlargement is not fully explained yet. However, the spin-echo resonance data may suggest that the Mn^{2+} ions system is in a mixed valence state and that an additional channel of interaction between magnetic ions is open.

Keywords: ferromagnetic semiconductors, magnetic properties
PACS: 71.20.Nr, 75.50.Dd

INTRODUCTION

Semiconductors exhibiting ferromagnetism are recently intensively investigated on account of the emerging field of spintronics. Of particular interest are materials that display electrically tunable magnetism. That is the case of most of IV-VI diluted magnetic semiconductors (DMS). In this class of materials, deviations from stoichiometry (metal vacancies) result in the carrier density sufficiently high to produce strong ferromagnetic interactions between the localized spins, and, further, the carrier concentration can be controlled in a wide range by thermal annealing or doping.

Among other IV-VI compounds, much interesting is rhombohedral GeMnTe displaying, in addition to ferromagnetism, ferroelectric properties. We study an effect of introducing into GeMnTe the second type of magnetic ion, Eu, on properties of the resulting quaternary alloy.

EXPERIMENT

In this work, we investigate Bridgman method grown Ge$_{1-x-y}$Mn$_x$Eu$_y$Te crystal with Mn content about 0.07 and Eu content 0.04. X-ray investigation (Fig. 1) revealed that the samples are single phase and showed that the crystal is rhombohedrally distorted with a lattice constant a_0 = 5.9754 Å and rhombohedral distortion angle α = 88.37°. The samples were p-type with practically temperature independent concentration of carriers, of the order of 10^{21} cm^{-3}.

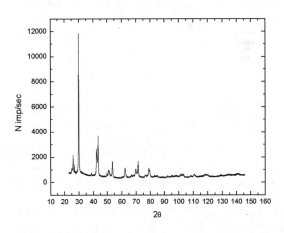

Figure 1. X-ray diffraction patterns for GeMnEuTe.

The magnetic measurements were performed in the temperature range 2-300 K using Lake Shore 7229 AC Susceptometer/DC Magnetometer. In the range of high temperatures, all the samples are Curie–Weiss paramagnets with the temperature dependence of the magnetic susceptibility described by the Curie–Weiss law. At low temperatures, the transition to a

CP893, *Physics of Semiconductors, 28th International Conference*
edited by W. Jantsch and F. Schäffler

ferromagnetic phase takes place (Fig. 2) as manifested by a peak on the $\chi(T)$ curve.

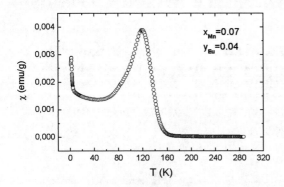

Figure 2. The magnetic susceptibility vs. temperature.

The magnetic hysteresis loop was clearly observed below the Curie–Weiss temperature (temperature evolution of the hysteresis loop is shown in Fig. 3).

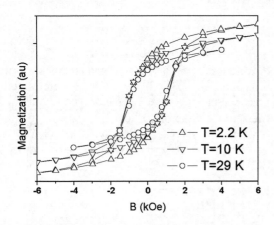

Figure 3. Magnetization hysteresis loops for GeMnEuTe at three temperatures below the Curie–Weiss temperature.

It is well known, from early 70's (see [1-2]), that even a small admixture of MnTe in GeTe leads to a ferromagnetic behavior. GeMnTe is a strongly degenerate semiconductor with 10^{20}-10^{21} cm^{-3} holes and the source of ferromagnetism is the RKKY interaction between mobile holes and localized magnetic moments. The Curie temperature depends on both the Mn content and the carrier concentration and its highest reported value (for $x_{Mn} = 0.6$) does not exceed 160 K.

As expected, the Eu substitution in GeMnTe does not essentially change the properties of the host crystal still displaying the RKKY interaction driven-ferromagnetism. However, it drastically changes the Curie temperature. We found that in our samples T_C is typically above 100 K and thus substantially exceeds

the values of T_C reported in Ge$_{1-x}$Mn$_x$Te bulk crystals and layers with similar composition, i.e. ~40 K [2]. The origin of this substantial Curie temperature enlargement is yet not fully explained. One of the hypotheses assumes that addition of Eu ions to GeMnTe can block a creation of antiferromagnetic Mn^{2+}– Mn^{2+} pairs, which presence decreases the Curie temperature. Anyway, the increase of T_C seems to be too large to be explained by the above hypothesis. The result of nuclear magnetic resonance studies may shed some light on observed anomaly. The spin-echo resonance does not correspond to the anticipated position of Mn^{2+} ion, but occurs at lower frequencies. This may suggest that that the system is in mixed valence state and that additional channel of interaction between magnetic ions is open.

CONCLUSIONS

Two important features give IV–VI materials the distinguished position within the family of DMS. First, the variety of magnetic properties observed in the Mn based IV–VI alloys. Second, the semi-metallic electric properties with the well developed methods of carrier concentration controlling. However, the ferromagnetic characteristics (the magnetic anisotropy, coercive field and cryogenic Curie temperatures) are not superior to other magnetic materials. Thus, applications (if any) related to ferromagnetic properties of these materials will be limited to hybrid systems with IV–VI electronic devices incorporating the ferromagnetic element with controlled magnetic properties. The case of GeTe-based ferromagnetic semiconductors seems to be promising. Preliminary data presented here show that the Eu substitution enhances the ferromagnetism in the sense that it enlarges the Curie temperature, and T_C in crystals containing only few percent of Mn and Eu substantially exceeds liquid nitrogen temperature. This property, in addition to ferroelectricity, opens a wide field of potential applications.

ACKNOWLEDGMENTS

This research was supported by grant from the Polish Ministry of Science No. 2 P03B 053 25.

REFERENCES

1. M. Rodot, J. Lewis, H. Rodot, G. Villers, J. Cohen, and P. Mollard, *J. Phys. Soc. Japan* **21**, Suppl., p. 627 (1966).
2. R. W. Cochrane, M. Plischke, and J. O. Ström-Olsen, *Phys. Rev. B* **8**, 3013 (1974).

Exchange Interaction Effects on the Optical Properties of $Eu_xPb_{1-x}Te$

A. B. Henriques[1], G. D. Galgano[1], B. Díaz[2], P. H. O. Rappl[2], and E. Abramof[2]

[1]*Instituto de Física, Universidade de São Paulo,*
Caixa Postal 66318, 05315-970 São Paulo, Brazil
[2]*LAS-INPE, Av. dos Astronautas, 1758 - Jd. Granja,*
12227-010, São José dos Campos, Brazil

Abstract. We measured the absorption band-edge in $Eu_xPb_{1-x}Te$ in the ferromagnetic order induced by an external magnetic field (Faraday configuration). A narrow dichroic line, superimposed on a rising monotonous background, describes the spectrum. Here we examine if this line could be associated to an excitonic character of the electronic transition. Measurements of the absorption line width dependence on x (the molar fraction of Eu) allowed us to obtain an estimate for the characteristic radius of the excited wave function, and hence of the hypothetical exciton binding energy, which is found to be ~120 meV. When the magnetic field is removed, anti-ferromagnetic order is restored, and the absorption intensity decreases by more than one order of magnitude. Such a large change in the absorption cannot be explained in the framework of the excitonic absorption model.

Keywords: Optical absorption, magneto-optics
PACS: 78.20.-e

INTRODUCTION

Europium divalent monochalcogenides combine a very high magnetic moment of the Eu^{2+} spins, which are in a $^8S_{7/2}$ configuration, with an energy gap that can be transparent in part of the visible spectrum. This makes them very attractive for applications in magneto-optical devices; however, practical devices operating at room temperature are not possible due to their very low critical temperatures. Nevertheless, these materials have unique properties and have caught continuous interest from the scientific community. A few years ago, on EuTe samples grown by molecular beam epitaxy (MBE), a narrow photoluminescence (PL) line was observed for the first time, at photon energies close to the absorption gap[1]. The discovery of a new PL line prompted us to investigate the absorption spectra of europium chalcogenides grown by MBE, which lead to our discovery of a highly dichroic doublet of sharp absorption lines in EuTe and EuSe, when the sample was submitted to a strong enough magnetic field, such that ferromagnetic arrangement of the localized Eu^{2+} spins was achieved[2]. This absorption line is well explained by an electronic transition from a localized $4f^7$ $^8S_{7/2}$ electronic state to a state where the Eu^{3+} core is left at a $4f^6$ ^7F_J (J=0,...,6) state, and an electron is transferred to a 5d t2g state[2]. It

has been argued that the band-edge absorption spectra of Eu chalcogenides could be associated to excitonic transitions (i.e., formation of bound electron-hole pairs)[3]. In this work we investigate a possible excitonic nature of the $4f^7$ $^8S_{7/2}$ $\rightarrow$ $4f^6$ ^7F_J 5d t_{2g} transition by studying dilute $Eu_xPb_{1-x}Te$ systems.

RESULTS AND DISCUSSION

Figure 1 shows the absorption band-edge of $Eu_xPb_{1-x}Te$ measured in the σ^- polarization for a field B=9.6T. (For the σ^+ polarization a line with similar intensity and width appears at higher energy and it will not be discussed here). The curve shown is denominated *induced* absorption because the zero field absorption spectrum, which is characterized by an almost monotonous rising background in this energy range (1.9-2.25 eV), was subtracted from the raw spectrum. This was done in order to isolate the lowest energy single line the absorption related to the σ^- $4f^7$ $^8S_{7/2}$ $\rightarrow$ $4f^6$ ^7F_J 5d t_{2g} transition from the background absorption. In the energy interval above 2.25 eV, contributions to the absorption from other lines appear, and we therefore ignored that interval in the present analysis.

CP893, *Physics of Semiconductors, 28th International Conference*
edited by W. Jantsch and F. Schäffler
© 2007 American Institute of Physics 978-0-7354-0397-0/07/$23.00

As the molar fraction x of Eu in the samples decreases, the position of the absorption peak, E_{max}, is displaced to higher energies, because the total exchange interaction energy between the excited electron and the localized Eu^{2+} spins decreases.[4] The shape of the absorption line does not change, but the line width increases. In order to obtain a good estimate for the full width at half maximum (FWHM) dependence on the Eu concentration, the absorption spectrum was fitted using the theory described in Ref. 2, assuming every transition to be described by a Voigt line shape, with the FWHM as the only adjustable parameter. (The Voigt line shape was chosen, because it gives a slightly better fit, and hence a better estimate of the FWHM, than a Gaussian[4] one).

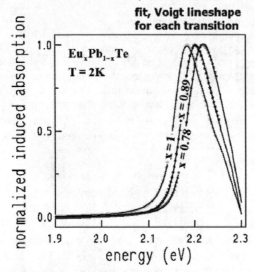

FIGURE 1. Absorption band-edge in $Eu_xPb_{1-x}Te$ in the σ^- polarization, at B=9.6T and T=2K.

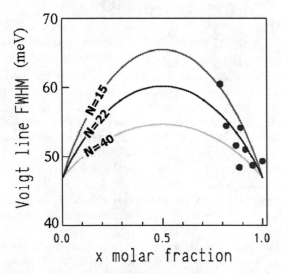

FIGURE 2. FWHM of the lowest energy σ^- line as a function of the molar fraction of Eu in the samples.

Figure 2 shows the FWHM obtained as a function of Eu concentration. It an ideal alloy structure, the only source of broadening is the statistical fluctuation of Eu content within the excited wave function radius. Then he FWHM dependence on x will be given by[4,5]

$$\left(\text{FWHM}_{Eu_xPb_{1-x}Te}\right)^2 = \left(\text{FWHM}_{EuTe}\right)^2 + \frac{8x(1-x)(J_{df}S)^2 \ln 2}{N},$$

where N is the number of Eu^{2+} ions that are enclosed by the electronic wave function, and $J_{df}S$=150 meV[4]. The best-fit value is N=22, although the uncertainty is large (15<N<40). Using the lattice parameter for EuTe (rocksalt, a=6.600 Å), we can estimate the characteristic radius of the excitation to be $\left(\frac{3N}{16\pi}\right)^{1/3} a = 7.2$ Å. This value is in approximate agreement with our earlier estimate, based on a simplified theoretical model applied to measurements done on only two samples[4].

The source of localization could be the attractive hole potential[3], in which case the exciton binding energy can be estimated, i.e. $\frac{ke^2}{2\varepsilon a_B}$, and it is found to be in the range 100-140 meV for ε=8.2 (see Ref. 6). Such a large exciton binding energy describes a very strongly bound electron-hole pair, which would not be perturbed by a modest magnetic field of only B=10T. However, we also measured the intensity of the absorption spectrum as a function of B, and it was found that the peak intensity of the absorption coefficient associated with the σ^- $4f^7$ $^8S_{7/2} \dashrightarrow 4f^6$ ^7F_J 5d t_{2g} lowest energy transition at B=0 is 27 times smaller than at B=9.6T. Such a large difference cannot be explained by a (plausible) excitonic character of the absorption, and the mechanisms that lead to such a huge dependence of the absorption intensity on B are presently unclear.

A. B. H. thanks Pinchas Dahan for profitable discussions. FAPESP and CNPq – funding agencies, supported this work.

REFERENCES

1. W. Heiss *et al*, Phys. Rev. B **70**, 035209 (2004).
2. A. B. Henriques *et al*, Phys. Rev. B **72**, 155337 (2005).
3. T. Kasuya, J. Magn. Magn. Mater. **195**, 141 (1999).
4. L. K. Hanamoto *et al*, J. Phys.: Condensed Matter. **16**, 5597 (2004).
5. $J_{df}S=\Delta E_{max}/\Delta x$, see Ref. 4.
6. M. Umehara, Phys. Rev. B **65**, 205208 (2002).

Magnetotransport and Antiferromagnetic Behavior in ErP Epitaxial Layers on GaInP(001)

A. Nakamura[1], T. Ito[1], H. Ohnishi[2], A. Koizumi[2], and Y. Takeda[2]

[1]Department of Applied Physics, Nagoya University
[2]Department of Crystalline Materials Science, Nagoya University,
Chikusa-ku, Nagoya 464-8603, Japan

Abstract. We have investigated transport and magnetic properties in ErP ultrathin films grown on the GaInP (001) surface. Hall resistance and transverse magnetoresistance measurements yield the carrier density of ~1.4x10^{20} cm^{-3} and the electron and hole mobilities of 1250–1450 cm^2/Vs at 10 K. The resistivity anomaly in the longitudinal megnetoresistance is interpreted in terms of the spin-disorder scattering in the antiferromagnetic phase below 3.5 K.

Keywords: Semimetal, Rare-earth monopnictides, Semiconductor-metal structures, Spin scattering
PACS: 73.61.At, 75.30.Kz, 75.47.-m, 73.43.Qt

INTRODUCTION

Heterostructures consisting of metal and semiconductor materials have attracted much attention from the viewpoint of quantum transport and spintronics. Semimetallic rare-earth monopnictides such as ErAs and ErP can be epitaxially grown on III-V compound semiconductors. Most effort has been devoted to ErAs/GaAs heterostructures for resonant tunneling diode and high speed device applications. We have successfully grown ErP quantum disks on InP substrates, and observed semimetal to semiconductor transition due to the quantum size effect on the semimetal band structure[1]. Rare-earth monopnictides show antiferromagnetic spin order due to 4f electron spins at low temperature[2,3]. However, little attention has been paid to such magnetic properties, though these materials have the potential for producing magnetic semimetal-semiconductor heterostructures.

In this paper, we report on carrier densities, mobilities and a resistivity anomaly caused by spin-disorder scattering near the Neel temperature T_N in ErP epitaxial layers grown on GaInP lattice-matched to GaAs.

EXPERIMENT

A GaInP/ErP/GaInP heterostructure was grown by metalorganic vapor phase epitaxy. The In content x in Ga$_{1-x}$In$_x$P is 0.52 to be lattice-matched to GaAs, and the lattice mismatch to ErP is −1.09 %. The substrate temperatures were 610 C and 540 C for the GaAs buffer layer and the GaInP/ErP/GaInP layer, respectively. The details of the growth procedures are given elsewhere[1,4]. The epitaxial growth of the ErP layer with the NaCl type structure was confirmed by the EXAFS measurement. The heterostructure is composed of a 2-nm-wide GaInP buffer layer and a 10-nm-wide GaAs buffer layer on a semi-insulating GaAs(001) substrate followed by a 11-nm-wide ErP layer. The ErP layer was capped by a 20-nm-wide GaInP layer. Hall and transverse- and longitudinal-resistance were measured using a van der Pauw method at temperature 2 – 300 K in the magnetic field up to 8T.

RESULTS AND DISCUSSION

Figure 1 shows the Hall resistance (ρ_{xy}) and transverse magnetoresistance (ρ_{xx}) for the magnetic field oriented perpendicular to the surface at temperatures between 10 and 300 K. We analyzed the data assuming an isotropic hole Fermi surface centered at Γ with hole density $n_h = n$ and mobility μ_h, and three equivalent ellipsoidal electron Fermi surfaces at X with electron density $n_e = n/3$ and anisotropic electron mobilities $\mu_{e,1}$ and $\mu_{e,2}$[5]. The obtained density n is 1.4x10^{20} cm^{-3} at 300 K. This result indicates that ErP is a low density semimetal with a carrier density of ~1x10^{20} cm^{-3}, which is slightly lower than that of ErAs

CP893, *Physics of Semiconductors, 28th International Conference*
edited by W. Jantsch and F. Schäffler
© 2007 American Institute of Physics 978-0-7354-0397-0/07/$23.00

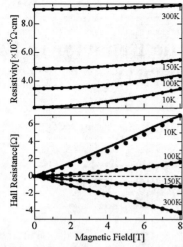

FIGURE 1. Hall resistance and transverse magnetoresistance at 10 to 300 K in ErP/GaInP. The solid curve is a fit to the data.

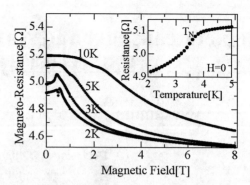

FIGURE 2. Logitudinal magnetoresistance at different temperatures between 2 and 10 K. The inset shows the temperature dependence of resistance without a magnetic field.

($\sim 4 \times 10^{20}$ cm^{-3})[3]. The mobilities at 10 K are $\mu_{e,1}$ =1450 cm^2/Vs and μ_h =1240 cm^2/Vs, and with increasing temperature to 300 K they decrease to $\mu_{e,1}$ =390 cm^2/Vs and μ_h =190 cm^2/Vs. The temperature dependence of the mobilities also indicates the semimetallic behavior in electron (hole) transport. The mobility $\mu_{e,2}$ is $\sim$100 cm^2/Vs, which is approximately independent of temperature.

To investigate magnetic properties we measured longitudinal magnetoresistance in the magnetic field up to 8 T at temperatures below 20 K. Shown in Fig. 2 are magnetoresistance curves at different temperatures. The resistance anomaly showing a cusp was observed at $\sim$ 0.4 T below 4 K, while the resistance at 10 K monotonically decreased with increasing magnetic field. Such an anomaly suggests spin-disorder scattering as the magnetic field takes the system from the antiferromagnetic phase to the paramagnetic phase[3]. The neutron scattering experiment in bulk ErP crystals has shown that the antiferromagnetic order consists of *ferromagnetically* aligned sheets perpendicular to a <111> direction with neighboring sheets aligned *antiferromagnetically* with respect to each other[2]. If we take into account the elastic scattering between the conduction electrons with spins and the 4f Er spins, the resistivity depends on the spin ordering[6]. At low temperatures below 4 K, the applied magnetic field in the [100] direction induces the spin disorder in the antiferromagnetic phase resulting in the increase in resistivity due to spin-disorder scattering of carriers. With further increase of the magnetic field the system changes to the paramagnetic phase, and consequently the resistivity decreases upon an increase of the field.

The inset of Fig.2 shows the temperature dependence of the resistance (R) at the zero magnetic

field. A significant drop in resistance was observed around 3.5 K, which indicates the antiferromagnetic spin order at lower temperatures, because the spin-disorder scattering is suppressed in the antiferromagnetic phase. From the point of maximum dR/dT, T_N was found to be 3.5 K.

CONCLUSIONS

We have investigated magnetotransport properties in ErP epitaxial layers grown on GaInP (001) surface on GaAs substrates. It is found that ErP is a low density semimetal with a carrier density of 1.4 x10^{20} cm^{-3} and mobilities of $\sim$ 1000 cm^2/Vs at 10 K. In the longitudinal magnetoresistance curves, the resistivity anomaly due to the spin-disorder scattering in the antiferromagnetic phase was observed at low temperatures. The Neel temperature was found to be 3.5 K, indicating that ErP is an antiferromagnetic semimetal at low temperature.

REFERENCES

1. L. Bolotov, T. Tsuchiya, A. Nakamura, T. Ito, Y. Fujiwara and Y. Takeda, *Phys. Rev.* B **59**, 12236-12239 (1999).
2. H. R. Child, M. K. Wilkinson, J. W. Cable, W. C. Koehler and E. O. Wollan, *Phys. Rev.* **131**, 922-931 (1963).
3. S. J. Allen, Jr., N. Tabatabaic, C. J. Palmstrom, G. W. Hull, T. Sands, F. DeRosa, H. L. Gilchrist and K. C. Garrison, *Phys. Rev. Lett.*, **62**, 2309-2312 (1989).
4. A. Koizumi, H. Ohnishi, T. Inoue, T. Yamauchi, I. Yamakawa, H. Ofuchi, M. Tabuchi, A. Nakamura and Y. Takeda, *Thin Solid Films* (2006) in press.
5. S. J. Allen, Jr., F. DeRosa, C. J. Palmstrom and A. Zrenner, *Phys. Rev.* B **43**, 9599-9609 (1991).
6. P. G. de Gennes and J. Friedel, *J. Phys. Chem. Solids* **4**, 71-77 (1958).

Inter-Wire Antiferromagnetic Exchange Interaction in Ni/Si-Ferromagnetic/Semiconductor Nanocomposites

P. Granitzer[1], K. Rumpf[1], M. Hofmayer[1], H. Krenn[1], P. Pölt[2], A. Reichmann[2], F. Hofer[2]

[1] Institute of Physics, Karl-Franzens-University, Universitaetsplatz 5, 8010 Graz, Austria
[2] Institute for Electron Microscopy, Technical University of Technology, Steyrergasse 17, 8010 Graz, Austria

Abstract. A matrix of mesoporous silicon offering an array of quasi 1-dimensional oriented pores of high aspect ratio perpendicular to the sample surface has been produced. This porous silicon (PS) skeleton is filled with Ni in a further process-step to achieve ferromagnetic metallic nanostructures within the channels. This produced silicon based nanocomposite is compatible with state-of-the-art silicon technology. Beside the vertical magnetic surface anisotropy of this Ni-filled composite the nearly monodisperse distribution of pore diameters and its regular arrangement in a quasi 2-dimensional lattice provides novel magnetic phenomena like a depression of the magnetization curve at magnetic fields beyond 2T, which can be interpreted as a field induced antiferromagnetic exchange interaction between Ni-wires which is strongly influenced by magnetostrictive stresses at the Ni/Si-interface.

Keywords: Ni-nanostructures; magnetic anisotropy; exchange interaction; porous silicon;
PACS: 61.46.-w; 75.30.Gw; 75.75.+a;

INTRODUCTION

PS is a widely used material in prospect of applications. Mostly used is micro PS with its light emitting properties [1] and macro porous structures with pores in the μm-range which offer quite smooth pore walls [2] and are used as photonic crystals.

The fabricated structures exhibit pores which can be classified between meso and macro pores. These kinds of pores show dendritic growth and quite often a star-like cross-section. In this mesoporous regime the pore diameter and the associated pitch can be changed only in a small regime by accurate adjustment of the electrochemical parameters. The obtained pore length is up to 50 μm exhibiting an aspect ratio in the range of about thousand. Ni-filling of this Si-based template leads to an interesting ferromagnetic nanocomposite.

EXPERIMENTS AND DISCUSSION

The meso-PS template is fabricated electro-chemically in a HF-solution as electrolyte [3]. The achieved samples consist of pores with square-like shape and a quasi-regular quadratic-like arrangement which is proved by FFT-analysis of SEM-pictures. The distribution of the pore diameters, tunable between 30 and 100 nm, is quite homogeneous. Figure 1 shows the quasi-regular porous structure and an associated top view FFT-picture. The channels are loaded with Ni in a deposition process carried out galvanically in a $NiCl_2$-bath slightly modified as described in ref. 4. Magnetic measurements performed by SQUID-magnetometry show a bimodal behavior. Additional to the low-field hysteresis loops a depression in the magnetization curve is observed in the high-field range of a few Tesla. In both field ranges the samples show a substantial difference in the in-plane and perpendicular anisotropy, with preference of the latter.

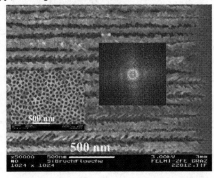

Figure 1: SEM-images of the oriented pores of a sample as well as the top view of the same sample (left inset). A diffraction-analysis of this pore arrangement is shown in the right inset.

CP893, *Physics of Semiconductors, 28th International Conference*
edited by W. Jantsch and F. Schäffler
© 2007 American Institute of Physics 978-0-7354-0397-0/07/$23.00

The anisotropy of the coercive field between easy axis and hard axis magnetization is due to the differently shaped incorporated metallic structures and the magnetostatic interaction among them whereas the negative magnetization peak occurring at high fields (figure 2) above 2 T can be interpreted as field induced antiferromagnetic (AFM) exchange.

Exchange coupling like RKKY-interaction [5] seems to be inapplicable because of the too large distances (PS-spacing) between the Ni-structures. Authors of Ref. 6 observed a negative magnetization at fields between 0.5kOe and 1.5 kOe and explained the occurrence of this peculiar magnetic behavior by an AFM coupling between Ni grains separated by Al.

The depression of the magnetization occurs only for easy axis magnetization whereas hard axis magnetization does not show this behavior.

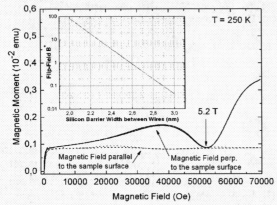

Figure 2: Depression of the magnetization curve occurring at 5.2 T during easy axis magnetization. The dotted curve represents hard axis magnetization. The diamagnetic contribution of the silicon substrate is subtracted. Inset: Flip-field B^* vs barrier thickness D.

THEORY AND RESULTS

From inspection of the magnetization curve, Fig. 2, we can substantiate three important facts: (i) a depression in the magnetization signal occurs at fields between 4 and 6 T which are an order of magnitude higher than the expected dipolar coupling fields between saturated wires, (ii) the absence of any hysteresis rules out effects of on-site magnetic anisotropy. Thus we argue that solely an electronic exchange mechanism across a quantum tunnelling barrier (Si) is responsible to mediate AFM coupling between neighbouring magnetic Ni-wires. Furthermore (iii) this exchange coupling is active only above a threshold field > 4T. An estimate of this exchange is taken from interlayer coupling between planar ferromagnetic films separated by an insulating barrier, as published by Bruno [8]:

$$J_{af} = \frac{1}{4\pi} \frac{\hbar^2 \kappa_{F_F}^2}{mD^2} \text{Im}\left(\Delta r^2 e^{-2\kappa_F D}\right) \frac{2\pi k_B T \cdot m \cdot D / \hbar^2 \kappa_F}{\sin\left(2\pi k_B T \cdot m \cdot D / \hbar^2 \kappa_F\right)}$$

Beside the Si barrier thickness D the "damped" (imaginary) part of the Fermi wavevector $\kappa_F = \sqrt{2m\Delta E_B / \hbar^2}$ at the center of the barrier is the crucial parameter. $\Delta r = (r_\uparrow - r_\downarrow)/2$ is the difference of reflection coefficients for spin-up and spin-down tunnelling electrons, injected by the Stoner split majority ($\uparrow$) and minority ($\downarrow$) bands of Ni. The Si quantum barrier (QB) ΔE_B is positive, thus the reflection coefficients taken within the barrier are mainly imaginary. As extensively explained in Ref. [7], these damped waves in the barrier mediate an AFM exchange coupling which turns the magnetic moment ($\mu=1.5\cdot10^9$ μ_B) of adjacent wires in opposite directions. From IR transmission we estimate a Schottky barrier $\Delta E_B = 0.43$ eV, and consequently $\kappa_F = 3.4\cdot10^9$ m^{-1}. The Stoner splitting in Ni (=0.11 eV) causes an imbalance of impinging spin currents at the barrier, which yields [taking $E_{F\uparrow}$(Ni) = 10 eV] a finite Im(Δr^2) ~10^{-3}. The AFM coupling between wires is extremely dependent on the barrier thickness D. For D < 2.6 nm it represents a molecular field of $B_{flip} = J_{af}/\mu$ > 1T and enhances this field up to 10 T for D < 2.3 nm (see inset of Fig.2). The system seems to provide a high amount of such barrier thicknesses because our measurements show B_{flip} around 5.5T and indicate increasing parallel magnetization of the AFM arranged wires for $B > B_{flip}$. At present, we are not able to explain the turn-on of this exchange J_{af} at B>4T, but we are convinced from temperature-dependent measurements that magnetostrictive effects induced by the Ni wires tunes the QB ΔE_B correspondingly to promote an AFM interaction between FM Ni wires from a certain threshold field on. The model is rather crude because we did not take into account the inherent cylindrical symmetry of the barrier interface.

ACKNOWLEDGMENTS

We thank the Austrian FWF for his grant (project P18593) and the Austrian MNA nanonetwork for the support.

REFERENCES

1. L. T. Canham, et al., *Nature* **368**, 133 (1994).
2. U. Grüning, et al., *Appl. Phys. Lett.* **68**, 747 (1996).
3. P. Granitzer, et al., *Mat. Res. Soc. Symp. Proc.* **872**, J13.13 (2005).
4. K. Nielsch, et al., *IEEE Trans. Magn.* **38**, 2571 (2002).
5. Y. Qiang, et al., *Phys. Rev. B* **66**, 064404 (2002).
6. E. Fonda, et al., *Phys. Rev. B* **71**, 184411 (2005).
7. P. Bruno, *Phys. Rev. B* **49**, 13231 (1994).

Anomalous Hall effect in a two-dimensional electron system: unified analysis of side-jump and skew scattering mechanisms

S. Y. Liu[*,†], Norman J. M. Horing[*] and X. L. Lei[†]

[*]Department of Physics and Engineering Physics, Stevens Institute of Technology,
Hoboken, New Jersey 07030, USA
[†]Department of Physics, Shanghai Jiaotong University, 1954 Huashan Road, Shanghai 200030, China

Abstract. We present a unified kinetic equation approach to analyze the side-jump and skew scattering anomalous Hall contributions in a two-dimensional electron system with extrinsic spin-orbit coupling and also spin-orbit coupling induced directly by the driving electric field. Considering long-range electron-impurity scattering up to the second Born approximation, we derive the side-jump and skew scattering contributions to the anomalous Hall conductivity on an equal basis. Our numerical analysis shows that in a typical two-dimensional semiconductor with magnetization, both the side-jump and skew anomalous Hall conductivities are of the same order of magnitude. For an attractive electron-impurity scattering potential, their signs are the same as that of the ordinary Hall conductivity. Also, we make it clear that the anomalous Hall effect is relatively small in comparison with the ordinary one in the diffusive regime.

Keywords: Anomalous Hall Effect; Side-Jump Scattering; Skew Scattering; Extrinsic Spin-Orbit Interaction
PACS: 73.50.Dn,72.20.Fr, 73.63.Hs

A nonvanishing magnetization in spin-split systems may give rise to an extraordinary Hall current. This so-called anomalous Hall effect (AHE) has been observed in various solid-state systems, such as itinerant ferromagnets, dilute magnetic semiconductors, *etc.* Essentially, the AHE arises from spin-orbit (SO) coupling and can be classified into two types, intrinsic and extrinsic AHE, according to the origins of the SO interaction.

The extrinsic AHE stems from a SO coupling induced by electron-impurity scattering.[1] There are two mechanisms responsible for this AHE: a side-jump process[2], and a skew scattering.[3] The side-jump AHE arises from a sidewise shift of the center of the electron wave packet, while the skew scattering AHE corresponds to an anisotropic enhancement of the wave packet due to electron-impurity scattering.

In present paper, we propose a unified kinetic equation approach to investigate the side-jump and skew scattering AHE mechanisms-on the same footing-in a two-dimensional (2D) electron system considering extrinsic SO coupling induced by long-range electron-impurity scattering and also SO interaction induced directly by the external driving electric field. Note that the latter SO coupling has been ignored in all previous studies of AHE. We show that both of these SO couplings make contributions to the side-jump anomalous Hall current (AHC), completely independently of any electron-impurity scattering. The skew AHC relates only to the extrinsic SO interaction. It is proportional to n_i^{-1} (n_i is the impurity density) and appears when electron-impurity scattering is

considered up to the second Born approximation (SBA). Performing a numerical calculation of the AHE in a typical 2D semiconductor system, we find that side-jump and skew scattering anomalous Hall conductivities are of the same order of magnitude. For an attractive electron-impurity scattering potential, their signs are the same as that of the ordinary Hall conductivity.

We consider a quasi-2D semiconductor in the $x - y$ plane, driven by a homogeneous magnetization $\mathbf{M} \equiv (0,0,M)$ and a uniform in-plane dc electric field $\mathbf{E}$. In this system, the motion of an electron with momentum $\mathbf{p} \equiv (p_x, p_y) \equiv (p \cos \phi_\mathbf{p}, p \sin \phi_\mathbf{p})$ ($\phi_\mathbf{p}$ is the momentum angle in polar coordinates) can be described by Hamiltonian, $\hat{H} = \hat{H}_0 + \hat{H}_{\text{imp}} + \hat{H}_E$. The free electron Hamiltonian, $\hat{H}_0$, is a diagonal 2×2 matrix: $\hat{H}_0 = \text{diag}[\varepsilon_1(p), \varepsilon_2(p)]$ with $\varepsilon_\mu = p^2/2m^* + (-1)^\mu M$ ($\mu = 1, 2$, m^* is the electron effective mass). $\hat{H}_{\text{imp}}$ describes the electron-impurity interaction. It contains not only an ordinary scattering potential term, V, but also a term related to the extrinsic SO coupling. H_E describes an applied external electric field, and, in the Coulomb gauge, it can be written as $\hat{H}_E = -e\mathbf{E} \cdot \mathbf{r} - \lambda [\sigma \times \mathbf{E}] \cdot \mathbf{p}$, with λ as a SO coupling constant. Note that, in $\hat{H}_E$, we have considered the effect of the SO coupling induced directly by the external driving dc electric field.

In present paper, we examine the AHC flow along the x-axis, J_x, when the electric field is applied along the y-axis, *i.e.* $\mathbf{E} = (0, E, 0)$. From the Hamiltonian, it follows that J_x consists of three components: $J_x = J_x^{\text{f}} +$

CP893, *Physics of Semiconductors, 28th International Conference*
edited by W. Jantsch and F. Schäffler
© 2007 American Institute of Physics 978-0-7354-0397-0/07/$23.00

$J_x^{\text{imp}} + J_x^E$. J_x^E is the result of the SO coupling term induced directly by the external electric field. Considering only linear order in electric field, J_x^E takes the form, $J_x^E = e^2 E \lambda \sum_{\mathbf{p}} \{n_F[\varepsilon_1(p)] - n_F[\varepsilon_2(p)]\}$, with $n_F(\varepsilon)$ as the Fermi function. J_x^{imp} comes from the SO coupling term of $\hat{H}_{\text{imp}}$. To determine J_x^{imp}, one has to analyze the function $< \hat{\psi}_{\mu\mathbf{p}}^+ \hat{\psi}_{\mu\mathbf{k}} >$ with $\hat{\psi}_{\mathbf{p}}^+$ and $\hat{\psi}_{\mathbf{p}}$ as the electron creation and annihilation operators, respectively. From the Heisenberg equation for the operator $\hat{\psi}_{\mu\mathbf{p}}^+ \hat{\psi}_{\mu\mathbf{k}}$, it follows that to linear order in E, J_x^{imp} is equal to J_x^E.

It should be noted that J_x^{imp} and J_x^E have the characteristics of the side-jump AHC, which originates from the shift of the electron wave-packet center towards the direction transverse to the driving electric field. Such a shift is exhibited by the single-particle current operators of J_x^{imp} and J_x^E, involving the antisymmetric tensor ε_{lmn}. Hence, the side-jump AHC, J_x^{sj}, can be expressed as $J_x^{\text{sj}} = J_x^{\text{imp}} + J_x^E$. It is evident that J_x^{sj} is completely independent of electron-impurity scattering.

J_x^{f} arises from the free-electron Hamiltonian $\hat{H}_0$: $J_x^{\text{f}} = e \sum_{\mathbf{p}} (p_x/m^*) [\hat{\rho}_{11}(\mathbf{p}) + \hat{\rho}_{22}(\mathbf{p})]$ with $\hat{\rho}_{\mu\mu}(\mathbf{p})$ ($\mu = 1, 2$) as the component of the distribution function $\hat{\rho}(\mathbf{p})$. Obviously, J_x^{f} is nonvanishing only if there exists a component of $\hat{\rho}_{\mu\mu}(\mathbf{p})$ which depends on the momentum angle through $\cos\phi_{\mathbf{p}}$. This implies that J_x^{f} results from an anisotropy due to electron-impurity scattering, and hence it just is a component of the skew AHC, J_x^{ss}: $J_x^{\text{ss}} = J_x^{\text{f}}$.

To determine the nonvanishing J_x^{ss}, we derive a kinetic equation for $\hat{\rho}(\mathbf{p})$ from the Dyson equation of the lesser nonequilibrium Green's function using the generalized Kadanoff-Baym ansatz. In this, the nonequilibrium self-energies are expressed in terms of a T-matrix which is evaluated in the SBA. Solving the obtained kinetic equation to first order in λ, we find that J_x^{ss} can be written as $J_x^{\text{ss}} = e^2 E \sum_{\mathbf{p},\mu} (p/m^*) \cos^2\phi_{\mathbf{p}} \Phi_{1\mu}^c(p)$, with

$$
\begin{aligned}
\Phi_{1\mu}^c(p) &= (-1)^\mu 4\tau_\mu n_i \pi^2 \lambda \Phi_{0\mu}^s(p) \sum_{\mathbf{k},\mathbf{q}} V_{\mathbf{p}-\mathbf{k}} V_{\mathbf{k}-\mathbf{q}} \\
&\times V_{\mathbf{q}-\mathbf{p}} pk \sin(\phi_{\mathbf{k}} - \phi_{\mathbf{p}}) \delta(\varepsilon_{\mu p} - \varepsilon_{\mu k}) \\
&\times \delta(\varepsilon_{\mu p} - \varepsilon_{\mu q}) [pk \sin(\phi_{\mathbf{k}} - \phi_{\mathbf{p}}) \\
&\quad + qp \sin(\phi_{\mathbf{p}} - \phi_{\mathbf{q}}) - qk \sin(\phi_{\mathbf{k}} - \phi_{\mathbf{q}})], (1)
\end{aligned}
$$

$\Phi_{0\mu}^s(p) = -\tau_\mu \{\partial n_F[\varepsilon_\mu(p)]/\partial \varepsilon_\mu(p)\} \{\partial \varepsilon_\mu(p)/\partial p\}$, and $\tau_\mu^{-1} = 2\pi \sum_{\mathbf{k}} |V_{\mathbf{p}-\mathbf{k}}|^2 (1 - \cos\phi_{\mathbf{k}}) \delta(\varepsilon_{\mu p} - \varepsilon_{\mu k})$.

Considering an attractive, long-range electron-impurity scattering potential, V, we numerically evaluate the AHE in a InSb/AlInSb quantum well. In Fig. 1, we plot the calculated total anomalous Hall conductivity $\sigma_{xy} = \sigma_{xy}^{\text{ss}} + \sigma_{xy}^{\text{sj}}$, and its component $\sigma_{xy}^{\text{sj}} = \sigma_{xy}^{\text{imp}} + \sigma_{xy}^E$ as functions of magnetization, M (the quantities σ_{xy}, $\sigma_{xy}^{\text{ss,sj}}$, and $\sigma_{xy}^{\text{imp},E}$ are defined as $\sigma_{xy} = J_x/E$, $\sigma_{xy}^{\text{ss,sj}} = J_x^{\text{ss,sj}}/E$, and $\sigma_{xy}^{\text{imp},E} = J_x^{\text{imp},E}/E$). It is evident the signs of σ_{xy}^{ss} and

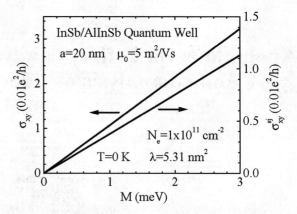

FIGURE 1. Magnetization dependencies of σ_{xy} and σ_{xy}^{sj} in a InSb/AlInSb quantum well. The width of the quantum well is $a = 20$ nm. The electron density is $N_e = 1 \times 10^{15}$ m^{-2}. The lattice temperature is $T = 0$ K and the mobility in the absence of magnetization is $\mu_0 = 5$ m^2/Vs.

σ_{xy}^{sj} (as well as that of the ordinary Hall conductivity) are the same. With increasing magnetization, σ_{xy} and σ_{xy}^{sj} increase linearly. A qualitative comparison between σ_{xy} and σ_{xy}^{sj} indicates that, for the given value $\mu_0 = 5$ m^2/Vs, both the contributions from side-jump and skew scattering to anomalous Hall conductivity, σ_{xy}^{ss} and σ_{xy}^{imp}, are of the same order of magnitude. Note that, for the InSb/AlInSb quantum well with $\mu_0 = 5$ m^2/Vs, the ordinary Hall conductivity is equal to $103.4 e^2/h$, which is much larger than the anomalous Hall conductivity.

In summary, we have determined the AHE in a 2D semiconductor considering both extrinsic SO coupling and also SO interaction induced directly by the driving electric field. A qualitative comparison of the contributions from side-jump and skew scatterings has been carried out.

This work was supported by the Department of Defense through the DURINT program administered by the US Army Research Office, DAAD Grant No. 19-01-1-0592, and by projects of the National Science Foundation of China and the Shanghai Municipal Commission of Science and Technology.

REFERENCES

1. J. Sinova *et al.*, Int. J. Mod. Phys. B **18**, 1083 (2004).
2. L. Berger, Phys. Rev. B **2**, 4559 (1970); **5**, 1862 (1972).
3. J. Smit, Physica **21**, 877 (1955); **24**, 39 (1958).

Energy Transport Between Hole Gas and Crystal Lattice in Diluted Magnetic Semiconductor

J.M. Kivioja[1], M. Prunnila[1], S. Novikov[2], P. Kuivalainen[2], and J. Ahopelto[1]

[1]VTT Micro and Nanoelectronics, Tietotie 3, Espoo, P.O. Box 1000, FI-02044 VTT, Finland
[2]Electron Physics Laboratory, Helsinki University of Technology, P.O.BOX 3500, FI-02015 HUT, Finland

Abstract. The temperature dependent energy transfer rate between hole gas and lattice has been investigated in thin $Mn_xGa_{1-x}As$ (x=3.7% and 4.0%) films by heating the hole system with power density P_d and measuring the hole temperature T. The heating experiments were carried out in temperature range of 250 mK-1.3 K and the temperature dependency of resistivity provided the hole thermometer. When the hole temperature greatly exceeds the lattice temperature we find that $P_d \sim T^n$, where n is in the range of 4 - 5.

Keywords: ferromagnetic semiconductor, MnGaAs, carrier-phonon energy relaxation
PACS: 63.20.Kr, 71.38.-k, 75.50.Dd, 72.25.Dc

INTRODUCTION

Recent years have seen a growing interest in the field of diluted magnetic semiconductors due to their ability to combine magnetism and integrated electronics. Various electrical and material properties of magnetic semiconductors have been extensively reported in the literature. Here, we focus to study thermal relaxation of holes in magnetic semiconductor, which is a new subject in this field. In this work the temperature dependent energy loss rate between charge carriers and lattice is experimentally investigated in MnGaAs.

SAMPLES

The MnGaAs samples were grown on semi-insulating GaAs (100) substrate by molecular beam epitaxy (MBE). First an undoped GaAs buffer layer (230 nm) was grown at 580 °C. Then low temperature MBE of a 100 nm thick $Mn_xGa_{1-x}As$ device layer was performed at 230 °C. In the experiments we studied two samples with manganese concentrations of x=3.7 % and 4.0 % and Curie temperatures of 60 K and 62 K, respectively.

The MnGaAs films were patterned utilizing UV-lithography and wet etching. The MnGaAs mesas were contacted with superconducting electrodes (Nb or Al) for preventing thermal leakage during the heating experiments. Samples were electrically characterized

down to 250 mK using He^3-sorption cryostat and standard lock-in techniques.

RESULTS AND DISCUSSION

Figure 1 presents measured resistivity ρ as a function of temperature. The resistivity of both samples show a peak around 60 K. The position of the peak gives the Curie temperature. Furthermore, the Hall-resistivities ρ_{xy} (not shown) exhibit the standard

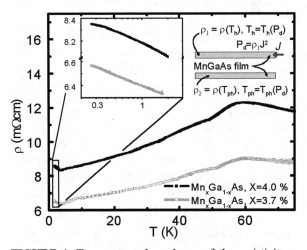

FIGURE 1. Temperature dependency of the resistivity ρ. The right inset shows the schematic top view of the heating experiments and also how $\rho(T)$ is utilized in determining the hole and phonon temperatures (see Fig. 2 for the results).

CP893, *Physics of Semiconductors, 28th International Conference*
edited by W. Jantsch and F. Schäffler
© 2007 American Institute of Physics 978-0-7354-0397-0/07/$23.00

anomalous Hall effect: at low magnetic fields B (<0.4 T) ρ_{xy} shows a rabid increase with increasing B and then it almost saturates at $B \sim 0.4$ T. Additionally, $\rho_{xy}(B)$ shows hysteretic behavior. The observed features in ρ and ρ_{xy} are well known signatures of ferromagnetism [1].

Below T $\sim$ 5 K both samples exhibit a "Kondo-like" $\rho(T) \sim \log(T)$ behavior (left inset in Fig. 1) [2]. This well defined temperature dependency of the resistivity provides a local thermometer, which is utilized in the heating experiments: the resistivity of adjacent electronically isolated films gives the hole T_h and phonon temperatures T_{ph} in the spirit of Refs. [3,4] (see the right inset of Fig. 1). The thermometers were first calibrated by slowly adjusting the bath temperature of the cryostat. Then one of the 5 μm wide adjacent MnGaAs mesas was heated by applying a DC current density J at constant bath (cryostat) temperature. The change in the resistivities, which were measured with a small ac-signal, give the response of T_h and T_{ph} to heating power density $P_d = \rho J^2$. These responses are plotted in Fig. 2 at various bath temperatures.

The temperatures of electrically isolated phonon and hole thermometers have very different responses. The hole temperature shows a strong response while the phonon temperature shows only extremely weak increase, which is observable at the highest heating powers and lowest bath temperatures. This indicates that the thermal coupling between GaAs substrates and cryostat's sample holder (copper) was extremely good, contradictory to studies utilizing silicon substrates [3,4]. Further, this also shows that the "bottle-neck" in the heat path is the hole-phonon energy relaxation rate.

Figure 2 shows also curves $P_d \propto T^n$ with n = 4,5. We can observe that the experimental T_h fall between these dependencies at high power density. More careful inspection reveals that the sample with x = 3.7 % (4.0 %) is described better with n=4 (n=5). On the other hand, the sensitivity of our hole (and phonon) thermometer is rather limited, which makes clear distinction between these two power laws difficult. Thus, we conclude that our preliminary experiments indicate that $P_d \propto T^n$ with n = 4 - 5 for both x = 3.7 % and x = 4.0 %. Note that as the hole-phonon energy relaxation rate is given by $\tau_{h-ph}^{-1} \propto T^{n-2}$ [4] our results also suggest that in $Mn_x Ga_{1-x} As$ $\tau_{h-ph}^{-1} \propto T^{2-3}$.

In semiconductors the elastic intra-valley [5] and inter-valley [4] scattering processes affect the carrier-phonon relaxation at low temperatures. In low mobility hole systems the latter is expect to have a strong effect, because it does not require diffusion. The role of ferromagnetism in the energy relaxation is not yet clear. However, we have also performed heating

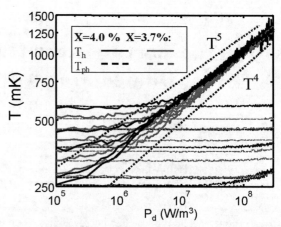

FIGURE 2. Hole-gas temperature (T_h) and temperature of the lattice (T_{ph}) as a function of heating power density at various base temperatures.

measurements at various perpendicular magnetic fields between -2 T and 2 T and our conclusion is that the hole-phonon relaxation rate in $Mn_x Ga_{1-x} As$ has negligible magnetic field dependency.

SUMMARY

Our results show that the energy loss rate from charge carriers to lattice in $Mn_x Ga_{1-x} As$ samples with x=3.7 % and x=4.0 % follows a power law $P_d \propto T^{4-5}$, which indicates that the hole-phonon energy relaxation time has $\tau_{h-ph}^{-1} \propto T^{2-3}$ behavior. We observed no magnetic field dependency in the energy relaxation.

ACKNOWLEDGMENTS

The Academy of Finland (grant 205478) is acknowledged for financial support.

REFERENCES

1. F. Matsukura, H. Ohno, A.Shen, and Y. Sugawara, Phys. Rev. B. 57, 2037 (1998).
2. H.T. He *et al.* Appl. Phys. Lett. 87, 162506 (2005).
3. J.M. Kivioja, I.J. Maasilta, J.T. Karvonen, and J.P. Pekola, Physica E 18, 21 (2003).
4. M. Prunnila, P.Kivinen, A.Savin, P. Törmä, and J.Ahopelto, Phys. Rev. Lett. 95, 206602 (2005).
5. A. Sergeev, M. Yu. Reizer, and V. Mitin, Phys. Rev. Lett. 94, 136602 (2005).

Local environment effects on exchange interactions in dilute magnetic semiconductors

K. Sato*, P. H. Dederichs[†] and H. Katayama-Yoshida*

*The Institute of Scientific and Industrial Research, Osaka Univ., Ibaraki, Osaka 567-0047, Japan
[†]Institut fuer Festkoerperforschung, Forschungszentrum Juelich, D-52425 Juelich, Germany

Abstract. We discuss local environment effects on exchange interactions in dilute magnetic semiconductors. The effects of local impurity configurations are taken into account by embedding a large cluster into the effective medium calculated by the coherent potential approximation. We find a large discrepancy in calculated exchange interactions by our cluster embedding method and by the Liechtenstein's method, because in our method the multiple scattering effect between site i and j is fully included. It is also found that the calculated exchange interactions strongly depend on the position of the impurities in the cluster other than site i and j. The average of the configuration dependent interactions approximately converge to the two impurity embedding results.

Keywords: local environment effect, coherent potential approximation, exchange interaction, cluster embedding
PACS: 85.75.-d, 75.50.Pp, 75.30.Hx

Recent first-principles calculations based on the density functional theory have proven to describe the electronic structure and magnetism of dilute magnetic semiconductors (DMS) with good accuracy. In particular, combining standard statistical methods with first-principles methods, the measured Curie temperatures of DMS are reasonably reproduced for the well studied systems such as (Ga, Mn)As and (Zn, Cr)Te [1, 2, 3]. The most successful approach is a hybrid method of Monte Carlo simulations (MCS) and first-principles calculations of effective exchange interactions by using Liechtenstein's prescription for the CPA [4]. In this method, the configuration dependence of the exchange coupling constants J_{ij} due to the presence of other impurities is averaged out by using the coherent potential approximation (CPA) and the calculated exchange interactions depend only on the distance between the two sites i and j. In the MCS, first we generate a random distribution of impurities in a supercell, and perform MCS assuming the configuration independent CPA interactions for each generated configuration, and then take the configuration average of the simulation results. Thus, rigorously speaking, this hybrid method is inconsistent with the averaging procedure.

In this paper, we would like to discuss local environment effects on the exchange interactions in DMS in order to propose a consistent procedure for Curie temperature calculations. To take the effects of local impurity configurations into account, we embed into the CPA medium a large cluster which includes in addition to site i and j several other shells with random occupancies, but fully aligned moments. Within the cluster, multiple scattering at the different magnetic impurities

is fully included and the calculated exchange parameters J_{ij} reflect the given local impurity configurations. In the present calculations, we calculate the electronic structure of DMS by using the Korringa-Kohn-Rostoker coherent potential approximation (KKR-CPA) method based on the local density approximation. We use the KKR-CPA package MACHIKANEYAMA2002 developed by Akai [5]. The scattering path operators are calculated for the embedded clusters and then the total energy change due to the rotation of magnetic moments at sites i and j is mapped on a classical Heisenberg model to estimate effective exchange interactions J_{ij} [4].

Calculated results are shown in Figs. 1-(a), (b) and (c) for (Ga, Mn)As, (Ga, Mn)N and (Ga, Cr)N, respectively. Mn and Cr concentrations are fixed to 5% for considered cases. For the realization of random impurity configurations, we prepare an $8 \times 8 \times 8$ supercell and choose magnetic sites randomly in the supercell. Then, for each (i, j) impurity pair in the supercell, J_{ij} is calculated by taking a local impurity distribution into account. We consider two kinds of clusters, one is the smallest cluster which consists of only 2 impurities at site i and j (2-impurity embedding) and the other considers the positions of impurities on the first nearest neighbor shells around the site i and j. For configuration average, we generate 10 different random configurations. For the simplicity of the calculations, we assume a zinc blende crystal structure for (Ga, Mn)N and (Ga, Cr)N.

The exchange interactions J_{ij} calculated by the Liechtenstein's formula and by the 2-impurity embedding method are shown in Fig. 1. We should notice that in the Liechtenstein's formula the multiple scattering effects is not fully considered, e.g. repeated back and forth scatter-

CP893, *Physics of Semiconductors, 28th International Conference*
edited by W. Jantsch and F. Schäffler
© 2007 American Institute of Physics 978-0-7354-0397-0/07/$23.00

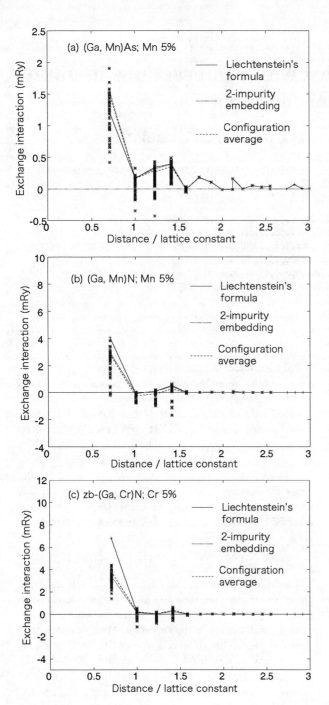

FIGURE 1. Configuration dependent exchange interactions in (a) (Ga, Mn)As, (b) (Ga, Mn)N and (c) (Ga, Cr)N by the cluster embedding method (asterisks). The 2-impurity embedding results and the averages of configuration dependent J_{ij} are also shown.

ing between site i and j is not taken into account, therefore already for the 2-impurity embedding (the smallest cluster) the calculated J_{ij} differ from the J_{ij} given by the Liechtenstein's formula. The discrepancy is large for the

nearest neighbors in particular in (Ga, Cr)N, however the effect is already very small for the 2nd neighbors and negligible for farther pairs. As shown in the figures, J_{ij} strongly depend on the positions of the other impurities in the clusters resulting in a large fluctuation. The fluctuation is so large that the calculated J_{ij} can change their sign in particular for the 2nd and 3rd neighbor interactions. Schilfgaarde *et al.* obtained similar results to the present ones by using large supercells [6, 7]. In spite of the considerable fluctuation in the configuration dependent J_{ij}, the configuration average of J_{ij} approximately converges to the 2-impurity embedded results.

In this paper we discuss the local environment effects on exchange interactions in DMS. It is found that, (1) the Liechtenstein's formula and the 2-impurity embedding method give different values of J_{ij} due to the incomplete treatment of the multiple scattering effects in the Liechtenstein's formula. This effect is large for near neighbors but negligible for distant pairs. (2) The calculated J_{ij} exhibit large fluctuations depending on the positions of other impurities in the cluster and (3) the averages of the configuration dependent interactions approximately converge to the 2-impurities-embedded-in-CPA results. However, we expect that the Curie temperatures are reduced by the fluctuations.

ACKNOWLEDGMENTS

This research was partially supported by a Grant-in-Aid for Scientific Research in Priority Areas "Quantum Simulators and Quantum Design" (No. 17064014) and "Semiconductor Nanospintronics", a Grand-in-Aid for Scientific Research for young researchers, JST-CREST, NEDO-nanotech, the 21st Century COE and the JSPS core-to-core program "Computational Nano-materials Design".

REFERENCES

1. L. Bergqvist, O. Eriksson, J. Kudrnovský, V. Drchal, P. Korzhavyi and I. Turek, *Phys. Rev. Lett.* **93**, 137202 (2004).
2. K. Sato, W. Schweika, P. H. Dederichs and H. Katayama-Yoshida, *Phys. Rev. B* **93**, 201202R (2004).
3. T. Fukushima, K. Sato, H. Katayama-Yoshida and P. H. Dederichs, *Jpn. J. Appl. Phys.* **43**, L1416 (2004).
4. A. I. Liechtenstein, M. I. Katsnelson, V. P. Antropov and V. A. Gubanov, *J. Magn. Magn. Mater.* **67**, 65 (1987).
5. H. Akai, http://sham.phys.sci.osaka-u.ac.jp/kkr/
6. M. van Schilfgaarde and O. N. Mryasov, *Phys. Rev. B* **63**, 233205 (2001).
7. J. L. Xu and M. van Schilfgaarde, *Phys. Rev. Lett.* **94**, 97201 (2005).

Anisotropic Magnetic-Field Evolution of Valence-Band States in One-Dimensional Diluted Magnetic Semiconductors

Yukihiro Harada*, Takashi Kita*, Osamu Wada* and Hiroaki Ando†

*Department of Electrical and Electronics Engineering, Faculty of Engineering, Kobe University, Rokkodai 1-1, Nada, Kobe 657-8501, Japan
†Department of Physics, Faculty of Science and Engineering, Konan University, Okamoto 8-9-1, Higashi-Nada, Kobe 658-8501, Japan

Abstract. We have theoretically studied the anisotropic magnetic-field evolution of the valence-band states in CdMnTe quantum wires by using a multiband effective-mass method. The Zeeman diagram depends on the direction of the magnetic field against the wire direction. The optical transition probability has been found to show a dramatic change in the polarization because of the valence-band mixing. The calculated magneto-optical properties are carefully compared with experimental results observed in CdTe/CdMnTe tilted superlattices.

Keywords: Quantum Wire; Magnetic Semiconductor; Magneto-optical effects
PACS: 78.67.Lt, 75.50.Pp, 78.20.Ls, 78.55.Et

INTRODUCTION

Diluted magnetic semiconductors (DMS's) have attracted great interest because of the functional magnetic effects caused by the *sp-d* exchange interaction of spins between carriers and magnetic ions.[1] On the other hand, low-dimensional heterostructures can artificially control the *s* and *p* electronic states. The exchange interaction enables to change the electronic states in a nondestructive way. Recently, we have experimentally demonstrated anisotropic magneto-optical effects in $(CdTe)_{0.5}(Cd_{0.75}Mn_{0.25}Te)_{0.5}$ tilted superlattices (TSL's) fabricated by fractional monolayer growth on to a CdMgTe(001) vicinal surface.[2] The TSL's are equivalent to [1-10]-oriented quantum wires (QWR's) lying on the (001) plane. The observed magneto-optical properties have been found to depend on the direction of the external magnetic field in the Voigt configuration. The Zeeman shift in the parallel magnetic field to the QWR direction is smaller than that in the perpendicular field. Furthermore, it has been demonstrated by applying the parallel magnetic field that the in-plane polarization of the QWR luminescence is rotated sensitively.

In this paper, we perform detailed theoretical calculations to demonstrate such anisotropic phenomena.

THEORETICAL MODEL AND METHOD

Characteristics of the magneto-optical effects in one-dimensional DMS's have been studied by calculating the valence-band states of an ideal CdMnTe QWR surrounded by infinite potential barriers. We assumed that the conduction and valence bands are decoupled, and that the spin-orbit split-off band can be neglected. We applied a simple effective-mass model to describe the electron states in the conduction band. On the other hand, the valence-band mixing induced by the one-dimensional quantum confinement is treated by using the multiband effective-mass method based on the 4-band Luttinger-Kohn Hamiltonian [3] for the analysis of the hole states in the valence bands. In addition, the *p-d* exchange interaction have been introduced by adding the Heisenberg type Hamiltonian as described in Ref. 4. Besides, the heavy and light holes are defined as the $j = \pm 3/2$ and $\pm 1/2$ components in the base function set u_j^v comprised by the Bloch functions at Γ_8 as represented in Ref. 4, respectively. We assumed that the Landau quantization effect is negligible. In the following calculation, we used the parameters of $Cd_{0.90}Mn_{0.10}Te$ [5, 6], and assumed a rectangular QWR with a cross-section of 13x10 nm^2. This QWR cross-section reproduces the experimental linear optical polarization of the CdTe/CdMnTe TSL's in the zero-magnetic field.[2]

CALCULATED ANISOTROPIC MAGNETO-OPTICAL PROPERTIES

Figure 1 shows the calculated magnetic-field dependence of the Zeeman shift energy of the highest valence subband at Γ_8. Circles, squares, and triangles represent results for $W \perp B \parallel k$, $W \perp B \perp k$, and $W \parallel B \perp k$, respectively, where W, B, and k are the direction of the QWR, the applied magnetic field direction, and the wave vector of the emitted light, respectively. W is parallel to the

CP893, *Physics of Semiconductors, 28th International Conference*
edited by W. Jantsch and F. Schäffler

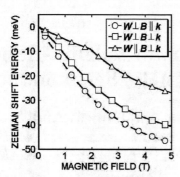

FIGURE 1. Calculated magnetic field dependence of the Zeeman shift energy of the highest valence subband at Γ_8. Circles, squares, and triangles represent results for $W \perp B \parallel k$, $W \perp B \perp k$, and $W \parallel B \perp k$, respectively.

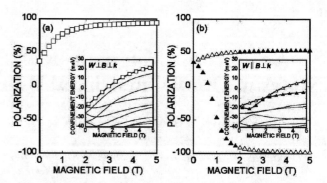

FIGURE 2. Calculated magnetic field dependence of the linear polarization of the optical transition probability at Γ_8 in the Voigt configuration. The polarization is defined by $(I_\parallel - I_\perp)/(I_\parallel + I_\perp)$, where $I_\parallel$ and $I_\perp$ are parallel and perpendicular components of the optical transition intensity to the QWR, respectively. (a) and (b) are calculated results placed at $W \perp B \perp k$ and $W \parallel B \perp k$, respectively. Squares represent the transition from the highest valence subband at $W \perp B \perp k$. Opened and closed triangles show the results of the transitions from the highest and the second-highest valence subbands at $W \parallel B \perp k$, respectively. The inset shows calculated Zeeman diagram of the valence subbands near the band edge.

[010] direction. k is perpendicular to the growth plane (001). The Zeeman shift energy clearly depends on the configuration. The Zeeman shift energy in the Faraday configuration ($W \perp B \parallel k$) is larger than that in the Voigt configurations ($W \perp B \perp k$ and $W \parallel B \perp k$), because the applied magnetic field direction in the Faraday configuration coincides with the strongest quantization direction along the short axis of the QWR. On the other hand, in the Voigt configuration, the Zeeman shift energy at $W \parallel B \perp k$ is smaller than that at $W \perp B \perp k$. Since the in-plane quantum confinement tends to prevent the quantization axis of the hole spin from rotating into the magnetic field direction at $W \parallel B \perp k$, the exchange interaction is suppressed, which results in the anisotropic behavior in the Voigt configuration. A cusp structure observed near 2 T at $W \parallel B \perp k$ is originated from the valence-band crossing between the highest and the second-highest subbands as shown in the inset of Fig. 2(b). Thus, the above findings qualitatively reproduce our recent experimental results observed in the CdTe/CdMnTe TSL's. [2]

Figure 2 shows the magnetic field dependence of the linear polarization of the optical transition probability at Γ_8 calculated in the Voigt configuration. The polarization is defined by $(I_\parallel - I_\perp)/(I_\parallel + I_\perp)$, where $I_\parallel$ and $I_\perp$ are parallel and perpendicular components of the optical transition intensity to the QWR, respectively. Figure 2(a) and (b) are calculated results placed at $W \perp B \perp k$ and $W \parallel B \perp k$, respectively. Squares represent the transition from the highest valence subband at $W \perp B \perp k$. Opened and closed triangles show the results of the transitions from the highest and the second-highest valence subbands at $W \parallel B \perp k$, respectively. The optical transition polarization in 0 T is about 37 %. At $W \perp B \perp k$, the polarization increases with the magnetic field monotonically. This indicates that the quantization along the perpendicular to the QWR direction is strengthened. On the other hand, at $W \parallel B \perp k$, the polarization of the transition from the highest valence subband shows an abrupt

change near 2 T. With increasing magnetic field in this configuration, the heavy-hole dominant subband (polarized parallel to the QWR) is the topmost level up to ~ 2 T. And then, as shown in the inset of Fig. 2(b), the highest valence subband intersects with the second-highest band coupled strongly with the light-hole dominant subband (polarized perpendicular to the QWR) in ~ 1 T. The strong coupling causes a substantial anticrossing behavior. The redshifted level intersects with the topmost subband near 2 T. Since the character of the topmost level is changed from the heavy-hole dominant state to the light-hole dominant state, the polarization shows the sudden jump. Such valence-band crossing plays a key role in the anisotropic Zeeman shift and optical polarization depending on the magnetic-field direction.

REFERENCES

1. J. K. Furdyna, *J. Appl. Phys.* **64**, R29 (1988).
2. S. Nagahara, T. Kita, O. Wada, L. Marsal, and H. Mariette, *Phys. Rev. B* **69**, 233308 (2004).
3. J. M. Luttinger, *Phys. Rev.* **102**, 1030 (1956).
4. Y. Harada, T. Kita, O. Wada, L. Marsal, H. Mariette, and H. Ando, *phys. stat. sol. (c)* **3**, 667 (2006).
5. J. A. Gaj, R. Planel. and G. Fishman, *Solid State Commun.* **29**, 435 (1979).
6. T. Z. Kachlishvili, *Solid State Commun.* **80**, 283 (1991).

Ab initio investigation of quasi-one-dimensional nano-structures in dilute magnetic semiconductors

T. Fukushima*, K. Sato*, H. Katayama-Yoshida* and P. H. Dederichs†

*The Institute of Scientific and Industrial Research, Osaka University, 8-1 Mihogaoka, Ibaraki, Osaka 567-0047, Japan.
†Institut fuer Festkoerperforschung, Forschungszentrum Juelich, D-52425 Juelich, Germany.

Abstract. A new control method of quasi-one-dimensional nano-structures in dilute magnetic semiconductors (DMS) is demonstrated by using *ab initio* calculations and Monte Carlo simulation of spinodal decomposition under layer-by-layer crystal growth condition. We show that growth positions of the quasi-one-dimensional nano-structures in the DMS can be controlled by making a periodic atomic-patterning of magnetic impurities on the semiconductor substrate before the thermal non-equilibrium crystal growth by *e.g.* molecular-beam epitaxy.

Keywords: dilute magnetic semiconductor, Monte Carlo simulation, spinodal decomposition, quasi-one-dimensional nano-magnet
PACS: 75.50.Pp

INTRODUCTION

Much attention has been paid to semiconductor nano-spintronics because of new multi-functionalities using both the spin and the charge of the electron. Dilute magnetic semiconductors (DMS) have been expected as one of the materials which realize the semiconductor nano-spintronics. Although many theoretical and experimental researches have been performed, the origin of ferromagnetism in the DMS is still under discussion and recognized to be non-trivial problem. Recently, it is pointed out that magnetic percolation effect and inhomogeneity of magnetic impurity distribution are very important for understanding the magnetism in the DMS [1, 2]. Fukushima *et al.* showed that the DMS undergoes spinodal decomposition due to attractive force between magnetic impurities, and proposed that randomly distributed magnetic impurities over the cation sublattice form quasi-one-dimensional nano-structures, called "Konbu-phase", by using the Monte Carlo simulation of the two dimensional spinodal decomposition under layer-by-layer crystal growth condition.[3] The purpose of this Letter is to design a new fabrication method of "Konbu-phase" in the DMS based on *ab initio* calculations and Monte Carlo simulation with layer-by-layer crystal growth condition. We show that growth positions of the nano-structures in the "Konbu-phase" of the DMS can be controlled by "Nano-scale seeding" under the thermal non-equilibrium crystal growth condition. As a typical example, we take (Zn, Cr)Te system. Our simulation method, however, is easily generalized to all of the DMSs.

CALCULATION METHOD

The layer-by-layer crystal growth condition with the two dimensional spinodal decomposition is simulated by the Monte Carlo method in the Ising Hamiltonian, $H = -(1/2)\sum_{i\neq j} V_{ij}\sigma_i \cdot \sigma_j$, where V_{ij} is effective pair interaction between magnetic impurities at site i and j, σ_i is occupation number at site i. The V_{ij} is calculated by generalized perturbation method proposed by Ducastelle and Gautier, which utilizes occupation fluctuations in the coherent potential approximation (CPA) medium. [4] The KKR-CPA (Korringa-Kohn-Rostoker) method within the local density approximation is employed to calculate the CPA medium. Readers can find calculation details in Refs. [5] and [6]. In the generalized perturbation method, we can calculate the V_{ij} from Cr-Cr, Zn-Zn and Zn-Cr pair potential energy in the CPA medium, i.e., $V_{ij}^{\text{Cr-Cr}} = V_{ij}^{\text{Zn-Zn}} + V_{ij}^{\text{Cr-Cr}} - 2V_{ij}^{\text{Zn-Cr}}$, where $V_{ij}^{\text{A-B}}$ denotes the effective pair interaction associated with two sites, i and j, occupied by A and B atoms, respectively. Sato *et. al.* and Fukushima *et.al.* showed that most of the V_{ij}'s are negative and the interactions between magnetic impurities are attractive. [2, 3] By using the Monte Carlo method, the spinodal decomposition is simulated as follows. Starting from random distribution of impurities, first we choose one impurity site, then try to diffuse the impurity to another site, which is chosen randomly from the nearest neighbors site by obeying Metropolis algorithm. When we simulate the layer-by-layer crystal growth, atomic diffusion is restricted to first-layer, and only the nearest neighbors sites can become candidate for the trial site. After annealing the first layer we fix the resulting configuration of the first layer, then deposit the next layer and start the annealing. The grouth posi-

CP893, *Physics of Semiconductors, 28th International Conference*
edited by W. Jantsch and F. Schäffler
© 2007 American Institute of Physics 978-0-7354-0397-0/07/$23.00

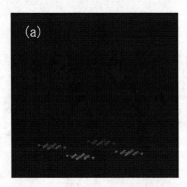 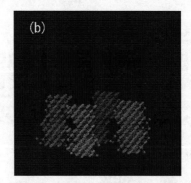 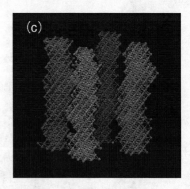

FIGURE 1. Control of the growth positions of the "Konbu-phase" by the "Nano-scale seeding" in the layer-by-layer growth condition using the two-dimensional spinodal decomposition. (a) Seeding on the substrate, (b) During the intermediate crystal growth, (c) Shape of the Konbu-phase controlled their position by the seeding.

tions of the nano-structures are controlled by periodic atomic-patterning ("Nano-scale seeding"), before starting the layer-by-layer crystal growth simulation.

RESULTS

Results of controlling the growth positions of the nano-structures in the "Konbu-phase" in (Zn, Cr)Te are shown in Fig. 1. In the figure, only Cr atoms in (Zn, Cr)Te are shown by the red points. Nearest neighbor Cr atoms are connected by white bars. In our simulation, 1000 Monte Carlo steps are performed to anneal each layer at scaled annealing temperature $k_B T / V_{01} = 0.5$, where k_B is Boltzmann constant and V_{01} is the effective pair interaction between the nearest neighbor Cr atoms. In Fig.1 (a), each seed consists of 12 Cr atoms and covers 1.44 nm^2. As shown in Fig. 1 (b), Cr atoms pile up on the seeds and finally the nano-pillars are formed on the seeds (Fig. 1 (c)). As shown in Fig. 1, we can see the control of the growth positions by the seeding is almost perfect. If the vapor pressure or impurity concentration is kept constant during the crystal growth as in the present simulations, the fluctuation of the width of the nano-pillars are very small. Due to large magnetic shape anisotropy, the "Konbu-phase" is expected to have high blocking temperature (T_B). [7] The present simulation suggests the possibility to use "Konbu-phase" of the DMS as nano-spintronics materials for a Tera-bit density memory.

SUMMARY

In this Letter, new control method of the quasi-one-dimensional nano-structures, called "Konbu-phase", in the DMS has been demonstrated by using *ab initio* calculations and Monte Carlo simulation of layer-by-layer crystal growth of the DMS. We have showed that the growth positions of the nano-structure in the "Konbu-

phase" of the DMS can be controlled by the "Nano-scale seeding" . Recently, the "Konbu-phase" was observed experimentally in (Al, Cr)N and (Ga, Cr)N systems. [8, 9] High-T_B "Konbu-phase" allows us to realize the semiconductor nano-spintronics application. We hope our new idea for control method of the "Konbu-phase" is confirmed by experimentalists.

ACKNOWLEDGMENTS

This research was partially supported by a Grant-in-Aid for Scientific Research in Priority Areas "Quantum Simulators and Quantum Design" (No. 17064014) and "Semiconductor Nanospintronics" , a Grant-in-Aid for Scientific Research for young researchers, JST-CREST, NEDO-nanotech, and the 21st Century COE.

REFERENCES

1. K. Sato, W. Schweika, P. H. Dederichs, and H. Katayama-Yoshida, *Phys. Rev. B* **70**, 201202 (2005).
2. K. Sato, H. Katayama-Yoshida, and P. H. Dedrichs, *Jpn. J. Appl. Phys.* **44**, L948 (2005).
3. T. Fukushima, K. Sato, H. Katayama-Yoshida, and P. H. Dederichs, *Jpn. J. Appl. Phys.* **45**, L416 (2006).
4. F. Ducastelle, and F. Gautier, *J. Phys. F* **6**, 2039 (1976).
5. H. Akai (2000), URL http://sham.phys.sci.osaka-u.ac.jp/kkr.
6. H. Akai, *J. Phys. Soc. Jpn* **51**, 486 (1982).
7. P. Gambardella, A. Dallmeyer, K. Maiti, M. C. Malagoli, W. Eberhardt, K. Kern, and C. Carbone, *Nature* **416**, 301 (2002).
8. L. Gu, S. Y. Wu, H. X. Liu, R. K. Singh, N. Newman, and D. J. Smith, *J. Magn. Magn. Mater.* **290**, 1395 (2005).
9. R. K. Singh, S. Y. Wu, H. X. Liu, L. Gu, D. J. Smith, and N. Newman, *Appl. Phys. Lett.* **86**, 012504 (2005).

Ab initio study of GaN/Mn$_x$Ga$_{1-x}$N digital heterostructure

M. Marques*, L. G. Ferreira[†], L. K. Teles**, L. M. R. Scolfaro[‡], J. Furthmüller [§] and F. Bechstedt [§]

*Departamento de Microondas e Optoeletrônica, Divisão de Engenharia Eletrônica, Instituto Tecnológico de Aeronáutica, 12228-900 São José dos Campos, SP, Brazil
[†]Instituto de Física Gleb Wataghin, Universidade Estadual de Campinas, Caixa Postal 6165, 13083-970 Campinas, SP, Brazil
**Departamento de Física, Instituto Tecnológico de Aeronáutica, Centro Técnico Aeroespacial, 12228-900 São José dos Campos, SP, Brasil
[‡]Instituto de Física, Universidade de São Paulo, CP66318, 05315-970 São Paulo, SP, Brazil
[§]Institut für Festkörpertheorie und Theoretische Optik, Friedrich-Schiller-Universität, 07743 Jena, Germany

Abstract.
The energetic and magnetic properties of wurtzite GaN/Mn$_x$Ga$_{1-x}$N digital heterostructures are investigated by first-principles total energy calculations, within the spin density functional theory, and Monte Carlo simulations. At 700^{0}C, up to the concentration of 8% Mn, the 2D alloy is stable. However, above this concentration, there is a strong tendency to the formation of MnN clusters with an AFM ground state defined by ferromagnetic Mn rows coupled antiferromagnetically with other Mn rows. The behavior of the magnetization with temperature is completely different in these two concentration regimes, with the 2D MnN-cluster being very stable, whereas the 2D alloy presents low magnetic transition temperatures.

Keywords: Spintronics, DMS, Transition Metals Nitrides, Ab initio
PACS: 71.20.Be

INTRODUCTION

Nowadays, materials under intense investigation are the diluted magnetic semiconductors (DMS) based on III-V materials. [1]They have properties whose can be used in the new field of spintronics, which aims at the use of spin of carriers for electronic devices. The DMS allow an interplay between magnetic and electronic properties and are structurally compatible with most epitaxially grown III-V semiconductors. Among the III-V DMS, Mn-doped GaAs system has been the most studied. These materials have a maximum Curie temperature T_c of 110 K. [2] Moreover, the solubility of the transition metals in these semiconductors is rather small. More recently, a different approach was suggested, in which superlattices are used. [3] These structures, called digital ferromagnetic heterostructures (DFH), are formed by a thin magnetic layer or submonolayer, embedded into bulk semiconductor. Such structures have higher concentration of transition metal atoms than bulk alloys. Aside from this new DFH approach, calculations based on mean field theory [4] showed that using nitride based systems a T_c above room temperature could be achieved. However, there are theoretical works, using first principles calculations, which predict lower transition temperatures for the (Ga,Mn)N system [5]. Experimentally, a variety of Curie temperatures for the (Ga,Mn)N system has been obtained[6, 7]. The conflicting results show that the mag-

netism observed in the nitride-based DMSs is yet not well understood.

In this work, we carry out rigorous and systematic theoretical studies of GaN/Mn$_x$Ga$_{1-x}$N wurtzite digital heterostructures. The energetic preferences among the different magnetic configurations are investigated by total energy calculations. The thermodynamic properties are derived by combining first principles (Kohn-Sham equations) and Monte Carlo (MC) calculations [8].

RESULTS

In Fig. 1(a) we present the distribution of atoms in the MC cell (Ga, Mn spin up and Mn spin down) for 8 and 10% Mn in the thermodynamic equilibrium at 700^{0}C. One clearly sees that at 8% Mn the distribution of Mn atoms is random and the spins do not present any clear tendency for +1 or -1. However, at 10% Mn, there is the tendency for the formation of MnN 2D clusters, with a strong antiferromagnetic coupling.

The next step in the Monte Carlo simulations is the study of the temperature behavior of the magnetization. For the layered GaN/Mn$_x$Ga$_{1-x}$N systems, we chose the distributions of atoms obtained at 700^{0}C, because it is about the typical growth temperature of GaMnN samples. Therefore, we made new MC runs allowing only the Mn spins to flip. In order to analyze the behavior

CP893, *Physics of Semiconductors, 28th International Conference*
edited by W. Jantsch and F. Schäffler
© 2007 American Institute of Physics 978-0-7354-0397-0/07/$23.00

of the magnetization we define the Correlation per pair (C) as

$$C = \frac{\sum\limits_{i=1}^{N} \sum\limits_{j=1}^{6} S_i S_j}{\sum\limits_{i=1}^{N} \sum\limits_{j=1}^{6} (S_i S_j)^2} \qquad (1)$$

with the atom j being a first neighbor of atom i, and N the total number of sites in the MC cell. The correlation per pair can assume different values depending on the arrangement of spins in the cell: (i) If $C \sim 1$ the system is ferromagnetic; (ii) if $C \sim 0$ the system does not present magnetic order, and (iii) $C < 1$ corresponds to a AFM ordering of Mn spins. Therefore, with this parameter we can detect the kind of magnetic order in the system. Fig. 1(b) presents the correlation per pair as function of temperature for concentrations of 8 and 10% Mn. The starting distribution of spins were of two types: (i) all spins up, or (ii) the AFM configuration. The first important result is that the case with 8% Mn (stable alloy) is completely different from the others in that it does not present any tendency to cluster formation. In this regime of a stable 2D random alloy, the correlation is independent of the starting configuration of spins, except at very low temperatures. With increasing temperature, C decays to zero, meaning a paramagnetic material. The FM state (value 1 for the correlation) only occurs in a combination of very low temperatures (about 25 K) and a FM starting configuration. If we start the calculation with an AFM configuration, at the same temperature, the correlation value is about 0.7, meaning a ferrimagnetic state. For concentration of 10% Mn, when we have the formation of clusters, the behavior is completely different. In this case, the correlation per pair depends on the starting configuration. If the MC simulation is started with a FM configuration, this state ($C=1$) is maintained until high temperatures when there is a transition to the AFM state defined by $C \sim -1/3$. The transition temperatures increase with increasing Mn concentration. Nevertheless, if the starting configuration is AFM, the value -1/3 for the correlation is kept until very high temperatures. The lowest energy is for the AFM state, therefore the FM state is metastable.

CONCLUSIONS

Summarizing, we have used spin density-functional theory-based calculations and Monte Carlo thermodynamics to study the electronic structure and magnetic properties of the nitride digital heterostructures. The 2D alloys are only stable up to 8% Mn at the usual growth temperature of the GaMnN systems. Above this Mn concentration, there is a strong tendency to form MnN clus-

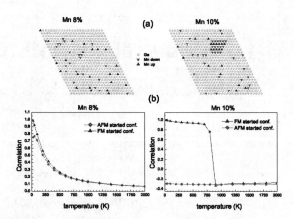

FIGURE 1. (a) Distribution of atoms and spins of the ground state in the MC cell in the thermodynamic equilibrium for concentrations of 8 and 10 % and (b)Correlation versus temperature for the concentrations of 8 and 10% Mn. The distribution of atoms was that of equilibrium at 700°C. The starting configurations for the Monte Carlo runs were either FM or AFM.

ters. The clusters, when in thermal equilibrium, also have an AFM arrangement of alternating spin up and spin down ferromagnetic lines. The arrangement in the clusters of alternating rows may have a fortuitous small net magnetic moment.

ACKNOWLEDGMENTS

We acknowledge the support provided by brazilian agencies CNPq and FAPESP.

REFERENCES

1. H. Ohno, *Science.* **281**, 951 (1998).
2. H. Ohno, A. Shen, F. Matsukura, A. Oiwa, A. Endo, S. Katsumoto, and Y. Iye, *Appl. Phys. Lett.* **69**, 363 (1996).
3. R. K. Kawakami, E. Johnston-Halperin, L. F. Chen, M. Hanson, N. Guebels, J. S. Speck, A. C. Gossard, and D. Awschalom, *Appl. Phys. Lett.* **77**, 2379 (2000).
4. T. Dietl, H. Ohno, F. Matsukura, J. Cibert, and D. Ferrand, *Science* **287**, 1019 (2000).
5. L. Bergqvist, O. Eriksson, J. Kudrnovský, V. Drchal, P. Korzhavyi, and I. Turek, *Phys. Rev. Lett.* **93**, 137202–1 (2004).
6. H. Hory, S. Sonoda, T. Sasaki, Y. Yamamoto, S. Shimizu, K. Suga, and K. K, *Physica B* **324**, 142 (2002).
7. M. E. Overberg, C. R. Abernathy, S. J. Pearton, N. A. Theodoropopoulou, K. T. McCarthy, and A. F. Hebarb, *Appl. Phys. Lett.* **79**, 1312 (2001).
8. M. Marques, L. G. Ferreira, L. K. Teles, L. M. R. Scolfaro, J. Furthmüller, and F. Bechstedt, *Phys. Rev. B* **73**, 224409 (2006).

First-principles calculations under carrier doping treatment in CuAlO$_2$ based dilute magnetic semiconductor

H. Kizaki, K. Sato and H. Katayama-Yoshida

ISIR-SANKEN, Osaka University, 8-1 Mihogaoka, Ibaraki, Osaka 567-0047, Japan

Abstract. We investigate the electronic structure and magnetic properties under carrier doping treatment in CuAlO$_2$ based dilute magnetic semiconductors ((Cu$_{0.95}$, Fe$_{0.05}$)AlO$_2$, (Cu$_{0.95}$, Co$_{0.05}$)AlO$_2$ and (Cu$_{0.95}$, V$_{0.05}$)AlO$_2$) from first-principles for semiconductor spintronics. Hole carriers are introduced by substitutional Mg impurities on Al sites in these materials. Electorons are introduced by substituting Si by Al. The Korringa-Kohn-Rostoker method combined with the coherent potential approximation within the local density approximation is employed for the present purpose. It is shown that Curie temperature of (Cu$_{0.95}$, V$_{0.05}$)(Al$_{1-x}$, Mg$_x$)O$_2$ and (Cu$_{0.95}$, Fe$_{0.05}$)(Al$_{1-x}$, X$_x$)O$_2$ (X=Mg, Si) affected by changing the carrier density, in contrast to the case of (Cu$_{0.95}$, Co$_{0.05}$)(Al$_{1-x}$, X$_x$)O$_2$, where Curie temperature is insensitive to the carrier density.

Keywords: Spintronics, First-principles calculation, Materials design, CuAlO$_2$
PACS: 75.50.Pp

Dilute magnetic semiconductors (DMS) are materials of much scientific and industrial interest due to their promising potential for spintronics. A key of technology for practical device applications in DMS is how to increase the Curie temperature, being at or above room temparature. So far, the electronic structures and magnetic properties of CuAlO$_2$ based DMS have been calculated to propose a new candidate for realizing a high T_C and a large magnetization magnetic semiconductor [1]. CuAlO$_2$ shows p-type conductivity

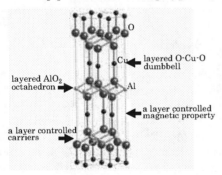

FIGURE 1. The crystal structure of CuAlO$_2$ with delafossite structure. Small black, large black, and small gray dots represent Cu, O and Al, respectively

at room temperature with a wide band gap energy of about 3.5eV(direct) and 1.8eV(indirect) [2]. It is known that CuAlO$_2$ has the hexagonal delafossite structure with a=2.86Å, c=16.96Å [2]. The material belongs to space group of $R\bar{3}m$ (FIG. 1). Thin films of CuAlO$_2$ show p-type conductivity up to 1 S cm^{-1} with a hole concentration of an order of 10^{17} cm^{-3} and mobility of 10cm^{2}V^{-1}s^{-1} at 300K [3]. The delafossite CuAlO$_2$ phase has an advantage of possessing two cation sites,

Cu^{+1} and Al^{+3} sites, for possible magnetic ion substitution. CuAlO$_2$-based DMS has two advantages. One is that CuAlO$_2$ is p-type semiconducting oxide without any intentional doping. The other is to make use of characteristic crystal structure.

In this paper we investigate the effect of carrier doping in (Cu$_{0.95}$, Fe$_{0.05}$)AlO$_2$, (Cu$_{0.95}$, Co$_{0.05}$)AlO$_2$ and (Cu$_{0.95}$, V$_{0.05}$)AlO$_2$ from first-principles. Hole carriers are introduced by substitutional Mg impurities on Al sites in these materials. Electrons are introduced by substituting Si by Al. T_C's are calculated as a function of Mg or Si concentration.

The electronic structure and the magnetic properties of CuAlO$_2$-based DMS are calculated by using the Korringa-Kohn-Rostoker method combined with the coherent potential approximation within the local spin density approximation (KKR-CPA-LSDA). We use the KKR-CPA package MACHIKANEYAMA2002 developed by Akai [4]. The scalar relativistic approximation is employed. The lattice relaxation isn't taken into account and experimental lattice parameters are used throughout the calculations [5]. 288 independent k-sampling points in the irreducible part of the first Brillouin zone are chosen in the calculations. No spin-orbit coupling effect is taken into account.

In order to estimate the T_C's of CuAlO$_2$-based DMS, we calculate the electronic structure and the total energy (TE) of both ferromagnetic and paramagnetic CuAlO$_2$-based DMS. Then, $\Delta E=TE$(paramagnetic state)-TE(ferromagnetic state) are calculated. These ΔE's allow us to estimate the T_C by using the classical Heisenberg model within the mean-field approximation. T_C's are calculated for x=0.025, 0.05, 0.075, 0.10 and 0.125 on Mg, and for x=0.025, 0.05 and 0.075 on Si.

CP893, *Physics of Semiconductors, 28th International Conference*
edited by W. Jantsch and F. Schäffler

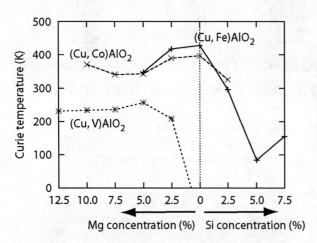

FIGURE 2. Curie temperature of $(Cu_{0.95}, V_{0.05})(Al_{1-x}, Mg_x)O_2$ (dotted lines), $(Cu_{0.95}, Fe_{0.05})(Al_{1-x}, X_x)O_2$ (solid lines) and $(Cu_{0.95}, Co_{0.05})(Al_{1-x}, X_x)O_2$ (dashed lines), where X denotes Mg or Si, as a function of x (carrier density).

FIGURE 2 shows calculated Curie temperatures of $(Cu_{0.95}, V_{0.05})(Al_{1-x}, Mg_x)O_2$, $(Cu_{0.95}, Fe_{0.05})(Al_{1-x}, X_x)O_2$ and $(Cu_{0.95}, Co_{0.05})(Al_{1-x}, X_x)O_2$. As shown in FIG. 2, it is found that, in case of (Cu, Fe)(Al, X)O_2 and (Cu, V)(Al, Mg)O_2, T_C values change dramatically as changing the carrier concentration by Mg or Si doping. In contrast to these systems, (Cu, Co)(Al, X)O_2 system is remarkably insensitive to carrier doping.

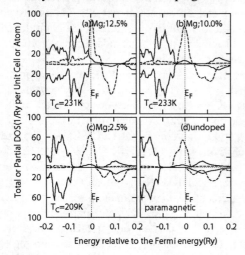

FIGURE 3. Total DOS per unit cell (solid lines) and partial density of V-d states per V atom (dashed lines) in ferromagnetic (Cu, V)AlO$_2$. (a)Mg: 12.5%, (b)Mg: 10.0% and (c)Mg: 2.5% are additionally introduced into (Cu, V)AlO$_2$. In (d), no additional carrier doping treatment is performed.

In order to investigate the origin of the ferromagnetism in CuAlO$_2$-based DMS, density of states (DOS) in each $(Cu_{0.95}, V_{0.05})(Al_{1-x}, Mg_x)O_2$ (x=0, 0.025, 0.10 and 0.125) is calculated. FIGURE 3 shows DOS's in the ferromagnetic state. As shown in FIG. 3, as increas-

ing the hole concentration by Mg doping, the Fermi level is shifted to lower energy region. As a result, the Fermi level gradually approaches around the center of V-d-states, leading to the more contribution of ferromagnetism due to double-exchange interaction. In case of FIG. 3 (d), however, V-d-states of the down-spin side hybridize with host conduction band, so that paramagnetic state stabilize because of the contribution of antiferromagnetic superexchange interaction caused by bandwidth broadening. Next, in case of FIG. 3 (a) and (b), in spite of hole doping, T_C shows not so many changes. Here the V-d-states hybridize with host valence band (FIG. 3 (a)). Therefore, the doped holes occupy not only V-d-states but host valence states. As a result, the T_C between FIG. 3 (a) and (b) is less sensitive to hole doping as compared to FIG. 3 (c) and (d). The behavior of T_C in carrier doped (Cu, Fe)AlO$_2$ and (Cu, Co)AlO$_2$ can be also understood above explanations.

We have investigated the electronic structure of carrier doped CuAlO$_2$ based DMS and estimated T_C's from KKR-CPA-LSDA total energy calculations within the mean-field approximation. It was shown that in case of (Cu, Fe)AlO$_2$ and (Cu, V)AlO$_2$, T_C values changed dramatically as changing the carrier concentration. In contrast to these systems, (Cu, Co)AlO$_2$ system was remarkably insensitive to carrier doping. These behaviors could be understood by competition between double exchange and superexchange interaction mechanism. For accurate estimation of T_C, Monte Carlo simulations with realistic exchange coupling constants are desirable. Such kind of calculation is now under preparation.

ACKNOWLEDGMENTS

This research was partially supported by a Grant-in-Aid for Scientific Research in Priority Areas "Quantum Simulators and Quantum Design" (No. 17064014) and "Semiconductor Nanospintronics", a Grand-in-Aid for Scientific Research for young researchers, JST-CREST, NEDO-nanotech, the 21st Century COE and the JSPS core-to-core program "Computational Nano-materials Design".

REFERENCES

1. H. Kizaki, K. Sato, A. Yanase and H. Katayama-Yoshida, *Jpn. J. Appl. Phys.*, **44** (2005) 1187.
2. H. Kawazoe, M. Yasukawa, H. Hyodo, M. Kurita, H. Yanagi and H. Hosono, *Nature*, **389** (1997) 939.
3. T. Epicier and C. Esnouf, *Philos. Mag. Lett.*, **61** (1990) 285.
4. H. Akai, http://sham.phys.sci.osaka-u.ac.jp/kkr/
5. R. W. G. Wyckoff: *Crystal Structures*(Wiley, New York, 1986) 2nd ed., Vol. 1 *p*.292

Spin photocurrent and current-induced spin polarization in an InGaAs/InAlAs two-dimensional electron gas

Chunlei Yang,[1] Lu Ding,[1] Hongtao He,[1] Lijie Cui,[2] Yiping Zeng,[2] Jiannong Wang,[1] and Weikun Ge[1*]

[1]*Department of Physics, Hong Kong University of Science and Technology, Kowloon, Hong Kong, China*
[2]*Institute of Semiconductors, Chinese Academy of Sciences, P.O. Box 921, Beijing 100083, China*

Abstract. Spin photocurrent and current-induced spin polarization were experimentally observed in a two-dimensional electron gas with Rashba spin splitting. The sign of the spin photocurrent was found to be strongly dependent on the polarization, the incidence angle and the wavelength of the laser. The relative ratio of the spin photocurrent (or Kerr rotation signal intensity) in different samples is in good agreement with the ratio of the Rashba coefficient determined by the SdH oscillation, which reveals the same mechanism behind the spin photocurrent and current-induced spin polarization.

Keywords: Spin photocurrent, current-induced spin polarization, Rashba spin-orbit coupling.
PACS: 72.25.Fe, 72.25.Pn

The structural inversion asymmetry (SIA) induced spin-orbit coupling (Rashba interaction [1]) in a two-dimensional electron gas (2DEG) system has attracted more and more attention due to its potential applications in spintronics devices [2]. The zero field spin splitting in a Rashba system is expected to bring the converse effects of spin photocurrent [3, 4] and current-induced spin polarization [5, 6] in a two-dimensional electron gas system.

We report the experimental evidence of circularly polarized optical-excitation-induced spin photocurrent in (001) grown InGaAs/InAlAs 2DEGs under oblique incidence of radiation for interband excitation, which is 2 orders of magnitude stronger than similar observations using far-infrared excitation for intersubband transitions. The current-induced spin polarization in the same samples is measured using the Kerr rotation experiment. These results are consistent with the spin splitting of the energy bands as examined by the beating of the Shubnikov–de Haas (SdH) oscillations.

Two samples (named D and E) studied here were $In_xGa_{1-x}As/In_{0.52}Al_{0.48}As$ 2DEGs grown on semi-insulating (001) InP substrate with well thickness of 14 nm. The SIA was achieved by δ–doping of only one side of the barrier layer (on top of the well). Sample E was grown with a graded indium composition from 0.53 to 0.75 for the quantum well, instead of the uniform indium composition of 0.70 for sample D.

Hall measurements at 1.6 K showed that the carrier concentration was 1.5×10^{12} cm^{-2} and 1.4×10^{12} cm^{-2} for samples D and E, respectively. The SdH oscillations allow us to determine the Rashba spin-orbit interaction parameter α [7] of the value of 3.0×10^{-12} eVm and 6.3×10^{-12} eVm for samples D and E, respectively.

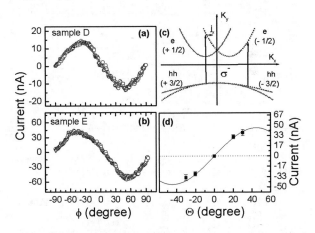

FIG. 1 **(a)** and **(b)** are the polarization angle dependence of the spin photocurrent in the 2DEG sample D and E, respectively, with oblique incidence angle of 30^0 and laser power of 100 mW (λ=880nm) at 10 K. **(c)** is a schematic diagram with spin-split valence and conduction bands to show the microscopic origin of the spin photocurrent. **(d)** is the incidence angle dependence of the spin photocurrent.

Figs. 1 (a) and (b) show the dependence of the photocurrent of the two samples on the laser beam

CP893, *Physics of Semiconductors, 28th International Conference*
edited by W. Jantsch and F. Schäffler
© 2007 American Institute of Physics 978-0-7354-0397-0/07/$23.00

polarization, represented by angle ϕ between the optical axis of the $\lambda/4$ modulator and the polarization plane of the incident light, with $\lambda=880$ nm. It clearly shows that when ϕ changes from $-\pi/4$ to $+\pi/4$, the current varies from one maximum to the other maximum of opposite direction, in good agreement with the fitting using $\sin2\phi$ [3, 4]. This reveals that the spin photocurrent changes its sign when the light changes its polarization. Inter-band excitation using circularly polarized light will produce a spin photocurrent, for which the microscopic mechanism [4] can be schematically described as shown in fig. 1(c). The imbalanced momentum relaxation of electrons in the conduction band results in a net current due to the absorption of the circularly polarized light. Fig. 1(d) shows the incidence angle dependence of the spin photocurrent. At normal incidence, since there is no y-component of optically induced electron spin polarization, no current is created. With the increase of Θ, leading to a larger y-component of the electron spin polarization, the spin photocurrent first gets larger but finally gets smaller because of the increased reflection.

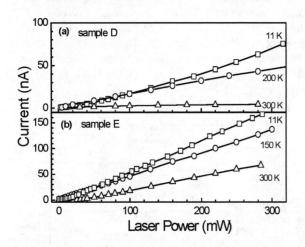

Fig 2. Laser power dependence of the spin photocurrent for sample D **(a)** and sample E **(b)** at various temperatures.

Furthermore, we find that the photocurrent is almost linearly dependent on the laser power, as shown in Fig 2. For sample D, the current drops faster when the temperature is higher than 200 K, leaving a very small signal at 300 K. But for sample E, the current only drops about a factor of 4 from 11 K to room temperature. We believe that the larger photocurrent of sample E is due to its much larger spin splitting, as also revealed by the SdH experiment. In addition to the incident direction and the polarization dependence of the spin photocurrent, we have found that it also changes its direction when the laser wavelength is changed [8]. Due to the selection rules for light hole and heavy hole (such as $-3/2 \rightarrow -1/2$ for

heavy hole, $-1/2 \rightarrow +1/2$ for light hole with $\Delta j = +1$), electrons excited from the heavy hole and the light hole bands by the same circularly polarized light will jump to opposite spin splitting branches ($+1/2$ or $-1/2$) in the conduction band, which will result in reversed current in the SIA case.

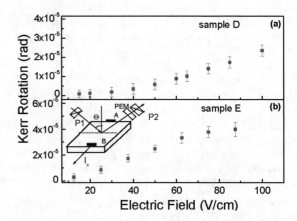

FIG. 3 Electric field (E_x) dependence of the Kerr rotation of sample D **(a)** and E **(b)** to show the currentinduced spin polarization S_y at 10 K. The experimental setup is schematically shown in the inset of Fig. 3(b), of which $P1$ and $P2$ represent the polarizer and analyzer, respectively.

Kerr effect was used to monitor the spin polarization along the y-direction under an external electric field in the x-direction, as shown in the inset of Fig. 3. The Kerr rotation was extracted from the signal difference between positive and negative electric fields. The detected Kerr signal increases with the increase of the external field, which is in agreement with the theoretical prediction that the spin polarization S_y is proportional to E_x [5, 6]. This experiment shows that there is another choice to take non-magnetic semiconductor as the spin source for spintronic devices using spin-orbit coupling. .

References

[1] S. Datta and B. Das, Appl. Phys. Lett. **56**, 665 (1990).
[2] Y. A. Bychkov and E. I. Rashba, J. Phys. C **17**, 6039 (1984).
[3] S. D. Ganichev, E. L. Ivchenko, S. N. Danilov, J. Eroms, W. Wegscheider, D. Weiss, and W. Prettl, Phys. Rev. Lett. **86**, 4358 (2001).
[4] S. D. Ganichev and W. Prettl, J. Phys. Condens. Matter **15**, R935 (2003), and references therein.
[5] V. M. Edelstein, Solid State Commun. **73**, 233 (1990).
[6] J. I. Inoue, G. E.W. Bauer, and L.W. Molenkamp, Phys. Rev. B **67**, 033104 (2003).
[7] G. Engels, J. Lange, Th. Schapers, and H. Luth, Phys. Rev. B **55**, R1958 (1997); J. Appl. Phys. **83**, 4324 (1998).
[8] C. L. Yang, H. T. He, Lu Ding, L. J. Cui, Y. P. Zeng, J. N. Wang, and W. K. Ge, Phys. Rev. Lett. **96**, 186605 (2006).

Scattering Induced Spin Separation at Zero Bias

S.D. Ganichev[1], V.V. Bel'kov[1,2], S.A. Tarasenko[2], S.N. Danilov[1], S. Giglberger[1], Ch. Hoffmann[1], E.L. Ivchenko[2], D. Weiss[1], C. Gerl[1], D. Schuh[1], W. Wegscheider[1], W. Prettl[1]

[1] *University of Regensburg, Regensburg, Germany 93040*
[2] *A.F. Ioffe Physico-Technical Institute, Russian Academy of Sciences, St. Petersburg, Russia 194021*

Abstract. We show that in gyrotropic semiconductor structures spin-dependent asymmetry of electron scattering induces a spin separation which, in contrast to the spin Hall effect, does not require an electric current to flow. The effect is observed in GaAs/AlGaAs quantum well structures at free-carrier absorption of terahertz (THz) radiation. Microscopic theory based on asymmetry of photoexcitation and relaxation is developed being in a good agreement with experiment.

Keywords: Spin photocurrents, Drude absorption, Spin-dependent scattering.
PACS: 73.21.Fg, 72.25.Fe, 78.67.De.

INTRODUCTION

The spin-orbit coupling provides a versatile tool to generate and manipulate the spin degree of freedom in low-dimensional semiconductor structures. The spin Hall effect, where an electrical current drives a transverse spin current and causes a nonequilibrium spin accumulation near the sample boundary, the spin-galvanic effect, where a nonequilibrium spin polarization drives an electric current or the reverse process, in which an electrical current generates a nonequilibrium spin polarization, are all consequences of spin-orbit coupling. In order to observe a spin Hall effect a bias driven current is an essential prerequisite.

Here we provide evidence for an elementary effect causing spin separation which is fundamentally different from that of the spin Hall effect. In contrast to the latter it requires no an electric current to flow: it is spin separation achieved by spin-dependent scattering of electrons in media with suitable symmetry. We show that by free carrier (Drude) absorption of terahertz radiation spin separation is achieved in a wide range of temperatures. Moreover the experimental results show that simple electron gas heating by any means is already sufficient to yield spin separation due to spin-dependent energy relaxation processes of nonequilibrium carriers.

To demonstrate an existence of the pure spin current due to asymmetric scattering we converted the spin current into an electric current. It is obtained by application of a magnetic field which polarizes spins.

MODEL

It is well known that in gyrotropic quantum well structures spin degeneracy in the band structure is removed due to bulk inversion asymmetry (BIA) or structure inversion asymmetry (SIA). This property is crucial for spintronic allowing spin manipulation by external electric field and giving rise to various spin-dependent phenomena. Formally removal of spin degeneracy is described by **k**-linear terms in the electron effective Hamiltonian.

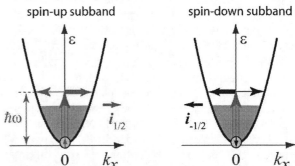

FIGURE 1. Microscopic picture of the photoexcitation asymmetry.

While removal of spin degeneracy is well known practically unknown is the fact that in gyrotropic media also electron-phonon interaction becomes to be spin dependent. Indeed, due to the same arguments electron-phonon interaction also have an asymmetric part described by **k**-linear terms. In contrast to the

CP893, *Physics of Semiconductors, 28th International Conference*
edited by W. Jantsch and F. Schäffler

previous examples it does not modify the single-electron spectrum but can give rise to spin-dependent effects, like spin currents. The microscopic mechanism of the effect is related to the asymmetry of optical excitation and requires Drude absorption of radiation. Indirect optical transitions are accompanied by a momentum transfer from static defects or phonons to electrons. A spin current induced by these transitions appears due to asymmetry of the scattering processes in the k-space. The asymmetry results in nonequal rates of indirect optical transitions for opposite wave vectors within each spin subband. This causes flows $i_{\pm 1/2}$ of electrons in the spin-up and spin-down subbands, as sketched in Fig. 1, left and right panels, respectively. Here, the different thicknesses of the horizontal arrows indicate the difference in electron-phonon interaction strength for positive and negative wave vectors. The flows $i_{+1/2}$ and $i_{-1/2}$ are oppositely directed because the electron-phonon asymmetry is spin dependent and changes its sign from one band to another. Therefore the net electric current vanishes. To reveal the spin flux, we apply an external magnetic field which results, due to the Zeeman effect, in different equilibrium populations of the spin subbands. The currents flowing in the opposite directions become nonequivalent, leading to a spin-polarized net electric current. A characteristic feature of the mechanism caused by optical excitation is the sensitivity to the light polarization.

EXPERIMENTAL RESULTS

The experiments are carried out on (001)-oriented n-type GaAs/AlGaAs heterostructures. A molecular THz laser has been used as radiation source delivering 100 ns pulses with a radiation power up to 1 kW. Several lines in the wavelength range between 77 and 496 μm have been selected. The terahertz radiation causes indirect optical transitions within the lowest size-quantized subband. The samples are irradiated under normal incidence along the growth direction. The magnetic field B is applied parallel to the heterostructure interface. In experiments the angle α between the polarization vector of the linearly polarized light and the magnetic field is varied. The photocurrent is measured both in the direction perpendicular and parallel to the magnetic field.

Irradiation of the samples at $B = 0$ does not lead to any photocurrent. A current response is obtained only when a magnetic field is applied. The current detected in two directions, perpendicular and parallel to the in-plane magnetic field, increases linearly with B due to the increasing spin polarization and changes sign upon reversal of the magnetic field direction.

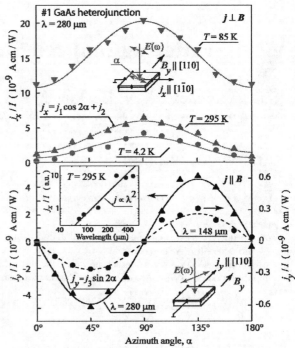

FIGURE 2. Photocurrents as a function of azimuth angle α at different temperatures, $B = 0.3$ T.

The photocurrent is measured as a function of magnetic field, temperature, mobility, carrier concentration and polarization of radiation. The polarization dependence of the current in the longitudinal geometry is described by $\sin 2\alpha$, while it follows a $\cos 2\alpha$ dependence for the transverse geometry, see Fig. 2. The observed polarization dependencies of the photocurrent correspond to that given by phenomenological considerations. With increasing the radiation wavelength the current raises as a wavelength square.

Microscopic analysis taking into account the scattering asymmetry-induced contribution to the photocurrent is carried out being in a good agreement with experiments. All main experimental properties of the terahertz photocurrent, namely magnetic field, temperature, mobility, and concentration dependencies provide evidence that the observed photocurrent is solely determined by the spin degree of freedom. It can only be understood if the photocurrent is proportional to the equilibrium spin polarization.

REFERENCES

1. S. D. Ganichev *et al.*, arXiv: cond mat 0605556 (2006).
2. V. V. Bel'kov *et al.*, *J. Phys.: Condens. Matter* **17**, 3405 (2005).
3. S. A. Tarasenko and E. L. Ivchenko, *JETP Letters* **81**, 231 (2005).

Electrical spin injection in light emitting Schottky diodes based on InGaAs /GaAs QW heterostructures

N.V. Baidus[1,3], M.I. Vasilevskiy[1], M.J.M. Gomes[1], V.D. Kulakovskii[2], S.V. Zaitsev[2], M.V. Dorokhin[3], P.B. Demina[3], E.A. Uskova[3] and B.N. Zvonkov[3]

[1]Centro de Física, Universidade do Minho, Braga, Portugal
[2]Institute of Solid State Physics, RAS, Chernogolovka, Russia
[3]Physical-Technical Research Institute, N.I. Lobachevskii University, Nihzniy Novgorod, Russia

We demonstrate efficient hole spin injection from a ferromagnetic metal (Ni) contact in a forward biased light emitting Schottky diode (LESD) fabricated on a GaAs based heterostructure with a quantum well (QW). The spin polarization of injected holes was detected by measuring circular polarization of the electroluminescence (EL) from the near surface InGaAs/GaAs QW. An intermediate gold layer has been used in order to improve the spin injection efficiency. Over 40% degree of circular polarization of the EL has been observed at T= 2 K for the LESD structure with Au-Ni-Au Schottky contact.

Keywords: hole spin injection, Schottky diode, quantum well
PACS: 72.25.Hg, 72.25.Mk

INTRODUCTION

Efficient spin injection into semiconductors and spin transport through metal-semiconductor interfaces are of great importance for spintronics [1]. It is typically studied by measuring circular polarization of the heterostructure's electroluminescence (EL). Despite the low quantum efficiency of the EL from Schottky diodes (SD's), conductivity mismatch problem and problems related with the ferromagnetic metal (FM)-GaAs interface, the electrical injection of spin polarized carriers has been observed in several works [1-2].

In an earlier work [3] we have shown the possibility to realize considerable EL in a forward biased Au-SD´s based on InAs/GaAs quantum-size heterostructures. Here we investigated the EL of InGaAs/GaAs QW heterostructures with Ni and Au/Ni/Au Schottky contacts in magnetic fields up to 10 T. We demonstrate that this emission is caused by the injection of spin polarized holes into the semiconductor.

EXPERIMENTAL

The structures were grown on n-GaAs substrates by MOVPE at atmospheric pressure. An $In_xGa_{1-x}As$/GaAs QW (thickness of 6 nm and x = 0.16) was placed some 20 nm below the surface. A FM Schottky contact (0.5 mm in diameter) was made by deposition of nickel or a three layer Au/Ni/Au film. A similar structure with nonmagnetic Au contact was used as a reference sample.

The EL measurements were performed under forward bias at 1.8 K using a superconducting magnet. The experiments were carried out in Faraday geometry, with the magnetic field normal to sample surface.

RESULTS AND DISCUSSION

The degree of circular polarization was determined as $P=(I_+-I_-)/(I_++I_-)$, where $I_+(I_-)$ is the EL intensity of the right (left) circularly polarized component obtained by integrating the area under the corresponding part of a spectrum.

CP893, *Physics of Semiconductors, 28th International Conference*
edited by W. Jantsch and F. Schäffler
© 2007 American Institute of Physics 978-0-7354-0397-0/07/$23.00

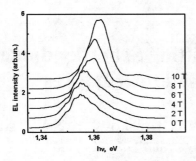

FIGURE 1. EL spectra of SD with Ni contact at 1.8K for different values of magnetic field (σ^+ polarization).

The peculiarity of EL from a forward biased SD with n-type GaAs is the injection of holes from the metal into the semiconductor. The EL properties of such structures without magnetic field were described in [3]. The dependence of the integrated EL intensity on forward bias is a quadratic function. This fact is accounted for the mechanism involving the hole injection by tunneling through a thin oxide layer existing at the metal-semiconductor interface [4].

Fig. 1 displays typical EL spectra obtained for structures with Ni Schottky contacts. The magnetic field (B) leads to an increase of the EL intensity and a blue shift of the EL band related to the electron-hole radiative recombination in the InGaAs QW. The magnetic field also splits the band into a number of peaks corresponding to the electron-hole transitions between different Landau levels (LL's). With the increase of B, the higher energy emission peaks disappear due to emptying of the upper LL's in the conduction band.

Fig. 2 demonstrates that the QW emission is circularly polarized. The degree of circular polarization (P) is highest at the main peak (corresponding to the lowest LL for electrons). Fig. 2 shows a non-monotonous dependence of P on the magnetic field with a local minimum at 5–6 T and maximum at 7.5–9 T for different samples. The positions of the minima and maxima are practically independent of the operating current. This type of $P(B)$ dependence is characteristic of all the investigated SD's including those with non-magnetic contact, therefore we think that the oscillations originate from the properties of the electron gas in the QW in the magnetic field and not from those of the injector.

The polarization degree strongly depends on the FM type and the quality of the metal-semiconductor interface. The maximum polarization degree (42%) was observed for a SD with Au/Ni/Au contact, compared to approximately 10% for the reference sample.

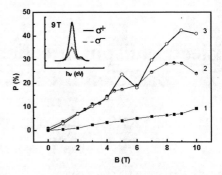

FIGURE 2. Circular polarization degree dependence on magnetic field: SD's with different Schottky contacts: 1-Au, 2 - Ni, 3 – Au/Ni/Au. The inset shows the EL spectra measured at 9 T for two circular polarizations.

There are several effects that contribute to the circular polarization of the EL in magnetic field. First, the Zeeman splitting of the hole energy levels in the QW leads to a difference between the population of spin-up and spin-down levels and, hence, to different intensities of σ^+ and σ^- EL components. This explains the results for SD's with Au contacts. The reason for the highly enhanced EL polarization in the case of SD's with FM contacts must be the spin polarized hole injection into the QW.

Thus, we have demonstrated the high circular polarization of the EL from QW heterostructures with a FM Schottky contact indicating an efficient spin injection. The degree of circular polarization is a non-monotonic function of the magnetic field originating from several processes, such as the filling of electron LL's in the QW.

ACKNOWLEDGMENTS

This work was supported by FCT (Portugal) through Project POCTI/FIS/58524/2004. NVB wishes to acknowledge FCT fellowship SFRH / BPD / 14436 / 2003.

REFERENCES

1. I. Zutič, J. Fabian, and S. Das Sarma, *Rev. Mod. Phys.* **76**, 323 (2004).
2. V. F. Motsnyi, P. Van Dorpe, W. Van Roy, E. Goovaerts, V. I. Safarov, G. Borghs and J. De Boeck, *Phys. Rev. B.* **68**, 245319 (2003).
3. N. V. Baidus, P. B. Demina, M. V. Dorokhin, B. N. Zvonkov, E. I. Malysheva, and E. A. Uskova, Semiconductors, **39**, 17 (2005).
4. H. C. Card, E. H. Rhoderick, *Solid State Electronics*, **16**, 365 (1973).

Effects of Spin-Dependent Tunneling in III-V Semiconductor Heterostructures

I. N. Yassievich, P. S. Alekseev, S. A. Tarasenko and V. I. Perel'

A.F. Ioffe Physico-Technical Institute, 194021 St. Petersburg, Russia

Abstract. Theory of spin-dependent tunneling of conduction electrons in III-V heterostructures has been developed. The dependence of the tunneling process on the electron spin orientation leads to (i) spin polarization of the carriers transmitted through the barrier under oblique incidence and (ii) generation of an in-plane electric current under tunneling of spin-polarized carriers. The effects become stronger in double-barrier structures where the tunneling via resonant spin-split levels can be controlled by applying the gate voltage.

Keywords: Electron tunneling, Spin-orbit interaction, Resonant states
PACS: 72.25.Dc, 72.25.Mk, 73.61.Ey

INTRODUCTION

Physics of spin-dependent-tunneling phenomena in semiconductor heterostructures has attracted a great deal of attention. Such an interest is stimulated by possibilities of using the tunneling structures for spintronic applications. Significant progress has been made in experimental and theoretical investigation of spin-polarized transport in magnetic tunneling junctions. On the other hand, it has been pointed out that electron tunneling could be spin dependent even in nonmagnetic semiconductor structures [1, 2, 3, 4, 5, 6].

Here we present a theory of spin-dependent tunneling of electrons in symmetrical heterostructures based on III-V compounds. The process of tunneling is spin-dependent because of lack of the inversion center in zinc-blende-lattice semiconductors. Microscopically, the effect originates from k-cubic (Dresselhaus) spin-orbit splitting of electron states. The effect of spin-dependent tunneling could be employed for spin injection and detection of spin-polarized carriers by electrical means.

MICROSCOPIC ORIGIN

We consider the transmission of electrons from the left region of the tunneling structure (emitter) to the right region (collector). The effective Hamiltonian of conduction electrons in zinc-blend-lattice semiconductors contains the spin-dependent k-cubic Dresselhaus term. In the case, where the electron kinetic energy is substantial smaller than the band offsets, the main spin-dependent contribution to the effective Hamiltonian has the form [6]:

$$H_D = \gamma(\sigma_x k_x - \sigma_y k_y)\frac{\partial^2}{\partial z^2}, \qquad (1)$$

where γ is a material constant, σ_x and σ_y are the Pauli matrices, $x\|[100]$ and $y\|[010]$ are the coordinates in the interface plane, and $z\|[001]$ is the growth direction. Essentially, H_D induces a spin-dependent correction to the effective electron mass along z. It is the correction that determines the spin-dependent tunneling because particles with different effective masses tunnel through the structure with the different probabilities.

The Hamiltonian (1) is diagonalized by spinors which correspond to the electron states "+" and "−" with the opposite spins. The orientations of the electron spins $\mathbf{s}_\pm$ in the states "+" and "−" depend on the direction of the wave vector with respect to the crystallographic axes

$$\mathbf{s}_\pm = (1/2)\left(\ \mp k_x/k_\|, \quad \pm k_y/k_\|, \quad 0\ \right), \qquad (2)$$

where $\mathbf{k}_\| = (k_x, k_y, 0)$ is the wave vector in the interface plane. Solution of the Schrödinger equation with the term (1) included in the Hamiltonian allows one to derive coefficients of transmission $t_\pm$ and reflection $r_\pm$ for carriers with the spins $\mathbf{s}_\pm$. Calculations of the spin-dependent transmission coefficients for single-barrier and resonant double-barrier structures based on zinc-blende-lattice semiconductors have been carried out in Ref. [6] and Ref. [7], respectively.

Under normal incidence of electrons, $k_x, k_y = 0$, the spin-orbit term (1) vanishes and the transmission coefficients t_+ and t_- coincide. However, for oblique tunneling, when $k_\| \neq 0$, the transparency does depend on the spin orientation. In the case of electron tunneling through a single-barrier structure, the polarization efficiency $\mathscr{P} = (|t_+|^2 - |t_-|^2)/(|t_+|^2 + |t_-|^2)$ is given by

$$\mathscr{P} = \tanh\left(2\gamma\frac{m^* k_\|}{\hbar^2} a q_0\right),$$

where m^* is an effective electron mass in the barrier layer, a is the barrier width and q_0 is the reciprocal length

CP893, *Physics of Semiconductors, 28th International Conference*
edited by W. Jantsch and F. Schäffler

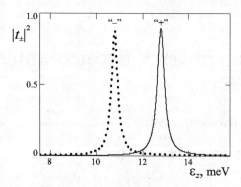

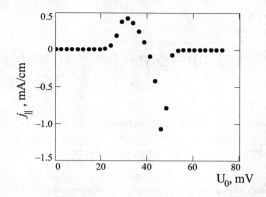

FIGURE 1. Dependencies of the transmission coefficients $|t_\pm|^2$ on ε_z for the in-plane wave vector $k_\parallel = 10^6$ cm^{-1}. The curves correspond to Al$_x$Ga$_{1-x}$Sb double-barrier heterostructure with aluminium contents in banks $x = 0.15$, in barriers $x = 0.3$ and in the well $x = 0$, the well width 2.6 nm, the barrier width 6.0 nm, and the gate voltage $U_0 = 24$ mV [8].

FIGURE 2. Gate voltage dependence of the interface current $j_\parallel$. The dependence corresponds to Al$_x$Ga$_{1-x}$Sb double-barrier heterostructure described in the caption to Fig. 1, the temperature 9 K, the electron density $1.8 \cdot 10^{18}$ cm^{-3}, and the spin polarization degree 10% [8].

of decay of the wave function in the barrier. Increase of the barrier width a leads to enhancement of the polarization efficiency $\mathscr{P}$ but drastically decreases the barrier transparency, hampering practical application of the single-barrier structures.

In double-barrier structures the tunneling occurs mainly via resonant levels which are formed in a quantum well between the barriers. At finite wave vector $k_\parallel$ the levels are spin split. This is shown in Fig. 1 where the dependencies of the double-barrier structure transparency $|t_\pm|^2$ on the incident electron energy along the growth direction $\varepsilon_z = \hbar^2 k_z^2 / 2m^*$ is plotted for the fixed in-plane wave vector $k_\parallel$. Tunneling of carriers with the wave vector $\mathbf{k}_\parallel \neq 0$ via the spin levels leads to spin polarization of the transmitted carriers and can be controlled by applying the gate voltage [8].

TUNNELING SPIN-GALVANIC EFFECT

Generation of an electric current by spin-polarized carriers represents the effect inverse to the spin injection. Now we assume the electrons, which tunnel from the emitter to the collector, to be partially spin-polarized. Spin-dependent asymmetry of tunneling leads to the in-plane flow of the transmitted electrons near the barrier, i.e. to the interface electric current $\mathbf{j}_\parallel$. The direction of this interface current is determined by the spin orientation of the electrons and symmetry properties of the barrier. In particular, the current $\mathbf{j}_\parallel$ reverses its direction if the spin orientation changes the sign. Theory of the tunneling spin-galvanic effect has been developed in Ref. [9] by using the spin-density-matrix technique. In Refs. [7, 8] the theory has been extended for resonant tunneling in double-barrier structures. Figure 2 presents the gate voltage dependence of the interface current $j_\parallel$ calculated

numerically for Al$_x$Ga$_{1-x}$Sb double-barrier heterostructure. The gate voltage dependence of the interface current reveals resonant non-monotone behavior.

In conclusion, theory of spin-dependent tunneling of conduction electrons is developed for heterostructures grown from III-V semiconductor compounds. The effect of the spin-dependent tunneling could be employed for creating spin injectors and detectors based on nonmagnetic tunneling structures.

ACKNOWLEDGMENTS

This work was supported by the RFBR, the DFG, programs of the RAS and "Dynasty" Foundation.

REFERENCES

1. A. Zakharova, F.T. Vasko, and V. Ryzhii, *J. Phys.: Condens. Matter* **6**, 7537 (1994).
2. A. Voskoboynikov, S.S. Liu, and C.P. Lee, *Phys. Rev. B* **58**, 15397 (1998); *ibid* **59**, 12514 (1999).
3. E.A. de Andrada e Silva, G.C. La Rocca, *Phys. Rev. B* **59**, 15583 (1999).
4. T. Koga, J. Nitta, Y. Takayanagi, and S. Datta, *Phys. Rev. Lett.* **88**, 126601 (2002).
5. A.E. Botha and M.R. Singh, *Phys. Rev. B* **67**, 195334 (2003).
6. V.I. Perel', S.A. Tarasenko, I.N. Yassievich, S.D. Ganichev, V.V. Bel'kov, and W. Prettl, *Phys. Rev. B* **67**, 201304 (2003).
7. M.M. Glazov, P.S. Alekseev, M.A. Odnobludov, V.M. Chistyakov, S.A. Tarasenko, and I.N. Yassievich, *Phys. Rev. B* **71**, 155313 (2005).
8. P.S. Alekseev, V.M. Chistyakov, and I.N. Yassievich, *Semiconductors* **40** (December 2006).
9. S. A. Tarasenko, V.I. Perel', and I.N. Yassievich, *Phys. Rev. Lett.* **93**, 056601 (2004).

Drastic Magnetoresistance Enhancement on Spin-Dependent -Transport and Appearance of Spin-Glass-Like Behavior for Magnetite Nanoparticle Sinter Calcined at Low Temperature

H. Kobori [1], K. Ohnishi[1], A. Sugimura[1] and T. Taniguchi[2]

[1] Department of Physics, Faculty of Science and Engineering, Konan University, Japan

[2] Department of Earth and Space Science, Graduate School of Science, Osaka University, Japan

Abstract. We have studied the spin-dependent-transport and magnetization for magnetite nanoparticle sinter (MNPS) calcined at low temperature. As compared with a bulk crystal, the drastic enhancement of negative differential magnetoresistance has been obtained for the MNPS. Below the Verwey transition temperature, we have observed the difference of magnetization between zero-field-cooling and field-cooling. This phenomenon indicates that localized spins in amorphous-like grain-boundary region in the MNPS are spin-glass-like.

Keywords: magnetite, nanoparticle, spin, transport, magnetoresistance, spin glass.
PACS: 71.55.Jv, 72.25.-b, 72.25.Mk, 75.10.Nr, 75.47.-m

INTRODUCTION

Decreasing the diameter of a magnetite particle, it has been reported that a single magnetic domain is formed in the particle below ~100nm, and it shows the super-paramagnetic behavior below ~20nm. For the assembly of randomly spin-polarized magnetite nano-particles, we expect a large negative change of magneto-resistance (MR), because of the half-metallicity of magnetite. The large differential negative magneto-resistance (ND-MR) leads to the possibility of the application to a high sensitive magneto-sensor. In this case, the inter-grain and intra-grain-boundary conduction is considered to be important. The NDMR for the assembly of magnetite particles has been reported for powder compacts and poly-crystalline thin films [1]. In this paper, we present the study of physical properties of the MR and magnetization for magnetite nano-particle sinter (MNPS) calcined at low temperature. The magnetization measurement has been carried out with zero-field-cooling (ZFC) and field-cooling (FC) with 0.1T. The experimental results that we have obtained are compared with those of the bulk crystal.

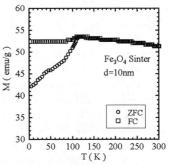

FIGURE 1. The magnetization of the MNPS for zero-field-cooling and field-cooling with 0.1T.

EXPERIMENTAL PROCEDURES

The magnetite nano-particles (MNP's) were prepared by the chemical wet synthesis, and the average diameter of those is ~10nm. The magnetite nano-particle sinter (MNPS) were made of the compacted MNP's by the heat-treatment at 500°C for 5 hours in the atmosphere of Ar(90%)/H$_2$(10%) gas. The MNPS samples were set to the closed-cycle He refrigerator and the temperature were varied between 4K and 250K. The magnetic field were applied to

CP893, *Physics of Semiconductors, 28th International Conference*
edited by W. Jantsch and F. Schäffler
© 2007 American Institute of Physics 978-0-7354-0397-0/07/$23.00

MNPS samples up to 0.7T by utilizing the electromagnet. The magnetization measurements were performed by use of the superconducting quantum interference device (SQUID).

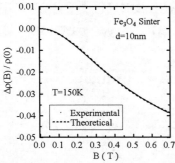

FIGURE 2. The change of magneto-resistivity for the MNPS at 150K.

RESULTS AND DISCUSSION

Magnetite is a ferri-magnetic material and the Curie temperature is 585°C. It is a mixed-valence iron oxide and has an inverse spinel cubic structure. The unit cell contains 8 units AB_2O_4, with 8 A-sites, 16 B-sites and 32 oxygens. The tetrahedral 4-coordinated A-site is occupied by Fe^{3+}, whereas the octahedral 6-coordinated B-site is occupied by Fe^{3+} and Fe^{2+}. The electrical conduction is caused by the hopping of a conduction electron with the minority spin from Fe^{2+} to Fe^{3+} in B-site. Fe^{3+} in B-site includes 5 d-electrons with the majority spin. The temperature dependence of the resistivity of the MNPS did not show the indication of the Verwey transition. The Verwey transition is a temperature-induced metal-insulator transition, and the electrical resistivity abruptly increases by 2 orders of magnitude at 123K with decreasing the temperature. We consider that the MNPS contains the large region of amorphous-like grain-boundary. The electrical conduction is mainly dominated by the grain-boundary conduction (GBC), as compared with the inter-grain conduction (IGC). In this model, localized spin orientation in grain-boundary is considered to be relatively random. We have found that below ~100K, the MR of the MNPS shows an aging phenomenon. The MR for the magnetic-field-down did not coincide with that of the magnetic-field-up. The MR came to be a smaller value at zero magnetic field for repeated measurements. In addition, we have observed that below ~100K, the magnetization of the MNPS for field-cooling (FC) deviates from that of zero-field-cooling (ZFC). Figure 1 shows the magnetization of the MNPS for ZFC and FC with 0.1T. The difference of magnetization between ZFC and FC increases with decreasing the temperature below ~100K. These phenomena indicate that localized spins in the MNPS are spin-glass (SG) like. Above ~100K, the aging phenomenon of the MR for the MNPS disappeared. Figure 2 shows the change of magneto-resistivity for the MNPS at 150K. The dots and dotted line are the experimental and theoretical results, respectively. Here $\Delta\rho(B)$ means $\rho(B) - \rho(0)$ with the resistivity $\rho(B)$ at the magnetic field B. $\Delta\rho(B)/\rho(0)$ is proportional to $M(B)^2$ at low magnetic field, where $M(B)$ is the magnetization. If we assume the magnetization $M(B)$ is expressed by the Langevin function, $L(\beta) = \coth(\beta) - 1/\beta$, we get

$$\Delta\rho(B)/\rho(0) = \alpha(T)L^2[\gamma(T)B]$$

Here $\alpha(T)$ and $\gamma(T)$ are the temperature dependent parameters. In Fig.2, we find a good agreement between the experimental and theoretical results. The above fact means that although the spin orientation is spatially random like a paramagnet, in a short range spins are relatively ordered like a spin-cluster. Figure 3 shows the temperature dependence of $\Delta\rho(B)/\rho(0)$ at 0.7T for the MNPS. Regarding the experimental results below ~100K, saturated values obtained by sufficiently repeated measurements are used because of the aging phenomenon. It is found that $\Delta\rho(B)/\rho(0)$ at 0.7T shows the maximum (4.0%) at ~110K (near the Verwey transition temperature V_T) for the absolute value. For the bulk crystal, the sharp peak of $\Delta\rho(B)/\rho(0)$ has been observed at the V_T. In addition, $\Delta\rho(B)/\rho(0)$ at 1T and 290K is ~0.1% [2]. Whereas, $\Delta\rho(B)/\rho(0)$ for the MNPS is ~2.3% at 0.7T and 250K. We conclude that the considerable enhancement of the MR on the spin dependent transport is obtained for the magnetite nano-particle sinter as compared with the bulk crystal.

REFERENCES

1. H. Zeng, C.T.Black, R. L. Sandstrom, P. M. Rice, C. B. Murray and S. Sun, *Phys. Rev.* **B73**, 020402-1-4 (2006).
2. M. Ziese and H. J. Blythe, *J. Phys.: Condens. Matter* **12**, 13-28 (2000).

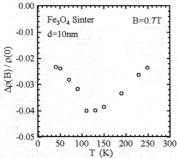

FIGURE 3. The temperature dependence of the change of magneto-resistivity at 0.7T for the MNPS.

Mesoscopic Hall Effect driven by Chiral Spin Order

J. -i. Ohe*, T. Ohtsuki[†] and B. Kramer**

*I. Institut fuer Theoretische Physik Universtitaet Hamburg Jungiusstrasse 9 D-20355 Hamburg, Germany
[†]Department of Physics, Sophia University, Kioi-cho 7-1, Chiyoda-ku, Tokyo 102-8554, Japan
**School of Engineering and Science, International University Bremen, Campus Ring 1, 28757 Bremen, Germany

Abstract. A Hall effect due to the spin chirality in mesoscopic systems is investigated numerically. We consider 4-terminal Hall systems including local spins with vortex domain wall geometry, where strong spin chirality appears near the vortex center. The Fermi energy of the conduction electrons is assumed to be comparable to the exchange coupling energy where the adiabatic approximation cannot be applied. Our results show Hall effect where voltage drop and spin current arise in transverse direction.

Keywords: Anomalous Hall Effect, Spin Hall Effect, Spin Chirality
PACS: 72.25.Dc, 72.10.Fk, 73.23.-b

Recent research on the anomalous Hall effect has shown that spin chirality of local spin system induces Hall conductance via exchange coupling [1]. The anomalous Hall effect can be seen in ferromagnetic metallic systems where the time reversal symmetry (TRS) is broken. When the TRS is preserved, the spin current in transverse direction is driven by a longitudinal voltage drop. Such a spin current, the so-called spin Hall current [2], can be seen in bulk semiconductor systems with a spin-orbit interaction.

In this report, we show that mesoscopic systems with internal chiral magnetic order exhibit Hall effects in such a way that both the charge and the spin Hall conductance occur simultaneously. We consider a 2-dimensional electron system that interacts with local spins via exchange coupling. The local spin has vortex structure with a finite out-of-plane component that determines the spin chirality. Our numerical results show that the Hall conductance can be obtained when the system has spin chirality. Furthermore, spin Hall current is observed even if the system does not have spin chirality. This spin Hall current does not require an electric field inside the system unlike conventional spin Hall effects [2].

We consider a 2-dimensional electron system with exchange interaction,

$$H = -t \sum_{<i,j>,\sigma,\sigma'} c_{i\sigma}^{+} c_{j\sigma'} - J \sum_{i,\sigma,\sigma'} c_{i\sigma}^{+} \sigma c_{i\sigma'} \cdot \mathbf{S}(x,y), \quad (1)$$

with the nearest-neighbor hopping with an energy of $t = \hbar^2/2m^*a^2$ (m^* the effective mass, a the lattice constant). Operator $c_{i\sigma}^{+}(c_{i\sigma})$ creates (annihilates) an electron of a spin σ at lattice site i. σ's are the Pauli matrices, and $J(>0)$ is the exchange coupling constant. The local spin $\mathbf{S}(x,y)$ has vortex geometry in the x-y plane in addition to the uniform S_z component and is written as $\mathbf{S}(x,y) =$

$S(\cos\phi(x,y)\sin\theta, \sin\phi(x,y)\sin\theta, \cos\theta)$, where S is the modulus of the local spin. The vortex is determined by setting $\phi(x,y) = -\tan^{-1}(y/x)$. The center of the vortex is located at the origin. We assume that the dynamics of the local spins is much slower than that of the conducting electron, and treat local spins as static. A scheme of the system is shown in Fig. 1 in which we assume 4-terminal geometry. The leads are labeled as 1-4 and the $+x(y)$-direction is set to the direction from the lead as $1(4)$ to $3(2)$. We also consider the chirality of a local spin system, $Ch_{ijkl} \equiv E_{ijk} + E_{ikl}$, where $E_{ijk} = \mathbf{S}_i \cdot (\mathbf{S}_j \times \mathbf{S}_k)$ for a plaquette of a square lattice labeled as (i, j, k, l) counter-clockwise. The anomalous Hall effect in ferromagnetic metals is induced by the spin chirality of each lattice in bulk systems. For the proposed system, the local spin system does not have chirality $Ch_{ijkl} = 0$ when $\theta = 0, \pi/2, \pi$. Like bulk anomalous Hall effect, we expect that the Hall effect can be obtained except for these values of θ.

We calculate spin-resolved transmission amplitudes by using the recursive Green function method [3]. By

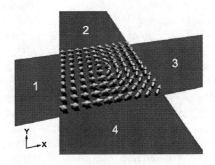

FIGURE 1. Scheme of a proposed system. Arrows represents local spins that embedded in the 4-terminal geometry.

CP893, *Physics of Semiconductors, 28th International Conference*
edited by W. Jantsch and F. Schäffler
© 2007 American Institute of Physics 978-0-7354-0397-0/07/$23.00

employing the Landauer-Buttiker formula, we assume that the net current of the lead 2 and 4 is zero. The current of lead I_l is $I_l = \sum_\sigma (N_l - R_{l\sigma,l\sigma})\mu_l - \sum_{l \neq l'\sigma\sigma'} T_{l\sigma,l'\sigma'}\mu_{l'}$, where N_l is the number of the propagating channel of the lead l, $T_{l\sigma,l'\sigma'}(R_{l\sigma,l'\sigma'})$ is the transmission (reflection) amplitude from the σ'-spin channel of lead l' to the σ-spin channel of the lead l. μ_l is the chemical potential of a reservoir attached to the lead l. The Hall conductance is defined as $G_{\mathrm{H}} = -r_{yx}/(r_{xx}^2 + r_{yx}^2)$, where $r_{yx} = (\mu_2 - \mu_4)/I_1$ and $r_{xx} = (\mu_1 - \mu_3)/I_1$ is the Hall resistance and the (longitudinal) resistance, respectively. The spin Hall conductance is defined as $G_{\mathrm{sH}}^v = (I_{2+}^v - I_{2-}^v)/(\mu_1 - \mu_3)$, where $I_{2\pm}^v$ is the current of lead 2 with a polarization in the $\pm v$ ($v = X, Y, Z$) direction.

The Hall conductance as a function of the energy of the conduction electron and the angle of the local spin θ is shown in Fig. 2. The exchange coupling constant and the value of the local spin is set to $JS = 1.0t$. The system size is $30a \times 30a$. The Hall conductance can be observed when the local spin system has spin chirality ($\theta \neq 0, \pi/2, \pi$). The sign of the Hall conductance changes when the sign of S_z is changed. The amplitude of the Hall conductance oscillates with the energy. This is because the Hall effect is proportional to the momentum of the x-direction, hence it decreases when the Fermi energy is close to the energy where new propagating channels open. We should note that the (charge) Hall effect also induces the spin current polarized parallel to the local spins near the interface between the lead 2 or 4 and the sample. In contrast to the situation in ferromagnetic metal systems, we assume that the Fermi energy is comparable to the exchange coupling energy such as magnetic semiconductors. The adiabatic approximation that neglects the minority spin components cannot be applied to this system. We can expect the spin current that is not parallel to the local spins. We also plot the spin Hall conductance for each polarization direction in Fig. 2. We can obtain each components of spin Hall conductance that is not parallel to the local spin system. From this figure, $G_{\mathrm{sH}}^{Y,Z}$ vanishes at $\theta = 0, \pi$ while G_{sH}^X vanishes at $\theta = 0, \pi/2, \pi$. At $\theta = \pi/2$, the local spins near the interface between the sample and the lead 2 almost direct to the x-direction. Therefore, the suppression of the Hall conductance at $\theta = \pi/2$ results in the suppression of G_{sH}^X. The direction of polarization rotates while electrons propagate in the sample due to precession induced by the exchange coupling. This precession is an important feature of the mesoscopic spin Hall effect that is also obtained in the 2-dimensional electron system with spin-orbit interaction [5]. In contrast, only z-component of the spin current is expected in bulk spin-orbit systems.

In conclusion, we investigated the Hall effect in mesoscopic systems which have spin chirality. We have shown that both voltage drop and spin current are driven in the

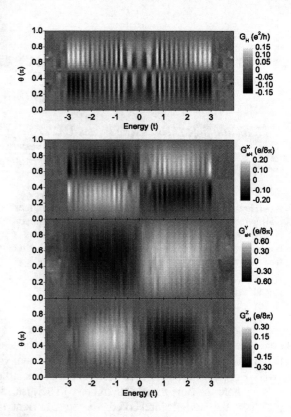

FIGURE 2. Hall conductance (G_{H}) and spin Hall conductances ($G_{\mathrm{sH}}^{X,Y,Z}$) as a function of the Energy of conduction electrons and the angle of local spins θ.

transverse direction. This spin Hall current should be distinguished from the conventional spin Hall effect observed in bulk spin-orbit systems.

The authors are grateful to M. Yamamoto, S. Kettemann and Y. Avishai for valuable discussions. The work has been supported by the Deutsche Forschungsgemeinschaft via SFBs 508 and 668 of the Universität Hamburg, and by the European Union via the Marie-Curie-Network MCRTN-CT2003-504574.

REFERENCES

1. K. Ohgushi, S. Murakami, and N. Nagaosa, *Phys. Rev. B* **62**, R6065–R6068 (2000).
2. S. Murakami, N. Nagaosa and S. -C. Zhang, *Science* **301**, 1348 (2003).
3. T. Ando, *Phys. Rev. B* **40**, 5325 (1989).
4. M. Yamamoto, T. Ohtsuki, and B. Kramer, *Phys. Rev. B* **72**, 115321 (2005).
5. L. Sheng, D.N. Sheng, and C.S. Ting, *Phys. Rev. Lett.* **94**, 016602 (2005).

Spin Hall Current Induced By Electric Field Pulse

Masayuki Yamamoto and Bernhard Kramer

I.Institut für Theoretische Physik, Universität Hamburg, Jungiusstraße 9, 20355 Hamburg, Germany

Abstract. We have numerically investigated the spin Hall current induced by an electric field pulse in a two dimensional electron system without impurities in the presence of Rashba spin-orbit coupling. By solving the time-dependent Schrödinger equation, the dynamics of a wave packet has been calculated in a system subject to a time-dependent potential that represents an electric field pulse. It is found that a spin Hall current is generated when the external electric field is switched on by tilting the potential. This spin Hall current reaches its maximum value and then decreases to zero after the electric field is switched off. The maximum value is proportional to the duration of the electric field pulse. The stationary charge current decreases with increasing strength of the spin-orbit coupling.

Keywords: Spin Hall Effect, Rashba Spin-Orbit Coupling
PACS: 72.25.Dc, 71.70.Ej

The spin Hall effect (SHE), the generation of a transverse spin current by an external electric field via spin-orbit coupling, is one of the most exciting phenomena in the field of spintronics [1]. Recently, it has been reported that a spin Hall current in two dimensional electron system (2DES) can be generated just after an external electric field is switched on [2]. In the present work, we want to investigate this transient effect in some detail. We present numerical results for the spin Hall current in a clean 2DES induced by an electric field pulse in the presence of Rashba spin-orbit coupling (RSO). The transient spin Hall current is calculated as a function of time for several pulse durations and strength of RSO.

Let us consider a 2DES with RSO [3]. The single-electron Hamiltonian is given by

$$H_0 = \frac{p^2}{2m^*} + \frac{\alpha}{\hbar} \left(\sigma_x p_y - \sigma_y p_x \right), \qquad (1)$$

where m^* denotes the effective mass, α the strength of RSO, and σ_i and p_i ($i = x, y$) are the Pauli matrices and the components of the momentum, respectively.

We represent this system in the tight-binding language [4] and assume the presence of a time-dependent potential,

$$H(t) = - \sum_{\langle i,j \rangle, \sigma, \sigma'} V_{i\sigma, j\sigma'} c_{i\sigma}^\dagger c_{j\sigma'} + \sum_{i,\sigma} U_i(t) c_{i\sigma}^\dagger c_{i\sigma}, \quad (2)$$

with

$$V_{i,i+\hat{x}} = e^{-i\theta\sigma_y}, \quad V_{i,i+\hat{y}} = e^{i\theta\sigma_x}, \qquad (3)$$

and

$$U_i(t) = \begin{cases} -\Delta U + \frac{2\Delta U (i_x - 1)}{N_x - 1} & (\tau_1 < t < \tau_2) \\ 0 & (\text{otherwise}) \end{cases}, \quad (4)$$

where $c_{i\sigma}^\dagger (c_{i\sigma})$ denotes the creation (annihilation) operator of an electron on site i with spin σ, $V_{i,i+\hat{x}}(V_{i,i+\hat{y}})$ the

hopping matrix elements in the x-(y-) directions and $U_i(t)$ the time-dependent on-site potential at the time t. The hopping term is restricted to nearest neighbours. The parameter θ represents the strength of RSO and is related to α in Eq.(1) by

$$\alpha \simeq 2\theta V_0 a \qquad (\theta \ll 1), \qquad (5)$$

where $V_0 = \hbar^2 / 2m^* a^2$ is the unit energy and a the unit length corresponding to the tight-binding lattice spacing. In the following simulation, the system size is assumed to be $N_x \times N_y = 300 \times 300$ and the strength of the potential $\Delta U = 2.99$.

In order to solve numerically the time-dependent Schrödinger equation, we have used the method based on the higher-order decomposition of exponential operators [5]. By applying the basic formula for the fourth-order decomposition to the time evolution operator, the state vector $|\psi(t + \delta t)\rangle$ at time $t + \delta t$ can be obtained as [6],

$$
\begin{aligned}
|\psi(t + \delta t)\rangle &= \exp(-iH(t)\delta t/\hbar)|\psi(t)\rangle \\
&= S(-ip\delta t/\hbar, \ t + (1 - p/2)\delta t) \\
&\quad \times S(-i(1 - 2p)\delta t/\hbar, \ t + \delta t/2) \\
&\quad \times S(-ip\delta t/\hbar, \ t + p\delta t/2)|\psi(t)\rangle \\
&\quad + O(\delta t^5),
\end{aligned}
\qquad (6)
$$

with

$$S(x,t) = e^{xH_1/2} \cdots e^{xH_4/2} e^{xH_5(t)} e^{xH_4/2} \cdots e^{xH_1/2}, \quad (7)$$

where the parameter p is given by $p = (2 - 2^{1/3})^{-1}$. The Hamiltonian is decomposed into five parts $H(t) = H_1 + \cdots + H_4 + H_5(t)$. The single time step is assumed to be $\delta t = 0.1\hbar/V_0$ in the following.

To prepare the initial wave packet, we numerically diagonalize a subsystem (10×10) located at the center of

CP893, *Physics of Semiconductors, 28th International Conference*
edited by W. Jantsch and F. Schäffler
© 2007 American Institute of Physics 978-0-7354-0397-0/07/$23.00

the system. There are two eigenstates for each energy level due to Kramers degeneracy ($\chi = \pm$). These states have the same charge but opposite spin distributions. We choose the eigenstates for the lowest energy level as the initial states $|\psi_\chi(0)\rangle$. They are, of course not eigenstates of the entire system, and will evolve during time according to the time dependent Schrödinger equation.

The time evolution can be divided into the three regions. Equilibrium evolution ($0 < t < \tau_1$): the potential is flat and the wave packet broadens with zero average velocity. (2) Acceleration period ($\tau_1 < t < \tau_2$): the potential is tilted by ΔU. The wave packet is accelerated in the $-x$-direction. (3) Steady state ($\tau_2 < t$): the potential is flat again. The wave packet travels with a constant velocity while continuing to broaden.

We have calculated the electric and spin currents of this non stationary state. They are defined by

$$j_i(t) = -e \sum_{\chi = \pm} \langle \psi_\chi(t) | v_i | \psi_\chi(t) \rangle, \qquad (8)$$

and

$$j_i^{\text{spin}}(t) = \frac{\hbar}{2} \sum_{\chi = \pm} \langle \psi_\chi(t) | \frac{v_i \sigma_z + \sigma_z v_i}{2} | \psi_\chi(t) \rangle, \qquad (9)$$

where the velocity is given by $v_i = \hbar^{-1} \partial H / \partial k_i$ ($i = x, y$).

Figure 1 shows results for the electric and spin Hall current as a function of the time for various acceleration time periods. One observes that a spin current is generated when the potential is tilted in addition to the charge current. After the potential is assumed to be flat again, the spin current reaches its maximum value, oscillates, and decreases to zero while the charge current remains constant. The maximum value of the spin current is proportional to the acceleration time period (Fig. 1 inset).

Figure 2 shows results for the electric and spin Hall current as a function of the time for different strengths of RSO. It is found that the electric current decreases as the strength of RSO increases. The inset in Fig. 2 shows that the loss of an electric current is well fitted by a quadratic function of the strength of RSO.

REFERENCES

1. For summary of the spin Hall effect, see, e.g., J. Schliemann, cond-mat/0602330; H.-A. Engel, E.I. Rashba and B.I. Halperin, cond-mat/0603306.
2. R. Raimondi and C. Gorini, cond-mat/0601525.
3. E.I. Rashba, Sov. Phys. Solid State **2**, 1109 (1960); Y.A. Bychkov and E.I. Rashba, J. Phys. C **17**, 6039 (1984).
4. T. Ando, Phys. Rev. B **40**, 5325 (1989).
5. M. Suzuki, Phys. Lett. A **146**, 319 (1990).
6. T. Kawarabayashi and T. Ohtsuki, Phys. Rev. B **51** 10897 (1995); T. Nakanishi, T. Ohtsuki and T. Kawarabayashi, J. Phys. Soc. Jpn. **66**, 949 (1997); T. Kawarabayashi and T. Ohtsuki, Phys. Rev. B **67**, 165309 (2003).

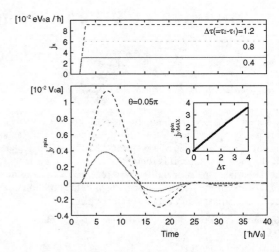

FIGURE 1. (color online) The electric current j_x (top) and the spin Hall current j_y^{spin} (bottom) as a function of the time for several acceleration time periods $\Delta\tau = \tau_2 - \tau_1$, as indicated. The strength of RSO is $\theta = 0.05\pi$. A spin current is generated when the potential is tilted at $\tau_1 = 2.0\hbar/V_0$. After the potential is assumed to be flat again at τ_2, the spin current reaches its maximum value $j_{y\text{MAX}}^{\text{spin}}$ and then decreases to zero. Inset: the maximum value of the spin current, $j_{y\text{MAX}}^{\text{spin}}$, as a function of the acceleration time period $\Delta\tau$.

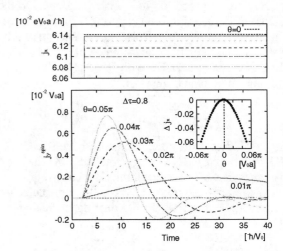

FIGURE 2. (color online) The electric current j_x (top) and the spin Hall current j_y^{spin} (bottom) as a function of the time f or different strengths of RSO θ, respectively. The acceleration time period is $\Delta\tau = 0.8\hbar/V_0$. The electric current j_x decreases as the strength of RSO θ increases. Inset: the difference between the electric current with and without RSO, $\Delta j_x = j_x(\theta) - j_x(0)$, as a function of the strength of RSO θ.

Spin-Hall Effect in Semiconductor Heterostructures with Cubic Rashba Spin-Orbit Interaction

O. Bleibaum and S. Wachsmuth

Institute for Theoretical Physics, Otto-von-Guericke University, 39016 Magdeburg, PF4120, Germany

Abstract. We investigate the structure of spin-diffusion equations for dirty semiconductor heterostructures with weak cubic Rashba interaction. Our investigation shows that the spin-current tensor determines the boundary conditions for the model in question, which are needed to solve the diffusion equations. Using this fact we calculate the edge spin-accumulation in a spin-Hall experiment and the anomalous Hall-current after optical excitation.

Keywords: Spin Transport, Spin Diffusion, Electric Spin Generation
PACS: 75.50.Pp, 85.75.Mm

At present there is much interest in investigations of spin-charge coupling effects in non-magnetic semiconductor heterostructures with Rashba spin-orbit interactions. Effects which permit electric generation of non-equilibrium magnetizations, like the homogeneous spin accumulation [1] in an electric field or the spin-Hall effect [2], have received particular attention. However, while the mechanism responsible for the homogeneous spin accumulation has already been understood for decades, the intrinsic spin-Hall effect is still a rather controversial issue.

The first investigations of intrinsic spin-Hall effects in such systems focused on the expectation value of the spin-Hall current operator

$$\hat{J}_{yz} = \frac{1}{2}\{\hat{v}_y, \sigma_z\} \qquad (1)$$

of models with linear Rashba interaction (see, e.g., the recent review [2]). ($\hat{v}_y$ is y-component of the velocity operator and σ_z is the Pauli matrix.). These investigations have shown that the spin-Hall current is non-zero in clean systems in electric fields. This fact has led to the conclusion that there is a non-vanishing spin-Hall effect in such systems which manifests itself in non-equilibrium magnetizations at boundaries. However, further investigations of the spin current tensor have shown that the results are not robust. The spin-Hall conductivity of macroscopic samples vanishes already in the presence of a weak amount of disorder. Therefore, we expect that there is no intrinsic spin-Hall effect in macroscopic dirty systems with linear Rashba interaction.

The absence of intrinsic spin-Hall currents in dirty macroscopic systems with linear Rashba interaction has not remained the only problem casting doubts on the predictions of the intrinsic spin-Hall effect. The spin-current tensor of linear Rashba models is also non-zero in equilibrium. Therefore, it is not clear that it really characterizes macroscopic transport phenomena [3]. This fact manifests itself also in the spin diffusion equations [4]. Spin diffusion equations for dirty systems have been derived by a number of authors. However, their solution, derived under the assumption that the spin-current tensor vanishes at hard-wall boundaries, yields finite equilibrium spin-accumulations at the boundaries, which seem to contradict physical intuition [4]. Alternative definitions for the spin-current tensor and alternative boundary conditions have been suggested. However, they either fail to establish a connection with the magnitude of the boundary magnetization, or yield results which are in contradiction to those presented in the literature before.

Surprisingly, the situation in the cubic Rashba model

$$H = \frac{\boldsymbol{p}^2}{2m} + i\frac{N}{2}(p_-^3\sigma_+ - p_+^3\sigma_-) + V(\boldsymbol{r}) + (\boldsymbol{F},\boldsymbol{r}) \qquad (2)$$

differs from that in the linear Rashba model [H is the Hamiltonian, $\boldsymbol{p} = p_x\boldsymbol{e}_x + p_y\boldsymbol{e}_y$ is the momentum, $p_\pm = p_x \pm ip_y$, $\boldsymbol{r} = x\boldsymbol{e}_x + y\boldsymbol{e}_y$ is the position vector, N characterizes the Rashba interaction strength, $V(\boldsymbol{r})$ is a disordered Gaussian white-noise potential with zero average and standard deviation $\langle\langle V(\boldsymbol{r})V(\boldsymbol{r}')\rangle\rangle = \delta(\boldsymbol{r}-\boldsymbol{r}')\hbar/(2\pi\nu\tau)$, τ is the scattering time, ν the density of states per spin, and $\boldsymbol{F}$ a constant field. $\boldsymbol{e}_x$ and $\boldsymbol{e}_y$ are the unit vectors in the two-dimensional plane. $\boldsymbol{e}_z$ is a unit vector perpendicular to the plane. Indices $i, k, \ldots$ replace the labels x, y and z in sums.] The cubic Rashba model describes heavy holes in III-V semiconductor quantum wells. The spin-Hall current is even non-zero in such systems in the dirty limit, in which the energy level splitting due to the Rashba interaction is small compared to the disorder energy. This fact offers the opportunity to address the question of how the non-vanishing spin-Hall current manifests itself in the spin-diffusion equations, how these equations differ from those for systems with linear Rashba interaction,

CP893, *Physics of Semiconductors, 28th International Conference*
edited by W. Jantsch and F. Schäffler
© 2007 American Institute of Physics 978-0-7354-0397-0/07/$23.00

and whether the spin-Hall current determines the boundary conditions for such systems or not.

To answer these questions we have derived spectral spin-diffusion equations for systems with weak cubic Rashba spin-orbit interaction in the dirty limit. In doing so, we have restricted the consideration to ohmic contributions to the transport coefficients. The diffusion equations were extracted from a product of retarded and advanced Green's functions, as detailed in Ref. [5]. Our calculation shows that the spectral spin diffusion equation reduces to the simple equation

$$\partial_t \boldsymbol{S} + \boldsymbol{\Omega} \circ \boldsymbol{S} + \text{Div} \boldsymbol{J} = -\partial_\varepsilon \boldsymbol{j}_\varepsilon. \tag{3}$$

Here $\boldsymbol{S}$ is the spin density, $\boldsymbol{\Omega}$ is a symmetric tensor of second rank with matrix elements $\boldsymbol{\Omega}_{ik} = \Omega \delta_{ik}(1 + \delta_{i3})$ $(i, k = 1, 2, 3)$

$$\Omega = 16 \frac{N^2 m^3}{\hbar^2} \varepsilon^3 \tau, \tag{4}$$

ε is the kinetic energy of the particles, $\circ$ is the dyadic product, $\boldsymbol{j}_\varepsilon$ is the energy current for spins and $\boldsymbol{J}$ is the tensor of transport currents. The components of the tensor $\boldsymbol{J}$ are given by

$$J_{lk} = -D\nabla_l S_k + DF_l \partial_\varepsilon S_k + \delta_{kz} \frac{3}{2} \frac{\hbar}{m} \tau \Omega (\boldsymbol{e}_z \times \boldsymbol{\nabla})_l n$$
$$-\delta_{kz} \frac{3}{2} \frac{\hbar}{m} \tau \Omega (\boldsymbol{e}_z \times \boldsymbol{F}_l) \partial_\varepsilon n. \tag{5}$$

Here n is the particle density, $D = \varepsilon \tau / m$ is the diffusion coefficient and $l = 1, 2$. The tensor $\boldsymbol{J}$ agrees with the expectation value of the spin-current tensor. Its yz component coincides with the expectation value of the operator (1). There are no spin-charge coupling coefficients in the spin-current tensor which couple the spin density to the particle density. There are only terms which couple the spin density to derivatives of the particle density. The spin current tensor of dirty systems with cubic Rashba interaction therefore vanishes in equilibrium. This distinguishes the situation in systems with cubic Rashba interaction from that in systems with linear Rashba interaction, and leads to the conclusion that Eq. (3) has just the structure of conventional diffusion equations for non-conserved quantities. The spin-current tensor coincides with the tensor of transport currents in the diffusion equation and consequently also determines the boundary conditions.

The fact that the spin-Hall current enters explicitly the spin-diffusion equations (3)-(5) is not the only fact which distinguishes systems with cubic Rashba interaction from that with linear Rashba interaction. A glance at these equations also reveals that an ohmic magnetization can not be induced by means of external electric fields or concentration gradients in homogeneous systems. Thus, the spin-Hall effect is the only effect which permits electric spin-generation in the ohmic regime. To calculate

the magnitude of the edge spin-accumulation we focus on the situation in the half-space $y > 0$. We assume that there is an additional scattering mechanism which keeps the system in energy equilibrium but does not affect momentum relaxation. This is the typical situation at low temperatures, where momentum relaxation is governed by scattering at impurities but energy relaxation is due to electron-phonon interaction. To calculate the edge spin-accumulation we solve Eq.(3) in the ohmic regime subject to the boundary condition $J_{yk} = 0$ for $y = 0$ and find

$$S_z(y) = -3 \frac{\hbar \tau v F_x}{m} \sqrt{\frac{\Omega}{2D}} \exp(-\sqrt{2\Omega/D}\, y), \tag{6}$$

if the field $\boldsymbol{F} = F_x \boldsymbol{e}_x$ is applied in x-direction. Here all transport coefficients are those at the Fermi energy. Eq. (6) shows that the penetration length $l = \sqrt{D/2\Omega} \propto \tilde{n}^{-1}$ of the magnetization is independent of disorder and decreases with increasing particle concentration $\tilde{n}$. It shares this property with the penetration length in nearly clean systems, in which the Rashba level splitting is large compared to the disorder energy [6]. For the same reason, however, the magnitude of the magnetization increases with increasing particle concentration. This behavior contrasts with that in clean systems. Thus, from the point of view of electric spin generation, systems with weak cubic Rashba interaction and sufficiently large particle density are as suitable as systems with strong Rashba interaction.

Finally, we would like to draw attention to the fact that the existence of spin-charge coupling effects manifests itself also in particle currents. There it leads to additional contributions to the spectral current of the structure

$$\delta \boldsymbol{j} = -\frac{3\hbar}{2} \frac{\tau}{m} \Omega \boldsymbol{e}_z \times (\boldsymbol{\nabla} - \boldsymbol{F} \partial_\varepsilon) S_z \tag{7}$$

in experiments in which the magnetization is due to optical orientation. We refer the reader to Ref. [5] for further details.

REFERENCES

1. V. M. Edelstein, Solid State Commun. **73**, 233 (1990).
2. J. Sinova, S. Murakami, Shun-Qing Shen, and Mahn-Soo Choi, cond-mat/0512054v1 (2005).
3. E. I. Rashba, Phys. Rev. B **68**, 241315(R) (2003), J. Supercond. **18**, 137 (2005).
4. O. Bleibaum, Phys. Rev. B **73**, 035322 (2006), see also cond-mat/0503471 (2005).
5. O. Bleibaum and S. Wachsmuth, cond-mat/0602517v1 (2006).
6. K. Nomura, J. Wunderlich, J. Sinova, B. Kaestner, A. H. MacDonald and T. Jungwirth, Phys. Rev. B **73**, 245330 (2005).

Spin and Charge Transport Properties in Quasi-One Dimensional Anomalous Hall System

Katsunori Wakabayashi*,† and Manfred Sigrist†

*Department of Quantum Matter, AdSM, Hiroshima University, Higashi-Hiroshima 739-8530, Japan
†Theoretische Physik, ETH-Hönggerberg, Zürich 8093, Switzerland

Abstract. The ferromagnetic system with orbital hybridization and onsite spin-orbit coupling shows finite anomalous and spin Hall conductivity. In this paper, we study the edge effect on charge and spin transport properties in quasi-one dimensional anomalous Hall system. It is found that the existence of the intriguing spontaneous edge spin current which flows even in the absence of the internal magnetic field, unless either orbital hybridization hopping or spin-orbit interaction is turned off. The origin of the surface spin current is the consequence of the quantum interference effect between parity violation due to the orbital hybridization and spin-orbit interaction.

Keywords: anomalous Hall effect, spin current, edge effect, spintronics
PACS: 72.25.-b,71.70.Ej,73.21.Hb,78.67.Lt,73.20.-r

Spin-dependent transport phenomena has attracted a lot of interests recently due to intriguing new physical phenomena that are observed experimentally or predicted theoretically. Some of these will serve as a basis for future device applications in the spintronics paradigm, where not only the charge degree of freedom but also spin degree of freedom is used to code and transfer the information.

In order to characterize and explore the spin and charge transport properties in spintronics devices, anomalous Hall effect (AHE) is an important tool for characterising the physical properties of ferromagnet and diluted magnetic semiconductor[1]. The AHE observed in ferromagnetic materials is a phenomenon that the transverse resistivity contains a contribution proportional to the magnetization, in addition to the usual Hall effect. Recent theoretical progress has shown that AHE can be caused not only by the impurity scattering, but also by the geometric Berry phase effect of the system[2, 3, 4]. In this paper, we investigate the edge effects on anomalous Hall system, on the basis of tight-binding model.

We consider the ferromagnetic quantum wire with orbital hybridization and onsite spin-orbit couplings as shown in Fig. 1 (a), on the basis of the tight-binding model[5]. Here we consider the N-leg ladder system where each site has p_x and p_y orbitals and the onsite spin-orbit interaction $\lambda \hat{l}_z \hat{\sigma}_z$ is assumed. We take x-axis for the longitudinal translational invariant direction, and y-axis for the transverse direction. The origin $y = 0$ is fixed at the middle of the ribbon. Since we take the with of ribbon as $L = (N-1)a$, $|y| \leq L/2$. We also reserve $r(= 1\ 2\ 3\ \cdots\ N)$ for the index of leg. The Hamiltonian of the system is $H = H_0 + H_1 + H_{SOI} + H_M$ where H_0 is

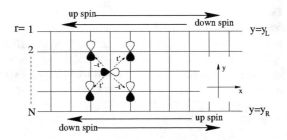

FIGURE 1. The ribbon system with N-legs. The width of ribbon is $L = (N-1)a$. Since the origin of y-axis is the middel of the ribbon, y varies $y_R \leq y \leq y_L$. Here $y_L = L/2$ and $y_R = -L/2$.

the electron hopping between same orbitals with transfer integral t and H_1 is the hopping between different orbitals with the transfer integral t'. H_{SOI} and H_M are the spin-orbit interaction and Zeeman term describing the internal magnetic field of the ferromanget, respectively. The central consequence is the appearance of spontaneous surface spin current which flows even in the absence of the internal magnetic field unless either the orbital hybridization or spin-orbit interaction is absent.

The spin current flowing from j-site to i-site can be evaluated as the expectation value of the current operator:

$$J_{ijs} = \frac{et_{ij}}{\hbar}\mathrm{Im}(c^{\dagger}_{kis}c_{kjs} - \mathrm{h\,c}) \tag{1}$$

In absence of Zeeman magnetic field, net charge current is zero. However, the finite spontaneous spin current appears along the edges. In Fig. 2(a), the distribution of spin current is depicted for ribbon width $N = 20$, $t'/t = 0\ 2$ and $\lambda/t = 0\ 1$. We can clearly see the large spin

CP893, *Physics of Semiconductors, 28th International Conference*
edited by W. Jantsch and F. Schäffler
© 2007 American Institute of Physics 978-0-7354-0397-0/07/$23.00

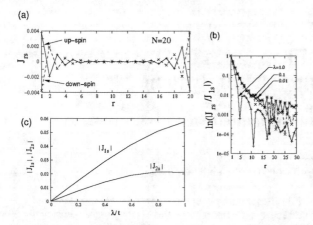

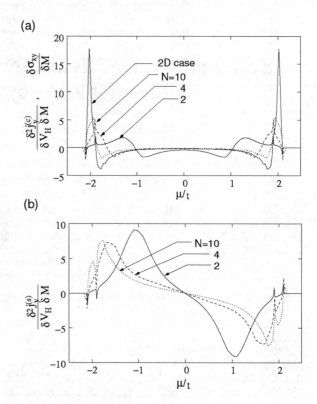

FIGURE 2. (a) The ditribution of spin current for ribbon width $N = 20$ and spin-orbit coupling $\lambda\ t = 0\ 1$. (b) Semi-log plot of the spin current distribution from r=1 to r=N/2 for $\lambda\ t = 0\ 01\ 0\ 1\ 1\ 0$. Here we have fixed $N = 60$ and $\mu = 0$. (c) The spin-orbit coupling dependence of the spin current which flows on 1st and 2nd legs for same parameter set.

current along the edges, and interestingly current decays with oscillation. The exponential decay of spin current can be seen from the semi-log plot of the distribution of spin current as in Fig. 2(b). Here the distribution of spin current for ribbon width $N = 60$ is plotted in the range of $1 \leq r \leq N\ 2$. In the small $r \leq 10$, the exponential decay is clearly seen. Also, the current rapidly decays with increasing the spin-orbit coupling. In Fig. 2(b), the spin-orbit coupling dependence of the spin current on the outermost legs, i.e. $r = 1\ 2$ is shown. The spin current on the edges develops linearly in the small λ regime.

The application of infinitesimal transverse Hall voltage and internal Zeeman magnetic field gives rise to the finite net charge and spin current in the longitudinal direction. Here, the Hall conductivity for the ribbon system is defined as

$$\sigma_{\text{Hall}}^{(c\ s)} = \frac{\delta j^{(c\ s)}}{\delta V_{\text{Hall}}} \qquad (2)$$

The susceptibility of $\sigma_{\text{Hall}}^{(c\ s)}$ to the Zeeman field M, i.e. $\delta\sigma_{\text{Hall}}^{(c\ s)}\ \delta M$ should be consistent with the susceptibility of the anomalous Hall conductivity in 2-dimensional system, i.e. $\delta\sigma_{xy}\ \delta M$. In Fig. 3, the susceptibilities of the charge and spin Hall conductivity to the Zeeman field for various ribbon width are shown. We can see that the wider ribbon qualitatively well reproduces the result for the 2-dimensional system. We should note that above approach is quite close to the evaluation of the Hall conductance by the Streda formula in quantum Hall system[6].

In conclusion, edge effect on charge and spin transport properties in anomalous Hall system has been studied. The quantum wire with orbital-hybridization and onsite

FIGURE 3. Chemical potential dependence of (a) charge Hall conductivity and (b) spin Hall conductivity for $t'\ t = 0\ 2$ and $\lambda\ t = 0\ 1$.

spin-orbit interaction shows the spontaneous surface spin current which flows even in the absence of the internal magnetic field. The origin of the surface spin current is the consequence of the quantum interference effect between parity violation due to the orbital hybridization and spin-orbit interaction.

Financial support from the Swiss National Science Foundation and NCCR MaNEP are gratefully acknowledged.

REFERENCES

1. Z. Fang, N. Nagaosa, K. S. Takahashi, A. Asamitsu, R. Mathieu, T. Ogasawara, H. Yamada, M. Kawasaki, Y. Tokura, K. Terakura, Science **302**, 92 (2003).
2. N. Nagaosa, J. Phys. Soc. Jpn. **75**, 04001 (2006).
3. M. Onoda and N. Nagaosa, J.Phys. Soc. Jpn. **71**, 19 (2002).
4. T. Jungwirth, Qian Niu, and A. H. MacDonald, Phys. Rev. Lett. **88**, 207208 (2002).
5. K. Wakabayashi, R. Monnier and M. Sigrist, preprint.
6. P. Streda, J. Phys. C, **15**, L717 (1982).

Spin-splitting characterization of an InGaSb 2DEG by using magnetoresistance measurements with tilted magnetic fields

M. Akabori, V.A. Guzenko[*], T. Kakegawa, T. Sato,
Th. Schäpers[*], T. Suzuki, S. Yamada

*Center for Nano Materials and Technology, Japan Advanced Institute of Science and Technology,
1-1, Asahidai, Nomi, Ishikawa, 923-1292 Japan*
*Institute of Thin Films and Interfaces (ISG 1), Research Centre Jülich, D-52425 Jülich, Germany

Abstract. We investigated spin-splitting properties in a metamorphic $In_{0.89}Ga_{0.11}Sb/In_{0.88}Al_{0.12}Sb$ two-dimensional electron gas (2DEG) by means of magnetoresistance measurements with tilted magnetic fields. In magnetoresistance curves with perpendicular magnetic field, we observed clear Shubnikov-de Haas oscillations with the Zeeman-type spin-splitting over 1 T, and spin-splitting vanishing around 1 T. By tilting the 2DEG, we also observed the equidistant separation between the spin-split Landau levels and the coincidence of the spin-up and spin-down levels from the neighboring Landau levels. From these results, we concluded that the dominant zero-field spin-splitting is the Dresselhaus-type but with some contribution of the Rashba term. Additionally, we obtained a 2DEG g-factor $|g| \approx 31$ from the coincidence method.

Keywords: InGaSb/InAlSb 2DEG; tilted magnetic fields; magnetoresistance; Zeeman spin splitting; Zero-field spin splitting; Dresselhaus term; Rashba term
PACS: 71.70.Ej; 73.61.Ey

INTRODUCTION

Since narrow gap semiconductor (NGS) two-dimensional electron gases (2DEGs) are expected to have large spin-splitting as well as high electron mobilities due to small electron effective masses, these NGSs may be suitable base materials for the non-magnetic semiconductor spintronics devices, e.g. spin field effect transistors (spin-FETs).[1] Based on acquired experience in growth and characterization of InGaAs[2,3] and InGaSb[4,5] quantum wells having high indium contents, we have performed magnetoresistance (MR) measurements on an InGaSb-2DEG in the tilted magnetic fields and analyzed its spin-splitting (SS).

EXPERIMENTAL PROCEDURE

We grew metamorphic InGaSb/InAlSb 2DEGs on semi-insulating GaAs (001) by a conventional molecular beam epitaxy (MBE) with a Sb cracker cell. The indium contents for the InGaSb and the InAlSb were fixed to 0.89 and 0.88, respectively. Since thicker

InAlSb buffer provides less threading dislocations[4], a 6μm-thick InAlSb buffer layer was selected for the present study. The thickness of the InGaSb channel layer was 30 nm. 2DEG is located at a depth of about 160 nm. After the growth, we fabricated Hall-bar samples by using conventional photolithography techniques. The channel width was 50 μm, and the probe distance was 200 μm. The channel directions were defined to [110], [-110] and [010] for the investigation of transport anisotropy. For MR measurements, magnetic field B up to 8 T was applied to Hall-bar samples, which was mounted into the tiltable sample holder and placed into a ⁴He-flow cryostat.

EXPERIMENTAL RESULTS AND DISCUSSION

Figure 1 shows MR and Hall-resistance (HR) curves of various channel directions at tilt angle $\theta=0°$, i.e. with B perpendicular to the plane of 2DEG. There was no clear anisotropy in MR and HR curves, which suggest that our metamorphic technique realizes high

CP893, *Physics of Semiconductors, 28th International Conference*
edited by W. Jantsch and F. Schäffler
© 2007 American Institute of Physics 978-0-7354-0397-0/07/$23.00

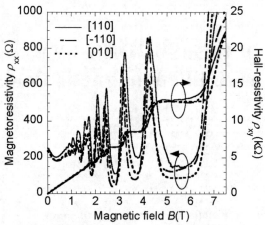

FIGURE 1. MR and HR curves of [110], [-110] and [010] channels at 1.5K.

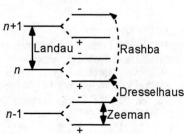

FIGURE 2. Schematic illustration of spin-split LLs with ZFSS.

quality 2DEG. We also observe clear peak splitting of the Shubnikov-de Haas (SdH) oscillations at high magnetic field $B > 1$ T, which corresponds to the Zeeman-type SS. Moreover, such Zeeman-type SS vanished around $B = 1$ T, despite of high electron mobility $\mu \approx 10^5$ cm^2/Vs. We consider that the origin of the vanishing is zero-field spin-splitting (ZFSS). Figure 2 shows a schematic illustration of the spin-split Landau levels (LL) with ZFSS.[6] Since the Rashba-type splitting should enhance SdH peak splitting at low magnetic fields, whereas the Dresselhaus-type splitting has an opposite effect, the result indicates that the Dresselhaus term is dominant rather than the Rashba term in the present sample.[5]

Figure 3 shows MR curves of a [010] channel sample for various tilt angles. With tilted magnetic fields, we also observe double frequency in SdH oscillation at $\theta \approx 45°$-$49°$ (not shown in Fig. 3), which corresponds to the equidistant separation between the spin-split LL, and phase inverse of SdH oscillation without peak splitting at $\theta \approx 70°$, which corresponds to the coincidence of the spin-up and spin-down levels from the neighboring LL. Without the Rashba-type SS, the sample should show no phase inversed oscillation; therefore some contribution of the Rashba term could be concluded. Moreover, from these tilt angles and the effective mass of the 2DEG ($m^* = 0.022 m_0$),[7] we

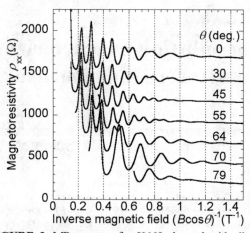

FIGURE 3. MR curves of a [010] channel with tilted magnetic fields. Every offset is 250 Ω.

obtained a g-factor $|g| \approx 31$ of the present 2DEG, which is quite small in comparison with the InSb bulk value ($g = -51$). However, we consider that it is reasonable with assuming the channel bandgap $E_g \approx 0.3$eV at low temperature and the Fermi energy of the 2DEG $E_F = 0.07$ eV, measured from the conduction band edge E_C.[8]

SUMMARY

We investigated SS properties in an InGaSb/InAlSb 2DEG through MR measurements. With perpendicular magnetic field, we observed clear SdH oscillations with the Zeeman-type SS over $B > 1$ T as well as SS vanishing around $B = 1$ T. The vanishing was interpreted as the dominance of the Dresselhaus term. Through MR measurements with tilted magnetic fields, we found the tilt angles where the sample showed double frequency oscillations and phase inversed oscillation. From these results, we concluded that there was still some contribution of the Rashba term. Furthermore, g-factor of the investigated 2DEG was estimated to be $|g| \approx 31$.

REFERENCES

1. S. Datta and B. Das, Appl. Phys. Lett. 56 (1990) 665.
2. S. Gozu *et al.*, Jpn. J. Appl. Phys. 37 (1998) L1501.
3. Y. Sato *et al.*, J. Appl. Phys. 89 (2001) 8017.
4. T. Sato *et al.*, ICDS-23 (2005) 205; Physica B 376-377 (2006) 579.
5. T. Sunouchi *et al.*, EP2DS-16 (2005) PC1; M. Akabori *et al.*, Physica E, in press (2006).
6. B. Das *et al.*, Phys. Rev. B 41 (1990) 8278.
7. K. Fujii *et al.*, Proc. of NGS-12 (2006) 61.
8. J. Nitta *et al.*, Appl. Phys. Lett. 83 (2003) 4565.

Long-range spin transport in (110) GaAs quantum wells

O. D. D. Couto Jr.*, F. Iikawa†, J. Rudolph*, R. Hey*, P. V. Santos* and K. H. Ploog*

*Paul-Drude-Institut für Festkörperelektronik, Hausvogteiplatz 5–7, 10117 Berlin, Germany
†Universidade Estadual de Campinas, IFGW, CP-6165, Campinas-SP, 13083-970, Brazil

Abstract. We report on long-range (>60 μm) coherent spin transport via surface acoustic waves in (110) GaAs quantum wells. The long transport distances, attributed to the quenching of the exciton exchange interaction and to the inhibition of the D'yakonov Perel' spin relaxation mechanism, allow the manipulation of the electron spin during the acoustic transport via external magnetic fields. Potential applications include for quantum information processing.

Keywords: (110) GaAs Quantum Wells, Surface Acoustic Waves, Spintronics
PACS: 42.55.Px, 73.63.Hs, 78.67.Pt

A basic requirement for spintronic devices is an efficient spin transport. In this context, long spin lifetimes and long transport distances combined with manipulation of the electron spin degrees of freedom are essential [1, 2]. GaAs quantum well (QW) structures grown along the $\hat{z}$=[110] direction exhibit, due to their special symmetry, much longer spin relaxation times for spins polarized along $\hat{z}$ than conventional (100) QWs and appear as potential candidates for such applications.

In this work, we employ the mobile type-II potential modulation induced by the piezoelectric field of a surface acoustic wave (SAW) to transport spins in an intrinsic (110) GaAs QW. The modulation traps electrons and holes in the positive and negative potential valleys, respectively, and separates the carriers spatially [3, 4]. This effect decreases the electron-hole (e-h) exchange interaction, increasing the recombination lifetime and allowing efficient transport. Spin manipulation is obtained by means of an external magnetic field. The absence of inversion symmetry of the zinc-blende material is exploited to control the spin dephasing mechanisms. The most relevant one in GaAs based structures is the D'yakonov Perel'(DP) mechanism [5, 6], where the lack of inversion symmetry causes a **k**-dependent internal effective magnetic field $\mathbf{B}_{eff}(\mathbf{k})$, which can lead to the dephasing of a spin ensemble. The advantage of the (110) GaAs QWs is that $\mathbf{B}_{eff}$ is oriented perpendicularly to the QW plane ($\mathbf{B}_{eff} \propto k_y\hat{z} \parallel$ [110]), meaning that this field does not contribute to the dephasing of a spin population oriented along $\hat{z}$.

The acoustically induced spin transport experiments were carried out on a 18-nm-thick undoped GaAs QW with $Al_{0.3}Ga_{0.7}As$ barriers grown by molecular-beam epitaxy on a GaAs (110) substrate. In order to increase the piezoelectric fields, we coated the sample with a 500 nm ZnO layer. Rayleigh SAWs propagating along the $\hat{x}$-direction of the (110) surface were generated apply-

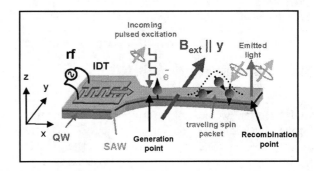

FIGURE 1. Experimental sketch: a SAW generated by an IDT, traps and transports spin polarized electrons ($\bar{e}$) along the wave channel in the $\hat{x}$-direction ($\parallel$ [001]). After recombination, the circularly polarized light is detected by a CCD. An external magnetic field $\mathbf{B}_{ext} \parallel$ [1$\bar{1}$0] is used for spin manipulation.

ing a radio-frequency (rf) signal to a focusing interdigital transducer (IDT), designed for operation at a wavelength of $\lambda_{SAW} = 5.6$ μm and a frequency of $f_{SAW} = 510$ MHz [7]. The spin transport measurements were performed by generating carriers at a position on the SAW path using a pulsed (40 MHz) laser beam at 780 nm wavelength, focused to a diameter <2 μm. In order to create carriers with spins polarized along the growth direction, the incident beam was right circularly polarized using a $\lambda/4$ plate. The generated spin packets are then trapped by the SAW piezoelectric potential and transported by the wave. An external magnetic field along $\hat{y}$ was used to induce spin precession [see Fig. 1]. The PL emitted from the transport path was spatially resolved, and its circular polarization was analyzed by a $\lambda/4$ plate and a polarization displacement prism. The latter displaces the right (I_R) and left (I_L) circularly polarized components of the PL, which are then detected simultaneously in separate regions of a charge-coupled-device (CCD) camera. Using a delay line between excitation

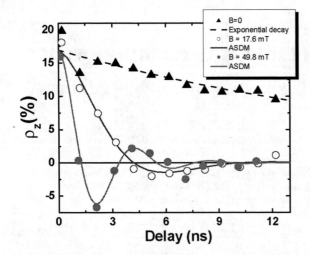

FIGURE 2. Time evolution of the spin polarization ρ_z under SAW power of 20 dBm. Without external magnetic fields (triangles), the decay is exponential (dashed line). Under magnetic fields with different amplitudes, at 18 mT (circles) and 49.8 mT (dots), we observe damped oscillation of ρ_z, well described by the anisotropic spin dephasing model (ASDM) (solid lines).

and detection, we are able to follow the time evolution of the transported spin packets all along the SAW propagating channel. The spin polarization is determined by $\rho_z = (I_R - I_L)/(I_R + I_L)$.

Figure 2 displays the spin polarization ρ_z without external magnetic field (triangles) as a function of the delay time, for transport along the $\hat{x}$-direction at 15 K. The decay can be fitted by an exponential curve (dashed line), providing a spin lifetime of $\tau_z = (22 \pm 2)$ ns. Taking into account the propagation velocity of the spin packets of $v_{spin} = 2.8$ μm/ns (which can be very accurately determined by fitting the mean packet position as a function of the delay), we obtain a spin decay length of $L_s = (63 \pm 5)$ μm. To our knowledge, this is the longest spin lifetime obtained for this system and is comparable to the ones obtained using n-doping of [001] QWs [8] or confinement via dynamic quantum dots [9]. The long spin lifetimes and transport lengths in (110) QWs are attributed to two effects. The first is associated with the fact that the DP mechanism becomes inefficient for spins oriented along the growth axis ($\hat{z} \parallel$ [110]) [10], considerably increasing the transport distances. The second is the reduction of the e-h exchange interaction due to the type-II potential profile induced by the SAW, which leads to a quenching of the Bir-Aronov-Pikus mechanism [11].

The long spin lifetimes allowed for the manipulation of the spin precession during transport using an external magnetic field $\mathbf{B}_{ext}$ applied along the $\hat{y}$-direction. The spin dynamics under constant field is shown in Figure 2 for 17.6 mT (circles) and 49.8 mT (dots). We observe damped oscillations of the spin polarization, since the

electron spin precesses around $\mathbf{B}_{ext}$. After 12 ns, ρ_z has vanished for both magnetic field strengths. This quick loss of spin polarization occurs because of the fluctuating effective magnetic field along the [110] direction. Although the carriers are confined and transported along the [001] direction, they are free to move and scatter along the [1$\bar{1}$0]. The random scattering causes the fluctuation of $\mathbf{B}_{eff}$ due to the already mentioned linear dependence on momentum k_y, so that in this direction $\langle \mathbf{B}_{eff} \rangle = 0$, but $\langle \mathbf{B}_{eff}^2 \rangle \neq 0$. This effect considerably decreases the spin lifetimes in the QW plane. The measured time dependence of ρ_z can be very well described by the anisotropic spin dephasing model (ASDM) [12] (solid lines in Fig. 2), which provides a spin lifetime along the [001] direction $\tau_x = 1.2$ ns and a total spin lifetime of $\tau_s = 2/(1/\tau_x + 1/\tau_z)^{-1} = 2.4$ ns. This value for τ_x reflects a spin dephasing rate in the QW plane $(1/\tau_x)$ 17 times higher than the one along the $\hat{z}$ direction $(1/\tau_z)$. Although smaller, τ_x in (110) GaAs QWs is expected to be at least 4 times larger than the spin relaxation time in their (001) counterparts [6].

In summary, we have demonstrated long spin lifetimes and transport distances in intrinsic (110) GaAs QWs. Spin manipulation using external magnetic fields was also shown, and the time evolution behavior of the spin polarization was very well understood in terms of the spin dephasing anisotropy between the growth direction and QW plane. These achievements clearly demonstrate the feasibility of using SAW fields for spin manipulation in spintronic devices using (110) GaAs QWs.

REFERENCES

1. S. Datta and B. Das, *Appl. Phys. Lett.* **56**, 665-667 (1990).
2. I. Zutić, J. Fabian, and S. Das Sarma, *Rev. Mod. Phys.* **76**, 323-410 (2004).
3. T. Sogawa, P. V. Santos, S. K. Zhang, S. Eshlaghi, A. D. Wieck, and K. H. Ploog, *Phys. Rev. Lett.* **87**, 276601 (2001).
4. S. Furuta, C. H. W. Barnes, and C. J. L. Doran, *Phys. Rev. B* **70**, 205320 (2004).
5. M. I. D'yakonov and V. I. Perel' *Sov. Phys. JETP* **33**, 1053-1059 (1971).
6. M. I. D'yakonov and V. Y. Y. Kachorovskii *Sov. Phys. Semicond.* **20**, 110-112 (1986).
7. M. M. de Lima Jr., F. Alsina, W. Seidel, and P. V. Santos, *J. Appl. Phys.* **94**, 7848-7855 (2003).
8. J. M. Kikkawa, and D. D. Awschalom, *Phys. Rev. Lett.* **80**, 4313 (1998).
9. J. A. H. Stotz, R. Hey, P. V. Santos, and K. H. Ploog, *Nat. Mat.* **4**, 585-588 (2005).
10. Y. Ohno, R. Terauchi, T. Adachi, F. Matsukura, and H. Ohno, *Phys. Rev. Lett.* **83**, 4196 (1999).
11. G. L. Bir, A. G. Aronov, and G. E. Pikus, *Sov. Phys. JETP* **42**, 705-712 (1976).
12. S. Döhrmann, D. Hägele, J. Rudolph, D. Schuh, M. Bichler, M. Oestreich, *Phys. Rev. Lett.* **93**, 147405 (2004).

Transport study of the annealing-induced transition from $Ga_{1-x}Mn_xAs$ alloys to GaAs:Mn/MnAs hybrids

M. T. Elm, J. Teubert, P. J. Klar, W. Heimbrodt, C. Michel, P. Thomas and S. Baranovskii

Dept. Physics & Material Sciences Center, Philipps University, Marburg, Germany

Abstract. The magneto-resistance properties of a $Ga_{0.98}Mn_{0.02}As$ alloy grown by molecular beam epitaxy and corresponding GaAs:Mn/MnAs hybrid samples obtained by controlled thermal annealing at different temperatures between 350 and 600 °C were studied. Thermal annealing at first leads to a non-randomness of the Mn distribution within the alloy and at higher temperatures finally to the formation of mesoscopic MnAs clusters within the surrounding GaAs:Mn matrix. The change in the transport behavior can be modelled realistically using a network model based on activated transport and accounting for the magnetic properties of the $Ga_{1-x}Mn_xAs$ matrix and the MnAs clusters. Comparison of experiment and theory shows that the modification of the magneto-transport properties due to annealing is dominated by changes of the $Ga_{1-x}Mn_xAs$ matrix, i.e. reduction of x. The number of the MnAs clusters formed is too small to considerably influence the transport.

Keywords: magnetic semiconductors, magneto-transport, spintronics, disorder
PACS: 75.50.Pp, 75.25.Dc, 75.20.My, 72.80.Ng

INTRODUCTION

The ferromagnetic $Ga_{1-x}Mn_xAs$ alloy is a model system for semiconductor spintronics. Thermal annealing of such alloys at low temperatures leads to a non-randomness of the Mn distribution within the alloy and at higher temperatures finally to the formation of mesoscopic MnAs clusters. Furthermore, the size of the clusters increases with increasing annealing temperature whereas the cluster density decreases accordingly. This morphology change can be monitored by atomic force microscopy and by ferromagnetic resonance studies. Here, we focus on changes of the transport behavior.

EXPERIMENTAL DETAILS AND THEORETICAL MODEL

A 50 nm thick ferromagnetic $Ga_{0.98}Mn_{0.02}As$ sample with a $T_C \approx 45$ K was grown by LT-MBE. Corresponding paramagnetic-ferromagnetic GaAs:Mn/MnAs hybrid structures were obtained by thermal annealing of pieces of the specimen at different temperatures ranging from 350 to 600 °C for 10 min. All samples were Hall-bar structured and bonded with gold wires. The magneto-resistance (MR) measurements were performed in fields up to 10 T and temperatures between 2 and 280 K.

The calculations were performed using a network model [1] based on activated band transport and accounting for the magnetic properties (ferromagnetic and paramagnetic phase) of the material in a mean-field fashion. The annealing is modelled assuming that the Mn content x of the $Ga_{1-x}Mn_xAs$ material is reduced when MnAs clusters are formed. Moreover, we assume that the clusters are distributed randomly within the host matrix. Their effect on the transport and the incorpoartion of these effects into the model are described in Ref. [2].

RESULTS AND DISCUSSION

The annealing-induced structural transition from the ferromagnetic alloy to the paramagnetic-ferromagnetic granular hybrid is accompanied by significant changes of the transport behavior (Fig. 1). Already at the low annealing temperatures, the electronic transport changes from a metallic regime in the as-grown sample to an activated transport regime with a strong non-Arrhenius behavior in the sample annealed at 400 °C (left graph of Fig. 1). Both the non-Arrhenius temperature dependence as well as the increase of the slope with increasing annealing temperature can be understood on the basis of our model: The activation of carriers takes place out of an energetically broadened distribution of acceptor states, leading to a nonlinear temperature dependence of the Fermi energy and thus finally to a resistivity dependence of the non-Arrhenius type [3]. In the model, the density of acceptors is a Gaussian distribution centered at the acceptor energy $E_A = 110$ meV with a standard deviation σ. Thermal annealing is not only assumed to reduce the Mn-content x of the matrix but also to narrow the energetic width σ of the acceptor reservoir. The increase of the slope of the temperature dependence of the resistivity cannot be explained with a simple reduction of the

CP893, *Physics of Semiconductors, 28th International Conference*
edited by W. Jantsch and F. Schäffler
© 2007 American Institute of Physics 978-0-7354-0397-0/07/\$23.00

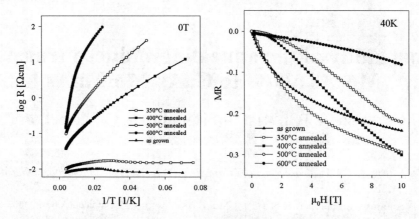

FIGURE 1. Measured temperature dependence of the resistivity (left) and magneto-resistance at 40 K (right).

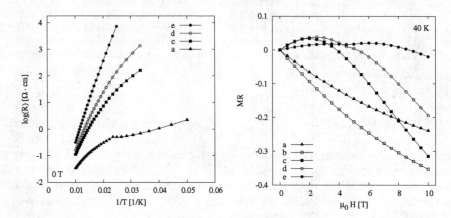

FIGURE 2. Calculated temperature dependence of the resistivity (left) and magneto-resistance at 40 K (right).

density of acceptor states, since such a reduction only leads to a shift of the curve but hardly affects its slope. Reducing both, Mn content in the host matrix as well as energetic width σ of the acceptor state distribution, and thus taking into account the influence of the annealing, we are able to model the measurements qualitatively and almost quantitatively (left graph of Fig. 2). The x value decreases from 0.02 to 0.0075 in the matrix and σ decreases from 55 to 20 meV in the calculated curves (a) to (e). The large σ value for curve (a) somewhat mimics the metallic state. The anomaly in curve (a) arises due to the inclusion of the ferromagnetic-paramagnetic phase transition at $T_C \approx 45$ K in the model.

The right graphs of Figs 1 and 2 show a comparison of measured and calculated MR curves at 40 K. The as grown sample exhibits a weaker negative MR effect than the sample annealed at 350 °C where the cluster formation slowly sets in. With increasing annealing temperature the negative MR effects are less pronounced and eventually almost disappear. The MR experiments also are well reproduced by the theory. In the model, the negative MR arises from the effective reduction of the activation energy due to the Giant-Zeeman splitting of the va-

lence band states in the paramagnetic phase. On the one hand this effect is less pronounced in the as grown sample at 40 K, just below the Curie temperature, because of the presence of a small spontaneous magnetization. On the other hand the effect decreases with decreasing x in the matrix at higher annealing temperatures.

Furthermore, the calculations show that in samples with low MnAs cluster densities, too low to form a percolation network, the transport properties of the matrix define the transport behavior of the entire hybrid despite the higher conductance of the MnAs clusters. The MnAs clusters only play an indirect role by reducing the Mn content x in the surrounding $Ga_{1-x}Mn_xAs$.

REFERENCES

1. C. Michel, P. J. Klar, S. D. Baranovskii and P. Thomas, *Phys. Rev. B* **69**, 165211 (2004).
2. C. Michel, C. H. Thien, S. Ye, P. J. Klar, W. Heimbrodt, S. D. Baranovskii, P. Thomas, M. Lampalzer, K. Volz, W. Stolz and B. Goldlücke *Superlatt. and Microstruct.* **37**, 321 (2005).
3. C. Michel, P. J. Klar, S. D. Baranovskii and P. Thomas and B. Goldlücke *Appl. Phys. Lett.* in press.

Theory of Spin Transport Across Domain-Walls in (Ga,Mn)As

Rafał Oszwałdowski*, Jacek A. Majewski¶, and Tomasz Dietl¶§

* Institute of Physics, Nicolaus Copernicus University, Grudziądzka 5, PL 87-100 Toruń, Poland
¶ Institute of Theoretical Physics, Warsaw University, PL 00-681 Warszawa, Poland
§ Institute of Physics, Polish Academy of Sciences and ERATO Semiconductor Spintronics Project of Japan Science and Technology Agency, PL 02-668 Warszawa, Poland

Abstract. We present results of numerical calculations of domain-wall resistance in the ferromagnetic semiconductor (Ga,Mn)As. We employ Landauer-Büttiker formalism and the tight binding method. Taking into account the full valence band structure we predict the magnitude of the domain-wall resistance without disorder and compare it to experimental values. Next we add disorder to the model and study numerically both small and large disorder regime.

Keywords: dilute magnetic semiconductors, magnetic domains, disorder
PACS: 75.47.Jn, 72.25.Dc, 75.50.Pp

INTRODUCTION

Recently, current-induced domain-wall displacement [1] and intrinsic domain-wall resistance [2,3] have been observed in ferromagnetic semiconductor (Ga,Mn)As. These results attract a lot of attention as they address the question of spin dynamics in the presence of spatially inhomogeneous spin texture as well as they open the doors for novel concepts of high density memories and logic devices.

We study intrinsic domain-wall resistance (DWR) in perpendicular anisotropy (Ga,Mn)As films employing recent theory that combines an empirical multi-orbital tight-binding approach with a Landauer-Büttiker formalism for spin transport [4]. In this scheme, the entire complexity of the valence band structure is taken into account. Since the mean free path of the carriers is typically shorter than the domain wall (DW) width, carrier scattering has to be taken into account. This is accomplished within the 1D Anderson model by assuming random values of on-site energies.

METHOD AND RESULTS

We assume the in-plane current to flow along the x-axis, and the Bloch DW profile to be described by magnetization $M(x)$ according to: $M_x=0$; $M_y=1/\cosh(x/\lambda_W)$; $M_z=\tanh(x/\lambda_W)$, where λ_W denotes the DW length parameter.

Band Structure Contribution to the DWR

It was found in early studies [5] that the resistance of DWs vanishes in the adiabatic limit $\lambda_W k_F \gg 1$. However, in the presence of spin-orbit coupling, DWR is non-zero even in the adiabatic limit [6]. This asymptotic DWR must be taken into account in (Ga,Mn)As, where the DW width is of the same order as Fermi wavelength [7]. In Fig. 1 we present our results for (Ga,Mn)As DWR for relevant values of Mn content and Fermi level E_F. Calculations have been performed for $\lambda_W = 5$ nm, which corresponds to the predicted DW width [8].

However, even the highest value of Fig. 1 is an order of magnitude lower than the DWR determined

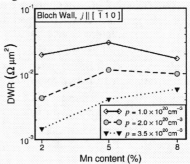

FIGURE 1. Domain-wall resistance in (Ga,Mn)As calculated for valence band structure of GaAs but neglecting disorder.

CP893, *Physics of Semiconductors, 28th International Conference*
edited by W. Jantsch and F. Schäffler
© 2007 American Institute of Physics 978-0-7354-0397-0/07/$23.00

experimentally [3]. Thus, the measured value of DWR cannot be explained by assuming ballistic transport, where rotating magnetization is considered as the only source of scattering.

Disorder Effects in DWR

Given the short mean free path l in (Ga,Mn)As, comparable to λ_W and k_F^{-1} [9], a large role of disorder can be anticipated. Apart from practical implications, this issue is interesting theoretically, since negative DWR in the presence of disorder was predicted theoretically [10,11]. We neglect band structure effects assuming a simple parabolic band, but now introduce random on-site energies in particular atomic layers according to the time-honored 1D Anderson model [12]. The disorder is characterized by the width d of the random energy distribution. For a given disorder configuration, adopting experimentally relevant values of the ratio of spin splitting Δ to Fermi energy E_F, we calculate DWR as a difference between resistance with and without DW. Then we perform averaging for many disorder configurations, and use root-mean-square value as a measure of DWR variance. Using the Drude formula we obtain from the calculated resistivity (without DW) the value of $k_F l$, which corresponds to a particular magnitude of d.

We find, as could be expected, that disorder has no effect on DWR as long as $l \gg \lambda_W$. However, when d increases and thus l decreases, an additional effect, is observed. It is well known, [12] that the variance of resistance calculated in the Anderson model, steeply grows for increasing disorder.

In Fig. 2 we show that the rms of the DWR quickly increases. Each point was calculated averaging over 100 disorder configurations. For values of d yielding $k_F l < 100$, the relative DWR error is larger than one for any spin-splitting Δ. Thus, in this experimentally relevant regime, reliable predictions based on configurational averaging over 1D disorder would require a very high number of configurations.

It is interesting to use the same approach to investigate the possibility of negative DWR in the large disorder limit. To compare more directly with the work of Jonkers et al., [11] we use $k_F \lambda_W / \pi \approx 4$, and $\Delta / E_F \approx 0.8$ in our calculations. We denote the transmission coefficient for the structure with (without) a DW by T (T_0). We calculate T and T_0 for $k_{||} = 0$.

In agreement with the results of [11] we find that for some disorder configurations $T / T_0 > 1$. Percentage of such configurations grows with increasing disorder. This suggests that under some conditions it is possible to obtain, on average, $T / T_0 > 1$ for majority of the tunneling channels $k_{||}$.

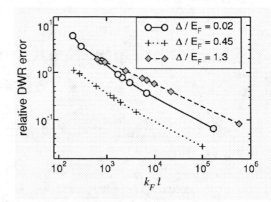

FIGURE 2. Dependence of relative variance of domain-wall resistance on the mean free path l. The DW width is of the order of 10 nm. For the shortest l (highest disorder) also the r-m-s error fluctuates. Note the log-log scale.

If this were the case, a negative DWR would be realized. We must note, however, that with increasing d, the variance of T/T_0 increases, yielding the calculated average uncertain.

ACKNOWLEDGMENTS

This work was partly supported by EU NANOSPIN project (EC:FP6-2002-IST-015728). R.O. acknowledges an additional support by Nicolaus Copernicus University Grant 381-F.

REFERENCES

1. M. Yamanouchi, D. Chiba, F. Matsukura, and H. Ohno, *Nature* **428**, 539-542 (2004); M. Yamanouchi, D. Chiba, F. Matsukura, T. Dietl, and H. Ohno, *Phys. Rev. Lett.* **96**, 096601 (2006).
2. H. X. Tang S. Masmanidis, R. K. Kawakami, D. D. Awschalom, and M. L. Roukes., *Nature* **431**, 52-56 (2004).
3. D. Chiba, M. Yamanouchi, F. Matsukura, T. Dietl, and H. Ohno, *Phys. Rev. Lett.* **96**, 096602 (2006).
4. P. Sankowski, P. Kacman, J.A. Majewski, T. Dietl, *Physica E* **32**, 375-378 (2006); cond-mat/0607206.
5. G. G. Cabrera and L. M. Falicov, *phys. stat. sol. (b)* **61**, 539-549 (1974).
6. Anh Kiet Nguyen, R. V. Shchelushkin, and A. Brataas, cond-mat/0601436.
7. R. Oszwałdowski, J. A. Majewski, and T. Dietl, cond-mat/0605230.
8. T. Dietl, J. König, and A. H. MacDonald, *Phys Rev. B.* **78**, 241201 (1997).
9. F. Matsukura, M. Sawicki, T. Dietl. D. Chiba, and H. Ohno, *Physica E* **21**, 1032-1035 (2004).
10. G. Tatara and H. Fukuyama, *Phys. Rev. Let.* **78**, 3773-3776 (1997).
11. P. A. E. Jonkers, S. Pickering, H. De Raedt, and G. Tatara, *Phys. Rev. B* **60**, 15970-15974 (1999).
12. B. Kramer and A. MacKinnon, *Rep. Prog. Phys.* **56**, 1469-1564 (1993).

Thermoballistic Description of Spin-Polarized Electron Transport in Diluted-Magnetic-Semiconductor Heterostructures

R. Lipperheide and U. Wille

Abteilung Theoretische Physik, Hahn-Meitner-Institut Berlin, Glienicker Str. 100, D-14109 Berlin, Germany

Abstract. In our previously developed thermoballistic description of electron transport in semiconductor structures, the ballistic and diffusive transport mechanisms are unified. By allowing spin relaxation to take place during the ballistic electron motion between randomly distributed equilibration points, a thermoballistic spin-polarized current is constructed. Here, we adopt the thermoballistic description to treat spin-polarized transport in heterostructures formed of a nonmagnetic semiconducting sample sandwiched between two finite-width layers of diluted magnetic semiconductors. We evaluate the magnetoresistance and the current spin polarization for a specific case and compare the results to those of a purely diffusive treatment.

Keywords: Theory, Thermoballistic transport, Spin-polarized transport, Heterostructures, Diluted magnetic semiconductors
PACS: 72.10.-d, 72.25.Dc, 73.40.Lq, 75.50.Pp

1. INTRODUCTION

Spin-polarized electron transport in heterostructures formed of a nonmagnetic semiconductor (NMS) and two (metallic or semiconducting) magnetic contacts is a topic of current interest in spintronics research [1-4]. For ferromagnetic metal (FM) contacts, the efficiency of spin injection into the semiconductor has been found to be very low. It has been demonstrated [5] that this result is related to the large conductivity mismatch between the metal contacts and the semiconductor. One way to circumvent the mismatch problem is provided by the use of contact layers made up of diluted magnetic semiconductors (DMS). A number of experiments using paramagnetic and ferromagnetic DMS have yielded promisingly large values of the spin injection efficiency, and a novel magnetoresistance effect has been observed [6] and theoretically analyzed [6-8] within the diffusive transport theory.

In the present contribution, we treat spin-polarized transport in DMS/NMS/DMS heterostructures within the thermoballistic description which combines elements of the ballistic and diffusive transport mechanisms.

2. THERMOBALLISTIC SPIN-POLARIZED TRANSPORT

Our unified semiclassical description of (spinless) electron transport in semiconductor structures [9] is based on the concept of a "thermoballistic electron current". To construct this current, we consider (assuming a one-dimensional geometry) "ballistic transport intervals" $[x', x'']$ spanned between two equilibration points x' and x'' which are randomly distributed over a semiconducting sample. The *ballistic* current $J(x', x'')$ across the interval $[x', x'']$ is determined by the chemical potentials at x' and x'' and by the maximum of the band edge profile in that interval. The *thermoballistic* current $J(x)$ at position x inside the sample is obtained by summing up the contributions $J(x', x'')$ from all intervals $[x', x'']$ that enclose x, each weighted with the probability $\exp(-|x'' - x'|/l)$ of occurrence of the interval (l = momentum relaxation length). Requiring the current $J(x)$ entering at one end of the sample to be equal to that leaving at the other end and identifying the sample average of $J(x)$ with the (conserved) physical current J, we derive the J-V characteristic in terms of a "reduced resistance" [9].

Spin polarization is included in the thermoballistic description [10] by allowing spin relaxation (with ballistic spin relaxation length l_s) to occur during the electron motion across the interval $[x', x'']$. The *ballistic spin-polarized* current $J_-(x', x''; x)$ is expressed in terms of a spin transport function $A(x)$, which is related to the spin-resolved chemical potentials and to the equilibrium polarization P of the sample. The *thermoballistic spin-polarized* current $J_-(x)$ is obtained in analogy to the thermoballistic current $J(x)$. Using the balance equation connecting $J_-(x)$ with the associated density, we set up a scheme for calculating the function $A(x)$. The current spin polarization $P_J(x)$ is given by the ratio $J_-(x)/J(x)$. In Ref. [10], we have applied the thermoballistic description in a study of spin-polarized transport in FM/NMS/FM heterostructures.

CP893, *Physics of Semiconductors, 28th International Conference*
edited by W. Jantsch and F. Schäffler

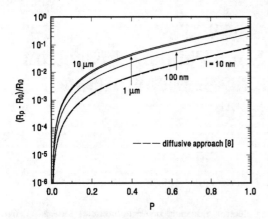

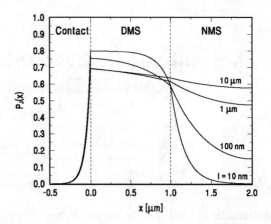

FIGURE 1. Magnetoresistance R_p relative to the zero-field resistance R_0 for a symmetric DMS/NMS/DMS heterostructure ("parallel configuration"), plotted as a function of the DMS equilibrium polarization P for various values of the momentum relaxation length l (width of DMS layers: 1 μm; width of NMS layer: 2 μm; $l_s = 2.5$ μm; for remaining parameter values, see Ref. [10]).

FIGURE 2. Zero-bias current spin polarization $P_J(x)$ for the structure of Fig. 1, with $P = 0.8$. The curve calculated from the diffusive approach of Khaetskii et al. [8] agrees, within the accuracy of the drawing, with our curve for $l = 10$ nm.

3. TRANSPORT IN DMS/NMS/DMS HETEROSTRUCTURES

One way to apply the thermoballistic description to spin-polarized transport in DMS/NMS/DMS heterostructures consists in treating the whole structure as a single semiconducting sample, so that the material parameters (in particular, the equilibrium polarization P) become step functions of position and the ballistic intervals $[x', x'']$ may enclose one or both of the DMS/NMS interfaces. In this case, the ballistic spin-resolved currents are to be matched at the interfaces before the thermoballistic current $J(x)$ is formed. Alternatively, we may treat the different layers of the structure separately, evaluating for each layer the spin transport function $A(x)$ and the current spin polarization $P_J(x)$ in terms of constant parameters and then matching the respective functions at the interfaces. This procedure amounts to considering the interfaces to be equilibration points. While, for reasons of principle, the first alternative is to be preferred, it is more difficult to implement than the second one.

For a symmetric DMS/NMS/DMS structure ("parallel configuration"), we treat the different layers separately and calculate the magnetoresistance R_p relative to the zero-field resistance R_0 [see Fig. 1] as well as the zero-bias current spin polarization $P_J(x)$ [see Fig. 2] for various values of the momentum relaxation length l. For $l \to 0$, our results turn out to match those calculated within the diffusive approach of Khaetskii et al. [8] (neglecting in R_p the field dependence of the DMS conductivity). For intermediate l-values ($l \approx l_s$) and in the ballistic regime, the resistances and the polarization deviate considerably from their diffusive limits, leading to an en-

hancement of $(R_p - R_0)/R_0$ by almost one order of magnitude and to a substantial increase of the spin injection into the NMS, respectively.

4. CONCLUSIONS

By treating spin-polarized electron transport in DMS/NMS/DMS heterostructures within the thermoballistic description, we have been able to study the dependence of the magnetoresistance and of the zero-bias current spin polarization on the momentum relaxation length, and thus have revealed the behavior of these quantities in a parameter range where the diffusive approach is no longer applicable. More detailed studies, in which all structure parameters are systematically varied, remain to be done.

REFERENCES

1. *Semiconductor Spintronics and Quantum Computation*, edited by D. D. Awschalom, D. Loss, and N. Samarth (Springer-Verlag, Berlin, 2002).
2. G. Schmidt and L. W. Molenkamp, Semicond. Sci. Technol. **17**, 310 (2002).
3. I. Žutić, J. Fabian, and S. Das Sarma, Rev. Mod. Phys. **76**, 323 (2004).
4. G. Schmidt, J. Phys. D: Appl. Phys. **38**, R107 (2005).
5. G. Schmidt et al., Phys. Rev. B **62**, R4790 (2000).
6. G. Schmidt et al., Phys. Rev. Lett. **87**, 227203 (2001).
7. Z. G. Yu and M. E. Flatté, Phys. Rev. B **66**, 235302 (2002).
8. A. Khaetskii et al., Phys. Rev. B **71**, 235327 (2005).
9. R. Lipperheide and U. Wille, Phys. Rev. B **68**, 115315 (2003).
10. R. Lipperheide and U. Wille, Phys. Rev. B **72**, 165322 (2005); Mater. Sci. Eng. B **126**, 245 (2006).

Planar Andreev Spectroscopy in InAs

F. Magnus,[1] G. Burnell,[2] Y. Miyoshi,[1] K.A. Yates[1], Y. Bugoslavsky,[1] S. K. Clowes,[1] P. W. Josephs-Franks,[3] M.G. Blamire,[2] and L. F. Cohen[1]

1. Blackett Laboratory, Imperial College, Prince Consort Road, London SW7 2BZ, United Kingdom

2. Department of Materials Science and Metallurgy, University of Cambridge, Pembroke Street, Cambridge CB2 3QZ, United Kingdom

3. National Physical Laboratory, Teddington TW11 0LW, United Kingdom

Abstract. Andreev reflection spectroscopy is a well established method to measure the transport spin-polarization in magnetic films. Here we discuss the prospects for using planar Andreev junctions to detect spin accumulation in the non-magnetic semiconductor InAs. Here we compare Andreev spectra from planar fabricated Pb/InAs junctions and point-contact measurements. Planar junctions yield considerably lower smearing than point-contacts but the barrier parameter Z is highly dependent on the processing method in planar structures.

Keywords: Andreev spectroscopy, superconductivity, spintronics, nanoelectronics.
PACS: 74.50 +r, 74.45 +c, 07.05 Kf, 85.30 Hi

The successful development of spintronic devices requires improved experimental methods of measuring spin-polarized currents within device structures. Point contact Andreev spectroscopy (PCAR), where a superconducting probe is used to interrogate the transport spin-polarization, has been successfully employed to characterize magnetic films [1]. However, using Andreev reflection to study spin accumulation in non-magnetic metals or semiconductors has not been demonstrated previously. In the semiconductor case, there are several additional factors which can severely affect the Andreev spectrum such as interface quality [2], high Fermi velocity mismatch [3], and non-linear conductance backgrounds. Although PCAR spectroscopy has the advantage of speed, control of interfaces is extremely limited and planar Andreev devices could prove an attractive alternative. Here we compare results from point contacts and planar structures on InAs and discuss the implications for spin detection.

Point-contacts were made by pressing a mechanically sharpened Nb tip on to the sample surface, as reported elsewhere [4]. Planar contacts were fabricated onto an undoped InAs film, grown by molecular-beam epitaxy on a semi-insulating GaAs substrate. A combination of conventional photolithography and microfabrication techniques and focused ion beam (FIB) milling was used in the processing. The film was covered with SiO_x, (100 nm, rf sputtered) in which apertures were opened by use of a focused ion beam (FIB) (sample 1) or by a photo-

lithographic lift off process (sample 2) to define the contact area. In both cases a set of superconducting Pb tracks, 50 µm wide, crossing the contact areas, were defined using a photolithographic lift-off process and thermal evaporation. The two processing routes are illustrated in Fig. 1. The differential conductance was measured four-terminally using standard lock-in techniques for all the samples.

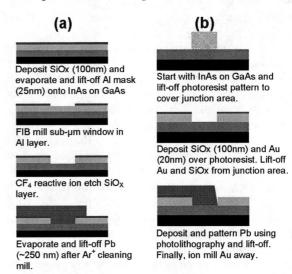

FIGURE 1. Processing of Pb/InAs junctions. (a) Sample 1, using FIB milling. (b) Sample 2, using photolithography.

CP893, *Physics of Semiconductors, 28th International Conference*
edited by W. Jantsch and F. Schäffler
© 2007 American Institute of Physics 978-0-7354-0397-0/07/$23.00

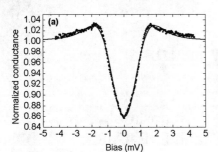 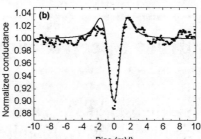 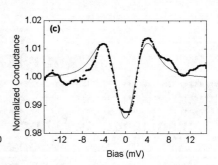

FIGURE 2. Normalized conductance spectra (points) with BTK fits (lines). (a) Sample 1, planar 1 μm × 1 μm sized Pb/InAs junction at 2 K. Parameters: Δ = 0.4 meV, Z = 3.8, ω = 0.6 meV. (b) Sample 2, planar 50 μm × 50 μm Pb/InAs junction at 2 K. Parameters: Δ = 0.4 meV, Z = 2.0, ω = 0.6 meV. (c) Nb/InAs point contact at 4.2 K. Parameters: Δ = 0.7 meV, Z = 1.4, ω = 1.6 meV.

Fig. 2 compares the normalized conductance spectra obtained from the planar Pb/InAs junctions of sample 1 and sample 2 to spectra obtained using Nb point-contacts on InAs. We find that, in junctions with InAs, the Andreev spectrum is superimposed on a large V-shape background, the origin of which is still unknown. To eliminate any spectral structure which is not due to the superconductor we normalize by dividing by the T > T$_C$ spectrum. This should leave only the Andreev features provided that the background conductance is not temperature dependent over the relevant temperature range [5]. The spectra are then fitted using the generalized Blonder-Tinkham-Klapwijk (BTK) theory [6,7] where Z is the interface parameter, Δ is the energy gap and P the polarization. An additional parameter is the generic spectral broadening parameter ω (details in ref. [4]). It should be noted that the normalization procedure is critical to obtaining a good fit and potentially small changes in normalization can have a significant effect on the fitting parameters [4].

The theoretical limit imposed by the Fermi velocity mismatch sets a lower bound for $Z \approx 0.95$. The results from sample 1 are shown in Fig. 2(a). The BTK fit indicates a highly non-transparent interface most likely due to FIB damage. The fabrication method for sample 2 was designed to avoid this problem and as Fig. 2(b) shows, Z is lower for sample 2. But photoresist residue is still likely to contaminate the interface. The point-contact spectrum is noisy and shows much higher smearing than the planar junctions. This is in part due to the higher temperature but, more significantly, there is an indication of very strong surface scattering. All three junctions exhibit a strongly suppressed superconductor energy gap in agreement with several studies of Andreev reflection on semiconductors [2,8] but the planar structures have a strikingly low gap value.

Low values of Z and ω are crucial if accurate values for P are to be extracted once there is a spin

accumulated signal to detect. In addition with the Z and ω values achieved for sample 1 for example, only differences in P of greater than 10-30% would be detectable. So clearly improvements are needed here. The high smearing found for the point-contact junction which is a rather typical result, renders this route impractical.

In summary, results on planar Andreev structures on InAs demonstrate that the interface parameter and the smearing are highly dependent on the fabrication methods used to prepare the junctions. Further development of the processing is needed to minimize the interface barrier so that polarization can be determined reliably.

REFERENCES

1. S. K. Clowes, Y. Miyoshi, Y. Bugoslavsky, W. R. Branford, C. Grigorescu, S. A. Manea, O. Monnereau, and L. F. Cohen, *Physical Review B* **69**, 214425 (2004).
2. K. Neurohr, A. A. Golubov, T. Klocke, J. Kaufmann, T. Schapers, J. Appenzeller, D. Uhlisch, A. V. Ustinov, M. Hollfelder, H. Luth, and A. I. Braginski, *Physical Review B* **54**, 17018-17028 (1996).
3. I. Zutic and O. T. Valls, *Physical Review B* **61**, 1555-1566 (2000).
4. Y. Bugoslavsky, Y. Miyoshi, S. K. Clowes, W. R. Branford, M. Lake, I. Brown, A. D. Caplin, and L. F. Cohen, *Physical Review B* **71** 104523 (2005).
5. W.K. Park, L.H. Greene, J.L. Sarrao and J.D. Thompson, *Physical Review B* **72** 052509 (2005)
6. G. E. Blonder, M. Tinkham, and T. M. Klapwijk, *Physical Review B* **25**, 4515-4532 (1982).
7. I. I. Mazin, A. A. Golubov, and B. Nadgorny, *Journal of Applied Physics* **89**, 7576-7578 (2001).
8. R. P. Panguluri, K. C. Ku, T. Wojtowicz, X. Liu, J. K. Furdyna, Y. B. Lyanda-Geller, N. Samarth, and B. Nadgorny, *Physical Review B* **72**, 054510 (2005).

The conductance of the quantum wire touching the gated Aharonov-Bohm ring

I.A. Shelykh[a)], N.T. Bagraev[b)], N.G. Galkin[b)], L.E. Klyachkin[b)]

[a)]*School of Physics & Astronomy, University of Southampton, SO17 1BJ Southampton, UK*
[b)]*Ioffe Physico-Technical Institute, 194021 St.Petersburg, Russia*

Abstract. We analyse the conductance of the Aharonov - Bohm (AB) one- dimensional quantum ring touching a quantum wire. The period of the AB oscillations is shown to be dependent strongly on the chemical potential and the Rashba coupling parameter that is in a good agreement with the studies of such a device prepared on the Si(100) surface.

Keywords: Spin-orbit interaction, Aharonov-Bohm ring, quantum wire.
PACS: 71.70.Ej; 75.20.Hr; 73.20.Dx

INTRODUCTION

The mesoscopic physics became the intense research field in last two decades. The gated AB rings present a special interest as they can be used as basic components for the realization of the spin interference devices [1]. The conductance of such a structure depends both on the magnetic and electric fields applied perpendicular to the plane of the AB ring. The former provides the AB phaseshift between the waves propagating in the clockwise and anticlockwise direction thus resulting in the conductance oscillations with the period in the range hc/2e – hc/e as a function of the amplitude of the backscattering on the contacts between the ring and the leads [2]. The electric field applied perpendicular to the plane of the ring provides the change of the carrier's wavenumber by shifting the subband's bottom inside the AB ring and by lifting the symmetry of the quantum well as a result of the Rashba spin - orbit interaction (SOI) [3]. The latter depends linearly on the gate voltage and creates the dynamical phaseshift between the waves propagating within the AB ring, which results in the Aharonov - Casher (AC) conductance oscillations [3].

In the present paper we analyze the conductance of the quantum ring touching the quantum wire that are narrow enough to support only one spin-degenerated propagating channel (Fig. 1). The drain-source voltage causing the electric current in the system is taken to be weak enough, so the Landauer-Buttiker formula can be used for the calculation of the conductance at zero temperature [4]:

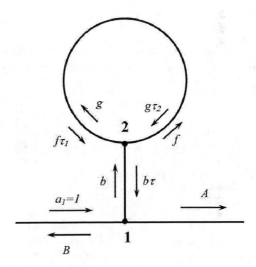

FIGURE 1. The amplitudes of the waves touching the quantum wire. The lead connecting the wire and the ring is introduced for the sake of the simplification of the calculations. Its length is then put equal to zero.

$$G = \frac{e^2}{h}\Big[T_\uparrow(\Phi,\alpha,k_F) + T_\downarrow(\Phi,\alpha,k_F) \Big] \quad (1)$$

where $T_{\uparrow,\downarrow}(\Phi,\alpha,k_F)$ is the transmission coefficient for the carriers of the two opposite spin directions dependent on the magnetic flux, Φ, the Rashba coupling parameter, α, and the Fermi wavenumber, k_F. We suppose also that the spin of the carrier is affected only by the Rashba SOI, because the Zeeman splitting can be neglected in weak magnetic fields.

CP893, *Physics of Semiconductors, 28th International Conference*
edited by W. Jantsch and F. Schäffler
© 2007 American Institute of Physics 978-0-7354-0397-0/07/$23.00

METHODS

In order to calculate the conductance of the device, we used the 3x3 scattering matrix, because the length of a short lead connecting the AB ring and the wire is supposed to be equal to zero. Within the adiabatic approximation the spin of the carrier follows the direction of the effective magnetic field created by the Rashba SOI, and the phase factors of the clockwise and anticlockwise propagating waves read

$$\tau_{1,2\uparrow} = \exp\left[i\left(2\pi k_{\pm}a \pm \frac{e\Phi}{\hbar c} \pm \theta_B\right)\right] \quad (2a)$$

$$\tau_{1,2\downarrow} = \exp\left[i\left(2\pi k_{\mp}a \pm \frac{e\Phi}{\hbar c} \mp \theta_B\right)\right] \quad (2b)$$

where the wavenumbers $k_{\pm}$ differ only if the Rashba SOI is taken into account and θ_B notes the Berry phase. [2].

RESULTS

The conductance calculated as a function of α, is seen to exhibit irregular oscillations determined by the

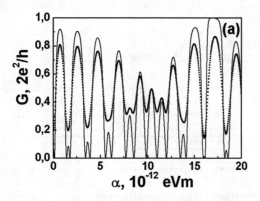

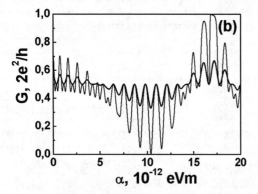

FIGURE 2. The dependence of the conductance on the Rashba SOI parameter for $\Phi/\Phi_0 = 0$ (a) and $\pi/2$ (b). $\mu = 10$ meV, T=0 and T=0.25 K. The radius of the ring is a = 0.5 μm.

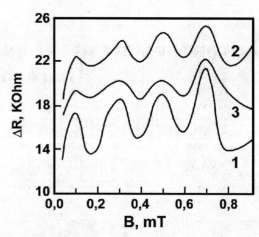

FIGURE 3. The AB conductance oscillations of the quantum wire touching the AB ring embedded in p-type Si-QW on the Si (100) surface that are observed by varying the Rashba SOI. T = 77 K; α, 10^{-12} eVm: 1 – 2; 2 – 4.2; 3 – 9.5.

variations of $k_{\pm}$ due to the AC effect and of θ_B with α if the external magnetic field is absent (Fig. 2a).

If the magnetic field and the Rashba SOI are present, the transmission amplitudes for the two spin components differ, because the transmitted and reflected currents become spin-polarized (Fig. 2b). The interplay between the AB and AC conductance oscillations shown in Figs. 2a and 2b appear to be revealed by studying the conductance of the quantum wire touching the AB ring that were electrostatically prepared inside the p-type Si-QW on the n-Si (100) surface (Fig. 3). The shape of the AB oscillations observed depends on the chemical potential and the Rashba SOI parameter, as it is predicted in Fig. 2b. In particular, these two quantities determine the relation between the amplitudes of the AB oscillations and the Aronov-Altshuler-Spivak oscillations of the half period [5].

SUMMARY

The dependence of the conductance of the quantum wire touching the AB ring on the Rashba SOI parameter has been shown to define by both the geometrical Berry phase and the AC phase.

REFERENCES

1. R. Schuster et al., *Nature* **385** 417-420 (1997).
2. I. A. Shelykh et al., *Phys. Rev. B* **71**, 113311-4 (2005).
3. A. G. Aronov and Y. B. Lyanda-Geller. *Phys. Rev. Lett.* **70**, 343-347 (1993).
4. M. Büttiker, *Phys. Rev. Lett.*, **57**, 1761-1764 (1986).
5. B. L. Altshuler et al., *Sov. Phys. JETP Lett.* **33**, 94-97 (1981).

1284

Electrical Spin Injection into InGaAs Quantum Dot Ensembles and Single Quantum Dots

M. Hetterich, W. Löffler, J. Fallert, T. Passow, B. Daniel, J. Lupaca-Schomber, J. Hetterich, S. Li, C. Klingshirn, and H. Kalt

Institut für Angewandte Physik and DFG Center for Functional Nanostructures (CFN), Universität Karlsruhe (TH), Wolfgang-Gaede-Straße 1, D-76131 Karlsruhe, Germany

Abstract. Electrical spin injection from an n-type ZnMnSe spin aligner into III-V p-i-n diode structures with InGaAs quantum dots (QDs) in the active layer is investigated. Analysis of the circular polarization degree (CPD) of the device emission indicates the spin polarization of the injected electrons. Values > 70% are obtained for the electroluminescence (EL) from the wetting layer and QDs with high ground-state energy. Towards the low-energy end of the emission spectrum, the CPD drops strongly. Temperature-dependent measurements suggest, that this is due to spin relaxation taking place at a stage, when the electrons are not yet finally captured in the dots, i.e. in the GaAs spacer or the wetting layer. Furthermore, we demonstrate electrical spin injection into single InGaAs QDs, a prerequisite for future single spin manipulation experiments within the context of quantum information processing.

Keywords: Spin injection, quantum dots, single dot spectroscopy, spin-LEDs.
PACS: 72.25.Dc, 72.25.Hg, 72.25.Rb, 75.50.Pp

INTRODUCTION

In recent years, the idea of a spin-based quantum information processing has attracted a lot of attention. Some of the prerequisites for the realization of the latter are the ability to spin-polarize electrons, store them at defined sites and address them individually, e.g. to read out the spin state. In this contribution, we investigate electrical spin injection from an n-type ZnMnSe spin aligner into III-V p-i-n diodes containing InGaAs/GaAs quantum dots (QDs). The latter have been shown to be very promising for spin storage [1, 2]. The circular polarization degree (CPD) of these spin light-emitting diodes (spin-LEDs) in a magnetic field is analyzed and provides a direct measure for the electron spin polarization in the QDs [3, 4]. Temperature-dependent and spectrally resolved CPD measurements enable some insight into the spin relaxation mechanisms involved. Finally, we also demonstrate electrical spin injection into *single* QDs.

FABRICATION AND EXPERIMENT

The devices studied were grown by molecular-beam epitaxy (MBE) on Zn-doped p-GaAs(001) substrates. Their bottom III-V part consists of 475 nm GaAs:C ($p \sim 5 \times 10^{17}$ cm^{-3}), 100 nm i-GaAs, the optically active InGaAs QDs, and a 50 nm thick i-GaAs spacer. The II-VI part contains a 750 nm Zn$_{0.95}$Mn$_{0.05}$Se:Cl ($n = 2 \times 10^{18}$ cm^{-3}) spin aligner. On top, we deposited 200 nm of ZnSe:Cl ($n = 5 \times 10^{18}$ cm^{-3}) to improve the quality of the In contact. Standard photolithography was used to define individual devices. Further details may be found in [3, 4] and references therein.

For the injection experiments, the spin-LEDs were mounted in a magneto-cryostat ($B = 0$–14 T, $T = 4$–300 K), and the CPD of the electroluminescence (EL) in Faraday geometry was determined by measuring the σ^- and σ^+ polarized components of the device emission. To achieve a high spatial resolution for the single dot measurements, we integrated a micro-EL set-up with a 20× microscope objective (NA = 0.4) in our magneto-cryostat.

RESULTS AND DISCUSSION

Figure 1 shows the spectrally resolved CPD of the light emitted by a spin-LED at different measurement temperatures. In the high-energy region (wetting layer and QDs in the ensemble emitting at high-energies), the EL shows a strong circular polarization (CPD ~ 0.6) at low temperatures. Indeed, even higher values > 0.7 have been obtained for similar other devices [4].

CP893, *Physics of Semiconductors, 28th International Conference*
edited by W. Jantsch and F. Schäffler

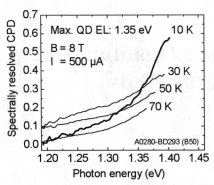

FIGURE 1. Temperature dependence of the spectrally resolved CPD.

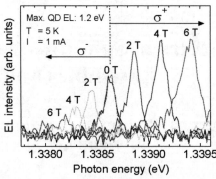

FIGURE 2. *B*-dependent EL spectra of a single QD, in which spin-polarized electrons are injected electrically.

This indicates that efficient spin injection into the III-V structure is indeed taking place. However, for QDs with lower emission energies, the CPD drops strongly. Since excited states do not contribute significantly to the EL of the devices discussed here, Pauli blocking effects cannot account for this energy dependence [4]. Instead, the electron spin is clearly lost for electrons injected into low-energy dots. On the other hand, recent all-optical measurements [1] and theoretical considerations [2] suggest no significant spin relaxation during exciton lifetime in the QDs themselves. We therefore believe, that spin polarization is already lost, before the electrons are finally captured in the dots, i.e. during the phonon-assisted energy relaxation process. At that stage, they are still mobile in the GaAs spacer or the wetting layer, and the D'yakonov-Perel' mechanism should contribute significantly to spin relaxation. Calculations show, that due to the applied voltage and the band bending at the III-V/II-VI interface the spin-polarized electrons have to tunnel through a potential barrier to reach the QDs in our devices [4]. For the low-energy QD states the effective barrier height is higher, i.e. tunneling is slower and there is more opportunity for spin scattering. This may explain, why spin relaxation is stronger for QDs with low ground-state emission. Evidence, that mobile states are indeed involved in the spin relaxation process comes from T-dependent measurements (Fig. 1). The high-energy CPD drops upon heating to ~20% at $T = 70$ K. However, this is not related to spin relaxation but simply caused by the fact, that at higher T the upper Zeeman level in the spin aligner is populated, i.e. the initial spin polarization degree of the injected electrons is lower. On the other hand, the slope of the energy-dependent CPD strongly decreases for higher T. In a certain spectral region this even implies an initial rise of the CPD with temperature and suggests spin relaxation to become less efficient. We attribute this effect to motional narrowing processes, indicating that mobile states should indeed play an important role in the spin relaxation process.

As a prerequisite for future spin manipulation experiments, the ability to address individual QDs is crucial. Therefore, we have started to investigate spin injection into single QDs (see [4] for details). The latter are addressed by micro-EL in the high-energy tail of the spectrum, where not too many dots contribute to the EL and the spin injection efficiency should be high. Preliminary results are shown in Fig. 2. For $B = 0$ T, a sharp emission peak (half-width resolution-limited) from a single QD with no circular polarization is observed. For finite magnetic fields, the Zeeman splitting of the transition is observed. With increasing B, the spin polarization of the injected electrons grows. Accordingly, the σ^+ transition rises, while the σ^- peak practically disappears for $B = 6$ T, indicating nearly full spin polarization. On the other hand, for some emission lines (not shown) a vanishing CPD is found, which explains the lower average values in the ensemble measurements. The reasons for this effect are currently under investigation.

In conclusion, the results presented demonstrate that spin-polarized electrons can be injected into InGaAs QDs with high efficiency, and that individual spin states in single QDs can be addressed optically.

ACKNOWLEDGMENTS

This work has been performed within project A2 of the CFN. It has been further supported by a grant from the Ministry of Science, Research and the Arts of Baden-Württemberg (Az: 7713.14-300).

REFERENCES

1. M. Paillard, X. Marie, P. Renucci, T. Amand, A. Jbeli, and J. M. Gérard, *Phys. Rev. Lett.* **86**, 1634 (2001).
2. E. Tsitsishvili, R. v. Baltz, and H. Kalt, *Phys. Rev. B* **67**, 205330 (2003).
3. W. Löffler et al., *Appl. Phys. Lett.* **88**, 062105 (2006).
4. M. Hetterich et al., to be published in *phys. stat. sol. (b)* **243** (2006).

Spin-dependent Transverse Magnetic Focusing in InSb- and InAs-based Heterostructures

J. J. Heremans[1], Hong Chen[1],
M. B. Santos[2], N. Goel[2], W. Van Roy[3], G. Borghs[3]

[1]Department of Physics, Virginia Tech, Blacksburg, VA 24061, USA
[2]Department of Physics & Astronomy, & Center for Semiconductor Physics in Nanostructures,
The University of Oklahoma, Norman, OK 73019, USA
[3]IMEC, Kapeldreef 75, B-3001, Leuven, Belgium

Abstract. Spin-dependent ballistic transport was observed in InSb/AlInSb and InAs/AlGaSb heterostructures. Split transverse magnetic focusing maxima in InSb are consistent with spin-split trajectories of carriers as well as spin-flipping events occurring when carriers reflect off a lithographic barrier. Similar results are observed in InAs. The temperature dependence reveals that the ballistic focusing maxima survive up to ~150 K for InSb and ~60 K for InAs, whereas the splitting in the maxima disappears at lower temperatures, indicating the latter's separate origin.

Keywords: spin-orbit interaction; transport; ballistic; mesoscopic.
PACS: 72.25.Dc; 73.23.Ad; 73.63.Hs

INTRODUCTION

We present mesoscopic transverse magnetic focusing (TMF) experiments in high mobility InSb/AlInSb and InAs/AlGaSb heterostructures, where the large spin-orbit interaction (SOI) leads to the observation of features consistent with spin-split ballistic transport. The spin of electrons and holes in semiconductors has attracted much interest in the context of spin-dependent electronics. Further, TMF has been used to study ballistic transport, including spin-dependent transport, in semiconductors [1-3]. The narrow-gap semiconductors InSb and InAs and their heterostructures exhibit strong SOI, leading to a spin-splitting in semiclassical trajectories of carriers and to spin-dependent reflection off lithographic barriers [4]. Their large mean free paths, moreover, allow the fabrication of mesoscopic devices in which spin-dependent transport can be exploited for spin manipulation. The n-type InSb/AlInSb heterostructure, MBE grown on GaAs substrate [5], contains a 20-nm-wide InSb well, flanked by $Al_{0.09}In_{0.91}Sb$ barrier layers and Si δ-doped layers. At 0.4 K, the material as grown yields a mobility $\mu = 1.6\times10^5$ cm^2/Vs, and two-dimensional density $N_S = 2.3\times10^{11}$ cm^{-2}, resulting in a mobility mean-free-path $l_P \approx 1.3$ µm. Also grown by MBE on GaAs, the undoped InAs heterostructure contains a 15-nm-wide InAs quantum well, flanked by $Al_{0.2}Ga_{0.8}Sb$ layers, with, in the experiments below, $\mu = 2.8\times10^5$ cm^2/Vs, $N_S = 6.8\times10^{11}$ cm^{-2}, and $l_P \approx 3.7$ µm

at temperature $T = 0.4$ K. Mesoscopic structures are patterned on the materials using standard optical and electron beam lithography and damage-less wet chemical etching.

EXPERIMENT

Figure 1 shows TMF spectra (collector voltage over injected current) of an InSb sample with injector and collector apertures spaced by 0.6 µm (geometry:

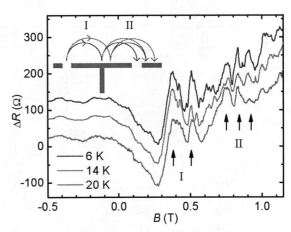

FIGURE 1. TMF spectra of the 0.6 µm InSb sample show doublet and triplet structures for the first and second focusing maxima, respectively. Traces are offset by 50 Ω. Inset: Schematic plot of the focusing structure and spin-split ballistic trajectories.

CP893, *Physics of Semiconductors, 28th International Conference*
edited by W. Jantsch and F. Schäffler
© 2007 American Institute of Physics 978-0-7354-0397-0/07/$23.00

inset in Fig. 1). A semiclassical calculation predicts focusing maxima at magnetic field multiples of $B = 0.42$ T, when the cyclotron orbits fit an integer multiple of times within the injector-collector separation [1-3]. Instead, we observe a doublet structure ($B_1 = 0.37$ T and $B_2 = 0.50$ T) at the position of the first maximum (0.42 T) and a triplet structure at the second maximum (0.84 T). We note that the splitting cannot originate from universal conductance fluctuations since these are not expected at $T = 20$ K. The doublet structure is hence likely caused by an orbital effect, namely by the presence of spin-splitting in the cyclotron orbits, themselves a result of spin-split Fermi contours due to the large SOI in InSb. A same effect has been reported on GaAs/AlGaAs heterostructures [3]. For the second maximum, electrons reflect off the lithographic barrier, which may cause electrons to flip spin states [4], creating four separate trajectories (Fig. 1 inset). Notice that the two spin-flipped trajectories land at the same location at the collector. Therefore only three peaks are expected at $2B_1 = 0.74$ T, $B_1 + B_2 = 0.84$ T, and $2B_2 = 1.0$ T, within 10% of the observed values of 0.76 T, 0.83 T, and 0.90 T, respectively. The consistency of the experimental results with spin-split ballistic trajectories and spin-dependent reflection is bolstered by the further experiments below.

Figure 2 depicts the temperature dependence of another TMF structure on InSb with 1.2 μm separation, twice that of the sample discussed above, resulting in a TMF trajectory length about twice as long as the mean-free-path. The TMF signal is hence not as pronounced as in Fig. 1, and a linear background is subtracted to extract the focusing peaks. The low-T spectra again display split TMF maxima: a peak with a strong shoulder near 0.22 T, and a triplet

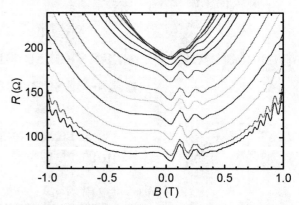

FIGURE 3. TMF spectra of the 2.0 μm InAs sample. From top to bottom, $T = 60, 50, 45, 40, 35, 30, 25, 20, 15, 12.5, 10, 7.5, 5,$ and 4 K. The split maxima merge at ~20 K, at lower T than the TMF maxima smoothing out at ~60 K.

structure between 0.4 and 0.7 T. The fact that the splitting merges at ~80 K whereas the ballistic peaks remain discernible up to ~150 K (similar to the ballistic results in Ref. 6) confirms that the splitting is a feature additional to and of different origin than the main TMF maxima, reinforcing the spin-splitting interpretation.

Figure 3 shows TMF spectra on an InAs/AlGaSb sample with 2.0 μm separation. Low-T spectra show a doublet at the first TMF maximum and a flattening of the second maximum, indicating unresolved multiple split peaks. The splitting in InAs is less pronounced than in InSb, consistent with the latter's stronger SOI. Especially, the Dresselhaus SOI term dominates in InSb, while in our InAs heterostructures the Rashba term is expected to of double the magnitude of the Dresselhaus term. The roles of either contribution in spin-split ballistic transport merits further full study, beyond the scope of the present work. Figure 3 also exhibits a different temperature dependence of the splitting compared to the main ballistic peaks, a phenomenon hence common to our InSb as well as InAs observations.

ACKNOWLEDGMENTS

The authors acknowledge support from the National Science Foundation under Grant Nos. DMR-0618235 (J.J.H.) and DMR-0080054, DMR-0209371 (M.B.S.).

REFERENCES

1. H. van Houten et al. *Phys. Rev. B* **39**, 8556 (1989).
2. J. J. Heremans et al., *Appl. Phys. Lett.* **61**, 1652 (1992).
3. L. P. Rokhinson et al., *Phys. Rev. Lett.* **93**, 146601 (2004).
4. Hong Chen et al., *Appl. Phys. Lett.* **86**, 032113 (2005).
5. S. J. Chung et al., *Physica E* **7**, 809 (2000).
6. Hong Chen et al., *Appl. Phys. Lett.* **84**, 5380 (2004).

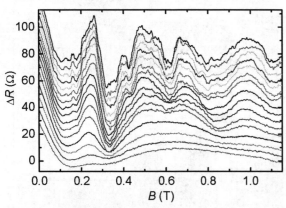

FIGURE 2. TMF spectra of the 1.2 μm InSb sample with linear background subtracted. From top to bottom, $T = 4.5, 6, 8, 10, 13, 16, 20, 25, 30, 40, 50, 60, 80, 100, 125,$ and 150 K. Traces are offset by 5 Ω. The split maxima merge at ~80 K, at lower T than the TMF maxima smoothing out at ~150 K.

Oblique Hanle Measurements of InAs/GaAs Quantum Dot Spin-Light Emitting Diodes

G. Itskos[1], E. Harbord[1], S.K. Clowes[1], E. Clarke[1], P. Van Dorpe[2],
W. Van Roy[2], L.F. Cohen[1] and R. Murray[1]

[1]*Blackett Laboratory, Imperial College London, Prince Consort Rd, London, SW7 2AZ, UK*

[2]*IMEC, Kapeldreef 75, Leuven, B-3001, Belgium*

Abstract. We report here electrical spin injection through an Fe contact into a quantum dot light emitting diode structure using the oblique Hanle geometry. The measured spin polarization in the ground state of the dots is estimated to be 7.5% at 15 K while the injected spin polarization into the structure is estimated to be 20%.

Keywords: quantum dots, spin-LED, electrical spin injection, spin relaxation.
PACS: 73.21La, 78.55-m, 78.67Hc

INTRODUCTION

Efficient injection, manipulation and detection of spin polarized carriers is crucial to the implementation of spintronics devices and quantum computing. There have been many studies of spin relaxation in bulk and quantum well structures but the focus has now turned towards quantum dots (QDs) where strong spatial confinement of trapped carriers is predicted to result in long spin coherence times. Efficient optical spin injection in QDs has been demonstrated in both the ensemble and the single-dot limit but the development of electrically driven spin-based QD devices remains the ultimate goal.

EXPERIMENTAL DETAILS

Figure 1 shows the band diagram of the QD-based spin-light emitting diode (spin-LED)[1]. Holes are injected through the 200 nm thick p-$Al_{0.3}Ga_{0.7}As$ layer and are captured in the dots. Spin polarized electrons are injected (ballistically) through the Schottky diode formed at the interface of the thin (10 nm) Fe layer and the 60 nm thick n-$Al_{0.1}Ga_{0.9}As$ layer. The active region consists of a single layer of QDs grown at a low deposition rate. Electroluminescence (EL) occurs due to recombination of excitons in the ground state of the QDs at a wavelength of ~1200 nm. The processed device is held at 15 K in a closed cycle cryostat at 45° to the applied magnetic field. The optical polarization of the emitted light is analyzed using a combination of

a quarter wave plate and a linear polarizer and detected by a spectrometer equipped with a Ge photodiode.

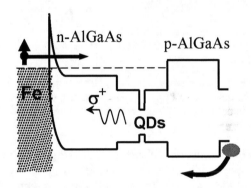

FIGURE 1. Band diagram of the spin LED. Injected holes (unpolarized) and electrons (polarized) relax into the QDs. Light is emitted through the top (Fe) contact.

RESULTS AND DISCUSSION

Conventional surface emitting LEDs emit unpolarized light. In this device spin polarized electrons are injected from the Fe contact into the semiconductor where they relax into the dots. Circularly polarized light will then be emitted along the growth (z) direction provided there is a non-zero S_z component of the electron spin[2]. The EL emission is collected from the top of the device through the Fe contact that must be thin to minimize light absorption. This means that due to shape anisotropy the Fe

CP893, *Physics of Semiconductors, 28th International Conference*
edited by W. Jantsch and F. Schäffler
© 2007 American Institute of Physics 978-0-7354-0397-0/07/$23.00

magnetization lies in the film plane. Injected electrons will therefore have their spins aligned perpendicular to z. Application of a high magnetic field rotates the magnetization (Faraday geometry) so that electrons with predominantly S_z polarization are injected. Alternatively application of a relatively weak magnetic field (Oblique Hanle geometry) causes the injected spins to precess around B with a Larmor frequency $\Omega = g^*\mu_B B/\hbar$ where g^* is the effective Landé factor. The B field is applied at an angle of $\varphi = 45°$ with z.

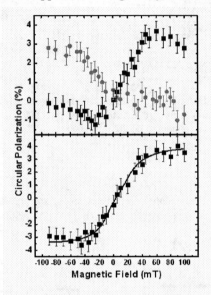

FIGURE 2. Upper panel: circular polarization P (squares) and photoluminescence (circles). Lower panel: normalized P taking into account Zeeman splitting and MCD. All measurements were carried out at T=15K

Figure 2 contains the summary of the results from the oblique Hanle experiment. The upper panel shows (squares) the circular polarization P of the ground-state excitonic EL as a function of oblique magnetic field. The polarization is defined as $P = (\Gamma^+ - \Gamma^-)/(\Gamma^+ + \Gamma^-)$, where Γ^+, Γ^- are the respective σ^+, σ^- circular polarized components of the QD exciton, obtained by area integration. The data must be normalized to take into account the contribution of intrinsic, non-spin injection effects, such as the Zeeman splitting in the QDs and the magneto-optical circular dichroism (MCD) arising from the transmission of light through the thin Fe contact. The correction is achieved by obtaining the circular polarization of the QD photoluminescence signal excited by an unpolarized He-Ne laser (upper panel, circles) and subtracting it from the corresponding EL data. The lower panel of figure 2 shows the normalized Hanle curve which can be fitted by the Lorentzian function[3]:

$$S_Z(B) = S_{0X} \cdot (T_S/\tau_r) \cdot [(\Omega T_S)^2 \cos\varphi \sin\varphi] / [1 + (\Omega T_S)^2]$$

where T_S (defined by $1/T_S = 1/\tau_S + 1/\tau_r$) is the QD ground state exciton spin lifetime, τ_S is the exciton spin relaxation time and τ_r the exciton recombination time.

Fits to the data yield a half-width of $B_{1/2} = 21.5\pm2.9$ mT from which we derive a scaled ground state exciton spin lifetime of $g^*T_S = \hbar/\mu_B B_{1/2} = 510\pm70$ ps. From the saturation value of the curve we get the steady-state QD spin polarization to be equal to $(7.5\pm0.7)\%$. Then the spin injection efficiency from the Fe film to the semiconductor, before QD recombination, can be derived from $\Pi = (7.5\pm0.7)\% \cdot \tau_r/T_S$. Assuming a value of $g^* = -1.7$[4] and an exciton recombination lifetime[5] of 800 ps from time-resolved studies in our dots, Π is estimated $\sim20\%$.

The spin polarization at the Fe Fermi level is close to 45% and Π is smaller than that by a factor of two. The polarization loss is attributed to D'yakonov-Perel (DP) spin dephasing mechanism[2] that acts in the ballistically (hot) injected electrons during their thermalization in the AlGaAs and GaAs part of the spin-LED structure. Indeed, similar results have been reported for spin-LEDs having bulk active regions[3]. Increases in the spin injection efficiency may be possible through improvements in the magnetic contacts and device design. The most notable result is the apparent loss of spin after capture by the dots. At this stage we cannot be sure whether the spin dephasing affects carriers occupying the ground state of the dots and/or during relaxation through the excited states of the dot. Spin-filp mechanisms, such as electron-hole exchange and hyperfine interactions have been shown to be strong in InAs/GaAs dots. We are currently investigating this aspect of QD spin-LEDs. One approach is to tailor the QD electronic structure (through for instance annealing) to modify the radiative lifetime or influence the relaxation rate within the dots through control of the excitation rate.

ACKNOWLEDGMENTS

The authors acknowledge useful discussions with Drs Patrick Howe and Edmund Clarke. EH thanks EPSRC for a studentship as part of the Ultrafast Photonics Consortium.

REFERENCES

1. G. Itskos *et al., Appl.Phys.Lett.,* **88** 022113 (2006) (and references within)
2. F. Meier and B.P. Zachachrenya in *Optical Orientation* (North-Holland, Amsterdam, 1984)
3. V.F. Motsnyi *et al., Phys.Rev.B* **68**, 245319 (2003).
4. T. Nakaoka *et al., Phys.Rev.B* **70** 235337 (2004)
5. S. Malik *et al., Phys.Rev. B* **63** 155313 (2001)

Detection of Magnetic Domain Wall in a Permalloy Wire using a Semiconductor and Ferromagnetic Hybrid Structure

Yoshiaki Sekine[*], Tatsushi Akazaki[*], Junsaku Nitta[†,¶]

[*]*NTT Basic Research Laboratories, Nippon Telegraph and Telephone Corporation,*
3-1 Morinosato-Wakamiya, Atsugi, Kanagawa 243-0198, Japan
[†]*Graduate School of Engineering, Tohoku University, 6-6-02 Aoba, Aramaki-aza, Aoba-ku, Sendai,*
Miyagi 980-8579, Japan
[¶]*CREST-JST, Japan Science and Technology Agency, 4-1-8 Honchou, Kawaguchi, Saitama 331-0012, Japan*

Abstract. Using the local Hall effect (LHE), we have succeeded in detecting a magnetic domain wall (DW) trapped in a permalloy $Ni_{80}Fe_{20}$ wire and in clearly distinguishing whether the DW structure is a head-to-head or a tail-to-tail DW. The LHE method has an advantage of large signal and makes it possible to investigate the inner DW structure.

Keywords: domain wall, local Hall effect, two-dimensional electron gas, stray field
PACS: 75.60.Ch, 75.60.-d, 73.61.Ey

INTRODUCTION

In the field of spintronics [1], intensive research has been carried out to develop devices that control the position of a magnetic domain wall (DW), such as a logic device performing NOT-operations [2] and a magnetic race-track memory [3]. To investigate a DW position, DWs trapped in a notch or hole structure formed in ferromagnetic wires were detected using the giant magnetoresistance [4,5], anisotropic magnetoresistance [6], and extraordinary Hall effect [7]. Compared with these methods, the local Hall effect (LHE) method [8] has the advantage of having sufficient sensitivity to measure DW velocity [9]. In this work, we have succeeded in detecting a DW trapped in a notch in a permalloy $Ni_{80}Fe_{20}$ wire using the LHE method. Furthermore, we were able to clearly distinguish whether the DW structure is a head-to-head or a tail-to-tail DW.

SAMPLE FABRICATION

The layer of an InGaAs two-dimensional electron gas (2DEG) with a 2.5-nm-thick InP barrier layer was grown by the molecular-organic chemical vapor deposition. A Hall bar with three $0.8{\times}0.8\ \mu m^2$ Hall crosses was fabricated by the electron beam (EB) lithography and electron-cyclotron dry etching. A 60-nm-thick and 300-nm-wide $Ni_{80}Fe_{20}$ wire was deposited on the InP surface layer. A tapered end, right-angle end, and

centered notch were made in the wire by the EB lithography and lift-off technique. Gold was deposited on the $Ni_{80}Fe_{20}$ wire to a thickness of 5 nm to prevent the oxidation of $Ni_{80}Fe_{20}$. A scanning electron microscopy (SEM) image and the schematic cross-sectional view of the sample are shown in figures 1(a) and (b), respectively. The three Hall crosses are just under the tapered end, notch, and right-angle end. The stray magnetic field from each region of the magnetic wire is detected by the Hall crosses. Using a lock-in-amplifier

(a)

(b)
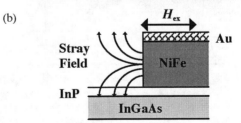

FIGURE 1. (a) SEM image of the sample. Three Hall crosses are just under the tapered end, centered notch, and right-angle end of the $Ni_{80}Fe_{20}$ wire. (b) Schematic view of the sample. The InGaAs 2DEG detects the stray magnetic field from the wire. The sweeping direction of H_{ex} is parallel both to the wire and to the 2DEG.

CP893, *Physics of Semiconductors, 28th International Conference*
edited by W. Jantsch and F. Schäffler
© 2007 American Institute of Physics 978-0-7354-0397-0/07/$23.00

with a frequency of 172 Hz, the Hall resistivities, ϱ_{yx}, of the three Hall crosses were measured at 300 K while sweeping an external magnetic field, H_{ex}, parallel both to the wire and to the 2DEG. In the magnetization reversal processes, DW nucleation, trapping, and annihilation occur at the right-angle end, centered notch, and tapered end, respectively. Note that the DW always nucleates at the right-angle end. Therefore, trapped DW is expected to be a head-to-head or a tail-to-tail DW with decreasing or increasing H_{ex}, respectively.

RESULTS AND DISCUSSION

Figure 2 shows ϱ_{yx} of the three Hall crosses as a function of H_{ex}. Here, ϱ_{yx} of the probe at the right-angle end, centered notch, and tapered end are defined as $\varrho_{yx}1$, $\varrho_{yx}2$ and $\varrho_{yx}3$, respectively. The left and right axes represent $\varrho_{yx}1$ or $\varrho_{yx}3$ and $\varrho_{yx}2$, respectively. The scale of the left axis ten times as large as that of the right axis. Sharp jumps of $\varrho_{yx}1$ and $\varrho_{yx}3$ are observed around the coercive force, and the curves of $\varrho_{yx}1$ and $\varrho_{yx}3$ show clear hysteresis loops with sweeping H_{ex}. The sharp jumps correspond to the DW nucleation or annihilation, and the jumps are in opposite directions. These rapid changes are approximately 10 Ω. These

sharp jumps of of $\varrho_{yx}1$ and $\varrho_{yx}3$ occur at ±22 and ±26 mT, respectively. As expected, the DW nucleates at the right-angle end in the lower coercive force of 22 mT, and annihilates at the tapered end in the higher coercive force of 26 mT. Between these lower and higher coercive forces, $\varrho_{yx}2$ shows a dip with decreasing H_{ex} and a peak with increasing H_{ex}. The dip and peak correspond to the trapped head-to-head and tail-to-tail DWs, respectively. This is because the stray magnetic field from the head-to-head and tail-to-tail DWs are opposite. These results clearly show that the DW can be detected by the LHE method. Moreover, it is possible to investigate the inner DW structure. The peak and dip heights are approximately 1 Ω, and one-tenth that of the sharp jumps of $\varrho_{yx}1$ and $\varrho_{yx}3$. These heights depend on the stray field from the DW. The small changes of $\varrho_{yx}2$ indicate that the trapped DWs have inner DW structures that reduce the stray field.

In summary, the DW trapped at the notch in the $Ni_{80}Fe_{20}$ wire was detected by the LHE method. Furthermore, we succeeded in distinguishing whether the DW structure is the head-to-head or the tail-to-tail DW from the change of ϱ_{yx}. The LHE method has the advantage of large signal and makes it possible to investigate the inner DW structure. These results will be useful for the development of future DW devices.

REFERENCES

1. G. Prinz, *Science* 282 (1998) 1660.
2. D. A. Allwood, Gang Xiong, M. D. Cooke, C. C. Faulkner, D. Atkinson, N. Vernier, and R. P. Cowburn, *Science* **296**, 2003 (2002).
3. S. S. P. Parkin, U.S. Patent No. 6,834,005 (21 December 2004).
4. T. Ono, H. Miyajima, K. Shigeto, and T. Shinjo, *Appl. Phys. Lett.* **72**, 1116 (1998).
5. A. J. Zambano, and W. P. Pratt, Jr., *Appl. Phys. Lett.* **85**, 1562 (2004).
6. K. Miyake, K. Shigeto, K. Mibu, T. Shinjo, and T. Ono, *J. Appl. Phys.* **91**, 3468 (2002).
7. H. W. Schumacher, D. Ravelosona, F. Cayssol, J. Wunderlich, C. Chappert, V. Mathet, A. Thiaville, J. P. Jamet, J. Ferré, and R. J. Haug, *IEEE Trans. Magn.* **37**, 2331 (2001).
8. J. Nitta, T. Schäpers, H. B. Heerche, T. Koga, Y. Sato, and H. Takayanagi, *Jpn. J. Appl. Phys.* **41**, 2497 (2002).
9. Y. Sekine and J. Nitta, in *Narrow Gap Semiconductors*, Inst. Phys. Conf. Ser. **187**, edited by J. Kono and J. Léotin: Taylor & Francis, New York, 2006, pp. 461-466.

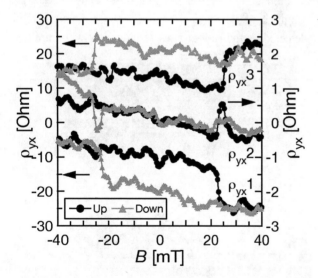

FIGURE 2. The $\varrho_{yx}1$, 2, and 3 with sweeping H_{ex} measured by a lock-in-amplifier at 300 K. The sharp jumps of $\varrho_{yx}1$ and 3 correspond to the nucleation and annihilation of the DW, respectively. The dip and peak of $\varrho_{yx}2$ with decreasing and increasing H_{ex} show the trapped head-to-head and tail-to-tail DWs, respectively.

Study of Spin Dynamics in Quantum Hall Regime by Time Resolved Kerr Rotation Spectroscopy

Daisuke Fukuoka[1], Naoki Tanaka[1], and Kiyofumi Muro[2]

[1]*Graduate School of Science and Technology, Chiba University, Chiba 263-8522, Japan*
[2]*Department of Physics, Faculty of Science, Chiba University, Chiba 263-8522, Japan*

Abstract. Time-resolved Kerr rotation (TRKR) spectroscopy has been applied to a two-dimensional (2D) electron gas in GaAs/AlGaAs hetero-junction to probe the electron and nuclear spin dynamics in quantum Hall regime. A large and long-lasting Kerr rotation signal was ascribed to the high-mobility 2D-electron gas, since the Kerr signal from etched high purity GaAs substrate was much smaller and shorter. In a configuration where an out-of-plane magnetic field quantizes 2D-electrons into Landau levels, the spin coherence time, T_2^* exhibits a drastic increase. Furthermore, both T_2^* and effective g factor exhibit an oscillation behavior as a function of the magnetic field. Under a circularly polarized pump, we observed an Overhauser shift up to 40 μeV, which corresponds to 30 % dynamic nuclear polarization (DNP).

Keywords: 2D-electron gas, time-resolved Kerr rotation, dynamic nuclear polarization, spin dynamics
PACS: 71.10.Ca, 73.43.-f, 75.40.Gb

INTRODUCTION

A high-mobility 2D-electron gas in the quantum Hall regime presents a variety of spin related phenomena based of the long spin coherence. However, so far, few works have been reported on the dynamical behaviors of the spin dynamics of 2D-electron gas [1] [2]. In the present work, we have applied a time-resolved Kerr rotation spectroscopy on the high-mobility 2D electron gas in a GaAs/AlGaAs hetero-junction on a (100) non-doped GaAs substrate.

EXPERIMENTS

2D-electron spin coherence measurements were performed on a modulation doped GaAs/AlGaAs hetero-junction grown by molecular beam epitaxy on (100) GaAs substrate. The electron sheet density and mobility are 2.4×10^{11}/cm^2 and 2.3×10^5cm^2/Vs, respectively at T = 1.5 K and dark condition.

A 100 fs Ti:Sapphire laser with a pulse repetition rate of 76 MHz was tuned to the band gap of GaAs, 1.53 eV. A folded beam delay unit enabled a time delay between pump and probe pulses, Δt ranging form −2.4 to 8.2 nsec. Circularly polarized pump beam (1 mW) and linearly polarized probe beam (0.5 mW) were focused on the sample surface with a spot size of 250 μmφ. Kerr rotation of the order of 1 μrad could be measured as a function of the time delay with the combination of an optical bridge and a balanced photo-diode detector. A 50 kHz photo-elastic modulator was used to modulate the helicity of a circular pump beam or to generate 100 kHz amplitude modulation of the circularly polarized light for the measurement of DNP. The sample was placed in a liquid He cryostat with optical windows (SpectroMag, Oxford). As shown in Figure 1, measurements were carried out in the Voigt configuration and the 45° tilted field configuration.

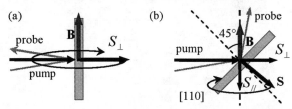

FIGURE 1. Two measurement geometries (a) Voigt configuration, (b) 45° tilted field configuration.

Precessing spin, $S_\perp$ can be measured in the Voigt configuration, while both of the precessing spin, $S_\perp$ and non-precessing spin, $S_{//}$ can be measured in the 45° tilted field configuration. The Kerr rotation evolutions are expressed in the following equations, respectively;

$$\theta_{K,Voigt} = S_\perp \exp\left(\frac{-\Delta t}{T_2^*}\right)\cos\left(\frac{g^*\mu_B B\Delta t}{\hbar}\right) \quad (1)$$

$$\theta_{K,45°} = S_{//} \exp\left(\frac{-\Delta t}{T_1}\right) + S_\perp \exp\left(\frac{-\Delta t}{T_2^*}\right)\cos\left(\frac{g^*\mu_B B\Delta t}{\hbar}\right) \quad (2)$$

CP893, *Physics of Semiconductors, 28th International Conference*
edited by W. Jantsch and F. Schäffler
© 2007 American Institute of Physics 978-0-7354-0397-0/07/$23.00

RESULTS AND DISCUSSIONS

Using the helicity modulation of the circular pump beam, TRKR signals presented typical free induction decays in the Voigt configuration. The g^* decreased monotonically from 0.43 to 0.42, and T_2^* decreased from 350 to 150 ps in the magnetic field from 0 to 7 T.

Figure 2 (a) and (b) show TRKR signals in the 45° configuration, and T_2^* and g^* estimated from the Fourier transform of TRKR signal as function of magnetic field. Spin coherence time, T_2^* increased drastically in the out-of-plain filed below 0.5 T, and then presented peaks around 2.25, 3.25, 4.5 and 6.25 T. The amplitude of Kerr signal also showed peaks at the fields. The evolution of g^* correlates with the evolution of T_2^*. Assuming the electron density $3.1\times10^{11}/cm^2$, the peaks of T_2^* well coincide with the integer filling factors. This is considered to be caused by the suppression of the scattering-driven spin decoherence. The increase of the 2D-electron density from dark condition ($2.4\times10^{11}/cm^2$) may be induced by the optical pumping. These oscillatory behaviors of T_2^* and g^* resemble the results of V. Sih et. al. [1].

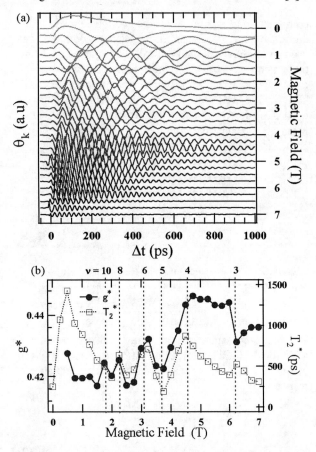

FIGURE 2. (a) The TRKR signal in the 45° configuration at T = 1.5 K. (b) g^* (solid circle) and $T2^*$ (open square) as a function of magnetic field. Vertical dashed lines represent the filling factors assuming the electron density $3.1\times10^{11}/cm^2$.

However, even filling factor corresponds to the dip of T_2^* in their results. This difference might be ascribed to the large difference of the 2D-electron mobilities of the samples. Evolution of g^* can be understood by the Landau level dependence of g^*-factor [3].

Figure 3 shows the spin precession energies observed in three different modulation schemes, i.e., σ^+-σ^- helicity modulation and σ^+ or σ^- amplitude modulations. σ^- polarization pumping brought a large negative Overhauser shift while σ^+ polarization pump brought a small positive shift. Overhauser shift for σ^- pumping reached to 40 μeV at 7 T, which corresponds to 30 % polarization of total nuclear spin. So far, all optical nuclear magnetic resonance based on TRKR was limited in the 2D-electron gas on a (110) substrate. However, the long electron spin coherence in the quantum Hall regime may allows all optical NMR study in the high-mobility 2D-electrons in (100) GaAs substrate.

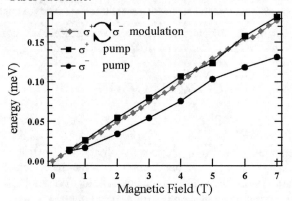

FIGURE 3. Spin precession energy in the 45° tilted configuration as a function of magnetic field at T = 1.5 K.

We have successfully applied TRKR spectroscopy on the spin study of 2D-electrons in the quantum Hall regime. The increase of spin coherence based on the orbital quantization and the consequent dynamic nuclear spin polarization have been observed.

We acknowledge Prof. K. Oto for the valuable discussions. This work is supported by a Grant-in-Aid for Sci. Res. on priority Areas "High Field Spin Science in 100T" (No.451) from MEXT, Japan.

REFERENCES

1. V. Sih, W. H. Lau, R. C. Myers, A. C. Gossard, M. E. Flatte, and D. D. Awschalom, Phys. Rev. B 70, 161313, (2004)
2. M. A. Brand, A. Malinowski, O. Z. Karimov, P. A. Marsden, R. T. Harley, A. j. Shields, D. Sanvitto, D. A. Ritchie, and M. Y. Simmons, Phys. Rev. Lett. 89, 236601, (2002)
3. M. Dobers, K. v. Kilitzing, and G. Weimann, Phys. Rev. B 38, 5453, (1988)
4. G. Salis, D. T. Fuchs, J. M. Kikkawa, D. D. Awschalom, Y. Ohno, and H. Ohno, Phys. Rev. Lett. 86, 2677, (2001)

Spin Susceptibility Enhancement of a Spin Polarized Two Dimensional Electron Gas Determined by Raman Spectroscopy

F. Perez[1], C. Aku-Leh[1, 2], B. Jusserand[1], D. Richards[2], and G. Karczewski[3]

[1] Institut des Nanosciences de Paris, UMR 7588, CNRS/Université Paris VI et VII, Campus Boucicaut, 140 rue de Lourmel, 75015 PARIS, France
[2] Department of Physics, King's College London, Strand, London WC2R 2LS, United Kingdom
[3] Institute of Physics, Polish Academy of Sciences, al. Lotnikòw 32/46, 02-668 Warszawa, Poland

Abstract. We show Raman Scattering measurements by spin flip excitations of a spin polarized two-dimensional electron gas embedded in a doped CdMnTe quantum well. Depolarized Raman spectra exhibit a coexistence of the collective Spin Flip Wave and the Single Particle Spin Flip Excitation. At vanishing wavevector, we show that these excitations provide direct determination of Z, the bare and Z^*, the enhanced Zeeman energies. We link these two quantities with recent magneto-transport measurement of the spin susceptibility enhancement due to Coulomb exchange and correlations.

Keywords: Electronic Raman Scattering, spin-polarized electron gas, Zeeman splitting, semi-magnetic quantum well
PACS: 72.25.Dc, 73.21.-b, 78.30.-j, 78.55.-m

Low dimensional electron gases embedded in semiconductors quantum wells have proven themselves to be excellent specimens to reveal Coulomb effects physics. Due to Coulomb exchange and correlations, the spin susceptibility χ is enhanced compared to the Pauli one χ_0. This enhancement χ/χ_0, also given by the mass (m^*/m_b) and g-factor (g^*/g_b) enhancement (b indices stand for band values), i-e $\chi/\chi_0 = m^* g^* / m_b g_b$, has been recently investigated by many groups using magneto-conductance measurements on two-dimensional electron gases (2DEG) [1]. Experimental techniques employed by the above cited groups can accurately determine the product $m^* g^*$ as a function of the electron density for low spin polarization degree ζ, thus enabling a comparison with recent determination of spin polarized 2DEG correlation energy [2] and thickness and disorder correction [3]. In this work we have investigated the same enhancement using Spin Flip Electronic Raman Scattering (SFR) under Magnetic Field [4]. We have used CdMnTe modulation doped quantum wells exhibiting giant Zeeman effect $Z(B)$ rather than GaAs heterostructures where Landau quantization dominates [5]. SFR measurements were carried out on a 15 nm thick $Cd_{1-x}Mn_xTe$ modulation doped (Iodine) quantum well with 0.75% Mn. The

barriers were made of $Cd_{1-x}Mg_xTe$ with 15% Mg. The sample was mounted in the core of a 5 T superconducting magnet providing a field in the plane of the quantum well, and all were immersed in superfluid helium. The Voigt configuration was used. A Ti:sapphire laser with incident power densities below 1 W/cm^2 (to avoid heating the Mn^{2+} ions) was tuned to resonate close to 1.65 eV transition energy between the first and the second electron (hole) level respectively. Electron density varied from 5.0 to 2.0 10^{11}cm^{-2}. Compared to transport, this allows (1) direct measurement of both the bare $Z(B)$ and the enhanced $Z^*(B)$ Zeeman energies and (2) to investigate the continuous dependence of the enhancement with the spin polarization degree.

Figure 1 shows depolarized Raman spectra for vanishing wavevector $q \sim 0$, obtained for different magnetic fields ranging from 0 to 2.0T. Each spectrum shows the coexistence of a low energy narrow line and a higher energy broader line, both dispersing with the applied magnetic field. The narrow line is observed even for the weakest magnetic fields with a Raman shift which increases with the field strength and saturates at 2.0T. The broad Raman feature is clearly separated from the low energy line for fields above 0.3T, when the line corresponds to a well defined mode of the SP2DEG. In previous work [4,6], we have

CP893, *Physics of Semiconductors, 28th International Conference*
edited by W. Jantsch and F. Schäffler
© 2007 American Institute of Physics 978-0-7354-0397-0/07/$23.00

already shown that the narrow line corresponds to the collective Spin Flip Wave (SFW), whose energy at vanishing wavevector q, due to the Larmor theorem coincides with the bare Zeeman energy $Z(B)$ due to the exchange coupling between conduction band electrons and Mn electrons. The additional high energy line which is only seen in depolarized spectra is assigned to single particle spin flip excitations $E_{\downarrow\uparrow}$. At vanishing wavevector, these excitations are degenerate and correspond to the renormalized Zeeman energy $Z^*(B)$, energy responsible for the conduction band splitting. The inset of Fig.1 reproduces $Z(B)$ and $Z^*(B)$, which is clearly enhanced due to Coulomb exchange and correlations.

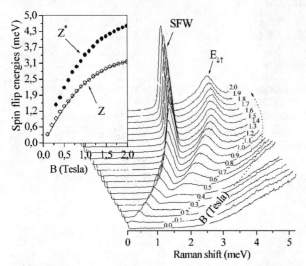

FIGURE 1. SFR spectra in Voigt ($q \sim 0$) for various magnetic field. The inset reproduces magneto-dispersions of the two lines *SFW* and $E_{\downarrow\uparrow}$, respectively corresponding to Z and Z^*. As shown by the curve Z(B) is well reproduced by the Brillouin curve with parameters : x=0.75%, T_{Mn}=1.7K.

The link between the Zeeman enhancement Z^*/Z and the spin susceptibility enhancement is as follows. We assume a 2D parabolic band for each spin sub-bands and the same mass enhancement for each spin population $m_\uparrow^* = m_\downarrow^* = m^*$. The latter is expected to be a weak assumption for low ζ. In such a case ζ is simply given by : $\zeta = m^* Z^* / 2\pi\hbar^2 n_{2D} = Z^*/2E_F$, where E_F is the Fermi energy of the unpolarized 2DEG and n_{2D} is the electron density. Let ζ_0 be the bare spin polarization degree : $\zeta_0 = m_b Z / 2\pi\hbar^2 n_{2D}$. By definition, the spin susceptibility enhancement is given by $\chi/\chi_0 = d\zeta/d\zeta_0$, leading to :

$$\frac{\chi}{\chi_0} = \frac{d\zeta}{d\zeta_0} = \frac{m^*}{m_b}\frac{dZ^*}{dZ} \qquad (1)$$

The quantity dZ^*/dZ is here fully equivalent to g^*/g_b for the non-magnetic samples. We show here,

how the knowledge of both the individual and collective spin flip excitation energies leads directly to the determination of the g-factor enhancement in the spin susceptibility.

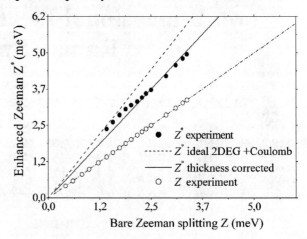

FIGURE 2. Comparison of $Z^*(Z)$ deduced from experiment with the calculated one (see text).

Figure 2 compares $Z^*(Z)$ determined from Fig.1 with the same quantity calculated using Eq. 1, definition of ζ and the well known formula :

$$\frac{\chi}{\chi_0} = \left(1 + \frac{r_s^2}{2}\frac{\partial^2 \varepsilon_{xc}}{\partial \zeta^2}\right)^{-1}$$

where ε_{xc} is the exchange-correlation part of the ground-state energy in Rydberg given by [2], r_s is the coupling strength. The recent evaluation of the finite thickness correction [3] was included. The density has been extracted from spin conserving excitations dispersion [7]. A density of n_{2D}=4.4 10^{11}cm^{-2} corresponding to r_s=1.7 was found. For this value the mass enhancement is negligible and was not considered. Without any fitting parameters, the thickness corrected value reproduces the enhanced Zeeman energy $Z^*(Z)$ well, within 10%.

In Conclusion, we show here for the first time direct spectroscopic determination of the Zeeman enhancement in a Spin Polarized 2DEG out of Landau Quantization [5]. We demonstrate the Coulomb origin of this enhancement.

This work was supported by EPSRC, King's College London and the CNRS.

1. Y.W. Tan *et al.*, *Phys. Rev. Lett.* **94**, 016405-1 (2006); and references therein.
2. C. Attacalite *et al.*, *Phys. Rev. Lett.* **88**, 256601 (2002)
3. S. De Palo *et al.*, *Phys. Rev. Lett.* **94**, 256405 (2005)
4. B. Jusserand *et al.*, *Phys. Rev. Lett.* **91**, 086802 (2003)
5. A. Pinczuk *et al.*, *Phys. Rev. Lett.* **68**, 3623 (1992)
6. F. Perez *et al.*, *Physica Stat. Sol. B*, **243**(4), 873 (2006)
7. C. Aku-leh *et al.*, Poster **TuA 3r.41**, presented at ICPS 2006

Coherent Oscillatory Spin-Dynamics in High-Mobility 2D Electron Gases

W.J.H.Leyland[a,b], R.T.Harley[a], M.Henini[c], A.J.Shields[d] and D.A.Ritchie[b]

[a]School of Physics and Astronomy, University of Southampton SO17 1BJ, UK
[b]Cavendish Laboratory, Madingley Road, Cambridge CB4 3HE , UK
[c]School of Physics and Astronomy, University of Nottingham NG7 4RD, UK
[d]Toshiba Research Europe Ltd, Cambridge CB4 4WE, UK

Abstract. Measurements of electron spin dynamics at low temperatures ($T<5K$) in a series of high mobility 2D electron gases in modulation doped GaAs/AlGaAs quantum wells show damped coherent oscillations. The frequency corresponds to the conduction band spin-splitting at the Fermi energy and the damping is related to the momentum scattering time obtained from the electron mobility. The behaviour corresponds to D'yakonov-Perel' spin relaxation in a quasi-collision-free regime.

Keywords: Spin-dynamics, 2DEG, coherent.
PACS: 72.25.Fe, 72.25.Rb

INTRODUCTION

The dominant mechanism of electron spin relaxation in III-V semiconductors is the motionally-slowed, in-flight precession mechanism proposed by D'yakonov, Perel' and Kacharovskii[1,2]. Precession is driven by the effective magnetic field due to spin-orbit coupling. It is normally assumed that the momentum scattering rate of the electrons τ_p*^{-1} is much greater than the mean precession frequency $<\Omega>$ so that scattering leads to relatively slow spin relaxation. Here we investigate the possibility of a weak scattering regime in which the electron spins precess coherently through large angles before scattering. Our preliminary published work[3] indicated that quasi-collision-free conditions occur in high mobility 2D electron gases at low temperatures. Here we describe a study at $T<5K$ of five (100)-oriented modulation-doped GaAs/AlGaAs quantum well samples with widths L_z from 5 nm to 20 nm. PL and PLE spectra gave the electron density N_s (between 1.75 10^{11} cm^{-2} and 3.5 10^{11} cm^{-2}) and electron confinement energy E_{1e}. Hall mobility gave the transport relaxation time τ_p (between 5.1 ps and 26.7 ps). Ultrafast polarised optical pump-probe reflectivity[3] was used to track the spin evolution of a small (~1% of N_s) population of spin-polarised electrons injected at the Fermi energy.

RESULTS AND DISCUSSION

Fig. 1 shows the pump-probe signal corresponding to the time dependence of the average electron spin perpendicular to the quantum well plane $<S_z>$ in three samples. Damped oscillatory variation occurs with frequency increasing for lower L_z. Initially-injected spin-polarised electrons have wavevectors distributed around the Fermi surface and so precess about different axes in the quantum well plane. However the precession frequency is essentially isotropic under these conditions[3] so that, in the absence of scattering which would randomize the precession axes, $<S_z>$ should show coherent oscillations with only light damping due to residual anisotropy of the frequency. The observed strong damping can therefore be assigned to effects of momentum scattering of the electrons.

Fig 2 shows the precession frequency $|\Omega(k_F)|$ at the Fermi surface and the ratio of scattering rates τ_p/τ_p* for the samples, extracted using a Monte Carlo simulation method neglecting anisotropy of $\Omega(k)$ and assuming elastic momentum scattering with an adjustable rate τ_p*. An initial arbitrary population of 10^5 electrons with spin along z is injected. These all precess at the same frequency which may be adjusted in the simulation and undergo random changes of wave vector on scattering. The axis of precession of each

CP893, *Physics of Semiconductors, 28th International Conference*
edited by W. Jantsch and F. Schäffler
© 2007 American Institute of Physics 978-0-7354-0397-0/07/$23.00

electron is as specified by the vector **k** and is changed by scattering events as the wave vector is changed.

The conduction band spin splitting, corresponding to $\Omega(\mathbf{k})$, varies as $\mathbf{k}^3$ in bulk zinc-blend semiconductors and in two dimensions this will give a leading term $\langle k_z^2 \rangle k_{x,y}$ where $\mathbf{k}_{x,y}$ is the in-plane component. Therefore we expect that the observed precession frequency should, to a first approximation, be linear in $E_{1e}(E_F)^{0.5}$ as is observed (Fig 2a).

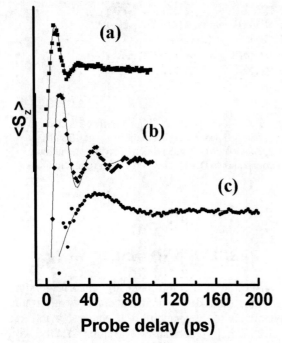

(a)

$\langle S_z \rangle$

(b)

(c)

Probe delay (ps)

FIGURE 1. Time evolution of spin polarization of electrons injected at the Fermi energy in three samples at temperatures below 5K. (a) L_z= 6.7 nm N_s = 3.3 10^{11}cm^{-2}, (b) L_z= 10 nm N_s = 3.1 10^{11}cm^{-2} and (c) L_z= 20 nm N_s = 1.75 10^{11}cm^{-2}. Solid curves indicate results of Monte Carlo simulation described in text.

The ratio $\tau_p/\tau_p{}^*$ (Fig 2b) is close to unity for the widest quantum well (lowest value of $E_{1e}(E_F)^{0.5}$) but increases monotonically as well width is reduced. Electron-electron scattering will reduce $\tau_p{}^*$ relative to τ_p.[3] Such scattering is forbidden by the Pauli principle for electrons at the Fermi energy in a fully degenerate (T=0 K) system, so the observed increasing ratio is consistent with departure from full degeneracy in the samples with narrower wells. As we describe elsewhere, this trend becomes more pronounced as temperature is increased[3,4]; $\tau_p{}^{*-1}$ increases rapidly with temperature leading to exponential spin decay in all the samples with a maximum in decay *time* near T= T_F

These results give a new and clear insight into the mechanism of spin-dynamics in III-V semiconductors and also demonstrate the short timescale of coherence of individual electron spins in a 2DEG when scattering

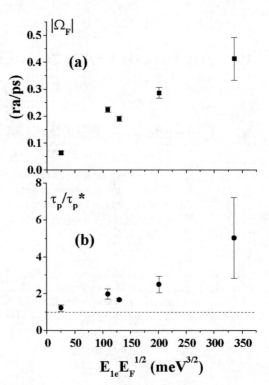

$|\Omega_F|$

(a)

(ra/ps)

$\tau_p/\tau_p{}^*$

(b)

$E_{1e}E_F{}^{1/2}$ (meV$^{3/2}$)

FIGURE 2. (a) Precession frequency at the Fermi surface $|\Omega(\mathbf{k}_F)|$ and (b) scattering time $\tau_p{}^*$ extracted from data of Fig 1. τ_p is the transport relaxation time from Hall measurements of the mobility.

is minimised. Note that our measurements are made in zero applied magnetic field. Much longer-lived oscillations have been reported in externally applied magnetic field or when the spin polarized electron population experiences a non-zero average spin-orbit field due to an imposed drift momentum[5]; in these cases the electrons were in a strong scattering regime.

ACKNOWLEDGMENTS

This work has been supported by EPSRC, the Royal Society grant 2005/R1-JP, RFBR, and "Dynasty" Foundation- ICFPM.References

REFERENCES

1   D'yakonov M I and Perel' V I 1971 Sov. Phys. JETP 33 1053
2   D'yakonov M I and Kachorovskii V Yu 1986 Sov. Phys. Semicond. 20 110
3   Brand M A et al 2002 Phys. Rev. Lett. 89 236601.
4   Glazov M.M. et al 2006 (proceedings of this conference)
5   For review see: Semiconductor Spintronics and Quantum Computation, ed D D Awschalom et al (Berlin: Springer)

Recombination and Spin Dynamics of Excitons in III-V/II-VI:Mn Heterovalent Double Quantum Wells

A. A. Toropov, Ya. V. Terent'ev, S. V. Ivanov, P. S. Kop'ev, T. Koyama[*],
K. Nishibayashi[*], A. Murayama[*], and Y. Oka[*]

Ioffe Physico-Technical Institute, Russian Academy of Sciences, St. Petersburg 194021, Russia
[*]Institute of Multidisciplinary Research for Advanced Materials, Tohoku University, Sendai 980-8577, Japan

Abstract. Time-resolved magneto-photoluminescence spectroscopy is applied to elucidate dynamics of excitons in GaAs/AlGaAs/ZnSe/ZnCdMnSe heterovalent double quantum wells (QW). An essential slowdown of the recombination rate was observed, resulting from exciton localization due to the compositional disordering at the AlGaAs/ZnSe heterovalent interface. It was found that both exciton lifetime and spin lifetime can be controlled by varying the detuning of the single-QW electron levels.

Keywords: Heterovalent nanostructures, diluted magnetic semiconductors, double quantum wells, spin dynamics.
PACS: 73.40.Lq, 75.50.Pp, 78.20.Ls, 78.67.De

Heterovalent quantum wells are heterostructures built from semiconductor compounds of different chemical groups. These structures can display unusual characteristics since they integrate properties of chemically different materials. Recently we have developed a molecular-beam-epitaxy technique for fabrication of GaAs/AlGaAs/ZnSe/ZnCdMnSe heterovalent double quantum wells (DQW) [1]. Our intention was to combine in a single structure the effect of giant Zeeman splitting, usually observed in II-VI diluted magnetic semiconductors (DMS), and such properties of III-V nonmagnetic semiconductors as relatively slow electron spin relaxation, high carrier mobility, and well-developed growth technology. Optical-quality samples were fabricated, which allowed one to observe the effect of resonant electronic coupling between the III-V nonmagnetic GaAs/AlGaAs quantum well (QW) and the II-VI DMS ZnCdMnSe/ZnSe QW [1,2].

In this paper we report on comparative studies of time-resolved excitonic magneto-photoluminescence (PL) in two GaAs/AlGaAs/ZnSe/ZnCdMnSe DQW structures characterized by different strength of interwell electronic coupling. In both structures the width of the ZnCdMnSe QW was 9 nm and the thickness of the combined AlGaAs/ZnSe barrier between the QWs totals 3.2 nm. The formation procedure of the AlGaAs/ZnSe heterovalent interface in both structures was designed to produce a neutral compensated interface, with a nearly vanishing average electric dipole moment along the growth direction. Therefore the conduction- and valence- band offsets at the heterovalent interface approach the values of chemical band offsets [2]. The two samples differ in the width of the GaAs QW. The DQW structure with the 3.2-nm-wide GaAs QW can be considered as resonant since the average detuning of the ground electron levels in the two QWs (~10 meV) is comparable with the estimated levels anticrossing gap. The other structure contains the 5-nm-wide GaAs QW. The levels detuning in this sample is ~60 meV and the DQW structure can be considered as off-resonant.

In accordance with the band line-ups of the DQW structure (see e.g. Ref. [1]), the ground heavy-hole state is always confined in the nonmagnetic GaAs QW, while the electron ground state can be confined either in the GaAs QW, or in the ZnCdMnSe QW, depending on the mutual position of the single-QW electron levels (see inset in Fig. 1). The former case corresponds to type I excitons with relatively short radiative lifetime (less than 1 ns), whereas the confinement of the electron in the DMS ZnCdMnSe QW results in the formation of type-II excitons with longer radiative lifetime that can be in the nanosecond range.

According to this description, the recombination dynamics of excitons in the off-resonant DQW should be similar to that of type-I excitons in a conventional

CP893, *Physics of Semiconductors, 28th International Conference*
edited by W. Jantsch and F. Schäffler
© 2007 American Institute of Physics 978-0-7354-0397-0/07/$23.00

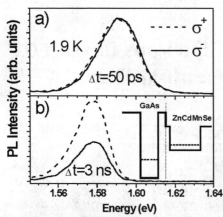

FIGURE 1. Circularly polarized PL spectra measured in the off-resonant DQW structure at the magnetic field of 6 T (applied in Faraday geometry) at different delay times: 50 ps (a) and 3 ns (b). The inset shows schematically the conduction band line up of the structure.

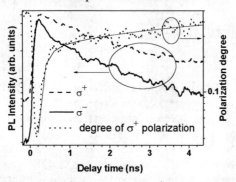

FIGURE 2. Decay curves of the σ^+ and σ^- polarized PL, measured at 1.57 eV in the off-resonant structure at 6 T. The dotted curve shows the respective degree of σ^+ polarization. Thin solid line demonstrates the fit by a two-exponential model with 200 ps and 5 ns time-constants.

GaAs/AlGaAs single QW. However, the measured PL spectra demonstrate certain admixture of the emission decaying on the scale of a few nanoseconds. Previously, this long-decaying PL was attributed to the emission of type-II excitons involving the electrons localized in the ZnCdMnSe QW due to microscopic fluctuations of the conduction band offset (CBO) at the AlGaAs/ZnSe interface [2]. This interpretation is confirmed by the time-resolved PL spectra, shown in Fig. 1. Indeed, the PL spectrum measured at the long decay of 3 ns is essentially σ^+ polarized (see Fig. 1 (b)), which indicates the efficient overlap of the electron wave function with the DMS region. Note that the interface disordering of this kind seems to be an inherent property of heterovalent DQWs. It results in inhomogeneous broadening of the exciton resonances and essential slowdown of the exciton recombination. In the resonant structure this mechanism is responsible for about two time's increase of the PL line width, as

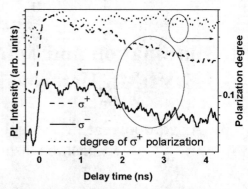

FIGURE 3. Decay curves of the σ^+ and σ^- polarized PL, measured in the resonant structure at 6 T. The dotted curve shows the respective degree of σ^+ polarization.

compared with the conventional GaAs QW of the same thickness. Moreover, most of the emission there originates from type-II excitons with the lifetime ranging from hundreds of picoseconds to tens of nanoseconds.

Figures 2 and 3 demonstrate different spin dynamics in the two samples. In the resonant structure (Fig. 3) the rise of spin polarization after excitation by a linearly polarized laser pulse occurs faster than time resolution of the set up, which is ~20 ps. This is in agreement with the fast spin relaxation rate usually observed in DMS QWs. In the off-resonant structure (Fig. 2) the rise of spin polarization occurs on the nanosecond time-scale. The involved spin relaxation time is surprisingly long for the DMS structure and its origin is not yet completely understood. The factors facilitating the long spin relaxation in the off-resonant structure can be weaker penetration of the QW electron wave function into the DMS region and 3D confinement of electrons localized due to the CBO fluctuations at the heterovalent interface. The observed long exciton and spin lifetimes accompanied by strong spin polarization at relatively weak magnetic fields make the structures of this kind promising for different spintronic applications.

This work was supported by the RFBR grant 06-02-16394-a, by the Ministry of Education, Science, and Culture, Japan, and by NEDO Nanotechnology Materials Program, Japan. A. A. T. acknowledges support from the Russian Science Support Foundation.

REFERENCES

1. A. A. Toropov, I. V. Sedova, S. V. Sorokin, Ya. V. Terent'ev, E. L. Ivchenko, and S. V. Ivanov, *Phys. Rev. B* **71**, 195312 (2005).
2. A. A. Toropov, I. V. Sedova, S. V. Sorokin, Ya. V. Terent'ev, E. L. Ivchenko, D. N. Lykov, S. V. Ivanov, J. P. Bergman, and B. Monemar, *phys. stat. sol. (b)* **243**, 819-826 (2006).

Spin Relaxation in 2D Electron Gases in the Strong Scattering Regime

M.M.Glazov[1], W.J.H.Leyland[2,3], E.L.Ivchenko[1], R.T.Harley[2], M.Henini[4], A.J.Shields[5] and D.A.Ritchie[3]

[1] Ioffe Physico-Technical Institute, Russian Academy of Sciences, 194021 St. Petersburg, Russia
[2] School of Physics and Astronomy, University of Southampton, Southampton SO17 1BJ, UK
[3] Cavendish Laboratory, Madingley Road, Cambridge CB4 3HE, UK
[4] School of Physics and Astronomy, University of Nottingham, Nottingham NG7 4RD, UK
[5] Toshiba ResearchEurope Ltd, Milton Road Science Park, Cambridge CB4 4WE, UK

Abstract. Measurements of spin dynamics of electrons in high-mobility, two dimensional electron gases (2DEGs) in GaAs/AlGaAs quantum wells from 5K to 300K show a rapid increase of spin relaxation time up to a peak near the Fermi temperature. Theoretical analysis based on the D'yakonov-Perel' mechanism shows that this variation is 'motional slowing' caused by electron-electron scattering and that the mobility of the electrons plays a minor role in the spin dynamics.

Keywords: Spin dynamics, 2DEG.
PACS: 72.25.Fe, 72.25.Rb.

INTRODUCTION

Three mechanisms are known for spin relaxation of electrons in zinc-blende semiconductors[1,2]; spin-flips associated with electron scattering due to spin orbit interaction, spin-flips induced by exchange interaction with holes and spin precession between scattering events in the effective magnetic field represented by conduction band spin-splitting. For n-type samples, particularly 2DEGs, spin reorientation via precession, i.e. the D'yakonov-Perel' (DP) mechanism[1,2], is dominant.

Usually a collision-dominated regime is assumed where spin relaxation is much slower than the average precession period and is actually inhibited by momentum scattering. There is exponential spin relaxation along a particular axis with rate[1,2]

$$\tau_s^{-1} = <\Omega^2> \tau_p^*$$

(1)

where $<\Omega^2>$ is the average square precession frequency perpendicular to the axis and τ_p^* is the electron momentum scattering time. This formula contains the 'motional slowing' characteristic of the

DP mechanism; increasing electron scattering produces slower spin relaxation. A common second assumption is that τ_p^* can be equated to the drift momentum relaxation time, τ_p, from the electron mobility[1,2]. In previous papers[3,4] we have shown that these assumptions can be invalid in 2DEGs. Here we present new data on spin dynamics from 5K to 300K of 2DEGs in GaAs/AlGaAs quantum wells which are fully characterized in terms of electron mobility and sheet density. The assumption of strong collisions is valid and motional slowing is directly observed, but τ_p^* is not the same as τ_p. Theoretical analysis shows that this is a result of electron-electron scattering which dominates τ_p^* but has almost no effect on the mobility and hence τ_p.

EXPERIMENTAL RESULTS

Fig. 1 shows representative results for two of the five samples investigated. They are modulation-doped single (100)-oriented quantum wells with widths L_z from 5 nm to 20 nm and electron concentrations N_s,

CP893, *Physics of Semiconductors, 28th International Conference*
edited by W. Jantsch and F. Schäffler

from PL and PLE measurements, of 3.5×10^{11} cm^{-2} to 1.75×10^{11} cm^{-2}. Hall mobility as a function of temperature gave τ_p in each case; mobilities at 5 K were in the range 30 m^{2}V^{-1}s^{-1} to 70 m^{2}V^{-1}s^{-1}. Ultrafast polarised optical pump-probe reflectivity[4] was used to investigate spin-relaxation of a small ($\sim$1% of N_s) nonequilibrium electron spin population. At very low temperatures the spin evolution is oscillatory, as described elsewhere[4]. As the temperature is increased the evolution becomes exponential and slows dramatically, qualitatively consistent with the motionally-slowed, DP mechanism. The spin relaxation time reaches a maximum near the Fermi temperature, T_F, of the 2DEG.

DISCUSSION

Fig. 2 is a qualitative picture of the behaviour of τ_s in a 2DEG from consideration of the two factors in Eq (1). At relatively low temperatures $\langle\Omega^2\rangle$ is proportional to the average in-plane kinetic energy and so is independent of (or linear in) T for a degenerate (or non-degenerate) 2DEG. If we equate τ_p^* with τ_p, ie ignore electron-electron (e-e) scattering, τ_p^{*-1} will follow the inverse of the mobility, constant at low temperatures and increasing roughly as T^2 at high temperatures. This gives a contribution to τ_s constant at low temperature and proportional to T at high temperatures (dashed curve in Fig. 2). For degenerate (or nondegenerate) 2DEG the e-e scattering rate[3] has the form T^2/N_s (or N_s/T). This gives a term in τ_s proportional to T^2 (T^{-2}) at low (high) temperatures (see dotted curve in Fig. 2). Thus a peak in the spin relaxation time at the Fermi temperature, as is observed experimentally, is a signature of dominant e-e scattering. Our detailed calculations (see Fig. 1) confirm this qualitative expectation; the dashed curves are calculated using τ_p obtained from mobility while the solid curves include the calculated e-e scattering. The excellent agreement of the solid curves with the experiment demonstrates the correctness of the interpretation.

ACKNOWLEDGMENTS

This work has been supported by EPSRC, the Royal Society grant 2005/R1-JP, RFBR, and "Dynasty" Foundation- ICFPM.

REFERENCES

1. For review see: Flatté M et al 2002 *Semiconductor Spintronics and Quantum Computation: chapter 4*, ed D D Awschalom *et al* (Berlin: Springer)

2. D'yakonov M I and Perel' V I 1971 *Sov. Phys. JETP* **33** 1053; D'yakonov M I and Kachorovskii V Yu 1986 *Sov. Phys. Semicond.* **20** 110

3. Glazov M. M. and Ivchenko E. L., *JETP Lett.* 75, 403 (2002); Glazov M. M.and Ivchenko E. L. *JETP* 99, 1279 (2004); Glazov M. M., et al, *Proc. Int. Symp. Nanostructures*, St Petersburg (June 2003).

4. Brand M A,et al 2002 *Phys. Rev. Lett.* **89** 236601; Leyland W.J.H. et al 2006 (proceedings of this conference)

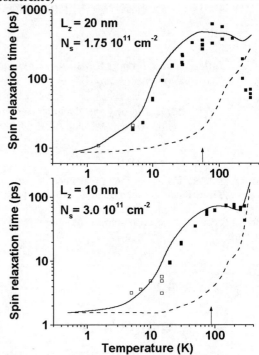

FIGURE 1. Spin relaxation time for two 2DEG samples with different well width, L_z, and sheet density, N_s. Arrow indicates T_F in each case. Solid (dashed) curves are theoretical with (without) electron-electron scattering.

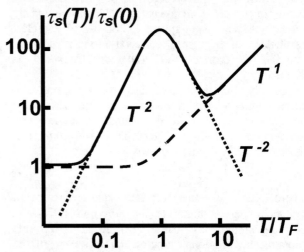

FIGURE 2. Qualitative variation of τ_s without (dashed) and with (solid) e-e scattering. Dotted curve is contribution of e-e scattering alone.

Spin Coherence of Holes in GaAs/AlGaAs Quantum Wells

Marcin Syperek[*,†], D. R. Yakovlev[†], A. Greilich[†], M. Bayer[†], J. Misiewicz[*],
D. Reuter[‡] and A. Wieck[‡]

[†] Experimental Physics 2, University of Dortmund, 44221 Dortmund, Germany
[*] Institute of Physics, Wrocław University of Technology, 50-370 Wrocław, Poland
[‡] Ruhr-University of Bochum, D-44780 Bochum, Germany

Abstract. Pump-probe time-resolved Kerr rotation technique has been used for experimental investigation of hole spin coherence in 15-nm wide GaAs/AlGaAs quantum well structure in regime of diluted two-dimensional hole gas. Due to the spectral width of 1.5 ps laser pulses which correspond to ~1 meV, selective excitation of trion and exciton states has been performed. In the case of resonant excitation of exciton only the electron spin beats have been observed in the presence of magnetic field. In the case of resonant excitation of the positively charged exciton two component decay of time-resolved Kerr rotation (TRKR) signal appeared. From the period of the quantum beat oscillation related to long decay component (up to 650 ps) of TRKR signal we obtained in-plain hole g-factor of ~0.048±0.005.

Keywords: coherence, GaAs, quantum well
PACS: 42.25.Kb, 78.55.Cr, 78.67.De

Recently the investigation of the coherent spin dynamics in semiconductor quantum wells and quantum dots attract much attention. This is due to the possible use of the spin degree of freedom for solid state quantum information processing or spintronic devices[1-3]. Till now the interest was mostly focused on the spin coherence of electrons and experimental information about spin coherence of holes is very limited. This is mostly due to many spin decoherence mechanisms of holes in the valence band of semiconductors (GaAs)[4], which prevents the observation of long-lived coherency. In the case of GaAs quantum wells (QWs), as far as we know, there is only one experimental work by Marie et al[5]. Authors study the coherence of holes in the n-type doped QWs by means of time-resolved photoluminescence.

In this paper we used time-resolved Kerr rotation (KR) experimental technique[6] to investigate the spin coherence of localized holes in p-doped GaAs/AlGaAs QW with a low density of hole gas. The great advantage of this method is possibility of observation of the spin coherence of holes or electrons after the recombination of an optically excited state.

The investigated sample was grown on (100) oriented GaAs substrate. It consists of (from the bottom) a buffer superlattice, a 20 nm $Al_{0.34}Ga_{0.66}As$ spacer, a δ-doped region with carbonate, and again a 305 nm $Al_{0.34}Ga_{0.66}As$ spacer. Then there is an active region consisting of a 15 nm-wide GaAs QW placed between 21 nm-wide AlAs/GaAs. After that a 308 nm $Al_{0.34}Ga_{0.66}As$ spacer layer is placed, followed by another δ-doped region with carbonate and an 80 nm $Al_{0.34}Ga_{0.66}As$ spacer layer. The entire structure is capped by a 5nm GaAs layer doped by a carbonate. The hole concentration and mobility in QW was determined to be 1.51×10^{11} cm^{-2} and 120 000 cm^2/Vs, respectively, as determined by the Hall measurement at temperature T= 4.2 K.

TRKR pump-probe experiment was performed using a mode-locked Ti:Sapphire laser with a repetition rate of 75.6 MHz. The temporal resolution of a single pulse was ~1.5 ps (~1meV full width at half maximum). The laser wavelength was tuned to the charged exciton line at 806.9 nm (1.536 eV). The laser beam was divided into the circularly polarized pump and linearly polarized probe beams. The average pump and probe power was kept at 0.5 mW and 0.1 mW, respectively. The diameter of a beam spot on the sample surface was ~200 μm. To detect the KR angle of the linearly polarized probe pulse, a homodyne technique based on a phase-sensitive balanced detection was used. The sample was placed in the optical cryostat with a superconducting magnet. The magnetic field was oriented perpendicular to the structure growth axis (Voigt geometry). The temperature was tuned in the range of T = 1.6 K to 10 K and magnetic field up to B = 10 T.

CP893, *Physics of Semiconductors, 28th International Conference*
edited by W. Jantsch and F. Schäffler
© 2007 American Institute of Physics 978-0-7354-0397-0/07/$23.00

In the case of the pump-probe Kerr rotation experiment the pump pulses coherently excite carriers that are spin polarized along the optical path. Then a coherent evolution of the spin or spin precession is tested by a probe pulse in a transverse magnetic field.

The inset (a) in Fig.1 shows an example of TRKR signal for investigated QW. We observed two sets of quantum beat oscillations. Note that they are observed in the entire range of magnetic field. The fast one we attributed to the Larmor precession of an electron spin inside an exciton until it recombines. The slow one was related to the precession of a hole spin. According to such assumptions a simple model was applied to extract the hole and electron part from the TRKR signal (see Fig. 1 inset (b)):

$$\Theta_{KR} = \sum_{i=hole,electron} A_i \exp\left(-\frac{\Delta t}{T^*_{2,i}}\right)\cos(\Omega_i \Delta t) \qquad (1)$$

where: Θ_{KR} is the Kerr rotation, $T^*_{2,i}$ is a spin coherence time, $\Omega_i = \mu_B|g_{\perp,i}|B_\perp$ is a frequency of Larmor precession, μ_B -Bohr magneton, $|g_{\perp,i}|$ is an in-plain g-factor, and Δt is a delay between pump and probe beams.

The existence of an additional long exponential decay component in TRKR signal was neglected due to its small amplitude (see Fig 1, inset (a)).

For fast oscillating part in accordance with the model we got the values of $T^*_{2,electon} = 48\pm5$ ps and $|g_{\perp,electron}| = 0.287\pm0.005$ in the entire range of $B_\perp$. This T^*_2 time for an electron in exciton also fits well to the recombination time of exciton in GaAs QW system which is ~50 ps [7,8]. Therefore, we concluded that the fast decay of electron signal is due to the radiative recombination of excitons.

Fig. 1 shows the results of application of the described model to extract the hole related part from TRKR experimental curves vs $B_\perp$. In this way we could obtain the value of T^*_2 of hole (see Fig. 1, inset (b)) and $|g_{\perp,hole}|$. The obtained value of $|g_{\perp,hole}| = 0.048\pm0.005$ remains in conformity with the one reported by Marie et. al. (calculations done by Ivchenko)[5]. A very interesting result is the observation of a very long spin precession of hole, which reaches 650 ps at $B_\perp = 1$ T and decreases down to 100 ps at $B_\perp = 10$ T. One of the possible explanations of such long-lived spin coherence is the localization of holes. Such localization can lead to the screening from the possible dephasing mechanisms. The performed TRKR experiment with temperature shows that above the temperature of 10 K the hole contribution of TRKR signal completely vanishes. This is in agreement with the localization mechanism due to the fluctuations of the confining potential in GaAs system.

In conclusions, the magnetic field and temperature dependent TRKR experiment was performed on the

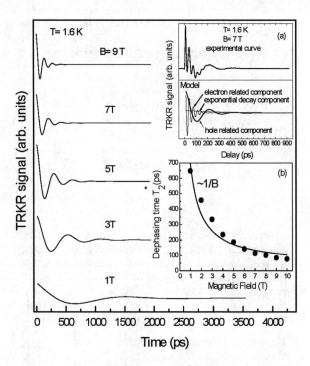

FIGURE 1. Hole related component of TRKR experimental curves obtained at different magnetic fields. Inset (a): top curve represents TRKR signal taken from experiment at B= 7 T and T= 1.6 K, at the bottom theoretical model which was used to fit experimental curve. Model consists of three components related to electron, hole and exponential decay component. Inset (b): Spin dephasing time of hole vs magnetic field.

p-doped 15 nm-wide GaAs QW. The two components of the decay of TRKR were resolved. The dephasing time of hole spins has been obtained to be 650 ps at 1 T and was related to the spin coherence of a localized hole. Also, the in-plain hole g-factor of 0.048 ± 0.005 was measured.

References

1. *Semiconductor Spintronics and Quantum Computation,* edited by D. D. Awschalom, D. Loss, and N. Samarth, Heidelberg: Springer-Verlag, 2002.
2. I. Žutić, J. Fabian, and S. Das Sarma, *Rev. Mod. Phys.* **76**, 323 (2004).
3. D. P. DiVincenzo, *Science* 270, 255 (1995); D. Loss and D. P. DiVincenzo, Phys. Rev. A **57**, 120 (1998).
4. *Optical Orientation,* edited by F. Meier and B. P. Zakharchenya, Amsterdam: North-Holland, 1984)
5. X. Marie, T. Amand, P. Le Jeune. M. Paillard, P. Renucci, L. E. Golub, V. D. Dymnikov, and E. L. Ivchenko, *Phys. Rev.* B **60**, 5811 (1999)
6. J. J. Baumberg, D. D. Awschalom, N. Samarth, H. Luo, J. K. Furdyna, *Phys. Rev. Lett.* **72**, 717 (1994)
7. E. Hanamura, *Phys. Rev.* B **38**, 1228 (1998).
8. B. Deveaud, F. Clérot, N. Roy, K. Satzke, B. Sermage, and D. S. Katzer, *Phys. Rev. Lett.* **67**, 2355 (1991)

Spin Relaxation in Quantum Wire

Tomoaki Kaneko, Mikito Koshino, and Tsuneya Ando

Department of Physics, Tokyo Institute of Technology, 2-12-1 Ookayama, Meguro-ku, Tokyo 152-8551

Abstract. The spin relaxation length is calculated numerically in quantum wires with strong spin-orbit interaction. The spin relaxation is perfectly suppressed in a quantum wire with a single channel and becomes important with the increases of the width or the channel number. The width dependence is much stronger than the result of classical simulations.

Keywords: spintronics,quantum wire,tight-binding model,spin relaxation length
PACS: 73.63.Nm, 72.25.Rb,72.25.Dc

The goal of spintronics is to utilize the spin degree of freedom in electronic devices [1]. In semiconductor quantum structure, the so-called structure inversion asymmetry is known to cause gate controllable spin splitting in the absence of a magnetic field [2, 3] and a spin device using this spin splitting was proposed [4]. In such systems, however, even spin independent scattering causes spin relaxation [5]. The purpose of this paper is to study the spin relaxation length in quantum wires with strong spin-orbit interaction.

For this spin relaxation, the parameter $\omega\tau$ plays a decisive role, where τ is the relaxation time and ω is the Larmor precession frequency due to an effective magnetic field arising from the spin-orbit interaction. In a two-dimensional system, for $\omega\tau \ll 1$, the spin relaxation length is given by $\Lambda_S = v_F/\omega$, which is independent of the mean free path Λ and determined only by ω and the Fermi velocity v_F, while for $\omega\tau \gg 1$, the spin relaxation length becomes comparable to the mean free path, i.e., $\Lambda_S \approx \Lambda$ [5].

In this study, a tight-binding model including spin-orbit interaction due to structure inversion asymmetry is employed and a recursion method is used to calculate the spin-dependent transmission coefficient in quantum wires [6]. The strength of the spin-orbit interaction is characterized by $\delta = \alpha k_F/\varepsilon_F$ where αk_F is the spin splitting at the Fermi energy ε_F with k_F being the Fermi wave number. The precession frequency is given by $\omega = 2\pi\delta v_F/\lambda_F$ where the Fermi wavelength is given by $\lambda = 2\pi/k_F$. Effects of disorder are included by a random and uniform distribution of the on-site potential and their strength is characterized by the mean free path Λ in the two-dimensional system. Then, we have $\omega\tau = 2\pi\delta\Lambda/\lambda_F$. Let W be the width of the wire. Then, the channel number, i.e., the number of the one-dimensional subbands below the Fermi level per spin, is given by $N = 2W/\lambda_F$.

Consider a quantum wire with length L, both ends of which are connected to an ideal lead without spin-

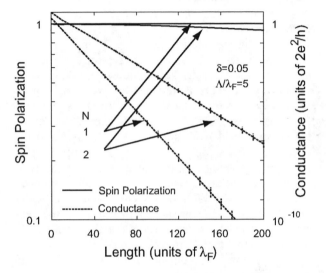

FIGURE 1. Examples of the calculated spin polarization and conductance as a function of L for $N = 1$ and 2. $\delta = 0.05$. $\Lambda/\lambda_F = 5$. In the wire with a single conducting channel, the spin relaxation is perfectly suppressed.

orbit interaction. Let $\psi_{i,\nu}^{(j)}$ be the two-component wave function of the out-going channel j from the incoming channel i with spin ν and unit amplitude. Then, the expectation value of spin σ_μ of the transmitted waves is given by

$$S_{\mu,\nu} = \sum_{i,j} \frac{\psi_{i,\nu}^{(j)\dagger} \sigma_\mu \psi_{i,\nu}^{(j)}}{\psi_{i,\nu}^{(j)\dagger} \psi_{i,\nu}^{(j)}}. \qquad (1)$$

A spin correlation function between the in-coming and out-going states of the quantum wire with L is defined by the sample average $\langle S_{\mu,\nu}\rangle$. The spin polarization function is defined by

$$P(L) = \sqrt{\sum_{\mu,\nu=x,y,z} |\langle S_{\mu,\nu}\rangle|^2}. \qquad (2)$$

CP893, *Physics of Semiconductors, 28th International Conference*
edited by W. Jantsch and F. Schäffler
© 2007 American Institute of Physics 978-0-7354-0397-0/07/$23.00

Numerical results given below show that $P(L)$ decreases exponentially with the increase of L. Then, the spin relaxation length Λ_S is defined by the relation

$$P(L) \propto \exp\left(-\frac{L}{\Lambda_S}\right). \tag{3}$$

Figure 1 gives examples of calculated spin polarization function and conductance for quantum wires with $N = 1$ and 2 for $\delta = 0.05$ and $\Lambda/\lambda_F = 5$. In a single-channel wire, the spin relaxation never takes place. This is because the spin precesses in the reversed direction in each backward scattering and therefore the precession angle depends only on the distance from the incident position. In a wire with two channels, a weak relaxation appears but its amount can practically be neglected.

Systematic calculations have been performed for wider wires with channel number $N = 5, 7, 10$, and 21, and the results are summarized in Fig. 2 for $\delta = 0.05$. In the figure the spin relaxation length is plotted against the mean free path for each N. The results in two dimensions mentioned above are represented by two straight lines ($\Lambda_S = v_F/\omega$ for $\omega\tau < 1$ and $\Lambda_S = \Lambda$ for $\omega\tau > 1$).

For the widest wire $N = 21$, the spin relaxation length is independent of Λ for small Λ and increases and approaches Λ for sufficiently large mean free path. This behavior is qualitatively the same as that in the two-dimensional system, although Λ_S for small Λ is much larger than v_F/ω. With the decrease of the wire width the relaxation length for short Λ increases but the general feature in the dependence on Λ remains qualitatively the same as that in the two-dimensional system.

A simulation in two-dimensional system with a finite width W and in the regime $\omega\tau \ll 1$, corresponding to $\Lambda/\lambda_F \sim 1$ in the present system, has been performed previously based on a classical Monte-Carlo method [7] and a classical spin-diffusion equation [8]. It gives the relation $\Lambda_S \propto (v_F/\omega)^2/W$. We can determine the proportionality constant in such a way that this equation gives the present Λ_S for $N = 21$ and $\Lambda/\lambda_F = 1$. Then the corresponding results for other values of N are shown by the horizontal arrows in the figure. It is clear that the present Λ_S determined full-quantum-mechanically increases much faster with the decrease of N than the classical result.

In summary, the spin relaxation is perfectly suppressed in a quantum wire with a single channel and becomes important with the increases of the width or the channel number. For sufficiently wide wires, the relaxation length Λ_S for a short mean free path Λ corresponding to $\omega\tau < 1$ is independent of Λ and approaches Λ for large Λ corresponding to $\omega\tau > 1$, where ω is the spin precession frequency and τ is the relaxation time. With the decrease of the channel number the relaxation length increases much more rapidly than that of the result of classical simulations.

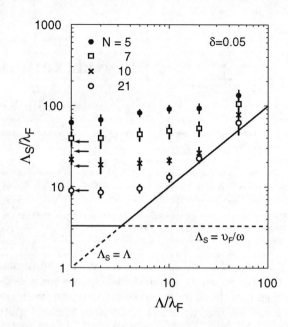

FIGURE 2. Calculated spin relaxation length Λ_S vs mean free path Λ for $\delta = 0.05$. The channel numbers are $N = 5, 7, 10$, and 21. When Λ_S becomes close to Λ, Λ_S starts to increase and crossovers into $\Lambda_S \propto \Lambda$. The straight lines show the known result in two dimensions. The horizontal arrows indicate the results of classical simulations.

ACKNOWLEDGMENTS

This work was supported in part by a 21st Century COE Program at Tokyo Tech "Nanometer-Scale Quantum Physics" by the Ministry of Education, Culture, Sports, Science and Technology, Japan.

REFERENCES

1. I. Zutic, J. Fabian, and S. D. Sarma, Rev. Mod. Phys. **76**, 323 (2004).
2. F. J. Ohkawa and Y. Uemura, J. Phys. Soc. Jpn. **37**, 1325 (1974).
3. Y. A. Bychkov and E. I. Rashba, J. Phys. C : Solid State Phys. **17**, 6039 (1984).
4. S. Datta, and B. Das, Appl. Phys. Lett. **56**, 665 (1990).
5. M. I. D'akonov, and V. I. Perel', Sov. Phys. JETP **33**, 1053 (1074).
6. T. Ando, Phys. Rev. B **40**, 5325 (1989).
7. A. A. Kiselev and K. W. Kim, Phys. Rev. B **61**, 13115 (2000).
8. A. G. Mal'shukov and K. A. Chao, Phys. Rev. B **61**, R2413 (2000).

Ultrafast Carriers Dynamics in GaSb/Mn Random Alloys

Shuji Ye, Joseph Knab, Jing-Yin Chen, Shumin Wang, Miyeon Cheon,
Hong Luo and Andrea Markelz

Department of Physics, University at Buffalo, SUNY, Buffalo, NY 14260

Abstract. Single color time resolved reflectivity change ($\Delta R/R$) measurements were performed at room temperature for two wavelength regions, 1.35-1.60 µm and 750 – 860 nm. The long wavelength measurements show that consistent with other low temperature (LT) grown III-V's, the GaMnSb samples have somewhat shorter recombination times ($\tau_r < 2$ ps) than the high temperature grown GaSb buffer layer ($\tau_r \sim 28$ ps at 1.6 µm). The recombination time decreases with increasing doping concentration. $\Delta R/R$ time dependence near the band edge indicates a possible metastable defect state produced after photo-excitation. For the measurements in the 750-860 nm range, $\Delta R/R$ has periodic oscillations for both in GaMnSb and epilayer samples. The oscillation period (T) is independent of the Mn concentrations, but dependent on the probe photon energy with T = 21 ps, 24 ps, and 25 ps for GaMnSb samples, and T = 19.3 ps, 20.5 ps, 22.0 ps for the epilayer sample at the probe wavelengths of 750 nm, 800 nm, and 860 nm, respectively. These values are in good agreement with recent theoretical calculations for modulation of $\Delta R/R$ due to coherent generation of acoustic phonon wave packets.

Keywords: coherent phonons, GaSb, magnetic semiconductors, transient reflectivity.
PACS: 73.20.-r 73.22.Lp 73.50.Gr 73.61.Ey

1. INTRODUCTION

Dilute magnetic semiconductors based on III-V semiconductors have attracted a great deal of attention owing to the discovery of carrier mediated ferromagnetism which can be controlled by electronic or optical carrier injection. GaSb is particularly interesting as a substrate material because its lattice parameter matches solid solutions of various ternary and quaternary III-V compounds whose band gaps cover the spectral range from ~0.8 - 4.3 µm. Recently above room temperature ferromagnetism for GaSb/Mn digital alloys has been achieved,[1] however this system's electronic properties are not yet ideal for device applications. Single color time resolved reflectivity change ($\Delta R/R$) measurements were performed at room temperature for two wavelength regions, 1.35 – 1.60 µm and 750 – 860 nm on GaMnSb random alloys as a function of pump/probe wavelength and Mn concentrations to study the defect states. At the longer wavelengths the recombination dynamics possibly indicate metastable trapping sites whereas at the shorter wavelengths we observe coherent acoustic phonon generation.

2. EXPERIMENT

The GaMnSb samples were grown by molecular beam epitaxy (MBE) with magnetic and electrical properties reported previously.[2] A 90nm thick GaAs buffer layer was grown on a semi-insulating GaAs(100) substrate at 580 °C followed by a 220 nm thick AlSb layer grown at 550 °C and a 90 nm thick GaSb layer grown at 500 °C. The 100 nm thick GaMnSb layer was grown at 275 °C. Mn concentrations were 1.45, 1.77, 1.86, 2.15 and 2.59%.

3. RESULTS AND DISCUSSION

3.1 Carrier Dynamics

The time-resolved reflection change ($\Delta R/R_0$) of the GaSbMn 1.45% alloy is shown in Fig. 1 as a function of pump/probe wavelength. $\Delta R/R_0$ time dependence increases in complexity as the wavelength approaches the band edge. The initially small positive $\Delta R/R_0$ rapidly decreases (less than 500 fs) after photo-excitation, and becomes negative then rapidly increases and changes sign again (< 2 ps) with a final

CP893, *Physics of Semiconductors, 28th International Conference*
edited by W. Jantsch and F. Schäffler
© 2007 American Institute of Physics 978-0-7354-0397-0/07/$23.00

slow decay to zero. The $\Delta R/R_0$ for the GaSb buffer layer has a single decay time recombination process τ_1 increasing with pump/probe wavelength.

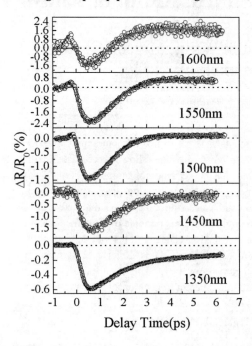

FIGURE 1. ΔR of GaMnSb random alloys with Mn concentration of 1.45% as a function of pump/probe wavelength. Open circles show the experimental results; solid lines represent multi-exponential decay fitting results, and dotted lines represent the baseline at t < 0.

For the GaMnSb samples two recombination processes are necessary to fit the data, τ_1 and τ_2. The shorter recombination time ($\tau_1 < 2$ ps) decreases with increasing Mn concentrations and is somewhat shorter than for the high temperature grown GaSb buffer layer ($\tau_1 \sim 28$ ps at 1.6 μm). The longer recombination time (τ_2) doesn't follow a regular trend with Mn concentration, varying from ten to several tens ps. A possible mechanism for the behavior is a metastable defect state that is populated after photo excitation and then slowly depopulates with time τ_2.

3.2 Coherent Phonon Generation

Although the $\Delta R/R_0$ time dependence is complex for photon energies high above the bandgap, at longer times (from ten ps to several hundreds ps), periodic oscillations are observed similar to those recently observed in other dilute magnetic III-V's semiconductors of InMnAs, and InGaMnAs.[3-5] The oscillatory amplitude of the reflection change of GaMnSb (800 nm) and GaSb (750nm) is shown in Fig.2. The amplitude and oscillation period is independent of Mn concentration but both depend on

the probe photon energy. The oscillation periods (T) from fits to the data are T = 21 ps, 24 ps, and 25 ps for GaMnSb samples, and T =19.3 ps, 20.5 ps, 22.0 ps for the epilayer sample at the probe wavelengths of 750 nm, 800 nm, and 860 nm, respectively. These values are in good agreement with recent theoretical calculations for modulation of $\Delta R/R$ due to coherent generation of acoustic phonon wavepackets.[5,6]

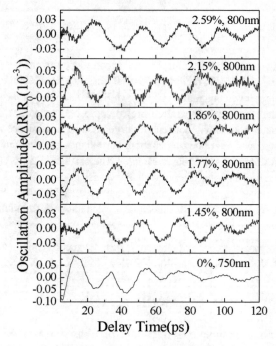

FIGURE 2. The oscillatory parts of the reflection change in GaMnSb at 800 nm wavelength and GaSb at 750nm.

ACKNOWLEDGMENTS

The authors are grateful to NSF ECS-0224206, ACS PRF39554-AC6, NSF CAREER PHY-0349256, and NSF IGERT DGE0114330 for support.

REFERENCES

1. X. Chen, M. Na, M. Cheon, S. Wang, H. Luo, and B. D. McCombe X. Liu, Y. Sasaki, T. Wojtowicz, J. K. Furdyna, S. J. Potashnik and P. Schiffer, *Appl. Phys. Lett.* **81**, 511 (2002).
2. G. B. Kim, M. Cheon, S. Wang, H. Luo, and B. D. McCombe, J. Superconductivity **18**, 87(2005).
3. J. Wang, G. A. Khodaparast, J. Kono, A. Oiwa, H. Munekata, J. Modern Optics **51**, 2771(2004).
4. J. Wang, J. Kono, A. Oiwa, H. Munekata, C. J. Stanton, Superlattices and Microstructures **34**, 563(2003).
5. J. Wang, Y. Hashimoto, J. Kono, A. Oiwa, H. Munekata, G. D. Sanders, and C. J. Stanton, Physical Review B **72**, 153311 (2005).
6. G. D. Sanders, C. J. Stanton, J. Wang, J. Kono, A. Oiwa and H. Munekata, Phys.Rev. B **72**, 245302 (2005).

Spin Dynamics Controlled by Spin-Dependent Recombination in GaAsN alloys at Room Temperature

V.K. Kalevich*, E.L. Ivchenko*, A.Yu. Shiryaev*, A.Yu. Egorov*, L. Lombez†, D. Lagarde†, X. Marie† and T. Amand†

*A.F. Ioffe Physico-Technical Institute, St.Petersburg 194021, Russia
†LNMO-INSA, Toulouse 31077, France

Abstract. We report on both experimental and theoretical study of conduction-electron spin polarization dynamics achieved by pulsed optical pumping at room temperature in GaAs$_{1-x}$N$_x$ alloys with a small nitrogen content (x = 2.1, 2.7, 3.5%). It is found that the photoluminescence (PL) circular polarization reaches 40-45% and this giant value persists within 2 ns. The results are explained by spin-dependent capture of free conduction electrons on deep paramagnetic centers. We have developed a nonlinear theory of spin dynamics in the coupled system of spin-polarized free and localized carriers that describes the experimental dependencies, in particular, electron spin quantum beats observed in a transverse magnetic field.

Keywords: Spin dynamics, semiconductor alloy, spin-dependent recombination.
PACS: 71.20.Nr, 72.25.Fe, 72.25.Rb, 78.47.+p, 78.55.Cr

INTRODUCTION

Spintronics devices require generation of high electron spin polarization in non-resonant excitation conditions and its conservation that must be sufficient to manipulate and store spin information. We show here that these goals can be achieved at room temperature in dilute nitride III-V semiconductor heterostructures under optical pumping. This is achieved on the base of spin-dependent capture of free electrons by deep paramagnetic centers and formation of coupled spin-system of free and localized carriers. We demonstrate that spin relaxation of the coupled spin-system is controlled by spin relaxation of deeply localized electrons.

EXPERIMENT AND DISCUSSION

The samples used for this work are undoped 0.1-μm-thick GaAs$_{1-x}$N$_x$ (x = 2.1, 2.7, 3.5%) layers grown by MBE on a (001) GaAs substrate [1]. We investigated spin properties in these structures by time-resolved polarized photoluminescence (PL). The samples are excited by circularly (σ^+) polarized 1.5 ps pulses generated by a mode-locked Ti-sapphire laser with a repetition rate of 82 MHz. The PL intensities co-polarized (I^+) and counter-polarized (I^-) with the excitation laser are recorded using a S1 photocathode

Hamamatsu Streak Camera with an overall time-resolution of 8 ps. We measure the PL circular polarization degree $\rho = (I^+ - I^-)/(I^+ + I^-)$ that is equal to electron spin polarization $P_e = (n^+ - n^-)/(n^+ + n^-)$ where n^+ and n^- are the densities of spin-up and spin-down free electrons.

Fig. 1 presents the PL and circular polarization

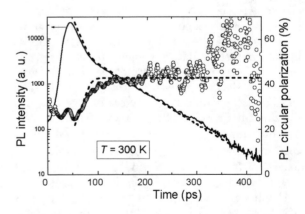

FIGURE 1. Time-resolved PL intensity (solid) and circular polarization (points) measured in GaAs$_{0.979}$N$_{0.021}$ alloy at room temperature. The excitation energy is $h\nu_{exc}$ = 1.39 eV which corresponds to the photogeneration of carriers below GaAs barrier. The detection energy corresponds to the conduction band – heavy-hole recombination [1]. Dashed curves are the result of the calculation in the model of Ref. [2].

CP893, *Physics of Semiconductors, 28th International Conference*
edited by W. Jantsch and F. Schäffler
© 2007 American Institute of Physics 978-0-7354-0397-0/07/$23.00

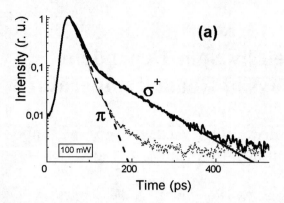 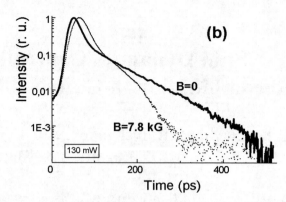

FIGURE 2. PL decay in $GaAs_{0.079}N_{0.021}$ under σ^+- and π-polarized excitation (a) and under σ^+-excitation in the absence and presence of a transverse magnetic field $B = 7.8$ kG (b). $T = 300$ K. Solid and dashed curves in (a) are calculated in the framework of the model proposed in Ref. [2].

dynamics in $GaAs_{0.079}N_{0.021}$. It is seen that the PL circular polarization reaches ~ 40% and this value persists within 2 ns which exceeds the photoelectron lifetime by more than an order of magnitude [1-3]. Both a change of the light polarization from circular to linear (Fig. 2a) and an application of the transverse magnetic field 7.8 kG (Fig. 2b) result in a decrease of the PL decay time by a factor of 4. We explain the observed large polarization and its persistence by spin-dependent capture of free electrons on deep para-magnetic centers assumed to be present in the alloys under study. Since the capture of a free electron in the same spin state as the one of a localized electron is blocked [4], and spin relaxation of paramagnetic centers is slow, the latter are dynamically polarized. This in turn causes an increase in the free electron polarization. After the polarization of the centers reaches a value close to 100%, the free-electron density is entirely controlled by spin relaxation in the conduction band. As a free electron spin flip is immediately followed by its capture on a paramagnetic center, it does not affect the average spin polarization of the free electron population. Thus the polarization does not decay with time, as we see in Fig. 1. In this time domain, PL polarization is insensitive to the free-electron spin-relaxation time τ_s while PL decay is solely controlled by τ_s: $I_{PL} \propto \exp(-2t/\tau_s)$. A value of τ_s found from the slow PL decay in Fig. 1 is ≈ 130 ps.

We have also observed strong PL polarization and its stability in compressively strained quantum wells InGaAsN/GaAs with small nitrogen content of the order of 1%.

We have developed the nonlinear theory of spin dynamics in the coupled system of free and localized carriers. The theoretical model is formulated in Ref. [2]. The details of theoretical analysis will be published elsewhere. Particularly, the observed effects of a transverse magnetic field and a circular-to-linear

change-over appear due to the deep-center depolarization, cutting off the spin filter and strong acceleration of free electron recombination. Electron spin quantum beats observed in transverse magnetic field (Fig. 3) are also described theoretically.

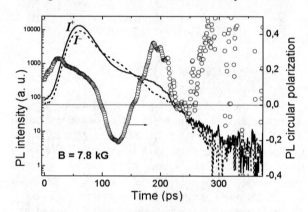

FIGURE 3. Room-temperature electron spin beats in the PL intensity components σ^+ (solid curve) and σ^- (dashed) and the PL circular polarization degree (circles) in $GaAs_{0.079}N_{0.021}$.

REFERENCES

1. A.Yu. Egorov, V.K. Kalevich, M.M. Afanasiev et al., *J. Appl. Phys.* **98**, 13539 (2005).
2. V.K. Kalevich, E.L. Ivchenko, M.M. Afanasiev et al., *JETP Lett.* **82**, 455-458 (2005).
3. L. Lombez, P.-F. Braun, H. Carrere et al., *Appl. Phys. Letters* **87**, 252115 (2005).
4. C. Weisbuch and G. Lampel, *Solid State Commun.* **14**, 141-144 (1974).

Demonstration Of Rashba Spin Splitting In GaN-based Heterostructures

W. Weber[*], S.D. Ganichev[*], S. Seidl[*], V.V. Bel'kov[†], L.E. Golub[†], W. Prettl[*], Z.D. Kvon[**], Hyun-Ick Cho[‡] and Jung-Hee Lee[‡]

[*]Fakultät Physik, University of Regensburg, 93040, Regensburg, Germany
[†]A.F. Ioffe Physico-Technical Institute, Russian Academy of Sciences, 194021 St. Petersburg, Russia
[**]Institute of semiconductor physics, Novosibirsk, 630090, Russia
[‡]Kyungpook National University, 1370, Sankyuk-Dong, Daegu 702-701, Korea

Abstract. The circular photogalvanic effect (CPGE), induced by infrared radiation, has been observed in (0001)-oriented GaN low dimensional structures. The photocurrent changes sign upon reversing the radiation helicity demonstrating the existence of spin splitting of the conduction band in k-space in this type of materials. The observation suggests the presence of a sizeable Rashba type of spin splitting, caused by the built-in asymmetry at the AlGaN/GaN interface.

INTRODUCTION

Gallium nitride is a potentially interesting material system for spintronics since it is expected to become ferromagnetic with a Curie-temperature above room temperature if doped with manganese [1]. Long spin relaxation times observed in this materials are another promising property for possible applications [2]. Little is known so far about spin-orbit interaction in GaN based heterojunctions like existence of Rashba spin splitting in the band structure which would provide a potential handle for spin manipulation. Strong spin-orbit effects are expected to be in narrow-gap materials only. A large piezoelectric effect which causes a strong electric field at the $Al_xGa_{1-x}N$/GaN interface and the strong polarization induced doping effect, on the other hand, may result in a sizeable Rashba contribution to spin splitting of the band ($\sim$1 meV) due to spin-orbit interaction [3]. Indeed a spin splitting of 9 meV was extracted from beatings of Shubnikov-de-Haas oscillations in $Al_{0.25}Ga_{0.75}N$/GaN heterostructures [4]. However, such beatings were ascribed to magneto-intersubband scattering by others [5]. On the other hand the observation of short spin relaxation times was attributed to D'yakonov-Perel mechanism which requires Rashba spin splitting. To investigate the presence of a sizeable spin splitting in this material class we employ the circular photogalvanic effect (CPGE) [6]. The CPGE as well as k-linear spin splitting of the band structure are only permitted in gyrotropic media. In such materials a linear relation between polar vectors (electric current) and axial vectors (spin) is allowed by symmetry. Both GaN/AlGaN heterostructures and bulk GaN belong to the family of wurtzite-type semiconductors which are gyrotropic.

EXPERIMENTAL TECHNIQUE AND SAMPLES

The experiments were carried out on $Al_{0.3}Ga_{0.7}N$/GaN heterojunctions grown by MOCVD on a C(0001)-plane sapphire substrate. The thickness of the AlGaN layers was varied between 30 and 100 nm. An undoped 33 nm thick GaN buffer layer, which was grown under a pressure of 40 Pa at 550 °C, is followed by an undoped GaN layer (2.5 μm). The electron mobility in the 2DEG was typically about 1200 cm^2/Vs at electron density (1-1.4) $\cdot 10^{13}$ cm^{-2} at room temperature. To measure the photocurrent two pairs of ohmic contacts have been centred along opposite sample edges. The experiments were carried out in two different spectral ranges: the mid-infrared (MIR) regime with wavelength between 9.2 and 10.8 μm and the terahertz (THz) regime at 77, 90, 148, 296 and 496 μm. The latter wavelengths were achieved by an optically pumped molecular NH$_3$ laser while a pulsed TEA CO$_2$ laser and a commercial Q-switched CO$_2$ laser with a peak power of about 1 kW were employed in the MIR-regime. While the THz radiation causes indirect Drude-like optical transitions in the lowest subband of the 2DEG, the MIR radiation can additionally induce direct optical transitions between the subbands. The helicity $P_{circ} = \sin 2\varphi$ of the incident light was varied from left handed circular (σ_-) to right handed circular (σ_+). Here φ is the angle between the initial polarization plane and the optical axis of the $\lambda/4$ plate or the Fresnel rhombus. The current j generated by the circularly polarized light in the unbiased samples was measured at room and liquid nitrogen temperatures via the voltage drop across a 50 Ω load resistor in a closed circuit configuration.

CP893, *Physics of Semiconductors, 28th International Conference*
edited by W. Jantsch and F. Schäffler
© 2007 American Institute of Physics 978-0-7354-0397-0/07/$23.00

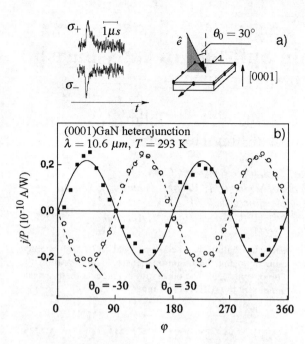

FIGURE 1. a) Geometry of the experiment and the temporal structure of the current response for right- and left-circularly polarized radiation. b) Photocurrent in GaN/AlGaN heterojunction normalized by the radiation power P as a function of the phase angle φ defining helicity. The current j is measured for the direction perpendicular to propagation of light (angle of incidence $\theta_0 = \pm 30°$). Solid and dashed lines show ordinate scale fits according to phenomenological theory.

EXPERIMENTAL RESULTS AND DISCUSSION

Irradiating the (0001) grown AlGaN/GaN heterojunction by circularly polarized light at oblique incidence, as sketched in Fig. 1b), causes a photocurrent signal measured across a contact pair. The measured current follows the temporal structure of the applied 40 ns laser pulses and is shown in the insets in Fig. 1a) for two polarization states. The current reverses its direction by switching the sign of the radiation helicity (see Fig. 1a). The fact that the current is proportional to the radiation helicity proves the circular photogalvanic effect as origin of the photocurrent. The signal proportional to the helicity is only observed under oblique incidence. The current vanishes for normal incidence and changes its polarity. The photocurrent in the layer flows always perpendicularly to the direction of the incident light propagation and its magnitude does not change by rotating the sample around the growth axis. All characteristic features persist from 4 K to room temperature. The observed photocurrents have the same order of magnitude as those measured in GaAs, InAs, and SiGe QWs [6].

The effect is observed for all wavelengths used between 9 and 496 μm. Data in Fig. 1b) shows the effect for a wavelength of 10.6 μm using a Q-switched CO_2 laser.

In addition to the CPGE current detected in the direction normal to the in-plane wave vector of radiation a signal is also observed along the in-plane propagation direction. This signal has equal magnitude and the same sign for right- and left-handed circularly polarized radiation and is ascribed to the linear photogalvanic effect and the photon drag effect [6].

The observation of the CPGE with strength comparable to that observed in GaAs and InAs heterostructures unambiguously demonstrates a substantial Rashba splitting of spin subbands in GaN heterojunctions. In contrast to zinc-blende based III-V QWs, where interference of BIA and SIA results in varying angles between electron spin and its momentum, $\boldsymbol{k}$, for different crystallographic directions, the electron spin in GaN heterojunctions is always perpendicular to $\boldsymbol{k}$. This is demonstrated by our experiments where the CPGE current always flows perpendicular to the incidence plane and does not change its amplitude if the in-plane direction is varied.

Acknowledgements: This work is supported by the DFG, RFBR, INTAS, RAS Dynasty Foundation - ICFPM and by the grant N R01-2003-000-10769 (2004), BK 21 of Korea Science and Engineering Foundation.

REFERENCES

1. T. Dietl, H. Ohno, F. Matsukura, J. Cibert, and D. Ferrand, *Science* **287**, 1019 (2000).
2. B. Beschoten, E. Johnston-Halperin, D. K. Young, M. Poggio, J. E. Grimaldi, S. Keller, S. P. DenBaars, U. K. Mishra, E. L. Hu, and D. D. Awschalom, *Phys. Rev. B* **63**, 121202 (2001).
3. V. I. Litvinov, *Phys. Rev. B* **68**, 155314 (2003).
4. Ikai Lo, J. K. Tsai, W. J. Yao, P. C. Ho, Li-Wei Tu, T. C. Chang, S. Elhamri, and W. C. Mitchel, K. Y. Hsieh, J. H. Huang, H. L. Huang, and Wen-Chung Tsai, *Phys. Rev. B* **65**, 161306 (2002).
5. N. Tang, B. Shen, Z.W. Zheng, J. Liu, D. J. Chen, J. Lu, R. Zhang, Y. Shi, Y. D. Zheng, Y. S. Gui, C. P. Jiang, Z. J. Qiu, S. L. Guo, J. H. Chu, K. Hoshino, T. Someya, and Y. Arakawa *J. Appl. Phys.* **94**, 5420 (2003).
6. S. D. Ganichev and W. Prettl, *Intense Terahertz Excitation of Semiconductors*, Oxford: Oxford University Press, 2006.
7. E. I. Rashba, *Fiz. Tverd. Tela* **2**, 1224 (1960) [*Sov. Phys. Solid State* **2**, 1109 (1960)].
8. Yu. A. Bychkov and E. I.ăRashba, *PisŚma Zh. Eksp. Teor. Fiz.* **39**, 66 (1984) [*JETP Lett.*, **39**, 78 (1984)].

Properties of the Two-Dimensional Electron Gas Confined in GaN/AlGaN Interface Studied by Electron Spin Resonance

A. Wolos,[1] W. Jantsch,[1] K. Dybko,[2] Z. Wilamowski,[2] and C. Skierbiszewski[3]

[1]*Institute of Semiconductor and Solid State Physics, Johannes Kepler Universität, A-4040 Linz, Austria*
[2]*Institute of Physics, Polish Academy of Sciences, Al. Lotnikow 32/46, 02-668 Warszawa, Poland*
[3]*Institute of High Pressure Physics, Polish Academy of Sciences, Ul. Sokolowska 29/37, 01-142 Warszawa, Poland*

Abstract. In this communication we report results of electron spin resonance investigations on the high-mobility two-dimensional electron gas confined at the GaN/AlGaN interface. On one spectrum we observe simultaneously Shubnikov – de Haas oscillations, magnetoplasma resonance, and a narrow resonance line with g-factor close to 2. From the period of the Shubnikov – de Haas oscillations we calculate the sheet carrier density, $1.9*10^{12}$ cm^{-2}. The lineshape of the magnetoplasma resonance is well described assuming the Drude model of relaxation with resonance frequency given by the standard formula for the lower branch of the coupled plasma-cyclotron mode. The plasma frequency obtained from the fit of the lineshape yields the same sheet carrier density as that determined from Shubnikov – de Haas oscillations. The mobility of the two-dimensional electrons determined from the fit equals to 120 000 cm^2/Vs. The correlation of the resonance line at g = 2 with the two-dimensional electrons is discussed.

Keywords: GaN/AlGaN, 2DEG, ESR, magnetoplasma
PACS: 73.40.kp, 76.30.pk, 76.40.+b

INTRODUCTION

Here we present results of electron spin resonance (ESR) studies of GaN/AlGaN heterostructures, aiming at investigations of spin- and electric properties of high-mobility two-dimensional electron gas (2DEG) confined at the interface.

SAMPLES AND THE EXPERIMENT

The GaN/AlGaN heterostructures were grown on bulk GaN substrates using plasma-assisted molecular beam epitaxy. Thanks to the high quality and low dislocation density of the substrate used the 2DEG formed at the interface with a sheet electron density of $2*10^{12}$ cm^{-2} exhibits a mobility of 70 000 cm^2/Vs (at liquid helium temperature), as determined from the transport measurements.

ESR of the 2DEG was investigated using a standard Bruker ELEXSYS E-580 spectrometer, operating at the frequency of 9.48 GHz (X-band).

EXPERIMENTAL RESULTS

Using the contactless resonance technique we obtained in a single spectrum the Shubnikov – de Haas (SdH) oscillations, magnetoplasma resonance, and a narrow resonance line with g-factor close to 2.

Figure 1(a) shows the measured SdH oscillations together with their Fourier transform. Only one oscillation frequency is recognized, from which a sheet carrier density of the 2DEG of $1.9*10^{12}$ cm^{-2} can be calculated. The obtained concentration agrees with the transport data.

Figure 1(b) shows a broad and strong resonance, which we attribute to the dimensional magnetoplasma

CP893, *Physics of Semiconductors, 28th International Conference*
edited by W. Jantsch and F. Schäffler

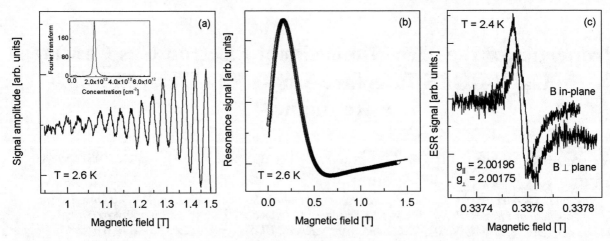

FIGURE 1. Resonance spectra measured at X-band for GaN/AlGaN heterostructure, B perpendicular to the sample plane: (a) Shubnikov – de Haas oscillations with the Fourier transform of the signal showing sheet electron density of $1.9*10^{12}$ cm^{-3}; (b) magnetoplasma resonance - open points with theoretical fit - solid line; (c) spin resonance line, whose correlation with 2D electrons is under further studies.

resonance. The coupled plasma-cyclotron modes have been observed, *e.g.* in 2D GaAs/AlGaAs micrometer-size heterostructures.[1] The resonance occurred in that case at the frequency of a few thousand GHz (for a magnetic field up to about 6 T). In our case, due to bigger dimensions of the sample (a few mm) the resonance occurs at the X-band frequency and a magnetic field of 0.4 T.

The asymmetric lineshape of the observed resonance can be successfully described assuming Drude model of relaxation with the resonant frequency given by:

$$\omega_{res} = -\frac{\omega_c}{2} + \sqrt{\omega_p^2 + \left(\frac{\omega_c}{2}\right)^2}. \quad (1)$$

Here ω_c stands for the cyclotron frequency and ω_p for the sample geometry-dependent plasma frequency at B=0.[1] In Fig. 1(b), the fit of the above model to the measured spectrum is shown. From the best fit parameters we can extract $\omega_p/2\pi$ = 27 GHz and μ = 120 000 cm^2/Vs. The obtained plasma frequency corresponds well to the sheet electron density determined from the SdH oscillations. The mobility obtained is higher than the mobility determined for the companion sample in transport measurements. Actually it is a typical result, as in contrast to the transport method optical measurements show properties of the best-quality areas of the sample.

Figure 1(c) shows the narrow resonance line, with an in-plane g-factor of 2.00196 and for perpendicular field we get 2.00175 (at T = 2.4 K). This line is a good candidate for conduction electron spin resonance, as it exhibits Pauli type of paramegnetism up to the room temperature. However, the small linewidth and anisotropy of the g-factor would suggest a rather small Bychkov-Rashba field for the GaN/AlGaN interface,

comparable to the magnitude determined for the 2D electrons in modulation-doped SiGe quantum wells.[2] This is not surprising in view of the fact that both materials have rather weak spin-orbit interaction, however it is in disagreement with the recent results of weak antilocalization experiments.[3] Nevertheless, the origin of this line, in particular its correlation with 2D GaN electrons, needs further investigations.

CONCLUSIONS

We have investigated high-mobility 2D electron gas in GaN/AlGaN heterostructure by ESR. This contactless method allows determination of basic electric parameters of the 2DEG, sheet carrier density and mobility. We have observed and analyzed coupling of plasma oscillations with cyclotron motion of the 2D electrons. The frequency of these magnetoplasma oscillations for a few mm sample width and a magnetic field of 0.4 T occurs at 9.48 GHz. For smaller structures, *e.g.* micrometer size, the frequency falls into THz region, making these structures interesting for the generation or detection of THz radiation. We have also observed a narrow spin resonance line, whose correlation with 2D GaN electrons is under further investigations.

REFERENCES

1. S. J. Allen, H. L. Stormer, and J. C. M. Hwang, *Phys. Rev.* **28**, 4875-4877 (1983).
2. H. Malissa, W. Jantsch, M. Muhlberger, F. Schaffler, Z. Wilamowski, M. Draxler, and P. Bauer, *Appl. Phys. Lett.* **85**, 1739-1741 (2004).
3. N. Thillosen, Th. Schapers, N. Kaluza, H. Hardtdegen, and V. Guzenko, *Appl. Phys. Lett.* **88**, 022111 (2006).

Picosecond spin relaxation of acceptor-bound exciton in wurtzite GaN

Hirotaka Otake, Takamasa Kuroda and Atsushi Tackeuchi

Department of Applied Physics, Waseda University, Tokyo 169-8555, Japan

Kazuyoshi Taniguchi, Takako Chinone, Ji-Hao Liang, Masataka Kajikawa and Naochika Horio

Stanley Electric Company, Ltd., Edanishi 1-3-1, Aoba, Yokohama 225-0014, Japan

Abstract. The spin relaxation process of acceptor-bound excitons in wurtzite GaN is observed by spin-dependent pump and probe reflectance measurement with subpicosecond time resolution. The time evolutions measured at 15-50 K have a single exponential component corresponding to spin relaxation times of 1.40 – 1.14 ps. The spin relaxation time, τ_s, is found to be proportional to $T^{-0.175}$, where T is the temperature. This temperature dependence is quite weak compared with that of A-band free excitons showing $\tau_s \propto T^{-1.41}$ at 150 - 225K.

Keywords: spin, GaN, exciton, spin relaxation, wurtzite
PACS: 72.25.Rb, 78.47.+p, 78.55.Cr, 72.25.Fe

INTRODUCTION

Spin dynamics in semiconductors has been investigated with great interest, not only for fundamental physics but also for the application such as spin-switch device. In 1990, we proposed the time-resolved spin-dependent pump and probe measurement method to observe the spin relaxation process with sub-picosecond time resolution [1]. Recently, we reported that the spin relaxation times of A-band free exciton in wurtzite GaN are 0.47-0.25 ps at 150-225K [2]. Here, we focus on the spin relaxation of acceptor-bound exciton (ABE) in wurtzite GaN.

An acceptor bound exciton consists of a shallow neutral acceptor and an exciton as shown in Fig. 1 [3]. Since a neutral acceptor bound exciton has two-hole state in the topmost valence band, only $J = 0$ is allowed by the Pauli Exclusion Principle. The additional electron in the ABE state then contributes to its unpaired spin resulting in $J = 1/2$. Consequently, spin dependent pump-probe measurement for the ABE state yields information about the electron spin relaxation.

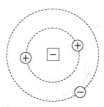

FIGURE 1. Schematic electronic structure of neutral acceptor bound exciton.

EXPERIMENTAL

The sample consists of 2.2 micron meters-thick GaN and a 40-nm-thick GaN buffer layer grown on a sapphire substrate by metalorganic chemical vapor deposition. Figure 2 shows the photoluminescence (PL) spectrum measured at 10 K. The PL peaks or shoulders lying at 3.495, 3.490, 3.484, 3.460 and 3.400 eV are attributed to B-band free exciton (FEB), A-band free exciton (FEA), donor-bound exciton (DBE), acceptor-bound exciton, FE-LO phonon replica, respectively [4]. To generate and detect the spin polarization, we used the spin-dependent selection rule of the optical transition between a circularly polarized

CP893, *Physics of Semiconductors, 28th International Conference*
edited by W. Jantsch and F. Schäffler

light and an electron spin. Frequency-doubled optical pulses generated from a mode-locked Ti: sapphire laser are used for pump and probe pulses. The energy of the laser pulses was tuned to the ABE PL peak.

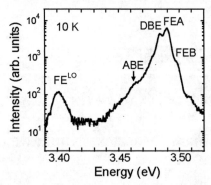

FIGURE 2. Photoluminescence spectrum of wurtzite GaN at 10 K.

DISCUSSION

The observed time evolution of spin relaxation has a single decay component which is attributed to electron spin relaxation. The spin relaxation time at 25 K is evaluated to be 1.35 ps using the single exponential fitting. This spin relaxation time is slightly longer than those of A-band free exciton of 0.47 ps at 150 K and shorter than those of the other III -V compound semiconductors.

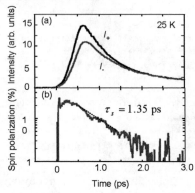

FIGURE 3. (a) Time evolution of reflection intensity at 25 K. I_+ (I_-) indicates right circularly polarized excitation and right (left) circularly polarized probe.
(b) Time evolution of spin polarization at 25 K. The dotted line representing the spin-relaxation time of 1.35 ps is fitted by the least-squares method.

The spin relaxation time becomes faster at higher temperatures. Figure 4 shows the temperature dependence of the spin relaxation time. The least squares method is used for curve fitting assuming

$$\tau_s = \alpha T^\beta,$$

where α and β are fitting parameters. The obtained results show that

$$\tau_s = 2.292 \times 10^{-12} T^{-0.175}.$$

This temperature dependence is quite weak compared with that of the FEA at 150 - 225K as shown in Fig. 4. The spin relaxation time of the FEA is proportional to $T^{-1.41}$ [2]. The candidate spin relaxation mechanism is the Bir-Aronov-Pikus process which is almost independent of temperature.

The observed picosecond spin relaxation shows the high potential of GaN as a promising material for the ultrafast optical devices.

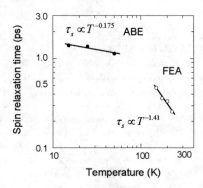

FIGURE 4. Temperature dependence of spin relaxation time of acceptor bound excitons and A-band free excitons. The solid lines are fitted by the least-squares method.

ACKNOWLEDGMENTS

This work was supported in part by a Grant-in-Aid for Scientific Research (No.18360042), The 21st Century COE Program (Physics of Self-Organization Systems), Academic Frontier Project and the High-Tech Research Center Project from Japan Ministry of Education, Culture, Sports, Science and Technology.

REFERENCES

1. A. Tackeuchi, S. Muto, T. Inata, and T. Fujii, Appl. Phys. Lett. **56**, 2213 (1990).
2. T. Kuroda, T. Yabushita, T. Kosuge, A. Tackeuchi, K. Taniguchi, T. Chinone, and N. Horio, Appl. Phys. Lett. **85**, 3116 (2004).
3. B. Monemar, W. M. Chen, P. P. Paskov, T. Paskova, G. Pozina, and J. P. Bergman, Phys. Stat. Sol. (b) **228**, 489 (2001).
4. G. Pozina, J. P. Bergman, T. Paskova, and B. Monemar, Appl. Phys. Lett. **75**, 4124 (1999).

Spin relaxation in SiGe islands

H. Malissa*, W. Jantsch*, G. Chen*, H. Lichtenberger*, T. Fromherz*, F. Schäffler*, G. Bauer*, A. Tyryshkin†, S. Lyon† and Z. Wilamowski**

*Institute of Semiconductor and Solid State Physics, Johannes Kepler University Linz, Austria
†Department of Electrical Engineering, Princeton University, USA
**Institute of Physics, Polish Academy of Sciences, Warsaw, Poland

Abstract. We investigate spin relaxation of electrons confined in SiGe structures produced by MBE growth of Ge islands on unstructured and structured Si substrates that cause strain in a Si layer above. These structures are investigated by photoluminescence spectroscopy and electron spin resonance both in continuous wave and pulsed mode. These structures show an ESR line-width and a g-factor of conduction electrons in Si with inhomogeneous broadening and no 2D anisotropy.

Keywords: Spintronics, Quantum dots
PACS: 85.75.-d, 78.67.Hc, 76.30.-v

In the past we were able to demonstrate that modulation doped 2D SiGe quantum wells defined by SiGe barriers show long spin lifetimes on the order of $1\,\mu s$ due to the small spin orbit interaction (SOI) in Si and a negligible hyperfine coupling due to the low abundance of ^{29}Si (less than 5%) and motional narrowing [1]. The Si device technology is well developed, which makes the SiGe material system an ideal candidate for spintronics and quantum computation applications, where long spin lifetimes are desirable due to the requirement that the spins must not decay during manipulation. On top of that, we have demonstrated that g-factor tuning can be achieved which allows for individual spin manipulation [2].

When electrons are confined in all three dimensions in quantum dot (QD) structures, the longitudinal spin relaxation time increases drastically [3], as has been shown in the case of Ga(In)As QDs in GaAs [4]. On the other hand, the transverse spin relaxation time remains on the order of 10 ns in III-V QDs [5].

When Ge is deposited on a Si(100) substrate, it forms a thin wetting layer of about 3 mono-layer thickness. Further Ge deposition leads to the formation of self-organized Ge QDs due to the lattice mismatch between Ge and Si (Stranski-Krastanow growth) with a random distribution of islands. The Ge QDs are overgrown with a 25 nm thick Si buffer, which is locally strained due to the buried Ge QDs. This leads to a lowering of the Δ_2 valleys in the Si conduction band (CB) which presents a potential that is attractive for electrons that are thus localized inside the Si layer, above the Ge QD [6]. When this procedure is repeated by again depositing Ge and overgrowing it with Si, the Ge QDs grow exactly above the first Ge QD locations due to the underlying strain distribution. This way up to 24 periods of QDs layers were grown, yielding more than 10^{10} QDs in total. The produced Ge QDs are dome shaped with a diameter of 100–120 nm at the base and a height of 6–8 nm.

When the Si(100) substrate is pre-patterned using electron beam or holographic lithography, regular arrays of small pits are produced after reactive ion etching [7]. This structured substrate is overgrown with a thin Si buffer. Ge deposition leads now to the formation of Ge QDs in those pits, which are laterally ordered. Repeating the growth procedure described above allows thus the formation of QD structures that are ordered in all three directions. In these pre-structured samples, the density of Ge QDs is by a factor of about 5 smaller compared to the self-organized QD structures.

In photoluminescence (PL) experiments these QDs show a wide band centered at 0.85 eV that originates from spatially indirect transitions from the lowest states in the strained Si CB to the valence band (VB) states of adjacent Ge QDs (see Fig. 1). This feature is much stronger in unstructured QD samples and scales approximately with QD density.

Continuous wave (cw) electron spin resonance (ESR) were done in a commercial X-band spectrometer operating at a microwave (MW) frequency of 9.48 GHz. The sample is located inside a rectangular TE_{102} MW cavity in a continuous flow liquid He cryostat with a base temperature of 2.5 K. The external magnetic field is modulated for phase sensitive lock-in detection.

Under illumination with bandgap light a single line appears with a line-width (lw) of 0.0220 mT at 344.1 mT (see Fig. 2), corresponding to a g-factor of $g = 1.998$ which is close to the g-factor obtained for electrons confined in 2D quantum wells (QWs) [1, 2] but shows no anisotropy when the sample is rotated around an axis perpendicular to the external magnetic field. This line is present in structured and unstructured QD samples but

CP893, *Physics of Semiconductors, 28th International Conference*
edited by W. Jantsch and F. Schäffler

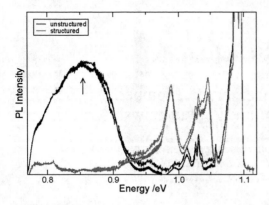

FIGURE 1. PL data from structured and unstructured (marked with arrow) samples. Features at higher energies originate from the substrate and wetting layer PL.

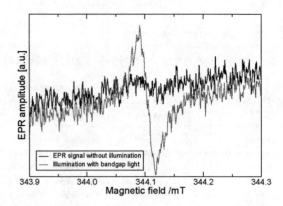

FIGURE 2. ESR line at $g = 1.998$ with and without illumination. This feature is much stronger in unstructured samples as compared to structured ones, corresponding to the higher QD density.

far more prominent in unstructured samples, which corresponds to the higher quantum dot density. Under illumination with monochromatic light with a tunable wavelength, we observe a threshold for photoexcitation of approximately 1.05 eV (blue-shifted with respect to the PL emission), which originates from the higher probability of spatially direct transitions followed by relaxation into the QD states in the excitation process.

In 2D QWs the g-factor and lw anisotropy is governed by the Bychkov-Rashba effect that originates from the one-sided modulation doping [1]. This effect scales with the electron velocity, and thus is expected to vanish for pure 0D structures.

In order to distinguish homogeneous and inhomogeneous spin relaxation, time resolved ESR experiments using appropriate MW pulse sequences [8] were done. For the unstructured sample, we obtain a value of $0.8\,\mu s$ for T_2 that is isotropic, whereas T_1 is anisotropic: in the case of H_0 perpendicular to the sample plane, we obtain $T_1 = 0.7\,\mu s$, and if H_0 is oriented in-plane, $T_1 = 1.2\,\mu s$. In terms of ESR lw, the homogeneous transverse lw is 0.0082 mT for all sample orientations. This isotropic behavior originates from the suppression of cyclotron motion as the dot diameter is smaller than the cyclotron radius. The longitudinal contribution to the lw is 0.0070 mT for H_0 perpendicular and 0.0022 mT for H_0 in-plane. The inhomogenously broadened lw determined from cw ESR experiments for perpendicular ($\Delta H = 0.0220$ mT) and for in-plane H_0 ($\Delta H = 0.0350$ mT) is considerably larger than the homogeneous contributions, which we attribute (i) to a fluctuation of the g-factor for different QD sizes and (ii) to the hyperfine interaction with the nuclear spins of ^{29}Si.

In summary, we were able to demonstrate that local strain in Si produced by buried Ge islands provides a confining potential for CB electrons that leads to QD like structures. The signal, observed in PL and ESR experiments scales with the number of QDs in our samples. The spin relaxation times are in the order of microseconds, which is shorter than the longitudinal, but longer than the transverse spin lifetimes in III-V QD systems. The anisotropy of the spin relaxation times indicates that the effective QD sizes are still rather large, and electron localization is still insufficient for the quenching of spin relaxation.

REFERENCES

1. Z. Wilamowski, W. Jantsch, H. Malissa, and U. Rössler, *Phys. Rev. B* **66**, 195315 (2002).
2. H. Malissa, W. Jantsch, M. Mühlberger, F. Schäffler, Z. Wilamowski, M. Draxler, and P. Bauer, *Appl. Phys. Lett.* **85**, 1739 (2004).
3. A. V. Khaetskii and Y. V. Nazarow, *Phys. Rev. B* **61**, 12639 (2000).
4. M. Kroutvar, Y. Ducommun, D. Heiss, M. Bichler, D. Schuh, G. Abstreiter, and J. Finley, *Nature* **432**, 81 (2004).
5. A. C. Johnson, J. R. Petta, J. M. Taylor, A. Yacoby, M. D. Lukin, C. M. Marcus, M. P. Hanson, and A. C. Gossard, *Nature* **435**, 925 (2005).
6. J. Novák, V. Holý, J. Stangl, T. Fromherz, Z. Zhong, G. Chen, G. Bauer, and B. Struth, *J. Appl. Phys.* **98**, 073517 (2005).
7. Z. Zhong, G. Chen, J. Stangl, T. Fromherz, F. Schäffler, and G. Bauer, *Phys. E* **21**, 588 (2004).
8. A. Schweiger and G. Jeschke, "Principles of Pulsed Electron Paramagnetic Resonance", Oxford University Press, Oxford, 2001.

Electron spin quantum beats in positively charged quantum dots

L. Lombez, P.-F. Braun, P. Renucci, O. Krebs[†], D. Lagarde, B. Urbaszek, X. Marie, T. Amand, P. Voisin[†]

Laboratoire de Nanophysique, Magnétisme et Optoélectronique-INSA, Toulouse 31077, France
[†]Laboratoire de Photonique et Nanostructures, Marcoussis, France 91460, France

Abstract. We report on electron spin quantum beats observed in transverse magnetic field of positively charged excitons in an ensemble of InAs/GaAs quantum dots. We show that two contributions must be taken into account to explain the damping of the circular polarization oscillations: the first one is due to the nuclear field fluctuations experienced by the electron spin from dot to dot. The second one is due to the dispersion on the transverse Landé g-factor, due to the inherent inhomogeneity of the system, and leads to a field dependent contribution to the damping. We have developed a model taking into account both contributions, which is in good agreement with the experimental data.

Keywords: Spin dynamics, hyperfine interaction, quantum dots, charged excitons.
PACS: 71.35.Pq, 71.70.Jp, 72.25.Fe, 78.67.Hc

INTRODUCTION

The dynamics and control of carrier spin in semiconductor quantum dots (QDs) is an important step towards future spintronic or quantum information processing applications. In this context, QDs are attractive since a long coherence time is expected at low temperature, as a result of the inhibition of classical spin relaxation mechanisms leading to relaxation and decoherence in bulk semiconductor and quantum well structures [1]. Yet, hyperfine interaction of localized electron with the QD nuclei leads to efficient spin dephasing [2]. The time evolution of optically generated electron spin coherence (ESC) in negatively charged InAs/GaAs QDs has been recently observed using time resolved Kerr pump-probe spectroscopy [3]. In this work, we have studied the ESC from time resolved photoluminescence spectroscopy of positively charged excitons X$^+$ under transverse magnetic field. We show that nuclear field fluctuations still lead to efficient spin dephasing, in this configuration.

EXPERIMENT AND DISCUSSION

Exciting singly charged QDs by an optical pulse results in the formation of a charged exciton complex X$^+$ which, in its ground state, consists of a spin singlet plus a single electron spin. So, the electron-hole exchange, an efficient interaction within neutral QD excitons [4], cancels out. The time and polarization resolved photoluminescence (TRPL) is thus a direct probe of the unpaired electron spin dynamics.

The samples used for this work consist of 10 planes of self assembled InAs QDs separated by 30 nm of GaAs; a beryllium doped delta doping layer is located 15 nm below each wetting layer. From strictly resonant TRPL, we deduce that there are less than 2 holes per dot in average. The samples are placed under an external transverse magnetic field $\vec{B} = B_x \vec{e}_x$ oriented along the Ox axis in the QD plane. They are excited by circularly (σ^+) polarized 1.5 ps pulses propagating along the growth axis Oz, generated by a mode-locked Ti-sapphire laser with a repetition rate of 80 MHz, thus generating a coherent superposition of $|+1/2\rangle_x$ and $|-1/2\rangle_x$ trion states. The PL intensities co-polarized (I^+) and counter-polarized (I^-) with the excitation laser are recorded using a S1 photocathode Hamamatsu Streak Camera with an overall time-resolution of 8 ps. We measure the photoluminescence circular polarization degree $P_c = (I^+ - I^-)/(I^+ + I^-)$, which corresponds directly to the electron average spin component $\langle S_z \rangle = -P_c/2$ along Oz.

Figure 1 presents the time evolution of $P_c(t)$ when the QDs are excited in the wetting layer (E$_{ex}$=1.44 eV). Oscillations, with a period corresponding to the X$^+$

CP893, *Physics of Semiconductors, 28th International Conference*
edited by W. Jantsch and F. Schäffler
© 2007 American Institute of Physics 978-0-7354-0397-0/07/$23.00

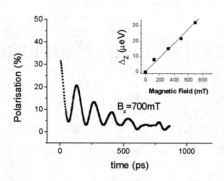

FIGURE 1. Circular polarization decay of X^+ trion as measured from TRPL in transverse magnetic field B_x, under σ^+ excitation. Inset: Zeeman splitting as a function of B_x.

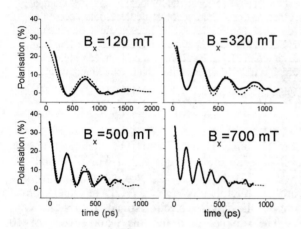

FIGURE 2. Time-resolved circular polarization decay of X^+ trion in transverse magnetic field B_x under σ^+ excitation. Bold line: experimental data. Dashed line: fit using a model including both g dispersion and nuclear field fluctuations, taking Δ_B=28 mT, $\Delta g/g_\perp$= 0.07 and T_2^* = 400 ps (see text).

ground state Zeeman splitting Δ_Z are clearly seen. The linear dependence of Δ_Z with B_x (see inset in Fig.1) yields an average electron transverse g-factor $g_\perp \approx 0.8$. Despite the relatively high magnetic field value, the ESC decays with a typical time of about 300 ps, one order of magnitude shorter than previously found in Faraday configuration [2]. Increasing the magnetic field leads to an increase of the polarization oscillations damping, as is seen on fig. 2 . We have explained this behaviour using two ingredients: the nuclear field fluctuations lead to a first contribution to the P_c oscillations damping, as predicted in the model of the "frozen" configuration of nuclear spins [5]. Note that here, in Voigt configuration, no dynamical polarization of the nuclei can occur [6]. So, these nuclear field fluctuations should be of similar amplitude to their amplitude at B_x=0, leading to a field independent contribution. Secondly, the magnetic field

dependent damping arises from the variations of the $g_\perp$ factor over the QD ensemble, leading to a spreading of the Larmor pulsations $\omega = g_\perp\mu_B B_x/\hbar$ with increasing B_x. We have included these variations in Merkulov's model using a gaussian distribution of electron g-factor. The equation of motion of the spin $\vec{S}$ in a fixed magnetic field is given by:

$$\vec{S} = (\vec{S}_0.\vec{n})\vec{n} + [\vec{S}_0 - (\vec{S}_0.\vec{n})\vec{n}]\cos\omega t \\ + [\vec{S}_0 - (\vec{S}_0.\vec{n})\vec{n}] \times \vec{n}\sin\omega t \tag{1}$$

where: $\vec{n} = (\vec{B} + \vec{B}_N)/|\vec{B} + \vec{B}_N|$, and $\vec{B}_N$ is the nuclear field in a given QD [5]. Expression (1) is then averaged taking gaussian variations of $\vec{B}_N$ and $g_\perp$, characterized respectively by the parameters Δ_B, measured at B_x=0 [2,5], and Δg. In addition, the QD charge varies from dot to dot, some of them may be neutral (X^0), and some may contain two holes (X^{2+}). The anisotropic exchange between electron and hole [4,7] would lead in principle to beats of $P_c(t)$. However, the latter quickly damp, due to the strong dispersion of the exchange parameters. Thus the (X^0, X^{2+}) effect on $P_c(t)$, which manifest by the asymmetry of the measured quantum beats, has been taken into account by simply adding an exponentially decaying contribution of parameter T_2^* to the X^+ contribution. The only adjustable parameters of the model are finally Δg, T_2^*, and the weight of QD with 0 or 2 holes, all independent of the magnetic field. We find, $\Delta g/g_\perp$= 0.07, which is consistent with previous studies [8]. The agreement between the model and the experiment can be seen on Fig. 2.

Finally, the spin quantum beat experiments presented here demonstrate the key role played by the nuclear field fluctuations on the electron spin coherence dynamics in QDs.

ACKNOWLEDGMENTS

We are grateful to V. M. Ustinov for sample growth. P.-F. B. thanks FSE for financial support.

REFERENCES

[1] Kroutvar *et al.*, Nature, **432**, 81 (2004)
[2] P.-F. Braun *et al.*, Phys. Rev. Lett. **94**, 116601 (2005)
[3] A. Greilich *et al.*, Phys. Rev. Lett. **96**, 227401 (2006)
[4] M. Senès *et al.*, Phys. Rev. B **71**, 115334 (2005)
[5] I. Merkulov *et al.*, Phys. Rev. B **65**, 205309 (2002)
[6] D. Paget *et al.*, Phys. Rev. B **15**, 5780 (1977)
[7] S. Laurent *et al.*, Phys. Rev. B **73**, 235302 (2006)
[8] M. Bayer *et al.*, Phys. Rev. B **82**, 1748 (1999)

Temperature Dependence of Exciton Spin Relaxation Rates in Semiconductor Quantum Dots

A. Reznitsky[1], A. Klochikhin[1,2], S. Permogorov[1], L. Tenishev[1], K. Mironenko[1], E. Tsitsishvili[3], R. v. Baltz[3], H. Kalt[4] and C. Klingshirn[4]

[1] *A.F.Ioffe Physical-Technical Institute, 194021, St.Petersburg, Russia*
[2] *Nuclear Physics Institute,188350, St.Petersburg, Russia*
[3] *Institute of Theory of Condensed Matter, University of Karlsruhe (TH), 76128 Karlsruhe, Germany*
[4] *Institute of Applied Physics, University of Karlsruhe (TH), 76128 Karlsruhe, Germany}*

Abstract. We have studied temperature dependence of the signals of optical orientation of excitons at resonant excitation of the ensemble of planar self-assembled CdSe/ZnSe quantum dots and show that spin memory in this system survives up to 100K. To describe the experimental results we apply the model that considers explicitly the effect of multi-phonon processes on the broadening of bright-exciton-phonon sublevels and demonstrate that calculated temperature dependences of spin relaxation rates are in good agreement with obtained experimental data.

Keywords: self-assembled quantum dots, excitons, optical orientation, optical alignment, temperature dependence.
PACS: 78.55.Et,   73.21.La,   78.67.Hc,   71.38.-

Nowadays a considerable attention is paid to comprehensive study of relaxation of an electron spin localized in a quantum dot (QD). Much less is known about the temperature dependence of the spin relaxation rates. Basically, the spin relaxation between discrete energy levels in QD's is hampered by the phonon bottleneck due to the energy conservation law. We demonstrate that multi-phonon processes transforming discrete levels into continuum bands relax the limitations connected with phonon bottleneck and allow to fit experimental findings.

The samples under study were grown by molecular-beam epitaxy of ultra narrow quantum wells (QWs) formed by insertion of CdSe with nominal thickness of 2.1 monolayers into ZnSe matrix [1] and revealed well developed planar quantum dots [2]. We have studied temperature dependences of the optical orientation of exciton spins and optical alignment of exciton dipole momenta at resonant excitation of the emitting states of excitons localized in self-assembled CdSe QDs.

Photoluminescense (PL) of localized excitons was excited by polarized light from Ar$^+$ laser (λ_{ex}=514.5nm). The laser beam was directed at small angle to the growth axis z, along which recombination emission was detected in back-scattering geometry. The linear polarization of the exciting light was achieved using a linear polarizer. Signal of PL passed through rotating half-wave plate followed by linear analyzer with fixed orientation and then was sent to spectrometer (for circular polarization measurements quarter-wave plates were placed after the linear polarizer in the exciting beam and before rotating half-wave plate for detection). For detection we used two-channel photon-counting system, which allowed parallel recording of the PL spectra in both polarizations I^{α}_{α} and I^{α}_{β} and calculation spectra of polarization degree $P^{\alpha}=(I^{\alpha}_{\alpha}-I^{\alpha}_{\beta})/(I^{\alpha}_{\alpha}+I^{\alpha}_{\beta})$. Here, symbols α and β stand for two components of polarization of exciting and/or detecting beams (x or y and σ_+ or σ_- for linear and circular polarizations, respectively), while superscript and subscript symbols indicate the polarization of excitation and detection, respectively. In order to exclude the polarization of PL which stems from the lateral anisotropy of the quantum dot the linear polarization degree has been detected for two orientations of polarizer x and y and spectra of optical alignment of excitons P_{lin} were obtained as $(P^x-P^y)/2$. Similar procedure with circular polarized excitations allowed to diminish the role of non-ideality of the used quarter-wave plates.

In Fig.1 the PL spectrum of the localized excitons and the spectra of polarization degrees P_{lin} and P_{circ} at resonant polarized excitation are shown. It was shown earlier [3, 4] that PL spectra of the samples under

CP893, *Physics of Semiconductors, 28th International Conference*
edited by W. Jantsch and F. Schäffler
© 2007 American Institute of Physics 978-0-7354-0397-0/07/$23.00

study are formed by the overlapping sub-bands corresponding to the recombination of the ground and metastable exciton states. As a consequence, at resonant excitation by polarized light both optical orientation and optical alignment signals can be detected, the relative intensity of which reflects the relative number of charged and neutral excitons.

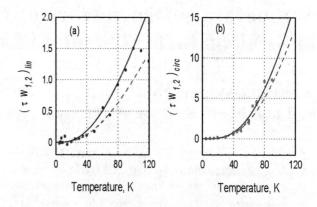

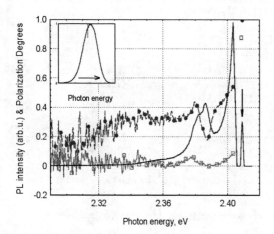

FIGURE 1. PL spectrum at resonant excitation at T=6K (black solid line) and spectra of optical orientation P_{circ} and optical alignment P_{lin} degrees of excitons (blue dashed line with closed symbols and red solid line with open symbols, respectively). The black vertical arrow indicates the spectral position of the excitation energy E=2.409 eV. Insert shows PL spectrum at above band gap excitation. Red vertical line in the insert indicates the photon energy used for resonant excitation.

In the two level approximation the temperature dependence of polarization degree of PL at polarized excitation can be obtained by solving the master equation for the populations of two spin states E_1 and E_2. In the simplest case of strictly polarized excitation the solution of this equation can be presented as

$$P(T) = \frac{1 + \tau[w_{2,1}(T) - w_{1,2}(T)]}{1 + \tau[w_{2,1}(T) + w_{1,2}(T)]}. \quad (1)$$

Here, τ is the PL decay time, $w_{1,2}(T)$ and $w_{2,1}(T)$ are transition rates between two spin sublevels, which are connected, as usual, by the ratio $w_{1,2}(T)/w_{2,1}(T)=\exp(E_{12}/kT)$. For degenerate states $E_1=E_2$ the rates are equal $w_{1,2}(T)=w_{2,1}(T)$ and tend to zero at $T\rightarrow 0$. These relations and Eq.(1) allow to connect the product $\tau w_{1,2}(T)$ and $P(T)$.

In Fig.2 the temperature dependence of the products $\tau w_{1,2}(T)$ calculated from the experimental values of polarization degrees P_{lin} and P_{circ} are shown.

FIGURE 2. Temperature dependences of the momentum relaxation rate (*a*) and the spin relaxation rate (*b*). Symbols are the experimental data obtained from polarization degrees P_{lin} and P_{circ} measured at photon energy of 2.405 eV in spectra shown in Fig.1. For calculated dependences (dashed and solid curves) the product $\tau w_{1,2}$ at T=5K was taken to be equal to $(2.5$ or $5) \, 10^{-4}$ (panel *a*) and $(10$ or $12) \, 10^{-4}$ (panel *b*), respectively.

We have performed the fitting of experimental data and have shown that the temperature dependence of transition rates $w_{1,2}(T)$ and $w_{2,1}(T)$ can be obtained by taking into account the broadening of electronic levels due to multi-phonon processes. These processes are not able by themselves to provide the spin-flip. However, they modify the spin relaxation indirectly leading to the transformation of the discrete exciton spin sub-levels into continuum bands.

The best fit of the experimental data presented in Fig.2 was achieved under assumption that the levels 1 and 2 are splitted for the states which demonstrate optical alignment signal (panel *a*) and are degenerated for those which give optical orientation signal (panel *b*). The estimated values of the parameters $\tau w_{1,2}$ which are of order $10^{-4} - 10^{-3}$ at T=5K, mean that at low temperature spins of the emission states do not relax during the radiative lifetime. This conclusion is in reasonable agreement with presently available experimental findings (see, for example [5]).

REFERENCES

1. S. Sorokin, et al., *J. Cryst. Growth* **201/202**, 461-464 (1999)
2. N. Peranio et al., *Phys. Rev. B* **61**, 16015-16024 (2000).
3. A. Klochikhin et al., *Phys.Rev.B* **68**, 085308-1-14 (2004)
4. A. Reznitsky et al., *AIP Conf. Proc.* **772**, 935-936 (2005)
5. Yu. G. Kusraev et al., *Phys.Rev.B* **72**, 15531-1-9 (2005)

Quenching of the Electronic Spin Relaxation and Decoherence by Localization on Donors

E. Aubry[1], G. Karczewski[2], J. Tribollet[1], F. Bernardot[1],
C. Testelin[1], and M. Chamarro[1]

[1] Institut des NanoSciences de Paris – Universités Paris-6 et Paris-7, CNRS UMR 7588 –
Campus Boucicaut – 140, rue de Lourmel – 75015 Paris – France
[2] Institute of Physics – Polish Academy of Sciences – Al. Lotnikow 32/46 – 02 668 Warsaw – Poland

Abstract. In pump-probe experiments, we compare the spin relaxation and decoherence times of electrons bound on neutral donors inside an intrinsic CdTe quantum well (QW), with those of free electrons in a doped CdTe QW. We demonstrate that the localization of the electrons on donors, slows down the spin relaxation and the spin decoherence by two orders of magnitude.

Keywords: Quantum well. II-VI semiconductors. Ultra-fast optical measurements.
PACS: 73.21.Fg 73.61.Ga 78.47.+p

INTRODUCTION

Electron spin is a promising candidate to form a qubit in the future quantum computers. Recently, an electron spin coherence time of about 30 ns[1] has been measured in remotely doped CdTe QWs, and has been interpreted as the coherence time of free electrons. But, as we have shown that the spin relaxation time of free electrons of a 2D gas in a CdTe QW, was in the order of two hundred of picoseconds[2], we are pushed to test whether the long spin coherence time measured in recent studies, could be affected by electronic localization in QW width fluctuations. For a more controllable electron localization, we have chosen to work with electrons bound to neutral donors.

SAMPLES AND SET-UP

We have studied two samples containing single CdTe/CdMgTe QWs with a width of 8 nm. The first one is a modulation-doped QW in which the electron gas, of concentration 10^{11} cm^{-2}, is delocalized over the whole QW. In the second sample, iodine donors of concentration about 10^{11} cm^{-2} are included at the center of the QW, inducing a localization of electrons on the neutral donors at low temperature.

The dynamics of the electronic spin has been studied using photo-induced Faraday rotation (PFR) experiments in the picosecond regime, allowing a narrow spectral resolution of 1 meV. The electronic spins are oriented by a circularly polarized pump, tuned to the trion transition in the case of the modulation-doped QW (mdQW), and to the exciton-bound-to-donor (D^{0}X) transition for the QW containing donors (dQW). The pump and probe pulses are degenerated in energy. The polarization of the pump pulses is σ^+/σ^- modulated at 42 kHz. The probe pulses are linearly polarized at 45° to the horizontal and vertical axes of the set-up; the PFR signal is measured[2] by a balanced optical bridge, which detects the difference in intensities of these two horizontal and vertical components. Measurements are made at 2 K.

SPIN RELAXATION

Figure 1 shows the PFR signal obtained in dQW. This signal possesses a three-exponential decay: a very fast initial decay with a characteristic time of about 10 ps, a slower decay of 80 ps, and a long-time decay of 15 ns. The initial and secondary decays are shorter than the radiative D^{0}X decay, measured to be 180 ps in time-resolved photo-luminescence measurements. Then, the long-time PFR signal is related to the only species present in the sample after the D^{0}X recombination, i.e., electrons bound to donors, and is the signature of a net spin polarization of the neutral donors. This remarkably long time is to be compared to the 195 ps of the spin relaxation in mdQW, not shown here[2]. Noticeably, the spin relaxation of the

CP893, *Physics of Semiconductors, 28th International Conference*
edited by W. Jantsch and F. Schäffler
© 2007 American Institute of Physics 978-0-7354-0397-0/07/$23.00

neutral donors is so long that we observe a non-zero PFR signal at negative pump-probe delay times: the electronic spins are not fully relaxed within the repetition period 13 ns of our pulsed laser. Hence, it is clear that the localization of the electrons on donors slows down their spin relaxation, the characteristic damping time being increased by two orders of magnitude, from 195 ps to 15 ns.

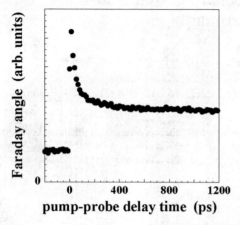

FIGURE 1. PFR signal measured on the D^0X line of the CdTe QW containing donors. The initial short-time decay is linked to the radiative recombination and the spin relaxation of D^0X. The non-zero signal for negative delay times is due to an electronic spin relaxation time longer than the repetition period of the laser.

The spin of the D^0X complex is the spin of the hole it carries, because its two electrons (one photo-created, one associated to the neutral donor) are in a singlet state. The middle PFR damping time of 80 ps gives an information about the hole spin relaxation, because the measured damping rate is equal to $1/\tau_{rad} + 1/\tau_h$, where $\tau_{rad} = 180$ ps is the D^0X radiative time and τ_h the hole spin relaxation time: we then obtain $\tau_h = 140$ ps. The initial fast PFR decay (10 ps) could be due to a fast hole spin relaxation affecting a fraction of the D^0X photo-created complexes. A hole spin relaxation with τ_h in the same order of magnitude or smaller than τ_{rad}, is necessary for the creation of the electronic spin polarization of the neutral donors.

SPIN DECOHERENCE

Figure 2 shows the PFR signal in a magnetic field B = 0.6 T, for both studied samples. This field being applied transversally to the direction of the beams (*i.e.*, in the plane of the QW), it causes a Larmor precession of the electronic spins, initially oriented along the pump beam direction. The Fig.2 shows the oscillatory behaviour of the PFR signal measuring the electronic spin component along the propagation direction of the light, the upper (lower) curve corresponds to the dQW

(mdQW) sample. A linear fit of the oscillations frequency as a function of magnetic field gives us the Landé factor $|g_e^\perp| = 1.3$ for dQW and 1.34 for mdQW, both are consistent with values already found in CdTe QWs[2]. Oscillations damping time decreases when magnetic field increases due to the presence of inhomogeneities associated to a local variation in the electron g-factor[3]. The value of the oscillations damping time extrapolated at zero magnetic field is equal to 15 ns in dQW and equal to 220 ps in mdQW. This zero-field damping time is probably affected by inhomogeneities of donor local environment such as donor-donor distance or nuclear field orientation which would be at the origin of different spin relaxation times[6].

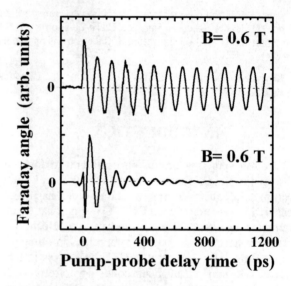

FIGURE 2. PFR signals in the presence of a B = 0.6 T transverse (in-plane) magnetic field, for both studied samples. Upper curve: CdTe QW containing donors; lower curve: modulation doped CdTe QW.

It is worth noting that the value of 15 ns for the oscillations damping time of a neutral donor is longer than the value of 2.5 ns reported for localized trions in GaAs[4], and shorter than 100 ns reported in bulk GaAs[5]. However, according to theoretical works[1], even longer relaxation times – then longer coherence times – are expected for lower donor concentrations[6].

REFERENCES

1. A. Zhukov *et al.*, 12th International Conference on II-VI Compounds, Poland (September 2005)
2. J. Tribollet *et al.*, Phys. Rev. B **68**, 235316 (2003)
3. J.A. Gupta et al., Phys.Rev. B **59**, R10421 (1999)
4. T.A. Kennedy *et al.*, Phys. Rev. B **73**, 45307 (2006)
5. J.M. Kikkawa *et al.*, Phys. Rev. Lett. **80**, 4313 (1998)
6. R.I. Dzhioev *et al.*, Phys. Rev. B **66**, 245204 (2002)

Nuclear spin effects in negatively charged InP quantum dots

S. Yu. Verbin[*,†], B. Pal[**], M. Ikezawa[**], I. V. Ignatiev[*,†] and Y. Masumoto[**]

[*]V. A. Fock Institute of Physics, St-Petersburg University, St-Petersburg 198504, Russia
[†]Venture Business Laboratory, University of Tsukuba, Tsukuba 305-8571, Japan
[**]Institute of Physics, University of Tsukuba, Tsukuba 305-8571, Japan

Abstract. Effects of both the dynamic nuclear polarization (DNP) created by circularly polarized light and the fluctuations of average nuclear spin in a quantum dot (QD) on the electron spin orientation are studied for singly negatively charged InP QDs. From the dependence of the negative circular polarization of photoluminescence on the applied longitudinal magnetic field, the hyperfine field B_N of *a few* mT appearing due to DNP and the effective magnetic field B_f of *a few tens* of mT arising from nuclear spin fluctuations (NSF) are estimated. A lifetime of about 1 μs is estimated for NSF.

Keywords: Electron Spin, Nuclear Spin, Hyperfine Interaction, InP Quantum Dots
PACS: 78.67.Hc, 71.35.Pq, 72.25.Fe, 72.25.Rb, 71.70.Jp

Strong localization of electrons in quantum dots (QDs) may enhance hyperfine interaction of electron spins with those of nuclei [1]. Various aspects of the hyperfine interaction of electron and nuclear spins have been studied for last three decades in different materials [2], including InP QDs [3]. Charge-tunable InP QDs with one resident electron per QD, on an average, have recently attracted considerable research interests due to the observation of millisecond range spin lifetime of resident electrons in these QDs [4, 5]. This observation makes it a promising candidate for quantum memory element in the emerging fields of quantum information technology and spintronics [6]. However, the influence of the hyperfine interaction between electron and nuclear spins on the long-lived electron spin orientation needs to be clarified.

Two effects of the electron-nuclear spin-spin interactions are possible. One of them is the so-called dynamic nuclear polarization (DNP). In the optical orientation of electron spins, the spin-polarized electrons dynamically polarize the nuclear spins due to the hyperfine coupling of the electron and nuclear spin subsystems [2]. In turn, the spin polarized nuclei produce an internal magnetic field B_N, which may influence electron spin dynamics. In presence of an externally applied magnetic field B_{ext}, electron spin subsystem should feel an effective magnetic field $B_{eff} = B_{ext} + B_N$.

Another effect arises from the nuclear spin fluctuations (NSF). Due to limited number of nuclear spins, typically $n \sim 10^5$, interacting with the electron spin in a QD, random correlation of nuclear spins may create a fluctuating nuclear polarization, $\Delta S_N \propto S_N/\sqrt{n}$, where S_N is the total spin of the polarized nuclei. Fluctuation ΔS_N acts on the electron spin subsystem as another internal magnetic field, B_f, with random magnitude and orientation [7]. Electron spin precession in this field results in the dephasing of electron spins in the QD ensemble and

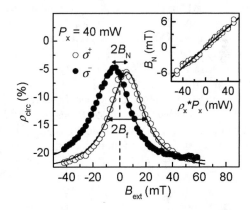

FIGURE 1. Dependence of ρ_{circ} on B_{ext}. Inset: Excitation power dependence of B_N.

in the three-fold decrease in magnitude of the total electron spin polarization [7, 8].

In the present paper we describe our experimental study of nuclear spin effects on long-lived spin polarization of resident electrons observed recently [4, 5] in singly negatively charged InP QDs.

The sample consists of a single layer of self-assembled InP QDs embedded between GaInP barriers grown on a n^+-GaAs substrate. The average base diameter (height) of the QDs is about 40 (5) nm with an areal density of about 10^{10} cm^{-2}. Semi-transparent indium-tin-oxide electrode was deposited on top of the sample to control the charge state of the dots by means of applied electric bias [4, 5]. For the present study on *singly negatively* charged QDs we apply an electric bias of $U_b = -0.1$ V, as it was found from a previous study of trionic quantum beats [9] on the same sample that at this bias the QDs contain one resident electron per dot (on an average).

Electron spins in the QD ensemble were polarized in

CP893, *Physics of Semiconductors, 28th International Conference*
edited by W. Jantsch and F. Schäffler
© 2007 American Institute of Physics 978-0-7354-0397-0/07/$23.00

our experiments by using the well-known optical orientation technique [2, 4, 5]. A *negative circular polarization* of the trionic (negatively charged exciton) photoluminescence (PL) with absolute value up to *a few tens* of percentage was observed for such QDs under quasiresonant excitation and was interpreted as a result of long-lived (hundreds of microseconds) spin memory of resident electrons [4, 5]. We monitor the degree of circular polarization $\rho_{circ} = (I_+^+ - I_+^-)/(I_+^+ + I_+^-)$, where $I_+^{+(-)}$ is the PL intensity for σ^+ excitation and detection of $\sigma^{+(-)}$ PL, as a function of an external magnetic field B_{ext} applied along the optical excitation axis (longitudinal magnetic field, Faraday geometry). The internal magnetic field B_f is expected to cause a three-fold reduction in the electron spin polarization (and correspondingly in ρ_{circ}) when $B_{eff} = B_{ext} + B_N \approx 0$. Influence of B_f may be suppressed by applying a longitudinal magnetic field exceeding B_f [7, 8]. A clear demonstration of this effect is seen in Fig. 1, where ρ_{circ} is plotted as a function of B_{ext} for σ^+ and σ^- excitations. For $B_{ext} > 50$ mT, ρ_{circ} approaches a constant value and a decrease from this constant value is seen for B_{ext} nearly, but not exactly zero. The behavior of ρ_{circ} as a function of B_{ext} is fitted with a Lorentzian, full width at half maximum of which estimates $B_f \approx 15$ mT. The shift of the Lorentzian from $B_{ext} = 0$ is due to B_N. The sign of B_N created by light should be opposite for the two counter circular polarizations (σ^+ and σ^-) of the excitation beam. As a result, the values of B_{ext} corresponding to $B_{eff} = B_{ext} + B_N \approx 0$ for σ^+ and σ^- excitations differ by $2B_N$ [Fig. 1]. A plot of B_N as a function of the product $\rho_x * P_x$ [$\rho_x = +1 (-1)$ for σ^+ (σ^-) excitation and P_x is the excitation power] shows that DNP builds up linearly with the excitation laser power [Fig. 1(inset)]. Even at high excitation power of about 50 mW a rather small dynamic nuclear magnetic field of about 6 mT is seen, in agreement with a previous report [3].

Theoretically proposed three-fold decrease of the electron spin polarization [7] due to hyperfine interaction with "frozen" NSF was not observed experimentally in case of very weak optical pumping of the InP QDs. This is related to a variation of the amplitude and orientation of the NSF in time (finite lifetime of NSF) which is able to totally destroy the electron spin polarization if the pump photons rarely come and restore the polarization. To estimate the lifetime of NSF we perform a time-domain measurement by using PL pump-probe technique [4, 5] shown schematically in the left inset of Fig. 2. A circularly (σ^+ or σ^-) polarized strong pump pulse creates spin orientation of the resident electrons [5]. The electron spin orientation is then probed by measuring $\Delta\rho$, the difference of ρ_{circ} of the probe PL for the σ^+ and σ^- pump, as a function of the pump-probe delay (τ). Figure 2 plots $\Delta\rho$ as a function of τ for

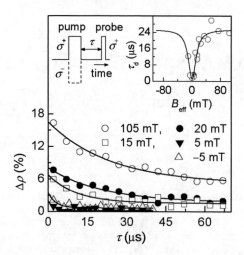

FIGURE 2. Decay of $\Delta\rho$ at a few values of B_{ext}. Left inset: Schematic of PL pump-probe method. Right inset: Dependence of τ_d on B_{eff}.

different values of B_{ext}. The spin decay time τ_d is estimated from a fit $\Delta\rho = A \exp(-\tau/\tau_d) + B$ to these data. A plot of τ_d as a function of B_{eff} is shown in the right inset of Fig. 2. We consider that near the minimum where $B_{eff} \approx 0$, electron spin dynamics is ruled by the NSF lifetime, which is estimated to be about 1 μs from our data.

In conclusion, the effect of nuclear spins on electron spin dynamics in InP QDs is studied. The values of NSF lifetime and of hyperfine fields B_N and B_f appearing due to DNP and due to NSF are estimated.

Authors thank V. K. Kalevich and I. Ya. Gerlovin for fruitful discussions. The work is partially supported by Grant-in-Aid for Scientific Research #17·5056, #13852003 and #18204028 from the MEXT of Japan and "R&D promotion scheme funding international joint research" promoted by NICT of Japan, by ISTC, grant 2679, by Russian Ministry of Sci. & Edu., grant RNP.2.1.1.362 and by RFBR, grant 06-02-17137-a.

REFERENCES

1. D. Gammon et al., *Phys. Rev. Lett.* **86**, 5176–5179 (2001).
2. F. Meier and B. P. Zakharchenya, *Optical Orientation* (North-Holland, Amsterdam, 1984).
3. See e.g., R. I. Dzhioev et al., *JETP Lett.* **68**, 745–749 (1998).
4. M. Ikezawa et al., *Phys. Rev. B* **72**, 153302-1–4 (2005).
5. B. Pal et al., *J. Phys. Soc. Jpn.* **75**, 54702-1–5 (2006).
6. D. D. Awschalom, D. Loss, and N. Samarth, *Semiconductor Spintronics and Quantum Computation* (Springer-Verlag, Berlin, 2002).
7. I. A. Merkulov et al., *Phys. Rev. B* **65**, 205309-1–8 (2002).
8. P.-F. Braun et al., *Phys. Rev. Lett.* **94**, 116601-1–4 (2005).
9. I. E. Kozin et al., *Phys. Rev. B* **65**, 241312(R)-1–4 (2002).

k-Dependence of the Electron Spin-Flip Time in GaAs

A. Amo[1], L. Viña[1], P. Lugli[2], A. I. Toropov[3] and K. S. Zhuravlev[3]

[1] SEMICUAM Dpto. de Física de Materiales, Universidad Autónoma de Madrid, E-28049 Madrid, Spain
[2] Lehrstuhl für Nanoelektronik, TU München, Arcisstrasse 21, D-80333 München, Germany
[3] Institute of Semiconductor Physics, Pr. Lavrentieva, 13, 630090 Novosibirsk, Russia

Abstract. The k-dependence of the electron spin flip time (τ_{sf}) in undoped GaAs is experimentally determined for the first time. Time-resolved optical orientation under strong optical injection is used to directly obtain τ_{sf}, which monotonically decreases by more than one order of magnitude when the electron k-vector varies from 0 to 2.5×10^6 cm^{-1}. Our results are well reproduced by a Monte-Carlo simulation of the electron-hole scattering and demonstrate that, at low lattice temperatures, the main spin flip mechanism of conduction band electrons is the Bir-Aronov-Pikus, i.e. a spin relaxation mechanism based in the exchange of spins between electrons and depolarized holes. We also show with the simulations that many body effects, such as phase space filling, result in an increase of τ_{sf} with excitation density.

Keywords: Electron spin flip, Pauli blockade, time-resolved polarization.
PACS: 72.25.Rb, 72.25.Fe, 71.35.Ee, 78.47.+p

The electron spin-relaxation processes in direct gap semiconductors have attracted the attention of the solid-state physics community for the past three decades. Optical orientation has proven to be an extremely powerful tool for the manipulation and study of the electron-spin degree of freedom in direct gap semiconductors: in particular, the spin relaxation mechanisms have been thoroughly studied in III-V materials, such as GaAs, both bulk[1] and low-dimensional. Surprisingly, despite the enormous body of experimental and theoretical results in this field, some fundamental aspects of the physics of electron spin relaxation in semiconductors have been neglected. One of these issues is the electron-momentum (k) dependence of the spin-flip processes, which is of great importance both from a fundamental point of view and in the design of applications that rely on the transport and injection of electrons with a preserved spin state. Another fundamental issue that has not been explored until very recently, is the physics of spin-dependent electron many-body processes[2,3] and phase-space filling effects.[4] In this communication we will present experimental results that shed some light on the two aforementioned issues.

We used a time- and energy- resolved photoluminescence (PL) setup (spectrograph + streak camera) in order to investigate the circularly polarized emission (σ^+ and σ^-) of a nominally undoped 2.5 μm thick GaAs epilayer of highest purity, after a non-resonant σ^+ pulsed excitation (1.5 ps duration). At low

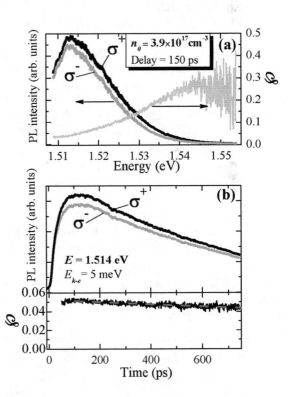

FIGURE 1. (a) PL spectra (left scale) and $\wp$ (right scale) for a delay of 150 ps and excitation density n_0 of 3.9×10^{17} cm^{-3}. (b) Upper panel: time evolution of the σ^+ and σ^- PL intensity for the excitation conditions of (a) at an emission energy of 1.514 eV ($E_{k-e} = 5$ meV); the lower panel shows the corresponding $\wp$ (dashed line is a fit to an exponential decay function).

CP893, *Physics of Semiconductors, 28th International Conference*
edited by W. Jantsch and F. Schäffler
© 2007 American Institute of Physics 978-0-7354-0397-0/07/$23.00

temperatures and low excitation densities the PL is dominated by excitonic features. However, at high excitation densities ($>1.2\times10^{17}$ cm^{-3}) the screening of the carriers leads to the formation of an electron-hole plasma [see Fig. 1(a)], characterized by quasi-degenerate Fermi-Dirac distributions of spin-up and spin-down electrons, as well as holes (holes are unpolarized after the first 100 fs). The imbalance between the electron spin-up and spin-down populations is evidenced through the spectral dependence of the degree of circular polarization [$\wp$; Fig. 1(a)]. The spin-flip dynamics of the electrons with a given electron kinetic energy in the conduction band ($E_{k\text{-}e}$) can be accessed by monitoring the time evolution of $\wp$ at a given emission energy [Fig. 1(b)]. The electron spin-flip time (τ_{sf}) for each $E_{k\text{-}e}$, which is twice the decay time of $\wp(E_{k\text{-}e})$, can be measured in this way.

Under our conditions of strong optical pumping in an undoped system (i.e., equal number of injected electrons and holes) the dominant electron spin relaxation mechanism is expected to be the so called Bir-Aronov-Pikus (BAP), which relies on the exchange interaction between the electrons and a population of depolarized holes.[5]

Figure 2 shows τ_{sf} for different $E_{k\text{-}e}$, and three different initial photoinjected carrier densities (n_0). τ_{sf} increases with increasing n_0, and decreases with increasing $E_{k\text{-}e}$. In order to investigate the effect of the degeneracy of the electron and hole populations on $\tau_{sf}(E_{k\text{-}e})$ we introduce a phenomenological, BAP-based model of the spin-flip time given by:

$$\tau_{sf}^{-1}\left(E_{k\text{-}e}\right) = \tau_{e\text{-}h}^{-1}\left(E_{k\text{-}e}\right) \times P_{spin\text{-}flip}\left(E_{k\text{-}e}\right),$$

where $\tau_{e\text{-}h}\left(E_{k\text{-}e}\right)$ is the electron-hole scattering time, and $P_{spin\text{-}flip}\left(E_{k\text{-}e}\right) = \left(P_0 \cdot E_{k\text{-}e}\right)^{\alpha}$ is the probability for an electron to flip its spin when it scatters with a hole. We have calculated $\tau_{e\text{-}h}\left(E_{k\text{-}e}\right)$ for our experimental conditions by means of a Monte-Carlo simulation (see inset of Fig. 2). The solid lines in Fig. 2 show the result of a fitting of the experimental τ_{sf} points to the phenomenological expression of $\tau_{sf}^{-1}\left(E_{k\text{-}e}\right)$ with the simulated $\tau_{e\text{-}h}\left(E_{k\text{-}e}\right)$. The fit was performed simultaneously for the three considered excitation densities in order to obtain universal values of the fitting parameters, P_0 and α, which yield $P_0 = 3.38 \cdot 10^2$ meV^{-1} and $\alpha = 0.65$.

The model very well explains the freezing of the electron spin-flip as the excitation density is increased: the higher the population, the lower the electron-hole scattering rate (and also spin-flip rate) due to the occupation of final states after the scattering events (inset of Fig. 2).[6] Thus, phase-space filling plays a major role in the spin-flip mechanisms of electrons under strong excitation, and should be taken into account in the design of spintronic devices.

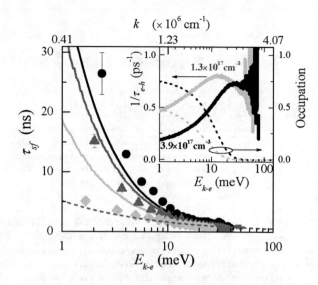

FIGURE 2. Measured spin-flip time as a function of the electron kinetic energy for initial excitation densities of 3.9×10^{17} cm^{-3} (circles), 2.4×10^{17} cm^{-3} (triangles) and 1.3×10^{17} cm^{-3} (diamonds). Solid lines compile the fitted spin-flip time as discussed in the text for each excitation density. The dashed line corresponds to the theoretical electronic non-degenerate case with a hole density comparable to the 3.9×10^{17} cm^{-3} excitation. The non-linear upper scale corresponds to the momentum of the electrons. The inset depicts the total electron-hole scattering rate (left scale) at 150 ps for excitation densities of 3.9×10^{17} cm^{-3} (black line) and 1.3×10^{17} cm^{-3} (green line); the dashed lines show the corresponding mean spin-up and spin-down electron occupation for those two cases (right axis).

ACKNOWLEDGMENTS

We thank C. Tejedor and L. C. Andreani for fruitful discussion. This work was partially supported by the Spanish MEC (MAT2005-01388; NAN2004-09109-C04-04), the *Comunidad Autónoma de Madrid* (S-0505/ESP-0200) and the Russian Basic Research Fund (grant no. 04-02-16774a). A. A. acknowledges a scholarship of the FPU program of the Spanish MEC.

REFERENCES

1. F. Meier and B. P. Zakharchenya eds., *Optical Orientation*, Amsterdam: North-Holland, 1984.
2. P. Nemec, Y. Kerachian, H. M. van Driel, and A. L. Smirl, Phys. Rev. B **72**, 245202 (2005).
3. Y. Zhang and S. Das Sarma, Phys. Rev. Lett. **95**, 256603 (2005).
4. M. Potemski, E. Perez, D. Martin, L. Vina, et al., Solid State Commun. **110**, 163 (1999).
5. P. H. Song and K. W. Kim, Phys. Rev. B **66**, 035207 (2002).
6. A. Amo, L. Viña, et al. Phys. Rev. B (submitted); cond-mat/0606173 (2006).

Spin Relaxation Anisotropy in Quantum Well Structures

L.E. Golub, N.S. Averkiev, A.S. Gurevich, V.P. Evtikhiev, V.P. Kochereshko,
A.V. Platonov, A.S. Shkolnik and Yu.P. E mov[1]

A.F. Ioffe Physico-Technical Institute, Russian Academy of Sciences, 194021 St. Petersburg, Russia

Abstract. Spin relaxation times of two-dimensional electrons in asymmetrical (001) AlGaAs quantum wells are measured by means of Hanle effect. Three different spin relaxation times for spins oriented along [110], [1$\bar{1}$0] and [001] crystallographic directions are extracted demonstrating anisotropy of the D'yakonov-Perel' spin relaxation mechanism. The relative strengths of Rashba and Dresselhaus terms describing the spin-orbit coupling in semiconductor heterostructures are obtained. It is shown that the Rashba spin-orbit splitting is about four times stronger than the Dresselhaus splitting in the studied structure.

Keywords: spin relaxation, spin splitting, quantum wells, polarized photoluminescence, Hanle effect
PACS: 73.21.Fg, 72.25.Rb, 73.63.Hs, 76.60.Jx

Spin relaxation of conduction electrons is an important field of research due to rapidly developing semiconductor spintronics. The D'yakonov-Perel' spin relaxation process is the dominant spin decoherence mechanism in undoped GaAs-based heterostructures. It consists in electron spin precession around an effective magnetic field which is caused by lack of inversion centrum in the bulk semiconductor of which the system is made (bulk inversion asymmetry, or BIA) or in the heterostructure (structure inversion asymmetry, or SIA).

The corresponding Hamiltonian of spin-orbit interaction has the form

$$H = \hbar \boldsymbol{\sigma} \cdot \boldsymbol{\Omega}(\boldsymbol{k}), \qquad (1)$$

where $\boldsymbol{\sigma}$ is a vector of Pauli matrices and $\boldsymbol{\Omega}$ is a precession frequency dependent on the electron quasimomentum $\boldsymbol{k}$.

The direction of the precession axis $\boldsymbol{\Omega}$ is determined by the carrier momentum $\boldsymbol{k}$ and by a kind of inversion asymmetry. SIA generates the effective field oriented perpendicular to $\boldsymbol{k}$. BIA results in the field which direction depends on the angle between the momentum and crystallographic axes. In (001) quantum wells (QWs), both SIA and BIA produce effective magnetic fields lying in the plane of the structure. In the coordinate system $x \parallel [1\bar{1}0]$, $y \parallel [110]$ the precession frequencies have the form

$$\boldsymbol{\Omega}_{\text{SIA}} = \alpha(k_y, -k_x), \qquad \boldsymbol{\Omega}_{\text{BIA}} = \beta(k_y, k_x). \qquad (2)$$

Spin-relaxation times are given by the following expressions [1, 2]

$$\frac{1}{\tau_z} = C(\alpha^2 + \beta^2), \qquad \frac{1}{\tau_{\pm}} = C\frac{(\alpha \pm \beta)^2}{2} \qquad (3)$$

for spin oriented along the growth axis (τ_z), along the axis [110] (τ_+), and along [1$\bar{1}$0] (τ_-). Here C is a factor determined by temperature and momentum relaxation time independent of the spin-orbit interaction parameters.

A very important case is spin relaxation in asymmetrical QWs where both Rashba and Dresselhaus spin-splittings are present. Their effect on spin relaxation is non-additive: interference of Rashba and Dresselhaus splittings in (001) grown structures leads to suppression of spin relaxation for the spin oriented along one of $\langle 110 \rangle$ axes and to its acceleration for perpendicular spin component in the structure plane [1, 2]. The microscopic reason for this anisotropy is low symmetry of the studied structure (C_{2v}) caused by the presence of both SIA and BIA.

For demonstration of the spin relaxation anisotropy, special asymmetrical GaAs/Al$_x$Ga$_{1-x}$As quantum wells are grown. The quantum well has a sloping barrier prepared by change of the Al source temperature resulting in varying of Al content from 4 to 28 % along the distance 270 Å under the MBE growth process [3].

We used the method of PL depolarization by transverse magnetic field (Hanle effect) for measurements of the spin relaxation times. The Hanle linewidth is determined by a lifetime of spin oriented perpendicular to the magnetic field $\boldsymbol{B}$. Therefore measuring PL circular polarization degree under different orientations of $\boldsymbol{B}$ in the QW plane one can extract the times τ_+ and τ_-, and then, with use of Eq. (3), determine the time τ_z.

[1] Present address: Institute of Physics, St. Petersburg State University, Ulyanovskaya 1, Petrodvorets, 198504 St. Petersburg, Russia

The degree of circular polarization of radiation has a Lorentzian form

$$P_{circ}(\boldsymbol{B}) = \frac{P_{circ}(0)}{1 + [\gamma(\theta)B]^2},$$

where the inverse half widths are given by

$$\gamma(\theta) = \sqrt{\gamma_+^2 \cos^2\theta + \gamma_-^2 \sin^2\theta}, \quad \gamma_\pm = \frac{g\mu_B\sqrt{\tau_z\tau_\pm}}{\hbar}. \quad (4)$$

Here θ is an angle between $\boldsymbol{B}$ and the axis $[1\bar{1}0]$, g is an electron factor Landé in the QW plane, and μ_B is the Bohr magneton. From the Hanle contour half width angular dependence $\gamma^{-1}(\theta)$ one can determine all three spin relaxation times.

Hanle effect measurements are performed at different orientations of magnetic field in the QW plane. Every Hanle contour is fitted by the Lorentz function with an adjustable parameter $\gamma(\theta)$. In Fig. 1 experimental Hanle curves are presented for two orientations of a magnetic field. One can see that optical orientation is almost totally suppressed in the field 0.3 T, however widths of two curves differ by 60 %.

Figure 2 presents the dependence of the inverse half width $\gamma(\theta)$. Dots are experimental results, the solid curve is plotted after Eq. (4) with the parameters $\gamma_\pm$ found above from fit of the Hanle curves at $\boldsymbol{B} \parallel [1\bar{1}0]$ and [110]. Figure 2 demonstrates that Eq. (4) perfectly describes angular variation of the Hanle effect. In its turn this means sufficient anisotropy of spin relaxation times.

Fitting the Hanle linewidth angular dependence by Eq. (4) and assuming $|g| = 0.35$ which is relevant for the AlGaAs heterostructures under study [3], yields

$$\tau_- = 0.8 \text{ ns}, \qquad \tau_+ = 0.3 \text{ ns}, \qquad \tau_z = 0.2 \text{ ns}.$$

This clearly demonstrates spin relaxation times anisotropy.

In the analysis we neglect anisotropy of the g-factor in the QW plane because it is inessential in the studied system [3]. The Hanle effect anisotropy is caused by anisotropy of spin relaxation.

Since the D'yakonov-Perel' spin relaxation is due to spin-orbit splitting of electron energy spectrum, we can extract the ratio of Rashba and Dresselhaus spin-splittings from the values τ_+ and τ_-. From Eqs. (3) we get

$$\left|\frac{\alpha}{\beta}\right| = \frac{\sqrt{\tau_-} + \sqrt{\tau_+}}{\sqrt{\tau_-} - \sqrt{\tau_+}} \approx 4.$$

To summarize, electron spin relaxation anisotropy is observed in the [001] grown QW. The anisotropy is measured by dependence of the Hanle linewidth on magnetic field orientation in the QW plane. It is demonstrated that the Rashba effect dominates the Dresselhaus effect in the studied structure. Spin relaxation times of electrons in the [001] QWs at liquid nitrogen temperature are determined for all three spin orientations.

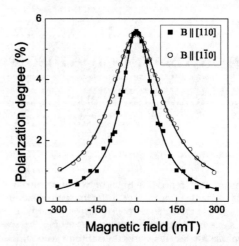

FIGURE 1. Hanle effect measurements for two orientations of a magnetic field in the QW plane. Solid lines represent fitting by the Lorentz function with the half widths $1/\gamma_+ = 0.12$ T and $1/\gamma_- = 0.075$ T.

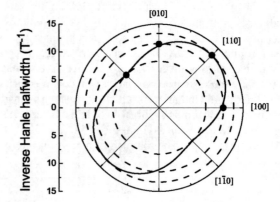

FIGURE 2. Hanle contour inverse half width for different magnetic field orientations in the QW plane (points) and the dependence Eq. (4) with $\gamma_\pm$ given above (solild line).

ACKNOWLEDGMENTS

Financial support from RFBR, RAS, Russian Ministry of Science and Education and INTAS is gratefully acknowledged. Work of L.E.G. is also sponsored by the Russian President grant for young scientists and Foundation for Russian Science Support.

REFERENCES

1. N.S. Averkiev and L.E. Golub, Phys. Rev. B **60**, 15582 (1999).
2. N.S. Averkiev, L.E. Golub and M. Willander, J. Phys.: Condens. Matter **14**, R271 (2002).
3. N.S. Averkiev, L.E. Golub, A.S. Gurevich, V.P. Evtikhiev, V.P. Kochereshko, A.V. Platonov, A.S. Shkolnik, and Yu.P. Efimov, Phys. Rev. B **74**, in press (2006).

Spin Orientation and Spin Currents Induced by Linearly Polarized Light

Sergey A. Tarasenko and Eugeniyus L. Ivchenko

A.F. Ioffe Physico-Technical Institute, Russian Academy of Sciences, 194021 St. Petersburg, Russia

Abstract. To date, optical orientation of free-carrier spins and spin currents have been achieved by circularly polarized light, while the linearly polarized light has been used for optical alignment of electron momenta. Here we show that, in low-dimensional structures, absorption of the linearly polarized light also leads to the spin polarization and spin photocurrent, and, thus, the electron and hole spins can be manipulated by light of zero helicity. The microscopic description of the both effects is developed for interband optical transitions in undoped quantum wells (QWs) as well as for direct intersubband and indirect intrasubband (Drude-like) transitions in n-doped QW structures.

Keywords: Optical orientation, Spin photocurrents, Linearly polarized light, Quantum wells
PACS: 72.25.Fe, 72.25.Dc, 78.67.De

PURE SPIN PHOTOCURRENTS

Pure spin currents are described by a non-equilibrium distribution where free carriers, electrons or holes, with the spin "up" propagate mainly in one direction and equal number of spin-down carriers propagates in the opposite direction. This state is characterized by zero charge current because electric currents contributed by spin-up and spin-down quasiparticles cancel each other, but leads to accumulation of the opposite spins at the opposite edges of the sample. Spin currents in semiconductors can be driven by an electric field acting on unpolarized free carriers (the so-called spin Hall effect). They can be induced as well by optical means under interband or intraband optical transitions in non-centrosymmetrical bulk and low-dimensional semiconductors [1, 2, 3, 4].

The appearance of a pure spin current in semiconductor quantum wells (QWs) under interband optical pumping with linearly polarized light is linked with the spin splitting of the energy spectrum, which is linear in the wave vector **k**, and the spin-sensitive selection rules for the optical transitions. The effect is most easily conceivable for direct transitions between the heavy-hole valence subband $hh1$ and conduction subband $e1$ in QWs of the C_s point symmetry, e.g., in (110)-grown QWs. In such structures the spin component along the QW normal $z' \| [110]$ is coupled with the in-plane electron wave vector. This leads to **k**-linear spin-orbit splitting of the energy spectrum as sketched in Fig. 1, where the heavy hole subband $hh1$ is split into two spin branches $\pm 3/2$. In the reduced-symmetry structures, the spin splitting of the conduction subband is usually smaller than that of the valence band and not shown for simplicity. Due to the selection rules the allowed direct optical transitions from the valence subband $hh1$ to the conduction subband

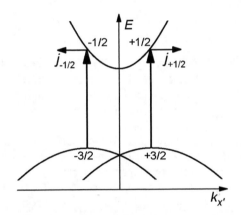

FIGURE 1. Microscopic origin of pure spin photocurrent caused by spin splitting of the band structure.

$e1$ are $|+3/2\rangle \rightarrow |+1/2\rangle$ and $|-3/2\rangle \rightarrow |-1/2\rangle$, as illustrated in Fig. 1 by vertical lines. In the presence of the spin splitting, electrons with the spins $\pm 1/2$ are photoexcited in the opposite points of the **k** space which results in a flow of electrons within each spin branch. The corresponding fluxes $\mathbf{j}_{+1/2}$ and $\mathbf{j}_{-1/2}$ are of equal strengths but of opposite directions. Thus, this non-equilibrium electron distribution is characterized by the nonzero spin current $\mathbf{j}_{spin} = (1/2)(\mathbf{j}_{+1/2} - \mathbf{j}_{-1/2})$ but a vanishing charge current, $e(\mathbf{j}_{+1/2} + \mathbf{j}_{-1/2}) = 0$.

In general, the flux of electron spins can be characterized by a pseudo-tensor **J** with the components J^{α}_{β} describing the flow in the β direction of spins oriented along α, with α and β being the Cartesian coordinates. The non-zero components of the photo-induced spin current are determined by the light polarization and the explicit form of spin-orbit interaction. The latter is governed by the QW symmetry and can be varied. In (110)-

CP893, *Physics of Semiconductors, 28th International Conference*
edited by W. Jantsch and F. Schäffler
© 2007 American Institute of Physics 978-0-7354-0397-0/07/$23.00

grown QWs the absorption of unpolarized light leads to a flow along $x' \parallel [110]$ of spins oriented along z'. This component can be estimated as

$$J_{x'}^{z'} = \gamma_{z'x'}^{(hh1)} \frac{\tau_e}{2\hbar} \frac{m_h}{m_e + m_h} \frac{\eta_{cv}}{\hbar\omega} I, \qquad (1)$$

where $\gamma_{z'x'}^{(hh1)}$ is a constant describing the $\mathbf{k}$-linear spin-orbit splitting of the $hh1$ subband, τ_e is the relaxation time of the spin current, m_e and m_h are the electron and hole effective masses in the QW plane, respectively, η_{cv} is the light absorbance, and I is the light intensity.

Another contribution to spin photocurrents may come from $\mathbf{k}$-linear terms in the matrix elements of the interband optical transitions. Taking into account $\mathbf{k} \cdot \mathbf{p}$ admixture of the remote condution band Γ_{15} to the valence-band and conduction-band states $X_{\mathbf{k}}, Y_{\mathbf{k}}, Z_{\mathbf{k}}$ and $iS_{\mathbf{k}}$, one derives the interband matrix elements of the velocity operator for bulk zinc-blende-lattice semiconductors [5]

$$\langle iS_{\mathbf{k}}|\mathbf{e}\cdot\mathbf{v}|X_{\mathbf{k}}\rangle = (P/\hbar)[e_x + i\beta(e_y k_z + e_z k_y)], \qquad (2)$$
$$\langle iS_{\mathbf{k}}|\mathbf{e}\cdot\mathbf{v}|Y_{\mathbf{k}}\rangle = (P/\hbar)[e_y + i\beta(e_x k_z + e_z k_x)],$$
$$\langle iS_{\mathbf{k}}|\mathbf{e}\cdot\mathbf{v}|Z_{\mathbf{k}}\rangle = (P/\hbar)[e_z + i\beta(e_x k_y + e_y k_x)],$$

where $\beta = QP'(2E'_g + E_g)/[PE'_g(E'_g + E_g)]$ is a material parameter, P, P' and Q are the interband matrix elements of the momentum operator at the Γ point multiplied by $\hbar/m_0$ (m_0 is the free electron mass), E_g and E'_g are the energy band gaps, and $x\parallel[100]$, $y\parallel[010]$, $z\parallel[001]$. For GaAs band parameters [6] the coefficient β can be estimated as 0.2 Å. Calculation shows that, in (110)-grown QWs, the spin photocurrent caused by $\mathbf{k}$-linear terms in the interband matrix elements has the form

$$J_{x'}^{z'} = \beta\varepsilon(e_{y'}^2 - e_{x'}^2)\frac{\tau_e}{\hbar}\frac{\eta_{cv}}{\hbar\omega}I, \quad J_{y'}^{z'} = \beta\varepsilon e_{x'}e_{y'}\frac{\tau_e}{\hbar}\frac{\eta_{cv}}{\hbar\omega}I, \quad (3)$$

where $\varepsilon = (\hbar\omega - E_g)m_h/(m_e + m_h)$ is the kinetic energy of the photoexcited electrons, $\mathbf{e} = (e_{x'}, e_{y'}, 0)$ is the light polarization vector, $y'\parallel[00\bar{1}]$. In contrast to Eq. (1), this contribution depends on the polarization plane of the incident light and vanishes for unpolarized light. The spatial separation of opposite spins, which depends on the light polarization, has been observed in Ref. [3]. However, estimations show that the contributions (1) and (3) in GaAs-based QWs are comparable in magnitude for the excitation with 100 meV above the band edge.

In (001)-grown QWs the absorption of linearly- or unpolarized light results in a in-plane flow of electron spins. In contrast to the low-symmetry QWs considered above, in (001)-QWs the linear-in-$\mathbf{k}$ terms in the matrix elements of optical transitions under normal incidence vanish, and the spin photocurrents are entirely related to the spin-orbit splitting of the free-carrier subbands.

Intrasubband optical transitions. Light absorption by free carriers, or the Drude-like absorption, is accompanied by electron scattering by acoustic or optical phonons, static defects etc. Scattering-assisted photoexcitation with unpolarized light also gives rise to a pure spin current [2, 4]. However, in contrast to the direct transitions considered above, the spin splitting of the energy spectrum leads to no essential contribution to the spin current induced by free-carrier absorption. The more important contribution comes from asymmetry of the electron spin-dependent scattering.

OPTICAL ORIENTATION BY LIGHT OF ZERO HELICITY

Optical excitation with linearly polarized light in QWs can also result in the spin orientation of photoexcited carriers. This effect is related to the reduced symmetry of QW structures as compared to bulk crystals and forbidden in bulk cubic semiconductors. Theory of the optical orientation by linearly polarized light has been developed in Refs. [7, 8] for the direct interband and indirect intrasubband transitions. Microscopically, the effect is a two-stage process involving (i) asymmetrical spin-dependent photoexcitation of the carriers followed by (ii) spin precession in an effective magnetic field induced by the Rashba or Dresselhaus spin-orbit coupling. Direction of the average spin is determined by the structure symmetry and geometry of photoexcitation. In (001)-grown QWs, the linearly-polarized normal-incidence excitation results in the spin orientation along the QW normal, with the spin sign and magnitude depending on the orientation of light polarization plane. Estimations show that the spin orientation by linearly polarized light can reach a few percents and is experimentally accessible.

Acknowledgments. This work was supported by the RFBR, RAS, President Grant for Young Scientists, Russian Science Support Foundation, and Foundation "Dynasty" - ICFPM.

REFERENCES

1. R.D.R. Bhat, F. Nastos, A. Najmaie, and J.E. Sipe, *Phys. Rev. Lett.* **94**, 096603 (2005).
2. S.A. Tarasenko and E.L. Ivchenko, *JETP Lett.* **81**, 231 (2005).
3. H. Zhao, X. Pan, A.L. Smirl et al., *Phys. Rev. B* **72**, 201302 (2005).
4. S.D. Ganichev, V.V. Bel'kov, S.A. Tarasenko et al., *Nature Physics* **2**, 609 (2006).
5. J.B. Khurgin, *Phys. Rev. B* **73**, 033317 (2006).
6. J.-M. Jancu, R. Scholz, E.A. de Andrada e Silva, and G.C. La Rocca, *Phys. Rev. B* **72**, 193201 (2005).
7. S.A. Tarasenko, *Phys. Rev. B* **72**, 113302 (2005).
8. S.A. Tarasenko, *Phys. Rev. B* **73**, 115317 (2006).

Non-Markoffian Theory of Electron Spin Decoherence in a Single Quantum Dot

T. Takagahara

Department of Electronics and Information Science, Kyoto Institute of Technology, Matsugasaki, Kyoto 606-8585 JAPAN
CREST, Japan Science and Technology Agency, 4-1-8 Honcho, Kawaguchi, Saitama 332-0012, JAPAN

Abstract. We investigate theoretically the electron spin relaxation and decoherence rates in a single quantum disk and clarify their dependence on the magnetic field strength, the temperature and the strength of quantum confinement. In the weak confinement regime, the spin relaxation rate at low temperatures is dominated by the two-phonon processes and its dependence on the magnetic field is rather weak. In the strong confinement regime, on the other hand, the spin relaxation rate at low temperatures is governed by the one-phonon processes and exhibits the characteristic B^4 dependence on the magnetic field(B). Non-Markoffian theory is developed for the electron spin decoherence rate due to the electron-phonon interactions based on the double Feynman diagrams. The dependencies of the electron spin decoherence rate on the magnetic field and the temperature are clarified.

Keywords: electron spin relaxation, electron spin decoherence, quantum disk, electron-phonon interactions
PACS: 73.21.La,72.25.Rb,71.70.Ej

In recent years, a single electron in a single quantum dot(QD) or a single donor electron is extensively studied from the interest in the application to the quantum information processing. The electron spin decoherence time is one of the most important parameters which determine the performance figure of merit of the quantum information processing. There are two kinds of spin relaxation time. Namely, T_1 is the spin population decay time which represents the time scale of the spin-flip between the spin-up state and the spin-down state. The second one is T_2 which is called spin decoherence time and represents the decay time constant of the off-diagonal coherence between two spin states. There are several experimental reports on the spin decay time, T_1 [1, 2, 3]. In a GaInAs QD at 1K and under a magnetic field of 4 Tesla, a very long T_1 time about 20 ms was reported [3]. Recently, the spin decoherence time T_2^* in a GaAs QD and its dependence on the magnetic field was reported [4]. Here an in-plane magnetic field is applied to induce the spin-flip Raman coherence via the trion state. The off-diagonal coherence induced between spin doublet states of a resident electron in a QD was monitored spectroscopically. Concerning the theory of spin decoherence, there are only few papers [5, 6] which are based on the Bloch equation derived in the second Born approximation and in the Markoff approximation. However, a quantitative theory is missing which can be compared with experimental results. The purpose of our study is to construct a general non-Markoffian theory based on a realistic model to predict quantitatively the electron spin decay/decoherence times and their dependence on the temperature and the magnetic field.

We formulated a microscopic theory to calculate the spin population decay time(T_1) and the spin decoherence time(T_2) of a single electron in a quantum dot based on the Fermi's golden rule and a method of the double Feynman diagram [7], respectively. In our theory, the relevant Hamiltonian is composed of the $k \cdot p$ Hamiltonian for the conduction band, the confinement potential, the phonon Hamiltonian and the electron-phonon interactions. First of all, we diagonalize the electronic part to obtain the discrete energy levels, including the cubic-in-k term for the conduction band (the Dresselhaus term) and the Rashba term due to the structural asymmetry along the growth direction. After that, we take into account the relaxation induced by the electron-phonon interactions.

Concerning the T_1 time, we clarified the importance of the two-phonon processes. For a realistic size of natural quantum dot in a GaAs quantum well under an in-plane magnetic field, our theoretical results suggest that the spin population decay rate($1/T_1$) by the two-phonon processes is a few orders of magnitude larger than that by the one-phonon processes. The two-phonon rate is weakly dependent on the magnetic field(B) in contrast to the one-phonon rate which exhibits $\sim B^4$ dependence at low temperatures due to the piezoelectric coupling. We also studied the case of self-assembled quantum dots under a magnetic field along the growth axis. According to the results, we notice that at low temperatures($\sim$1K) as in the experiments by Kroutvar et al. [3], a cross-over occurs between the relative weight of the one-phonon and the two-phonon processes around a few Tesla, above

CP893, *Physics of Semiconductors, 28th International Conference*
edited by W. Jantsch and F. Schäffler
© 2007 American Institute of Physics 978-0-7354-0397-0/07/$23.00

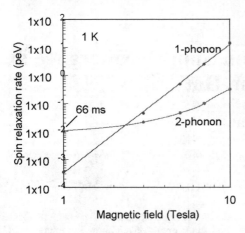

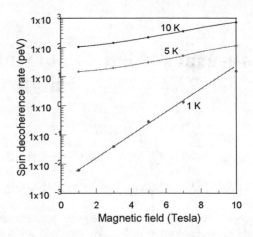

FIGURE 1. Electron spin relaxation rates in a GaAs quantum disk with a parabolic lateral confinement potential(characteristic energy of 30 meV) at 1K are plotted in units of pico eV as a function of the magnetic field applied along the growth direction. The contributions from the one-phonon and two-phonon processes are compared.

FIGURE 2. Electron spin decoherence rates in the same GaAs quantum disk as in Fig. 1 are plotted in units of pico eV for T=1, 5, and 10 K as a function of the magnetic field applied along the growth direction.

which the one-phonon processes are dominating the population decay rate($1/T_1$). It is also predicted that for a magnetic field below a few Tesla and at the temperature of $\sim$1K, where experimental data are not available, the spin T_1 time is determined by the two-phonon processes to be about 100 msec. These features are exhibited in Fig.1 for a strongly confined quantum disk with a harmonic lateral confinement potential(characteristic energy of 30 meV) under a magnetic field along the growth axis. It is important to note that the relative weight between the one-phonon and the two-phonon processes depends sensitively on the electronic energy level structure which is in turn dependent on the strength of quantum confinement.

In order to estimate the spin decoherence time, we consider the time-evolution of the off-diagonal coherence between the lowest spin doublet states of a resident electron in a QD. When this time-evolution is described by a simple damped oscillation, its Fourier-Laplace transform in the frequency domain exhibits a Lorentzian lineshape. Thus from the half-width of the Fourier-Laplace transform, the decoherence time can be estimated. This Laplace transform can be written in the resolvent form and can be expanded in a series with respect to the electron-phonon interactions. Then making use of the diagrammatic representation, we can sum up the higher order terms systematically. The non-Markoffian properties are taken into account in the frequency dependence of the self-energy operators [7]. Since the two-phonon processes play an important role in the spin relaxation processes as mentioned above, we have to take into account the fourth order self-energy operators corresponding to the two-phonon processes.

The calculated electron spin decoherence rates are exhibited in Fig. 2 for the same GaAs quantum disk as in Fig. 1 as a function of the magnetic field applied along the growth direction for T=1, 5, and 10 K. Unfortunately, experimental data of the electron spin decoherence rate are not available for the self-assembled InGaAs QDs and the comparison between the theory and experiments is left for the future. We also calculated the spin decoherence rate in a GaAs natural quantum dot under an in-plane magnetic field and clarified its dependence on the temperature and the magnetic field. Recent measurements of the spin decoherence rate($1/T_2^*$) in a similar system [4] show a few orders of magnitude larger values than our theoretical results, although the dependence on the magnetic field exhibits reasonable agreement between the theory and experiments. This discrepancy may arise from the fact that the measured values are subject to inhomogeneous contribution from, e.g., fluctuating nuclear fields.

REFERENCES

1. S. Cortez et al., Phys. Rev. Lett. **89**, 207401 (2002).
2. R. Hanson et al., Phys. Rev. Lett. **91**, 196802 (2003).
3. M. Kroutvar et al., Nature **432**, 81 (2004).
4. M. V. Gurudev Dutt et al., Phys. Rev. Lett. **94**, 227403 (2005).
5. Y. G. Semenov and K. W. Kim, Phys. Rev. Lett. **92**, 026601 (2004).
6. V. N. Golovach et al., Phys. Rev. Lett. **93**, 016601 (2004).
7. T. Takagahara, Chap.9 in *Quantum Coherence, Correlation and Decoherence in Semiconductor Nanostructures*, ed. T. Takagahara (Academic Press, San Diego, 2003).

Nanosecond excitonic spin relaxation in cubic GaN

Atsushi Tackeuchi, Hirotaka Otake, Yusuke Ogawa, Takafumi Ushiyama, and
Taisuke Fujita

Department of Applied Physics, Waseda University, Tokyo 169-8555, Japan

Fumiyoshi Takano and Hiro Akinaga

Nanotechnology Research Institute (NRI),
National Institute of Advanced Industrial Science and Technology (AIST),
1-1-1 Umezono, Tsukuba, Ibaraki 305-8568, Japan

Abstract. The excitonic spin relaxation in cubic GaN is observed by spin-dependent pump and probe reflectance measurements with sub-picosecond time resolution. The spin relaxation times at 15 – 75 K are found to be longer than 5 ns and short spin relaxation times on the picosecond order are not present. Although these long spin relaxation times are in striking contrast to the sub-picosecond spin relaxation of A-band free excitons in hexagonal GaN, they are consistent with the dependence that spin relaxation time becomes longer for wider-band-gap zincblende semiconductors.

Keywords: spin, spin relaxation, GaN, exciton, cubic, zincblende
PACS: 78.47.+p, 78.55.Cr, 72.25.Fe , 72.25.Rb

INTRODUCTION

Picosecond spin relaxation process in semiconductors became observable in the 1990s with the use of spin-dependent pump and probe measurements [1]. Investigations on spin dynamics in the GaN system are expected to yield information on the applicability of spin-related phenomena in the GaN system. Recently, we reported that the A-band free exciton in hexagonal GaN shows sub-picosecond spin relaxation [2]. Since cubic GaN has a crystallographic symmetry higher than hexagonal GaN, the spin relaxation process is expected to be different.

EXPERIMENTAL

For the sample preparation of cubic GaN, molecular beam epitaxy growth was carried out using solid-metal Ga source and a radio-frequency-excited nitrogen plasma source [3]. A 600 nm-thick cubic GaN layer was grown at a substrate temperature of 750 °C on a thin flat 3C-SiC layer (2-3 nm) obtained by carbonization of a Si (001) substrate surface.

The photoluminescence (PL) spectra using a He-Cd laser ($\lambda = 325$ nm) as the optical source are shown in

Fig. 1. The PL peak at 3.25 eV and the PL peak at 3.16 eV are attributed to an excitonic transition and a donor-acceptor recombination pair (DAP) transition, respectively [4, 5].

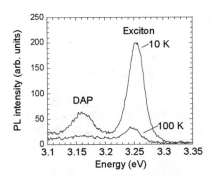

FIGURE 1. Photoluminescence spectra of cubic GaN at 10 K and 100K. PL peak at 3.25 eV and PL peak at 3.16 eV are attributed to an excitonic transition and a donor-acceptor recombination pair (DAP) transition, respectively.

We used the time-resolved spin-dependent pump and probe reflectance measurements to observe the time evolution of the spin polarization. The advantage of the pump and probe measurements is a high time

CP893, *Physics of Semiconductors, 28th International Conference*
edited by W. Jantsch and F. Schäffler
© 2007 American Institute of Physics 978-0-7354-0397-0/07/$23.00

resolution of sub-picosecond, which is determined by the convolution of optical pulses. The laser energy was matched to the photoluminescence peak at 3.25 eV which is attributed to free and bound excitonic transition.

DISCUSSION

The clear spin polarizations are observed below 75 K and disappear at 100 K as shown in Fig. 2. The time evolutions of the spin polarization rate are plotted in Fig. 3. The initial fast decay can be attributed to the coherent artifact which was generated due to pump beam refraction by the optical transient grating in the sample. The slow main decay can be attributed to the excitonic spin relaxation. The time evolution of the spin polarization at 15K-75 K shows a single exponential decay corresponding to the spin relaxation time longer than 5 ns.

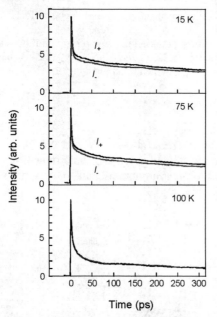

FIGURE 2. Observed time evolutions of spin dependent reflection intensity at 15 K-100 K at long time of 330 ps. I_+ (I_-) indicates the right circularly polarized excitation and right (left) circularly polarized probe. indicates the right circularly polarized excitation and left circularly polarized probe.

This long relaxation time is in striking contrast to the sub-picosecond spin relaxation of A-band free excitons in hexagonal GaN. In zincblende semiconductors, the spin relaxation time becomes longer for the wider-band-gap energy. Previously, we measured the spin relaxation time of bulk GaAs and found it to be 3.6 ns at 10 K [6]. The fact that the spin relaxation time in GaN is longer than that in GaAs is consistent with this trend. The candidate spin

relaxation mechanism is the Bir-Aronov-Pikus (BAP) process. The time evolutions of spin polarization do not change at 15 and 75 K. This fact agrees with the BAP process.

From the viewpoint of applications, the long spin relaxation time is attractive for memory applications or quantum computing, which requires a long coherence time.

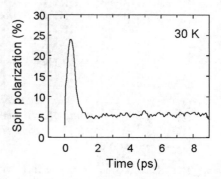

FIGURE 3. Time evolution of spin polarization: $(I_+-I_-)/(I_++I_-)$, at 30 K at short time of 10 ps.

ACKNOWLEDGMENTS

This work was supported in part by a Grant-in-Aid for Scientific Research (No. 18360042), The 21st Century COE Program (Physics of Self-Organization Systems), Academic Frontier Project and the High-Tech Research Center Project from Japan Ministry of Education, Culture, Sports, Science and Technology. This work was also partly supported by NEDO under the Nanotechnology Program.

REFERENCES

1. A. Tackeuchi, S. Muto, T. Inata, and T. Fujii, Appl. Phys. Lett. **56**, 2213 (1990).
2. T. Kuroda, T. Yabushita, T. Kosuge, A. Tackeuchi, K. Taniguchi, T. Chinone, and N. Horio, Appl. Phys. Lett. **85**, 3116 (2004).
3. D. Wang, Y. Hiroyama, M. Tamura, M. Ichikawa, and S. Yoshida, Appl. Phys. Lett. **76**, 1683 (2000).
4. R. Klann, O. Brandt, H. Yang, H. T. Grahn, K. Ploog, and A. Trampert, Phys. Rev. B, **52**, R11615 (1995).
5. H. Yaguchi, J. Wu, H. Akiyama, M. Baba, K. Onabe, and Y. Shiraki, phys. stat. sol. (b) **216**, 237 (1999).
6. A. Tackeuchi, R. Ohtsubo, K. Yamaguchi, M. Murayama, T. Kitamura, T. Kuroda, and T. Takagahara, Appl. Phys. Lett. **84**, 3576 (2004).

Ab initio Calculations of Zero-field Spin Splitting in Zinc Blende Semiconductors

A. Skierkowski and J. A. Majewski

Institute of Theoretical Physics, Faculty of Physics, Warsaw University, ul. Hoża 69, 00-681 Warszawa, Poland

Abstract. We present first-principles studies of the zero field spin splitting of conduction band in [110] strained GaAs. The calculations reveal strong anisotropy of the linear-k spin splitting in the (110) plane of the Brillouin Zone and very minor in the (001) plane. This provides qualitative understanding of the difference in the spin lifetimes in the GaAs/AlAs heterostructures grown along [100] and [110] crystallographic directions.

Keywords: zero field spin splitting, band structure, III-V semiconductors, Rashba effect
PACS: 71.55Eq, 71.70.Fk, 71.70.Ej, 72.25.Rb

INTRODUCTION

The present surge in interest for spin devices and spin relaxation effects calls for a detailed understanding of the spin dynamics in semiconductor nanostructures [1,2]. The spin splitting of the bands caused by the spin-orbit coupling induces a coherent spin precession that is an essential factor, together with spin-dependent and spin-independent scattering rates, determining spin lifetimes in semiconductors and their heterostructures [2]. These spin-related effects have been studied extensively both theoretically and experimentally, yet there are still many open questions concerning the microscopic origin of the spin-splitting of the energy bands, their dependence on material combinations, on quantum well widths, or external factors like strain and/or electric field [2]. For example, experimental studies have revealed that the spin lifetimes of conduction band electrons can be dramatically different in heterostructures grown along [001] and [110] crystallographic directions [3].

In this communication, we investigate the spin splitting of the conduction band in the (110) biaxially strained GaAs. In this case cubic T_d symmetry is reduced to uniaxial symmetry C_{2v}, which in turn causes the both Rashba (structure inversion asymmetry – SIA) and bulk inversion asymmetry terms (BIA) to appear in the k-linear spin splitting. Since [110] GaAs/AlGaAs heterostructures possess also C_{2v} symmetry, the present study sheds light on the peculiar behavior of the spin lifetimes in these structures in comparison to the standard [001] ones.

RESULTS AND DISCUSSION

We study the linear-k spin splitting by means of *ab initio* calculations, which turned out to provide useful tool in studies of this problem [4]. Owing to the nearly complete lack of experimental data concerning the linear-k spin splitting, this provides theoretical predictions for these quantities.

Computational procedure

The spin splitting of the conduction band in [110] strained GaAs has been calculated by the mean of the *ab initio* relativistic calculations that are performed in the framework of the local density approximation to the density functional theory and pseudopotential method. This approach has been applied previously to various studies of the spin splitting in semiconductors and their heterostructures. It provides, for example, very accurate description of the valence band spin splitting Δ_0 in III-V bulks [5,6]. The calculated linear-k spin-splitting has been also mapped on the simple two-band effective Hamiltonian traditionally used to the analysis of this type of problems [5-7].

Effective Hamiltonian

The linear-k spin splitting in the conduction band around the Γ-point can be modeled by the following 2x2 Hamiltonian $H(k) = \boldsymbol{\sigma} \cdot \boldsymbol{\Omega}(k) = H_{SIA}(k) + H_{BIA}(k)$,

CP893, *Physics of Semiconductors, 28th International Conference*
edited by W. Jantsch and F. Schäffler
© 2007 American Institute of Physics 978-0-7354-0397-0/07/$23.00

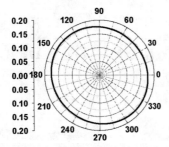

FIGURE 1. The angular dependence of the conduction band spin splitting for the wave vectors lying in the (001) plane. The angles 0° and 90° correspond to the directions [100] and [010], respectively.

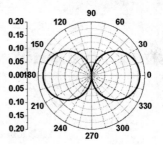

FIGURE 2. The angular dependence of the conduction band spin splitting for the wave vectors lying in the (110) plane. The angles 0° and 90° correspond to the directions [-110] and [001], respectively.

where σ is the vector of Pauli matrices and $\Omega(k)$ is the effective magnetic field dependent on the wave vector k. Rashba (SIA) contribution is represented by the x and y components of the vector Ω, whereas z-component originates from the BIA (Dresselhaus) term [8], leading to $\Omega_x = \alpha_{SIA}k_y$, $\Omega_y = -\alpha_{SIA}k_x$, and $\Omega_z = \alpha_{BIA}(-k_x + k_y)$. The spin splitting has been calculated numerically for the wave vector k in the Brillouin Zone and fitted to the analytical expression $\Delta E_{spin}(k) = 2|\Omega(k)|$. This allows us to determine the constants α_{SIA} and α_{BIA} describing the linear-k spin splitting. The spin lifetime is proportional to the square of the vector $\Omega(k)$ averaged over the angles. Therefore, the angular dependence of the vector $\Omega(k)$ in the plane perpendicular to the growth direction will determine the spin lifetime in the heterostructure.

Angular dependence of spin splitting

The calculated linear-k conduction band spin splitting in (110) strained GaAs for wave vectors lying in the (001) and (110) planes is depicted in Figs. 1 and 2, respectively. In these figures, the spin splitting has been normalized to the length of the in-plane vector. As one can see the spin splitting exhibits small anisotropy for wave vectors lying in the (001) plane, whereas the anisotropy in the (110) plane is huge. The linear-k spin splitting disappears only along the [001] axis, being not zero in the rest of the Brillouin Zone. Our calculations show that the SIA constant is roughly three times larger than the BIA, i.e., for the compressive biaxial strain of -0.5% these constants are respectively equal to 0.085 and 0.032 eVÅ.

The role of strain on the linear-k spin splitting in n-GaAs has been recently investigated using scanning Kerr microscopy, however, the results have been analyzed employing only SIA part of the effective Hamiltonian [9].

CONCLUSIONS

We have performed *ab initio* calculations of the zero field linear-k spin splitting of the conduction band in the [110] strained GaAs. We have found that the spin splitting exhibits very strong anisotropy in the (110) plane, whereas the spin splitting shows only weak anisotropy in the (001) plane. This sheds light on the qualitatively huge difference in the spin lifetimes in the [110] and [001] heterostructures as observed in experiment. It opens also new opportunities in tuning the spin lifetime of electrons through the growth of heterostructures onto suitable crystallographic planes or applying external stress in relevant direction.

REFERENCES

1. G.A. Prinz, *Science* **283**, 330 (1999).
2. I. Zutic, J. Fabian, and S. Das Sarma, *Rev. Mod. Phys.* **76**, 323 (2004).
3. Y. Ohno, R. Terauchi, T. Adachi, F. Matsukura, and H. Ohno, *Phys. Rev. Lett.* **83**, 4196 (1999).
4. A. N. Chantis, M. van Schilfgaarde, and T. Kotani *Phys. Rev. Lett.* 96, 086405 (2006) and references therein.
5. J. A. Majewski, M. Städele, and P. Vogl, *Mat. Res. Soc. Symp. Proc.* **449**, 887 (1997).
6. J. A. Majewski, S. Birner, A. Trellakis, M. Sabathil, and P. Vogl, *phys. stat. sol (c)* **1**, 2003 (2004).
7. J. A. Majewski and P. Vogl, *"Physics of Semiconductors 2002"*, Proc. 26th Int. Conf. Phys. Sem., Edinburgh, 29 July - 2 August 2002, Institute of Physics Conference Series Number 171, edited by A. R. Long and J. H. Davies, Institute of Physics Publishing, Bristol and Philadelphia, 2003, P305.
8. R. Eppenga and M. F. H. Schuurmans, *Phys. Rev. B* **37**, 10923 (1988).
9. S. A. Crooker and D. L. Smith, *Phys. Rev. Lett.* **94**, 236601 (2005).

^{71}Ga Nuclear Magnetic Relaxation Measurements in Zinc-blende GaN

R D Morris, A J Kent, H L Geen, C T Foxon and S V Novikov

School of Physics and Astronomy, University of Nottingham, University Park, Nottingham NG7 2RD, UK.

Abstract. We report measurements of ^{71}Ga nuclear magnetic relaxation in cubic, zinc-blende, GaN. The spin-lattice and spin-spin relaxation times, T_1 and T_2, were measured as a function of temperature using pulse NMR. The spin-lattice relaxation mechanism is dominated by hyperfine interactions between the Ga nuclei and conduction electrons. In the highest carrier density samples, the electron system is degenerate and T_1 is proportional to $1/T$. However, in the lowest carrier density sample $T_1 \sim 1/T^{\frac{1}{2}}$. These two results correspond, respectively, to the metallic and semiconducting regimes. The T_2 relaxation time was found to be only weakly dependent on the temperature and the NMR line width subject to quadrupolar broadening effects due to crystal defects.

Keywords: Zinc-blende GaN, nuclear magnetic relaxation
PACS: 76.60.-k; 81.05.Ea

INTRODUCTION

The wide-band-gap semiconductor GaN continues to attract considerable interest due to its applications in electronic and optoelectronic devices, such as high frequency transistors and blue/UV lasers. Despite the significant technological achievements in recent years, there are still significant gaps in our understanding of the basic physical properties of GaN. Nuclear magnetic resonance (NMR) measurements of spectra and nuclear magnetic relaxation rates give a unique insight to the electronic and structural properties of the material, as has been shown in measurements on the, common, hexagonal (wurtzite) crystalline form of GaN [1].

GaN can also be crystallized in the cubic zinc-blende structure. The non-polar nature of cubic GaN is beneficial for a number of possible applications including deep-UV light emitters. In this paper we describe measurements of ^{71}Ga nuclear magnetic relaxation in cubic GaN.

THE EXPERIMENT

The cubic GaN samples used in the experiments were grown by plasma-assisted MBE. A description of the growth process is given elsewhere [2]. The cubic structure was confirmed by x-ray (ω-2θ) measurements. Using Hall (van der Pauw) measurements, it was found that all the samples showed n-type conductivity as a result of unintentional doping, and had electron concentrations lying in the range 10^{15} to 10^{18} cm^{-3}. The samples were finely powdered and pulse NMR measurements were made on the ^{71}Ga nuclei at a frequency of 20 MHz in a home-made single-coil spectrometer. The spin-lattice relaxation time, T_1, was determined using a standard saturation-recovery pulse sequence. An exponential fit to the magnetization recovery curve was used to extract a value for T_1. The spin-spin relaxation time, T_2, was measured using a $\pi/2$-τ-$\pi/2^{90°}$-(spin echo) pulse sequence.

RESULTS AND DISCUSSION

Spin-lattice Relaxation

Figure 1 shows the dependence on the temperature, T, of T_1 for samples MS716 and MS777, which had electron concentrations of 2.5×10^{17} and 1.0×10^{15} cm^{-3} respectively.

For the higher electron concentration sample, MS716, $T_1 \sim T^{-1}$. This is typical behavior for a metallic sample in which the nuclear relaxation is due to electron-nuclear hyperfine couplings. In a metal T_1T is a constant, given by the Korringa relation:

$$T_1T = \left(\frac{\gamma_e}{\gamma_n}\right)^2 \frac{\hbar}{4\pi k_B K^2}, \qquad (1)$$

CP893, *Physics of Semiconductors, 28th International Conference*
edited by W. Jantsch and F. Schäffler
© 2007 American Institute of Physics 978-0-7354-0397-0/07/$23.00

where γ_e and γ_n are, respectively, the electronic and nuclear gyromagnetic ratios and K is the Knight shift:

$$K = \frac{1}{3\pi}\mu_0\gamma_e^2|\psi_F(0)|^2\Omega\left(\frac{3m^{*3}N}{8\pi}\right)^{\frac{1}{3}}. \quad (2)$$

Here m^* is the electron effective mass, N is the electron concentration and $|\psi_F(0)|^2\Omega$ measures the relative electronic charge at the nucleus. To obtain (1) it is assumed that the electron system is degenerate. This is an acceptable approximation in the case of sample MS716 for which we calculate the Fermi temperature, $T_F \approx 100$ K. From the results, $T_1T = 970$, this gives $K = 5.4 \times 10^{-5}$, which is in good agreement with the value obtained from measurement of the ^{71}Ga NMR frequency shift.

For the lower electron concentration sample, MS777, $T_1 \sim T^{-\frac{1}{2}}$, which is the behavior expected for semiconductors. This appears reasonable since, for this sample, T_F is only 2.5 K. Assuming the electron system is described by a Maxwell-Boltzmann distribution function; the following expression for T_1 is obtained

$$\frac{1}{T_1} = \frac{4}{9}\pi\mu_0^2\gamma_e^2\gamma_n^2|\psi(0)|^4\Omega^2N\left(\frac{m^{*3}k_BT}{2\pi^5}\right)^{\frac{1}{2}}. \quad (3)$$

From these measurements we obtain $|\psi(0)|^2\Omega \sim 10^4$.

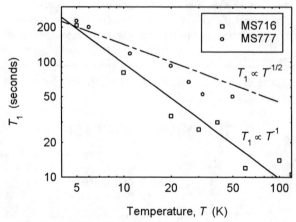

FIGURE 1. Temperature dependence of the spin-lattice relaxation time for two samples, MS716 and MS777.

The other samples measured fell in between these two limiting cases with the overall trend of T_1 decreasing with increasing electron concentration in the metallic regime (see Table 1), and the temperature dependence of T_1 showing metallic behavior at low temperatures ($T < T_F$) and tending towards semiconducting behavior at the higher temperatures.

Spin-spin Relaxation

The dephasing time of the spin-echo signal, T_2, was about 250 μs. This suggests that the intrinsic spin-spin relaxation is due to dipole-dipole interactions: for a powder sample of a material having a simple cubic lattice, the spin-spin relaxation time is given by [3]

$$\frac{1}{T_2} \approx 0.36\mu_0\gamma_n^2\hbar\sqrt{I(I+1)}\frac{1}{d^3}, \quad (4)$$

where d is the lattice constant. This gives T_2 of order 100 μs, which is in reasonable agreement with the measurements. However, we also observe significant NMR line broadening, reflected in a T_2^* value of only 31 μs. Gallium nuclei have $I = 3/2$ and so the NMR line could be subject to quadrupole broadening. This is expected to be zero in the case of a perfect cubic lattice due to symmetry arguments. However, crystal imperfections may give rise to quadrupolar broadening [4]. In this case the broadening may be used as a measure of the defect density in the material. Further work is underway to obtain quantitative results.

TABLE 1. Sample parameters at $T = 5$ K				
Sample	N cm^{-3}	T_1 (s)	T_2 (μs)	T_2^* (μs)
MS716	2.5×10^{17}	207	267	30.7
MS718	6.0×10^{16}	80	245	30.6
MS730	7.0×10^{17}	60	335	30.5
MS777	1.0×10^{15}	196	250	--

CONCLUSIONS

We have measured the ^{71}Ga nuclear magnetic relaxation times in a series of cubic GaN samples. The spin-lattice relaxation is due to electron-nuclear hyperfine interactions and we have observed both metallic and semiconductor-like dependence of T_1 on T in samples with differing electron concentrations. Strong broadening of the NMR line reflected by a short T_2^* was observed and attributed to quadrupolar broadening due to crystalline defects.

The authors acknowledge support for this project from EPSRC of the UK.

REFERENCES

1. M. Corti, A. Gabetta, M. Fanciulli, A. Svane and N. E. Christensen, *Phys. Rev. B* **67**, 064416 (2003).
2. S. V. Novikov, K. W. Edmonds, A. D. Giddings, K. Y. Wang, C. R. Staddon, R. P. Campion, B. L. Gallagher and C. T. Foxon, *Semicond. Sci. Tech.* **19**, L13 (2004).
3. A. Abragam, *Principles of Nuclear Magnetism*, Oxford: Clarendon Press, 1961.
4. M. H. Cohen and F. Reif, *Solid State Physics* **5**, 321 (1957).

Self-quenching of hyperfine-induced electron spin relaxation in InAs/GaAs quantum dots due to dynamic nuclear polarization

B. Eble*, O. Krebs*, A. Lemaître*, K. Kowalik*,†, A. Kudelski* and P. Voisin*

*CNRS-Laboratoire de Photonique et Nanostructures, Route de Nozay, 91460 Marcoussis, France
†Institute of Experimental Physics, Warsaw University, 69 Hoża, 00-681 Warszawa, Poland

Abstract. We report on the optical orientation of singly charged exciton X^+ in a single self-assembled InAs/GaAs quantum dot. We show that the hyperfine interaction with the nuclei is responsible for a partial spin relaxation. This effect manifests only under modulated excitation polarization, while under steady optical pumping conditions, we measure a nuclear polarization large enough to screen its own fluctuations. This explains the high degree of circular polarization commonly reported for X^+.

Keywords: Semiconductor quantum dot, nuclear polarization, charged exciton, spin relaxation
PACS: 71.35.Pq, 72.25.Fe,72.25.Rb, 78.67.Hc

Coherent manipulation of electron spin in semiconductors is currently a very exciting challenge. In this respect localization of electrons in quantum dots is certainly a prerequisite. Yet, the confinement on nanometer scale increases the amplitude of statistical fluctuations of the effective magnetic-like field due to the hyperfine interaction with the nuclear spin of the host materials [1]. In the case of self-assembled InGaAs/GaAs quantum dots the latter amounts to a few tens mT, giving rise to ensemble dephasing (termed further hyperfine induced spin relaxation (HSR)) in a characteristic time of 500ps. This effect has been reported in Ref. [2] for an ensemble of p-doped quantum dots for which the photoluminescence of positive trions X^+ (one electron with two holes) could directly monitor the average electron spin S_z^e. Yet, measurements of single quantum dots do not clearly reveal similar spin relaxation, since strong X^+ circular polarization up to 70% is generally reported [3, 4, 5], whereas the maximum theoretical polarization should be limited to about 50%. Since hyperfine interaction conserves the total spin of the electron-nucleus system, HSR should be accompanied by dynamic nuclear polarization (DNP) [3, 6, 8]. The latter could result in an effective magnetic field large enough to screen the transverse nuclear field fluctuations responsible for the HSR. We addressed this issue by measuring both circular polarization and optically induced nuclear polarization of a single quantum dot.

The detailed description and charactrization of the self-assembled InGaAs/GaAs quantum dot samples can be found in Ref. [7]. The InAs QDs were grown in the Stranski-Krastanov mode 25 nm above a 200nm-thick n⁺-GaAs layer and covered by an intrinsic GaAs (25 nm)/Al$_{0.3}$Ga$_{0.7}$As (120 nm)/GaAs (5 nm)

multilayer. The QD charge is controlled by an electrical bias applied between a top Schottky contact and a back ohmic contact.

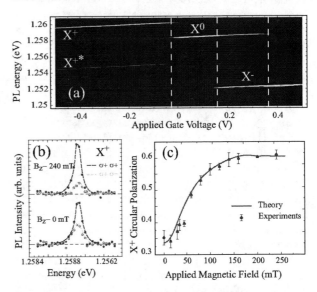

FIGURE 1. (a) Contour plot of the PL intensity from a single InAs QD at T=5 K versus the detection energy and applied bias under intra-dot excitation at 1.31 eV. (b) Polarization resolved spectra of X^+ line at -0.2V for two different magnetic fields. (c) Circular polarization of X^+ line versus external magnetic field. For (b) and (c), the excitation polarization is provided by a 50kHz-photo-elastic modulator, and the polarization- resolved detection is performed by a time-gated Si-avalanche photodiode.

The HSR described in Refs. [1, 2] corresponds to the spin dephasing of electrons due to the random orientation of magnetic-like nuclear fields in an ensemble of

CP893, *Physics of Semiconductors, 28ᵗʰ International Conference*
edited by W. Jantsch and F. Schäffler
© 2007 American Institute of Physics 978-0-7354-0397-0/07/$23.00

singly charged QDs. Actually, the nuclear field B_n has a correlation time $\tau_c \approx 10^{-4}$s. It can thus be considered as *frozen* during the period of electron Larmor precession $T_L = h/g_e\mu_B B_n \sim 0.5$ ns as well as during the lifetime $\tau_r \approx 0.7$ns of the photo-created trion X^+ . In the case of a single QD, the HSR will thus manifest if the time over which the measurement is carried out is long enough to ensure that the nuclear field statistically samples all its possible orientations. In the PL measurements reported below this important requirement is satisfied since the integration time (~ 10 s) is five orders of magnitude longer than τ_c.

Figure 1 presents the measurements of circular polarization ρ_c on a single X^+ state with excitation polarization modulated at 50 kHz between σ^+ and σ^- in order to prevent DNP. Note that the X^+ complex can be formed in a n-Schottky structure by decreasing the voltage until the neutral exciton line disappears and by choosing intra-dot excitation conditions (here 1.31 eV) to photo-create holes in the QD [3]. In zero magnetic field, a first remarkable observation is the strong fall of circular polarization from $\sim$65% to $\sim$35% when passing from constant (not shown) to modulated excitation polarization. Under such excitation, HSR becomes likely the dominant mechanism determining the average circular polarization of X^+. To confirm this interpretation we have measured the dependence of ρ_c on a longitudinal magnetic field, which allows for the progressive screening of the transverse nuclear field fluctuations. As shown in Fig.1(c), for $B_z \geq 150$ mT the circular polarization of X^+ recovers a high level of 62%. In addition we could perform a good theoretical fit of $\rho_c(B_z)$ by using the expression derived in Ref. [1] for the explicit field-dependent average spin $\langle S_z^e(t, B_z)\rangle$ and $\rho_c = \int \langle S_z^e(t, B_z)\rangle \exp(-t/\tau_r)/\tau_r dt$ for the time-integrated circular polarization. In this model, there are only two fitting parameters : the initial spin polarization of X^+ in its ground state ρ_c^0, which is actually imposed by the saturation plateau of ρ_c in strong magnetic field (62%) and the characteristic nuclear field dispersion Δ_B which determines the fall of polarization in zero magnetic field. The good agreement obtained with $\Delta_B = 33 mT$ demonstrates that under modulated excitation polarization the spin dynamics of X^+ is really governed by the hyperfine interaction with the nuclei.

Figure 2 presents measurements of nuclear polarization in zero magnetic field and under constant excitation polarization. This is achieved by measuring the trion splitting induced by the nuclear field (or Overhauser shift) between the σ^+ and σ^- polarized components of the X^+ line [3, 8, 4]. To avoid possible artefact of the optical set-up, the excitation polarization defined by the angle of a quarter-wave plate with respect to a linear polarizer is varied from σ^+ to σ^-. We measure an Overhauser shift of about 10 μeV in circularly polarized excitation, similar to the value recently reported by

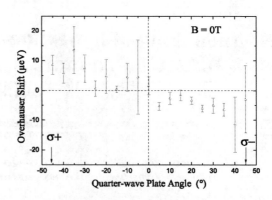

FIGURE 2. Overhauser-shift of a positive trion in zero magnetic field against the quarter wave plate angle which defines the excitation polarization. The reversal of nuclear polarization guarantees that this small splitting is not due to an artefact of the set-up.

C. W. Lai *et al.*[4]. In principle, an external magnetic field of a few Gauss is required to prevent the fast ($T_2 \approx 10^{-4}$ s) depolarization of the nuclei due to their mutual dipolar interaction. The Knight field produced by the electron itself could to some extent play this role[4], but obviously the resulting nuclear polarization achieved under such conditions remains much smaller ($\approx$5%) than the photo-created electron spin polarization (ρ_c^0=62%). Yet, this corresponds to an effective field above 100 mT which finally explains the strong circular polarization observed for X^+ in zero magnetic field under constant σ^+ (or σ^-) excitation.

ACKNOWLEDGMENTS

This work has been supported by contract BoitQuant of *Fonds National pour la Science* and the European network of excellence SANDIE.

REFERENCES

1. I. A. Merkulov, A. L. Efros and M. Rosen, Phys. Rev. B **65**, 205309 (2002).
2. P.-F. Braun *et al.*, Phys. Rev. Lett. **94**, 116601 (2005).
3. B. Eble *et al.*, cond-mat/0508281, (2005).
4. C. W. Lai *et al.*, Phys. Rev. Lett. **96**, 167403 (2006).
5. A. Ebbens *et al.*, Phys. Rev. B **72**, 073307 (2005).
6. F. Meier and B. Zakharchenya, Optical Orientation, vol. 8 of Modern Problem in Condensed Matter Sciences (1984).
7. S. Laurent *et al.*, Phys. Rev. Lett. **94**, 147401 (2005).
8. D. Gammon *et al.*, Phys. Rev. Lett. **86**, 5176 (2001).

Optical Enhancement of ^{15}N Nuclear Magnetic Resonance in Zinc-blende Ga^{15}N

R D Morris, A J Kent, H L Geen, C T Foxon and S V Novikov

School of Physics and Astronomy, University of Nottingham, University Park, Nottingham NG7 2RD, UK.

Abstract. We have observed enhancement of the nuclear dipolar alignment of ^{15}N in cubic Ga^{15}N by optical pumping. Illumination of the sample with polarized band-gap light creates spin polarization of the electronic conduction band. Polarization is transferred to the ^{15}N nuclei by Overhauser-type transitions, where it is detected by NMR measurements. An average increase of the ^{15}N nuclear polarization by ~ 30% over the thermal equilibrium value was observed. The relatively weak enhancement has been attributed to the significant background carrier density in the material, even in the low temperature regime, supported by supplementary Hall (Van der Pauw) measurements.

Keywords: Zinc-blende GaN, nuclear magnetic relaxation, optical enhancement
PACS: 76.60.-k; 81.05.Ea

INTRODUCTION

Nuclear magnetic resonance (NMR) is a powerful tool for chemical and structural analysis. However, the technique suffers from low sensitivity due to small thermal equilibrium values of the nuclear magnetic polarization. Sensitivity can be improved by increasing the applied magnetic field and/or decreasing the temperature. An alternative method is to "hyperpolarize" the nuclei. In semiconductors this can be achieved by optical pumping with circular-polarized band-gap light as has previously been demonstrated in GaAs and InP [1, 2]. The optical pumping excites spin polarized electrons which transfer their polarization to the nuclei by Overhauser cross relaxation processes (electron-nuclear spin flip-flop transitions). Using this technique, the degree of nuclear polarization can be moved far beyond the Boltzmann equilibrium value.

It has been proposed that hyperpolarized semiconductors can be used as substrates for transferred-optically-pumped NMR (TOPNMR) [3], in which the polarization of the semiconductor is transferred to a sample deposited on its surface. The high resistance of GaN to chemical attack would appear to make it an ideal substrate for TOPNMR. Also, GaN can be grown using the rare isotope ^{15}N which has nuclear spin-½ and so does not suffer from the spectroscopic barrier to polarization transfer at a surface experienced using quadrupolar nuclei, e.g. Ga.

In this paper we describe initial measurements of the optically pumped ^{15}N polarization in Ga^{15}N.

THE EXPERIMENT

The cubic, zinc-blende, GaN epilayer was grown on (100) GaAs by plasma-assisted MBE using isotopically pure ^{15}N as a source. Details of the growth of cubic GaN can be found in Ref. [4]. Cubic material was used because the optical pumping mechanism is understood for this polytype. Using Hall (van der Pauw) measurements, it was found that the sample showed n-type conductivity as a result of unintentional doping, and had an electron concentration of 7×10^{17} cm^{-3} at 4.2 K.

A 4.5×10 mm^2 rectangle was cleaved from the grown wafer and placed in an open-solenoid NMR coil. The pulse NMR measurements were made at a frequency of 20 MHz with the sample held at 5 K in an optical-access cryostat mounted in the bore of the NMR magnet. The illumination was provided by a frequency-doubled mode-locked picosecond Ti:Sapphire oscillator tunable in the range 3.55-2.49eV. The beam was circular polarized using a Fresnel rhomb and applied to the sample in a direction parallel to the applied B_0-field. The optical power density at the sample was estimated to be ~100mW/cm^2.

The nuclear polarization was measured using saturation-recovery sequences: *sat*-τ_{pump}-30s-π/2-*FID*,

CP893, *Physics of Semiconductors, 28th International Conference*
edited by W. Jantsch and F. Schäffler

where *sat* is a saturation sequence to destroy the magnetisation, $\tau_{pump} \sim T_1$ and *FID* is the free-induction decay. Optical-pumping was applied during the period τ_{pump}. For comparison, dark measurements were made using the same pulse sequence, but without illumination during τ_{pump}. The degree of nuclear alignment was measured by the intensity of the peak in the Fourier transform of the FID.

RESULTS AND DISCUSSION

Fig. 1 shows the ^{15}N FIDs at $B_0 = 4.63$ T, for the sample in the dark and optically pumped for 1800 s. A clear increase in the signal under optical pumping is seen. We can discount the possibility that this is related to a change in temperature of the sample under optical pumping because a carbon thermometer bonded to the sample was used to monitor its temperature which was maintained constant.

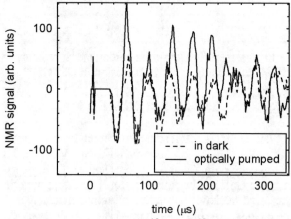

FIGURE 1. Nuclear FID for ^{15}N in Ga^{15}N in the dark and under illumination with band-gap light.

The Fourier transform of the FID data is shown in Fig. 2. From this, we deduce that the signal enhancement upon optical pumping is 30%. This maximum signal enhancement was obtained at pump photon energy of about 3 eV. This is less than the band gap energy of the cubic GaN (≈ 3.3 eV from photoluminescence (PL) measurements). We believe this could be due to optical pumping of defect states. It has been proposed that electrons localized at defects are more effective at transferring their polarization to the nuclei. We also found that the signal enhancement showed no dependence on the sense of polarization of the pump light. This is consistent with earlier reports of measurements on strongly doped GaAs samples [5].

At 30%, the maximum enhancement is much less than previously observed for GaAs [1] (using our setup we also measured up to 260 × enhancement from a semi-insulating GaAs wafer). We believe this is also

due to the relatively high background electron concentration in the GaN sample. Interaction with the sea of relatively weakly polarized electrons depolarizes the nuclei. Based on the incident optical power density and the lifetime of photo-induced carriers ($\sim$ ns from time-resolved PL measurements), we estimate that optical pumping leads to an increase in the electron concentration by only 0.01%. Therefore, even if the optically injected electrons are 100% spin polarized, the overall increase in polarization of the electron system will be very small.

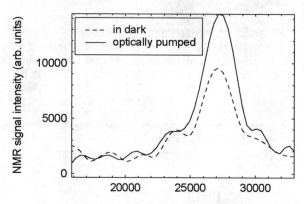

FIGURE 2. Fourier transform of FID data shown in Fig. 1.

CONCLUSIONS

We have detected, using NMR, optically-pumped enhancement of ^{15}N nuclear polarization in cubic Ga^{15}N. A maximum enhancement of $\sim$ 30% was measured, which is small compared to the enhancements previously observed in GaAs and InP. We believe this is due to the high background carrier concentration in the GaN material. Further work is underway to produce compensated material which should exhibit larger polarization enhancement under optical pumping.

The authors acknowledge support for this project from EPSRC of the UK.

REFERENCES

1. P. L. Kuhns, A. Kleinhammes, T. Schmiedel, W. G. Moulton, P. Chabrier, S. Sloan, E. Hughes and C. R. Bowers, *Phys. Rev.* B **55**, 7824 (1997).
2. C. A. Michal and R. Tycko, *Phys. Rev.* B **60**, 8672 (1999).
2. R. Tycko, *Solid State NMR* **11**, 1 (1998).
4. S. V. Novikov, K. W. Edmonds, A. D. Giddings, K. Y. Wang, C. R. Staddon, R. P. Campion, B. L. Gallagher and C. T. Foxon, *Semicond. Sci. Tech.* **19**, L13 (2004).
5. S. E. Barrett, R. Tycko, L. N. Pfeiffer and K. W. West, *Phys. Rev. Lett.* **72**, 1368 (1994).

Dynamic nuclear polarization of a single InAs/GaAs quantum dot : positive versus negative trions

B. Eble*, O. Krebs*, A. Lemaître*, K. Kowalik*,†, A. Kudelski*, B. Urbaszek**,
T. Amand**, X. Marie** and P. Voisin*

*CNRS-Laboratoire de Photonique et Nanostructures, Route de Nozay, 91460 Marcoussis, France
†Institute of Experimental Physics, Warsaw University, 69 Hoża, 00-681 Warszawa, Poland
**Laboratoire de Nanophysique Magnétisme et Optoélectronique, INSA, 31077 Toulouse Cedex 4, France

Abstract. We report on electron spin manipulation in a single charge-tunable self-assembled InAs/GaAs quantum dot. The hyperfine interaction between the optically oriented electron and nuclear spins leads to the polarization of the quantum dot nuclei. The sign of the resulting Overhauser-shift depends on the trion state X^+ or X^- which demonstrates the transfer of spin polarization to the nuclei from the unpaired electron either in the initial state for X^+, or in the final state for X^-.

Keywords: Semiconductor quantum dot, nuclear polarization, charged exciton
PACS: 71.35.Pq, 72.25.Fe,72.25.Rb, 78.67.Hc

The spin degree of freedom of electrons confined in quantum dot (QD) attracts a lot of attention because of its expected long relaxation time. Indeed, once the electron is confined in a quantum dot, its low temperature spin dynamics is almost no longer subject to the random perturbations which lead to relaxation and decoherence in bulk or quantum wells. Yet, the quantum confinement itself leads to new sources of relaxation. The most important is likely the confinement-enhanced exchange interaction between carriers which has been largely investigated in the recent years [1, 2, 3]. Its anisotropic part produces the well-known splitting of electron-hole pair states (named further excitons and labeled X^0) into linearly polarized states [4]. This effect which is dramatic for both spin orientation and detection by optical methods, can yet be suppressed by charging the quantum dot with a single additional carrier, electron or hole. The resulting singly-charged exciton (named further trion and labeled X^+ or X^-) becomes thus a good spin probe of the unpaired electron (in X^+) or hole (in X^-), which simultaneously opens the way towards optical pumping of the resident carrier spin. However, a second spin dependent interaction, which is also enhanced by the confinement perturbs the trion spins : the hyperfine interaction of a conduction band electron with the QD nuclei acts indeed as a random effective field of about 30 mT. Besides, this interaction may also give rise to a considerable magnetic-like field due to optically induced nuclear polarization [6, 7]. Here, we address this aspect in a single self-assembled InAs/GaAs QD under optical orientation of the trion complexes X^+ or X^-.

To study the nuclear polarization of a single QD optical orientation experiments have been performed in a small magnetic field $B_z \approx 0.2$ T provided by a permanent

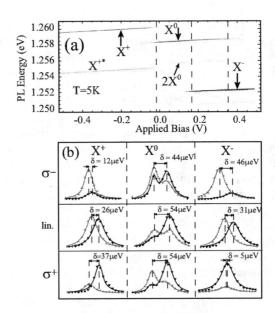

FIGURE 1. (a) Gray-scale plot of the PL intensity from a single InAs QD versus detection energy and voltage under intradot excitation at 1.31 eV. (b) Zoom of polarization-resolved PL spectra (gray for σ^-, dark for σ^+) in 0.2 T magnetic field for the fixed voltage marked by arrows in (a) panel. Excitation polarization is indicated on the left-hand side. We used a standard micro-photoluminescence (PL) setup with a spectral resolution of 30 μeV and a precision on line position of about 1 μeV after deconvolution by a Lorentzian fit.

magnet parallel to the QD growth axis z. The optical excitation and detection were both performed along the z axis. The PL circular polarization reads out the spin of the unpaired electron (hole) for X^+ (X^-) which besides determines the hole (electron) spin left in the QD after

CP893, *Physics of Semiconductors, 28th International Conference*
edited by W. Jantsch and F. Schäffler

optical recombination.

The sample was grown by molecular beam epitaxy on a semi-insulating GaAs (001) substrate. The InAs QDs are grown in the Stranski-Krastanov mode 25 nm above a 200nm-thick n^+-GaAs layer and covered by an intrinsic GaAs (25 nm)/Al$_{0.3}$Ga$_{0.7}$As (120 nm)/GaAs (5 nm) multilayer. The QD charge is controlled by an electrical bias between a top Schottky contact and a back ohmic contact.

Figure 1(a) shows the single QD PL intensity plotted against bias and detection energy. Between 0 V and ~ 0.15 V the neutral exciton X^0 is identified by its fine structure. Above 0.15 V the X^- trion red-shifted by ~ 6 meV shows up indicating the charging of the QD with one electron [3, 5]. It first competes with the neutral exciton line which finally disappears above 0.35 V when the QD is charged with 2 electrons. For stronger electric field (negative bias) the neutral exciton line disappears as a result of the electron tunnelling out of the QD. It is replaced by a 3 meV blue-shifted line assigned to the X^+ trion.

Figure 1(b) shows PL spectra resolved in circular polarization for different charge states and different excitation polarizations. Under linearly polarized excitation (lin.), the Zeeman interaction simply separates the $\sigma^\pm$-polarized components of the trion lines by $\delta_Z = |g_X|\mu_B B_{ext}$ where g_X is the exciton g-factor and μ_B=58μeV/T is the Bohr magneton. We find for the three lines an average Zeeman splitting $\delta_Z \approx 28\mu$eV in agreement with an exciton g-factor of ≈ 3 [4]. Under circularly polarized excitation a significant deviation from the sole Zeeman interaction is now observed : the X^+ splitting gets larger in σ^+ excitation by +10 μeV and smaller in σ^- by -15 μeV. This indicates the polarization of the QD nuclear spins due to the hyperfine interaction with the optically oriented electrons, which produces the so-called Overhauser shift (OHS) denoted further δ_n. Remarkably a symmetrical but reversed effect occurs for X^- with a shift δ_n=+15 μeV in σ^- and δ_n=-25 μeV in σ^+, whereas the PL from X^- and X^+ shows the same helicity. This reversal demonstrates that in the case of X^- for which the total electron spin is zero, the mechanism leading to nuclear polarization doesn't operate during its lifetime but takes place after optical recombination through the interaction with the spin polarized electron left in the QD. An other remarkable feature is the OHS asymmetry observed when changing the excitation from σ^+ to σ^-. This also appears in Fig. 2 which reports the voltage dependence of trion line splitting. This asymmetry reveals that polarizing the nuclear spins in the direction which produces a larger effective field for the electron is more difficult than in the opposite direction. This results from the dependence of the nuclear polarization rate on the total electron spin splitting[6, 8]. Noteworthily, the maximum of nuclear

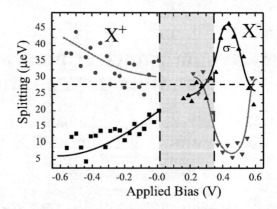

FIGURE 2. Spin splitting of X^+ and X^- PL lines against applied bias at B_z =0.2 T, under σ^+ (gray) and σ^- (dark) polarized excitation at 1.31 eV. The horizontal dashed line corresponds to the Zeeman splitting measured under linerly-polarized excitation and the gray-shaded area represents the region of X^0 stability. Solid lines are a guide for the eye.

polarization measured on X^- is reached when the QD is filled with 2 electrons before optical excitation. This regime ensures indeed both a strong spin polarization of the hole in X^- state (i.e. of the final unpaired electron state) [3], and a short correlation time of the hyperfine interaction in the final state allowing for the compensation of the electron spin splitting [8].

In conclusion, we have shown that a significative nuclear polarization can be induced by optically polarized trions in a single InAs/GaAs quantum dot, with a very different signature according to the trion state X^+ or X^-. It demonstrates that the nuclear polarization results from the hyperfine interaction with an unpaired electron *within* the quantum dot.

ACKNOWLEDGMENTS

This work has been supported by contract BoitQuant of *Fonds National pour la Science* and the European network of excellence SANDIE.

REFERENCES

1. P.-F. Braun *et al.*, Phys. Rev. Lett. **94**, 116601 (2005).
2. I. A. Merkulov, A. L. Efros and M. Rosen, Phys. Rev. B **65**, 205309 (2002).
3. S. Laurent *et al.*, Phys. Rev. Lett. **94**, 147401 (2005).
4. M. Bayer *et al.*, Phys. Rev. B **65**, 195315 (2002).
5. B. Urbaszek *et al.*, Phys. Rev. Lett. **90**, 247403 (2003).
6. F. Meier and B. Zakharchenya, Optical Orientation, vol. 8 of Modern Problem in Condensed Matter Sciences (1984).
7. D. Gammon *et al.*, Phys. Rev. Lett. **86**, 5176 (2001).
8. B. Eble *et al.*, cond-mat/0508281, (2005).

Optically enhanced nuclear spin polarization in InP

A. Brunetti*, M. Vladimirova*, D. Scalbert*, H. Folliot† and A. Lecorre†

*Groupe d'Etude des Semi-conducteurs, UMR 5650 CNRS-Université
Montpellier 2, Place Eugène Bataillon, 34095 Montpellier Cedex, France
†Laboratoire d'Etudes des Nanostructures à semiconducteurs, UMR FOTON 6082, INSA de Rennes, 20 avenue
des buttes de Coësmes, 35043 Rennes Cedex, France

Abstract.
Optically induced nuclear spin polarization is studied via time-resolved magnetooptical Kerr effect in Voigt configuration in n-doped InP. The hyperfine field acting on electrons is detected via a phase shift of the electron spin precession. The dependence of the hyperfine field on external field and the polarization time of the nuclei are discussed within a simple model neglecting nuclear spin diffusion.

Keywords: dynamic nuclear polarization, InP, time-resolved Kerr rotation
PACS: 76.70.Fz, 78.47.+p, 81.05.Ea

Optically enhanced nuclear polarization induced by cross relaxation between photoexcited electrons and nuclei attracts considerable interest in view of potential applications in biological solid state NMR [1], and quantum computation [2, 3]. In a previous work we have shown that in n-doped InP the photocreated holes may influence indirectly the nuclear polarization via spin-dependent recombination of the photoexcited carriers [4]. This effect is revealed by the direction of the optically induced nuclear field, which is opposite to the direction it has in GaAs [5] when the light direction is perpendicular to the external magnetic field. The nuclear field is deduced from the Larmor frequency ω_L of electron spins measured by time-resolved magnetooptical Kerr rotation technique in Voigt geometry [5]. Here we focus on nuclear field value and onset time, and their dependence on the applied magnetic field. Our results suggest a very short correlation time for the hyperfine interaction.

The studied sample is a 3.5μm thick InP n-doped layer ($n = 3 \times 10^{16}$ cm^{-3}) deposited on a [001] InP substrate. Fig.1 shows the color map of the Kerr rotation. The titanium-sapphire laser light (~ 100 fs pulse duration) at E=1.417eV is switched on just before acquisition, and scans are repeated with a 20 s time interval during 5 minutes (x-axis). The oscillations of the Kerr rotation angle shift with illumination time, because of the variation of ω_L on a time scale of a few minutes, typical for the nuclear field build up. Since ω_L decreases, the nuclear field develops in the direction opposite to that of the external field. This result contradicts previous measurements on n-doped GaAs [5], but can be explained if one assumes that donor-bound electron spins are cooled down below the lattice temperature by optical excitation [4].

From the phase shift of the electron spin precession as

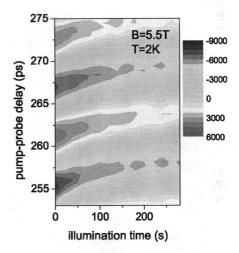

FIGURE 1. Color map of the time-resolved Kerr rotation showing a slowing down of electron spin precession with illumination time.

a function of time, one estimates the nuclear spin polarization time under illumination (Fig. 2). The variations of nuclear field and nuclear polarization time with magnetic field are shown in Fig. 3a and 3b, respectively.

Let us neglect spin diffusion effects, and assume cw optical excitation, which is reasonable because nuclear response time is much longer than the period of the laser pulse train. Solving the rate equation for the nuclear spin polarization yields its time evolution after light has been switched on

$$I_z(t) = I_z^{\infty}\{1 - \exp[-(\frac{1}{T_1} + \frac{1}{T_{1e}})t]\} \qquad (1)$$

CP893, *Physics of Semiconductors, 28th International Conference*
edited by W. Jantsch and F. Schäffler

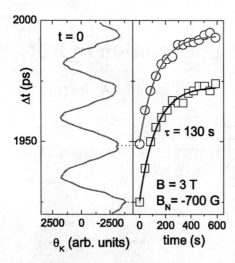

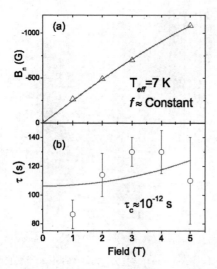

FIGURE 2. Oscillations of Kerr rotation with pump-probe delay (left). Shift of these oscillations with illumination time revealing the build-up of the nuclear spin polarization (right).

FIGURE 3. Nuclear field (a) and nuclear polarization time (b) versus external magnetic field (curves are fits to the data, see text).

where T_1 and T_{1e} are the nuclear spin relaxation times, respectively due to interaction with the lattice and with electrons trapped on donors. It can be shown [4] that in the Voigt geometry and taking into account the spin-dependent recombination

$$I_z^\infty = \frac{4}{3} f \frac{G\tau_s}{N_D + G\tau_s} I(I+1)(\rho J_0/3 - S_0) \quad (2)$$

$I = 9/2$ is the nuclear spin of indium, $f = T_1/(T_1 + T_{1e})$ is the leakage factor, J_0 and S_0 are the hole and electron spin thermal polarizations respectively, G is the carrier

excitation rate, τ_s is the electron spin relaxation time, N_D is the neutral donor concentration, and ρ is the radiative yield. From the power dependence of B_N we estimate that $\frac{G\tau_s}{N_D + G\tau_s} \sim 1$ [4]. Hence the field dependence of B_N is entirely determined by the product of f with the Brillouin functions governing J_0 and S_0. The fit of B_N (Fig. 3a) gives an effective temperature $T_{eff} = 7$ K and f constant.

According to Eq. (1) the nuclear polarization time is given by $1/\tau = 1/T_1 + 1/T_{1e}$. In order to estimate the value of f let us first assume that $T_1 \ll T_{1e}$. In this case $\tau \approx T_1$ and $f \approx T_1/T_{1e}$. Fig. 3b shows that τ is approximately constant within the error bars for fields up to 5 T, hence T_1 is also nearly constant. Besides T_{1e} varies as $T_{1e} \propto 1 + \omega^2 \tau_c^2$, where $\hbar\omega$ is the energy required for a mutual electron-nucleus spin flip, and τ_c the correlation time for the fluctuations of the hyperfine interaction [6]. Taking f as constant sets an upper limit for $\tau_c \sim 10^{-12}$ s. This very short correlation time may be due to spin exchange between free electrons and electrons trapped on donors [7], or to hopping of electron spin between different donor sites [8]. We can then estimate the relaxation time of nuclei at a distance from the donor equal to the Bohr radius a_B, which give the largest contribution to B_N [7]. We find $T_{1e}(a_B) \sim 50$ s, hence τ should be much smaller in contradiction with the observed polarization time of the nuclei. On the contrary, if we assume $T_1 \gg T_{1e}$ then $\tau \approx T_{1e}$, and $f \approx 1$. Since τ is nearly constant it also implies a short $\tau_c \sim 10^{-12}$ s and $\tau \approx 50$ s, in good agreement with experimental results.

To summarize we studied the optically induced nuclear field acting on electron spins and the polarization time of nuclear spins in n-doped InP, in Voigt geometry by using time-resolved magnetooptical Kerr effect. The analysis of the results indicates a leakage factor close to unity, however an analysis including nuclear spin diffusion effects maybe necessary to confirm this conclusion.

REFERENCES

1. R. Tycko, Solid State Nucl. Magn. Reson. **11**, 1 (1998).
2. D.P. DiVincenzo, Science **270**, 255 (1995); B.E. Kane, Nature **270**, 255 (1995).
3. T. D. Ladd, J. R. Goldman, F. Yamaguchi, Y. Yamamoto, E. Abe and K. M. Itoh, Phys. Rev. Lett. **89**, 17901 (2002).
4. A. Brunetti, M. Vladimirova, D. Scalbert, H. Folliot, and A. Lecorre, Phys. Rev. B **73**, 121202-4 (2006).
5. J.M. Kikkawa, D.D. Awschalom, Science **287**, 473 (2000).
6. M. I. Dyakonov and V. I. Perel in *Optical Orientation*, F. Meier and B.P. Zakharchenya, Eds. (North-Holland, Amsterdam, 1984).
7. D. Paget, Phys. Rev. B **25**, 4444 (1982).
8. R. I. Dzhioev et al, Phys. Rev. B **66**, 245204 (2002).

Spin precession monitored by laser pulse

Monique Combescot and Odile Betbeder-Matibet

Institut des NanoSciences de Paris, CNRS, Universite Pierre et Marie Curie, Paris, France

Abstract. We propose to induce the spin precession of an electron trapped on an impurity by means of an unabsorbed laser pulse made of circularly polarized photons. These photons induce a splitting of the spin degenerate electron level which comes from electron-exciton interaction: the electron sees the virtual excitons coupled to unabsorbed photons through Coulomb interaction and also through Pauli exclusion if its spin and the one of the exciton electron are the same while it sees them by Coulomb interaction only if they are different. The exchange processes producing this splitting - which induce a spin precession of the trapped electron - are nicely visualized through the Shiva diagrams we have recently proposed to represent our new many-body theory for composite excitons.

Keywords: laser induced spin manipulation, semiconductor spintronics, interacting composite excitons.
PACS:71.35.-y

INTRODUCTION

Spin manipulation using ultrafast laser pulses are of great current interest due to their possible applications in spintronics and quantum computing. Unabsorbed photons seem to be particularly promising because the effects they produce, which come from interactions with the virtual excitons to which they are coupled, stop when the laser pulse stops.

The first example of unabsorbed photons changing the semiconductor properties, is the exciton optical Stark effect in which the exciton line blue-shifts when the semiconductor is irradiated by a laser pulse tuned in the transparency region. This absorption line shift provides an interesting mechanism for ultrafast optical gates.

We have explained this exciton shift by the interaction between the real exciton produced by the absorbed photon and the virtual excitons coupled to the unabsorbed laser pulse. Excitons interact through both, Coulomb interactions and Pauli exclusion between the carriers making the excitons. It turns out that this Pauli exclusion and the carrier exchanges it induces, dominate the exciton shift at large detuning, in the absence of any Coulomb process, due to a bare dimensional argument.

The effect we propose [1] to make precessing the electron spin has a great similarity with the exciton optical Stark effect: a trapped electron sees the excitons through Coulomb interaction and also through Pauli exclusion if, and only if, the trapped electron has the spin of the exciton electron. This difference in electron exchanges leads to a difference in the energy change of electrons with up and down spins. Due to this energy difference, the electron spin precesses around the laser beam direction, this precession stopping when the laser pulse stops.

FORMALISM

We follow a procedure similar to the one we have used for the exciton optical Stark effect, except that we now use the formalism we have developed in our new many-body theory for composite excitons [2]. Although the seeds of this exciton many-body theory are already present in our approach to the exciton optical Stark effect, this old work is not written in terms of the Coulomb and Pauli scatterings, which are the keys to easily treat interacting composite excitons with all carrier exchanges included in an exact way.

These scatterings appear through four commutators, two are related to Pauli exclusion and two are related to Coulomb interactions. These four commutators allow to calculate any physical quantity in an easy way, these quantities ultimately reading in terms of the Coulomb and Pauli scatterings only, these scatterings being expressed in terms of the exciton wave functions only.

CP893, *Physics of Semiconductors, 28th International Conference*
edited by W. Jantsch and F. Schäffler

DIAGRAMMATIC REPRESENTATION

Instead of explaining how to calculate the splitting of the electron spin levels in a precise way, we have prefered to concentrate on the physical processes producing this splitting and their Shiva diagram representations.

At large detuning, the splitting is dominated by a pure electron exchange in the absence of any Coulomb process, these Coulomb processes being either between the trapped electron and one of the virtual excitons, or inside the virtual excitons: this means that, in the large detuning limit, these virtual excitons appear as free electron-hole pairs.

This leading term is represented by the Shiva diagram of figure (a): one photon creates an electron hole pair which exchanges its electron with the trapped electron, so that the pair which recombines to restore the unabsorbed photon is made with different carriers from the one which is created - as in all semiconductor optical nonlinearities.

The next order term in detuning contains one Coulomb interaction, either inside the virtual electron-hole pair to form the exciton, as in figure (b), or between this virtual pair and the trapped electron as in figure (c).

Due to dimensional arument, the terms with one Coulomb interaction, which contain one e^2 factor, have as extra factor, the square root of the exciton Ryberg divided by the exciton detuning, the pure exchange leading term being of the order of the square of the laser Rabi frequency divided by the detuning

CONCLUSION

The possible electron exchanges between a trapped electron and the virtual excitons coupled to unabsorbed photons make precessing the trapped electron spin through the energy splitting they induce between up and down spin states. The physical processes leading to this splitting, are made transparent by the Shiva diagram representation of the composite exciton many-body theory, we have just proposed.

REFERENCES

1. M.Combescot, O.Betbeder-Matibet, *Solid State Communications*, **132**, 129 (2004).
2. For a short review, M.Combescot, O.Betbeder-Matibet, *Solid State Communications*, **134**, 11 (2005), and references therein

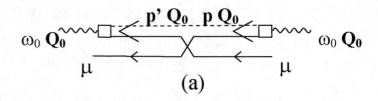

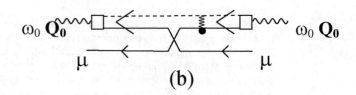

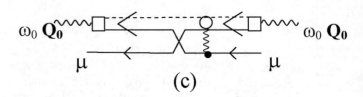

FIGURE : Shiva diagrams for electron exchange with the vitual exciton coupled to photons.

Electron spin dynamics during transport using moving quantum dots

J.A.H. Stotz[*][†], P.V. Santos[*], R. Hey[*] and K.H. Ploog[*]

[*]*Paul-Drude-Institut für Festkörperelektronik, Hausvogteiplatz 5–7, 10117 Berlin, Germany*
[†]*Department of Physics, Queen's University, Kingston, ON, K7L 3N6, Canada*

Abstract.
We present measurements showing that the long coherence lengths achieved during the transport of electron spins using surface acoustic waves result from the confinement of the spins within moving quantum dots. This confinement reduces the D'yakonov-Perel' spin dephasing effects that are prominent in GaAs quantum wells. As a result, the spin coherence lengths are independent of the number of electrons in each dot thus providing the ability to transport a single electron spin in a well-defined moving potential.

Keywords: Spin transport, Surface Acoustic Waves, Spin Precession, GaAs, Quantum Well
PACS: 72.25.Dc, 72.25.Rb, 77.65.Dq

The possibility of using electron spins to perform complex computations provides an inviting outlook beyond the limitations of continually shrinking transistors to gain performance in current computer architectures. In particular, confined spins in a semiconductor system has been proposed as a prototype system for quantum computation.[1] Previously, we have demonstrated that the long-range transport and manipulation of confined spin carriers can be realized using the tailored piezoelectric potentials generated by surface acoustic waves (SAWs).[2] Specifically, the piezoelectric fields of two orthogonally propagating SAWs on an undoped GaAs quantum well (QW) sample produce an array of mobile confinement potentials, referred to as dynamic quantum dots (DQDs). In this contribution, we show that the dramatic increase in the coherence of electron spins during transport within DQDs is a direct result of the confinement imposed on the carriers.

The spin transport experiments were performed on a sample consisting of an undoped, 20 nm-thick GaAs(001) QW with $Al_{0.3}Ga_{0.7}As$ barriers placed 390 nm below the surface; the sample was grown by molecular-beam epitaxy. Split-finger interdigitated transducers generated two 120-μm-wide SAW beams with a wavelength of 5.6 μm propagating along orthogonal $\langle 110 \rangle$ surface directions. The DQDs are produced by the superposition of the two plane SAWs and move along the $\langle 100 \rangle$ direction with a velocity $v_{DQD}=\sqrt{2}v_{SAW}$, where $v_{SAW} = 2907$ m/s is the velocity of the SAW. As shown in Fig. 1(a), spin-polarized electrons and holes are photogenerated at a spot G using a circularly polarized laser beam focused to a 2-5 μm-sized spot. The transport of photogenerated carriers away from the generation point G is very efficient; the weak photoluminescence (PL)

region near in Fig. 1(a) comprises only 1% of the total PL intensity in the absence of DQDs. Most electrons and holes are, therefore, captured by the DQDs and transported along the DQD channel towards a semitransparent metal strip M, where the piezoelectric potential is partially screened, and the electrons and holes can recombine. The PL spot at M is well-defined. With a diameter of 6 μm, it is only slightly larger than the width of a single DQD channel (4 μm). The polarization ratio $\rho_z = (I_R - I_L)/(I_R + I_L)$ of the luminescence at M is measured as the transport distance x between G and M is varied (I_R and I_L are the right and left circular polarization components, respectively, of the PL near M). The mapping of the spatial dependence of ρ_z is shown in Figs. 1(b) and 1(c) for varying spin concentrations and temperatures, respectively. As a result of the rapid hole-spin scattering, ρ_z is a good measure of the electron spin population at M.

The spatial dependence of the polarization ratio ρ_z is plotted in Fig. 1(b) for varying carrier concentrations within each dot. The oscillations are the result of the precession of the electron spin vector (originally aligned perpendicular to the surface via optical excitation) with the Larmor precession frequency $\Omega_L = \mu_B |g_e| B_{int}/\hbar$, where μ_B is the Bohr magneton and g_e is the effective, electron g-factor. B_{int} is an effective, internal magnetic field originating from the spin splitting of the conduction band for the nonzero average electron momentum $\bar{p} = m_e^* v_{DQD}$ during transport, where m_e^* is the effective mass of the electron; B_{int} is parallel to the transport direction for spin travelling along the $\langle 100 \rangle$-direction. The experimentally determined spatial dependence of ρ_z (symbols) is fitted with an exponentially damped sinusoidal function (solid lines) of the

CP893, *Physics of Semiconductors, 28th International Conference*
edited by W. Jantsch and F. Schäffler
© 2007 American Institute of Physics 978-0-7354-0397-0/07/$23.00

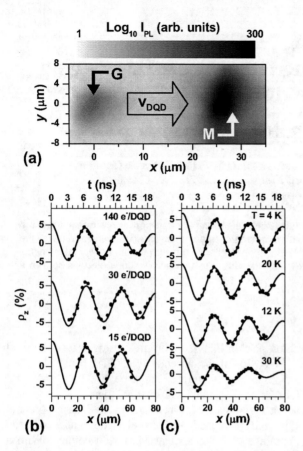

FIGURE 1. (a) Photoluminescence image showing the DQD-mediated transport of carriers photogenerated at G towards the edge of a metal strip M. The spatial dependence of the polarization ratio ρ_z of the electron spin transport via DQDs is shown in (b) and (c) for varying electron spin concentrations and temperatures, respectively. The sample temperature in part (b) is 12 K except for the lowest curve, which was measured at a temperature of 4.2 K. The temperature dependent measurements (c) were performed with 140 e$^-$/DQD. The upper time axis is determined by $t = x/v_{DQD}$.

form $\rho_z = \rho_0 e^{-x/l_s} \cos(\Omega_L x/v_{DQD})$, where ρ_0 represents the extrapolated, initial spin polarization at G and l_s is the spin coherence length.

Considering the size of the DQDs (between 1×1 and 2×2 μm^2), the electron densities n in Fig. 1(b) span an order of magnitude (from 10^{14} to 10^{15} cm^{-3}). Over this range, the spin lifetimes in both bulk n-type GaAs[3] and GaAs QWs[4] have been shown to be strongly dependent on n. However, the coherence lengths l_s for the entire concentration range are comparable and are approximately 100 μm. Therefore, the coherence of electron spins in DQDs does not reduce with decreasing n as observed in QWs and bulk GaAs. This demonstrates that the normally dominating D'yakonov-Perel' (DP) spin-dephasing mechanism[5] in the DQDs is not governed by the same motional narrowing effects. Instead, the work

presented here indicates that it is the confinement potential of the DQDs that controls DP dephasing and enables the long electron spin lifetimes and spin transport lengths observed here.

The temperature for the lowest electron concentration in Fig. 1(b) was lowered to 4.2 K to improve the PL efficiency. However, as shown in Fig. 1(c), there is little variation in the spin coherence lengths l_s for the temperatures below 20 K. All possess coherence lengths between 100 and 110 μm. As a result, the measurements varying the electron concentration [cf. Fig. 1(b)] were not affected by the change in temperature. When the temperature is increased to 30 K, however, there is a dramatic reduction of l_s to 39 μm attributed to the onset of the strongly temperature dependent DP spin dephasing. For sample temperatures of 20 K and below, the temperature invariance of l_s shown here indicates that the DP mechanism is limited–in support of the observations of Fig. 1(b). Instead, the spin coherence length is influenced by a temperature independent, and thus far unidentified, spin dephasing mechanism.

We have shown that the mechanism governing the transport of electrons spins inside DQDs results from the confinement of the electron spins in the moving piezoelectric potential. In particular, the invariance of the spin coherence length to the local electron density within the DQD is quite different than that observed in other measurements. This is significant because the DQD system enables single spins to be transported in well-defined confinement potentials, which is particularly interesting for applications in solid state quantum computing.

ACKNOWLEDGMENTS

The authors would like to thank W. Seidel, S. Krauß, and M. Höricke for their technical support regarding sample fabrication and preparation. In addition, the support of the Nanoquit consortium (BMBF, Germany) is acknowledged, and J.A.H. Stotz thanks NSERC Canada for financial support.

REFERENCES

1. D. Loss, and P. DiVincenzo, *Phys. Rev. A* **57**, 120–126 (1998).
2. J. A. H. Stotz, R. Hey, P. V. Santos, and K. H. Ploog, *Nat. Mater.* **4**, 585–588 (2005).
3. J. M. Kikkawa, and D. D. Awschalom, *Phys. Rev. Lett.* **80**, 4313–4316 (1998).
4. J. S. Sandhu, A. P. Heberle, J. J. Baumberg, and J. R. A. Cleaver, *Phys. Rev. Lett.* **86**, 2150–2153 (2001).
5. M. I. D'yakonov, and V. I. Perel', *Sov. Phys. Solid State* **13**, 3023–3026 (1972).

Electron Spin Manipulation, Detection, and Relaxation in a High Mobility Silicon Quantum Well

Junya Matsunami, Mitsuaki Ooya, and Tohru Okamoto

Department of Physics, University of Tokyo, 7-3-1 Hongo, Bunkyo-ku, Tokyo 113-0033, Japan

Abstract. We performed electrically detected ESR measurements on a high-mobility Si/SiGe heterostructure sample. The negative change in the longitudinal resistivity observed in a specific Landau level configuration demonstrates that the ESR signal is caused by the reduction of the spin polarization. The longitudinal spin relaxation time T_1 was found to be of the order of 1 ms in the in-plane magnetic field of 3.55 T. The very long T_1 is qualitatively explained by the suppression of the effect of the Rashba fields due to high frequency spin precession.

Keywords: Electron spin resonance, silicon quantum well, spin relaxation
PACS: 76.30.-v, 73.21.Fg, 72.25.Rb, 73.43.-f

INTRODUCTION

Recently there has been a great attention to electron spin in semiconductors in the context of the spintronics applications [1]. Electron spin resonance (ESR) is a promising technique to manipulate spins directly, and electrical detection is preferable for the read-out of the local spin states. It has been shown that the ESR signal is detected as positive change $\Delta\rho_{xx}$ in longitudinal resistivity ρ_{xx} in quantum Hall systems formed in GaAs/AlGaAs heterostructures [2]. However, the origin of the positive $\Delta\rho_{xx}$ has not been clarified because the spin depolarization and the electron heating can both cause the positive $\Delta\rho_{xx}$.

For fabricating spintronics devices, Si appears to be a suitable host material. Electron spin relaxation times are expected to be long because the spin-orbit coupling and electron-nuclear spin interaction are weak. Recently longitudinal and transverse spin relaxation times T_1 and T_2 of the order of μs have been reported in the ESR measurements on Si quantum well samples [3,4]. However, these measurements were restricted to the frequency of 9.4 GHz (corresponding to the resonance field of 0.34 T) apparently because they were performed with the X-Band ESR spectrometers.

We report electrically detected ESR measurements on a high-mobility Si/SiGe heterostructure sample in a magnetic field of 3.55 T [5]. The negative $\Delta\rho_{xx}$ observed in the specific Landau level (LL) configuration demonstrates that the ESR signal is caused by the reduction of the spin polarization. We obtained T_1 and T_2 by extending the measurements to the in-plane magnetic field configuration. The very long values of T_1 ~1 ms were obtained and qualitatively explained by the suppression of the effect of the Rashba fields due to high frequency spin precession.

EXPERIMENTS

We used a high-mobility Si/SiGe heterostructure sample. Details of the growth and characterization have been reported elsewhere [6,7]. Four probe ac resistivity measurements were performed for a 600x50 μm Hall bar sample located in a ^{3}He refrigerator. The ESR signal was observed during the magnetic field sweep under continuous 100 GHz millimeter wave radiation.

RESULTS AND DISCUSSION

Figure 1(a) illustrates the LL configuration we have selected to determine the origin of $\Delta\rho_{xx}$. The realization of the LL configuration was confirmed by the tilt-angle dependence of the Shubnikov-de Haas oscillations. In contrast to the previous studies, μ lies *above* a spin-down LL (LL(down,0)) and *below* a spin-up LL (LL(up,2)). Thermally excited holes in LL(down,0) and electrons in LL(up,2) give finite ρ_{xx}.

Figure 1(b) shows the negative $\Delta\rho_{xx}$ observed in the specific LL configuration. Electron heating cannot be the cause because dρ_{xx}/dT is positive. To explain it, we discuss the ESR-induced carrier dynamics in Fig. 1(a). Since the orbital index does not change during

CP893, *Physics of Semiconductors, 28th International Conference*
edited by W. Jantsch and F. Schäffler
© 2007 American Institute of Physics 978-0-7354-0397-0/07/$23.00

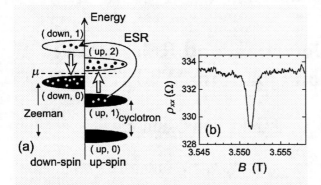

FIGURE 1. (a) ESR-induced carrier dynamics and (b) the ESR signal for the specific LL configuration.

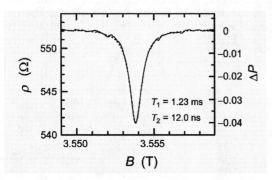

FIGURE 2. ESR signal observed in the in-plane magnetic field configuration. The solid and dashed line shows the experimental data and the result of the fitting, respectively.

the spin-flip, the photoexcitation occurs mainly from the filled LL(up,1) to the empty LL(down,1). When T_1 is much longer than the electron-lattice relaxation time, the photoexcited carriers relax their energy to the lattice without spin relaxation. The number of the thermally excited carriers decreases via the pair-annihilation with the photoexcited carriers. The negative $\Delta\rho_{xx}$ is understood as a consequence of the upward (downward) shift of the chemical potential for spin-down (spin-up) electrons. This clearly demonstrates that the reduction of the spin polarization P is successfully read out electrically.

Figure 2 shows a negative $\Delta\rho$ observed in the in-plane magnetic field configuration. Electron heating cannot explain it because $d\rho/dT$ is positive. We consider that the negative $\Delta\rho$ is caused by the spin depolarization as in the case of the specific LL configuration discussed above. It is well-known that ρ increases with the spin polarization P in silicon 2D electron systems [8]. A reduction ΔP of P explains the negative $\Delta\rho$ because $d\rho/dP$ is positive.

We transform $\Delta\rho$ into ΔP as shown in the right vertical axis of Fig. 2. Since P can be written as a function of the in-plane magnetic field $B_{\parallel}$ and T, we

can calibrate the relation between ρ and P by using the in-plane magnetoresistance $\rho(B_{\parallel})$. The obtained $B_{\parallel}$-dependence of ΔP is directly related to T_1 and T_2 by the Bloch equations as $\Delta P/P = (\gamma B_1)^2 T_1 T_2/\{1+(\omega-\gamma B_{\parallel})^2 T_2^2\}$, where γ is the electron gyromagnetic ratio, B_1 is the amplitude of the component of the oscillating magnetic field, and ω is its frequency, respectively. The dashed line in Fig. 2 shows the result of the fitting of the ESR signals by the equation. From the amplitude of the ESR signal, T_1 is estimated to be of the order of 1 ms whereas T_2 deduced from the linewidth is about 10 ns. The obtained T_1 is far the longest value ever reported for 2D systems as far as we know, and sharply contrasts with those reported in the previous studies on lower-mobility Si quantum wells in low magnetic fields ($B \cong 0.34$ T) in which both T_1 and T_2 were found to be of the order of μs.

The very long T_1 is qualitatively explained by the suppression of the effect of the Rashba fields due to high frequency spin precession. The longitudinal spin relaxation rate $1/T_1$ is written by the Fourier transform of the correlation function of the Rashba fields at the Larmor frequency ω_L, which decreases with increasing ω_L.

In summary, we performed electrically detected ESR measurements on a high-mobility Si/SiGe heterostructure sample in a magnetic field of 3.55 T. It was confirmed that $\Delta\rho_{xx}$ is caused by the reduction of P. The very long values of $T_1 \sim 1$ ms were obtained in the in-plane magnetic field and were qualitatively explained by the suppression of the effect of the Rashba fields due to high frequency spin precession.

We thank Y. Shiraki for providing us with the Si/SiGe sample and S. Yamamoto for helpful advice on the use of the millimeter wave system. This work was supported by the Sumitomo Foundation, Grant-in-Aid for Scientific Research (B) (No. 18340080) and Grant-in-Aid for Scientific Research on Priority Area "Physics of new quantum phases in superclean materials" (No. 18043008) from MEXT, Japan.

REFERENCES

1. I. Zutic, J. Fabian, and S. Das Sarma, *Rev. Mod. Phys.* **76**, 323 (2004).
2. D. Stein, K. v. Klitzing, and G. Weimann, *Phys. Rev. Lett.* **51**, 130 (1983).
3. Z. Wilamowski and W. Jantsch, *Phys. Rev. B* **69**, 035328 (2004).
4. A. M. Tyryshkin *et al.*, *Phys. Rev. Lett.* **94**, 126802 (2005).
5. J. Matsunami, M. Ooya, and T. Okamoto, *Phys. Rev. Lett.* **97**, 066602 (2006).
6. A. Yutani and Y. Shiraki, *Semicond. Sci. Technol.* **11**, 1009 (1996); *J. Cryst. Growth* **175/176**, 504 (1997).
7. T. Okamoto *et al.*, *Phys. Rev. B* **69**, 041202(R) (2004).
8. T. Okamoto *et al.*, *Phys. Rev. Lett.* **82** 3875 (1999).

Local Control of Carrier Spin States in a Semiconductor by Microscale Ferromagnetic Wires

S. Halm[1], E. Neshataeva[1], F. Seifert[1], T. Kümmell[1], E. Schuster[2], W. Keune[2], J. Puls[3], F. Henneberger[3], and G. Bacher[1]

[1] Werkstoffe der Elektrotechnik, Universität Duisburg-Essen,47057 Duisburg, Germany
[2] Angewandte Physik, Universität Duisburg-Essen,47048 Duisburg, Germany
[3] Institut für Physik, Humboldt-Universität Berlin,12489 Berlin, Germany

Abstract. Employing fringe fields from microscale Fe/Tb multilayer ferromagnets (FMs) with remanent out-of-plane magnetization, we are able to define a local, remanent carrier spin polarization in an underlying ZnCdMnSe dilute magnetic semiconductor quantum well (DMS QW). The fringe fields of the FMs "imprint" a locally varying magnetization into the DMS QW by orienting the magnetic moment of the incorporated Mn^{2+} ions. Optically excited charge carriers align their spin along the local DMS magnetization due to the s-pd exchange interaction. Using polarization resolved, magnetic field dependent photoluminescence (PL) spectroscopy we demonstrate a remanent DMS carrier spin polarization of 5 % in the vicinity of ferromagnetic Fe/Tb wire structures.

Keywords: dilute magnetic semiconductors, Fe/Tb ferromagnets, hybrids, spin manipulation, spintronics.
PACS: 85.75.-d, 75.50.Pp, 78.66.Hf, 75.75.+a, 78.20.Ls

INTRODUCTION

The integration of ferromagnetic and semiconducting materials in hybrid heterostructures presents a promising way for the development of devices with completely new functionalities [1,2]. One important aspect is the possibility to control the charge carriers' spin degree of freedom in the semiconductor [3,4]. Several routes are currently being followed to obtain this goal, e. g., ferromagnetic proximity polarization [5,6] or magnetic fringe fields [7,8]. In this paper we present micro-magnetoluminescence measurements on Fe/Tb – ZnCdMnSe hybrids which demonstrate the feasibility of local, remanent semiconductor (SC) carrier spin control via magnetic fringe fields.

EXPERIMENT

The SC sample was grown by molecular beam epitaxy on a (001) GaAs substrate and consists of a 1 μm thick ZnSe buffer layer, followed by 18 monolayers of $Zn_{0.76}Cd_{0.16}Mn_{0.08}Se$ forming the DMS quantum well and a 25 nm thick ZnSe cap layer. Electron beam lithography and lift-off technique was used to define arrays of different ferromagnetic

nanostructures on top of the semiconductor. The FMs consisted of 40 bilayers of 35 Å Fe and 19 Å Tb capped by 50 Å Cr to prevent oxidation. The deposition was done by thermal evaporation in ultra-high vacuum. The structured FM-SC hybrid sample was mounted on the cold finger of a helium flow cryostat (T ≥ 3.5 K) and inserted into the bore of a superconducting electromagnet (B ≤ 5 T). Photoexcitation of the SC was done by an InGaN solid state laser (λ_{Laser} = 403 nm) which was focussed onto the sample by a 50x microscope objective. The collected PL was dispersed by a 0.55 m monochromator. A modulation technique with a photoelastic modulator and a two-channel gated photon counter was used to determine the circular optical polarization degree of the PL with high accuracy.

Figure 1 shows the circular polarization degree $\rho = (I^+ - I^-)/(I^+ - I^-)$ of the QW PL measured on a reference area without FMs at T = 4 K (I^+ and I^- are the intensities of circularly right and left polarized PL, respectively). The external magnetic field B_{ext} was swept from -5 T to +5 T (filled symbols) and backwards (open symbols, only the range | B_{ext} | ≤ 1 T is shown). As is typical for a DMS QW, the PL becomes strongly polarized when an external magnetic

CP893, *Physics of Semiconductors, 28th International Conference*
edited by W. Jantsch and F. Schäffler

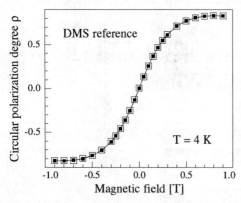

FIGURE 1. Circular optical polarization degree of the DMS PL as a function of external magnetic field on a sample area without FMs at 4 K.

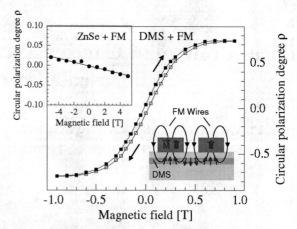

FIGURE 2. Circular optical polarization degree of the DMS PL under the influence of both external magnetic field and magnetic fringe fields from microscale ferromagnetic Fe/Tb wire structures. Lower inset: cross-sectional sketch of the hybrid structure. Upper inset: Circular polarization degree of the PL from the ZnSe layers in presence of the Fe/Tb wires.

field is applied in Faraday geometry. The Mn^{2+} ions in the DMS QW orient their magnetic moment along the external field and generate a magnetization in the SC. Optically excited charge carriers are coupled to this magnetization via the so called s-pd exchange interaction [9] and align their spins along the moments of the Mn^{2+} ions. Due to angular momentum conservation, the spin polarization of the recombining carriers can be detected directly via the circular polarization degree of the emitted photons. No difference in polarization can observed for the up and the down sweep of the external magnetic field.

The aim of our FM-SC hybrid structures is to employ the spatially confined fringe fields from microscale FMs instead of an external magnetic field in order to obtain local control over the SC carrier spins (lower inset Fig. 2). Fe/Tb multilayer FMs are especially suited for this purpose since they show a strong remanent out-of-plane magnetization [10]. In the main graph of Fig. 2 we studied the influence of a $(20\,\mu m)^2$ square shaped array of 1 μm wide and 20 μm long ferromagnetic Fe/Tb wires on the spin orientation of the charge carriers in the underlying DMS QW. A clear hysteresis in the DMS PL polarization degree can be observed (filled and open symbols represent up and down sweep of B_{ext}, respectively). It is the result of the additional fringe field of about ~20 mT, applied to the DMS by the ferromagnetic wires. The fringe field shifts the curve from Fig. 1 towards the left (right) for downwards (upwards) magnetized wires, respectively. To exclude the possibility of a purely optical effect of the FMs on the PL polarization, e.g., via circular dichroism, we analyzed the circular polarization degree of the PL from the ZnSe layers in presence of the ferromagnetic wires (see upper inset Fig. 2). No appreciable polarization could be observed in the relevant range of magnetic fields of $|B_{ext}| \leq 1$ T. For the DMS QW, however, a remanent charge carrier spin

polarization of ± 5 % remains at $B_{ext} = 0$ T. The sign of the spin polarization depends on the magnetization direction of the FMs, which can be changed by applying an external field larger than the coercive field of ~ 2.5 T. This proves that the local spin states of semiconductor charge carriers can be controlled via ferromagnetic fringe fields.

ACKNOWLEDGMENTS

This work was financially supported by the Deutsche Forschungsgemeinschaft within the priority program SPP 1133 "Ultrafast magnetization processes" and in part by the Sonderforschungsbereich SFB 491.

REFERENCES

1. G. A. Prinz, *Science* **250**, 1092-1097 (1990).
2. N. Samarth, S. H. Chun, K. C. Ku, S. J. Potashnik and P. Schiffer *Sol. State Comm.* **127**, 173-179 (2003).
3. D. D. Awschalom, D. Loss and N. Samarth *Semiconductor Spintronics and Quantum Computation.*, Berlin Heidelberg New York: Springer Verlag, 2002.
4. I. Žutić, J. Fabian, S. Das Sarma, *Rev. Mod. Phys.* **76**, 323-410 (2004).
5. R. K. Kawakami et al., *Science* **294**, 131-134 (2001).
6. R. J. Epstein et al., *Phys. Rev. B.* **65**, 121202 (2002).
7. H. Schömig et al., *J. Appl. Phys.* **95**, 7411-7413 (2004).
8. A. Murayama and M. Sakuma, *Appl. Phys. Lett.* **88**, 122504 (2006)
9. J. Furdyna, *J. Appl. Phys.* **64**, R29-R64 (1988).
10. F. Richomme et al., *Phys. Rev. B* **54**, 416-426 (1988).

Spin orientation by electric current in 2D and 3D semiconductors

L.E. Golub

A.F. Ioffe Physico-Technical Institute, Russian Academy of Sciences, 194021 St. Petersburg, Russia

Abstract. The effect of spin orientation by electric current is reviewed. It is shown that this phenomenon is possible only in gyrotropic media. Different types of gyrotropic bulk semiconductors and two-dimensional heterostructures are considered. Microscopic reason for appearance of an average spin in an external electric field is a spin-orbit interaction. Experimental observations of the effect are discussed.

Keywords: electrical spin orientation, spin splitting, quantum wells, spin relaxation
PACS: 72.25.Pn, 85.75.-d, 78.67.De

INTRODUCTION

The manipulation of the spin degree of freedom in conducting systems by electric field is at the heart of semiconductor spintronics. Spin control in low-dimensional systems is particularly important for combining magnetic properties with the versatile electronic characteristics of semiconductor heterojunctions.

In the present report the effect of spin orientation by electric current is reviewed. Historically, the possibility of this phenomenon in semiconductors has been noticed for bulk tellurium in Ref. [1]. Experimentally this effect was observed in Ref. [2]. Possibility for electrical spin orientation in 2D semiconductors was noticed in Ref. [3]. Then, simultaneously two communications [4, 5] appeared where spin density under electric current flow was calculated for symmetrical and asymmetrical 2D systems, respectively. General theory taking into account all possible types of system symmetry and scattering has been developed in Ref. [6]. In 2004, three experiments were performed demonstrating spin orientation by electric current: in a 3D deformed III-V crystal [7] and in 2D heterostructures [8, 9].

THEORY

Creation of a net spin density S by an electric current j described by a linear relation

$$S_i = Q_{im} j_m \qquad (1)$$

is possible only in media where a second-rank pseudotensor $\hat{Q}$ exists. Such media are called *gyrotropic*. In order to be gyrotropic, a system should lack for a space inversion center. Bulk gyrotropic semiconductors are tellurium, wurtzite II-VI compounds, and deformed III-V

crystals, while bulk GaAs and other III-V semiconductors are not gyrotropic. In contrast, nonzero components Q_{im} can exist in 2D heterostructures grown from any material.

Phenomenologically, in Eq. (1) for bulk tellurium $Q_{zz} \neq 0$ (z is the main axis), in deformed III-V and wurtzite II-VI semiconductors $Q_{xy} = -Q_{yx} \neq 0$, and in thin films grown along the axis $z \parallel [001]$, $Q_{xx} = -Q_{yy}$ are nonzero, where $x \parallel [100]$, $y \parallel [010]$.

In 2D systems the direction of spin S under current flow depends on how an inversion center is removed. Gyrotropy in heterostructures stems from two sources: structure inversion asymmetry (SIA) and bulk inversion asymmetry (BIA). If SIA is dominant then S lies in the structure plane: $Q_{xy} = -Q_{yx} \neq 0$, i.e. $S \perp j$. If, otherwise, BIA dominates, then, for structures grown along $z \parallel [001]$, $Q_{xx} = -Q_{yy} \neq 0$, i.e. spin is created in the 2D plane as well. If the structure is grown along low-symmetrical direction $z \parallel [110]$ or [113], then Q_{zx} is nonzero ($x \parallel [1\bar{1}0]$), i.e. S is parallel to the growth axis.

Microscopic reason for appearance of an average spin in an external electric field is a spin-orbit interaction. The corresponding part of the Hamiltonian has the form $H_{SO} = \alpha_{im} \sigma_i k_m$, where $\hat{\alpha}$ is the second-rank pseudotensor, σ_i are Pauli matrices, and k_m is the wavevector component. The presence of such k-linear terms in the Hamiltonian results in the spin orientation under electric current flow. The direction of spin density is determined by the structure of the tensor $\hat{\alpha}$: $\hat{Q} \sim \hat{\alpha}$.

The spin-orbit interaction H_{SO} results in that energy spectrum consists of two spin subbands with the splitting Δ proportional to the particle momentum. For example, in a symmetrical (110) structure $\Delta = 2\alpha k_x$, where $\alpha \equiv \alpha_{zx}$ and $x \parallel [1\bar{1}0]$. Due to this splitting, a drift in an electric field is different for particles in these two sub-

CP893, *Physics of Semiconductors, 28th International Conference*
edited by W. Jantsch and F. Schäffler
© 2007 American Institute of Physics 978-0-7354-0397-0/07/$23.00

bands. The drift momenta differ by $2k_0$:

$$\langle k \rangle_{\pm 1/2} = \langle k \rangle \mp k_0, \qquad (2)$$

where $\langle k \rangle = (m/e\hbar n)j$ is the drift momentum without spin-orbit interaction (m is the effective mass, n is 2D density), and $k_0 = \alpha(m/\hbar^2)$, Fig. 1.

Presence of an external electric field is not enough for creation of spin density. In addition to the current flow, an exchange of particles between the spin subbands is necessary, i.e. spin relaxation. An example of spin orientation via spin-flip scattering is illustrated in Fig. 1. Due to nonequal scattering probabilities $|1/2\rangle \rightarrow |-1/2\rangle$ and $|-1/2\rangle \rightarrow |1/2\rangle$ shown by arrows of different thickness, occupation of one spin subband ($|-1/2\rangle$ in Fig. 1) is higher than the other. As a result, net spin polarization is created under current flow.

The amplitude of spin density under current flow in the Boltzmann gas can be estimated as $S \approx \hat{\alpha}\langle k \rangle / k_B T$ which yields

$$S_i = r \frac{\alpha_{im} j_m}{k_B T} \frac{m}{e\hbar n}. \qquad (3)$$

The factor $r \sim 1$ depends on details of momentum scattering and spin relaxation. It is calculated in Ref. [6] for various scattering potentials. Note that for Fermi electrons $k_B T$ in Eq. (3) should be changed to $2E_F/3$.

If the dominant spin relaxation mechanism in the structure is not spin-flip scattering but the D'yakonov-Perel' mechanism, then spin density is also given by Eq. (3) with another constant $r \sim 1$ [6].

Recently, a new model of electrical spin orientation due to spin-dependent scattering is proposed [10]. It is demonstrated that net spin density can be created in gyrotropic systems without spin splitting of energy spectrum but due to k-linear terms in the scattering amplitude.

EXPERIMENTS

First observation of electrical spin orientation has been performed in bulk tellurium by means of transmission experiments [2]. Current-induced rotation of the light polarization plane has been detected.

In Ref. [7] the effect has been observed on strained bulk InGaAs structures by the same method.

In 2D systems, two experiments on electrical spin orientation have been performed. In Ref. [8], p-type [113] and [110] quantum wells have been studied. It has been shown that transmission of terahertz radiation is different for current $j \parallel [110]$ and $[1\bar{1}0]$ indicating the presence of spin along the growth axis.

Another method has been applied in Ref. [9], where polarized photoluminescence has been investigated. Appearance of circular polarization of photoluminescence

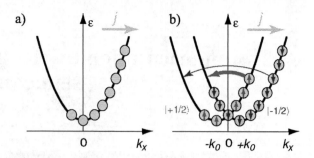

FIGURE 1. Comparison of current flow in (a) spin-degenerate and (b) spin-split subbands. (a) Electron distribution under drift in an electric field. (b) Spin polarization due to spin-flip scattering (after [8]).

under electric current flow has been demonstrated on p-type (001) quantum wells. Polarized radiation propagating in the structure plane shows that spin density is created in the 2D plane perpendicular to the current.

CONCLUSION

It is shown that electric current flow in gyrotropic systems leads to appearance of a net spin polarization. Microscopic reason is the spin-orbit interaction. The spin density is appeared under simultaneous action of electric field and spin relaxation. Experimental observations of the effect in bulk and 2D semiconductors are discussed.

Acknowledgments. Financial support from RFBR, RAS, Russian Ministry of Science and Education, Russian President grant for young scientists and Russian Science Support Foundation is gratefully acknowledged.

REFERENCES

1. E.L. Ivchenko and G.E. Pikus, JETP Lett. **27**, 604 (1978).
2. L.E. Vorob'ev, E.L. Ivchenko, G.E. Pikus, I.I. Farbstein, V.A. Shalygin, and A.V. Sturbin, JETP Lett. **29**, 441 (1979).
3. F.T. Vas'ko and N.A. Prima, Sov. Phys. Solid State **21**, 994 (1979).
4. A.G. Aronov and Yu.B. Lyanda-Geller, JETP Lett. **50**, 431 (1989).
5. V.M. Edelstein, Solid State Commun. **73**, 233 (1990).
6. A.G. Aronov, Yu.B. Lyanda-Geller, and G.E. Pikus, Sov. Phys. JETP **73**, 537 (1991).
7. Y. Kato, R.C. Myers, A.C. Gossard, and D.D. Awschalom, Phys. Rev. Lett. **93**, 176601 (2004).
8. S.D. Ganichev, S.N. Danilov, Petra Schneider, V.V. Bel'kov, L.E. Golub, W. Wegscheider, D. Weiss, and W. Prettl, cond-mat/0403641 (2004); J. Magn. Magn. Mater. **300**, 127 (2006).
9. A.Yu. Silov, P.A. Blajnov, J.H. Wolter, R. Hey, K.H. Ploog, and N.S. Averkiev, Appl. Phys. Lett. **85**, 5929 (2004).
10. S.A. Tarasenko, cond-mat/0607074 (2006).

InAs diode heterostructure as an effective electron spin aligner

Ya.V. Terent'ev, O.G. Lyublinskaya, A.A. Toropov, V.A. Solov'ev, and S.V. Ivanov

Ioffe Physico-Technical Institute, St. Petersburg 194021, Russia

Abstract. Photoluminescence (PL) has been studied in InAs diode structures grown by molecular beam epitaxy (MBE). In contrast to an InAs homogeneous layer, the p-n structure in a magnetic field applied in Faraday geometry demonstrates very high degree of PL circular polarization, which exceeds 80% in the field as low as 1T at T=2K (bulk layer gives only ~20% in the range of fields up to 4T). The polarization decays relatively slow with temperature. About 20% of the polarization degree was observed at the temperature as high as 50K in a magnetic field 2T. We believe that the effect originates from a strong built-in electric field of the p-n junction, that counteract the localization of photoexcited electrons on donors and enables effective spin alignment due to the Zeeman effect in the InAs conduction band.

Keywords: InAs, Zeeman splitting, p-n junction, photoluminescence.
PACS: 71.70.Ej; 78.55.Cr.

An effective spin aligner is one of the keystones of spintronics. Semiconductors doped with magnetic ions such as Mn^{2+} (so-called diluted magnetic semiconductors, or DMS) are commonly used for that purpose. Spin aligning is provided here by the giant Zeeman effect originating from exchange interaction between free carriers and the d-shell of a magnetic ion. Unfortunately, exchange interaction is very sensitive to a temperature, so DMS are effective only at helium temperatures. Alternatively one can use narrow gap semiconductors. Having strong spin-orbit interaction they provide a large enough value of g-factor (up to -15 for InAs and -49 for InSb) without any doping. In this paper we present the preliminary studies of the capability of InAs heterostructures as spin aligners.

PL of InAs regular undoped epilayers and p^+-n^0-n^+ structures has been measured in a magnetic field B applied in Faraday geometry. Circular σ^+ and σ^- polarized spectra have been recorded at the temperature range of 2-60K in the fields up to 4T. The samples were fabricated by MBE. In the diode structures a strongly asymmetric p-n junction was formed by the heavily p-doped (p~10^{18}cm^{-3}) and undoped InAs parts. The latter has background electron concentration n^0 as high as ~5×10^{16} cm^{-3} at T=80 K that is the same for the samples with simple homogeneous InAs epilayers. Note that so high value of n^0 is characteristic for any intentionally undoped

InAs epilayers grown by MBE and evidences rather large concentration of uncontrolled donor centers.

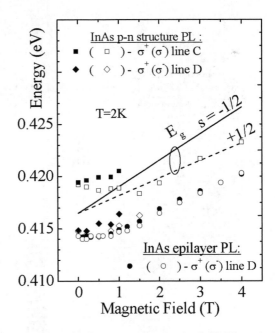

FIGURE 1. PL lines versus magnetic field. The calculated band gap E_g for different electron spins is also plotted.

CP893, *Physics of Semiconductors, 28th International Conference*
edited by W. Jantsch and F. Schäffler
© 2007 American Institute of Physics 978-0-7354-0397-0/07/$23.00

The PL spectrum of InAs regular epilayers has exhibited two lines. The first line with the energy 2-3 meV smaller than the band gap (416,75 meV [1]) is attributed to the recombination of electrons on shallow donors and free holes (therefore it is denoted as D). The other peak red-shifted by 15 meV emerges from the recombination of donor-acceptor pairs (DAP). We will focus here only on line D. Figure 1 shows the energy of the latter line versus magnetic field. It demonstrates behavior that is specific for the effect of magnetic freeze-out of electrons [2]. Surprisingly, the line doesn't split in the field, but possess some circular polarization (see Fig. 2). The polarization degree is about 20% in magnetic fields up to 4T.

The maximum of the curve we explain in terms of spin-dependent magnetic freeze-out of electrons [3]. PL from diode samples has been excited within the n^0-part of the structure. In weak magnetic fields (<1T) PL has two strongly overlapping components: D that coincides with the PL line of the regular epilayer, and C that originates from interband transitions (Fig. 1). In weak fields we have observed splitting of the line C into σ - polarized bands, but in a stronger field the higher energy (σ^+) term and the component D vanish. So, the remarkable increase in the emission circular polarization was observed. More than 80% of polarization was detected at B=2T and T=2K. In stronger fields the polarization saturates. A temperature rise reduces the effect, but even at T=50K polarization of 20% is still remaining (Fig. 3).

Summarizing, InAs epilayers fabricated by MBE demonstrate low degree of PL circular polarization and thus poor spin alignment even at a magnetic field of 4T on account of fast localization of non-equilibrium electrons on shallow donors. Diode structures show almost 100% polarization of PL originating here from interband transitions. We believe that the electric field of the p-n junction counteracts the localization of photo-excited carriers on donors, thus enabling spin alignment due to the Zeeman effect in an InAs conduction band. A moderate rate of polarization decay with temperature makes InAs diode structures a good candidate for spin aligner at the temperatures ranging up to ~50K.

This work was supported by Russian Foundation for Basic Research (grant # 06-02-17279-a).

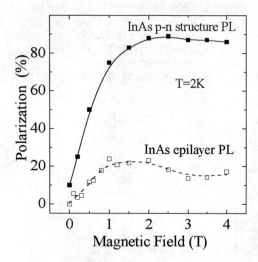

FIGURE 2. PL polarization degree defined as $(I^{\sigma^-} - I^{\sigma^+})/(I^{\sigma^-} + I^{\sigma^+})$, %, where I^{σ^-} (I^{σ^+}) is the maximum intensity of σ^- (σ^+) polarized PL peak. The curves are guides for eyes.

REFERENCES

1. Y. Lacroix, S.P. Watkins, C. A. Tran, and M.L.W. Thewalt, *J. Appl. Phys.* **80**, 6416-6424 (1996).
2. Y. Yafet, R.W. Keyes and E.N. Adams, *J. Phys. Chem. Solids* **1**, 137-142 (1956).
3. Ya.V. Terent'ev, O.G. Lyublinskaya, A.A. Toropov, V.A. Solov'ev, S.V. Sorokin, and S.V. Ivanov, "Anomalous Spin Splitting of Shallow Donor Bound Electrons in InAs-based Heterostructures under Electrical Injection Conditions" in *Narrow Gap Semiconductors*, edited by J. Kono and J. Leotin, Proc. of the 12th Int. Conf. on Narrow Gap Semicond., Institute of Physics Conf. Series 187, NY, London, 2006, pp. 57-62.

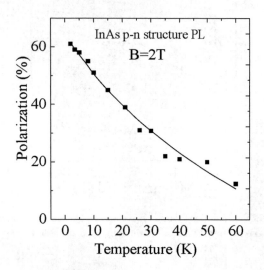

FIGURE 3. Polarization of PL from InAs p-n structure versus temperature. The curve is a guide for eyes.

Spin coherence of two-dimensional electron gas achieved via resonant excitation of trions and excitons

E A Zhukov*,†, D R Yakovlev*,**, M Bayer*, M M Glazov**, E L Ivchenko**, G Karczewski‡, T Wojtowicz‡ and J Kossut‡

*Experimental Physics 2, University of Dortmund, 44221 Dortmund, Germany
†Faculty of Physics, M.V. Lomonosov Moscow State University, 119992 Moscow, Russia
**A.F. Ioffe Physico-Technical Institute, 194021 St. Petersburg, Russia
‡Institute of Physics, Polish Academy of Sciences, PL-02668 Warsaw, Poland

Abstract. Generation mechanisms of long-lived spin coherence of two-dimensional electron gas (2DEG) have been studied theoretically and experimentally, the latter by means of a picosecond pump-probe Kerr rotation technique. CdTe/(Cd,Mg)Te quantum wells with a diluted two-dimensional electron gas have been addressed. Strong Coulomb interaction between electrons and holes, which results in large binding energies of neutral and negatively charged excitons (trions), allows selective addressing of exciton and trion states with resonant optical excitation. Different scenarios of coherence generation have been analyzed,namely, direct trion photocreation, formation of trions from photogenerated excitons and electron-exciton exchange scattering.

Keywords: spin dynamics, excitons, trions, time-resolved optical spectroscopy
PACS: 72.25.Fe, 72.25.Rb, 73.21.Fg, 73.61.Ga

INTRODUCTION

We study experimentally and theoretically the generation processes of electron spin coherence in quantum well structures. The regime of the low-dense two-dimensional electron gas (2DEG) is in the center of our attention. CdTe/(Cd,Mg)Te quantum wells (QW) have been chosen for these studies due to the stronger Coulomb interaction and larger binding energies of excitons as compared to III-V QWs.

EXPERIMENTAL DETAILS

We consider the case where the Fermi energy of 2DEG is of a millielectronvolt only and does not exceed the binding energy of negative trions (typically from 2 to 5 meV), and the exciton binding energy falls in the range 12 to 20 meV. Also resonant optical excitation of the trions and excitons has been exploited. Picosecond pump-probe Kerr rotation technique has been used for experimental investigation of spin coherence. Experiments have been performed at low temperatures $2-100$ K and in external magnetic fields up to 7 T. Spectral width of 1.5 ps laser pulses does not exceed 1 meV, which allows selective photoexcitation of either trion or exciton states. Under the resonant excitation of trions, the electron spin beats observed in the presence of an in-plane magnetic field are long-lived and characterized by a dephasing time up to 30 ns which exceeds considerably the radiative decay

of the trion states of 30 ps. In the case of resonant excitation of excitons, twocomponent decay with characteristic times of 30 ps and $5-20$ ns has been found. Their relative contributions are strongly sensitive to the excitation density and temperature. The faster decay is assigned to the spin precession of an electron bound in an exciton, this signal disappears with radiative annihilation of excitons. The longer decay is due to the spin coherence induced in the 2DEG and arising as a consequence of binding of the photogenerated excitons and free electrons into trions.

THEORY AND COMPARISON WITH EXPERIMENT

In short, the experimental set-up can be summarized as follows: the sample containing 2DEG is excited by the intensive pump pulse which induces the resonant interband transitions. Then a much weaker linearly-polarized probe pulse with the same carrier frequency as the pump arrives and the rotation of the polarization plane of the reflected probe pulse is analyzed as a function of the delay between the two pulses. An external magnetic field B is applied in the QW plane along the x-axis and leads to the precession of the electron spin with the Larmor frequency $\Omega = g_e \mu_B B / \hbar$, where g_e is the electron in-plane g-factor and μ_B is the Bohr magneton. As for two-dimensional heavy holes bound into excitons or trions, their in-plane g-factor is very small and can be ignored.

CP893, *Physics of Semiconductors, 28th International Conference*
edited by W. Jantsch and F. Schäffler

For the spin-polarized electrons the reflection coefficient for the right ($+$) and left ($-$) circularly polarized light has the following form

$$r_{\pm}(\omega) = \frac{i\Gamma_{0,\pm}}{\omega_{0,\pm} - \omega - i(\Gamma_{0,\pm} + \Gamma_{\pm})} \qquad (1)$$

with the resonant frequency ω_0, radiative broadening Γ_0 and nonradiative broadening Γ dependent on the light helicity. These three parameters are, in general, determined by the spin polarization of carriers and their complexes as well as their concentrations and the delay between the pulses.

We analyze theoretically three scenarios of coherence generation: the direct trion photocreation, formation of trions from photogenerated excitons and electron-exciton exchange scattering.

Resonant Excitation of Trions

In the first scenario the circularly polarized pump creates the singlet trions whose spins are controlled by the heavy-hole spin polarization. In a 2D system the interband absorption of circularly polarized light generates holes and electrons with fixed spin projections. As a result the background electron gas becomes spin polarized also under direct generation of singlet trions because the electrons with spin opposite to that of photoexcited electrons are picked out. (Similar considerations were applied to localized trions [1, 2]). An external magnetic field applied in the plane of the structure leads to the rotation of the spin polarization of background electrons and, therefore, to the modulation of $\Gamma_{0,\pm}$ and oscillations of Kerr signal.

The electron spin is given by

$$S_z(t) = N_0[-|1 - \eta|\sin(\Omega t - \Phi)e^{-t/\tau_s} + \eta' e^{-t/\tau^T}], \quad (2)$$

where $\eta \equiv \eta' + i\eta'' = \tau_0^{T-1}/(\tau^{T-1} - \tau_s^{-1} - i\Omega)$, $\Phi = \arctan[(1 - \eta')/\eta'']$, τ_s is the electron spin relaxation time and τ^T is the lifetime of trion spin including the trion lifetime τ_0^T and spin relaxation time τ_s^T, i.e., $\tau^T = \tau_0^T \tau_s^T/(\tau_0^T + \tau_s^T)$.

The specific feature of this regime, namely, the initial phase Φ dependence on the magnetic field, is illustrated in Fig. 1.

Resonant Excitation of Excitons

Diluted 2DEG. If the pump photon energy is tuned to the exciton transition then, at low temperates where $k_B T < E_B^T$ (k_B is the Boltzmann constant, E_B^T is the trion binding energy), the photogenerated excitons tend to bind into trions as far as they find cross-polarized pre-existing electrons, and the trion thermal dissociation can be neglected. Experimentally, the exciton contribution to the Kerr oscillating signal is determined by the Larmor spin precession of bound-to-exciton electrons. It follows then that,

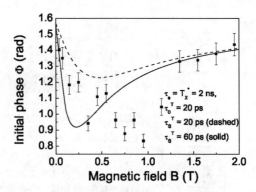

FIGURE 1. The initial phase of spin beats vs. the in-plane magnetic field under the pulsed resonant photoexcitation of trions. Points represent the experimental data, solid and dashed curves are theoretical fits with the parameters indicated in the panel.

in the pump-probe experiment, the correlation between the electron and hole spins held by the electron-hole exchange interaction is suppressed, see Refs. [3, 4]. Therefore, the spin s^X of an electron bound into an exciton precesses in an in-plane magnetic field with the same frequency as that of a free electron. Note that if the exciton-bound heavy holes are unpolarized the excitons can be labelled by the electron spin s^X. Moreover, the generated trions are unpolarized as well.

Dense 2DEG. An increase in the 2DEG density and its Fermi level leads to the dissociation of trions due to the state-filling and screening effects. Therefore, the third scenario involves only two subsystems, 2DEG and spin-polarized excitons resonantly excited by the circularly polarized optical pulse. The electrons being initially unpolarized can gain the spin polarization due to the electron-electron exchange interaction in the flip-flop electron-exciton scattering processes.

ACKNOWLEDGMENTS

EAZh stays in Dortmund have been financed by the DFG via grants 436 RUS 17/79/04 and 436 RUS 17/93/05. ELI research visit in Dortmund has been supported by the Gambrinus guest-professor program of the Dortmund University. The work was also partially supported by RFBR and Dynasty Foundation – ICFPM.

REFERENCES

1. A. Shabaev et al., *Phys. Rev. B* **68**, 201305 (2003).
2. T.A. Kennedy et al., *Phys. Rev. B* **73**, 45307 (2006).
3. T. Amand et al., *Phys. Rev. Lett.* **78**, 1355-1358 (1997).
4. M. Dyakonov et al., *Phys. Rev. B* **56**, 10412-10422 (1997).

Theory on measuring electron spin decoherence times by nonlinear optical spectroscopy of quantum dots

R.-B. Liu*, S. E. Economou†, L. J. Sham† and D. G. Steel**

*Department of Physics, The Chinese University of Hong Kong, Shatin, N.T., Hong Kong, China
†Department of Physics, University of California San Diego, La Jolla, CA 92093, The United States
**The H. M. Randall Laboratory of Physics, University of Michigan, Ann Arbor, MI 48109, The United States

Abstract. Nonlinear optical spectra of charged excitons (trions) in quantum dots are theoretically studied. The spin decoherence time excluding the inhomogeneous broadening can be measured by the fifth order differential transmission spectra.

Keywords: Nonlinear spectroscopy, Spin relaxation, Quantum dot
PACS: 76.70.Hb, 42.65.An, 78.67.Hc

INTRODUCTION

The electron spin relaxation in quantum dots is a most concerned and yet poorly characterized effect for spin-based quantum technologies, including spintronics and quantum computation. The decoherence is usually dominated by the inhomogeneous broadening, which induces the dephasing time T_2^*. Spin echo in microwave ESR experiments is a conventional approach to measuring the spin decoherence time T_2 excluding the inhomogeneous broadening, which, however, is less feasible for III-V compound quantum dots due to the ultrafast timescales in such systems ($T_2 \lesssim 10^{-6}$ sec and $T_2^* \lesssim 10^9$ sec). Optical manipulation of electron spin via Raman processes [1] can be an alternative but it still demands stabilization and synchronization of picosecond pulses in microsecond time-spans. High-resolution hole-burning optical spectroscopy have been successfully applied to characterize the slow relaxation processes in atomic systems [2]. Here we present the theoretical study of nonlinear optical spectroscopies of the spin coherence. We will shown that the spin decoherence time T_2 can be measured by the fifth-order differential transmission spectroscopy.

MODEL AND FORMALISM

The systems to be studied are quantum dots doped with single electrons. Without loss of generality, we consider light beams with a designated circular polarization and assume the selection rules for optical transitions are such that the angular momentum along the quantum dot growth direction is conserved. To break the rotational symmetry so that the spin coherence can be generated via Raman processes [3], a magnetic field is applied normal to the growth direction which induces a Zeeman splitting ω_0. The relaxation processes in the system are parameterized by the exciton recombination rate Γ_1, the exciton dephasing rate Γ_2, the spin relaxation rate $\gamma_1 = 1/T_1$, and the spin decoherence rate $\gamma_2 = 1/T_2$.

The optical excitation and the relaxation can be formulated into the master equation

$$\partial_t \rho_{\tau,\pm} = -i(\mathscr{E}_g \mp \omega_c/2 - i\Gamma_2)\rho_{\tau,\pm} - iE(t)\rho_{\tau,\tau}$$
$$+ iE(t)\rho_{\mp,\pm} + iE(t)\rho_{\pm,\pm}, \quad (1a)$$

$$\partial_t \rho_{\tau,\tau} = -2\Gamma_1 \rho_{\tau,\tau} + 2\Im\left[E^*(t)\rho_{\tau,\pm}\right], \quad (1b)$$

$$\partial_t \rho_{\pm,\pm} = -\gamma_1 (p_{\mp}\rho_{\pm,\pm} - p_{\pm}\rho_{\mp,\mp}) + \Gamma_1 \rho_{\tau,\tau}$$
$$- 2\Im\left[E^*(t)\rho_{\tau,\pm}\right], \quad (1c)$$

$$\partial_t \rho_{\pm,\mp} = \Gamma_1 \rho_{\tau,\tau} - i(\pm\omega_c - i\gamma_2)\rho_{\pm,\mp}$$
$$+ iE^*(t)\rho_{\tau,\mp} - iE(t)\rho_{\tau,\pm}^*, \quad (1d)$$

where $\rho_{i,j}$ denotes the density matrix elements between the trion state $|\tau\rangle$ and the spin states $|\pm\rangle$, the Zeeman splitting ω_c has included the inhomogeneous broadening $\varepsilon = \omega_c - \omega_0$, $\mathscr{E}_g$ is the energy gap, $p_{\pm}$ is the initial population of the spin states, and the optical field $E(t) = \sum_j E_j e^{-i\Omega_j t}$ contains all different frequency components. To calculate the nonlinear optical susceptibility to an arbitrary order, the master equation can be transformed into the frequency-domain and expanded order by order of the optical field. Considering the inhomogeneous broadening, the final result should be averaged with the distribution $g(\varepsilon)$. We take the Gaussian broadening, i.e., $g(\varepsilon) = e^{-\varepsilon^2/(2\sigma^2)}/(\sqrt{2\pi}\sigma)$, with $\sigma = 1/T_2^*$.

RESULTS AND DISCUSSIONS

The linear optical susceptibility presents the resonances $(\Omega - \mathscr{E}_g \pm \omega_c/2 + i\Gamma_2)^{-1}$. In typical GaAs quantum dots, the exciton dephasing rate is much greater than the spin inhomogeneous broadening ($\Gamma_2 \gg \sigma$), so the resonance width in the linear optical spectra will be

CP893, *Physics of Semiconductors, 28th International Conference*
edited by W. Jantsch and F. Schäffler
© 2007 American Institute of Physics 978-0-7354-0397-0/07/$23.00

dominated by the trion state broadening, revealing little information about the spin relaxation.

In the third order response, the spin coherence is generated by Raman processes like $\rho_{-,-} \xrightarrow{E_1} \rho_{\tau,-}^{(1)} \xrightarrow{E_2^*} \rho_{+,-}^{(1\bar{2})}$, corresponding to the Raman resonance

$$\rho^{(1\bar{2})} \sim \left(\Omega_{1\bar{2}} - \omega_c + i\gamma_2\right)^{-1}, \qquad (2)$$

where $\Omega_{i\bar{j}} \equiv \Omega_i - \Omega_j$ (as for similar notation hereafter). Thus the spin decoherence time T_2 can be deduced from the optical spectra. But when the inhomogeneous broadening is included, since $\gamma_2 \ll \sigma$, the Raman resonance will be be smeared out to be

$$\int \rho_{+,-}^{(1\bar{2})} g(\varepsilon) d\varepsilon \sim -i\pi g\left(\Omega_{1\bar{2}} - \omega_0\right), \qquad (3)$$

which discloses the inhomogeneous broadening but no information of the spin decoherence time T_2. The optically induced spin population will also enter the third order susceptibility, appearing as a resonance like

$$\rho_{\pm,\pm}^{(1\bar{2})} \sim \left(\Omega_{1\bar{2}} + i\gamma_1\right)^{-1}, \qquad (4)$$

which is independent of the Zeeman splitting and hence unaffected by the inhomogeneous broadening. Thus the spin relaxation time $T_1 = \gamma_1^{-1}$ can be deduced from the sharp resonance around $\Omega_{1\bar{2}} = 0$. A typical example of the third order differential transmission spectrum, calculated from $\rho_{\tau,\pm}^{(21\bar{1})}$, is shown in Fig. 1, which confirms our analysis above.

Coming to the fifth order nonlinearity, the spin coherence in the fourth order of optical field will present very rich resonance structures. For instance, such a double resonance as

$$\rho_{+,-}^{(43\bar{2}\bar{1})} \sim \left(\Omega_{3\bar{1}} + \omega_c + i\gamma_2\right)^{-1} \left(\Omega_{43\bar{2}\bar{1}} - \omega_c + i\gamma_2\right)^{-1}, \qquad (5)$$

can arise from the excitation and relaxation pathway:

$$\rho_{+,+} \xrightarrow{E_3} \rho_{\tau,+}^{(3)} \xrightarrow{E_1^*} \rho_{-,+}^{(3\bar{1})} \xrightarrow{E_4} \rho_{\tau,+}^{(43\bar{1})} \xrightarrow{E_2^*} \rho_{\tau,\tau}^{(43\bar{2}\bar{1})} \xrightarrow{\Gamma_1} \xrightarrow{} $$

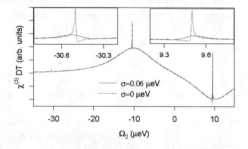

FIGURE 1. The third order differential transmission (DT) spectrum for $\omega_0 = 20\ \mu$eV, $\Gamma_1 = 10\ \mu$eV, $\Gamma_2 = 6\ \mu$eV, $\gamma_1 = \gamma_2 = 6$ neV, and $\sigma = 0.06\ \mu$eV (solid line). The inhomogeneous broadening is artificially switched off for the dotted line. The pump frequency $\Omega_1 = -10.5\ \mu$eV (measured from the gap). The insets single out the resonances around $\Omega_{2\bar{1}} = \pm\omega_0$.

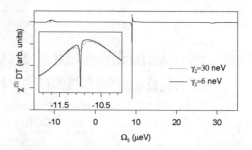

FIGURE 2. The fifth order DT spectra for $\gamma_2 = 6$ neV (solid line) or 30 neV (dotted line) and $\sigma = 0.6\ \mu$eV (other parameters are the same as in Fig. 1). The pump frequencies are set such that $\Omega_1 = 9\ \mu$eV, $\Omega_3 - \Omega_2 = \Omega_1 - \Omega_5 = 7\ \mu$eV when Ω_3 is scanned. The probe frequency $\Omega_4 = 22\ \mu$eV. The resonance of interest is amplified in the inset.

$\rho_{+,-}^{(43\bar{2}\bar{1})}$, where the last step is the spin coherence generation by spontaneous emission [related to the first term in the righthand side of Eq.(1d)] [3]. When the inhomogeneous broadening is included, the double resonance in Eq. (5) presents the hole burning effect for the spin coherence: When one of the excitation frequencies (e.g., $\Omega_{43\bar{2}\bar{1}}$) is fixed around the resonance, the scanning of the other frequency (e.g., $\Omega_{3\bar{1}}$) will result in a sharp resonance with width $\sim \gamma_2$, regardless of the inhomogeneous broadening. As compared to the third-order spectroscopies for optical coherence hole burning [2], here we need the fifth order nonlinearity since the generation of the lowest-order Raman coherence requires two optical fields. The fifth order differential transmission of a probe light at frequency Ω_4 can be measured if the pump frequencies are set such that $\Omega_{53\bar{2}\bar{1}} = 0$. As shown in Fig. 2, the sharp resonance with width $\sim \gamma_2$ is clearly seen in the fifth order differential transmission as a function of Ω_3. Thus the electron spin relaxation and decoherence can be characterized.

ACKNOWLEDGMENTS

This work was partially supported by the Hong Kong RGC Direct Grant 2060284.

REFERENCES

1. P. Chen, C. Piermarocchi, L. J. Sham, D. Gammon, and D. G. Steel, *Phys. Rev. B*, **69**, 075320 (2003).
2. D. G. Steel and J. T. Remillard, *Phys. Rev. A* **36**, 4330 (1987).
3. M. V. Gurudev Dutt *et al*, *Phys. Rev. Lett.* **94**, 227403 (2005).

Stray-field-induced modification of coherent spin dynamics

L. Meier*,†, G. Salis*, C. Ellenberger†, E. Gini** and K. Ensslin†

*IBM Research, Zurich Research Laboratory, Säumerstrasse 4, 8803 Rüschlikon, Switzerland
†Solid State Physics Laboratory, ETH Zurich, 8093 Zürich, Switzerland
**FIRST Center for Micro- and Nanosciences, ETH Zurich, 8093 Zürich, Switzerland

Abstract. Electron spins in an InGaAs semiconductor quantum well are used as a magnetometer of magnetic stray fields from an array of Fe bars. Using time-resolved Faraday rotation, the coherent precession of quantum-well spins in the inhomogeneous field between the Fe bars is measured for varying external magnetic fields and different geometries of the Fe bars. Compared with reference stripes made of Au, we find an enhancement of the spin precession frequency proportional to the Fe magnetization, in line with a decrease of the spin decay time, which is attributed to the inhomogeneous magnetic stray field in the quantum-well layer.

Keywords: magnetic stray field, ferromagnetic gates, time-resolved Faraday rotation
PACS: 78.47.+p, 78.67.De, 85.75.-d

Small ferromagnetic structures can be the source of a highly non-uniform and rather strong magnetic stray field that is of potential interest for the coherent manipulation of electron spins in close-by semiconductor quantum structures. The influence of magnetized ferromagnetic structures on the Zeeman splitting of electrons in a semiconductor quantum well (QW) has been investigated using luminescence spectroscopy [1, 2, 3]. Here, we demonstrate that the local magnetic stray field of magnetized Fe bars can be probed by time-resolving the precession of electron spins in an InGaAs QW below the Fe bars [4]. We find that electron spins precess faster in a QW situated below an array of magnetized Fe bars than below non-magnetic Au bars. The increase in precession frequency is proportional to the magnetization of the Fe bars, as measured using the magneto-optical Kerr effect (MOKE). The precession signal decays faster below the Fe grating, which we attribute to an averaging over the inhomogeneous stray field in between the Fe bars.

The QW structure consists of a 40 nm thick $In_{0.09}Ga_{0.91}As$ layer 20 nm below the surface; see [4] for the exact layer structure. Using electron-beam lithography, thermal evaporation and lift-off techniques, arrays of 100 μm long and 80 nm thick bars have been defined on the GaAs surface. The Fe bars were capped with 10 nm Al to prevent oxidation. We have fabricated bars with widths of 3, 2, 1 and 0.5 μm. The gaps in between the bars were chosen to be of the same dimensions as the bar width.

We employ time-resolved Faraday rotation (TRFR) [5] to track the coherent spin dynamics of QW electrons in the time domain and obtain precise values of the electron spin precession frequency v. TRFR is measured in the Voigt geometry with pump and probe beams along z and an external magnetic field B_{ext} applied along

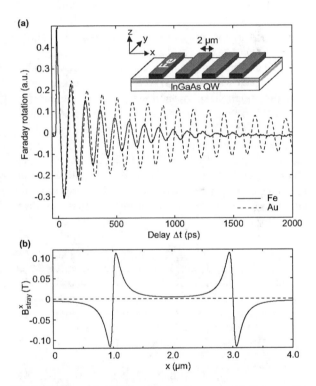

FIGURE 1. (a) TRFR signal of arrays of 2 μm wide bars with $B_{ext} = 1.05$ T applied along x. Fits yield $v = 7.72$ (8.14) GHz and $T_2^* = 1580$ (365) ps for Au (Fe). Inset shows a schematic view of a sample. (b) Micromagnetic simulation of the stray-field component along x in the center of the QW layer (the gap between two Fe bars is located at $1 < x < 3$ μm).

x [see inset of Fig. 1(a)]. Spin-polarized electrons are generated by a circularly polarized pump pulse at time $\Delta t = 0$ (spin polarization is along z). The Faraday rotation $\Theta(\Delta t)$ of a probe pulse that arrives at the QW at

CP893, *Physics of Semiconductors, 28th International Conference*
edited by W. Jantsch and F. Schäffler
© 2007 American Institute of Physics 978-0-7354-0397-0/07/$23.00

time Δt is proportional to the electron spin polarization along z at time Δt, and can be expressed as $\Theta(\Delta t) = \Theta_0 \cos(2\pi \nu \Delta t) \exp(-\Delta t / T_2^*)$, where T_2^* is the spin lifetime of the ensemble and $\nu = g \mu_B B_{tot}/h$ is given by the g-factor g of QW electrons, the Bohr magneton μ_B and the total local magnetic field B_{tot}, which includes B_{ext}, the magnetic stray field of the ferromagnetic grating B_s, and an effective magnetic field B_n resulting from hyperfine interaction with polarized nuclear spins. Fitting this equation to measurements of $\Theta(\Delta t)$ yields ν, from which B_{tot} can be determined.

A numerical simulation of the magnetic stray field of two Fe bars is obtained with the micromagnetic simulation tool OOMMF [6]. At $B_{ext} = 0$, the bars are magnetized along their long (easy) axis, and no stray field is expected along x. As B_{ext} is increased, the magnetization turns into the x-direction and saturates at $B_{ext} = 100$ to 200 mT, depending on the bar width. The stray field in the QW is strongly inhomogeneous and decays from 100 mT close to the bar edge to values below 12 mT just 500 nm away from the edge. In Fig. 1(b), the x-component of the stray field in the QW layer is shown for the Fe bars magnetized by $B_{ext} = 1$ T.

In the experiment, samples with Fe bars are compared with samples with non-magnetic Au bars. When the Fe bars are magnetized by applying B_{ext}, ν increases as compared to measurements on a reference grating made of non-magnetic Au, see Fig. 1(a). Fits to the experimental data of the $2\,\mu m$ samples at $B = 1.05$ T yield a precession frequency that is 0.42 GHz higher on the Fe than on the Au grating. A part of this difference can be related to a modified g-factor below the Fe bars as compared with that below the Au bars, possibly due to the different strain that the two materials exert on the QW. In Fig. 2(a), the dependence of ν on B_{ext} for both the Fe and Au sample is shown. It can be clearly seen that for Fe, ν is not linear in B_{ext} for $|B_{ext}| < 0.2$ T. Assuming that this deviation stems from the reversal of the Fe magnetization that saturates around 0.1 T, a linear fit at higher fields yields the electron g-factors. We find slightly different g-factors below the two gratings: $|g_{Fe}| = 0.535$ and $|g_{Au}| = 0.523$. In Fig. 2(b), $\nu - \nu_0$ is plotted for the $2\,\mu m$ Au and Fe samples, where $\nu_0 = g \mu_B B_{ext}/h$. Neglecting effects from nuclear polarization (which are below 0.01 GHz [4]), $\nu_{Fe} - \nu_0$ reveals the average stray field that is sampled by the photoexcited QW electron spins. The curve is proportional to the magnetization of the Fe grating, as measured by MOKE (see Ref. [4]). Note that the metallic bars on the sample surface act as an optical mask that covers the region below the bars such that the stray field is sampled only in between the bars. For the averaged stray field at magnetic saturation, $\langle B_s \rangle = h(\nu_{Fe} - \nu_0)/g_{Fe}\mu_B$, we find 37 mT. This is slightly more than the calculated stray field x-component shown in Fig. 1(b), averaged between two bars, of 25 mT. Because of the averaging of the in-

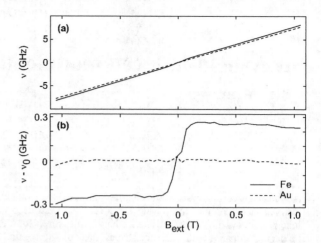

FIGURE 2. (a) Precession frequency ν vs. B_{ext} for the $2\,\mu m$ wide Au and Fe bars, showing a nonlinear dependence for the Fe bars. In (b), the difference of ν to a $\nu_0 = g\mu_B B_{ext}/h$ is shown, where g is obtained by a linear fit to $\nu(B_{ext})$ in the region of saturated magnetization.

homogeneous stray field, the lifetime T_2^* is reduced by a factor of about 4 on the Fe grating, as compared with that on the Au grating.

Varying the geometry of the Fe bars leads to a change of $\nu_{Fe} - \nu_0$ vs. B_{ext}. We find that the field at which $\nu_{Fe} - \nu_0$ saturates increases with decreasing bar width. This agrees with the observed increase in the saturation field of the Fe magnetization. On the other hand, we find a non-monotonic behavior of $\nu_{Fe} - \nu_0$ with the gap width, whereas a monotonic decay with increasing gap width is expected. This might be attributed to the presence of negative x-components of B_s in the QW close to the edge of the bars [see Fig. 1(b)], combined with a non-uniform sampling of this region due to near-field optical effects [4].

We acknowledge financial support from the Swiss National Science Foundation via NCCR Nanoscience.

REFERENCES

1. J. Kossut, I. Yamakawa, A. Nakamura, G. Cywiński, K. Fronc, M. Czeczott, J. Wróbel, F. Kyrychenko, T. Wojtowicz, and S. Takeyama, *Appl. Phys. Lett.* **79**, 1789 (2001).
2. H. Schömig, A. Forchel, S. Halm, G. Bacher, J. Puls, and F. Henneberger, *Appl. Phys. Lett.* **84**, 2826 (2004).
3. M. Sakuma, K. Hykomi, I. Souma, A. Murayama, and Y. Oka, *Appl. Phys. Lett.* **85**, 6203 (2004).
4. L. Meier, G. Salis, C. Ellenberger, K. Ensslin, and E. Gini, *Appl. Phys. Lett.* **88**, 172501 (2006).
5. S. A. Crooker, D. D. Awschalom, and N. Samarth, IEEE J. Sel. Top. Quantum Electron. **1**, 1082 (1995).
6. http://math.nist.gov/oommf/

Spin-dependent transmission through a mesoscopic ring: determination of the spin-orbit interaction strengths from the final spin orientation and spin flips

P. Vasilopoulos* and X. F. Wang†

*Department of Physics, Concordia University, 7141 Sherbrooke Ouest, Montréal, Québec, Canada, H4B 1R6
†Department of Physics and Astronomy, The University of Manitoba, Winnipeg, Manitoba R3T 2N2 Canada

Abstract. The electronic, spin-dependent transmission through a ring is studied in the presence of the Rashba and Dresselhaus terms of the spin-orbit interaction (SOI), respectively, of strengths α and β, and of a magnetic field B. We demonstrate a direct connection between α, β, and the final spin orientations. For $B = 0$ the outgoing spins trace rings normal to the y ($\beta = 0$), x ($\alpha = 0$) axis. For $\beta = 0$ ($\alpha = 0$) incident spins polarized along the y (x) axis exit the ring parallel to the y (x) axis. The values of α and β are extracted from the final spin orientation. For finite B this precession picture does not hold: spin flips occur when α (β) is varied as the angles describing the spin orientation change drastically in a very narrow range of α (β).

Keywords: Spin-orbit interaction, transmission, spin precession
PACS: 72.25.-b, 71.70.Ej, 03.65.Vf, 85.35.-p

INTRODUCTION AND FORMALISM

By inserting a mescoscopic ring into a circuit, one can study quantum transport through it. In the presence of SOI electron spins acquire different phases when traveling through the ring's two arms clockwise or anticlockwise; this leads to the Aharonov-Casher (AC) effect [1]. By controlling the strength of the SOI, with gate voltages, the phase difference ϕ_{AC} can be changed, the spin-dependent transmission can be modulated, and the ring can be used as a spin-interference device [2]. Here we consider a one-dimensional (1D) ring, symmetrically connected to two leads, cf. Fig. 1, in the presence of a magnetic field B and of *both* terms of the SOI. B and the SOI fields have perpendicular and radial components.

Eigenvalues and eigenfunctions. The 1D ring, of radius a, is in the $(x$-$y)$ plane, at $z = 0$, the components of the field B are $B_z = B\cos\gamma_3$ and $B_r = B\sin\gamma_3$, and the vector potential $\mathbf{A} = (A_r, A_\theta, A_z) = (0, B_z r/2 - B_r z, 0)$. In the presence of the RSOI (H_α) and DSOI (H_β) the one-electron Hamiltonian reads ($\lambda = g\mu_B/2$)

$$H = \hbar\omega_0(-i\partial/\partial\theta + \phi/\phi_0)^2 + \lambda\boldsymbol{\sigma}\cdot\mathbf{B} + H_\alpha + H_\beta; \quad (1)$$

here $\omega_0 = \hbar/2m^*a^2$, $\boldsymbol{\sigma} = (\sigma_x, \sigma_y, \sigma_z) \equiv (\sigma_r, \sigma_\theta, \sigma_z)$ are the Pauli matrices, $\phi = B_z\pi a^2$ the magnetic flux piercing the ring, $\phi_0 = h/e$, μ_B the Bohr magneton, and g the g factor. The SOI can result from asymmetric confinement along the z direction [3] (H_α) or from the crystal structure changing along it. The usual forms of H_α and H_β are [4] $H_\alpha = (\alpha/\hbar)[\sigma_x(\hat{p}_y + eA_y) - \sigma_y(\hat{p}_x + eA_x)]$ and $H_\beta = (\beta/\hbar)[\sigma_x(\hat{p}_x + eA_x) - \sigma_y(\hat{p}_y + eA_y)]$. Here $\alpha \propto \langle E_R\rangle$ and $\beta \propto \langle E_D\rangle$ are the RSOI and DSOI strengths. $\langle E_R\rangle = \langle E_R\rangle\mathbf{e}_z$ is the RSOI field and $\langle \mathbf{E}_D\rangle = \langle E_D\rangle\mathbf{e}_z$ an *effective*

DSOI field similar to the RSOI one. However, in general $\langle E_R\rangle$ and $\langle E_D\rangle$ can have a radial component as well, see [5] for the RSOI. Thus, we consider them in the form $\mathbf{E}_R = E_R(\sin\gamma_1\mathbf{e}_r + \cos\gamma_1\mathbf{e}_z)$, $\mathbf{E}_D = E_D(\sin\gamma_2\mathbf{e}_r + \cos\gamma_2\mathbf{e}_z)$ and assume that H_α and H_β remain the same.

With $\tan\varphi_n = C\beta/(\alpha + D)$, C, D constants, the eigenvectors of Eq. (1) are [6] $\Psi_{n\sigma} = e^{in\theta}\chi_{n\sigma}(\theta)/(2\pi)^{1/2}$ with $\chi_{n\sigma}(\theta) = [\cos(\delta_{n\sigma}/2), \sin(\delta_{n\sigma}/2)e^{i\varphi_n + i\theta}]^T$, $[...]^T$ the transpose of the vector $[...]$, and $\cot(\delta_{n+}) = f(\alpha, \beta, B)$.

If the Zeeman term is negligible, δ_{n+} and φ_n are independent of n and σ, $\delta_{n+} \equiv \delta$ and $\varphi_n \equiv \varphi$. Then the eigenvalues of Eq. (1) take the simple form $E_{n\sigma} = \hbar\omega_0[n + \phi/\phi_0 - \phi_{AC}^\sigma/(2\pi)]^2$, with the phase ϕ_{AC}^σ given by

$$\phi_{AC}^\sigma = -\pi\{1 + 2\sigma[\bar{\alpha}^2 + \bar{\alpha}\sin\gamma_1 + \bar{\beta}^2 C_{\gamma_2}^2 + 1/4]^{1/2}\}, \quad (2)$$

$C_{\gamma_2} = \sin\gamma_2 - \cos\gamma_2$. That is, ϕ_{AC}^σ depends on α, β, and the angles γ_1, γ_2. It reduces to that of Ref. [7] for $\beta = 0$.

Transfer-matrix formulation. We consider the ring shown in Fig. 1. Electrons with energy E and spins along the direction (δ_i, φ_i) are incident from lead I to the ring and exit it through lead II with spins along the direction (δ_f, φ_f). We write the wave function in lead I as

$$\Psi_I(x) = [\mathcal{A}^+, \mathcal{A}^-]^T e^{ikx} + [\mathcal{B}^+, \mathcal{B}^-]^T e^{-ikx}, \quad (3)$$

with $\mathcal{A}^-/\mathcal{A}^+ = \tan(\delta_i/2)e^{i\varphi_i}$; the outgoing wave function $\Psi_{II}(x)$ in lead II is given by the same expression with $\mathcal{A}$, $\mathcal{B}$, and x replaced by C, D, and x', respectively. The transmission amplitude t^σ is obtained after matching the wave function and the spin-current density at each junction. If the Zeeman term is neglected, t^σ takes the same form as that for $\beta = 0$ [7], [6], i.e., ($\omega = 2ka\pi$)

CP893, *Physics of Semiconductors, 28th International Conference*
edited by W. Jantsch and F. Schäffler
© 2007 American Institute of Physics 978-0-7354-0397-0/07/$23.00

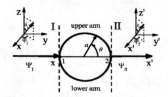

FIGURE 1.   A 1D ring, symmetrically connected to the leads I and II, and the orientations of the incident and outgoing spins.

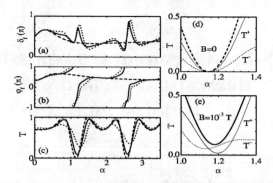

FIGURE 3.   Final angles $\delta_f(a)$, φ_f (b), and total transmission T (c) vs α for $\beta = 0$. The dashed, solid, and dotted curves are for $B = 0$, 10^{-3} T, and 2×10^{-3} T. The range $1 \leq \alpha \leq 1.4$ of panel (c), for the solid and dashed curves, is blown up in (d) ($B = 0$) and (e) ($B = 10^{-3}$ T) showing T, T^+, and T^-.

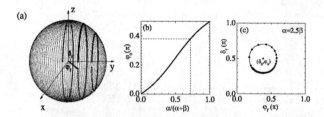

FIGURE 2.   (a) Final spin orientation (δ_f, φ_f) vs α for $\beta = 0$, $\delta_i = \pi/2$, and $\varphi_i = 0, \pi/8, \pi/16$ from inner to outer circle. (b) The angle φ_0 of the fixed axis vs $\alpha/(\alpha + \beta)$. For $\beta = 0$ and $\alpha \neq 0$, φ_0 is $\pi/2$. (c) Traces of (δ_f, φ_f) for $B = 0$ and $\alpha/\beta = 2.5$.

$t^\sigma = [8i\cos(-\phi/2\phi_0 + \phi_{AC}^\sigma/2)\sin(\omega/2)]/[1 - 5\cos\omega + 4\cos\phi_{AC}^\sigma + 4i\sin\omega]$ but with ϕ_{AC}^σ given by by Eq. (2).

The coefficients C^+, C^- of the transmitted wave function are related to those of the incident one $\mathcal{A}^+$, $\mathcal{A}^-$ by

$$\begin{bmatrix} C^+ \\ C^- \end{bmatrix} = U_R \begin{bmatrix} t^+ & 0 \\ 0 & t^- \end{bmatrix} U_L \begin{bmatrix} \mathcal{A}^+ \\ \mathcal{A}^- \end{bmatrix}. \qquad (4)$$

U_L (U_R) depend only on the angles δ and φ and express the precession of the reflected (transmitted) spins [6].

RESULTS

We first consider the case $B = 0$. In Fig. 2(a) we show the traces of (δ_f, φ_f) vs α on the surface of a unit sphere for different initial orientations $(\delta_i = \pi/2, \varphi_i)$ and $\beta = 0$. The traces form rings normal to the y axis: this can be proven analytically by noticing that $t^+ = -t^-$, $\cot\delta = -1/2\bar{\alpha}$ and $\phi = 0$: this gives $y_i = y_f$ or $\sin\delta_f \sin\varphi_f = \sin\delta_i \sin\varphi_i$.

For $\delta_i = \varphi_i = \pi/2$ the trace ring becomes a point since $\delta_f = \varphi_f = \pi/2$ for all α. That is, incident spins polarized along the y axis, exit the ring oriented along the y axis. We call this spin orientation the fixed axis (δ_0, φ_0); it is the y axis $(\pi/2, \pi/2)$ for $\beta = 0$. For $\alpha = 0$, $\beta \neq 0$, the trace rings are normal to the x axis since $x_i = x_f$ or $\sin\delta_f \cos\varphi_f = \sin\delta_i \cos\varphi_i$. The fixed axis is the x axis.

For $\alpha \neq 0$, $\beta \neq 0$, and $\delta_i = \pi/2$ the fixed axis lies in the $(x$-$y)$ plane. Denoting its direction by $(\delta_0 = \pi/2, \varphi_0)$, we plot φ_0 versus $\alpha/(\alpha + \beta)$ in Fig. 2 (b); the result is independent of the ring's radius. If α and β increase at the same rate, (δ_f, φ_f) will mark a ring normal to the fixed axis as shown in Fig. 2 (c) for an initial orientation

$(0.4\pi, 0.2\pi)$ and $\alpha/\beta = 2.5$. The fixed axis, shown by a star in Fig. 2 (c) and determined from Fig. 2 (b) for $\alpha/(\alpha + \beta) = 5/7$, is $(\pi/2, 0.379\pi)$. Successive dots on the ring correspond to $\delta\alpha = 0.1\alpha_0$ and $\delta\beta = 0.04\alpha_0$.

The direction (δ_f, φ_f) can be determined from the components $P_x = P\sin\delta_f \cos\varphi_f$, $P_y = P\cos\delta_f \cos\varphi_f$, and $P_z = P\cos\delta_f$ of the polarization, Then one can determine α and β as follows. (1) With $(\delta_i, \varphi_i) = (\pi/2, \varphi_i)$, we plot (δ_f, φ_f) vs φ_i and identify the value φ_0 which leads to the fixed axis $(\pi/2, \varphi_0)$. Then Fig. 2 (b) gives α/β. (2) We choose any $(\delta_i, \varphi_i) \neq$ fixed axis and draw a circle as in Fig. 2(b). Comparing the arc length (δ_i, φ_i) - (δ_f, φ_f) with the numerical one of step (1), gives α, β.

For finite B the picture shown in Fig. 2(a) no longer holds, $t^+ \neq \pm t^-$, and the spin precession is not as smooth a process as for $B = 0$. As shown in Fig. 3(a),(b) near certain values of α φ_f and δ_f change drastically, φ_f by 2π, δ_f by less, in a very narrow range of α. For $B = 0$ T, T^+, and T^- vanish at the points $\alpha_m = (\hbar^2/2m^*a)[4(m+1)^2 - 1]^{1/2}$, m integer, cf. panel (d). The drastic changes of φ_f and δ_f occur near these minima for a weak field $B = 10^{-3}$ T and contrasts sharply with their very smooth change for $B = 0$. This is not the case in panel (e) and near the T minimum T^- dominates since $T^+ \approx 0$. Simply a weak field B removes the $T^+ = T^-$ degeneracy seen in (d). The spin flips occur at $\alpha/\alpha_0 = 1.14, 2.56, 3.91$.

Acknowledgement. This work was supported by the Canadian NSERC Grant No. OGP0121756.

REFERENCES

1. Y. Aharonov *et al.*, Phys. Rev. Lett. **53**, 319 (1984).
2. J. Nitta *et al.*, Appl. Phys. Lett. **75**, 695 (1999).
3. Y. A. Bychkov *et al.*, J. Phys. C **17**, 6039 (1984).
4. G. Dresselhaus, Phys. Rev. **100**, 580 (1955).
5. A. V. Moroz *et al.*, Phys. Rev. B **60**, 14272 (1999).
6. X. F. Wang *et al.*, Phys. Rev. B **72**, 165336 (2005).
7. B. Molnár *et al.*, Phys. Rev. B **69**, 155335 (2004).

Zeeman Splitting of Zero–Dimensional Heavy–Hole States in a Strongly Strained Ge Quantum Well

O. B. Agafonov*, K.-M. Haendel*, R. Winkler[¶], U. Denker**, O. G. Schmidt**
and R. J. Haug*

*Institut für Festkörperphysik ,Leibniz Universität Hannover, Appelstraße 2, D-30167 Hannover
[¶]Department of Physics, Northern Illinois University, De Kalb, IL 60115
**Max-Plank-Institut für Festkörperforschung, Heisenbergstraße 1, D-70569 Stuttgart

Abstract. The method of magnetotunneling spectroscopy has been used for experimental probing of heavy–hole impurity states in Si/Ge double–barrier heterostructures in magnetic field up to 18 Tesla. The impurities were located in a strained Ge quantum well with a thickness of four monolayers. We have observed a giant anisotropy of Zeeman splitting for these zero–dimensional systems. The splitting was measured as a function of angle between the external magnetic field and the quantum well plane. A complete suppression of the splitting takes place when the magnetic field is oriented parallel to the sample surface and quantum well plane, while in the perpendicular field the observed splitting is maximal.

Keywords: Quantum well, magnetic field, spin–orbit effects.
PACS: R71.18.+y, 71.70.Fk, 73.21.Fg

INTRODUCTION

Spin–related phenomena in semiconductors draw attention of many researchers due to their possible application in spintronic devices and for quantum computing. A lot of these investigations are devoted to the study of spin–orbit interaction and to spin manipulation along with effective Landé factor g engineering. We report the results of our study of the influence of homogeneous magnetic fields B up to 18 Tesla on the current–voltage characteristics (IVC) of a resonant tunneling Si/Ge heterostructure in the temperature range from 100 mK to 1 K.

EXPERIMENT

The measurements were carried out on the samples fabricated of a Si/Ge double–barrier heterostructure with a 4 monolayer–thick strained Ge quantum well embedded in Si. This structure was grown by molecular–beam epitaxy on a boron–doped p^+–Si (100) substrate at 460° C. A series of vertical resonant tunneling diodes with the average in–plane dimensions of order of 1 μm were processed using electron–beam lithography. The schematic picture of the layer sequence of the structure used is given in Fig. 1 along with the theoretically calculated valence band profile.

The orientation of the external magnetic field B applied to the samples was varied in the range from $\Theta = 0°$ to $\Theta = 90°$, where Θ is the angle between the field direction and the quantum well plane.

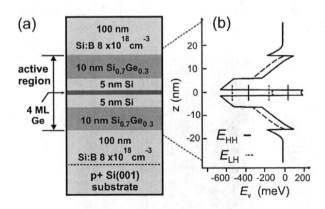

FIGURE 1. (a) Layer sequence of the studied Si/Ge heterostructure. (b) Self–consistently calculated valence band profile of an active region. The solid line illustrates the course of the heavy–hole subband E_{HH}. The dashed line corresponds to the light–hole subband E_{LH}.

CP893, *Physics of Semiconductors, 28th International Conference*
edited by W. Jantsch and F. Schäffler
© 2007 American Institute of Physics 978-0-7354-0397-0/07/$23.00

RESULTS AND DISCUSSION

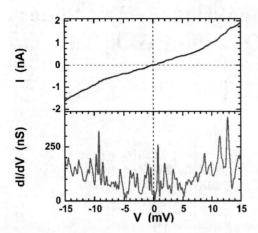

FIGURE 2. (a) Typical current–voltage characteristic of resonant tunneling diode at temperature 100 mK and B=0 T. (b) Differential conductance dI/dV.

The current–voltage characteristics of the samples reveal at low temperatures step–like features [1]. This behavior is observable at bias voltages much lower than voltages (of order of 300 mV) at which an onset of resonant tunneling of holes through two–dimensional states of the Ge quantum well sets in. We attribute these current steps to the tunneling process of holes through the zero–dimensional (0D) energy states created by boron dopant–atoms which have migrated from highly–doped contact layers into the region of the Ge quantum well. Tunneling through 0D heavy–hole (HH) state E_{HH} in the quantum well takes place each time E_{HH} is in resonance with the Fermi energy of emitter. An example of typical IVC inherent to our diodes is shown in Fig. 2 along with the corresponding differential conductance dI/dV.

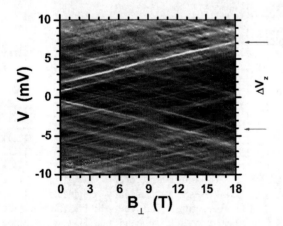

FIGURE 3. Gray–scale plot of differential conductance dI/dV at the temperature 100 mK measured in the magnetic field orientated perpendicular to the quantum well plane.

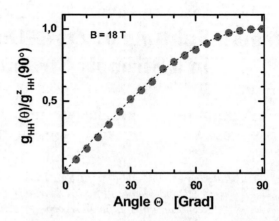

FIGURE 4. Angular dependence of g–factor of heavy–holes in the tilted magnetic field at 18 T. Θ is the angle between magnetic field and quantum well plane.

From the temperature–dependent broadening of the current step edges we have determined the energy–to–bias conversion factor [2] $\alpha \cong 0.5$.

In the magnetic field directed perpendicular to the quantum well plane we observed a linear splitting of differential conductance dI/dV peaks (see Fig. 3) attributed to the Zeeman splitting of heavy–hole states in Ge quantum well.

$$\Delta E_z = g_{HH}^z \mu_B B_\perp. \qquad (1)$$

As we see all levels reveal the same splitting. The gradient of the splitting $d\Delta V_z/dB_\perp = 0.73$ mV/T. The value of g–factor for this field orientation was determined as

$$g_{HH}^z = (\alpha e / \mu_B) \cdot (d\Delta V_z / dB_\perp) = 6.3. \quad (2)$$

The angular dependence of g_{HH} in the tilted magnetic field at 18 T is plotted in Fig. 4. The splitting turned out to be strongly anisotropic. In the perpendicular field $B_\perp$ the splitting is maximal. In an in–plane field $B_\parallel$ we observed a complete suppression of the splitting. This result correlates with the in [3] reported evidence of HH spin splitting which is determined only by $B_\perp$ component of magnetic field.

REFERENCES

1. K. -M. Haendel, R. Winkler, U. Denker, O. G. Schmidt, and R. J. Haug, *Phys. Rev. Lett.* **96**, 086403 (2006).
2. B. Su, V. J. Goldman, and J. E. Cunningham, *Phys. Rev. B* **46**, 7644 (1992).
3. R. W. Martin, R. J. Nicholas, G. J. Rees, N. J. Mason, and P. J. Walker, *Phys. Rev. B* **42**, 9237 (1990).

Novel Mechanism for Order-of-magnitude Enhancement of Rashba Effect in Wide Modulation-doped Quantum Wells

D.M. Gvozdić[1,2] and U. Ekenberg[2]

[1]Faculty of Electrical Engineering, University of Belgrade, P.O. Box 35-54, Belgrade, Serbia
[2]School of Information and Communication Technology, Royal Institute of Technology, SE-16440 Kista, Sweden

Abstract. The Rashba effect leading to subband splitting in quantum wells is frequently taken to be proportional to some average electric field. We here show that taking the spatial variation of the electric field into account gives important effects. In particular we demonstrate that one can apply a moderate electric field to a wide modulation-doped quantum well and get an order-of-magnitude enhancement of the Rashba splitting characteristic of the built-in interface field. For small asymmetry the wave function localization and spin projection of a subband can be rapid functions of the in-plane wave vector.

Keywords: Rashba effect, spintronics, modulation doping
PACS: 71.70.Ej, 73.21.Fg, 85.75.Hh

INTRODUCTION

Inversion asymmetry in quantum well structures leads to a spin-splitting for finite values of the in-plane wave vector $k_{//}$. In the case of structure inversion asymmetry (Rashba effect) [1] the spin splitting is usually assumed to be proportional to some average electric field. The spatial variation of the electric field has seldom been taken into account previously but we show that it can have strong effects in wide modulation-doped quantum wells where one takes advantage of the strong built-in electric field in the interface regions.

WIDE MODULATION-DOPED QUANTUM WELLS

We here consider 80 nm wide $In_{0.74}Ga_{0.26}Sb$ quantum wells with n-type doping in the $In_{0.7}Al_{0.3}Sb$ barriers. These materials essentially have the strong spin-orbit coupling of InSb. We have two weakly interacting electron gases in the interface regions. Here we can easily control the interface electric fields, carrier concentration, interaction between the electron gases and asymmetry with the doping profile including spacer layers widths. For a perfectly symmetric structure the two lowest subbands have symmetric and antisymmetric wave functions, respectively. A small but finite electric field is sufficient to localize each wave function to one of the interface regions.

ENHANCEMENT MECHANISM

Our self-consistent calculations are performed using an 8×8 **k·p** matrix approach in which the interaction between the conduction, heavy-hole, light-hole and split-off bands is included exactly. In this way we go beyond the commonly used approximations in the Rashba model [1].

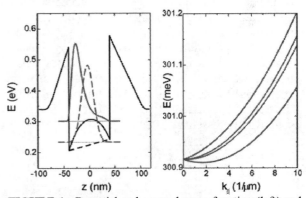

FIGURE 1. Potential and squared wave function (left) and subband dispersion (right) for an 80 nm InGaSb quantum well. Dashed lines: Uniform electric field. Solid lines: Modulation doping with $6·10^{11}$ electrons per cm^2. The average electric field is 4.4 kV/cm in both cases.

In Figure 1 we show the band diagram, squared wave function and subband structure for two cases. With a uniform electric field the spin splitting becomes quite small. In the modulation-doped case the splitting is enhanced by an order of magnitude. In this case the ground state wave function is localized at the left interface region where the strong local electric field yields a strong Rashba splitting.

This is a novel mechanism for efficient switching spintronic devices like the Datta-Das spin transistor [2]. It is sufficient to apply a rather small electric field and take advantage of the much stronger built-in field.

Our numerically determined expectation values of the electric field sometimes differ considerably between the components of a subband pair. Thus the common insertion of an expectation value of the electric field in the Rashba model is not well defined. Furthermore, when the two expectation values are similar this procedure yields a spin splitting that is roughly half of our numerical results.

STRONG $K_\parallel$-DEPENDENCE ON WAVE FUNCTION LOCALIZATION AND SPIN

In the previous section we took the asymmetry to be just sufficient to localize the wave functions to the interface regions. Interesting effects also occur for smaller asymmetry. At $k_\parallel = 0$ the wave functions have their largest amplitude in one interface region but with a non-negligible amplitude in the other interface region. The lowest spin-split subband pair has the strongest amplitude to the left, where the potential is deeper, while the second subband pair has a slightly higher energy and larger amplitude to the right. As $k_\parallel$ increases the spin subbands interact in a non-trivial and rather unexpected way. The wave functions of the anticrossing subbands can move in the perpendicular direction from one interface to the other and the calculated expectation value of the spin [3] can change its sign as $k_\parallel$ increases. We have found cases where one of these effects occurs. In Figure 2 both of them occur simultaneously in a narrow $k_\parallel$ range. To obtain this effect it is essential to include bulk inversion asymmetry (Dresselhaus effect) [4].

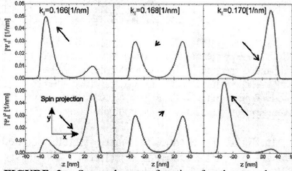

FIGURE 2. Squared wave function for the two lowest subbands for three values of the in-plane wave vector $k_{//}$ in the [11] direction. The insets show the expectation values of the spin in the xy-plane.

DISCUSSION

The wide modulation-doped quantum well is a valuable system for studying spin effects in which the interaction between two electron gases in slightly different interface potentials can be controlled to a high degree.

We have previously estimated the switch energy for different kinds of spin transistors [5]. We then concluded that with the original design [2] the n-type spin transistor would have problems to become competitive with conventional transistors. With our proposed mechanism a given spin splitting can be obtained with a gate voltage reduced by a factor 10 and much more promising prospects are opened.

The strong enhancement of the Rashba effect was shown for the lowest subband pair but a similar effect occurs for the second subband pair. Since the electric field there is inverted the direction of the spin precession during in-plane motion is reversed. This opens up for more complicated spintronic devices than the Datta-Das spin transistor [2], especially if the interface regions can be contacted separately.

The rapid spin flip in Figure 2 was shown for a constant electric field when $k_{//}$ was varied. It should be possible to obtain a similar effect at the Fermi level when the electric field is varied slightly. This will be considered elsewhere.

CONCLUSIONS

We have demonstrated useful and interesting effects in wide modulation-doped quantum wells with weakly interacting electron gases at the interfaces. The strong built-in electric field yields a novel mechanism for obtaining an enhancement of the spin splitting by an order of magnitude compared to the case with a uniform electric field. For smaller asymmetry the wave functions and spin projections can change rapidly as the in-plane wave vector is increased slightly.

REFERENCES

1. Y. A. Bychkov and E. I. Rashba, *J. Phys. C* **17**, 6039 (1984).
2. S. Datta and B. Das, *Appl. Phys. Letters* **56**, 665 (1990).
3. R. Winkler, "Spin-Orbit Coupling Effects in Two-Dimensional Electron and Hole Systems," *Springer Tracts in Modern Physics,* Vol. **191** (Springer, Berlin, 2003).
4. G. Dresselhaus, *Phys. Rev.* **100**, 580 (1955).
5. D.M. Gvozdić, U. Ekenberg and L. Thylén, *J. Supercond.* **18**, 349 (2005).

Spin-orbit Interactions in High In-content InGaAs/InAlAs Inverted Heterojunctions for Rashba spintronics Devices

Hyonkwan Choi, Yoshihito Kitta, Tomoyasu Kakegawa, Yeonkil Jeong, Masashi Akabori, Toshi-Kazu Suzuki, and Syoji Yamada

Center of Nano Materials and Technology, Japan Advanced Institute of Science and Technology
1-1, Asahidai, Nomi, Ishikawa 923-1292, Japan

Abstract. We studied novel $In_xGa_{1-x}As/In_xAl_{1-x}As$ (x=0.5 and 0.75) inverted modulation-doped heterojunctions (HJs) as a candidate material for realistic Rashba spintronics devices. Large Spin-orbit coupling constants, $\alpha > \sim 10 \times 10^{-12}$ eVm, have been estimated in these HJs with both the In contents. Also the larger α s were found in the HJs with thinner InGaAs channels due to the increase of the hetero-interface electric field. Moreover, higher In-content HJs seem to give larger α s, since they have a narrower bandgap as well as a smaller electron effective mass.

Keywords: Narrow-gap semiconductor, Spin-orbit coupling constant
PACS: R72.25.Dc; 73.40.-c

INTRODUCTION

Recently spin-orbit interaction (SOI) observed in narrow-gap semiconductor HJs has attracted much attention, since it could give a basic operation principle of various novel spintronics devices. So far, gated control of the SOI has been confirmed widely[1]. However, spin injection efficiency at the interface between the ferromagnetic (FM) electrode and the two-dimensional electron gas (2DEG) still remains in a few percent at present. In order to realize a HJ structure with a strong SOI as well as a possibility of high spin injection efficiency, we focused on the inverted InGaAs/InAlAs structures which have a thin and low potential barrier between the surface FM and 2DEG. In these samples, the spin-polarized electrons injected from the top FM electrode can more easily reach the 2DEG, but the details of the Rashba SO interaction have not been clarified yet.

EXPERIMENTAL DETAILS

We have grown inverted $In_xGa_{1-x}As/In_xAl_{1-x}As$ x=0.5 (and 0.75) modulation-doped HJ structures with 60 nm and 30 (40) nm channel thickness (d_c) by molecular beam epitaxy via metamorphic step graded buffer layer on semi-insulating GaAs (100) substrate [Fig. 1 (a)]. And also a normal InGaAs/InAlAs structure was grown for a reference [Fig. 1 (b)], where

the channel thickness was fixed to be 30 nm. For basic spin transport analysis, regular Van der Pauw (size=5x5 mm^2) and Hall bar samples (channel length of 50 μm and width of 200 μm with different channel directions [1-10], [110] and [100]) were prepared by photolithography. The SO coupling constant, α, is deduced by the fast Fourier transformation (FFT) and beating nodes Landau plot of the oscillations observed in the low field Shubnikov-de Haas (SdH) signals at ~1.5 K[2].

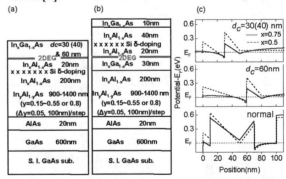

Figure 1. Schematic diagram for (a) inverted and (b) normal layer structures, and (c) corresponding potential profiles for the samples.

RESULTS AND DISCUSSION

The Van der Pauw samples were initially characterized by Hall measurements. Low temperature

CP893, *Physics of Semiconductors, 28th International Conference*
edited by W. Jantsch and F. Schäffler
© 2007 American Institute of Physics 978-0-7354-0397-0/07/$23.00

electron mobility reaches, however, up to ~2-3×10^5 cm^2/V·s in the x=0.75 HJs. Higher mobility in the x=0.75 samples than those in the x=0.5 ones is mainly due to the suppression of the alloy scattering.

Figure 2 shows the results of the SdH oscillations and the corresponding FFT results carried out to estimate the Rashba SO coupling constant (α) for d_c=60 and 30 nm samples. For the detailed spin transport analysis, the SdH oscillations were measured in the samples with different current directions [1-10], [110] and [100], respectively. As indicated in the traces in Fig. 2 there is almost no in-plane anisotropy for the beating pattern in d^2R_{xx}/dB^2s in the inverted In$_x$Ga$_{1-x}$As/In$_x$Al$_{1-x}$As HJs in the both cases of x=0.5 and 0.75, the large SO coupling constants, $\alpha > \sim 10$ (×10^{-12} eVm), comparable to those of the normal HJs were confirmed. Moreover, larger α s were found in the x=0.75 HJs than those in the x=0.5 ones. This is probably due to the difference of the energy bandgap (0.52 and 0.74 eV), electron effective mass (~0.04m$_o$ and ~0.06m$_o$) and interface electric field strength between the x=0.75 and 0.5 samples, respectively [3]. In addition, also larger α was found for the thinner InGaAs channel samples in the same In-content. For example, α s were ~23 and ~28 (×10^{-12} eVm) for the x=0.75 d_c = 60 and 40 nm samples, respectively. The origin of the larger α is probably due to the stronger interface electric field (<E>) resulting from the thinner triangular potential well at the HJ interface.

Table 1 shows the In-content and d_c dependencies of α in the inverted HJ samples. We calculated approximate values (α approx.) from the $\alpha \approx \hbar^2 \langle E \rangle / 2m^* E_g$ [3] and compared with the experiments. d_c dependency of α can be explained by <E> difference in both (x=0.5 and 0.75) the cases. However, in inverted HJ case, In-content dependency of α seems not to be interpreted only by the <E> difference. The disagreements between $\overline{\alpha}$ and α approx. suggests that possible other effects such as different interface penetration of electron distribution etc. are larger in the x=0.75 case.

TABLE 1. Comparison between the estimated $\overline{\alpha}$ (averaged for the current directions) and the calculated ones ($\alpha_{appprox.}$) with the interface electric fields, <E>, obtained from the potential calculations.

	d_c	$\overline{\alpha}$ (10^{-12} eVm)	α approx. (10^{-12} eVm)	<E> (10^5 V/cm)
	30 nm	20	13.2	14.0
x=0.5	60 nm	12	8.4	9.0
	normal	8	4.3	4.5
	40 nm	20	8.7	4.4
x=0.75	60 nm	16	6.3	3.2
	normal	20	5.3	2.7

CONCLUSIONS

We have investigated the Rashba spin-orbit coupling constant α and in-plane transport anisotropy in the inverted In$_x$Ga$_{1-x}$As/In$_x$Al$_{1-x}$As (x=0.5 and 0.75) structures. Low temperature 2DEG mobilities of ~3 and ~17 (x10^4 cm^2/Vsec) were obtained for x=0.5 and 0.75, which give mean free paths of 0.5 and 2 μm, respectively. Spin-orbit coupling constants α s of up to ~20 (x10^{-12} eVm) were obtained corresponding to the spin splitting of ~8 meV at Fermi energy. It is also confirmed that the α value likely increased with decreasing channel InGaAs layer thickness (d_c) probably due to the increase of the interface electric field strength. Contribution of the interface term enhanced in the x=0.75 case seems to be observed. In addition, there is almost no in-plane anisotropy for sheet electron density, n_s, mobility, μ_e, and α . These inverted HJs are thus enough to be utilized in spin transport experiments such as spin-injection, spin-Hall effect etc. toward spintronics device development

REFERENCES

1. Y. Sato, T. Kita, S. Gozu, S. Yamada, *J. Appl. Phys.* **89**, 8017 (2001).
2. Th. Schäpers, G. Engels, J. Lange, Th. Klocke, M. Hollfelder, and H. Lüth., *J. Appl. Phys.* **83**, 4324 (1998).
3. E. A. de Andarda e Silva, G. C. La Rocca, F. Bassani, *Phys. Rev. B* **50**, 8523 (1994).

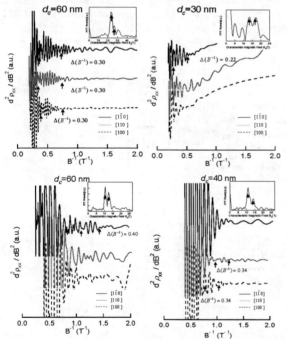

Figure 2. Magnetoresistance results of x=0.5 (upper panels) and 0.75 (lower) samples for the different d_c and current directions. The inset shows the fast Fourier transform (FFT) result for the [1-10] SdH oscillation.

CHAPTER 13

APPLICATIONS AND DEVICES

Strong Free Exciton Emission In An AlGaAs/GaAs HEMT Structure

Kazunori Aoki, Naozumi Sakamoto and Takayuki Tanigawa

Department of Electrical and Electronics Engineering, Faculty of Engineering, Kobe University, Rokkoda,,Nada, Kobe 657-8501, Japan

Abstract. Strong free exciton emission has been investigated in a AlGaAs/GaAs HEMT structure. As well as the significantly large emission line (e,A^0) at 830 nm, we have also observed very strong free exciton (FX) emission line at 818.3 nm of which intensity has been significantly large compared to the PL spectrum of the high purity n-GaAs. By the Arrhenius plot, the activation energy ΔE for the free exciton was obtained to be 7 meV. Removing the AlGaAs layer by the chemical etching, the fee exciton emission intensity was considerably reduced.

Keywords: strong free exciton cap emission, AlGaAs/GaAs HEMT structure, the Arrhenius plot.
PACS: 78.55.-m,78.55;Cr

INTRODUCTION

Normally, exciton emission in a high-purity GaAs is known to be composed of free exciton (FX) and exciton bound to the shallow impurities. It is quite typical that the FX emission intensity at 818.3 nm is not strong compared to the bound exciton emission intensity at 819 nm. In this paper, we investigate strong free exciton emission observed in the AlGaAs/GaAs HEMT structure[1-5], where the (D^0,X) emission line at 819 nm was observed by a shoulder only. The strong free exciton emission seems to come from AlGaAs/GaAs interface region which was confirmed by the depth-profile of the FX photoluminescence by the chemical etching.

EXPERIMENTAL PROCEDURE

Measurement was done by using a 4K-cryogenic refrigerator. The AlGaAs/GaAs structure is composed of the cap layer (5 nm), Si-doped AlGaAs layer (40 nm), nondoped AlGaAs layer (15 nm), nondoped GaAs layer (activation layer, 800 nm), and semi-insulating GaAs substrate (600 μm),respectively. The sample surface wasweakly excited using a 35 mW He-Ne laser beam which was spread over t he entire sample surface by a spatial filter. In order to remove the cap layer and the Si-doped AlGaAs layer, chem.-ical etching was made by Tartaric Acid: H_2O_2=5:1

and also using by H_2SO_4: H_2O_2=4:1.

EXPERIMENTAL RESULTS

Figure 1 shows the photoluminescence spectrum of the AlGaAs/GaAs HEMT structure which was compared to the spectrum of high-purity n-GaAs. Free exciton emission line at 818.3 nm was found to be significantly large when compared to the spectrum in the high-purity n- GaAs. Exciton bound to the

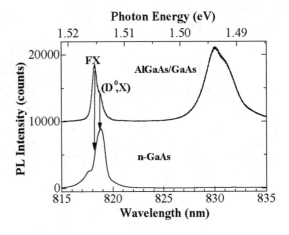

FIGURE 1. Photoluminescence spectrum in the AlGaAs/GaAs HEMT structure. As a reference, the spectrum in the high-purity n-GaAs is also shown.

CP893, *Physics of Semiconductors, 28th International Conference*
edited by W. Jantsch and F. Schäffler
© 2007 American Institute of Physics 978-0-7354-0397-0/07/$23.00

neutral donors (D^0,X) is shown as a shoulder. As well as the strong free exciton emission, we can find the large acceptor (and/ or donor-acceptor pair) emission line at 830 nm.

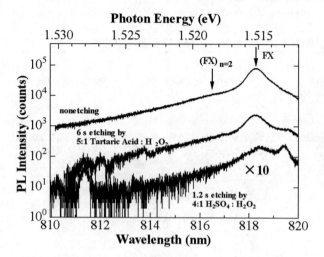

FIGURE 2. Photoluminescence spectra in the AlGaAs/GaAs HEMT structure. Chemical etching was done by Tartaric Acid:H_2O_2=5:1 and by H_2SO_4: H_2O_2=4:1.

In order to show that the FX line is actually due to the activation layer, the sample surface was removed by the chemical etching. By removing the modulation-doped AlGaAs layer, the two-dimensional electron gas in the activation layer disappears. Figure 2 shows the photoluminescence spectrum in the logarithmic scale, whereby the n=2 excited state of the free

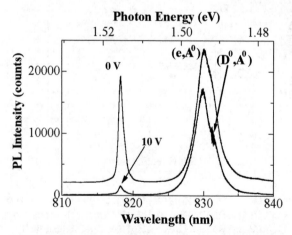

FIGURE 3. Free exciton emission spectrum of AlGaAs/ GaAs HEMT structure observed under the applied dc bias of 10V.

exciton can be seen. From the slope of the higher energy part of the spectrum, the effective exciton temperature T_x was estimated to be T_x=18 K. After the chemical etching by H_2SO_4:H_2O_2=4:1, the peak intensity of the free exciton emission was considerably decreased, while the (D^0,X) emission peak was clearly seen. From the result in Fig. 2, we confirm that the free excitons at 818.3 nm can be created partly by the two dimensional electron gas (as the majority carriers) and holes in the activation layer as well as by of the free electron (as the minority carriers) and free hole. By applying the dc bias, the free exciton emission intensity was largely decreased due to impact ionization avalanche, as shown in Figure 3,while the intensity of the (e,A^0) emission line decreased only by a small amount, where the (e,A^0) emission originates from the deeper part of the activation layer (800 nm). Under the dc bias, the effective exciton temperature increased monotonically by increasing the dc bias and was estimated to be T_x=37.0 K for 10 V.

CONCLUSION

. We have investigated the strong free exciton photoluminescence in the modulation-doped AlGaAs/ GaAs hetero-structure. By removing the modulation-doped AlGaAs layer, the emission intensity of the free exciton decreased significantly, from which we found that the free excitons are formed in the activation layer but only with the existence of the modulation-doped AlGaAs layer.

REFERENCES

1. G. Finkelstein, H. Shtrikman and I. Bar-Joseph, Phys. Rev. B53 , R1709 (1996).
2. D. C. Reynolds, D. C. Look, B. Jogai, P. W. Yu, K. Evans, C. E. Stutz and L. Rodomsky, Phys. Rev. **B50**, 7461 (1994).
3. J.X. Shen, Y. Oka, W. Ossau, G. Landwehr, K.J. Friedland, R. Hey, K. Ploog and G. Weimann,Solid State Commun. **106,** 495 (1998).
4. J.X. Shen, Y. Oka, C.Y. Hu, W. Ossau, G. Landwehr, K.J. Friedland, R. Hey, K. Ploog and G. Weimann,Phys. Rev. **B59**, 8093 (1999).
5. G. D. Gilliland, D. J. Wolford, T. F. Kuech and J. A. Bradley, Phys. Rev. **B49**, 8113 (1994).

Electron Mobility and Concentration on Submicrometer Scale – Investigation of Si and AlGaN/GaN Field Effect Transistors by AC Magnetoresistance Method

M. Sakowicz[1], J. Łusakowski[1], K. Karpierz[1], M. Grynberg[1], B. Majkusiak[2],
R. Tauk[3], A. Tiberj[3], W. Knap[3], Z. Bougrioua[4], M. Azize[4], P. Lorenzini[4],
F. Boeuf[5], and T. Skotnicki[5]

[1]IEP, Warsaw University, Hoża 69, 00-681 Warsaw, Poland
[2]IMO, University of Technology, Nowowiejska 15/19, 00-661 Warsaw, Poland
[3]GES CNRS - UMR 5650 Universite Motnpellier 2, Pl. E. Bataillon, 34950 Montpellier, France
[4]CRHEA-CNRS, B. Gregory, 06560 Valbonne, France
[5]ST Microelectronics, BP 16, 38921 Crolles, France

Abstract. Alternative current magnetoresistance (AC MR) method was applied to Si MOSFETs and AlGaN/GaN HEMTs at 4.2 K and 300 K. We show that the AC MR method allows to locally determine the quantum and transport relaxation times under the gate of micrometer and submicometer transistors.

Keywords: Field effect transistors, magnetoresistance, mobility
PACS: 73.40.Qt, 73.49.Qv

INTRODUCTION

Recently a direct current magnetoresistance method (DC MR) was applied to determine the mobility in nanometer Si metal-oxide-semiconductor field-effect transistors (MOSFETs) at 300 K [1]. To apply this method, one requires no knowledge of the electron concentration, threshold voltage or channel length. A disadvantage of the DC MR method is that it does not automatically take into account the series resistance (the source and drain resistance in the case of MOSFETs, and the source, drain and access resistance in the case of high electron mobility transistors – HEMTs). That is why, the measured resistance must be corrected by subtracting the series resistance which is difficult to determine. To avoid this problem, we propose an alternating current version of the MR method (AC MR method) in which one slightly modulates the gate potential and measures the AC component of the drain-source voltage while sweeping the magnetic field [2] at small constant drain-source current.

The first purpose of the present paper is to show the universality of the AC MR method by applying it to both MOSFETs and HEMTs of significantly different electron mobility. The second purpose is to show that by application of the AC MR method one can *locally*, (on the scale of the gate length) investigate the electron concentration and transport/quantum scattering times.

AC MR METHOD

Due to the $L << W$ condition (L and W are the device length and width, respectively), the transistor resistance in the magnetic field (B) is equal to $R = R_{SD0}(1 + \mu_{SD}^2 B^2) + R_{A0}(1 + \mu_A^2 B^2) + R_{C0}(1 + \mu_C^2 B^2)$. Subsequent terms describe the magnetoresistance of the source and drain, the access part and the gated part, respectively, with the corresponding magneto-resistance mobility denoted by μ_{SD}, μ_A, and μ_C. The subscript zero denotes the resistance at $B = 0$. The above formula is valid for $\mu^2 B^2 << 1$. To eliminate a non zero series resistance, one applies the AC MR technique to measure the derivative of the transistor resistance (with respect to the gate polarization, U_G) as a function of B. The measured signal is then proportional to $R' = R_{C0}' + (R_{C0}\mu_C^2)' B^2$, because R_A and R_{SD} are not effected by U_G. Tracing the experimental

CP893, *Physics of Semiconductors, 28th International Conference*
edited by W. Jantsch and F. Schäffler
© 2007 American Institute of Physics 978-0-7354-0397-0/07/$23.00

signal as a function of B^2 gives the coefficients $\alpha_A = R_{C0}'$ and $\beta_A = (R_{C0}\mu_C^2)'$, which allow to calculate the quantity p defined as:

$$p = \beta_A/\alpha_A = \mu_C^2(1-2(\mu_C'/\mu_C)/(\mu_C'/\mu_C + n'/n)), \qquad (1)$$

where n is the electron concentration in the gated part of the channel. The mobility in the gated part is determined by fitting Eq. 1 to experimentally determined $p(U_G)$ dependence, with $\mu(U_G)$ assumed to be approximated by a third order polynomial [2]. For $n \sim (U_G - U_{TH})$, $n'/n = (U_G - U_{TH})^{-1}$ and U_{TH} (the threshold voltage) can be determined form a transfer characteristics.

EXPERIMENT, RESULTS AND DISCUSSION

Three transistors were investigated: T1 - a sub-micrometer MOSFET ($L = 0.14$ μm) at 300 K; T2 - a micrometer MOSFET ($L = 10$ μm) at 4.2 K; T3 - a micrometer AlGaN/GaN HEMT ($L = 4$ μm) at 4.2 K. The transistors were placed in a variable temperature insert which was put into a 10 T superconducting magnet. They were connected to a current source; the gate potential was modulated. The AC component of the signal was measured with a lock-in technique. A parabola was fitted to the experimental data, and p (Eq. 1) was determined as a function of U_G. The square root of $p(U_G)$ dependence for the three transistors investigated is shown in Fig. 1. Then Eq. 1 was fitted to the $p(U_G)$ dependence to obtain $\mu_C(U_G)$ curves shown in Fig. 2.

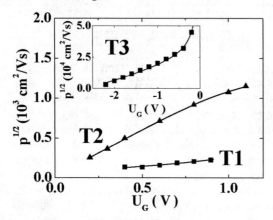

FIGURE 1. $p^{1/2}$ for T1 at 300 K (squares) and T2 at 4.2 K (triangles). Inset: $p^{1/2}$ for T3 at 4.2 K. Solid lines are fits of Eq. 1 to experimental data.

For T2 and T3 transistors we observed Shoubnikov-de Haas oscillations at large B that enabled to determine both the electron concentration and the quantum scattering time, τ_q. In determination

of those quantities we took into account that we are measuring derivative of resistance with respect to gate voltage. The transport scattering time, τ, was calculated from μ_C. This allows to determine τ/τ_q as a function of n. An example of such procedure for T2 transistor are shown in Fig. 3.

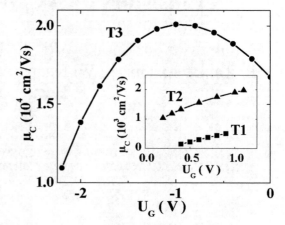

FIGURE 2. Electron channel mobility as a function of the gate voltage for T3 (at 4.2 K; main body of the figure) and T1 (at 300 K) and T2 (at 4.2 K) transistors (inset). Note different vertical scales of the main figure and the inset.

The method proposed thus allows to investigate scattering mechanism on micrometer and submicrometer scale both in MOSFETs and in HEMTs.

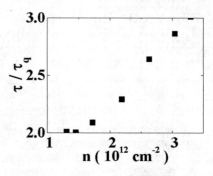

FIGURE 3. Ratio of transport to quantum relaxation time for T2 transistor at 4.2 K.

ACKNOWLEDGMENTS

This work was partially supported by a Polish Ministry of Scientific Research and Information Technology grant 3T11B04528.

REFERENCES

1. Y. M. Meziani *et al.*, *J. Appl. Phys.* **96**, 5761 (2004).
2. M. Sakowicz *et al.*, *J. Appl. Phys.*, accepted.

DRAM storage time of milliseconds demonstrated in self-organized quantum dots

A. Marent*, M. Geller*, A. P. Vasi'ev†, E. S. Semenova†, A. E. Zhukov†,
V. M. Ustinov† and D. Bimberg*

*Institut für Festkörperphysik, Technische Universität Berlin, Hardenbergstrasse 36, 10623 Berlin, Germany
†A. F. Ioffe Physico-Technical Institute, Russian Acadamy of Sciences, 26 Polytekhnicheskaya, St. Petersburg 194021, Russian Federation

Abstract.
Thermally activated hole emission from differently charged InAs/GaAs quantum dots (QDs) was investigated by using deep level transient spectroscopy. In samples with an additional AlGaAs barrier below the QD layer, we obtain a thermal activation energy of 560 meV for hole emission from the QD ground states over the AlGaAs barrier. This large activation energy leads to a hole storage time at room temperature of about 5 ms, which is a typical DRAM refresh time.

Keywords: quantum dots, DLTS, capacitance spectroscopy, memory
PACS: 73.21.La, 73.63.Kv

Self-organized quantum dots (QDs) [1] are promising building blocks for future non-volatile single-carrier memories. The first decisive milestone towards the realization of QD-based memories is a carrier retention time in the order of milliseconds at room temperature, the typical refresh time of a dynamic random access memory (DRAM). Previously investigated GaSb/GaAs QDs showed a hole storage time in the order of microseconds at room temperature [2]. Here, we investigate InAs QD-based structures with an additional AlGaAs barrier by useing charge-selective deep level transient spectroscopy (charge-selective DLTS). The additional AlGaAs barrier increases the activation energies sufficiently to reach the crucial storage time of milliseconds at 300 K.

Two different samples were investigated (see insets in Fig. 1). Both are n^+p diode structures ($n = 2 \times 10^{18}\,cm^{-3}$, $p = 2 \times 10^{18}\,cm^{-3}$) with a layer of InAs QDs, grown by molecular beam epitaxy (MBE). In the first sample, referred to as "Sample A", we include an additional nominally undoped $Al_{0.6}Ga_{0.4}As$ barrier of 20 nm thickness below the QD layer. The second sample, referred to as "Sample B", has an identical layer structure *without* the AlGaAs barrier (for details see [3]).

Figure 1 compares charge-selective DLTS spectra from both samples. The pulse bias height was fixed to 0.2 V for all spectra (i.e. $V_p = V_r + 0.2$ V) to observe on average the emission of less than one hole per QD. Therefore, instead of detecting simultaneously the emission from all QD states, as in usual DLTS, we observe the emission from differently charged QDs, i.e. different energy levels by changing the reverse bias [2]. Figure 1(a) shows the DLTS spectra for sample A. For reverse bias of $V_r = -3.2$ V the Fermi level reaches the QD ground state and

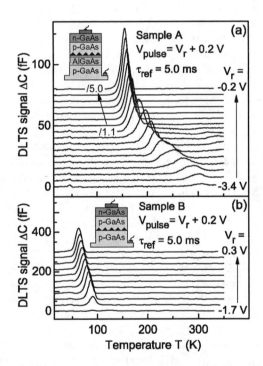

FIGURE 1. Charge-selective DLTS spectra of thermally activated hole emission from InAs QDs. Panel (a): sample A (with an AlGaAs barrier); Panel (b): sample B (without an AlGaAs barrier). The spectra are vertically shifted for clarity. Insets show sketches of the sample structures.

a peak in the DLTS spectrum appears at 300 K. This peak is related to thermally activated hole emission from the QD ground states over the AlGaAs barrier [inset in the upper left corner of Fig. 2(a)]. A further decrease of

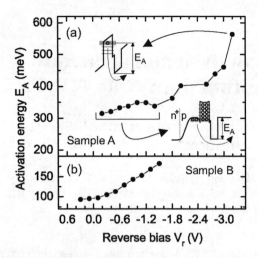

FIGURE 2. Dependence of the thermal activation energy on the reverse bias V_r for sample A [panel (a)] and sample B [panel (b)].

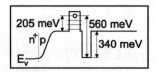

FIGURE 3. Energy diagram for the valence band of sample A as a result of the measured activation energies.

the reverse bias leads to QD state-filling and successive emission from higher QD states is observed. A peak in the DLTS appears at that temperature, where the average time constant of the thermally activated emission equals the applied reference time constant τ_{ref}. Therefore, the peak at 300 K ($V_r = -3.2$ V) for $\tau_{ref} = 5$ ms represents an average emission time constant (storage time) of 5 ms for hole emission from the QD ground states over the AlGaAs barrier.

For sample B Fig. 1(b) shows a pronounced DLTS peak at 90 K for the same reference time constant of 5 ms ($V_r = -1.5$ V), which again represents hole escape from the QD ground states. The carrier storage time at room temperature for InAs QDs without an AlGaAs barrier can be obtained by extrapolating the emission rate (see Eq. below) and is in the order of nanoseconds, in good agreement with previous experiments [2].

The thermal emission rate can be written as $e_{th} = \gamma T^2 \sigma_\infty \exp(-E_A/kT)$ [4]. From Arrhenius plots of the DLTS peak position for varying reference time constants τ_{ref} we obtain thermal activation energies for hole emission from differently charged QDs.

The thermal activation energies for sample A [panel (a)] and sample B [panel (b)] are shown in Fig. 2. The highest value for sample A of (560 ± 60) meV at $V_r = -3.2$ V is related to thermal activation from QD hole ground states over the AlGaAs barrier. With decreasing reverse bias a decrease in the activation energy is observed, due to QD state-filling. Between $V_r = -1.4$ V and $V_r = -0.2$ V we probe carrier emission from the valence band edge and the activation energy remains roughly constant with a mean value of 340 meV. This energy represents the AlGaAs barrier height [inset in the lower right corner of Fig. 2(a)]. The highest value for sample B of (180 ± 10)

meV is again related to thermal activation from QD hole ground states. At $V_r = -0.1$ V the QDs are completely filled and between $V_r = -0.1$ V and $V_r = 0.3$ V the mean value of 95 meV represents the Coulomb barrier height for completely charged QDs [2].

We can now combine the experimental results from both samples to obtain a consistent picture of the energy diagram for the valence band of sample A [Fig. 3]. We have to take into account, that the underlying emission process in DLTS experiments is phonon-assisted tunneling [5]. To obtain the ground state localization energy, we have to add the barrier height for tunneling through the triangular barrier, which can be estimated by comparison of the tunneling emission rate (Vincent et al. [6]) and the thermal emission rate for a given barrier height. We obtain a tunneling barrier height of about 25 meV. Hence, the entire ground state hole localization energy of the QD is 205 meV.

In conclusion, we have studied hole emission from InAs/GaAs QDs with and without an additional $Al_{0.6}Ga_{0.4}As$ barrier using charge-selective DLTS. The activation energy for the QD ground states increases from 205 meV up to 560 meV, due to the additional AlGaAs barrier. Accordingly, the hole storage time at room temperature reaches the important DRAM refresh time in the millisecond range.

The work was partly funded by the SANDiE Network of Excellence of the European Commission, contract number NMP4-CT-2004-500101 and SFB296 of DFG.

REFERENCES

1. D. Bimberg, M. Grundmann, and N. N. Ledentsov, *Quantum Dot Heterostructures*, John Wiley & Sons, Chichester, 1998.
2. M. Geller, C. Kapteyn, L. Müller-Kirsch, R. Heitz, and D. Bimberg, *Appl. Phys. Lett.* **82**, 2706–2708 (2003).
3. A. Marent, M. Geller, A. P. Vasiev, E. S. Semenova, A. E. Zhukov, V. M. Ustinov, and D. Bimberg, *submitted to Appl. Phys. Lett.* (2006).
4. D. V. Lang, *J. Appl. Phys.* **45**, 3023 (1974).
5. W. H. Chang, W. Y. Chen, T. M. Hsu, N. T. Yeh, and J. I. Chyi, *Phys. Rev. B* **66**, 195337 (2002).
6. G. Vincent, A. Chantre, and D. Bois, *J. Appl. Phys.* **50**, 5484 (1979).

Improved Geometric Control of the High-Field Linear Magnetoresistance by Metallic Bridges in InSb Arrays

S.K. Clowes[1], W.R. Branford[1,2], A.M. Gilbertson[1,3], T. Zhang[1], L. Buckle[3], A. Husmann[4], S.A. Solin[5], and L.F. Cohen[1]

[1]Blackett Laboratory, Imperial College, Prince Consort Rd., London, SW7 2BZ, United Kingdom
[2]Department of Chemistry, UCL, Gordon St., London WC1H OAJ, United Kingdom
[3]QinetiQ Ltd, Malvern Technology Centre, St. Andrews Rd., Malvern, WR14 3PS, United Kingdom
[4] Toshiba Research Europe Ltd, 260 Cambridge Science Park, Cambridge, United Kingdom
[5]Department of Physics and Centre for Materials Innovation, Washington University in St. Louis, 1 Brookings Drive, St Louis, Missouri 6314, U.S.A

Abstract. Gecmetric manipulation of the magnetoresistance of InSb remains topical. Here we aim to investigate the magnetoresistance properties of disc arrays contacted by gold bridges. In order for the gold bridges to significantly alter the magnetoresistance properties issues such as side wall contacting and low metal to semiconductor contact resistance have to be addressed. We demonstrate in this work that array structures with gold bridges have modest impact on the high-field response of InSb compared to unprocessed wafer material.

Keywords: InSb, linear magnetoresistance, geometric manipulation.
PACS: Replace 72.15.Gd, 72.20.Ht, 75.47.-m.

INTRODUCTION

The linear magnetoresistance (MR) of high mobility semiconductors, such as InSb[1] and PbTe[2] has long been known and thin epilayers of these materials have been exploited[3] for use in high-field sensors. A classical transport model of a uniform system cannot explain the non-saturating linearity of the resistance in field and various mechanisms have been suggested. Broadly, the proposed models can be divided into three categories; (1) Sample inhomogeneities[4,5] (2) geometric boundary effects[6] and (3) quantum effects[7,8]. Using a geometric model, Parish and Littlewood (PL) recently predicted[4] that the MR of an ($N \times M$) square array of interconnected conducting regions in an insulating matrix would become linear and non-saturating as the array becomes large ($N, M \geq 10$). This is promising for high magnetic field sensor applications.

We have recently reported the use of lithographic techniques to fabricate disk arrays from high mobility InSb thin films and compared the observed MR of these structures to the PL predictions[9]. We demonstrated that the array structures exhibited an MR with increased linearity. However we did not observe either sublinearity for odd arrays or a boost in the MR

over the van der Pauw geometry, as predicted by the PL model. Our previous attempt to physically reproduce the PL model consisted of an array of circles joined by interconnects, all made from InSb. The length to width ratio of the interconnects was designed to be approximately 1:1. However the actual connections were thinned by undercutting during patterning of the mesa using a nitric:lactic acid wet etch. As a consequence the bridges contributed at least half of the total measured resistance of the array and exhibited similar MR behavior as the as-grown unprocessed material. These features necessarily masked any underlying properties associated with the predicted geometric manipulation. In this paper we report on the preliminary results from an improved array design where the InSb bridges have been replaced with gold bridges.

EXPERIMENTAL

The array structures were fabricated from 1μm thick un-doped InSb epilayers on GaAs (001) using optical lithography (Fig. 1a). The arrays consist of 100μm diameter circles, connected nominally by 6μm wide and 5μm long InSb bridges. They were reactive ion etched (RIE) using a CH_4H_2 (90:10) chemistry to

CP893, *Physics of Semiconductors, 28th International Conference*
edited by W. Jantsch and F. Schäffler
© 2007 American Institute of Physics 978-0-7354-0397-0/07/$23.00

improve sidewall geometry. This was followed by a second lithographic step using a bi-level resist (to improve lift-off) in which the bridges and ohmic contacts were developed. A micrograph of the patterned resist is shown in the inset of Fig 1b. Another RIE step was used to etch away the InSb, which was followed by metallization using the same resist stage. Cr:Au contacts were evaporated using a rotating sample stage which was tilted by 30° to allow side wall contacting to the mesa. A scanning electron microscope image of a 12μm by 6 μm gold bridge in shown in Fig 1b.

The MR measurements were performed at room temperature using previously reported methods[9].

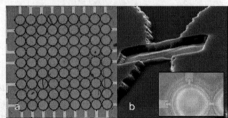

FIGURE 1. (a) Micrograph of InSb connected 9x9 array. (b) Scanning electron microscope image of gold bridges connecting array circles (inset) Micrograph of developed photoresist of bridges and Ohmics for RIE and metalization.

RESULTS

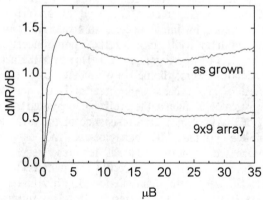

FIGURE 2. d(MR)/dB against μB for 9x9 array and the unprocessed wafer. The mobility of the of the InSb epilayer was μ=5.0 m²/Vs.

To demonstrate the efficacy of the gold bridges we have plotted in Fig 2 the slope of the MR as a function of field (d($\Delta R/R_0$)/dB) against μB. The curves were calculated by taking the first derivative of a seven-point, second order polynomial. At high-fields (>15μB) the transverse MR of the gold bridged arrays becomes virtually linear. In our previous work[9] we quantified the degree of linearity by fitting the high-field MR to $\Delta R/R_0 = \alpha|\mu B| + \beta(\mu B)^2$. We have applied this fitting analysis to modified gold bridged arrays

which gives a zero value quadratic term within experimental error. See Table 1 for the values of α and β.

TABLE 1. Linear(α) and quadratic(β) fitting parameters to high-field MR, including sheet resistance.

Array	R(Ω)	α	β
unprocessed	58	0.192	0.0008(2)
9x9 with Au bridges	388	0.095	0.0002(1)
10x10 with Au bridges	435	0.086	0.0001(1)

CONCLUSION

The modified array design with side-walled contacted gold connects has produced a structure that has an increased linearity in the high-field MR, over that of unprocessed material. Our new bridge design improves the high field linearity. However, full exploration of the geometric effects can only take place using InSb with a wafer designed to minimize the inherent MR[10]

ACKNOWLEDGMENTS

The work was funded by UK-EPSRC GR/R4202. WRB is supported by the Ramsay Memorial Fellowships Trust. SAS is supported by NSF grant ECS- 0329347 (US) and by NIH under grant 1U54CA11934201 (US).

REFERENCES

1. W. Schneider, H. Bruhns, and K. Hubner, Journal of Physics and Chemistry of Solids **41**, 313-321 (1980).
2. R. S. Allgaier, J. B. Restorff, and B. Houston, Journal of Applied Physics **53**, 3110-3116 (1982).
3. H. Weiss, *Structure and Applications of Galvanomagnetic Devices* (Pergamon, New York, 1969).
4. M. M. Parish and P. B. Littlewood, Nature **426**, 162-165 (2003).
5. C. Herring, Journal of Applied Physics **31**, 1939 (1960).
6. R. S. Allgaier, Journal of Applied Physics **59**, 1388-1390 (1986).
7. V. K. Arora and M. Jaafarian, Physical Review B **13**, 4457-4461 (1976).
8. A. A. Abrikosov, Europhysics Letters **49**, 789-793 (2000).
9. W. R. Branford, A. Husmann, S. A. Solin, S. K. Clowes, T. Zhang, Y. V. Bugoslavsky, and L. F. Cohen, Applied Physics Letters **86**, 202116 (2005).
10. T. Zhang, J. J. Harris, W. R. Branford, Y. V. Bugoslavsky, S. K. Clowes, L. F. Cohen, A. Husmann, and S. A. Solin, Applied Physics Letters **88**, 012110 (2006).

Characteristics of nano floating gate memory with Au nano-particles and SiON dielectrics

Min Seung Lee[1], Dong Uk Lee[1], Jae-Hoon Kim[1], Eun Kyu Kim[1], Won Mok Kim[2], and Won Ju Cho[3]

[1]Quantum-Function Spinics Lab. and Department of Physics, Hanyang University, Seoul 133-791, Korea
[2]Thin Film Materials Research Center, Korea Institute of Science and Technology, Seoul 130-650, Korea
[3]Semiconductor Nano-Electron Device & Process Lab. Department of Electronic Materials Engineer, Kwangwoon University, Seoul 139-701, Korea

Abstract. We fabricated the floating gated non-volatile memory devices with Au nano-particles embedded in $SiO_{1.3}N_1$ and SiO_2 dielectrics. The floating gate memory devices as a type of field effect transistor (FET) with the Au particle layer were fabricated with the thicknesses of tunneling barrier of 3 and 5 nm, control insulators of 45 nm by SiO_2 and $SiO_{1.3}N_1$ layers, respectively. Au thin films were deposited by using sputtering method and then, the size of Au nano-particles in the range of 1-5 nm could be controlled with nominal Au film thickness. The devices show current shift which due to programming and erasing works perform by a gate bias stress repeatedly.

INTRODUCTION

The nano-floating gate memory (NFGM) is an attractive candidate for the next generation memory devices, because the structure of NFGM is quite similar to the flash memory devices. Moreover they are promising candidates for low operating voltage, long retention time and fast programming/erasing speed. The reason is that possible at smaller injection tunneling oxide thickness. Specially, The NFGM structure is designed to use work function difference of metal nano-particles. Then by engineering the metal nano-particles work function, the oxide barrier height can be adjusted by about 2 eV, giving much freedom for NFGM optimization. [1-5]

EXPERIMENT

The NFGM devices with Au nano-particles were fabricated on the p-type (100) UNIBOND SOI wafers with a 100 nm top Si layer and a 200 nm buried oxide layer. Silicon active region was produced by photolithography and silicon etching with plasma reactive ion etching process. After a corner rounding of mesa-isolated silicon actives by wet etching of silicon to suppress the degradation of gate dielectrics, the 5 nm thick $SiO_{1.3}N_1$ layer as a tunneling insulator was deposited on the silicon channel. Also 3 nm thick SiO_2 layer as tunneling insulator was grown on the

silicon channel by using thermal oxidation method at 950 °C in pure oxygen ambient. In case of mesa-isolated SOI MOSFET devices the top corner shape of channel is important on the reliability, because the sharp corner leads to the local oxide thinning effect. Thus the oxide breakdown due to the crowding effect of electrical field could take place at the sharp corner. Moreover, a hump of subthreshold characteristics is appeared in drain current-gate voltage curves, because the parasitic transistor with lower threshold voltage is built at the sharp top corner. The deposition of 1 nm thick Au thin film as metal nano-particles, thickness of 45 nm $SiO_{1.3}N_1$ and SiO_2 layer as a control oxide was followed by sequential sputtering. $SiO_{1.3}N_1$ layers were deposited in reactive mode under Ar and N_2 mixture gas. The Au nano-particles were annealed at 800 °C for 10s to remove the surface defects because the surface defects play a role of charging sites between $SiO_{1.3}N_1$, SiO_2 insulator and Au nano-particles. Then, the aluminum layer with thickness of 200 nm was deposited on the $SiO_{1.3}N_1$ and SiO_2 control gate dielectric by thermal evaporation and the gate electrode was formed by lithography and aluminum etching with wet solution. Finally, the phosphorus plasma doping at elevated temperature was carried out for source-drain doping of NFGM devices. [6]

CP893, *Physics of Semiconductors, 28th International Conference*
edited by W. Jantsch and F. Schäffler

RESULT AND DISCUSSION

Figure 1 shows the schematic diagram of fabricated NFGM device structure. The length of gate electrode was in the range 2 to 20 μm and the density of nano-particles was estimated about 2×10^{12} cm^{-2}.

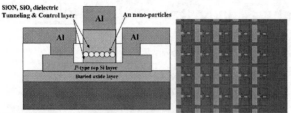

FIGURE 1. A schematic diagram of NFGM device structure with Au nano-particles

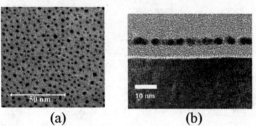

| (a) | (b) |

FIGURE 2. TEM images of plane view (a) and cross section view (b) the Au nano-particles embedded in SiO$_{1.3}$N$_1$ layer.

Figure 2 show the plane view (a) and cross-section view transmission electron microscopy (TEM) images of Au nano-particles embedded in SiO$_{1.3}$N$_1$ layer. The corresponding average of Au nano-particles was about 3 nm and the density of nano-particles was estimated about 2×10^{12} cm^{-2} from the plane view TEM analysis

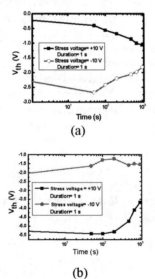

FIGURE 3. Retention characteristics of Au nano-particles NFGM with embedded in SiO$_{1.3}$N$_1$ insulator (a) and SiO$_2$ insulator (b)

Figure 3 (a) shows the retention time of NFGM with Au nano-particles embedded in SiO$_{1.3}$N$_1$ insulator and Figure 3 (b) SiO$_2$ insulator. Figure 3 (a) shows the threshold voltage shift between the writing (+10 V) and the erasing (-10 V) states was about 2.5 V. The memory window was decreased rapidly as time elapse. The reason of the degradation is considered to be a leakage current through SiO$_{1.3}$N$_1$ tunneling barrier, because there are many pinholes and weak spots in the SiO$_{1.3}$N$_1$ tunneling oxide deposited by sputtering. Figure 3 (b) shows the threshold voltage shift that is about 3.5 V. In this case, the memory window and retention time were improved then Figure 3 (a). The reason is that tunneling barrier was fabricated by thermal oxidation and thickness of 3 nm. The writing (+10 V) state was decreased as time elapse. A weak leakage current through control insulator composed by SiO$_2$ may be caused to the retention degradation.

In Summary, The NFGM devices were fabricated with Au nano-particles embedded in SiO$_{1.3}$N$_1$ and SiO$_2$ insulator. The memory windows due to the threshold voltage shift were about 2.5 V and 3.5 V, respectively. From these results, we expect that the Au nano-particles take advantage of apply highly integrated non-volatile memory device. Further improvement of the charge retention efficiency is expected by optimizing the quality of the oxide layers.

ACKNOWLEDGMENTS

This work was supported in part by the National Program for 0.1-Terabit Non Volatile Memory Device, the National Research Laboratory Program and the 2nd stage BK21 Program at Hanyang University. WMK acknowledges to the 'Center of Nanostructured Materials Technology' under '21st Century Frontier R&D Programs' of MOST, Korea.

REFERENCES

1. S. Tiwari, F. Rana, H. Hanafi, A. Harstein, E. Crabbé and K. Chan, *Appl. Phys. Letters* **68**, 1377-1379 (1996)
2. Z. T. Liu, C. Lee, V. Narayanan, G. Pei, and E. C. Kan, *IEEE Trans. Electron Devices* **49**, 1606-1613 (2002)
3. D.-W. Kim, T. Kim, and S. K. Banerjee, *IEEE Trans. Electron Devices* **50**, 1823-1829 (2003)
4. A. Chandra and B. M. Clemens, *Appl. Phys. Letters.* **87**, 253113-253113-3(2005)
5. J.-H. Kim, E. K. Kim, C. H. Lee, M. S. Song, Y.-H. Kim and J. Kim, *Physica E* **26**, 432-435 (2005)
6. W.-J. Cho, C.-G. Ahn, K. Im, J.-H. Yang, J. Oh, I.-B. Baek, and S. Lee, *IEEE Electron Devices Letters,* **25,** 366-368 (2004)

Thermoelectric Properties Of And Device Physics Based On InSb Semiconductors

J.Yamazaki[*1], J.Katsumata[1], N.Kaiwa[1], S.Yamaguchi[1, 2] and A.Yamamoto[3]

[1]Department of Electrical, Electronic and Information Engineering, Kanagawa University
3-27-1 Rokkakubashi, Kanagawa-ku, Yokohama 221-8686, Japan
[2]High-tech Research Center, Kanagawa University
3-27-1 Rokkakubashi, Kanagawa-ku, Yokohama 221-8686, Japan
[3]Energy Technology Research Institute, National Institute of Advanced Industrial Science and Technology, AIST
Tsukuba Central 2, 1-1-1 Umezono, Tsukuba 305-8568, Japan
[e-mail]r200570104@kanagawa-u.ac.jp

Abstract. The thermoelectric properties of InSb were studied. A miniaturized InSb-based thermoelectric device was designed and fabricated. Maximum of output voltage and output power were 6.1mV and 2μ W, respectively , at Δ T=100K.

Keywords: InSb, thermoelectric
PACS: 71.20.Nr

INTRODUCTION

In terms of the development of a new thermoelectric material, we have studied the thermoelectric properties of InSb and InAs semiconductors and fabricated miniaturized devices using them from a viewpoint of energy and environmental problems and of application for wearable devices using body heat. Particularly for InSb, the mobility of electron in a single crystal (78000cm^2/Vs at RT) is the highest among III-V of semiconductors, and this feature plays an important role when the responsivity to external current is required. Thermoelectric conversion can directly change heat energy into electric energy, and does not need movable parts and not produce radiation such as radioactive material.

EXPERIMENT

First, we calculated the thermoelectric properties of InSb as a function of temperature(T) from 10 to 700K and carrier concentrations from 10^{14} to 10^{20}cm^3, including such scatterings as ionized and neutral impurities, deformation potential acoustic phonons, piezoelectric phonons, and optical phonons. It was found that above room temperature optical phonons and neutral impurities are main causes for the scattering.

Based on the above results, we designed and fabricated a miniaturized InSb-based TE device with the size of 2mm×2mm×0.45mm(thickness)[1,2]. A temperature difference (Δ T) was applied to the device, and current dependences of output voltage (V_o) and output power (P_o) as a parameter of Δ T for the device were studied.

Result and Discussion

The maximum power factor (P_f) was estimated to be 9.9×10^3 W/mK^2 when Seebeck coefficient (α) and resistivity (ρ) were -1.3×10^4V/K and 1.7×10^6.m at 700K, respectively. P_f is derived from $P_f = \alpha^2/\rho$ and a value of $P_f = 10^3$W/mK^2 is an important criterion for practical use. Then we examined the properties of samples and found that a maximum P_f was 6.3×10^3W/mK^2 using α$=-1.9 \times 10^4$V/K and ρ$=5.5 \times 10^6$ Ω m, respectively. The maximum P_f was obtained when carrier concentration was in the mid of 10^{15}cm^3, which is nearly under degenerate condition. Moreover, thermal conductivity (κ) of InSb was measured using laser flush method and it was about 13W/mK at RT and decreased according to $T^{-0.66}$.

CP893, *Physics of Semiconductors, 28th International Conference*
edited by W. Jantsch and F. Schäffler
© 2007 American Institute of Physics 978-0-7354-0397-0/07/$23.00

Based on the above results, we fabricated a miniaturized InSb-based thermoelectric device.

Figure 1 shows current dependence of V_0 and P_0 as a parameter of Δ T of n-InSb and p-InAs 1-pair device. Maxima of V_0 and P_0 were 6.1mV and 2 μ W, respectively, at Δ T =100K. These values were much different from the designated values (106mV and 230 μ W). This discrepancy is due to the existence of large contact electrical resistance (R_e) and contact thermal resistance (R_t). The two kinds of resistances cause Δ T and P_0 to decrease according to the following expressions, where ΔT_{eff} is effective Δ T, L is device height, A is device area, ρ_c is contact resistance.

$$\Delta T_{eff} = \frac{\Delta T}{1 + 4R_t(\kappa / L)}$$

$$P = \frac{(\alpha \Delta T_{eff})^2}{4} \cdot \frac{A}{\rho_B L + 4\rho_c}$$

For this device ΔT_{eff} was as small as 5.7K at Δ T=100K. Using this value, R_t was estimated to be 8.63 ×10^{-3}m^{2}K/W.

Figure 2 shows ΔT_{eff} as a function of L. On the other hand, R_e was estimated to be 4.58×10^{-6} Ωm^2 using TLM method. That value is relatively high for a practical device. Using these values, the optimized device thickness was calculated to be 70mm. Such optimization occurs because of the fact that P_0 reaches a maximum at an appropriate device height in terms of κ. We found that if the contact resistances are reduced by a factor of 10, the energy coefficient of the device increases similarly, and the device size decreases to be several mm.

CONCLUSION

We studied the thermoelectric properties of InSb, and designed and fabricated a miniaturized InSb-based thermoelectric device. Maxima of output voltage and output power were 6.1mV and 2μ W, respectively at Δ T=100K.

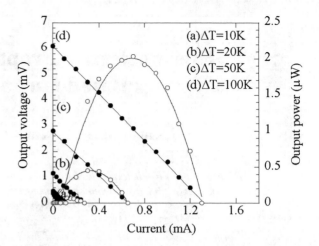

FIGURE 1. Current dependence of output voltage and output power as a parameter of temperature difference of InSb-InAs 1-pair device.

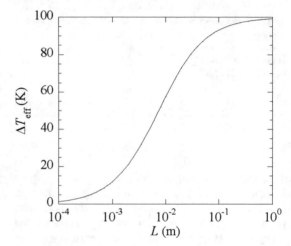

FIGURE 2. ΔT_{eff} as a function of L. of InSb-InAs 1-pair device.

ACKNOWLEDGMENTS

This study was partly supported by High-Tech Research Center Project from the Ministry of Education, Culture, Sports, Science and Technology , Japan.

REFERENCES

[1] S. Yamaguchi, T. Matsumoto, J. Yamazaki, N. Kaiwa, and A. Yamamoto, Appl. Phys. Lett., 87, 201902 (2005).

[2] S. Yamaguchi, Y. Nagawa, N. Kaiwa, and A. Yamamoto, Appl. Phys. Lett., 86, 153504 (2005).

Low-Field Mobility in Strained Silicon Inversion Layers and UTB MOSFETs for Different Substrate Orientations

E. Ungersboeck, V. Sverdlov, H. Kosina, and S. Selberherr

Institute for Microelectronics, TU Wien, Gußhausstraße 27–29/E360, 1040 Wien, Austria
{ungersboeck\sverdlov\kosina\selberherr}@iue.tuwien.ac.at

Abstract. To continue improvement of CMOS device performance process induced uniaxial stress is widely adopted in logic technologies starting from the 90 nm technology generation. In this work we model stress induced electron mobility enhancement in ultra thin body (UTB) MOSFETs for (001) and (110) substrate orientation using the Monte Carlo method. Uniaxial stress effects on the band structure are incorporated by adapting the non-local empirical pseudopotential method including spin-orbit interaction for arbitrary strain conditions. Stress induced change of the electron effective mass is found to be very important to explain mobility enhancement in UTB MOSFETs. Simulation results of electron mobility are in good agreement to recent experimental data.

Keywords: Monte Carlo method, uniaxial strain/stress, low-field mobility
PACS: 71.70.Fk, 72.20.Fr,72.10.-d

SIMULATION METHOD

Theoretical modeling of strain induced mobility enhancement for electrons and holes is an important issue with some critical questions still open [1, 2]. For this reason a simplified approach based on the empirically measured piezoresistance coefficients is often used by industry to predict mobility enhancement for electrons and holes.

In this work we analyze electron mobility enhancement by solving the Boltzmann equation using a MC method. The band structure of Si was calculated using the non-local empirical pseudopotential method (EPM) including spin-orbit coupling [3]. The effective masses were extracted from the curvature of the conduction bands at the minima along various directions and have been incorporated in the transport calculations. When the strain tensor in the crystal system contains off-diagonal components, a pronounced electron effective mass change is observed. Under $\langle 110 \rangle$ stress the constant energy surfaces of the two-fold degenerate Δ_2-valleys take the form of scalene ellipsoids $(m_l, m_{t,||}, m_{t,\perp})$, where $m_{t,||}$ and $m_{t,\perp}$ denote the transverse mass parallel and perpendicular to the stress direction. Band structure simulations indicate that uniaxial tensile stress along $\langle 110 \rangle$ decreases $m_{t,||}$ with respect to $m_{t,\perp}$. Analytical fits characterizing the changes of $m_l, m_{t,||}$, and $m_{t,\perp}$ as a function of applied $\langle 110 \rangle$ stress are reported in [3]. The observed effective mass change is consistent with a theoretical result in [4] and is in good agreement with a recently reported study [5].

The subband structure of the two dimensional electron gas was calculated using a one-dimensional Schrödinger-Poisson solver with modifications to account for the strain induced energy splitting between the subband ladders. Transport calculations have accounted for electron-phonon interaction and surface roughness scattering. The Monte Carlo method used for this work is based on the solution of the linearized Boltzmann equation and allows the exact treatment of the Pauli exclusion principle in the limit of vanishing driving fields.

MOBILITY IN UTB MOSFETS

In Si inversion layers the six-fold degenerate Δ_6 valley splits into up to three different subband ladders depending on the orientation of the substrate. For (001) substrate the masses of the lowest (unprimed) subband ladders are spherical and that the ladders are two-fold degenerate. On (110) substrate the masses of the unprimed subband ladders are anisotropic and the ladders are four-fold degenerate. The higher density of states and larger transport masses on (110) substrate yield a lower inversion layer mobility as compared to (001) substrate.

On (001) substrate the mobility can be enhanced if stress direction and channel direction are both [110]. The reasons are the stress induced valley splitting and the stress induced effective mass change. At relatively large body thicknesses, e.g. T_{SOI}=20 nm, $\Delta\mu_{eff}$ can be understood from a combination of the two effects yielding an anisotropic μ_{eff} as compared to the unstressed system (see Fig. 1).

In ultra-thin Si bodies, however, the strong quantum confinement induces a large intrinsic valley splitting, thus stress induced valley shifts have a negligible effect on the mobility. At T_{SOI}=2.4 nm, the larger (smaller) component of the mobility parallel (perpendicular) to the stress direction [110] results from the effective mass

CP893, *Physics of Semiconductors, 28th International Conference*
edited by W. Jantsch and F. Schäffler
© 2007 American Institute of Physics 978-0-7354-0397-0/07/$23.00

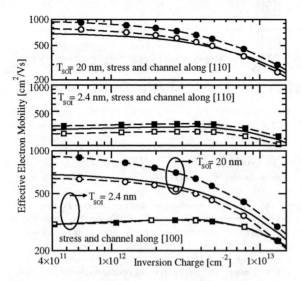

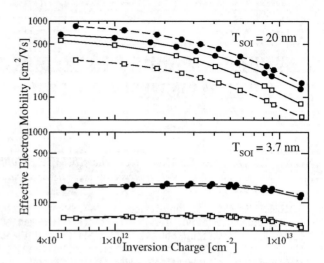

FIGURE 1. Simulated effective mobility for substrate orientation (001), two channel orientations and two body thicknesses of unstressed (solid lines) and 1 GPa stressed Si (dashed lines). The mobilities are plotted parallel (closed symbols) and perpendicular (open symbols) to the stress direction.

FIGURE 2. Simulated effective mobility for substrate orientation (110) of unstressed (solid lines) and 1 GPa stressed (dashed lines) Si for two body thicknesses. The mobility components are plotted parallel (closed symbols) and perpendicular (open symbols) to stress direction [001].

change only and is found in good agreement with experimental data [5]. Additionally, in Fig. 1 the effect of uniaxial stress on the mobility with channel direction and stress direction parallel to [100] is shown. The effect of uniaxial tensile stress is qualitatively different from wafers with stress and channel along [110]. Stress along [100] lifts the degeneracy of the fourfold (primed) ladder. Since effective mass does not change, mobility enhancement is only observed at large T_{SOI} and is a result of subband ladder splitting only.

Stress induced $\Delta\mu_{\mathrm{eff}}$ on (110) oriented substrates can be understood from similar arguments. Tensile stress along [001] does not alter the mobility at small T_{SOI}, because it does not change the effective masses, but merely increases the splitting between the primed and unprimed subband ladders. Fig. 2 shows that the stress induced mobility enhancement, observed at $T_{SOI} = 20.0$ nm, vanishes at $T_{SOI} = 3.7$ nm.

CONCLUSION

The effect of uniaxial stress on the electron mobility was analyzed by means of MC simulations. Experimentally observed mobility data were reproduced for bulk Si and Si inversion layers on (001) and (110) oriented substrates with large and small body thicknesses. Mobility enhancement can be understood only from a combination of three effects: (i) subband ladder repopulation, (ii) change in inter-subband scattering, and (iii) stress induced effective mass changes. While repopulation effects can increase the bulk and inversion layer mobili-

ties at relatively large body thicknesses ($T_{SOI} > 20$ nm), the population of higher subband ladders is intrinsically reduced by strong quantum confinement for very small body thickness ($T_{SOI} < 5$ nm). Thus, in the latter case, no mobility enhancement can be expected from stress induced repopulation effects and only the stress induced effective mass change can explain the experimentally observed mobility enhancement. In this aspect, stress conditions reducing the effective mass in transport direction (like uniaxial tensile stress along $\langle 110 \rangle$) are very beneficial to increase mobility in UTB-MOSFETs.

ACKNOWLEDGMENTS

This work has been supported by the Austrian Science Fund (FWF), projects 17285-N02 and I79-N16.

REFERENCES

1. M. V. Fischetti, F. Gamiz, and W. Hänsch, *J.Appl.Phys.* **92**, 7320–7324 (2002).
2. M. V. Fischetti, and Z. Ren, *J.Appl.Phys.* **94**, 1079–1095 (2003).
3. E. Ungersboeck, S. Dhar, G. Karlowatz, H. Kosina, and S. Selberherr, "Physical Modeling of Electron Mobility Enhancement for Arbitrarily Strained Silicon," in *11th International Workshop on Computational Electronics Book of Abstracts*, 2006, pp. 141–142.
4. G. L. Bir, and G. E. Pikus, *Symmetry and Strain Induced Effects in Semiconductors*, Wiley, New York, 1974.
5. K. Uchida, T. Krishnamohan, K. Saraswat, and Y.Nishis, "Physical Mechanisms of Electron Mobility Enhancement in Uniaxial Stressed MOSFETs and Impact of Uniaxial Stress Engineering in Ballistic Regime," in *Proc. Intl. Electron Device Meeting*, 2005, pp. 135–138.

Field characteristics of electron mobility and velocity in InAs/AlGaSb HFETs with high-k gate insulators

Toshihiko Maemoto, Masatoshi Koyama, Hiroshi Takahashi, Shigehiko Sasa, and Masataka Inoue

Nanomaterials Microdevices Research Center, Osaka Institute of Technology,
5-16-1, Ohmiya, Asahi-ku, Osaka 535-8585, Japan

Abstract. We report on the fabrication and characterization of InAs/AlGaSb heterojunction field-effect transistors (HFETs) with high-k gate insulators. These HFETs have been operated with a maximum extrinsic transconductance of 180 mS/mm at room temperature. The use of an 80-nm-thick Al_2O_3 gate insulator greatly lowered the gate leakage. The leakage current density was three orders of magnitude lower compared with other experimental studies of Shottky gate InAs HFETs. In addition, we evaluated the electron motility and drift velocity by increasing the field strength.

Keywords: Indium arsenide, heterojunction field-effect transistors (HFET's), high-k material, gate current
PACS: 68.65.Fg, 73.61.Ey, 85.30.-z

INTRODUCTION

The antimonide-based semiconductors, such as InAs combined with GaSb, AlSb and similar alloys, are compounds whose heterostructures have conduction band offsets that permit great flexibility in their band-gap engineering [1]. Additionally, the low-dimensional electrons in these nano-structures [2] are attracting interest because of their low effective mass and subsequent strong confinement in the quantum well. InAs/AlGaSb heterostructures have several advantages: high electron mobility, high electron drift velocity that are suitable for the production of high-speed heterostructure field-effect transistors (HFETs) [3, 4]. On the other hand, a technical issue for this material system is an enhanced gate leakage due to the elevated charge generated by impact ionization and through the Shottky junction. Recently, an Al_2O_3 insulator has been used as a high-k gate dielectric material able to control the FET leakage current [5]. In this paper, we demonstrate the performance of InAs/AlGaSb HFETs into which we have inserted a high-k gate dielectric insulator, and discuss the attendant field characteristics of electron mobility and velocity.

DEVICE FABRICATION

Figure 1 shows the schematic diagram of an InAs/AlSb HFET and its energy band structure.

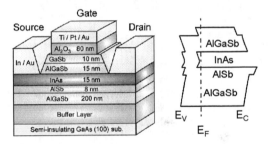

FIGURE 1. Schematic diagram of InAs/AlGaSb HFET structure and energy band structure.

The epitaxial layers were grown by molecular beam epitaxy (MBE) on a semi-insulating GaAs substrate. To improve the crystal quality of the InAs channel, we grew an un-doped 1.5 μm thick AlSb buffer as a buffer layer. Device isolation was accomplished by wet-chemical etching with a phosphoric acid-based etchant consisting of H_3PO_4, H_2O_2 and H_2O in a volume ratio of 1:1:100. Mesa isolation was carried out down to the middle of the bottom AlGaSb barrier, and the etched area was filled with a SiO_2 insulator deposited by electron beam evaporation. Next, the ohmic contact patterns were defined by photolithography, and the In/Au (20 nm/100 nm) ohmic layers were deposited by thermal evaporation. The gate metal (Ti/Au) and Al_2O_3 gate insulator were deposited by electron beam evaporation. In the end, the thicknesses of the gate metal and the Al_2O_3 were 100 nm and 80 nm, respectively. Hall measurements at 300 K revealed that

CP893, *Physics of Semiconductors, 28th International Conference*
edited by W. Jantsch and F. Schäffler

the electron mobility of an as-grown wafer reached 22,000 cm²/Vs and exhibited a sheet carrier density of 1.88×10^{12} cm⁻².

RESULTS AND DISCUSSION

The high-k gate InAs HFET characteristics measured at 300 K are shown in Fig. 2 (a). The gate voltage was varied from -2.5 to +1.0 V in 0.25 V steps. We demonstrated the operation of a 1-μm gate device with a 80-nm-thick Al_2O_3 insulator at room temperature, and a peak extrinsic transconductance, g_m was 180 mS/mm. Using the measured values for contact resistance and sheet resistance, we obtained a peak intrinsic g_m of 205 mS/mm ($V_{DS} = 0.5$ V).

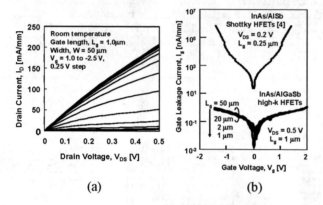

(a) (b)

FIGURE 2. (a) Drain V_{DS}-I_D characteristics of an 1-μm gate device measured at room temperature, and (b) gate leakage current characteristics for different gate lengths.

Figure 2 (b) shows that the gate leakage current densities were greatly decreased by inserting the Al_2O_3 gate insulator. We achieved a maximum gate current of less than 1 nA/mm at room temperature. In comparison with other results, regardless of gate length, we found that the gate current density of the InAs high-k gate HFET was three orders of magnitude lower than that of the InAs/AlSb Shottky gate HFET [4]. Evidently, this insulating layer significantly suppresses the leakage current in InAs HFETs.

We also estimated the field-effect mobility. Figure 3 (a) shows the mobility-field characteristics. The field effect mobility was affected by the lateral electric fields. With increases in the electronic field, the field effect motilities decreased from 16,300 cm²/Vs at 0.1 kV/cm to 4800 cm²/Vs at 1.7 kV/cm. The electron mobility in the InAs high-k FET tends to decrease with the field in a similar manner to that seen in the pulsed Hall-effect [6]. Next, we evaluated the drift velocity v. Electrons are accelerated according to the relation $v = \mu E$, where μ and E are the electron mobility and the lateral electric fields, respectively. Up to field strength of 0.8 kV/cm, the velocity rose in proportion

to the electric field. However, above 1.0 kV/cm, the mobility decreased, and the velocity saturated at 8.0 x 10⁶ cm/s. Taking into account the contact resistance, we noted that the velocity reached the high value of 1.05×10^7 cm/s at 1.7 kV/cm. Although the reason for the degradation of the velocity is not clear at the present, these results showing velocity suppression at high field strength are in good agreement with those reported for the pulsed Hall measurements [6]. This comparison of field effect characteristics clearly demonstrates the advantages of InAs/AlGaSb heterostructures for high-speed applications.

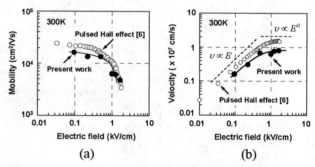

(a) (b)

FIGURE 3. (a) Electron mobility as a function of field, and (b) velocity-field characteristics of high-k HFETs.

CONCLUSION

We fabricated and characterized InAs/AlGaSb HFETs with a high-k gate insulator. In room temperature FET operations, the gate leakage was greatly reduced by the introduction of an 80-nm-thick Al_2O_3 gate insulator. The field effect mobility and drift velocity in high-k InAs HFETs were evaluated from FET characteristics, and these results were found to be useful for HFETs using high-k insulators.

ACKNOWLEDGMENTS

This work was partly supported by a Grant-in-Aid for Young Scientists (B) from the Ministry of Education, Culture, Sports, Science and Technology (MEXT) Japan (#17760284) and by the Sumitomo Foundation (#050282).

REFERENCES

1. H. Kroemer, *Physica E* **20**, 196-203 (2004).
2. T. Maemoto *et al.*, to be published in Journal of Physics.
3. K. Yoh *et al.*, *IEEE Electron Device Lett.* **11**, 526-528 (1990).
4. J. Bergman *et al*, 61th Device Research Conference, June 23-25 (2003) Salt Lake City, USA.
5. P. D. Ye *et al.*, *Appl. Phys. Lett.* **83**, 180-183 (2003).
6. M. Inoue *et al.*, 4th Int. Conf. on Advanced Heterostructure Transistor (1990).

Accurate Extraction of Conduction Parameter in MOSFETs on Si(110) surface

P. Gaubert[1], A. Teramoto[1], T. Hamada[2], T. Suwa[2], and T. Ohmi[1]

[1]New Industry Creation Hatchery Center, Tohoku University, Sendai 980-8579 Japan - [2]Graduate School of Engineering, Tohoku University, Sendai 980-8579, Japan

Abstract. This paper reports for the first time the intrinsic mobility attenuation factor for p-channel MOSFETs fabricated on (110) crystallographic oriented silicon. It has been demonstrated that some extraction methods working well for the conventional orientation cannot be applied anymore when it comes to the (110) orientation. The intrinsic attenuation factor found for the new orientation is ten times smaller than for the conventional one. Then the channel mobility of Si(110) p-MOSFETs is much less sensitive to the effective electric field variations than the Si(100) p-MOSFETs meaning that the shift to higher effective electric field coming from a higher doping concentration in the channel will affect in much less proportion the hole mobility of p-MOSFETs based on (110) oriented silicon.

Keywords: Mobility attenuation factor, MOS transistor, surface orientation, mobility, silicon.
PACS: 73.23.-b, 73.40.Qv, 73.43.Cd

INTRODUCTION

Major electronic companies try to improve devices performance by reducing the device size. Unfortunately the shrinking always comes with the appearance of new phenomenon such as the so-called punch through. This problem can be avoided by an increase of doping in the channel. But at the same time, for equivalent supply gate voltage, the mobility degrades because of the shift to higher effective electric field.

Among the numerous other technology to improve device performances, the replacement of the traditional (100) silicon by the (110) silicon oriented surface as base for future CMOS technology involved in digital and analog circuits seems to be very promising. Although the noise level of Si(110) p-MOSFET has been improved[1], it is still too high when compared to conventional p-MOSFETs and the major interest of the (110) orientation comes from a much better channel mobility in p-MOSFETs[2].

The purpose of this paper is to present for the first time the intrinsic mobility attenuation factor of p-MOSFETs based on (110) oriented silicon found to be ten times smaller than for the conventional orientation.

PARAMETER EXTRACTION METHODS

We are interested in this paper by the extraction of the conduction parameters such as the low field mobility μ_0, the access resistance R_{acc} and the intrinsic attenuation factor θ.

We used three different methods based on the I_d-V_g characteristic: the first has been presented by C. Ciofi et al.[3] and does not need any numerical differentiation, the second has been developed by G. Ghibaudo[4] and require the transconductance transfer characteristic and the last one has been presented by R. J. Schreutelkamp et al.[5][6] and includes series resistance effects.

RESULTS

p-MOSFETs fabricated on (100) and (110) silicon oriented N-type wafers were employed for this study. The oxide thickness t_{ox}=5nm, the doping concentration N_d=2x10^{17}cm^{-3}, the threshold voltage V_{th}=1.3V as well as the fabrication processes were identical on both wafers.

Values of the conduction parameters for p-MOSFETs based on Si(100) are presented on Tab. 1. We can see a very good agreement between the three methods as well as values presented in the literature.

CP893, *Physics of Semiconductors, 28th International Conference*
edited by W. Jantsch and F. Schäffler
© 2007 American Institute of Physics 978-0-7354-0397-0/07/$23.00

TABLE 1. Conduction parameters for conventional Si(100) p-MOSFETs extracted using the three different methods. Results presented for the Schreutelkamp method have been calculated for V_g-V_{th}=0.9V.

Si(100) pMOSFET	Ciofi method	Ghibaudo method	Schreutelkamp method
ΔW (μm)	-0.322	-0.331	/
ΔL (μm)	-0.121	-0.13	-0.1
θ (V^{-1})	0.348	0.3599	0.31
R_{acc} (Ω)	68.9	67.41	98
μ_0 (cm^2/Vs)	118	114	115

We then applied the same study for p-MOSFETs based on Si(110). Although extraction was successful with the Ciofi and Schreutelkamp methods, it was not possible to apply the Ghibaudo's one to our Si(110) p-MOSFETs. In the case of the Ghibaudo'method, the knowledge of the extrinsic attenuation factor θ^* which is characteristic of each MOSFET's gate dimension must be known in order to continue the extraction of the others conduction parameters. θ^* is obtained from the plot of $1/\sqrt{(g_m)}$ as a function of the gate voltage V_g:

$$\frac{1}{\sqrt{g_m}} = \frac{\left[1 + \theta^*\left(V_g - V_{th}\right)\right]}{\sqrt{G_m V_d}} \qquad (1)$$

g_m being the conventional transconductance and G_m the transconductance parameter defined as $G_m = WC_{ox}\mu_0/L$ with W and L respectively the width and length of the MOSFET channel and C_{ox} the oxide capacitance.

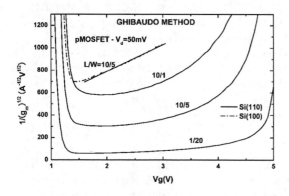

FIGURE 1. Required $1/\sqrt{(g_m)}$ versus V_g curves for the Ghibaudo method. It is presented for different silicon orientations and different gate dimensions. The fit on Si(100) was possible while it was not on Si(110).

The above equation is linear and a fitting must be done in order to obtain θ^*. As shown in Fig. 1, the fitting has been realized for the conventional orientation but has not been possible for the (110) one. The method developed by Ghibaudo could not be applied to our Si(110) p-MOSFET without any amelioration.

Conduction parameters obtained with both Ciofi and Schreutelkamp methods present relatively good agreement as shown on Tab. 2. Moreover, we found an intrinsic mobility attenuation factor θ ten times smaller than for the (100) orientation meaning that the channel mobility of hole on Si(110) p-MOSFETs is much less sensitive to effective electric field change.

TABLE 2. Conduction parameters for Si(110) p-MOSFET extracted using two different methods. Results presented for the Schreutelkamp method have been calculated for V_g-V_{th}=0.9V.

Si(110) pMOSFET	Ciofi method	Schreutelkamp method
ΔW (μm)	-0.42	/
ΔL (μm)	-0.43	-0.67
θ (V^{-1})	0.038	0.042
R_{acc} (Ω)	63	48
μ_0 (cm^2/Vs)	285	303

It has been found that the intrinsic mobility attenuation factor θ for Si(110) p-MOSFETs is much smaller than for Si(100) p-MOSFETs. Higher effective electric field will affect in much less proportion the hole mobility making highly doped channel Si(110) p-MOSFETs a key device of the CMOS technology based on Si(110) as viable competitor and even a future replacement for the conventional silicon CMOS technology.

ACKNOWLEDGMENTS

The authors gratefully acknowledge Ministry of Economy, Trade and Industry and The New Energy and Industrial Technology Development Organization for their financial support.

REFERENCES

1. P. Gaubert, A. Teramoto, T. Hamada, M. Yamamoto, K. Kotani and T. Ohmi, *IEEE Trans. Electron Devices*, **53**(4), 851-856 (2006).
2. A. Teramoto, T. Hamada, H. Hakahori, K. Nii, T. Suwa, K. Kotani, M. Hirayama, S. Sugawa and T. Ohmi, IEDM Tech. Dig., 801-804 (2003).
3. C. Ciofi, M. Macucci and B. Pellegrini, *Solid-St. Electron.*, **33**(8), 1065-1069 (1990).
4. G. Ghibaudo, *Electron. Lett.*, **24**(9), 543-545 (1988).
5. R.J. Schreutelkamp and L. Deferm, *Solid-St. Electron.*, **38**(4), 791-793 (1995).
6. R.J. Schreutelkamp and L. Deferm, Internal report IMEC, n° P30005-IM-FP-001, (1993).

Self-Consistent Wigner Monte Carlo Simulations of Current in Emerging Nanodevices: Role of Tunneling and Scattering

Viktor Sverdlov, Hans Kosina, Tibor Grasser and Siegfried Selberherr

Institute for Microelectronics, TU Wien, Gußhausstraße 27–29/E360, 1040 Wien, Austria
{sverdlov|kosina|grasser|selberherr}@iue.tuwien.ac.at

Abstract. Quantum effects determine transport in emerging nanoelectronic devices. At the same time, scattering is still important and may control current at room temperature. A Wigner function based approach, which accounts for the interplay between coherent quantum effects and dissipative scattering effects, is presented. The Wigner equation is solved by means of an advanced Monte Carlo technique. Influence of scattering, tunneling, and space charge effects on the electrical characteristics of single- and double-barrier nanoscale devices at room temperature is investigated.

Keywords: Device simulation, quantum transport, Wigner equation, Monte Carlo method
PACS: 72.10.Bg, 73.40.Qv, 85.30.De, 85.30.Mn, 85.30.Tv, 85.35.-p

INTRODUCTION

Quantum effects play a major role in determining transport in emerging nanoelectronic devices. There are, however, growing evidences that scattering still controls the current [1]. Recent studies demonstrate that the crossover from diffusive to ballistic transport in Si nanowire transistors occurs at approximately 2 nm [2], a much shorter distance than previously anticipated. Transport model for nanoelectronic devices must account for quantum mechanical and dissipative effects. The Wigner function formalism can handle both quantum effects and dissipation simultaneously. Realistic scattering processes are embedded into the Wigner equation via Boltzmann-like scattering integrals [3].

WIGNER MONTE-CARLO METHOD

The solution of the Wigner equation by Monte Carlo methods is hampered by the fact that the Wigner function is not positively defined and cannot be interpreted as a probability distribution. This so-called negative sign problem leads to exponentially growing variances of the Markov Chain Monte Carlo method [4]. We have developed a novel particle Monte Carlo strategy to control the variances. The Wigner potential operator is treated as a generation term [4]. It generates two numerical particles with opposite weights. Two particles stored at the annihilation mesh are chosen such that the weights in the related mesh elements are minimized. The weight sign of the particle continuing the trajectory is the same as the incoming one. To resolve the negative parts of the Wigner function, a certain fraction of negative trajectories has to be introduced. This computation strategy conserves current exactly and minimizes the weight stored. Several numerical methods have been improved to render the Wigner MC technique more robust, including the separation of a classical force, discretization of the Wigner potential. A self-consistent iteration scheme with the Poisson equation is introduced.

RESULTS

We apply the Wigner function formalism to demonstrate the role of tunneling, scattering, and space charge effects on the electrical characteristics of single and double barrier devices, considering n-i-n structures, double gate field-effect transistors, and resonant tunneling diodes as examples.

In order to estimate the tunneling component of current Wigner Monte Carlo simulations were carried out for a MOSFET with a gate length of 10 nm in the coherent mode. Good agreement to the results obtained from a Schrödinger solver is observed Fig. 1. The difference between quantum ballistic and semiclassical simulations is due to the additional contribution from electrons tunneling through the potential barrier.

Next, self-consistent Wigner Monte Carlo calculations for Si n-i-n structures with an intrinsic region of length W ranging from 20 nm to 2.5 nm were performed. Relative differences between I_{WIG} and the current I_{BALL} computed for a "ballistic" device with scattering inside the intrinsic region turned off is shown in Fig. 2. For $W = 2.5$ nm the relative differences in current due to quantum effects and scattering in the barrier are still of the order of 25% and cannot be neglected.

Finally, a typical output characteristic of a GaAs resonant tunneling diode, with and without space-charge ef-

CP893, *Physics of Semiconductors, 28th International Conference*
edited by W. Jantsch and F. Schäffler
© 2007 American Institute of Physics 978-0-7354-0397-0/07/$23.00

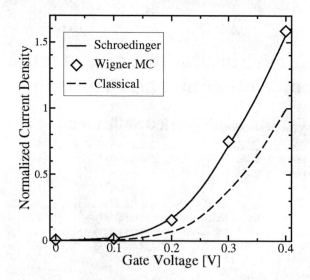

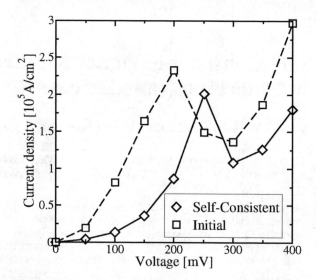

FIGURE 1. Normalized classical ballistic current density and relative quantum mechanical current density obtained with the Wigner Monte Carlo (open symbols). Wigner data are in good agreement with the current density found from the solution of the Schrödinger equation. Additional source-to-drain tunneling current component is clearly visible.

FIGURE 3. Typical *IV* curve of RTD, calculated self-consistently (solid line), contrasted against a non self-consistent characteristics.

and Poisson equation is mandatory for the correct determination of the resonance position.

fects taken into account, is shown in Fig. 3. Scattering with polar optical phonons as well as Coulomb scattering in the contacts is considered. A region of negative differential resistance common to transport via a resonant level is clearly visible after the resonance peak at 250 mV applied voltage. A self-consistent solution of the Wigner

CONCLUSIONS

The Wigner function approach is a comprehensive method to address simulation needs of emerging nano-electronic devices. It treats tunneling and realistic scattering mechanisms on equal footing. The method applied to single- and double-barrier nanostructures demonstrates the importance of both quantum-mechanical and scattering effects in emerging nanodevices.

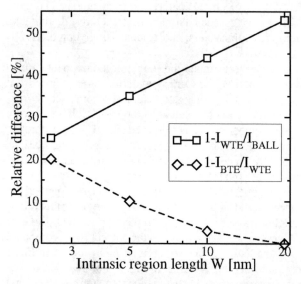

ACKNOWLEDGMENTS

We gratefully acknowledge financial support from the Austrian Science Fund FWF, project P17285-N02.

FIGURE 2. Relative difference between currents calculated with the Wigner and Boltzmann Monte Carlo methods (diamonds) and calculated with the Wigner MC for an *n-i-n* structure, with and without scattering in the intrinsic region.

REFERENCES

1. P. Palestri, D. Esseni, S. Eminente, C. Fiegna, E. Sangiorgi, and L. Selmi, *IEEE Trans.Electron Devices* **52**, 2727–2735 (2005).
2. M. Gilbert, R. Akis, and D. Ferry, *J.Appl.Phys.* **98**, 094303-1–8 (2005).
3. W. Frensley, *Reviews of Modern Physics* **62**, 745–791 (1990).
4. H. Kosina, and M. Nedjalkov, *Handbook of Theoretical and Computational Nanotechnology*, American Scientific Publishers, Los Angeles, 2006, vol. 10, chap. Wigner Function Based Device Modeling, pp. 731–763, (in print).

One-dimensional Sub-threshold Channels In Nanoscale Triple-gate Silicon Transistors

Gabri P. Lansbergen[1], Hermann Sellier[1], Jaap Caro[1], Nadine Collaert[2], Isabelle Ferain[2], Malgorzata Jurczak[2], Serge Biesemans[2] and Sven Rogge[1]

[1] *Kavli Institute of Nanoscience, Delft University of Technology,*
Lorentzweg 1, 2628 CJ Delft, The Netherlands
[2] *IMEC, Kapeldreef 75, 3001 Leuven, Belgium*

Abstract. We experimentally show the formation of sub-threshold channels at the edges of triple-gate silicon field-effect transistors, called FinFETs. These three dimensional nano-scale devices consist of a lithographically defined Si nanowire surrounded by a gate and have an active region as small as $50 \times 60 \times 35$ nm^3. By measuring the thermally activated transport, the sub-threshold channels are determined to have a cross-section of only 4 nm^2. The presence and size of these sub-threshold channels is independently confirmed by the Coulomb blockade conductance peaks visible below 60 K. These features reveal the formation of a quantum dot in the channel with a charging energy consistent with a 2 nm wide channel that extends from source to drain.

Keywords: Electronic transport in mesoscopic systems, Coulomb blockade, single electron tunneling.
PACS: 73.23.-b, 73.23.Hk, 73.61.Cw .

INTRODUCTION

A new type of field effect transistor, called FinFET, is currently being developed to solve the problematic issues encountered with the standard planar geometry when the channel length is reduced to a sub-100nm size [1]. In a triple-gate geometry (see Fig. 1) the gate action is expected to be stronger thus preventing leakage problems. We experimentally show that the triple-gate is also responsible for the formation of sub-threshold channels at the corners of the silicon body.

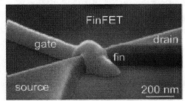

Figure 1. SEM image of the triple-gate FinFET

Such sub-threshold channels induce a lower threshold voltage and higher off-state current relative to the respective properties of the bulk, making it a serious technological issue in the design of triple-gate FETs [2]. Much simulation work concerning this so-called corner effect exists, but little experimental work has been published up to now [3] [4].

TRANSPORT CHARACTERISTICS

The electrical characteristics of the devices at room temperature show the expected FET-like behavior. To study the effect of the gate action on the transport properties in more detail, temperature dependant measurements were performed. The source-drain-conductance was measured as a function of temperature for various gate voltages, in a regime where the current is dominated by thermionic emission of carriers across the barrier imposed by the un-opened channel. It is known that the conductance can be described by [5]

$$G = SA^* \frac{e}{k_B} T \exp\left(-\frac{E_b}{k_B T}\right) \qquad (1)$$

where E_b is the barrier height, S is the cross-section of the channel and A^* is a material constant which is 2.1×120 A cm^{-2} K^{-2} for Si [5]. By fitting the data to Eq. 1, the barrier height as a function of gate voltage can be extracted.

The result, plotted in Fig. 2, shows some important device features. First of all, the linear relation between the barrier height and the gate voltage at $V_g < V_0$ shows a strong gate/channel coupling of 0.67, brought forth by the triple gate geometry of the device. Secondly, the gate coupling at $V_g > V_0$ is non-linear

CP893, *Physics of Semiconductors, 28th International Conference*
edited by W. Jantsch and F. Schäffler

due to residual barriers at the access regions between the channel and the source and drain contacts (see inset of Fig 2). These energy barriers in the access regions are due to a poor n-type doping caused by masking silicon nitride spacers next to the gate.

The fit of Eq. 1 also yields a channel cross section S of only 4 nm^2. The cross section of the Si body is 35x60 nm^2, meaning that the current is carried by only a small part of it.

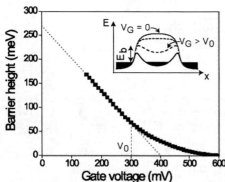

Figure 2. Barrier height in the channel versus gate voltage. Each data point results from fitting conductance data to Eq. 1. The inset shows the shape of the conductance band at three different gate voltages

COULOMB-BLOCKADE EFFECTS AND SUB-THRESHOLD CHANNELS

At low temperatures the conductance develops large fluctuations versus gate voltage. Figure 3 shows these patterns for FinFETs of various dimensions. The equally spaced peaks are energetically positioned in the region where $V_g > V_0$ (see inset Fig. 2). Here, the two residual barriers and the width of the conducting region confine an area inside the channel that effectively acts as a quantum dot. Transport at these gate voltages is subjected to Coulomb blockade effects.

The peak spacings are a direct result of the charging energy and level spacing of this quantum dot. The average spacing depends on the length of the Si body but shows no relation with its width, leading to the conclusion that another mechanism must be responsible for confinement in the direction perpendicular to the current.

The charging energy of the dot is a direct measure for its capacitance to the gate. From the capacitance the dot area of the device in Fig. 2 is determined to be 130 nm^2. If we assume, based on the observed peak spacing scaling with length and width of the body, that the channel length is equal to the body length, we find a channel width of 2 nm.

The existence of long and narrow sub-threshold channels is thus confirmed independently by both temperature dependent and Coulomb blockade measurements. We understand them as the result of the triple gate geometry producing a stronger electric field along the edges of the Si body and therefore deeper potential wells.

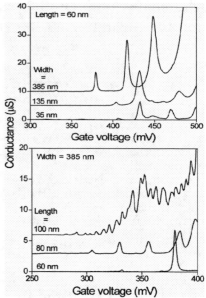

Figure 3. Conductance versus gate voltage at 4.2K for devices with various dimensions. **a)** Short channels of different widths have similar peak spacing. **b)** Devices with longer channels have smaller peak spacing

CONCLUSION

The triple-gate of the FinFET device induces stronger band bending along the edges of the silicon wire that make up the body. This leads to the formation of narrow sub-threshold channels that we observe as a current path confined to these edges. The presence and size of the corner effect has been confirmed by measurements of both the thermally activated current and the Coulomb blocked transport below 60 K.

REFERENCES

[1] Digh Hisamota *et al.*, IEEE Trans. Elec. Dev. **47** (12), 2320 (2000)

[2] J.G. Fossum *et al.*, IEEE Elec. Dev. Let. **24**(12), 745, (2003)

[3] B.S. Doyle *et al.*, IEEE Elec. Dev. Let. **24**(4), 263 (2003) & Weize Xiong *et al.*, IEEE Elec. Dev. Let. **25** (8), 541 (2004)

[4] H. Sellier *et al.*, submitted.

[5] S.M. Sze, Semiconductor device: Physic and technology, Wiley, New York (2002)

Modeling of Electron Transport in GaN-Based Materials and Devices

S. Vitanov*, V. Palankovski*, R. Quay† and E. Langer*

*Institute for Microelectronics, TU Wien, Gußhausstraße 27–29/E360, 1040 Wien, Austria
†Fraunhofer Inst. for Solid-State Physics (IAF), Tullastr. 72, Freiburg, Germany

Abstract. Material models which incorporate the basic characteristics of the underlying physics in a given semiconductor material are the core of device modeling. We employ a Monte Carlo (MC) technique to investigate stationary electron transport in GaN and AlGaN [1]. We obtain a set of model parameters which gives agreement with experimental data available for different physical conditions (doping, temperature, electric field, etc.). Such a calibrated set of models and model parameters delivers valuable data for low-field mobility, velocity saturation, energy relaxation times, etc. We use these data as a basis for the development of analytical models for the numerical simulation of GaN-based electron devices. As a particular example we analyze an AlGaN/GaN HEMT with l_g=300 nm from IAF using the two-dimensional device simulator Minimos-NT [2]. We study the impact of different models and efects (polarization charge, thermionic field emission, self-heating effects).

Keywords: Modeling, GaN, HEMT
PACS: 72.80.Ey, 73.61.Ey

INTRODUCTION

AlGaN/GaN based high electron mobility transistors (HEMTs) have been subject of extensive investigations in the last years. Their performance makes them suitable for power amplifiers in infrastructure base station applications. In order to fully develop the potential of the device, an accurate simulation model is needed.

SIMULATION RESULTS

We employ a single-particle MC technique to investigate stationary electron transport in GaN. Our model includes the three lowest valleys of the conduction band. Several stochastic mechanisms such as acoustic phonon, polar optical phonon, inter-valley phonon, ionized impurity scattering, and piezoelectric scattering are considered [1]. Fig. 1 compares experimental [3, 4, 5, 6, 7] and MC simulation data for the low-field electron mobility in GaN as a function of the free carrier concentration. The figure also includes an analytical model fitted to our MC simulation results. This model is incorporated in the two-dimensional device simulator MINIMOS-NT [2]. For device simulation, we consider electron energy relaxation times which depend on electron energy and lattice temperature. Fig. 2 compares our analytical model to MC simulation data for GaN.

Fig. 3 gives an example of a typical fully planar GaN/AlGaN structure. All layers are non-intentionally doped except the δ-doping which is introduced to provide additional carriers.

The crucial factor building the channel in HEMTs is the polarization charges at the AlGaN/GaN heterointerfaces. The positive charge at the channel/spacer interface is compensated by a negative surface charge at the barrier/cap interface. An optimum value of 1.1×10^{13} cm^{-2} is found. As can be seen in Fig. 4 (the electron concentration for V_{DS}=7 V, V_{GS}=0 V is shown) the device is a normally on transistor. Another unknown is penetration depth of the drain/source metal contacts which may build an alloy with the AlGaN supply layer. We assume a metal diffusion to the δ-doping in our simulations.

We further assess the impact of thermionic emission and field emission (tunneling) effects which critically determine the current transport across the heterojunctions. An optimal tunnel length of 7.5 nm is found.

Since the longitudinal electric field in the channel reaches peak values of above 500 kV/cm, a hydrodynamic approach is used to properly model the electron transport and energy relaxation. We further account for self-heating (SH) effects using a global temperature model. Fig. 5 shows simulated and measured data for the transfer curves. Fig. 6 compares measured and simulated output characteristics.

CONCLUSION

We incorporate a new material model in our two-dimensional device simulator. Our results allow not only to get a good agreement between simulation and measured electrical data of AlGaN/GaN HEMTs, but to gain understanding and insight in the effects taking place in the devices.

CP893, *Physics of Semiconductors, 28th International Conference*
edited by W. Jantsch and F. Schäffler
© 2007 American Institute of Physics 978-0-7354-0397-0/07/$23.00

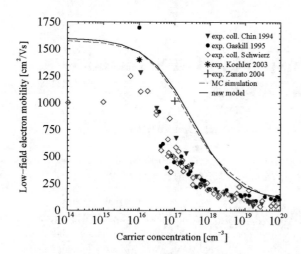

FIGURE 1. Mobility vs. concentration (Monte Carlo results and models used in the device simulator

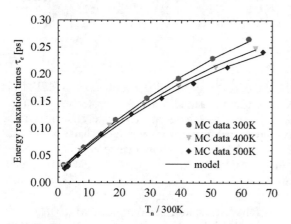

FIGURE 2. Electron energy relaxation times as a function of electron temperature for different lattice temperatures

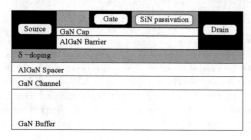

FIGURE 3. Layer structure of high electron mobility transistors considered in this work

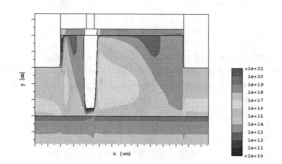

FIGURE 4. Electron concentration [cm^{-3}] in the device

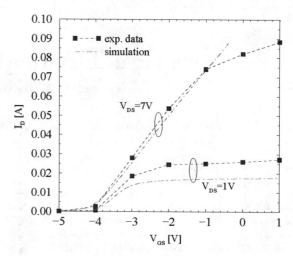

FIGURE 5. Transfer characteristics

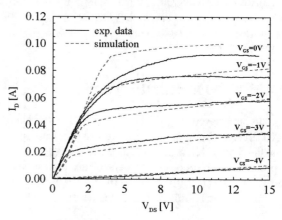

FIGURE 6. Output characteristics

ACKNOWLEDGMENTS

The authors acknowledge support from Austrian Science Fund (FWF), Project START Y247-N13, and by the TARGET European Network of Excellence.

REFERENCES

1. V. Palankovski, A. Marchlewski, E. Ungersböck, and S. Selberherr, Proc. 5th MATHMOD, CDROM, Vienna, pp. 14-1–14-9, 2006.

2. http://www.iue.tuwien.ac.at/software/minimos-nt.

3. V. Chin, T. Tansley, and T. Osotachn, J.Appl.Phys., vol. 75, no. 11, pp. 7365-7372, 1994.

4. D. Gaskill, L. Rowland, and K. Doverspike, Properties of Group III Nitrides, no. 11 in EMIS Datareviews Series, sec. 3.2, pp. 101-116, IEE INSPEC, 1994.

5. K. Köhler, S. Müller, N. Rollbühler, R. Kiefer, R. Quay, and G. Weimann, Proc. Intl. Symp. Compound Semiconductors, pp. 235-238, 2003.

6. D. Zanato, N. Balkan, G. Hill, and W. J. Schaff, Superlattices & Microstructures, vol. 36, no. 4-6, pp. 455-463, 2004.

7. F. Schwierz, Solide-State Electron., vol. 49, no. 6, pp. 889-895, 2005.

Quantum Non-Locality in Systems with Open Boundaries: Limitations of the Wigner function formalism

David Taj[*,†], Luigi Genovese[**] and Fausto Rossi[*]

[*]*Dipartimento di Fisica, Politecnico di Torino, 10129 Torino, Italy*
[†]*Dipartimento di Matematica, Università di Torino, 10100, Italy*
[**]*Dipartimento di Fisica e Sez. INFN, Università di Roma "Tor Vergata", 00133 Roma, Italy*

Abstract. Quantum non-locality is here put at variance with spatial contacts, as modelled within the Wigner-Function formalism: we shall show how these two concepts are indeed intrinsically incompatible when applied to transport through quantum devices. More specifically, by means of an exactly-solvable semiconductor model, we show that the application of the usual Up-Wind boundary scheme to the Wigner transport equation may produce highly non-physical results, like boundary-driven negative probability distributions.

Keywords: Quantum Transport. Applications and Devices
PACS: 72.10.Bg, 85.30.-z, 73.40.-c

Current micro/nanoelectronics technology pushes device dimensions toward limits where the traditional semi-classical Boltzmann theory can no longer be applied, and more rigorous quantum-transport approaches are required, in which a non-trivial interplay between phase coherence and dissipation/dephasing, also induced by the spatial boundaries [1], forces a real-space treatment.

Such a real-space description is naturally provided by the Wigner-Function Formalism (WFF) [1] in which the statistical quantum state of the electronic subsystem is fully described in terms of the Wigner function, defined over the phase-space as the Weyl-Wigner transform of the single-particle density matrix [2].

Different approaches based on the WFF have been proposed. On the one hand, starting from the pioneering work by Frensley, a few groups have performed simulations based on a direct numerical solution of the Wigner Transport Equation (WTE) by imposing the standard boundary-condition scheme of the semiclassical device modelling, also called U-scheme [3]. On the other hand, recent applications of the generalized SBE [3] suggested an intrinsic limitation of the conventional WFF in describing quantum-transport phenomena through systems with open boundaries, but no clear evidence of them has been reported so far via numerical WTE simulations [1]. Aim of this work is to solve this apparent contradiction, thus shedding light on the real limitations of the conventional WFF applied to open-device modelling.

We consider the one dimensional WTE in stationary conditions and in the absence of scattering mechanism, as reported for example in [1] (section IV):

$$v(k)\frac{\partial}{\partial z}f(z,k)+\int dk'\,\mathscr{V}(z,k-k')f(z,k')=0 , \quad (1)$$

where $\mathscr{V}(z,k) = \int_{-\infty}^{+\infty}dz'\,\frac{e^{-2ikz'}}{i\pi\hbar}\left[V(z+z')-V(z-z')\right]$ is the Weyl-Wigner superoperator corresponding to the device potential profile $V(z)$, while $v(k)$ denotes the electron group velocity. Following the standard U-scheme, we shall now impose the desired spatial boundary conditions for f at the left ($z=-\frac{l}{2}$) and right ($z=+\frac{l}{2}$) contacts, specifying the "incoming" electron distribution $f_b(k) = f(z_b(k),k)$, where $z_b(k) = \frac{l}{2}\left(\theta(-k)-\theta(+k)\right)$ denote the left and right boundary coordinate corresponding, respectively, to positive and negative carrier wavevectors k (θ being the usual Heaviside step function). By integrating Eq. (1) from the spatial boundary $z_b(k)$ to the current point z we get, in compact notation[1]: $f = f_b + \mathscr{W}f$, or $f = \frac{1}{1-\mathscr{W}}f_b$, with $\mathscr{W}(z,k;z',k') = -[\theta(k)\theta(z'-z_b(k))\theta(z-z')+ -\theta(-k)\theta(z'-z)\theta(z_b(k)-z')]\frac{\mathscr{V}(z',k-k')}{v(k)}$. By expanding the above formal solution in powers of the interaction superoperator/propagator $\mathscr{W}$ —and therefore of the potential $\mathscr{V}$— we get the well-known Neumann series expansion, $f = \sum_{n=0}^{\infty}\mathscr{W}^n f_b$.

Let us now focus on the case of a symmetric potential profile ($V(z)=V(-z)$), which in turn corresponds to an antisymmetric potential superoperator, i.e., $\mathscr{V}(z,k) = -\mathscr{V}(-z,k)$. Using this property together with the symmetric nature of our spatial boundaries, i.e., $z_b(k) = -z_b(-k)$, it is possible to show that the interaction propagator $\mathscr{W}$ is also preserving the potential symmetry, that is, $\mathscr{W}b\,(z,k) = \mathscr{W}b\,(-z,k)$ for any given symmet-

---

[1] The above formal solution can be also regarded as a sort of Schwinger-Dyson equation linking the desired Wigner function f to the free-particle one ($f_\circ(z,k) = f_b(k)$) through the potential superoperator $\mathscr{V}$.

CP893, *Physics of Semiconductors, 28th International Conference*
edited by W. Jantsch and F. Schäffler
© 2007 American Institute of Physics 978-0-7354-0397-0/07/$23.00

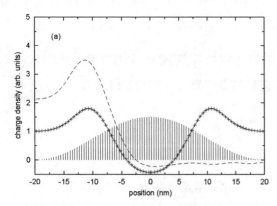

FIGURE 1. Spatial density simulations (see text). The potential profile is plotted in background with vertical lines.

ric function $b(z,k) = b(-z,k)$. This result is extremely important: it implies that for any symmetric potential profile and spatial boundaries the Neumann expansion gives always a Wigner function symmetric in the spatial coordinate: $f(z,k) = f(-z,k)$. Therefore, in total agreement with the numerical results of the generalized SBE presented in [3], the spatial charge density $n(z) = \int f(z,k)\,dk$ is always symmetric, no matter which is the shape of the injected carrier distribution $f_b(k)$. As anticipated, such symmetric behavior —which is an exact result of the treatment presented so far— has never been observed via finite-difference calculations.

In order to solve this apparent contradiction, let us now focus on a particular choice of the device potential profile: $V(z) = \frac{V_0}{2}[1 + \cos(2\kappa z)]$. For this particular potential superoperator it is possible to obtain the spatial charge distribution analytically, and this in turn allows to simulate a monoenergetic carrier injection from left only, i.e., $f_b(k) \propto \delta(k - k_0)$: the spatial density, reported in Figure 1 (solid curve), is always symmetric, in total agreement with the analysis proposed in [3] and, moreover, takes highly and non negligible negative values, which tells us that *the analytical solution $f(z,k)$ of the WTE is not necessarily a Wigner function, as it need not correspond to a well (i.e. positively) defined density matrix.*

Let us finally come to potential discrepancies between exact and finite-difference results: we have implemented a modified/corrected version of the Frensley finite-difference scheme, where both terms (kinetic and potential) are now discretized on the same spatial grid[2], and reported in Fig.1 a comparison between the two

versions (our is cross curve, conventional approach in dashed curve); for both cases the same 80×80 phase-space discretization has been employed. As we can see, while our numerical solution coincides with the analytical result (solid curve), the finite-difference result a la Frensley comes out to be strongly asymmetric, and such serious inconsistency, giving rise to the fictitious decoherence/damping dynamics, can now be explained on the basis of the non-symmetric discretization scheme adopted in [1],which in turn tends to limit the highly non-physical features of the Wigner-function formalism applied to systems with open boundaries.

The analysis presented so far allows us to draw a few important conclusions. First of all, the results of the analytically solvable device model previously considered clearly show that the usual boundary-condition scheme —successfully applied to semiclassical device modelling— is intrinsically incompatible with the non-local nature of quantum mechanics. We are forced to conclude that the application of the standard boundary-condition scheme to the Wigner equation in (1) is not physically justified, since it may provide solutions which are not Wigner functions, i.e., which do not correspond to the state of a quantum system. A clear and unambiguous proof of such non-physical outcomes are the negative values of the electron probability distribution reported in Fig.1 (analytical result). Generally speaking, what is intrinsically wrong in the usual Wigner-function treatment of open devices is the spatial separation between active region and reservoirs.

We finally stress that an alternative simulation scheme may be concretely realized following the prescription recently proposed in [4]: the basic idea is to replace the usual open description of quantum devices based on spatial boundaries (i.e., source/loss terms) with a closed-system treatment, where the interaction of the device electrons with the external reservoirs is simply described in terms of effective scattering rates acting on the device electrons only.

REFERENCES

1. See, e.g., W.R. Frensley, Rev. Mod. Phys. **62**, 3, p.745 (1990) and references therein.
2. See, e.g., F. Rossi and T. Kuhn, Rev. Mod. Phys. **74**, p.895 (2002) and references therein.
3. R. Proietti Zaccaria and F. Rossi, Phys. Rev.B 67, 113311 (2003).
4. R. Proietti Zaccaria *et al*, Appl. Phys. Lett. **84**, 139 (2004); R. Proietti Zaccaria *et al.*, Phys. Rev.B **70**, 195311 (2004).

---

[2] Within the modified discretization scheme, the kinetic part is still evaluated via left $(f_j - f_{j-1})$ or right $(f_{j+1} - f_j)$ derivatives (according to the sign of the wavevector), but the potential superoperator $\mathscr{V}_j$ is now replaced by its left $((\mathscr{V}_j + \mathscr{V}_{j-1})/2)$ or right $((\mathscr{V}_j + \mathscr{V}_{j-1})/2)$ spatial average.

Physical mechanism and ultimate improvement of Vfb shifts of SiN based SiON gate dielectrics

K. Kato, D. Matsushita, K. Muraoka, and Y. Nakasaki

Advanced LSI Technology Laboratory, Toshiba Corporate R&D Center
1 Komukai Toshiba-cho, Saiwai-ku, Kawasaki 210-8582, Japan

Abstract. N incorporated SiON gate insulating films normally exhibit negative Vfb shifts in proportion to N concentration. Physical mechanisms of the Vfb shifts were analyzed based on the first priciples calculations, and the mechanisms are well explained. Furthermore, the methods to reduce the defects; origins of Vfb shifts are experimentally studied, leading to ultimate improvements of the Vfb shifts.

Keywords: nitrogen, oxygen, gate, Vfb
PACS: 61.72.Ji, 71.15.Pd, 81.10.Jt

INTRODUCTION

In the trend of scaling down of MOSFETs, the thickness of gate insulating films is approaching the scaling limit. Since the physical thickness is finite, dielectric constants have to be increased to reduce the equivalent oxide thickness (EOT). N incorporated gate insulating films with a slight Si oxide at the interface is the most realistic measure to meet this demand because high-k materials have not been successfully applied yet[1]. Flat-band voltage (Vfb) of MOSFETs, however, normally shifts negatively in proportion to N concentration in the gate insulating films, as shown in Fig. 1. This shift increases further in p-MOSFETs. It is becoming an obstacle to further achievement.

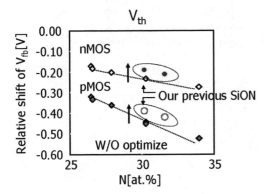

FIGURE 1. Vfb shifts of MOSFETs with SiON gate insulating as a function of N concentration.

THEORETICAL ANALYSES

We tried to understand the mechanisms of Vfb shifts based on first-principles calculations. Our calculations are based on density functional theory (DFT) and generalized gradient approximation (GGA) to describe nitrogen properties properly. The calculations are performed using ultrasoft pseudopotentials for nitrogen atoms. Although much is known about defects such as E' center in Si oxide, knowledge of defects in Si nitride is insufficient. A Si nitride film was prepared on Si(100) surfaces by introducing N atoms from the Si surfaces and relaxing the structures. A Si dangling bond (DB) or an N DB was artificially exposed in the Si nitride. The energy levels of Si DBs lie around the mid-gap of Si substrate, whereas those of N DBs lie far below, as show in Fig. 2(a). Hence, Si DBs can be positive charges in gate insulating films in both n-type and p-type MOSFETs, as shown in Fig. 2(b), providing a good explanation of the negative Vfb shifts. N DBs lying lower in the Si band gap cannot explain the Vfb shifts. To verify this assumption, we studied B migration and reaction in Si nitride. B atoms migrate actually from poly-Si to gate insulating films in p-MOSFETs. It is found that a single B cannot react with N nitride, but a pair of B atoms can react with N atoms in Si nitride. This results in generation of Si DBs in Si nitride, agreeing well with larger Vfb shifts in p-MOSFETs[2].

CP893, *Physics of Semiconductors, 28th International Conference*
edited by W. Jantsch and F. Schäffler
© 2007 American Institute of Physics 978-0-7354-0397-0/07/$23.00

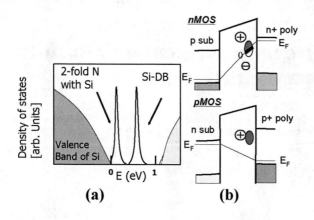

(a)   **(b)**

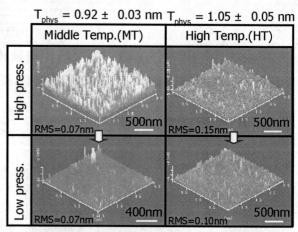

$T_{phys} = 0.92 \pm 0.03$ nm $T_{phys} = 1.05 \pm 0.05$ nm

FIGURE 2. (a) the energy levels of Si-DBs and N-DBs. (b) Positively charged Si-DBs in gate insulating films .

FIGURE 3. Leakage current profiles on Si nitride surfaces as a function of temperature and gas pressure.

Although nitridation of the 3rd layer from Si(100) surfaces is plausible[1], the Si nitride layer thickness slightly deviates, as found in oxidation of Si[3]. Since N atoms form a 3-fold configuration, this structure extends to up and down layers. The most stable structure found so far actually extends to 2 layers, furthermore accompanying SiN agglomeration or trapping of Si DBs. More semi-static approaches are essential for nitridation processes to avoid the Si DB generation.

Then, MOSFETs were fabricated with the Si nitride based SiON films as gate insulating films. In both n-type and p-type MOSFETs, the Vfb shifts were reduced to less than -0.1 V, being substantial reduction of over -0.3 V, as shown in Fig. 1. Vfb of MOSFETs for the newly designed process is reduced to the absolute minimum from the former results, breaking the phenomenological relationship between Vfb shifts and N concentration.

EXPERIMENTAL FORMATION

Based on the theoretical findings, we reconsidered the nitridation procedure[4]. Although atomically flatter Si nitride can be formed on Si surfaces normally by increasing temperature and reducing NH_3 gas pressure, it is not sufficient for reducing Si DB in Si nitride. To examine the number of defects (Si DB) in Si nitride, we observed leakage current profiles carefully at rather high temperatures by atomic force microscopy (AFM). As clearly seen in Fig. 3, leakage currents were dramatically reduced by reducing the high temperature slightly and the gas pressure substantially. More uniform Si nitride growth has been achieved at the Si nitride and Si interfaces.

Appropriate oxidation was performed on this defect minimized Si nitride. The oxygen depth profiles from the surface after subsequent oxidation are observed by angle resolved X-ray photoelectron spectroscopy (ARXPS). The oxygen atoms have penetrated through the Si nitride, and the concentration of O atoms reaches almost 100 % at the interface.

REFERENCES

1. Kato, K., Nakasaki, Y., Matsushita, D., and Muraoka, K., *Prceedings of ICPS-27* 395 (2005).

2. Wang, Z., Parker, C. G., Hodge, D. W., Robert, T. C., Yang, N., Misra, V., and Hauser, J. R., *IEEE EDL 21*, 170(2000).

3. Kato, K., Yamasaki, T., and Uda, T., *Phys. Rev. B 73*, 073302(2005); Yamasaki, T., Kato, K., and Uda, T., *Phys. Rev. Letters 91*, 146102(2003).

4. Matsushita, D., Muraoka, K., Nakasaki, Y., Kato, K., Kikuchi, S., Sakuma, K., and Mitani, Y., *IEDM Tech. Digest*, 847 (2005); *Symp. VLSI Tech.*, p172-173 (2004).

Electronic transport properties of strained Si thin films: Effective mass anomalies

Jun Yamauchi

Faculty of Science and Technology, Keio University, 3-14-1 Hiyoshi, Kohoku-ku, Yokohama 223-8522, Japan
Institute of Industrial Science, University of Tokyo, 4-6-1 Komaba, Meguro-ku, Tokyo 153-8580, Japan

Abstract. The effect of strain and layer thickness on the transport properties of $< 100 >$, $< 111 >$, and $< 110 >$ confined Si thin films is systematically investigated using the density functional calculation. The strain is uniformly applied to the plane perpendicular to the confined direction and the lattice along the direction is relaxed. Anomalously heavy effective mass, which is more than ten times of the strain-free bulk value, is found in the case of the $< 111 >$ confinement with relatively large strain. Similar results are obtained for the $< 110 >$ case. These heavy masses are attributed to the bulk property, where the two electron pockets, whose center is located about 0.84 $\Gamma - X$ in the non-strained case, merge into one pocket under the relatively large strain.

Keywords: strained Si, SOI, effective mass, density functional calculation, band structure, electron pocket
PACS: 73.50.-h,73.63.-b,73.61.Cw,73.43.Cd

INTRODUCTION

Recently, Silicon On Insulator (SOI) technology has been widely used for devices such as CPUs. The SOI structure consists of the silicon transport region sandwiched by insulating layers. For further high performance in MOSFET, strained SOI structure has been attracting researchers' interest because of its high mobility due to the suppression of intervalley phonon scattering[1]. On the other hand, successive downsizing of Si devices requires thin Si substrate. The function of *sub*-nm-body MOSFETs has been demonstrated[2]. However, there are few studies on intrinsic properties of Si film through the intermediate region from bulk to sub-nm-body using first-principles calculation. In the scientific and technological view points, it is interesting and important issue to clarify the effect of the strain and the confinement on the electronic transport properties of the Si region. I reported on the electronic structure of the *strain-free* SOI and germanium on insulator[3]. In this work, among the various properties, I focused on the effective mass behavior of *strained* Si thin films.

CALCULATIONAL METHOD

Hydrogen-terminated Si (100), (111) and $(110) - (1 \times 1)$ slab models are used as a model of Si film sandwiched by insulating layers. The plane perpendicular to the confinement direction is uniformly strained from -4 to $+4\%$ and the lattice constant along the confinement direction is relaxed. The band calculation is based on the density functional theory using a local density approxima-

tion and the pseudopotential scheme. The local density approximation(LDA) PW92[4] is adopted for the exchange correlation functional. The calculational condition is carefully checked. Cutoff energy is 20.25 Rydberg. Mesh of the sampled k-points are 8×8, 8×8, and 4×8 for (100), (111), and (110) slabs, respectively. The calculation is performed by the code TAPP[5]. In the case of the strained $< 111 >$ and $< 110 >$, it is necessary to optimize the internal coordinates, which is described by the internal displacement parameter ζ. The calculated ζ is 0.54, which shows excellent agreement with other theoretical value 0.53[6]. The effective mass is calculated from a fitting of eigenvalues to the 6th order polynomial.

RESULTS

The bulk Si has six equivalent electron pockets along the $\Gamma - X(< 100 >)$ lines. The $< 100 >$ confinement gives rise to the one isotropic electron pocket at the Γ and the four equivalent elliptic pockets. The pocket at the Γ is energetically lower and this effective mass is plotted as a function of the strain ratio and the substrate thickness in FIGURE 1. It is found that the effective mass shows a very smooth behaviors in the $< 100 >$ confined structure.

In the case of $< 111 >$ confinement, there are six equivalent elliptic electron pockets, whose longitudinal mass is plotted in FIGURE 2. Contrary to the $< 100 >$, the effective mass shows the very large values, which is more than ten times of the strain-free bulk value in the relatively large strained region both for tensile and compressive case. The reason of such anomalous behaviors is that the two conduction band bottom minima near the

CP893, *Physics of Semiconductors, 28th International Conference*
edited by W. Jantsch and F. Schäffler
© 2007 American Institute of Physics 978-0-7354-0397-0/07/$23.00

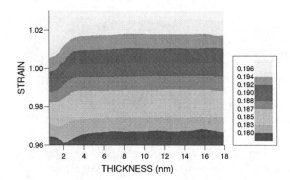

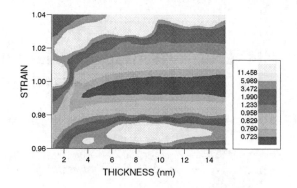

FIGURE 1. Effective mass of the < 100 > confined strained Si thin films as a function of strain ratio and substrate thickness. The strain is uniformly applied to the plane perpendicular to the confined direction and the lattice constant along the direction is relaxed. The strain ratio is the ratio of the lattice constant to that without strain in the plane perpendicular to the confined direction. The unit of the effective mass is the electron bare mass. The color scale is divided according to the data population.

FIGURE 2. Longitudinal effective mass of the < 111 > confined strained Si thin films as a function of strain ratio and substrate thickness. The configuration of this graph is similar to Figure 1. The color scale is divided according to the data population.

Brillouin zone boundary merge into one minimum due to the large strain. In FIGURE 3, the position of the conduction band minima and the effective mass are plotted both for the slab and the bulk. It is clearly shown that the anomalously heavy effective mass is obtained only when the position of conduction band minima is very near the Brillouin zone boundary.

The < 110 > confinement causes two kinds of equivalent two degenerate elliptic pockets, one of which corresponds to four pockets in the bulk. Similar enhancement of the effective mass is also found for this direction.

ACKNOWLEDGMENTS

This work was partially supported by a Grant-in-Aid for Scientific Research in Priority Areas "Development of New Quantum Simulators and Quantum Design"(No. 17064002) of MEXT. A part of this research was done in RSS21 project supported by Research and Development for Next-generation Information Technology of MEXT. The computations were performed using Research Center for Computational Science, Okazaki, Japan.

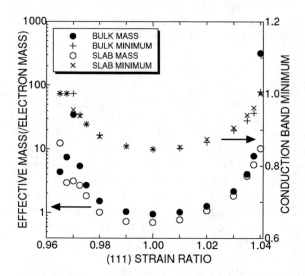

FIGURE 3. Longitudinal effective mass and the position of the conduction band bottom of the bulk and the confined slab Si as a function of strain ratio. The strain is uniformly applied to the (111) plane. The relaxed lattice constant is adopted for the rest direction. The scale of the effective mass is logarithmic. The thickness of the slab is about 15 nm depending on the strain ratio, which corresponds to 96 atomic layers. The position of the band bottom is measured by the half length of the < 100 > reciprocal lattice vector. In the strain free case, when the position is located at the X point, the value is one.

REFERENCES

1. S. Takagi, et al., J. Appl. Phys. **96** 1567 (1996).
2. K. Uchida et al., Tech. Dig. of IEDM, p.805, (2003).
3. J. Yamauchi, Thin Solid Films, **508** 342(2006).
4. J. P. Perdew and Y. Wang, Phys. Rev. B **45** 13244(1992).
5. J. Yamauchi, M. Tsukada, S. Watanabe and O. Sugino, Phys. Rev. B **54** 5586 (1996).
6. O. H.Nielsen and R. M. Martin, Phys. Rev. B **32** 3792(1985).

5μm Intersubband Raman Laser from GaInAs/AlInAs double Quantum Wells

Maxi Scheinert*, Hans Sigg*, Soichiro Tsujino*, Marcella Giovannini[†] and Jerome Faist[†]

*Laboratory for Micro-and Nanotechnologies, Paul-Scherrer-Institut, 5232 Villigen-PSI, Schweiz
[†]Physics Department, University of Neuchâtel, Rue A.L.Breguet 1, 2000 Neuchâtel, Schweiz

Abstract. We demonstrate an optically-pumped GaInAs/AlInAs based intersubband laser operating at a wavelength of $\sim 5.7\mu$m applying a simple three-level design. Using a sub-nanosecond long pulsed excitation laser tunable over the linewidth of the transition from the first level to the third level E_{13}, Raman shift in the lasing spectra was observed. Analyzing the lasing behavior we obtained the threshold at an absorbed pump power of 166W and an internal conversion efficiency between pump and intersubband laser of 3% at 70K.

Keywords: intersubband, raman, laser
PACS: 42.55Ye, 78.67De, 42.50Hz, 78.30Fs

Optically pumped intersubband lasers [1, 2] are based on a simple active layer design and waveguides with reduced losses due to the lack of electrical contacts. Raman lasing has been observed for different materials [3, 4] and can be strongly enhanced by bringing excitation and lasing energy in resonance with electronic transitions. For a three-level design in a double quantum well (DQW), the intersubband transition E_{13} is resonantly excited while the transition from the third to the second level E_{32} defines the lasing wavelength. These two transitions are in the Stokes resonance with the fundamental intersubband transition from E_2 to E_1 (E_{21}). Such an intersubband Raman laser was first demonstrated in a GaAs/AlGaAs material system with the lasing wavelength at 15μm [5].

Here, we demonstrate an InP-based optically pumped intersubband laser using a three-level DQW design. The GaInAs/AlInAs DQW structure was grown lattice matched on an undoped (100) InP substrate by molecular beam epitaxy. The active layer (Fig. 1) consisting of 60 DQW periods is embedded into a $\sim 1.1\mu$m thick waveguide structure.

In order to determine the pumping and lasing transition wavelength and confirm the design parameters, we measured the absorption spectra at several temperatures. The absorption peak for the excitation transition E_{13} is detected at 313meV for $T = 70$K and at 309meV for $T = 300$K. At 70K, the absorption linewidth of the E_{13} transition is 11meV with a peak absorption of 36%. The lasing transition E_{32} is only visible at high temperatures. It occurs at around 210meV and is close to the difference between E_{13} and E_{12}. Thus, a lasing transition energy of 215meV at 70K is expected.

As pump, 0.8ns long laser pulses obtained from a

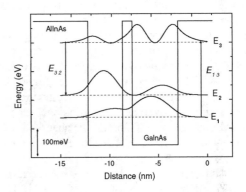

FIGURE 1. Calculated conduction band structure and square moduli of the wavefunctions of one period of the DQW structure. Each DQW is composed of 4.7nm GaInAs, 1.0nm AlInAs and 3.5nm GaInAs embedded into undoped 3.5nm and 3.0nm wide AlInAs barriers. The calculations for the transition energies E_{13} as pumping energy and E_{32} as lasing energy gives $E_{13} = 312$meV and $E_{32} = 219$meV. The depopulation energy of $E_{12} = 93$meV is around the double phonon resonance.

flash-lamp pumped active mode locked Nd:YAG excite a 50mm long periodically pooled (PP) Li-Niobate crystal. By parametric downconversion, strong infrared (IR) pulses at a wavelength around 3μm having a pulse energy of $\sim 20\mu$J and a linewidth of ~ 0.9meV are obtained. The light is coupled into the $\sim 200\mu$m thick samples via the 45° polished substrate facet. The multiple reflection of the pump light within the sample provides uniform excitation of the active layer (see inset of Fig. 2). The broad area cavity is formed by cleaving with a length of 5mm and a width of 3mm. To

CP893, *Physics of Semiconductors, 28th International Conference*
edited by W. Jantsch and F. Schäffler
© 2007 American Institute of Physics 978-0-7354-0397-0/07/$23.00

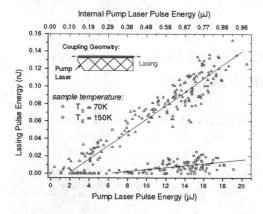

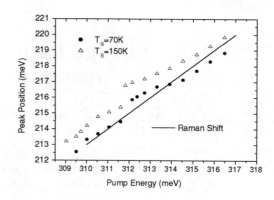

FIGURE 2. Lasing threshold curves for $T_S = 70$K and $T_S = 150$K with fit of the experimental data (dots). The scattering of the data points is due to fluctuations of the pump laser in power, pulse length and direction. The inset shows the coupling geometry.

FIGURE 3. Peak positions of the emission spectra versus pumping energy 70K and 150K. The shift of peak emission with pumping wavelength follows the Raman Shift indicated by the solid line.

minimize the atmospheric absorption, nitrogen purging was applied to the crucial parts of the setup.

For excitation at resonance energy - pumping energy coincides with E_{13} - strong lasing with a total output pulse energy from a single facet up to 20nJ is obtained at $T_S = 70$K. The lasing wavelength is found to be ~ 217meV ($= 5.71\mu$m) which is in agreement with the predicted value. An internal lasing efficiency of $\sim 3\%$ is obtained considering the amount of absorbed energy (36% of incident power) and the coupling losses for both, the excitation and the lasing.

Figure 2 shows threshold characteristics for a pump photon energy equal to 313meV at 70K and 150K. The internal threshold pump pulse energy (absorbed power) of the lasing is equal to 67nJ (86W) at 70K and 260nJ (321W) at 150K, respectively. Using a 100μm spot size of the excitation laser, the corresponding threshold intensity is equal to 1.1MW/cm^2 at 70K and 4.1MW/cm^2 at 150K. The maximum intensity at 70K is ~ 10 times larger than at 150K. The highest operation temperature is ~ 190K. Close to the threshold, the linewidth of the lasing spectrum is equal to 0.4meV which is by a factor of two smaller than the one of the pump laser. The lasing linewidth increases up to 0.6meV with higher pump intensity. Fig. 3 shows the linear shift for the peak position energy of the emitted lasing light in dependence on the pump energy. The difference between $\hbar\omega_p$ and $\hbar\omega_l$ is equal to ~ 95meV which coincides with the measured depopulation energy E_{12}. This observation indicates that the lasing occurs via Raman transition between the three levels and not via population inversion (PI), where the lasing energy is fixed to E_{32}. As we are in a two phonon resonant case, we also do not expect

phonon mode coupling as discussed in [6] and conclude from this that the Raman gain is weak, however stronger than the PI gain. The weak or eventually missing PI gain we tentatively ascribe to strong optical field effects by which carriers are excited away from the Γ-point leading to an increased state lifetime of level 2. This, combined with possible phonon reabsorption processes lifting carriers from level 3 to the continuum, may cause the non-existence of the PI.

In conclusion, we realized an optically pumped GaInAs/AlInAs laser emitting at the wavelength of 5.7μm. The linear dependence between excitation and lasing energy is a clear signature of a Raman laser which is in agreement with the relatively high threshold obtained. Most likely, carrier lifetimes are very short favoring the Raman process. Finally, Raman lasing might also be realized in other material systems like Si/SiGe where lifetimes are typically short.

The authors acknowledge S.Stutz for device preparation the financial support by the Swiss National Science foundation and by the European Community within the SHINE project.

REFERENCES

1. O.Gauthier-Lafaye, P.Boucaud, F.H.Julien et al., Appl.Phys.Lett. 71, 3619 (1997).
2. O.Gauthier-Lafaye, F.H.Julien et al., Appl.Phys.Lett. 74, 1537 (1999).
3. J.Nishizawa and K.Suto, J.Appl.Phys. 51, 2429 (1980).
4. H.Rong et.al., Nature 433, 725 (2005).
5. H.C.Liu, I.W.Cheung, A.J.SpringThorpe et al., Appl.Phys.Lett. 78, 3850 (2001).
6. H.C.Liu, C.Y.Song et al., Phys.Rev.Lett. 90, 077402 (2003).

Continuous-Wave Operation of Blue InGaN Laser Diodes Made by Plasma-Assisted MBE

C. Skierbiszewski[1,2], P. Perlin[1,2], I. Grzegory[1,2] and S. Porowski[1]

[1]Institute of High Pressure Physics, Polish Academy of Sciences, Sokolowska 29/37, 01-142 Warszawa, Poland
[2]TopGaN Ltd, Sokolowska 29/37, 01-142 Warszawa, Poland

Abstract. Room temperature, continuous-wave operation at 411 nm wavelength of InGaN multi-quantum wells laser diodes (LDs) made by plasma-assisted molecular-beam epitaxy (PAMBE) is demonstrated. The threshold current density and voltage of these LDs were 4.2 kA/cm^2 and 5.3 V, respectively. High optical power output of 60 mW was achieved. The lifetime of PAMBE LDs exceeds 5 h for 2 mW of optical power. The LDs are grown on low dislocation density bulk GaN substrates covered by dynamically stable thin metal Ga and In layer. We demonstrate that relatively low growth temperatures (600°C – 720°C) pose no intrinsic limitations for fabrication of nitride based LDs by PAMBE.

Keywords: Laser diodes, Gallium nitride.
PACS: 42.55.Px, 85.35.Be, 42.60.By, 73.21.Cd

INTRODUCTION

During last decade, the major achievements and developments in a field of the short wavelength InGaN laser diodes (LDs) has been made by metal-organic vapor-phase epitaxy (MOVPE) technique.[1] The key problem of molecular-beam epitaxy (MBE) is related with the decomposition of GaN, which undergoes at 800°C at vacuum conditions. To go above 800°C and achieve temperatures required for high quality growth (~1100°C which is about half of GaN melting point temperature), the matching overpressure of active nitrogen species in the range of 100 mbar – 1 bar is needed to stabilize GaN surface.[2] It is clear that for MBE, which relies on the negligible interaction of the atomic beams, such conditions are unattainable. However very recently, Kauer et. al.[3] managed to push the growth conditions in ammonia MBE reactor fairly close to these used by the MOVPE (by using very high ammonia flows - up to 200 sccm and reaching growth temperatures as high as 1000°C). They reported on 0.2 mW continuous-wave (cw) operation of InGaN LDs for 3 minutes.[3] On the other hand, recent progress in understanding growth mechanisms of nitrides by plasma-assisted MBE (PAMBE) led to obtain atomically flat GaN surfaces at low growth temperatures (where GaN surface is stable at vacuum conditions).[4,5] In PAMBE the active nitrogen is generated from N$_2$ molecules by RF plasma cell. It was evidenced experimentally that it is possible to achieve step-flow growth mode at temperatures below 800°C, when thin dynamic Ga (or In) layer is formed on the surface (i. e. for metal rich conditions).[4,5] This finding was confirmed by first principle *ab-initio* calculations, where substantial reduction of barrier for N adatoms diffusion on GaN surface was predicted.[6] The key element important for fundamental research as well as for industry is to prove that low temperature PAMBE can produce high quality structures which allow to show nitride based cw LDs. In this work we report on the first InGaN cw LDs made by PAMBE demonstrating potential of this technology.

EXPERIMENT AND DISCUSSION

The growth was performed in custom made VG90 Oxford MBE reactor equipped with Veeco RF plasma source (operating at 240 W for 0.8 sccm N$_2$ flow). Pressure during growth was $1.5 \cdot 10^{-5}$ Torr. The LDs structures were deposited on (0001) Ga- polarity side of the conductive, low dislocation density (~10^2 cm^{-2}) high pressure grown GaN bulk substrates. The 40 nm GaN:Si buffer layer and 450 nm Al$_{0.08}$Ga$_{0.92}$N:Si cladding were grown at Ga- rich conditions at temperature 720°C. The bottom waveguide, multi quantum wells (MQWs), electron blocking layer, top waveguide, top cladding and contact layer were grown at In- rich conditions at 600°C. The active region consists of five 3 nm In$_{0.1}$Ga$_{0.9}$N wells with 7 nm In$_{0.02}$Ga$_{0.98}$N barriers.[7] The devices were processed as

CP893, *Physics of Semiconductors, 28*[th] *International Conference*
edited by W. Jantsch and F. Schäffler
© 2007 American Institute of Physics 978-0-7354-0397-0/07/$23.00

ridge-waveguide, oxide-isolated lasers. The mesa structure was etched out in the wafer down to the depth of 0.3 μm. The 20 μm wide and 500 μm long stripes were used for the laser resonators. The oxidized Ni/Au ohmic contacts were deposited on the top surface of the device, while Ti/Au contacts were deposited on the backside of the highly conducting n-GaN substrate crystal.

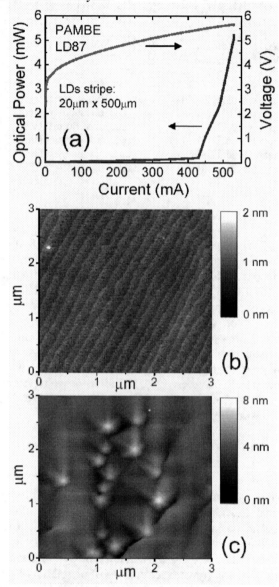

FIGURE 1. The light-current-voltage characteristic for 5 MQW LD at room temperature (a) and the Atomic Force Microscopy images of $In_{0.02}Ga_{0.98}N$ layers grown at 600°C on low (b) and high (c) dislocation density GaN substrates, respectively.

The cleaved laser mirror facets were coated by symmetrically reflecting mirrors. Figure 1a show the light-current-voltage characteristics of the LDs with lasing threshold current density and voltage of 4.2 kA/cm² and 5.3 V, respectively. The laser action

was registered up to 60 mW of optical output power (30 mW per facet) at 411 nm wavelength.[7] The lasing operation at 2 mW exceeds 5 hours. We expect increase of our LDs lifetime by optimizing the mirror region and reducing the operating voltage below 5V. As it was mentioned in introduction, for group III metal rich regime one can create conditions for two-dimensional step-flow growth mode, which in principle should give device quality structures by PAMBE. However, until very recently the efficiency of InGaN QWs grown by PAMBE was far behind those obtained by MOVPE. The poor quality of InGaN QWs from PAMBE was related with the growth on high threading dislocations (TDs) density substrates. In that case, for low temperature epitaxy, the dominant growth mode is dislocation mediated growth mechanism which result in spiral morphology (it gives spiral atomic steps on the surface around each TDs).[8] Spiral growth leads to formation of hillocks which deteriorates properties of InGaN QWs e.g. it can be a source of In segregation and InGaN alloy fluctuation along the QWs. When low TDs density GaN substrates (~10² cm⁻²) are used, the two-dimensional step-flow growth mode with parallel atomic steps is observed in PAMBE layers even at low growth temperatures (e.g. for $In_{0.02}Ga_{0.98}N$ layer grown at 600°C – see Figure 1b) and therefore smooth interfaces required for LDs are obtained.[9] For comparison, we show surface morphology of $In_{0.02}Ga_{0.98}N$ layer grown at 600°C on high TDs density GaN/sapphire template (5·10⁸ cm⁻²), where pyramids of 7 nm height are build around each TDs (Figure 1c).

In conclusion, we demonstrate first continuous-wave, blue InGaN laser diodes operating at room temperatures made by PAMBE. The low temperature PAMBE technology on low dislocation density GaN substrates opens new perspectives for next generation of nitride based optoelectronic devices.

We acknowledge partial support by Polish Ministry of Science and Higher Education Grant Nr 3T11B04729.

REFERENCES

1. S. Nakamura et. al., Appl. Phys. Lett. **73,** 832 (1998).
2. A. Ishizaka et. al., J. Phys.: Condens. Matter 6, L693 (1994)
3. M. Kauer et. al., Electronic Letters 41, No13, 23 (2005).
4. B. Heying et. al., Appl. Phys. Lett **77,** 2885 (2000).
5. C. Adelmann et. al., J. of Appl. Phys. **91,** 9638 (2002)
6. J. Neugebauer et. al, Phys. Rev. Letters **70,** 56101 (2003).
7. C. Skierbiszewski et. al., Appl. Phys. Lett **88,** 221108 (2006)
8. B. Heying et. al., J. Appl. Phys. **85,** 6470 (1999)
9. C. Skierbiszewski et. al., Semicond. Sci. Technol. **20,** 809 (2005)

Resonator fabrication for switchable two-color MIR detectors based on p-type SiGe quantum cascade injectors

M. Grydlik*, P. Rauter*, T. Fromherz*, C. Falub†, D. Gruetzmacher†, G. Isella** and G. Bauer*

*Institute for Semiconductor and Solid State Physics, University of Linz, Austria
†Paul Scherrer Institute, Villigen PSI, Switzerland
**Politecnico di Milano, Como, Italy

Abstract.

Recently, tunable SiGe quantum cascade injector structures designed for detection in the MIR spectra region have been demonstrated. The detectivity of this type of quantum well infrared photodetectors (QWIPs) can be switched between two bands centered around 6μm and 3μm by reversing the sign of the externally applied bias voltage. In order to suppress the observed spectral overlap of these bands and to increase the device detectivity, a process for integrating the detector into an optical resonator based on a low temperature ($T < 250°C$) etch mask deposition was developed

Keywords: SiGe QWIP, TMAH etching, resonator enhanced photodetection
PACS: 73.63.Hs, 78.67.De, 73.21.Fg

INTRODUCTION

Infrared detection employing optical transitions in quantum wells has attracted a lot of interest. In a recent work on SiGe QWIPs, we have demonstrated that a large wavelength tunability can be achieved by employing the injector concept originally developed for quantum cascade structures [1]. The detectivity of these tunable SiGe QWIPs at 77K is approximately $1.5x10^9 cmHz^{0.5}/W$. By using a resonator, the detector response can be limited to and enhanced in a narrow spectral region the width of which is determined by the resonators quality (Q)- factor. In the SiGe quantum cascade injector structures, the basis for photocurrent generation is the absorption in valenceband quantum wells (QWs), which is also allowed for radiation propagating parallel to the growth direction. Therefore, vertical cavity resonators can be used for these devices.

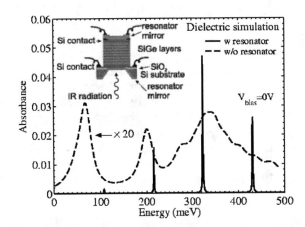

FIGURE 1. Simulation of the QWIP absorbance with (sharp lines) and without resonator mirrors (dashed lines). The absorbance without mirrors is multiplied by a factor of 20. Inset sketch - detector integrated with resonator.

EXPERIMENTAL

Details of the multilayers Si/SiGe sample structure are described in Ref. [1]. In Ref. [2] it was demonstrated, that the detectors grown on SOI substrate show a similar tunability as reported previously [1] for detectors grown on Si substrate. In Fig. 1 a simulation of the effect of a resonator on the absorption efficiency is shown. Using the absorption spectrum calculated for the QWIP structure by **k.p** band structure calculations [1], the sample transmission, reflection and absorption including multireflections at all interfaces in the sample was calculated for radiation propagating perpendicular to the sample surface. The intensity absorbed by the QWIP layer sequences is shown by the continuous spectrum in Fig. 1. Using the same band structure for the QWIP and assuming a free standing membrane consisting of QWIP layers coated with a gold layer on top and bottom of the membrane (for a sketch, see inset), the QWIP absorption was simulated. The simulated QWIP absorbance is indicated by the sharp peaks in Fig. 1.

To fabricate a vertical cavity resonator as sketched in the inset of Fig. 1, openings aligned to the detector mesas have to be etched from the backside of the sam-

CP893, *Physics of Semiconductors, 28th International Conference*
edited by W. Jantsch and F. Schäffler
© 2007 American Institute of Physics 978-0-7354-0397-0/07/$23.00

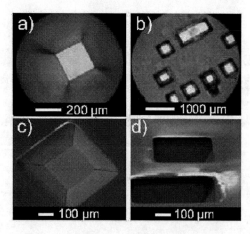

FIGURE 2. Free-standing membrane. (a,b) visible (c,d) electron microscopy

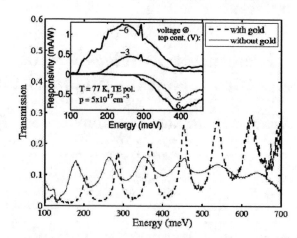

FIGURE 3. Transmission through the Si membrane with and without 5nm gold mirrors.Inset: responsivity of QWIP vs. energy for negative and positive bias voltage.

ple through the substrate. The buried oxide layer of the SOI substrate is used as an etch-stop. After removing the remaining SiO_2 layer by an HF etch, a free standing film consisting of the detector QW sequences results. On the top and bottom side of this detector film, broadband, high-reflectivity metal or Bragg- mirrors can be deposited.

The choice of a proper etchant is crucial for successful resonator fabrication. In our work, TMAH (Tetramethylammonium Hydroxide) at 90°C was used for the following reasons: a) TMAH has a large etch rate (30 μm/h) for the Si (001) lattice plane where as the etch rate for Si (111) lattice planes is an order of magnitude smaller. Therefore, TMAH etch grooves are bound by (111) planes b) The etch rate of TMAH for oxide is negligible. Therefore the etching process is effectively stopped by the 200 nm thick buried oxide of the SOI substrate.

For the long etch times required to etch from the wafer backside to the buried SiO_2, an etch mask with high resistance against TMAH is necessary. The best results were obtained using a mask consisting of a double layer of Si_3N_4 (200 nm), and the spin-on polymer BCB (Benzocyclobutene [5]). Using this mask during a 10h long TMAH wet-etch, free standing Si membranes were produced on a SOI test wafer. Electron and optical microscope pictures of the membrane are shown in Fig. 2. In the optical microscope (Fig. 2 a,b) the smooth surfaces of the membrane and the (111) sidewalls are visible. The sample shown in Fig. 2 (a,b) was illuminated from the backside resulting in a bright appearance of the Si membrane, indicating that it is transparent in the visible spectral region. Also the electron microscope pictures Fig. 2 (c,d) do not show significant surface roughness of the membranes and the sidewalls. The etch mask shown in Fig. 2 (c,d) is evidently not attacked by the TMAH etch.

On the top and bottom side of these membranes gold mirrors are deposited that form the resonator. The infrared transmission through a Si membrane (2μm) in Fig. 3 shows strong Fabry-Perot oscillations. Sufficiently large Q factors can be achieved for suppressing the spectral overlap of the two detection bands of the tunable SiGe QWIPs. Continuous and dashed line indicate transmission through the membrane before and after gold deposition respectively. Resonance peaks are observed at wavelengths within either responsivity band of the tunable QWIPs reported in Ref.[1] (inset of Fig. 3).

CONCLUSIONS

A process for fabricating a thin, free standing Si membrane by etching grooves from the backside of an SOI wafer has been developed, where the buried SiO_2 layer acts as an effective etch stop. Since only low temperature (T<250°C) process steps are involved, the process is perfectly suited for integrating SiGe based QWIPs grown on SOI substrates into vertical cavity resonators. Deposition of gold mirrors on Si membranes enhances and narrows transmission peaks, as expected from the calculations [1]. Work supported by FWF(SFB025) Vienna.

REFERENCES

1. P. Rauter, Appl. Phys. Lett. 83, 3879-3881 (2003).
2. M.Grydlik, Physica E 32 313-315 (2006).
3. L.Diehl et.al, Physica E 13, 829-834 (2002)
4. M.A. Ordal, et. al, Appl. Optics 24, 4493 (1985)
5. http://www.dow.com/cyclotene/

Competition Of Different Recombination Channels In Metamorphic 1.5 µm Range Quantum Dot Lasers On GaAs Substrate

L.Ya.Karachinsky[1,2], I.I.Novikov[1], T.Kettler[2], N.Yu.Gordeev[1], M.V.Maximov[1], Yu.M.Shernyakov[1], N.V.Kryzhanovskaya[1], A.E.Zhukov[1], E.S.Semenova[1], A.P.Vasil'ev[1], V.M.Ustinov[1], G.Fiol[2], M.Kuntz[2], K.Posilovic[2], A.Lochmann[2], O.Schulz[2], L.Reissmann[2], A.R.Kovsh[3], S.S.Mikhrin[3], V.A.Shchukin[2], N.N.Ledentsov[2], and D.Bimberg[2]

[1] *A.F.Ioffe Physico-Technical Institute, Russian Academy of Sciences, 26 Polytekhnicheskaya, St.Petersburg, 194021, Russia*
[2] *Institut für Festkörperphysik, Technische Universität Berlin, PN5–2, Hardenbergstr. 36, D-10623 Berlin, Germany*
[3] *NL-Nanosemiconductor GmbH, Konrad-Adenauer-Allee 11, 44227 Dortmund, Germany*

Abstract. 1.5 µm range laser heterostructures based on InAs/InGaAs QDs were grown on metamorphic (MM) (In,Ga,Al)As layers deposited on GaAs substrates using a defect reduction technique (DRT). The analysis of spontaneous emission efficiency corroborates the high contribution of non-radiative recombination in the total recombination current even at high current densities. Lasers showed record characteristics such as: pulsed output power > 7 W and cw output power > 220 mW, high degradation stability (> 800 h of cw operation at ~ 50 mW at 60°C junction temperature), modulation bandwidth of ~ 3 GHz limited by device overheating and the open-eye diagram at 2.5 Gbit/s.

Keywords: semiconductor laser, quantum dots, metamorphic growth, recombination, single-mode regime
PACS: 42.55.Px, 61.82.Fk, 68.65.Hb

INTRODUCTION

In last years a significant progress has been achieved in the field of semiconductor heterostructure lasers based on quantum dots (QDs) [1]. In spite of the fact that high-quality 1.3 µm range GaAs-based QD lasers have been demonstrated [2] since quite some time ago, an extension of the wavelength towards 1.5 µm keeping good device performance became possible only recently [3]. In present work we show the fundamental study of metamorphic lasers and laser characteristics we achieved recently. The details of structure and samples design can be found in [4-7]. To localize threading dislocations in a bottom buffer layer we used defect reduction technique (DRT) [8].

RESULTS AND DISCUSSION

The role of non-radiative recombination can be evaluated by studying the intensity of spontaneous emission as a function of injection current [4]. The measurements were performed on laser diodes with 250 µm cavity length. Following [4] we consider the following equation:

$$\frac{I}{P_{ext}} = \frac{e}{R} + \left(\frac{e^2 V}{R}\right)^{1/2}\left(\frac{1}{\tau_{nr}^2 B}\right)\left(\frac{1}{P_{ext}}\right)^{1/2} + \\ + \left(\frac{e^2}{R^3 V}\right)^{1/2}\left(\frac{C}{B^{3/2}}\right)(P_{ext})^{1/2}$$

(1)

where V is the volume of active medium, n - carrier concentration, B - the radiative recombination coefficient, τ_{nr} - nonradiative lifetime, C - Auger recombination coefficient, e - electron charge, I – injection current, R – linear coefficient between the real total output power and detected by detector P_{ext}. It is assumed that there are two principal non-radiative recombination channels: non-radiative recombination

CP893, *Physics of Semiconductors, 28th International Conference*
edited by W. Jantsch and F. Schäffler
© 2007 American Institute of Physics 978-0-7354-0397-0/07/$23.00

proportional to carrier density and Auger recombination, which is usually strong in long-wavelength lasers.

Figure 1 shows the dependence of the inverse spontaneous emission efficiency I/P_{ext} against injected carrier density $(P_{ext})^{1/2}$ plotted by using equation (1). The plot clearly shows the expansion of different recombination channels with increase in injection current. At low injection currents the non-radiative recombination process is dominant and the second term in (1) is the largest (region I). The radiative recombination starts to dominate at $\sqrt{P_{ext}}$ ~ 0.075 (W)$^{1/2}$ (region II) that corresponds to the current density about 5.46 kA/cm^2. The increase of I/P_{ext} at highest values of injection carrier density (region III) is likely due to the Auger recombination. Taking value of radiative recombination coefficient typical for InAs (B= $1.1 \cdot 10^{-10}$ cm^{3}s^{-1}) we could obtain non-radiative recombination time value τ_{nr} =1.4 ns. The data obtained show that at laser threshold non-radiative recombination is still significant and it influences on the device performance resulting in low temperature stability of short cavity samples and relatively low external quantum efficiency.

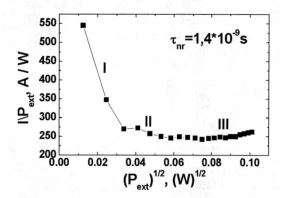

FIGURE 1. Plot showing interrelation between reciprocal of spontaneous emission efficiency I/P_{ext} and injected carrier density $(P_{ext})^{1/2}$. P_{ext} – is the power detected by the photodiode, I – injection current.

In spite of the high non-radiative recombination in metamorphic lasers several record results have been obtained for 1.5 µm range devices [5-7]. More than 7 W total output power operation in pulsed mode was shown in broad area lasers. It is shown that the narrow stripe lasers operate in continuous wave (cw) andsingle transverse mode at current densities up to 22 kAcm^{-2} without significant degradation. CW output power in excess of 220 mW at 10°C heat sink temperature is demonstrated. 800 mW single-mode output power in pulsed regime is obtained. It is also shown that the lasers demonstrate absence of beam filamentation up to the highest current densities studied. First studies on the dynamics of the lasers show a modulation bandwidth of ~3 GHz, limited by device heating. Eye diagrams at 2.5 Gbit/s and room temperature (RT) have been performed. Aging tests demonstrate > 800 h of cw operation at ~50 mW at 10°C heat sink temperature and > 200 h at 20°C heat sink temperature without decrease in optical output power.

CONCLUSION

1.5 µm range metamorphic laser heterostructures based on InAs/InGaAs QDs were grown on GaAs substrates using a DRT. By analysis of spontaneous emission efficiency in lasers fabricated from those heterostructures the high contribution of non-radiative recombination in the total recombination current was shown. In spite of this fact lasers showed record characteristics. The results clearly indicate that metamorphic InAs/InGaAs QD lasers are promising candidates for high-performance 1.5 µm edge- and surface-emitting lasers on GaAs substrates.

ACKNOWLEDGMENTS

This work was supported by the Joint Research Project between A.F.Ioffe Physico-Technical Institute, St.Petersburg, Russia and NL Nanosemiconductor GmbH, Dortmund, Germany, the EU Projects "SANDiE" (contract No NMP4-CT-2004-500101), DOTCOM, DLR, RFBR and Russian Federal Agency on Science and Innovations. A.E.Z. and L.Ya.K. acknowledges support from the Grants of the President of the RF for the support of young scientists (projects MD-4277.2004.2 and MK-941.2005.2, respectively).

REFERENCES

1 D. Bimberg, *J. Phys. D – Appl. Phys.* **38**, 2055-2058 (2005).

2 D.G. Deppe et al, *IEEE J. Quantum Electron.* **35**, 1238-1246 (1999).

3 N.N. Ledentsov et al, *Electron. Lett.* **39**, 1126-1128 (2003).

4 I.I. Novikov et al, *Semicond. Sci. Technol.* **20**, 33-37 (2005).

5 L.Ya. Karachinsky et al, *Electron. Lett.* **41**, 478-480 (2005).

6 L.Ya. Karachinsky et al, *Semicond. Sci. Technol.* **21**, 691-696 (2006).

7 T. Kettler et al, *Appl. Phys. Lett.* **89**, No 041113 (2006).

8 N.N.Ledentsov et al, *Proc. of SPIE* **6133**, 61330S (2006).

Near-Field Optical Microscopy of AlGaInP Laser Diode Emissions and Comparison with Far-Field Observation: Possible Non-Radiating Modes

Akihiro Tomioka[1,2*], Yasuaki Itakura[1], Shinji Kinoshita[1], Yuya Kurokawa[3], Yukiya Tanimura[3], and Wataru Susaki[1,2]

1Graduate School of Engineering, Osaka Electro-Communication University,
18-8 Hatucho, Neyagawa, Osaka 572-8530, Japan
2Academic Frontier Promotion Center, Osaka Electro-Communication University,
18-8 Hatucho, Neyagawa, Osaka 572-8530, Japan
3Department of Electronic Engineering and Computer Science,
Osaka Electro-Communication University, 18-8 Hatucho, Neyagawa, Osaka 572-8530, Japan
*Correspondence: tomioka@isc.osakac.ac.jp

Abstract. In situ emission profiles of AlGaInP multiple quantum well laser diodes (LDs) observed by a near-field scanning optical microscope (NSOM) showed that intact aperture probe did not couple with the lasing TE_{00} mode, indicating that the probe would couple with a longitudinal near-field. Emissions around the lasing region was detected by the NSOM, and they showed sharp peaks in the emission spectrum that may be ascribed to amplified spontaneous emissions located at wavelengths far from those of the multimode emissions. These near-field modes may therefore be non-radiating, only detectable by the NSOM. Using an intentionally enlarged aperture, each of the longitudinal multimodes was resolved spatially within an elliptic emission region.

Keywords: near field scanning optical microscope, laser diode, emission profile, TE mode, amplified spontaneous emissions, non radiating
PACS: 42.50.Pq, 42.55.Px, 42.60.Da, 72.40.+w, 78.30.Fs, 78.67.De

INTRODUCTION

Near-field scanning optical microscope (NSOM) is adequate to evaluate the optical property of quantum structures on nanometer scale[1]. However previous studies focused only on its high spatial resolution, neglecting possible differences between the far-field observation and the near-field one. Here we present a study concerning the optical coupling between the NSOM probe and the ideally linearly polarized field of TE_{00} lasing mode of laser diode (LD) and discuss on the existence of non-radiating cavity mode of LD, only detectable by the NSOM.

Detection by an Enlarged Aperture Probe

Using s NSOM probe with an enlarged aperture, a broad elliptic emission [Fig. 1(a)] was observed by a NSOM on the cleaved facet of AlGaInP multiple quantum well LD, similar to the far-field

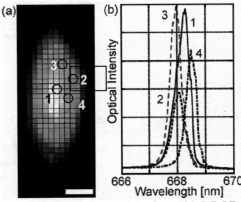

FIGURE 1. NSOM observation of an AlGaInP LD at the threshold driving current using an enlarged aperture probe. (a) The emission distribution on an end facet of the LD cavity, (b) local emission spectrum. Scale bar indicates 1μm.

CP893, *Physics of Semiconductors, 28th International Conference*
edited by W. Jantsch and F. Schäffler
© 2007 American Institute of Physics 978-0-7354-0397-0/07/$23.00

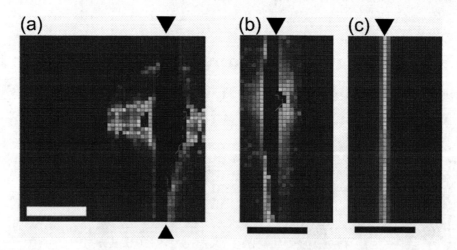

FIGURE 2. NSOM images of a LD emission observed at the intact probe-LD chip separation of 100 nm. (a), (b) Observation below (25 mA), and at (30 mA) the threshold driving current, respectively. (c) The mapping of photoelectric current produced by the free carriers excited by an optical near-field. No bias voltage was applied. Only part of the map was shown in (b) and (c). All the scale bars indicate 10 µm. The deduced location of the LD active region is indicated by a triangle.

observation of the lasing TE_{00} mode by a microscope, just where the active lasing region was located and along the electrode ridge. Local emission spectra [Fig. 1(b)] recorded with a spectrometer (Roper SP-2358 + PhotonMAX 97EMB), holding the NSOM probe at fixed positions, labeled as "1"-"4" in (a), within the emission region, showed a single peak on different wavelengths depending on the observation position, at the lasing threshold of the LD driving current. The spacing between these single peaks corresponded well with that of longitudinal multimodes observed by an optical spectrum analyzer (Advantest Q8384), which may indicate the spatial lateral separation of these multimodes, competing for optical gain, in a submicrometer scale on the end facet of the LD cavity. The peak width in (b) was deteriorated due to the limited resolution of the spectrometer (0.4 nm) and should actually be similar to the width of the multimodes (0.02 nm) observed by the optical spectrum analyzer.

Detection by an Intact Aperture Probe

When an intact, non-enlarged, aperture was used, an elliptic emission was disappeared on the NSOM emission profiles and observed a dark elongated region [Figs. 2(a) and (b)] running parallel to the quantum well layers[2], which indicates that linearly polarized light does not couple with a near-field aperture probe when the optical electric field is perpendicular to the probe long axis. This result is consistent with the reported theory[3] of fields near a metal slit of sub-wavelength scale, and also consistent with out previous interpretation deduced from the NSOM observation and the evanescent-field study of self-organized particles of organic dyes[4], where dye

molecules were unidirectionally oriented parallel to the substrate surface, therefore perpendicular to the probe's long axis[5]. This dark stripe was confirmed to correspond to the "active" region of the LD quantum structure [Fig. 2(c)], by another mapping experiment of photocurrent produced by the optical near-field at the probe tip. Emission profiles of other LDs from different manufacturers showed similar dark stripes consistently in the "active" lasing region when an intact aperture probe was used.

Around this dark stripe, additional emission was observed [Figs. 2(a) and (b)] for the driving currents both less than and above the threshold. Based on the proposed polarization property of an intact NSOM probe, these emissions should be polarized perpendicular to the end facet of the LD cavity, and therefore may be ascribed to the recombination between a light-hole and an electron, as described in text books[6], which is claimed to be irresponsible for the TE-mode lasing.

REFERENCES

1. For examples, S. K. Buratto, J. W. P. Hsu, J. K. Trautman, E. Betzig, R. B. Bylsma, C. C. Bahr and M. J. Cardillo, *J. Appl. Phys.*, **76**, 7720-7725 (1994).
2. A. Tomioka, T. Motokubota, Y. Itakura and S. Kinosita, accepted to *Mol. Cryst. Liq. Cryst.*
3. H. A. Bethe, *Phys. Rev.* **66**, 163-182 (1944).
4. Y. Ido, A. Tomioka, Y. Itakura, and T. Motokubota, *Nonlinear Opt. Quant. Opt.*, **34**, 265-269 (2005).
5. A. Tomioka, Y. Ido, Y. Itakura, and T. Motokubota, Jpn. *J. Appl. Phys.*, **45**, 417-420 (2006).
6. P. S. Zory, Jr., ed., *Quantum Well Lasers*, San Diego, USA: Academic Press, 1993, pp. 45-54.

Comparison of Near-Field Emission Profiles and Emission Spectra of AlGaAs Laser Diode with Far-Field TE- and TM-mode Optical Microscopy

Atsushi Fujimoto[1], Akihiro Tomioka[1,2*], Shinji Kinoshita[1], Takafumi Kai[3], Hiroyuki Kobo[3], and Wataru Susaki[1,2]

1Graduate School of Engineering, Osaka Electro-Communication University,
18-8 Hatucho, Neyagawa, Osaka 572-8530, Japan
2Academic Frontier Promotion Center, Osaka Electro-Communication University,
18-8 Hatucho, Neyagawa, Osaka 572-8530, Japan
3Department of Electronic Engineering and Computer Science,
Osaka Electro-Communication University,
18-8 Hatucho, Neyagawa, Osaka 572-8530, Japan
*Correspondence: tomioka@isc.osakac.ac.jp

Abstract. Near-field scanning optical microscope (NSOM) did not couple with the lasing field of the TE_{00} mode of laser diode (LD) cavity and detected additional emissions around the lasing region consistently, for both less than, and above, the lasing threshold. Based on the proposed polarization property of the NSOM probe, these emissions should be polarized perpendicular to the end facet of the LD cavity, and therefore may be ascribed to the recombination between a light-hole and an electron. Comparison of the local emission spectrum with the spectrum of far-field TE- and minor TM mode emissions suggested that the NSOM detected emissions are non-radiating cavity mode or they emerged as a result of optical coupling between the probe and the LD cavity.

Keywords: near field, laser diode, quantum well, emission profile, TE mode, TM mode, cavity mode, non radiating
PACS: 42.50.Pq, 42.55.Px, 42.60.Da, 42.60.Jf, 78.30.Fs, 78.67.De

INTRODUCTION

Luttinger-Kohn Hamiltonian explains that recombination between a heavy-hole and an electron conveys TE-mode emissions in compressively strained GaAs quantum wells[1]. The other emission predicted as the orthogonal polarization may emerge as a TM-mode, or with a different nature of e.g. non-propagating. Here we compare optical fields detected by a near-field scanning optical microscope (NSOM) with the far-field TE- and TM-modes, and discuss the origin.

MATERIAS AND METHODS

Commercially available laser diodes (LD) were placed on a custom NSOM holder with a precise temperature control to compare among emissions under different driving currents, with a sealed can opened to let the NSOM probe accessible to the end facet of the LD chip cavity. To observe far-field emission profile, laser beam was collimated with an f=4 mm aspheric lens and focused on a CCD with an f=300 mm zoom lens, which comprised a microscope to enlarge the laser emission profile.

RESULTS AND DISCUSSION

In situ emission profiles of commercially available laser diodes (LD) in operation were observed by a NSOM. In the center of the elliptical emission region, the lasing TE_{00} mode appeared as a dark region[2] running parallel to the quantum well layers [FIG. 1(a)], which was consistent with the interpretation that the NSOM probe couples only with the optical electric near-field parallel to the optical probe long axis[3] deduced from NSOM observation and evanescent-field study of self-organized particles of organic dyes[4], where dye molecules were unidirectionally oriented parallel to the substrate surface, therefore perpendicular to the probe's long axis. Around this

CP893, *Physics of Semiconductors, 28th International Conference*
edited by W. Jantsch and F. Schäffler
© 2007 American Institute of Physics 978-0-7354-0397-0/07/$23.00

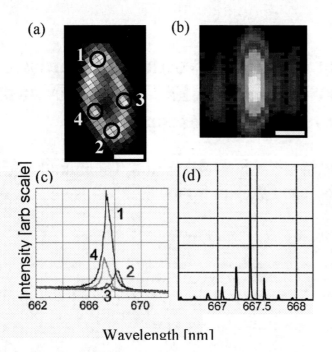

FIGURE 1. (a) The near-field, and (b) far-field TM-mode, emission distribution on an end facet of the LD cavity. (c) Local emission spectrum of (a). (d) Emission spectrum of (b). Scale bar indicates 1 μm.

dark region, additional emission was observed for the driving currents both less than, and above, the threshold. Independent mapping experiments of a photocurrent produced by an optical near-field at the probe tip consolidated the existence of the active region just where the dark region was observed in the near-field emission profile, consistently in different types of LDs with different semiconductor designs.

Far-field observation of TM-mode emissions, isolated by a Glan laser polarizer with a high extinction ratio of 1: 10^{-5} and observed using a microscope, showed a distinct intensity distribution [Fig. 1(b)] that was similar to the TE-mode emissions,

indicating that the NSOM-detected emissions are not belong to conventional TE-mode nor TM-mode emissions.

Local emissions collected by the NSOM probe displayed sharp spectrum peaks with full width around 0.7 to 1 nm [Fig. 1(c)], broader than the peak width (0.02 nm) of multi-mode laser emissions [Fig. 1(d)] recorded by a high-resolution optical spectrum analyzer. The peak positions were distributed across 1 nm difference, which was factor of five broader than the spread of multi-mode laser emissions observed at the lasing threshold. Those emissions identified by the NSOM were, therefore, not belong to the multi-mode laser emissions, and may be ascribed to amplified spontaneous emissions. Conventional far-field observation of the emission spectrum did not detect any emission at these wavelengths, even when we viewed only the TM-mode emissions. At lasing threshold with 320 μW of the major TE-mode emission, substantial light power (108 nW) was still observed as TM-modes, which was much larger than the residual power of TE-modes (3 nW) estimated from the non-zero extinction ratio of the polarizer, which indicates that the TM-mode was successfully isolated. Below the lasing threshold, the far-field TE- and TM-modes showed a large broad (41 nm full width) photoluminescence [Fig. 2] at the position 14 nm shorter than the lasing emission, which also did not correspond to the emissions identified by the NSOM, further supporting our interpretation that the NSOM-detected emissions are not belong to conventional TE- nor TM-mode. These near-field modes invisible in the far-field may therefore be non-radiating, only detectable by the NSOM, or they emerged as a result of optical coupling between the probe and the LD cavity, suggesting the possibility that the probe may work as a tool to modify or create optical fields inside the cavity.

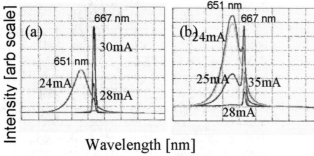

FIGURE 2. Far-field emission spectra of (a) TE-mode, and (b) TM-mode, at indicated driving currents. Intensities are plotted in arbitrary scale.

REFERENCES

1. G. Jones and E. P. O'Reilly, *IEEE J. Quant. Electr.* **29**, 1344-1354 (1993).
2. A. Tomioka, T. Motokubota, Y. Itakura and S. Kinosita, accepted to *Mol. Cryst. Liq. Cryst.*
3. A. Tomioka, Y. Ido, Y. Itakura, and T. Motokubota, Jpn. *J. Appl. Phys.*, **45**, 417-420 (2006).
4. Y. Ido, A. Tomioka, Y. Itakura, and T. Motokubota, *Nonlinear Opt. Quant. Opt.*, **34**, 265-269 (2005).

The Two-Dimensional Bigradient Effect and Its Application for GHz-THz Sensing

Dalius Seliuta*, Viktoras Gružinskis*, Vincas Tamošiūnas*, Aušrius Juozapavičius*, Irmantas Kašalynas*, Steponas Ašmontas*, Gintaras Valušis*[‡], Paul Steenson[§], Wai-Heng Chow[§], Paul Harrison[§], Alvydas Lisauskas[¶], Hartmut G. Roskos[¶], and Klaus Köhler[◊]

*Semiconductor Physics Institute, A. Goštauto 11, 01108 Vilnius, Lithuania
[§]IMP, School of Electronic and Electrical Engineering, University of Leeds, Leeds LS2 9JT, United Kingdom
[¶]Physikalisches Institut, J.W. Goethe-Universität, Max von Laue Str. 1, 60438, Frankfurt/M, Germany
[◊]Fraunhofer-Institut für Angewandte Festkörperphysik, Tullastr. 72, 79108 Freiburg, Germany

Abstract. A well-pronounced asymmetry in I-V-characteristics within low, 4.2–80 K, temperatures is demonstrated in asymmetrically in-plane shaped modulation-doped GaAs/AlGaAs structures. The results are explained by the presence of two different electric field gradients – the bigradient effect – induced by the geometrical shape. The features of the effect are revealed; the possibility to use it for GHz-THz sensing is explored via development of asymmetrically-shaped GaAs/$Al_{0.3}Ga_{0.7}$As-based and $In_{0.54}Ga_{0.46}$As-based bow-tie diodes. An effective bandwidth of 10 GHz – 1 THz and a sensitivity of about 5-6 V/W is achieved at room temperature.

INTRODUCTION

As a rule, gradients of an electric field in a semiconductor are produced via doping profiles. In this work, we show that in a modulation-doped GaAs/AlGaAs structure processed as a mesa with an asymmetrical in-plane shape (insert in Fig. 1) the "doping effect" can be realized in an otherwise uniform material – these structures tuned to the hot-electron regime behave like a conventional diode, i.e., its I-V-characteristics becomes asymmetric (Fig. 1) because two different electric field gradients are induced by the asymmetric shape.

THE TWO DIMENSIONAL BIGRADIENT EFFECT

The physics behind the effect is illustrated by calculated distributions of the electric field and the electron concentration along the structure as well as the I-V-curves given in Fig. 2. As one can see, the electric field value and its distribution is defined by the

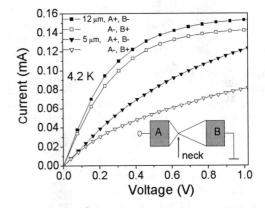

FIGURE 1. I-V-characteristics of the structures with different – 12 and 5 μm – neck size. **Insert** - shape of the sample. **Structure of the active part** (from the top): 20 nm i-GaAs cap layer; 60 nm Si doped, 2×10^{18}cm^{-3}, $Al_{0.3}Ga_{0.7}$As; undoped 10 nm $Al_{0.3}Ga_{0.7}$As spacer; 600 nm of i-GaAs; six periods of 9 nm AlGaAs/1.5 nm-GaAs layers; 0.6 μm i-GaAs layer; semi-insulating substrate. Samples are processed into 300 nm high mesas; their length is 500 μm, width and contact areas (grey A and B parts) size are 100 μm, A-shape length is 50 μm, B-shape one – 250 μm.

[‡] author to whom correspondence should be addressed: valusis@pfi.lt

CP893, *Physics of Semiconductors, 28th International Conference*
edited by W. Jantsch and F. Schäffler
© 2007 American Institute of Physics 978-0-7354-0397-0/07/$23.00

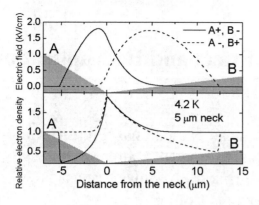

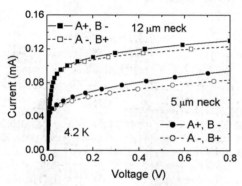

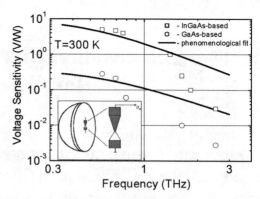

FIGURE 3. Voltage sensitivity as a function of frequency in GaAs-BT and InGaAs-BT diodes. Points − experimental data, solid lines show phenomenological fit using momentum relaxation time approach. The devices are of the same geometry as given in Fig. 1, the neck size is 12 μm. Sheet electron density in GaAs modulation-doped structure, at 300 K is $5.5 \times 10^{11} cm^{-2}$ and mobility is 4700 cm^2/Vs. InGaAs structure of 534 nm thickness is grown by MBE on InP substrate with one InAs layer in between. The electron concentration and mobility at room temperature are about $2 \times 10^{15} cm^{-3}$ and 13 300 $cm^2/V \cdot s$, respectively. **Insert** depicts silicon lens-coupled device. Note the metallization of the upper pad of the structure and the measurement scheme.

FIGURE 2. (Top plot) Calculated electric field and relative electron density distribution in the vicinity of the neck, $I=0.03$ mA. The background is decorated as the geometrical shape of the structure. (Bottom plot) Calculated I-V-characteristics for two structures with different necks. Note their similarity to the experimentally obtained data in Fig. 1.

current direction due to electron space charge accumulation in the vicinity of the neck. The phenomenon is well-pronounced within 4.2−80 K and is also affected by both the nonlocality in electron drift velocity and the real-space transfer effects [1].

GHZ-THZ SENSING

To adapt the idea for broad-band GHz-THz sensing at room temperature, we have modified the design to an asymmetric bow-tie diode: We have metallized one of the structure's pads in order to concentrate the incident radiation into the neck of the other half which contained the two-dimensional electron gas. The carriers are heated here non-uniformly by the incident radiation inducing a voltage signal over the ends of the device. Two types − silicon-lens-coupled asymmetrically-shaped GaAs/Al₀.₃Ga₀.₇As-based (GaAs-BT) and In₀.₅₄Ga₀.₄₆As-based (InGaAs-BT) − of bow-tie diodes are studied within the GHz-THz range. One can note that the sensitivity of both devices displays a similar frequency dependence: within 10 GHz−1 THz it is nearly independent of frequency

and amounts to about 0.3 V/W in the GaAs-BT and about 6 V/W in the InGaAs-BT. This increase is achieved mainly due to a higher value of the electron mobility. At frequencies above 1 THz (Fig. 3), the sensitivity drops faster than the phenomenological approach predicts due to weaker coupling of the incident radiation as illustrated by the finite-difference time-domain simulations [2].

The devices were studied using magnetron/klystron generators (10−37 GHz), and an optically-pumped molecular THz laser (0.584−2.52 THz). In all the experiments the incident electric field E was oriented along the diodes.

ACKNOWLEDGMENTS

The work was supported, in part, by NATO SfP project 978030. The research in Vilnius is performed under the topic *Study of semiconductor nanostructures for terahertz technologies* (No. 144.2).

REFERENCES

1. D. Seliuta, A. Juozapavičius, V. Gružinskis, S. Ašmontas G. Valušis, P. Steenson, W.-H. Chow, P. Harrison, A. Lisauskas, H. G. Roskos, and K. Köhler, *to be published*.

2. D. Seliuta, I. Kašalynas, V. Tamošiūnas, S. Balakauskas, Z. Martūnas, S. Ašmontas, G. Valušis, A. Lisauskas, H. G. Roskos, and K. Köhler, *Electron. Lett.* (in press).

Metal-Semiconductor-Metal Photodiode Ultraviolet Detector Based on High Quality ZnO

Ping Yu[1], Linghui Li[1], Jorge A. Lubguban[1], Yungryel Ryu[2], Tae-Seok Lee[2], and Henry W. White[1]

[1]*Department of Physics and Astronomy, University of Missouri-Columbia, Columbia, Missouri 65211, USA*
[2]*MOXtronics, Inc, 1309 Elsdon Ct, Columbia, Missouri 65203, USA*

Abstract. We present mechanism studies of a new metal-semiconductor-metal photodiode ultraviolet detector based on high quality ZnO. The detector structure consists of fringe-type Schottky contacts between high quality n-type ZnO and Ti or Au metals. High photoresponsivity has been observed at wavelengths above the band edge, which is explained by the generation and trapping of holes near the surface of ZnO. High rejection in the visible makes the device a potential candidate for visible-blind UV detectors.

Keywords: UV detector, ZnO, metal-semiconductor-metal structures.
PACS: 73.30.+y, 73.40.Sx, 73.23.Ra.

INTRODUCTION

Wide-bandgap semiconductors have shown great potential for ultraviolet (UV) detection [1]. During the past decade, wide-bandgap III-V GaN and AlGaN photodetectors have been extensively studied and show high photoresponsivity. However, these devices suffer from the problem of persistent photoconductivity due to deep level defects, grain boundaries and surface states in the material. As a wide-bandgap II-VI semiconductor, ZnO is a potential candidate material for UV detectors. Previous UV detectors based on ZnO showed either relatively low photoresponsivity or lacked the capability of visible rejection due to quality of the films. We present here a new metal-semiconductor-metal (MSM) detector based on high quality ZnO films. The mechanism of carrier generation and recombination has been studied to explain the observed photoresponse.

EXPERIMENTS AND RESULTS

Schottky contacts on n-type ZnO were made with Ti and Au metals. The electrodes on the ZnO MSM diode are finger shaped, as shown in the insert of Fig. 1. The distance (gap) between the fingers is 40 µm, and the width and length of an electrode finger are 40 µm and 800 µm, respectively. The electron concentration for n-type ZnO used for this study is in the upper 10^{16}cm^{-3}.

The DC photocurrent was measured using a current meter (Keithley Instruments 610B) under bias voltages between –5V to 5V applied to the detector. The frequency dependence of the photocurrent was studied using a lock-in amplifier (Stanford Research System SR810) and a chopper. A monochromatic light source was provided by a Shimadzu spectro-fluorophotometer (UV5301) using a 150W Xe lamp. The excitation light source was provided by scanning from 200 nm to 700 nm with a 2 nm slit width. To quantify the photoresponsivity, we measured the monochromatic light intensity at each wavelength using a UV enhanced Si detector (Newport 918-UV) and calculated the intensity according to the beam size.

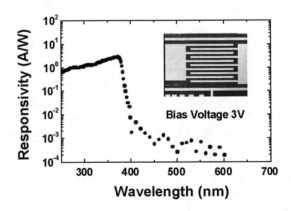

FIGURE 1. Spectral photoresponsivity of the MSM ZnO detector. Insert shows the fringe type structure of the device.

CP893, *Physics of Semiconductors, 28th International Conference*
edited by W. Jantsch and F. Schäffler
© 2007 American Institute of Physics 978-0-7354-0397-0/07/$23.00

Spectral photoresponsivity above the band edge of ZnO has been observed to be relatively flat, reaching the peak at 372 nm. Below the band edge the photoresponsivity drops quickly and reaches the noise floor in the visible. A tail of photoresponsivity near the band edge indicates density of states for carriers extending from the valence band edge into the forbidden gap. This tail can be explained by trapped holes after carrier generation. However, unlike undoped n-type GaN, the holes are not trapped by deep levels. Thus, a long–timescale, persistent photocurrent cannot be observed in the present device. This result is important for applications to UV detectors because persistent behavior adversely influences their performance.

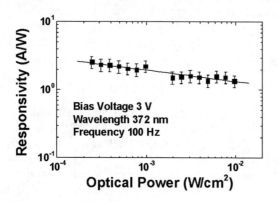

FIGURE 2. Photoresponsivity as a function of incident light power at a wavelength of 372 nm. The solid line is a linear fitting of the data.

In general, UV photovoltage detectors exhibit less than unity, or no gain. However, several authors reported gain present in GaN based Schottky detectors [2, 3]. The measured photoresponse for our detector has a relatively high value (2.7 A/W at 3 V bias and 372 nm), demonstrating possible gain presence. The high response could be due to the high quality of the ZnO film, so that holes can be trapped only by the surface states. The photoresponsivity dependence on light incident power at 372 nm is shown in Fig. 2. The responsivity is almost linear with incident power, and slightly decreases as the optical power increases. This behavior can be explained by recombination and repopulation of empty traps at the surface [3]. We could not observe responsivity saturation, as was observed previously in GaN at an optical power of 10^{-3} W/cm^2. However, more data is necessary to clarify the process by using a relatively high power Cd-He laser.

To study short-time photoresponsivity, the frequency response of lock-in signals was measured as shown in Fig. 3. The data is fitted by using the equation [4], $I(f) = I(0) / [1+(2\pi f\tau_r)^2]^{1/2}$ where $I(f)$ and $I(0)$ are photocurrents and f the chopper frequency.

The response time τ_r is determined to be 2.1 ms at 372 nm. This value is an order of magnitude smaller than that of undoped n-type GaN. By using a fourth harmonic generation of a YAG laser, we found a photoresponse of 50 μs. Since the measured response times at the low frequency (<1 kHz and 50% duty cycle) and the short pulse excitation (~ 8 ns) are all longer than the calculated RC time constant, we believe the transit time of carriers near the surface and between ohmic contacts plays an important role in the photoresponse.

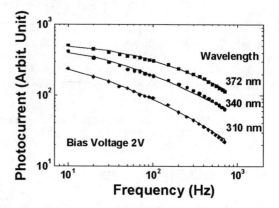

FIGURE 3. The photoresponse as a function of chopper frequency measured at three wavelengths: 372 nm, 340 nm and 310 nm.

In conclusion, a highly efficient MSM ZnO photodiode UV detector has been fabricated. A possible carrier process has been studied. The device shows excellent visible rejection, with more than 4 orders of magnitude difference between UV and visible responsivity. The results show that these devices are promising candidates for visible blind UV detectors.

ACKNOWLEDGMENTS

This work was supported by the Small Business Innovative Research (SBIR) Program of National Aeronautical and Space Administration (NASA) – Goddard Space Flight Center, Contract No. NNG05CA14C.

REFERENCES

1. E. Monry, F. Omnes, and F. Calle, *Semicond. Sci. Technol.* **18**, R33-R51 (2003).
2. D. Walker, et al., *Appl. Phys. Lett.* **74**, 762-764 (1999).
3. O. Katz, G. Bahir, and J. Salzman, *Appl. Phys. Lett.* **84**, 4092-4094 (2004).
4. C. H. Qiu and J. I. Pankove, *Appl. Phys. Lett.* **70**, 1983-1983 (1997).

Optical Properties Of IR Quantum Dot Detectors With Miniband Tunnel Extraction

F.F. Schrey[1], D.P. Nguyen[2], N. Regnault[2], R. Ferreira[2], G. Bastard[2], G. Strasser[1], K. Unterrainer[1]

[1]Technical University of Vienna, Institute for Photonics and Center for Micro- and Nanostructures, Floragasse 7, A-1040 Vienna, Austria
[2]Laboratoire Pierre Agrain - Ecole Normale Superieure, 24 rue Lhomond, F-75005 Paris, France

Abstract. We report on optical properties of InAs QD based mid- and far-infrared quantum dot infrared photodetectors (QDIP) in different host matrix environments. We show how a vertical periodic arrangement of the dots and the insertion of the QDs into an AlAs/GaAs quantum well superlattice (QW-SL) not only improve the device performance, but also how this design influences the absorption and polarization properties of the QDIP. Within an advanced model we can explain the behavior of these devices, which is dominated by the z-periodic symmetry of these structures.

Keywords: Quantum Dot, Photodetector, Superlattice.
PACS: 85.35.Be, 85.60.Gz, 73.21.Cd, 78.67.Hc

INTRODUCTION

Due to their electronic structure in the conduction band, QD based devices are predestined to be used as mid- and far-infrared (MIR/FIR) photodetectors with the advantage to offer more promising polarization selection rules[1-3] for detector applications than e.g. QW-based devices. In this paper we will show that embedding of InAs QDs into AlAs/GaAs SL structures can combine the advantages of both structures by applying a suitable QD/SL model to these devices.

DEVICES AND MODEL

All investigated samples are grown by molecular beam epitaxy (MBE) on smoothed semi-insulating (001) GaAs substrates. The parameters are chosen to obtain a lateral dot density of about 5×10^{10} dots/cm^2 per layer. For the application as photodetectors, the dots are modulation doped with one electron per QD and further processed by photolithography, wet chemical etching, and several polishing steps into QDIPs.[4] The samples differ in the number of QD layers, their vertical layer spacing or their SL period as summarized by Table 1.

The MD devices contain a vertically periodic arrangement of QDs and QWs, while the periodicity in the SD and DD device is broken for the QDs. The latter two act as control samples for our model presented below.

TABLE 1. Devices.

Device	SL period L (nm)	Number of QD layers	Number of AlAs barriers
MD-A	10	30	-
MD-B	11	20	20
MD-C	14	20	20
SD	11	20	60
DD	11	20	40

This model presumes a cylindrical symmetry and a z-periodic arrangement of the QD and AlAs layers with an effective Hamiltonian:

$$H = H_0 + \delta V = \frac{p^2}{2m^*} + V(\rho, z) + \delta V(r), \quad (1)$$

where the solutions of the corresponding Schrödinger equation can be written in the form:

$$\psi_{k_z}(x, y, z + L) = e^{ik_z L} \psi_{k_z}(x, y, z). \quad (2)$$

In this context $V(\rho, z)$ represents the isotropic part of the potential energy and $\delta V(r)$ the part without cylindrical symmetry, L the SL period length and m^* the effective electron mass $(0.07\ m_0)$[5]. Using the band offsets given in ref. 6, the solutions of the Schrödinger equation can be expressed in a Bessel basis for radial motion as given in refs. 6 and 7. As a consequence of these solutions, the QD has to be considered as a deep attractive perturbation for the carriers in

CP893, *Physics of Semiconductors, 28th International Conference*
edited by W. Jantsch and F. Schäffler
© 2007 American Institute of Physics 978-0-7354-0397-0/07/$23.00

AlAs/GaAs/InAs SL, and vice versa the energy scheme of the InAs QD's continuum is considerably restructured by the SL. This means that the combination of QDs and an SL cannot be regarded as a superposition of two independent subsystems.

EXPERIMENTS AND MODEL

Comparing the measured photocurrent (PC) signal for incident TM-polarized radiation with the calculated absorption coefficient from our model in Fig. 1(a), we observe a very good agreement between model and experiment. The high-energy absorption band in the model is suppressed in the PC measurement due to strong absorption in the optical system.

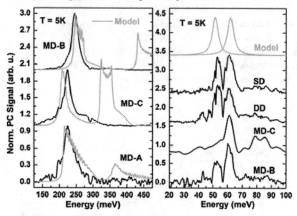

FIGURE 1. Normalized PC Signals for (a) bound-to-continuum and (b) bound-to-bound transitions.

Thus, the model is valid to predict and optimize such combined QD/SL structures for the bound to continuum transitions of these devices. In addition this model predicts correctly the spectral photoresponse of the bound-to-bound transitions within the dots for TE-polarized light as shown in Fig. 1(b).

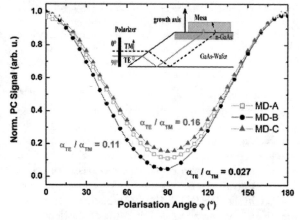

FIGURE 2. Dependence of PC the peak signal from Fig. 1 (a) on different polarization angles of the incoming light field (Inset: Sketch of the experimental geometry).

This holds even for the SD and DD devices as far as the low energy transitions are concerned, because these transitions are dominated by the QD properties, which are correctly mimicked by the model. For bound-to-continuum transitions the model cannot predict the spectra for the latter devices, because their broken symmetry violates the presumptions of the model. Fig. 2 presents the polarization dependence of the bound-to-continuum transitions of the MD devices. The indicated ratio of the TM response to the TE response is again in very good agreement with the predictions by the model.

CONCLUSION

We investigated the suitability of combined QD/SL systems for the use as mid-infrared quantum dot photodetectors. The model we developed for the periodic devices predicts not only the spectral response of the detectors, but also their polarization properties. Hence, our model allows designing the growth scheme for MIR QDIPs. We could show that vertical QD stacks within these SL structures should be preferred for the use as infrared photodetectors due to their higher spectral homogeneity, their high photocurrents, and low dark currents, as well as their possibility to design their spectral response by the surrounding SL.

ACKNOWLEDGMENTS

We would like to acknowledge the financial support by the Austrian Science Foundation FWF (SFB ADLIS, SFB IR-ON) and the European Community-IST projects SANDiE and POISE. Further, we would like to thank the Wolfgang Pauli Foundation (WPI Vienna) for their support.

REFERENCES

1. E. Finkman S. Maimon, V. Immer, G. Bahir, S. E. Schacham, F. Fossard, F. H. Julien, J. Brault, and M. Gendry, Phys. Rev. B 63, 045323 (2001).
2. E. T. Kim, A. Madhukar, Z. Ye, and J. C. Campbell, *Appl. Phys. Lett.* **84**, 3277 (1999).
3. S. W. Lee, K. Hirakawa, and Y. Shimada, *Appl. Phys. Lett.* **75**, 1428 (1999).
4. L. Rebohle, F. Schrey, S. Hofer, G. Strasser, and K. Unterrainer, *Appl. Phys. Lett.* **81**, 2079 (2002).
5. S. Hameau, Y. Guldner, O. Verzelen, R. Ferreira, G. Bastard, J. Zeman, A. Lemaitre, and J. M. Gerard, *Phys. Rev. Lett.* **83**, 4152 (1999).
6. F. F. Schrey, L. Rebohle, T. Müller, G. Strasser, and K. Unterrainer, D. P. Nguyen, N. Regnault, R. Ferreira, and G. Bastard, *Phys. Rev. B* **72**, 155310 (2005).
7. D. P. Nguyen, N. Regnault, R. Ferreira, and G. Bastard, *Phys. Rev. B* **71**, 245329 (2005).

Mid-infrared Excitation of Plasmonic Resonances in Highly Anisotropic Layered Semiconductor Structures

A. J. Hoffman[*], L. Alekseyev[*], D. L. Sivco[†], E. E. Narimanov[*], and C. Gmachl[*]

[*]Department of Electrical Engineering, Princeton University, Princeton, NJ 08544
[†]Lucent Technologies, Murray Hill, NJ 07974

Abstract. We fabricate degenerately doped quantum well superlattices and highly doped n^+-i-n^+ heterostructures and examine their optical anisotropy. We demonstrate that the n^+-i-n^+ metamaterial has sufficient anisotropy to exhibit negative refraction over a wide range of incident angles and wavelengths. Further, we show that the interval of high anisotropy, and thus negative refraction, can be controlled through the doping density in the structures.

Keywords: metamaterial, anisotropy, negative refraction
PACS: 78.20.Ci, 78.40.Fy, 78.30.-j, 78.67.De

INTRODUCTION

Optical metamaterials, have been the subject of great interest recently [1,2]. One property of these materials that has garnered much attention is negative refraction [3]. In order to obtain this behavior, materials consisting of artificial structures, with dimensions much smaller than the wavelength of light, have been designed and demonstrated repeatedly for the microwave region and recently, the optical region as well [1,2,4]. Since integrating these features into a 3-dimensional material suitable for the mid-infrared is difficult, we pursue a second method which requires only sufficient anisotropy in the dielectric tensor to achieve negative refraction [5]. Here, we report our work on degenerately doped quantum well superlattices and highly doped heterostructures, two

systems capable of providing the requisite anisotropy.

QUANTUM WELL SUPERLATTICE

A quantum well superlattice will exhibit intersubband absorption for the transverse magnetic polarization at wavelengths corresponding to allowed transitions between energy levels. The strength of the absorption can be controlled through the doping density of the wells [6]. Since an absorption resonance is necessarily accompanied by a change in the permittivity, it is possible to obtain the requisite anisotropy if the resonance is sufficiently narrow and strong.

In order to examine this phenomenon, we designed, grew, and characterized three InGaAs/AlInAs quantum well samples consisting of 85 Å quantum

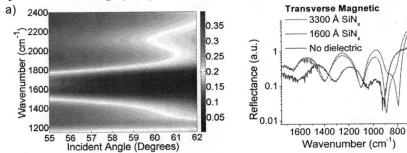
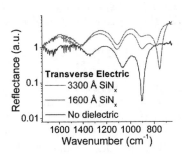

FIGURE 1. a) Plot of the measured reflection ratio R_{TM}/R_{TE} for a degenerately doped quantum well superlattice. Anomalous reflection caused by the E_{21} transition is seen in the asymmetry of the interference fringe around 1260 cm^{-1}. The dark blue region around 1650 cm^{-1} is due to intersubband absorption corresponding to the E_{32} transition. b) Plots of the specular reflectance for both polarizations that exhibit low reflection resonances. The resonances can be manipulated by use of a dielectric cap layer.

CP893, *Physics of Semiconductors, 28th International Conference*
edited by W. Jantsch and F. Schäffler
© 2007 American Institute of Physics 978-0-7354-0397-0/07/$23.00

a)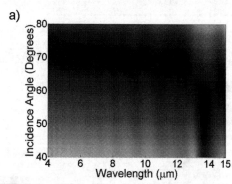

b)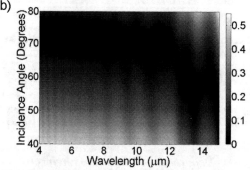

FIGURE 2. a) Plot of R_{TM}/R_{TE} for the lower-doped sample. The discontinuity in the polarization angle for 13 μm light indicates the transition into strong anisotropy. b) Numerical calculations for the sample shown in (a). The calculations require only sample thickness and doping density; free parameters are not used.

wells and barriers with the wells Si doped $> 2 \times 10^{19}$ cm^{-3}. We characterized the samples by performing reflection and transmission measurements as a function of polarization, incident angle, and wavelength. Our data display two regions of interest. The first is anomalous reflection in the vicinity of the E_{21} transition and is shown in Fig. 1(a), where E_{21} is the transition energy between the ground and first excited state of the quantum well. Here, the reflection data is plotted as a ratio of the transverse magnetic (TM) over transverse electric (TE) polarization to minimize experimental and background fluctuations. The enhanced value of the ratio around 1260 cm^{-1} is due to an increase in the TM reflectance. The fringes are due to interference effects and the dark blue region around 1650 cm^{-1} is a result of intersubband absorption corresponding to the E_{32} transition. The location of the enhanced reflection agrees with our prediction, but a determination of the actual anisotropy of the dielectric function is difficult. The second feature observed in the data are low reflection resonances and are shown in Fig. 1(b). These results are not related to negative refraction, but are interesting nonetheless. As is shown in the figure, the resonances can be spectrally shifted by application of a dielectric cap layer and even eliminated in the case of TE polarization.

HIGH-DOPED HETEROSTRUCTURE

We also study InGaAs/AlInAs heterostructures that are highly doped in the InGaAs layers. The layers in these structures are 80 nm thick, which is sufficient to eliminate quantization of the energy levels. For this system, the desired anisotropy is achieved when neighboring layers have dielectric constants with opposite signs. The transition into this strong anisotropy occurs when the frequency of the incident light exceeds the plasma frequency of the doped InGaAs layers and is marked by a discontinuity of the polarization angle for the metamaterial. The spectral

location of the discontinuity can be controlled through the doping in the InGaAs layers.

To study this system, we grew two samples with different doping densities in the InGaAs layers; both densities were greater than 0.8×10^{19} cm^{-3}. We performed transmission and reflection measurements as a function of polarization, incident angle and wavelength. The reflection measurements clearly displayed a discontinuity in the polarization angle at 13 μm for the lower doped sample and 10 μm for the higher doped sample. The reflection data is plotted as the ratio of TM/TE for reasons previously mentioned. Experimental data for the sample with critical wavelength $\lambda_0 = 13$ μm is shown in Fig. 2(a), and Fig. 2(b) shows a theoretical calculation for the same sample.

Our work on degenerately doped quantum wells demonstrates that they may provide a mechanism for realizing negative refraction. The work presented on n$^+$-i-n$^+$ heterostructures shows that we have obtained the anisotropy necessary to observe negative refraction. Our current research effort focuses on measuring effects due to this property of the material.

This work was supported in part by PRISM, Princeton University.

REFERENCES

1. V. M. Shalaev, W. Cai, U. Chettiar, H.-K. Yuan, A. K. Sarychev, V. P. Drachev, and A. V. Kildishev, Opt. Lett. **30**, 3356-3358 (2005)
2. S. Zhang, W. Fan, N. C. Panoiu, K. J. Malloy, R. M. Osgood, and S. R. J. Brueck, PRL **95**, 137404 (2005).
3. V. G. Veselago, Sov. Phys. Usp. **10**, 509 (1968)..
4. R. A. Shelby, D. R. Smith, and S. Schultz, Science **292**, 77 (2001).
5. V. A Podolskiy and E. E. Narimanov, Phys. Rev. B **71**, 201101, (2005).
6. H. Asai and Y. Kawamura, Phys. Rev B **43**, 4748-4759 (1991).

Red, Green and 1.54 μm Emissions from an Er-doped n-ZnO/p-Si Light Emitting Diode

S. Harako[1], S. Yokoyama[1], K. Ide[1], S. Komuro[2] and X. Zhao[1]

[1] Department of Physics, Tokyo University of Science, 1-3 Kagurazaka, Shinjuku-ku, Tokyo 162-8601, Japan
[2] Faculty of Engineering, Toyo University, Kawagoe, Saitama 350-8585, Japan

Abstract: Er-doped ZnO/Si hetero-junctions have been formed by laser ablating an Er-contained ZnO target onto p-Si (100) substrates. Light emitting diodes fabricated by using these samples exhibit bright green, red and 1.54 μm emissions under reverse current injections at room temperature. It is revealed that these light emissions arise from intra-4f transitions in Er^{3+} ions that are excited by impact excitation process. A low threshold voltage of ~10 V was achieved. Our results show a possibility of realizing the Si-based light emitting devices by doing Er.

INTRODUCTION

There has been great progress in the past decade on Er-doped semiconductors. Since the first report of stimulated emission at 1.54 μm from an Er-doped nanocrystalline Si waveguide,[1] new effort is focused on realizing a Si-based injection laser operating at the 1.54 μm wavelength region. Sufficient oxygen (O) co-doping with Er into Si dramatically enhances the 1.54 μm emission at room temperature (RT). However, the O-doping induces electrically insulating Si-O phase in Si. The Er-doped ZnO (ZnO:Er) is considered to be a candidate for fabricating a current injection type optical devices. ZnO layers on Si substrates have been extensively studied for light emitting diodes (LED's) and lasers emitting light based on band to band transitions and donor-acceptor (DA) pairs-related emissions in ZnO.[2-4] There is a lack, however, of fabricating ZnO/Si hetero LED's emitting light based on Er doping. In our previous work, ZnO:Er thin films with high Er density have been synthesized by laser ablation. The bright Er-related emissions have been demonstrated at RT.[5]

In this work, we report a n-ZnO:Er/p-Si LED worked at RT. The LED shows intense green, red and 1.54 μm emissions and operates at a very low threshold voltage, suggesting a promising Si-based light source of multi colors.

EXPERIMENTAL

The ZnO:Er thin film was formed on p-type Si (100) substrate (~10 Ω-cm) by ablating a ceramic target of ZnO containing 0.5wt% Er_2O_3. The Er density incorporated in the ZnO:Er layer was ~10^{20} cm^{-3}. A Q-switched YAG laser (266 nm, 1 J/cm^2) was used to ablate the target in a vacuum chamber with an O_2 pressure of 1x10^{-3} Torr. The ZnO:Er layer of 140 nm thick was formed at RT. After the ablation the sample was annealed at 700°C for 3 min in the O_2 atmosphere. A surface electrode was formed by depositing transparent indium-tin-oxide (ITO) layer with a thickness of 70 nm and a back

electrode by 100 nm Al, respectively. Afterwards, the sample was cut to chips to form the LED's. The EL spectra were measured by current injection using a pulsed current source (rectangular pulse, 10 ms). For PL measurements, the samples were excited by the 325 nm line of a He-Cd laser. Both the EL and PL signals were detected by a CCD detector in the visible region and by a Ge p-i-n diode in the infrared region, respectively, and were processed by a lock-in technique.

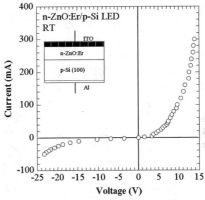

Figure 1. Current-voltage characteristics of a n-ZnO:Er/p-Si LED.

RESULTS AND DISCUSSION

The as-prepared ZnO:Er layers showed n-type characteristic and exhibited a resistivity of ~1 Ω-cm. After annealing the layers are still n-type but the risistivity increased to ~1000 Ω-cm. Although the relatively lower conductivity of the n-ZnO layer, excellent rectification characteristics have been demonstrated form the LED's, which suggested a good p-n junction formation in the n-ZnO/p-Si interface, as shown in Fig. 1 for one LED at RT. The insert shows a schematic drawing of the LED.

Figure 2 shows the EL and PL spectra in the visible region measured from the ITO surface of the LED at RT. The transmittance of the ITO film was about 85% in the visible region. The transmittance at 325 nm was ~50%, and at 1.54 μm was ~75%,

CP893, *Physics of Semiconductors, 28th International Conference*
edited by W. Jantsch and F. Schäffler

respectively. So that the PL intensity was lower than that measured from a bare ZnO:Er layer. The EL spectra were detected under a reverse current of 40 mA (533 mA/cm^2). Three distinct peaks at 536 nm, 556 nm and 665 nm were observed. These three sharp peaks were assigned to intra-4f transitions from spin-orbit split levels $^4H_{11/2}$, $^4S_{3/2}$ and $^4F_{9/2}$ to ground states $^4I_{15/2}$ of the Er^{3+} ions. These emissions, however, could not be observed in the PL spectra. The PL exhibited a sharp peak at 375 nm corresponding to bound exciton transitions and a broad band from 500 nm to 900 nm, which arose from the deep DA-related transitions. As described in Ref. 5, the 665 nm line could only be seen in the case of direct excitation of the Er^{3+} ions in ZnO. The photo-generated electron-hole (e-h) pairs transfer their energies to the first excited states $^4I_{13/2}$ and the second states $^4I_{11/2}$ rather than to higher levels. In agreement with this suggestion, a clear peak at 1538 nm was observed in the PL spectra, as shown in Fig. 3. So the sharp lines in red and green were caused by the impact excitation of the Er^{3+} ions. The reverse current of 40 mA, which corresponding to the reverse bias of 21 V, had generated a strong electric field and accelerated the electrons and holes to impact the Er^{3+} ions in the ZnO layer.

The EL spectra in the infrared region were shown in Fig. 3. A peak having the same position like PL at 1538 nm was obtained. This peak was caused by the transitions from $^4I_{13/2}$ to $^4I_{15/2}$ in the Er^{3+} ions. Under impacting excitation, the Er^{3+} ions are activated to various excited levels. Subsequently, cascade transitions occur, which gives rise to sharp emission lines in the visible and 1.54 μm regions. The clear different features in PL and EL spectra reveal that the observed EL was caused by impact excitations of the Er^{3+} ions but not by energy transfer from the e-h pairs. Also there was no detectable signal for the bound exciton emission at 375 nm in the EL measurements. A broad background EL band from 1100 nm to 1600 nm was also recorded, which was considered to be caused by some deep states activated by the accelerated minority carriers. There was also a peak at 1180 nm that did not appear in the PL spectra. This emission should originate in the e-h recombination near the p-n junction.

In order to investigate the emission mechanism of the Er^{3+} ions in the n-ZnO:Er/p-Si LED, the injection current dependence of the EL intensity has been carried out. The EL increased linearly with the increasing injection current and showed no saturation until the reverse voltage near to the break down limit. By assuming a certain cross section of Er^{3+} ions in impacting excitation, the EL intensities should exhibit linear dependence on the injection current, which leads to an exponential dependence of the EL on the biased voltage. The EL gives rise to a clear threshold at ~10 V, which corresponds to an electrical field of ~7x10^5 V/cm. The electrons and

holes cross the p-n junction are accelerated in this high filed to excite the Er^{3+} ions by impacting.

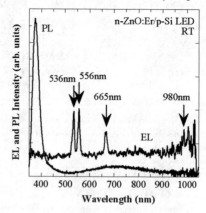

Figure 2. EL and PL spectra of a n-ZnO:Er/p-Si LED at visible wavelength region at RT.

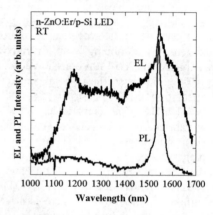

Figure 3. EL and PL spectra of a n-ZnO:Er/p-Si LED at infrared wavelength region at RT.

In conclusion, we have fabricated a n-ZnO:Er/p-Si LED by ablating a ZnO:Er$_2$O$_3$ target onto a p-type Si substrate. The LED shows intense green, red and 1.54 μm emissions at RT. A low threshold of about 10 V to activate the Er light emissions has been demonstrated. This low threshold and multi emitting colors indicate that ZnO:Er is a promising candidate in further opto-electronic device applications.

REFERENCES

1. X. Zhao, S. Komuro, H. Isshiki, Y. Aoyagi and T. Sugano: Appl. Phys. Lett. **74**, 120 (1999).
2. D. M. Bagnall, Y. F. Chen, Z. Zhu, T. Tao, S. Koyama, M. Y. Chen and T. Goto: Appl. Phys. Lett. **70**, 2230 (1997).
3. S. Cho, J. Ma, Y. Kim, Y. Sun, G. K. L. Wong and J. B. Ketterson: Appl. Phys. Lett. **75**, 2761 (1999).
4. B. Lin, Z. Fu and Y. Jia: Appl. Phys. Lett. **79**, 943 (2001).
5. S. Komuro, T. Katsumata, T. Morikawa, X. Zhao, H. Isshiki and Y. Aoyagi: Appl. Phys. Lett. **76**, 3935 (2000).

Avalanche Photodiode Structure for Photon Counting on $Si_{0.6}Ge_{0.4}$ Epitaxial Layer

Josef Blažej, Dominik Chren, Helmar Frank, Karel Hamal, Ivan Procházka, Bruno Sopko

Czech Technical University in Prague, Brehova 7, 115 19 Prague 1, Czech Republic

Abstract. We are presenting the results of the research and development of an avalanche photodiode structure, on the basis of SiGe epitaxial layer on Si wafer. The ultimate goal is to develop a solid state photon counting detector with picosecond timing resolution and stability and a spectral sensitivity beyond 1100 nanometers. The technology development steps on the $Si_{0.6}Ge_{0.4}$ epitaxial layer are presented together with the first results of the preparation of the shallow junction and its parameters. The ability of the avalanche structure to operate in a Geiger mode has been demonstrated for the first time. The serial resistance of the structure above its breakdown voltage has been measured. The diffusion and annealing model has been tuned for GeSi epitaxial layer and implantation. The resulting concentration profiles have been verified by two independent diagnostics methods. The rapidity of avalanche grow was compared with Si photon counting diode.

Keywords: SiGe, avalanche photodiode, picosecond resolution.
PACS: 42.79.Qx, 42.68.Wt

INTRODUCTION

Single Photon Avalanche Diodes (SPADs) have been developed in the early eighties [1]. Photon counting detectors based on Silicon have been developed in labs of the Czech Technical University [2]. The unique properties of the solid state photon counter are: high timing resolution and stability at room temperature, low operating voltage, simplicity and ruggedness. This detector has been applied in wide range of applications. SPAD detectors on Silicon may be employed in the wavelength region 220 – 1100 nm. For the wavelength above 1100 nm, Silicon is not suitable. Although photons in the wavelength range 1100 – 1600 nm can be detected using the Si based photon counters, the quantum efficiency is too low for practical applications. However, the wavelength region 1100 to 1600 nm is quite attractive for numerous applications. The near infrared photon counters based on Germanium have acceptable quantum efficiency ranging from visible up to 1550 nm and picosecond timing resolution. However, they have to be operated in cryogenic environment [3].

One of the semiconductor material candidates for the near infrared is SiGe. The theoretical models predict both the enhanced quantum efficiency in the near infrared and the increased timing resolution in comparison to Silicon based detectors [4]. To reach this performance the SiGe layer has to be at least several micrometers thick and the fraction of Germanium in Silicon has to be within the range of 20 – 70 %. The world first published attempts to manufacture SiGe based photon counters have been made by our group in the early nineties [5]. The SiGe material has been prepared by Germanium implantation into the Silicon. The structures have been operational as photon counting devices at room temperature; the timing resolution has been equal to a Silicon one. However, the SiGe preparation technology resulted in a low (< 1 %) concentration of Germanium within a nm thick layer, not sufficient to increase the structure sensitivity in the near infrared and the timing resolution.

SIGE STRUCTURE TECHNOLOGY

Recent achievements in SiGe mono-crystal growth permit to produce high conductivity silicon wafers with the SiGe epitaxial layer on their top with the Ge concentration > 30 % and with the quality acceptable for avalanche structure construction. The 4 inch diameter Silicon wafers with epitaxial layer have been acquired on a commercial basis, QINETIQ Ltd., Malvern Technology Centre, UK.

CP893, *Physics of Semiconductors, 28th International Conference*
edited by W. Jantsch and F. Schäffler

We have designed the avalanche structure in the SiGe epitaxial layer on the Silicon substrate. The p-n shallow junction will be created by ion implantation and following diffusion. The SPAD structures will be of circular shape with active area diameters of 60, 100, and 200 um and the break voltage of the structure will be 12 – 20 V.

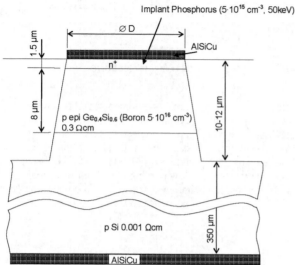

Implant Phosphorus ($5 \cdot 10^{15}$ cm^{-3}, 50keV)

FIGURE 1. Vertical mesa structure of SiGe SPAD prepared for development phase. D = 200 microns.

EXPERIMENTAL RESULTS

The parameters of ion implantation have been tuned to form a shallow p-n junction. In the final structure design the guard ring will be created by diffusion from implant deposition, also.

The first structures have been prepared by Phosphorus diffusion from an implanted layer and by MESA technology, see Figure 1. The mesa structure (etched through the epitaxial layer into the substrate) provides conditions similar to the structure with a guard ring; however it is more practical for experimental steps. The samples gave us the technological parameters for annealing and diffusion of the implanted layer. The vertical concentration profile of the SPAD structure has been measured by method of spreading resistance.

The Germanium, Boron, and Phosphorus concentration profiles of the same sample have been investigated using the secondary ion mass analysis [6]. The recorded profile of the P after the diffusion coincides well with the theoretical model. A Germanium average concentration of 48 % has been measured. The p-n shallow junction has been located in the depth of 118 nm.

The V-I characteristics of the diode samples have been analyzed and recorded on a Tektronix type 576 curve tracer, see Fig. 2. The p-n junction exhibits an avalanche break down characteristics; the break voltage is 14.2 V. A current 25 nA has been measured 2 V below the break voltage.

The first avalanche diode operation has been achieved when operating the diode structure in a passive quenching circuit formed by a 100 kΩ resistor and a 20 pF capacitor.

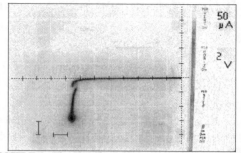

FIGURE 2. The V-I characteristics of the p-n junction in the third quadrant, horizontal sensitivity 2 V/div, vertical sensitivity 50 µA/div, dotted lines are zero axis.

The detector temporal resolution has been measured in linear regime with negative bias 5 V and 650 ps laser pulse with 532 nm has been detected. The energy on detector was 60 pJ. The response to 50 Ohm impedance has been analyzed on 400 MHz oscilloscope. The rise time was typically 960 ps. From knowledge of typical value for Si SPADs, 1.2 – 2.0 ns, the expected temporal resolution can be estimated as at least 2 times higher then for Si structure.

ACKNOWLEDGMENTS

This research has been supported by the Grant Agency of the Czech Rep., project No. 102/03/0316 and currently is supported by Ministry of Education in research framework MSM6840770015.

REFERENCES

1. S. Cova et al, *IEEE J.Q.Electronics* **19**, 630 (1983).
2. I. Prochazka et al, *Microelectronic Engineering* **19**, 643-648 (1992).
3. I. Prochazka et al, *Optics Letters* **21**, 17 (1996).
4. L. M. Giovane, et al, "Strong absorption GeSi on Si materials for 1.3 um photodetection" in *Proceedings of the 39th Electronic Materials Conference*, Fort Collins, CO, USA, 1997.
5. B. Sopko, J. Pavlu, I. Procházka and I. Mácha, "Detection of Near IR Radiation by GeSi Material" in *Proceedings of the ESSDERC'90*, A. Hilger, UK, 1990, pp. 413-415.
6. Bo Lojek, ATMEL Corporation, Colorado Springs, 1150 E. Cheyenne Mtn. Blvd., Colorado Springs, CO 80906, USA (private communication).

Band Alignment and Carrier Recombination in GaAsSb/GaAs Quantum Wells

K. Hild[1], S. J. Sweeney[1], S. R. Jin[1], S. B. Healy[2], E. P. O'Reilly[2], S. R. Johnson[3], J.-B. Wang[3] and Y.-H. Zhang[3]

[1] *Advanced Technology Institute, University of Surrey, Guildford, GU2 7XH, UK*
[2] *Tyndall National Institute, Lee Maltings, Cork, Ireland*
[3] *MBE group, Arizona State University, Tempe, Arizona, USA*

Abstract. Using a combination of experimental and theoretical techniques, we investigated the band alignment and the carrier recombination processes occurring in GaAsSb/GaAs structures. We find that for Sb fractions ~30%, the band alignment is slightly type II. From studies on lasers based upon this material we show that at the high carrier densities required to achieve threshold, at room temperature, the devices are dominated by carrier leakage and non-radiative Auger recombination.

Keywords: GaAsSb, band alignment, carrier recombination, semiconductor laser, VCSEL, optical communications
PACS: 42.55.Px, 61.50.Ks, 72.20.Jv, 78.60.–b, 79.20.Fv, 85.35.Be

INTRODUCTION

GaAsSb/GaAs quantum wells are of significant technological interest as they allow the possibility to produce vertical cavity surface emitting lasers emitting at 1.3μm. However, there is still a lot of uncertainty concerning the basic material properties such as the band alignment of the GaAsSb/GaAs QW system (type I / type II) for Sb concentrations ~30-40% as required to achieve 1.3μm emission [1],[2]. Secondly, the role of non-radiative recombination processes such as Auger recombination, known to be important in the InGaAs(P)/InP system at similar band gaps, has yet to be quantified. Here we present a combination of spectroscopic and device studies together with preliminary theoretical calculations to determine the band alignment and the dominant recombination processes. Our results suggest that the GaAsSb/GaAs band alignment is slightly type II. However, this is shown to have little influence on device properties due to the Coulombic attraction between the delocalized electrons and holes. Using a combination of pressure and temperature dependence techniques, we also find that at the high carrier densities required for lasing operation, the current is dominated by non-radiative recombination through a combination of carrier leakage and Auger recombination.

LASER STRUCTURES AND EXPERIMENTS

The samples studied were in the form of semiconductor lasers. The active region of the samples consists of 3, 7nm $GaAs_{0.64}Sb_{0.36}$ QWs within 5nm GaAs spacers and 8nm GaAsP barriers for strain compensation. The devices are measured as cleaved with cavity lengths of 500um. To reduce Ohmic heating the devices were driven pulsed with a pulse width of 200ns and a 10kHz repetition rate. Temperature dependence measurements over the range of 60-300K were performed with a standard closed cycle cryostat set-up. Hydrostatic pressure measurements over the range 0-10kbar were performed using a gas compressor.

BAND ALIGNMENT

In order to investigate the nature of the band alignment and the extent to which the different radiative and non-radiative processes influence the

CP893, *Physics of Semiconductors, 28th International Conference*
edited by W. Jantsch and F. Schäffler
© 2007 American Institute of Physics 978-0-7354-0397-0/07/$23.00

device characteristics, we performed spontaneous emission measurements whereby the light was collected in a direction perpendicular to the laser cavity through a window milled in the substrate of the lasers. This was to ensure that *pure* spontaneous emission was collected that had not been influenced by the effects of gain and/or loss along the laser cavity. This technique has been described in detail elsewhere [3] From those spontaneous emission spectra we observe a strong blue shift of the peak emission with excitation current (Figure 1). Also plotted is the equivalent data for a standard type I InGaAsP laser emitting at the same wavelength.

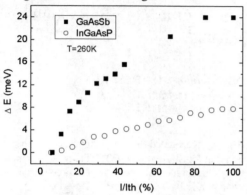

FIGURE 1. Comparison of the blue shift with excitation for the GaAsSb laser and an InGaAsP laser.

The shift for the GaAsSb/GaAs laser is much stronger and cannot be explained by band filling alone and is consistent with the carriers being delocalized and a type II band alignment. A comparably strong shift has also been observed in photoluminescence measurements of these structures [4]. Furthermore, utilizing self-consistent Schrodinger-Poisson calculations [5] in which the conduction band offset was treated as a free parameter, we observe that the peak emission shift with carrier density increases as one goes from a type I to a type II band alignment, consistent with our experimental findings

CARRIER RECOMBINATION

Figure 2 shows the measured temperature dependence of the threshold current (solid diamonds) and radiative current (open squares), the latter of which is determined from the spontaneous emission measurements [3]. It can be seen that the threshold current is very temperature sensitive whilst the radiative current maintains the ideal-like linear temperature dependence that one would expect for a QW [3] (see also inset). Thus, we conclude that at the typical carrier densities required for laser threshold, these 1.3μm GaAsSb/GaAs lasers are dominated by

non-radaitve recombination, accounting for ~90% threshold current at room temperature. From pressure dependence measurements, described elsewhere [6] we find that this is due to a combination of electron leakage from the QWs into the barrier layers together with non-radiative Auger recombination.

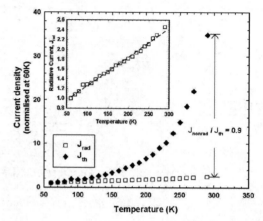

FIGURE 2. Temperature dependence of the threshold current and the radiative current in the GaAsSb/GaAs lasers.

CONCLUSIONS

In summary, using a combination of experimental and theoretical techniques, we find that the band alignment of the GaAsSb/GaAs interface (for Sb fractions ~30%) is slightly type II. However, due to the Coulombic attraction between the electrons and holes, this has little effect on device performance. We also investigated the dominant carrier recombination processes in GaAsSb/GaAs lasers emitting close to 1.3μm. We find that at the high carrier densities required to achieve threshold, the current is dominated by carrier leakage from the QWs together with non-radiative Auger recombination.

ACKNOWLEDGEMENTS

The authors gratefully acknowledge EPSRC (UK) for financial support.

REFERENCES

1. J.-B. Wang *et al*, Phys. Rev. B 70 p195339 (2004)
2. Q. Liu *et al*, J. Appl. Phys. 77 p1154 (1994)
3. S. J. Sweeney *et al*, IEEE Phot. Tech. Lett. 10, p1076 (1998).
4. G. Blume *et al*, IEE Proc. Optoelectron. **152,** p110 (2005)
5. S. B. Healy and E. P. O'Reilly, IEEE J. Q. E. **42**, p608 (2006)
6. K. Hild *et al, submitted to* Phys. Stat. Sol. (b).

Mechanism of Electron-Hole Pair Generation and Light Emission for Electro-Luminescence Devices with Silicon Nano-Crystals Prepared by Laser Ablation Method

A. Sugimura[1,2], M. Koyama[1], M. Inada[3], T. Yoshida[4] and I. Umezu[1,2]

[1]Department of Physics, Graduate school of Natural Science, Konan University, Kobe 658-8501, Japan
[2]Quamtum Nanotechnology Laboratory, Konan University, Kobe 658-8501, Japan
[3]National Institute of Information and Communications Technology, Kobe 651-2492, Japan
[4]Anan National College of Technology, Anan, Tokushima 774-0017, Japan

Abstract. Mechanism of electron-hole pair generation and light emission for electro-luminescence devices with silicon nano-crystals prepared by laser ablation method is studied. It is found that the properties of the present device are strongly influenced by the existence of the high electric field, which stems from the band discontinuity at the boundary between ITO and the Si nano-crystalline layer.

Keywords: Electroluminescence, Si nanocrystallites, pulsed laser ablation, luminescence, impact ionization.
PACS: 73.63.-b 78.60.Fi 78.67.-n

INTRODUCTION

Silicon nano-crystal material has attracted much interest because of its applicability to future light emitting devices. Although various aspects of this material have been studied extensively, from a standpoint of practical application, there still remain lots of subjects to overcome. Previously, we showed that Si nano-crystals prepared by the laser ablation method in the hydrogen atmosphere provide us good quality, high efficiency photo-luminescence (PL) when the ablation conditions are optimized[1]. Thus, we fabricated electro-luminescence (EL) device structures with this Si nano-crystal material and investigated mechanism of the electron-hole generation and the light emission in order to clarify the optimum device structure and the device performance limit.

DEVICE FABRICATION

To fabricate the EL device, (100) oriented p-type Si wafer was used as a substrates. Si nanocrystallites were deposited on it by PLA in hydrogen gas. In the present deposition condition, hydrogen-passivated Si nanocrystallites were formed with mean diameter of 4.6 nm [2] and the band gap energy was 1.9 eV [3]. Semitransparent n-type indium-tin-oxide (ITO) top electrodes with a thickness of 300 nm were then deposited by radio frequency (RF) sputtering method. Thus the fabricated device structure is such that the Si nano-crystal layer is sandwitched with n-type indium tin oxide (ITO) and p-type crystal Si layers.

RESULTS AND DISCUSSION

The I-V characteristics of the EL device measured at room temperature indicated a rectifying behavior. Figure 1 shows the integrated EL intensity as a function of the injection current measured at room temperature in logarithm scales. The slope of EL intensity lie on the two lines as indicated in Fig. 1. In the current region larger than 2 mA, the intensity is proportional to the square of the injection current. Reference 4 describes that the EL intensity super-linearly depends on the injected current when electron-hole pairs are created by the impact ionization processes, because the impact ionization rate depends on the hot electron energy. The electric field in the EL device is estimated to be about 1 MV/cm, which corresponds to the threshold value for the impact ionization process in bulk Si. These results suggest that the electron-hole pairs are created by the impact ionization process, and the luminescence is obtained by the radiative recombination of these electron-hole pairs. In the current region smaller than 2 mA, the EL

CP893, *Physics of Semiconductors, 28th International Conference*
edited by W. Jantsch and F. Schäffler
© 2007 American Institute of Physics 978-0-7354-0397-0/07/$23.00

intensity is proportional to the injection current. The impact ionization process is not expected, because electric field at this region is much less than 1 MV/cm. Thus, this result suggests that electron-hole pairs are created by direct injection of electrons and holes in the p-n junction structure, and the luminescence is obtained by the recombination of the pairs. The emission in this region was weak because of the unbalance between the electron and hole numbers.

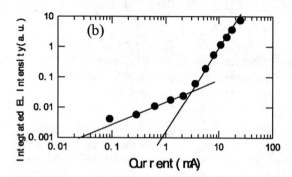

FIGURE 1. Integrated EL intensity as a function of injection current in logarithm scales.

Figure 2 shows the temperature dependence of the injection current measured at the applied voltage between 3 and 8 V. It is seen that there are two activation energies depending on the temperature range. The activation energy in the higher temperature region is larger than that in the lower region. This suggests that two carriers exist in the present device. Current component with larger energy barrier can be assigned to the electron current while that with the smaller barrier to the hole current, because the electron energy barrier is larger than the hole energy barrier. The measured activation energy value in the higher temperature region will correspond to the effective energy difference between the Fermi level of n-ITO and the conduction band edges of Si nanocrystallite, while that in the lower temperature region to the difference between the valence band edges of p-Si and Si nanocrystallite.

According to the band diagram discussed above, it is seen, that the electron-hole pair will not be generated sufficiently even when total injected carrier number is large. In the present paper, we observed very weak luminescence by the direct p-n injection as shown in Fig. 1. It can be explained by the fact that there is a bottleneck for the hole current at the n-ITO – Si nanocrystallite interface, where the current flow depends on the nonradiative recombination rate.

The comparison between the temperature dependences of the EL and PL intensities shows that the energy barrier for the excitons located on a radiative center in the EL device is smaller than that in

the PL experiment. It also shows that the non-radiative recombination rate is smaller in the EL device. These results are well explained by the fact that the voltage applied is very high. The observed photon energy of the EL device is around 1.8eV, which corresponds to the emission from a localized state. When the applied voltage is increased to as high as 12V, the 1.8eV emission band peak is shifted to the lower energy irreversiblly.

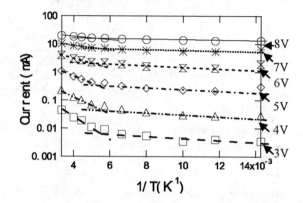

FIGURE 2. Temperature dependence of the injection current in the voltage region from 3 to 8 V.

CONCLUSION

According to the observed results above, it is found that the energy barrier for electrons in the ITO region is as high as 1.5eV, so that high electric field always exists during the device operation. It is also found that, under such high field condition, electrons and holes are more difficult to be captured by localized radiative centers and excitons sited on this center is easier to be escaped from it. In conclusion, the properties of the present device are found to be strongly influenced by the existence of the high electric field, which stems from the band discontinuity at the boundary between ITO and the Si nano-crystalline layer.

REFERENCES

1. M.Inada et al., *Materials Science & Engineering* B **101**, 283(2003).
2. M. Inada, H. Nakagawa, I. Umezu and A. Sugimura, *Applied surface science* **197-198**, (2002) 666-669.
3. T. Makino, M. Inada, K. Yoshida, I. Umezu and A. Sugimura, *Appl. Phys.* A (2004).
4. T. Yoshida, Y. Yamada and T. Orii, *J. Appl. Phys.* **83**, 5427 (1998).

Terahertz quantum-cascade laser dynamics in time-domain

J. Kröll[1], J.Darmo[1], S. Dhillon[2], X. Marcadet[3], M. Calligaro[3],
C. Sirtori[2,3] and K. Unterrainer[1]

[1]*Photonics Institute, Vienna University of Technology,Gusshausstrasse 25, A-1040 Vienna, Austria*
[2]*Matériaux et Phénomènes Quantiques, Université Paris 7, 75251 Paris Cedex 05, France*
[3]*Thales Research & Technology, Domaine de Corbeville, 91404 Orsay Cedex, France*

Abstract. We show results on the interaction between broadband terahertz radiation and a quantum cascade laser operating at 2.87 THz. By coupling terahertz pulses into the laser's waveguide the losses and gain in the frequency range 0.5 – 3.5 THz are determined.

Keywords: Terahertz time-domain spectroscopy, quantum cascade lasers
PACS: Spectroscopy time-resolved, 78.47.+p, Semiconductor lasers, 42.55.Px

INTRODUCTION

Over the past few years developments in terahertz technology have enabled the electro-magnetic spectrum of 0.1 – 10 THz to be covered and to be exploited in physics, biology and medicine [1]. In particular terahertz time-domain spectroscopy (THz-TDS) has shown huge potential for contactless sensing and non-destructive examination of materials and objects. Compared to the usual Fourier transform infrared spectroscopy (FT-IR), the THz-TDS can provide time-resolved spectral information on the picosecond time scale, and more importantly can monitor coherent effects.

Recently the terahertz quantum cascade laser (THz-QCL), a very promising light source for this frequency range, has emerged [2]. Such devices show remarkable performance compared to their size and have the potential to be designed to almost any required emission wavelength. At the moment their properties are assessed in the terms of output power, wavelength and linewidth of the emission using FT-IR spectroscopy. There is currently little or no information on losses and gain in these devices.

In this contribution we present unique THz-TDS measurements of QCLs that target these questions. By coupling broad-band THz pulses into the laser waveguide the internal processes within the active region and their dynamics are probed. We determine the losses and their spectral location, and the gain bandwidth as a result of the amplification of THz pulses around the gain of the THz QCL.

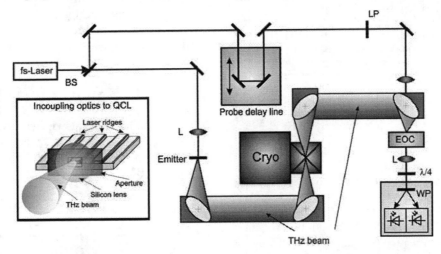

FIGURE 1. Scheme of the THz-TDS setup. Inset shows THz incoupling optics assembly of QCL (BS: beam splitter, LP: linear polarizer, EOC: electro-optic crystal, WP: Wollaston prism, L: lens, Cryo: cryostat, λ/4: quarter wave plate).

CP893, *Physics of Semiconductors, 28th International Conference*
edited by W. Jantsch and F. Schäffler

METHOD

As diagnostic tool a standard THz-TDS system is used (Fig. 1). Femtosecond Ti:sapphire laser pulses generate coherent THz pulses in a photo-conductive switch. The THz pulses are transmitted through the QCL's waveguide and detected with an electro-optic sensor consisting of a 300 μm thick gallium phosphide crystal. The THz QCL used in this study is a unipolar GaAs/AlGaAs heterostructure with a bound-to-continuum intersubband lasing transition [3]. The threshold current density of the device is 150 A/cm^2 and the emission line is centered at a frequency of 2.87 THz ($\lambda \sim 105$ μm). To optimize the incoupling efficiency, a silicon lens and an aperture are placed in direct optical contact with the laser facet (see the inset of Fig. 1).

EXPERIMENTAL RESULTS

We used modulation spectroscopy to analyze the few-cycle THz pulses transmitted through the THz-QCL. The measured signal shown in Fig. 2 is the difference between the THz pulse transmitted through the laser in active and passive mode and is the response of the laser's active region to the electric field of the injected THz pulse.

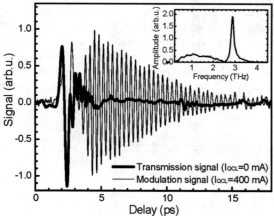

FIGURE 2. Time-domain signal of the transmitted reference pulse and the scaled modulation signal (Inset: spectrum of modulated signal).

In contrast to the reference pulse, the electric field of the modulated signal exhibits strong oscillatory behavior. The spectrum of this signal (inset in Fig. 2) consists of a strong peak around the position of the laser emission. The measured linewidth of the gain is ~150 GHz. The measured net gain experienced by the transmitted pulse at center frequency is about 15 cm^{-1}.

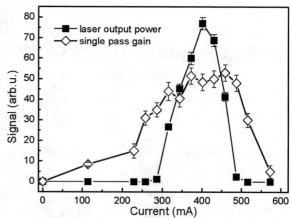

FIGURE 3. Measured single pass gain and laser output power as a function of the laser current density.

Figure 3 displays the dependence on the driving current of the gain and is compared to the laser power output. Amplification of the probe THz pulse is observed already far below the laser threshold current density. This behavior corresponds well to the laser theory – we probe the single pass net gain that is non-zero when at given pumping rate the mirror losses dominate the laser cavity losses. On the other hand, the roll-off of the gain is unambiguously delayed in comparison to the decay of the lasing. Here, the theoretically expected loss of the band structure alignment in the active zone as a key explanation for the switching-off the QCL laser is not proven and another mechanism has to be searched.

CONCLUSION

In summary, the measurement of the amplification of THz pulses by a THz QCL presents, to our knowledge, the first direct probe of the gain in THz quantum cascade structures. These results are valuable for the further development of quantum cascade lasers and the comprehension of the dynamic processes involved.

ACKNOWLEDGEMENT

The authors acknowledge support from the Austrian Fond zur Förderung der wissenschaftlichen Forschung (SFB-ADLIS) and from the EU project TeraNova (IST-511415).

REFERENCES

1. D. Mittleman, *Sensing with terahertz radiation* (Springer, New York 2003).
2. R. Köhler et al., *Nature*, vol. **417**, p. 156, 2002.
3. J. Alton, *et al.*, *Appl.Phys. Lett.*, vol. **86**, p. 71109, 2005.

Time-Resolved Studies of Gain Dynamics in Quantum Cascade Laser

Hyunyong Choi*, Zong-Kwei Wu*, Theodore B. Norris*, Tobias Gresch†, Marcella Giovannini†, Jérôme Faist†, Laurent Diehl** and Federico Capasso**

*Center for Ultrafast Optical Science and Department of Electrical Engineering and Computer Science, University of Michigan, Ann Arbor, Michigan 48109-2099 USA
†Institute of Physics, University of Neuchâtel, CH-2000 Neuchâtel, Switzerland
**Division of Engineering and Applied Sciences, Harvard University, Cambridge, Massachusetts 02138, USA

Abstract. Time-resolved mid-infrared pump-probe measurements in an operating quantum cascade laser below and above threshold reveal gain recovery dynamics to be driven by transport through the quantum cascade structure with two components: relaxation within a stage on a sub-picosecond scale and transport between stages on a picosecond scale. The fast recovery corresponds to resonant tunneling from the injector ground state into the upper lasing state, and is found to be incoherent due to strong dephasing via intraband electron-electron scattering. The slower component corresponds to miniband superlattice transport. Both components have been studied as a function of bias and temperature.

Keywords: quantum cascade lasers, gain dynamics, mid-infrared, resonant tunneling, transport
PACS: 42.55.Px, 78.47.+p, 78.67.-n

INTRODUCTION

Quantum cascade (QC) lasers are unipolar devices which rely on an interplay between the intersubband optical transitions, resonant tunneling and transport for their operation. So far, most information on their electrical and optical properties has been obtained only through measurements of steady-state light or voltage vs. current characteristics [1]. In order to understand the dynamics of carriers that govern the device physics, however, it is desirable to investigate directly in the time domain. One recent transport study in QC structures reported the observation of pronounced wavepacket oscillations for electron density of up to several 10^{11} cm^{-2} [2]. The structure used in that experiment, however, was not an operating laser, and so is not directly relevant to the dynamics under working conditions.

In this paper, we report time-resolved mid-infrared (IR) degenerate pump-probe experiments on an *operating* QC laser. Direct observations of pump-induced gain depletion, initial fast recovery, slow recovery of gain, and the effects of carrier heating are presented.

EXPERIMENT AND DISCUSSION

Details of the QC laser sample used in this experiment are given in Ref. [3]. For degenerate mid-IR pump-probe differential transmission (DT) measurements, 250 fs mid-IR pulses were tuned to 4.58 μm (QC laser wavelength) with pump pulse energies up to 800 pJ and probe pulse energy of 40 pJ. The pump and probe beams were collinearly combined and coupled through the QC laser waveguide core. The transmitted probe was collected using f/0.7 optics and focused on the liquid-nitrogen cooled InSb detector. The pump and probe polarizations were orthogonal and linearly polarized at 45 degree with respect to the lasing mode of the QC laser (growth or z-direction). A polarizer was placed before the detector to block the transmitted and scattered pump beam, and also to suppress coherent artifacts occurring from pump-probe coupling. In order to avoid any signals coupled with the substrate or cladding, a 10 μm spatial filter was carefully positioned to isolate the signal coupled with the waveguide core. The pump pulse was mechanically chopped at 2 kHz, and the DT signal was recorded using lock-in detection technique.

In Fig. 1(a), we show the gain recovery dynamics for a series of bias currents at 78 K; the inset displays one of the normalized curves at 300 mA including a fit to a two-exponential decay; (b) shows the two exponential time constants from the fits as a function of bias current. Depletion of the gain induced by the pump gives rise to a negative probe DT signal near zero time delay because of strong stimulated emission. Carrier heating contributions were shown to be negligible by using TE-polarized pump: since optical transitions occur on the intersubband transition only for TM polarization (z-direction), a TE-polarized pump will not induce intersubband transition via stimulated emission, but will only yield carrier heating due to excitation into the continuum. The results in Fig. 1(a) thus indicate that carrier heating is very small.

CP893, *Physics of Semiconductors, 28th International Conference*
edited by W. Jantsch and F. Schäffler
© 2007 American Institute of Physics 978-0-7354-0397-0/07/$23.00

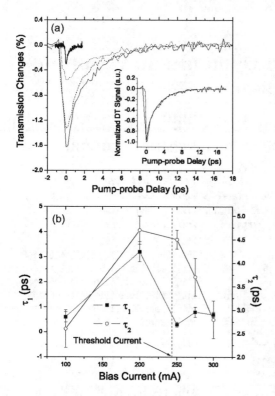

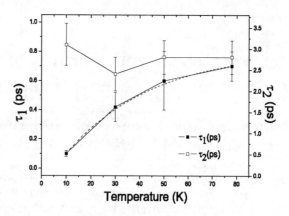

FIGURE 2. Temperature dependent fast and slow recovery time constants at $1.15 \times I_{th}$. Dashed line is its fit for the fast recovery components using $-0.78 \times e^{(-T/39)} + 0.81$.

FIGURE 1. (a) DT signals measured at 78 K. Dotted line, dashed line, and solid line are at 200 mA, 275 mA, and 300 mA, respectively. Thick solid line is the result of transverse electric (TE) pump and transverse magnetic (TM) probe at 300 mA. Inset: normalized DT signal for 300 mA bias current. (b) Gain recovery time constants for each bias current. τ_1 represents a fast component (filled square) and τ_2 a slow component (empty circle).

A "fast" component (< 1 ps) of the initial gain recovery was observed at all bias and temperature conditions investigated; this is attributed to carrier refilling from the injector ground state into the upper lasing state in the active region via resonant tunneling. No coherent tunneling oscillations were observed under any bias conditions. This indicates that coherent tunneling oscillations are strongly damped by dephasing collisions in these coupled states [5]. Strong dephasing comes from the extremely fast electron-electron scattering (< 100 fs) and the onset of plasmon emission in the upper lasing subband. As can be seen in Fig. 2, the resonant tunneling rate was found to decrease with increasing temperature over the range investigated from 10 K to 78 K. This is consistent with the resonant tunneling model of Eq. (1) [1] and Ref [5], which show that the resonant tunneling

rate decreases with increasing dephasing in the tunnel-coupled states, as described by

$$\frac{1}{\tau_1} = \frac{\Omega_R^2 \frac{1}{2}(\frac{1}{\tau_\perp})}{(\frac{1}{\tau_\perp})^2 + (\frac{\Delta E}{\hbar})^2} \quad (1)$$

where $1/\tau_1$ is the temperature dependent tunneling rate, $\hbar\Omega_R$ is the energy splitting between injector ground state and upper lasing state in the active region, $1/\tau_\perp$ is the dephasing rate, and ΔE is the energy detuning between injector ground state and upper lasing state in the active region at the absence of coupling.

Finally, we observe a "slow" recovery component with a time constant of $2 - 5$ ps at all bias currents and temperature ranges, as summarized in Fig. 1(b) and Fig. 2. The slow component is due to electron transport through superlattice miniband in the injector region [6]. Additional evidence comes from its inverse bias dependence [cf. Fig. 1(b)]: as bias current increases, the transport time through the miniband is found to depend inversely on the current, since the density is clamped above threshold.

REFERENCES

1. J. Faist *et al.*, in *Intersubband Transitions in Quantum Wells: Physics and Device Applications II*, edited by H. Liu and F. Capasso (Academic, New York, 2000), vol. 66, Chap. 1.
2. F. Eickemeyer *et al.*, Phys. Rev. Lett. **89**, 47402 (2002).
3. J. Faist *et al.*, IEEE J. Quantum Electron. **38**, 533 (2002).
4. P. W. Milonni and J. H. Eberly, *Lasers*, John Wiley & Sons, New York, (1988); A. Yariv, *Quantum Electronics*, John Wiley & Sons, New York, third edition, (1989).
5. K. Leo *et al.*, Phys. Rev. B **42**, 7065 (1990).
6. B. Deveaud *et al.*, Phys. Rev. Lett. **58**, 2582 (1987).

---

[1] This equation can be derived from the two-level density matrix theory [4], and is found to be exactly same as Eq. (4) of Ref [5]: tunneling rate is inversely proportional to the dephasing collision rate in the upper lasing state.

Mapping charge carrier distributions with THz microscopy

F. Buersgens*, H.-T. Chen† and R. Kersting*

*Photonics and Optoelectronics Group, University of Munich, Amalienstr. 54, 80799 Munich, Germany
†Los Alamos National Laboratory, MST-CINT, MS G756, Los Alamos, NM 87545, USA

Abstract. We report on THz microscopy for sensing charge carrier distributions in semiconductors. The contactless technique gives insight into the Drude response of electrons with a bandwidth of about 2.5 THz. We have achieved a spatial resolution of about 1.8 μm, which corresponds to a sensitivity sufficient to detect as few as 5000 electrons.

Keywords: Near-field scanning optical microscopy, Response to electromagnetic fields
PACS: 68.37.Uv, 74.25.Nf

INTRODUCTION

The current trend towards deep submicron semiconductor devices makes it challenging to map charge carrier distributions and their dynamics in an individual structure. The situation is even more complex in nano-size devices. Electrical leads for probing the carriers within the device would influence the quantum state of the nanostructure. In this contribution we present a novel microscopic technique that allows for contactless mapping of charge carriers with sufficient spatial resolution. Our approach provides a subpicosecond time-resolution, which gives insight into the Drude response of the charge carriers with a bandwidth of about 2.5 THz.

Many works have shown that THz waves are an excellent probe for monitoring charge carrier dynamics in the time domain. However, the long wavelength of THz radiation (1 THz corresponds to $300\,\mu$m) limits the spatial resolution that can be achieved by applying classical microscopy techniques. Recently, we have demonstrated an apertureless THz scanning near-field microscope (THz-SNOM) [1]. In this SNOM the dielectric permittivity of a surface is sampled by a metallic tip. Depending on the tip size resolutions down to 150 nm were achieved [2]. Charge carrier distributions in semiconductors can be probed by the THz SNOM because their Drude response modifies the dielectric permittivity of the semiconductor.

EXPERIMENTAL TECHNIQUE

In order to sense charge carriers in semiconductor structures, we use few-cycle THz pulses that have a center frequency of about 2 THz. These broadband pulses are generated by femtosecond laser excitation of n-doped InAs. In the microscope head (Fig. 1a) the pulses are focused to a diffraction limited spot and a scanning tungsten tip

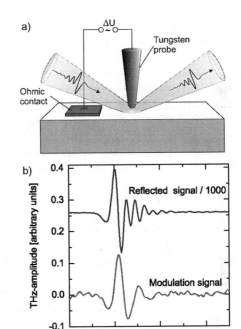

FIGURE 1. Head of the apertureless THz-SNOM (a) and electric field transients of the THz pulses (b). The upper curve in plot (b) shows the reflected THz pulse. The lower one shows the THz signal, which is achieved by electro-modulation of the semiconductor.

is used for achieving spatial resolution. Only the reflected pulses are transmitted through the head and are later time-resolved by electro-optic sampling [3]. However, the reflection depends on the impedance of the tip-surface system and thus on the charge carrier density underneath the tip. Moreover, the carrier density under the tip can be modulated by applying a bias between the needle and the electron gas.

CP893, *Physics of Semiconductors, 28th International Conference*
edited by W. Jantsch and F. Schäffler
© 2007 American Institute of Physics 978-0-7354-0397-0/07/$23.00

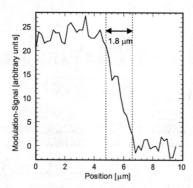

FIGURE 2. Electromodulation signal recorded across the edge of a grove etched into n-doped GaAs. A spatial resolution (10%-90%) of about 1.8 μm was deduced.

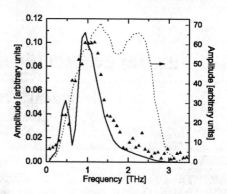

FIGURE 3. Amplitude spectra of the modulation signal (triangles) and of the reflected signal (dotted line). The solid line is the result of our model calculations.

For our experiments we use a MBE grown GaAs structure, which is n-doped at a level of $2 \cdot 10^{16}$ cm^{-3}. One electronic contact to the electron gas is an ohmic, whereas the tungsten needle forms a Schottky contact. At zero voltage, the depletion region under the needle is about 180 nm, whereas at -16 V it extends to 1100 nm. Applying an AC voltage and recording the differential signal leads to a THz modulation signal that shows exclusively the contribution of the modulated charges. A typical THz pulse and the corresponding modulation signal are shown in Fig. 1b).

RESULTS

The spatial resolution of the THz microscope was deduced by scanning in modulation mode across a structure where the electron gas was locally removed. The data of Fig. 2 reproduce the edge of the structure. A spatial resolution of 1.8 μm is deduced.

For a more quantitative insight we compare the experimental data with model calculations for the impedance of the tip-surface system [4]. In close analogy to macroscopic antennae, the tip-needle system exhibits a frequency dependent power-dissipation, which can be described by the relative efficiency

$$\eta_C(\omega) = \frac{RZ_0}{4\pi(R^2 + (\omega L - \frac{1}{\omega C})^2)} \qquad (1)$$

where Z_0 is the vacuum impedance, L is the inductance of the needle, C is the capacitance of the tip-surface system, and R accounts for energy losses. In our experiments, we modulate the charge carrier density under the tip and thus the capacitance of the Schottky contact. This leads to a spectral shift of the THz power dissipation by the tip-surface system and thus results in a modulation of the transmitted THz-Pulses.

The experimental data can be reproduced when considering both, the antenna properties of the tip-surface system and the depletion of the semiconductor. The model reproduces the spectrum of the modulation signal (Fig. 3) as well as the dependence of the modulation amplitude on the applied voltage [1]. The sensitivity of our technique can be expressed in terms of the number of electrons affected by the modulation. It depends on the depleted volume and thus on the width of the depletion zone, as well as on the surface area under the tip. For a bias of $\Delta U = 2$ V a volume of $3 \cdot 10^{-13}$cm^{-3} is depleted, which corresponds to the displacement of about 5000 electrons.

In summary we have shown that charge carriers in semiconductors can be detected by apertureless THz microscopy in a contactless way. The ultrashort duration of the THz pulses allows for studying charge carrier dynamics on microscopic scales directly in the time-domain. The spatial resolution was found to be 1.8 μm. From experimental data and model calculations we conclude that as few as 5000 electrons can be detected. It appears reasonable that further improvements of the technique may reach a sensitivity close to the single electron level.

The authors acknowledge support by NSF (ECS02-45461) and by DFG (KE 516/1-1).

REFERENCES

1. F. Buersgens, R. Kersting, and H.-T. Chen, *Appl. Phys. Lett.* **88**, 112115 (2006).
2. H.-T. Chen, R. Kersting, and G. Cho, *Appl. Phys. Lett* **83**, 3009 (2003).
3. Q. Wu, M. Litz, and X.-C. Zhang, *Appl. Phys. Lett.* **68**, 2924 (1996).
4. H.-T. Chen, S. Kraatz, G. Cho, and R. Kersting, *Phys. Rev. Lett.* **93**, 267401 (2004).

Thermal modelling of Antimonide-based quantum cascade lasers

Craig A. Evans*, Dragan Indjin*, Zoran Ikonić*, Paul Harrison* and Vladimir D. Jovanović†

*Institute of Microwaves and Photonics, School of Electronic and Electrical Engineering, University of Leeds, Leeds, LS2 9JT, UK
†Lehman Brothers, 25 Bank Street, London, E14 5LE, UK

Abstract.
    A quantum cascade laser (QCL) thermal model is presented. The model is used to calculate the active region temperature of an InGaAs/AlAsSb QCL under a range of operating conditions and device geometries. The active region temperature is a limiting factor of QCL performance and knowledge of the thermal dynamics inside these devices is crucial in order to improve their temperature performance. Buried heterostructures (BH) are found to offer the best thermal performance, allowing higher heat sink temperatures than alternative device geometries under both pulsed and continuous-wave (CW) operating conditions.

Keywords: quantum cascade lasers, thermal modelling
PACS: 44.05.+e,42.55.Px

INTRODUCTION

The active region temperature of QCLs can be considerably higher than that of the heat sink due to the very large power densities (of the order of GW/cm^3) in the device active regions. This is caused by the relatively large threshold currents and voltages and leads to strong local heating effects which affect the device performance considerably. At these higher temperatures, the population inversion is reduced due to two main mechanisms; increased electron leakage and thermal back-filling of the lower laser level. Therefore, in order to improve the temperature performance of these devices, the thermal dynamics inside the devices must be understood and special attention paid to the thermal management in order to improve the heat dissipation from the device active regions. Several different packaging techniques have been employed to realise QCLs emitting at and above room temperature in cw mode including epilayer-down mounted devices [1], thick electroplated gold on the device surfaces [2] and buried heterostructures [3].

THERMAL MODEL

The thermal model is based upon the standard two-dimensional heat diffusion equation

$$\rho(x,y,T)c_p(x,y,T)\frac{\partial T(x,y,t)}{\partial t} = \nabla \cdot [\kappa(x,y,T)\nabla T(x,y,t)] + S(x,y,t)$$

(1)

where T is the temperature (K), S is the source power density (W/m^3) and ρ, c_p and κ are the material parameters density (kg/m^3), specific heat capacity (J/kg K) and thermal conductivity (W/m K) respectively. It should be noted that the material parameters are temperature dependent as this causes Eqn. (1) to be non-linear. In order to apply Eqn. (1) to a typical QCL geometry, the device cross-section is mapped out into a non-overlapping mesh of control volumes and the derivatives in Eqn. (1) are approximated by finite-differences. The temperatures at the centre (or node) of each control volume are then calculated in each time step using Euler's Forward Method with a constant temperature boundary condition on the surface in contact with the heat sink and Neumann (zero-derivative) boundary conditions on all others. For solving the steady-state temperature profile (cw operation) the $\partial T/\partial t$ term in Eqn. (1) can be set to zero, but in our case, we keep the $\partial T/\partial t$ term in order to simulate pulsed mode as well as CW.

The source power density S is calculated from our simulated electric field–current density (F–J) curves from a previous work [4] and is given by $S = F \times J$. By extracting the current density for the particular working bias point from the F–J curves calculated at different lattice temperatures, S can be found as a function of temperature ($S = F \times J(T) = 1000\exp(T/1023)$ GW/m^3) and is used in the thermal model. This 'quantum source term' then describes the heat generation in the active region caused by dissipative quantum transport effects.

The thermal model also incorporates the anisotropic thermal conductivity of the QCL active region layers caused by the large number of interfaces in the

CP893, *Physics of Semiconductors, 28th International Conference*
edited by W. Jantsch and F. Schäffler
© 2007 American Institute of Physics 978-0-7354-0397-0/07/$23.00

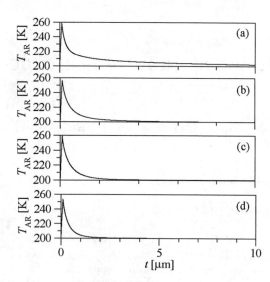

FIGURE 1. Cooling phases of (a) standard ridge (b) ridge with electroplated gold (c) epilayer down mounted ridge and (d) buried heterostructure mounted epilayer down.

TABLE 1. Results of fitting the cooling phases of each structure to a second-order exponential decay function

$$T_{AR} = a_0 + a_1 e^{-t/\tau_1} + a_2 e^{-t/\tau_2} \qquad (t > 100 \text{ ns})$$

Device	a_0	a_1	$\tau_1 (\mu s)$	a_2	$\tau_2 (\mu s)$
a	203.0	47.5	0.19	32.1	2.67
b	203.1	75.5	0.17	13.7	1.98
c	200.1	32.4	0.14	52.3	0.47
d	200.1	43.7	0.12	45.3	0.33

superlattice-like active region. These interfaces increase the rate of phonon scattering causing a reduction (typically an order of magnitude) in the cross plane thermal conductivity ($\kappa_\perp$) compared to the bulk constituent materials [5].

SIMULATION RESULTS

A standard InP-based 10 μm wide ridge waveguide mounted substrate side down was used to simulate the effect of the driving conditions in pulsed mode on the active region temperature. The active region temperature increases with duty cycle (pulse width × repetition frequency) and it is found that this temperature increase is greater when the frequency is kept constant and the pulse width increased rather than vice versa. This is due to the rate of temperature increase during the pulse being far greater than the rate of heat dissipation in between pulses. For high duty cycle operation, the heat accumulated during the first pulse can have insufficient time to completely dissipate and so greater heating occurs during the next pulse. This heat accumulation effect increases with each pulse until saturation occurs. The active region temperature is also found to increase with an increasing ridge width, this is intuitively due to an increased emitting volume which increases the power dissipated in the active region. The active region temperature also rises with increased etch depth and this is associated with a larger spreading resistance into the substrate.

The ability of different device structures to dissipate heat was characterised by extracting thermal time constants from the cooling phases of the devices in pulsed

mode. Fig. 1 shows the cooling phases of (a) a standard ridge and (b) a ridge with thick electroplated gold mounted substrate side down and a (c) double channel ridge and (d) buried heterostructure mounted epilayer side down. The thermal time constants are extracted by fitting the cooling phase to a second order exponential decay function $T_{AR} = a_0 + a_1 e^{-t/\tau_1} + a_2 e^{-t/\tau_2}$. Table 1 shows the results of these fits. It can be seen that the epilayer down mounted devices have smaller thermal time constants and in particular the buried heterostructure which has thermal time constants $\sim$8 times smaller than a standard ridge waveguide.

CONCLUSIONS

A QCL thermal model has been presented. Buried heterostructures have been shown to have the best temperature performance. The model should be particularly useful for improving the temperature performance of THz QCLs where the reduced conduction band offset and smaller energy gaps between subbands makes the population more sensitive to temperature.

REFERENCES

1. J. S. Yu, S. R. Darvish, A. Evans, J. Nguyen, S. Slivken, and M. Razeghi, *Appl. Phys. Lett.*, vol. 88, no. 041111, 2006.
2. J. S. Yu, S. Slivken, S. R. Darvish, A. Evans, B. Gokden, and M. Razeghi, *Appl. Phys. Lett.*, vol. 87, no. 041104, 2005.
3. M. Beck, D. Hofstetter, T. Aellen, J. Faist, U. Oestrele, M. Ilegems, E. Gini, and H. Melchior, *Science*, vol. 295, p. 301–305, 2002.
4. C. A. Evans, V. D. Jovanović, D. Indjin, Z. Ikonić, and P. Harrison, ' *Appl. Phys. Lett.*, vol. 87, no. 141109, 2005.
5. G. Chen, *Phys. Rev. B*, vol. 57, pp. 14 958–14 973, 1998.

Bipolar THz Laser: The way out of fundamental gain limitations.

Leonid D. Shvartsman and Boris Laikhtman

The Racah Institute of Physics, The Hebrew University, Jerusalem, 91904, Israel

Abstract. All nanostructure based THz lasers of standard design have principal limitations of gain value. The origin of these limitations is the necessity to engineer both THz gap and population inversion simultaneously. We present here estimations for these limitations and suggest to use InAs/GaSb coupled quantum wells as a way to overcome them. This is the only heterostructure where THz lasing can be based not on intersubband but on interband transitions. A proper design of this structure leads to a hybridization gap coming from anti-crossing of the GaSb valence band and InAs conduction band naturally appearing in the THz range. Two more advantages of this design are (i) a large value of the interband dipole matrix element and (ii) W-shaped spectrum leading to a singular density of states. These advantages lead to a gain orders of magnitude higher than for intersubband THz lasing.

Historically, the reduction of the emitted frequencies from visible range to near and mid-IR led to domination of intersubband lasing over interband one because the former appeared to be more effective. However, we will show that further decrease of frequencies naturally favors the reverse process, i.e.: for THz lasing interband approach has a better promise. This conclusion results from the existence of the fundamental gain limitations for THz intersubband lasing that do not exist in the interband scheme. Some delay of the realization of this is connected with the fact that typical band gap is far beyond the THz region and there is only one exception, InAs/GaSb heterostructures.

To demonstrate the advantages of the interband lasing we compare gain for intersubband and interband transitions.

$$g_{isb} = \frac{2e^2}{m_0^2\omega} \frac{\Gamma|M_{n,n-1}|^2}{ncL} \int \left[f_{e,n}(k) - f_{e,n-1}(k) \right] \delta\left(E_{n,n-1}(k) - \hbar\omega \right) d^2k \quad (1)$$

$$g_{ib} = \frac{2e^2}{m_0^2\omega} \frac{\Gamma|M_{eh}|^2}{ncL} \int \left[f_e(k) - f_h(k) - 1 \right] \delta\left(E_{eh}(k) - \hbar\omega \right) d^2k \quad (2)$$

These expressions have alike structure but a rather different meaning. Integral part roughly describes the population inversion, while the prefactor is responsible for the probability of the optical transition. For near-IR range, but not for THz as we show below, population inversion term favors the intersubband approach (1) because of parallelism of the subbands. Sometimes it is enough to compensate the disadvantage in prefactors. Let us consider these factors one by one.

The matrix element for interband transitions (2) is always higher than for intersubband ones (1). More than that, according to the estimate $M_{ee} \sim \sqrt{nmh\omega}$ for intersubband gain g_{isb} the matrix element falls with the emitted frequency. On the other hand, due to a very special band offset at the InAs/GaSb interface matrix element M_{eh} in (2) does not depend on the frequency. Therefore this factor always favors an interband approach (1).

With the depopulation selectivity a comparative analysis is less trivial. The result depends on the frequency range. For intersubband THz lasers the depopulation selectivity is rather poor because of relatively small level separation:

$$g_{isb} = \frac{4\pi e^2}{m_0^2\omega} \frac{\Gamma|M_{n,n-1}|^2}{ncL} J\tau_{n-1,1}^2 \left(1 - \frac{\tau_{n-1,1}}{\tau_{n,n-1}}\right)\left(1 - \frac{3\Delta\tau}{2\tau_{n-1,1}}\right) \quad (3)$$

The above expression is given for $\Delta\tau = \tau_{n,1} - \tau_{n-1,1} \ll \tau_{n,1}$, and all the substantial dependence of the gain on the emitted frequency is in

CP893, *Physics of Semiconductors, 28th International Conference*
edited by W. Jantsch and F. Schäffler
© 2007 American Institute of Physics 978-0-7354-0397-0/07/$23.00

$\Delta\tau$ (3). Our calculations lead to the estimate: $\Delta\tau/\tau_{n-1,1} \approx \sqrt{m}L\omega/\sqrt{k_BT}$, where L is the spatial size of the electron wave function. A numerical estimate for $T = 77K$ and $L = 50$ Å shows that ratio (8) becomes of the order of unity at 4 THz. It means that for this frequency still there exists a weak depopulation selectivity, while for lower frequencies the prospects for intersubband lasing is rather poor.

Another concept that was widely discussed in this context is a wave function engineering. In [1,2] an existence in adjacent well of a level resonant with lower radiative levels "n-1" is used in order to improve the depopulation selectivity. We doubt this concept for two reasons. First, the natural width of this resonance is typically around 4THz. Indeed, quantum beats between nearly resonant levels in adjacent wells occur at the frequency: $\hbar\Omega = \sqrt{(\varepsilon_{n-1}-\varepsilon_{n'-1})^2+4F^2}$, where F is the tunnel penetrability of the barrier between wells at the considered energy. For typical parameters of the quantum wells [1,2] it gives the above value of 4THz. This frequency happens to be nearly the same for both the upper and the lower radiative states and therefore the situation is effectively reduced to the considered above "off-resonance" case (3). In other words the depopulation time for upper and lower radiative states is nearly the same and equals $\tau_{dp} = (\hbar\Omega)^2\tau_{LO}/2F^2$. Second, the narrow resonance if reached, would be accompanied with current instability that inevitably brings the system out of the resonance.

We suggest to use InAs/GaSb coupled quantum wells as a way to overcome this fundamental limitation [3]. This is the only heterostructure where THz lasing can be based not only on intersubband but also on interband transitions (see Figure 1). A proper design of this structure leads to two options for "P-space cascade". In one of them interband THz lasing is associated with a regular V-type dispersion and optical transitions between conduction band of InAs QW and valence band of GaSb QW (Figure 1). In a second version the interband transition occurs over a hybridization gap coming from anti-crossing of the GaSb valence band and InAs conduction band naturally appearing in the THz range and leading to W-type dispersion of carriers [3]. Two more advantages of this design are (i) a large value of the interband dipole matrix element and (ii) W-shaped spectrum leading to a singular density of states. These advantages lead to a gain much higher than for intersubband THz lasing. Calculations show that the ratio of the gains for InAs-GaSb interband THz lasing and GaAs intersubband lasing is:

$$\frac{g_{ib}}{g_{isb}} = \frac{\pi}{2}\frac{|M_{eh}|^2}{|M_{n,n-1}|^2}\frac{n_0}{n_{e,n}-n_{e,n-1}}[f_{e1}(k_\omega)+f_h(k_\omega)-1]$$

Here n_0 is a number of states in an energy interval corresponding to the typical width of radiative subbands, that can be estimated as: $n_0 \approx 2m/(\pi\hbar\tau_{LO})$, where m is reduced e-h mass, k_ω is a carrier wave vector corresponding to radiative e-h transitons at the given frequency. The ratio of the gains can reach few hundreds.

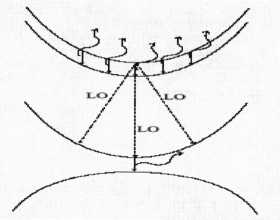

FIGURE 1. The scheme of optical transitions for bipolar InAs-GaSb CQWs. In addition to the traditional intersubband approach realized in electron subbands the interband transition is added. The material gain in this structure is the sum of the gains of the interband and intersubband transitions,

We acknowledge the support of the Israel Science Foundation founded by the Israel Academy of Sciences and Humanities

REFERENCES

1. Q. Hu, B. S. Williams, S. Kumar, H. Callebaut, S. Kohen, and J. L. Reno, Semicond. Sci. Technol. 20 (2005) S228–S236
2. S. Kumar, B. S. Williams, Q. Hu, J. L. Reno, Appl. Phys. Lett. 88, 121123 (2006)..
3. L.D.Shvartsman, B.Laikhtman, Proc.SPIE Vol. 6120, Paper 61200K (2005)

Silicon Stokes terahertz laser

S. G. Pavlov[1]*, H.-W. Hübers[1], J. N. Hovenier[2], T. O. Klaassen[2], D. A. Carder[3], P. J. Phillips[3], B. Redlich[3], H. Riemann[4], R. Kh. Zhukavin[5] and V. N. Shastin[5]

[1] *Institute of Planetary Research, German Aerospace Center, Rutherfordstrasse 2, 12489 Berlin, Germany*
*e-mail: sergeij.pavlov@dlr.de
[2] *Kavli Institute of Nanoscience Delft, Delft University of Technology, Postbus 5046, 2600 GA Delft, The Netherlands*
[3] *FOM-Institute for Plasma Physics, Postbus 1207, 3430 BE, Nieuwegein, The Netherlands*
[4] *Institute of Crystal Growth, Max-Born-Str. 2, 12489 Berlin, Germany*
[5] *Institute for Physics of Microstructures, Russian Academy of Sciences, GSP-105, 603950 Nizhny Novgorod, Russia*

Abstract. A Raman-type silicon laser at terahertz frequencies has been realized. Stokes-shifted stimulated emission has been observed from silicon crystals doped by antimony donors when optically excited by an infrared free electron laser. The Raman lasing was obtained due to resonant scattering on electronic states of a donor atom.

Keywords: Raman laser, terahertz, silicon laser.
PACS: 78.45+h, 42.65.Es, 71.55.Cn, 41.60.Cr

INTRODUCTION

In the past few years new concepts to generate light in silicon have attracted an increasing interest in Si-based optoelectronics and semiconductor research. Two potential key features of Si-based lasers are their low-cost production and on-chip integration with CMOS technology. The first silicon laser was realized on direct optical transitions between atom-like states of shallow donors [1]. This laser operates in the terahertz (THz) spectral region (50 - 230 μm) under mid-infrared optical excitation of group-V donor centers at low temperature [2]. In the near infrared, numerous approaches for a silicon laser were examined to overcome problems associated with its indirect bandgap. Examples are silicon nanocrystals, Si/SiO_2 and Si/SiGe superlattices, erbium-doped silicon and silicon light-emitting diodes [3]. However, to date, the only successfully realized near infrared silicon laser (~ 1.67 μm) [4] is based on Raman scattering by the zone-centered optical phonon.

RAMAN-TYPE TERAHERTZ SILICON LASER: EXPERIMENTAL

We report on the realization of a Raman-type silicon laser at THz frequencies. Stokes stimulated emission has been observed from silicon crystals doped by antimony donors[5] when optically excited by an infrared free electron laser. For the first time Raman lasing was obtained due to resonant scattering on impurity states mediated by all-intracenter excitation of the bound electron (Fig. 1).

Silicon crystals doped to the level of $\sim 4 \times 10^{15}$ cm^{-3} shaped to polished rectangular parallelepipeds with dimensions of $5 \times 7 \times 7$ mm^3, have been pumped in $\langle 111 \rangle$ or $\langle 110 \rangle$ crystal directions and the terahertz emission has been observed in the orthogonal direction (Fig. 1, on the left). A clear threshold-type increase of the THz output has been observed at pump photon flux densities above 10^{23} cm^{-2} sec^{-1} (Fig. 1, on the right).

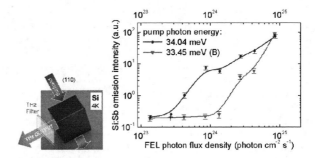

FIGURE 1. Schematic of the experiment (on the left) and Raman silicon laser thresholds at different pump photon energies (on the right).

CP893, *Physics of Semiconductors, 28th International Conference*
edited by W. Jantsch and F. Schäffler
© 2007 American Institute of Physics 978-0-7354-0397-0/07/$23.00

Despite the low lattice temperature (< 10 K) and low doping concentrations of the silicon crystals a significant Raman gain, ~ 7.4 cm GW^{-1}, has been observed. This is similar to the Raman gain reported for the near infrared silicon laser [4]. The photon energy of the THz laser emission $\hbar\omega_S$ is equal to the pump photon energy $\hbar\omega_{PUMP}$ reduced by the energy gap ΔE between the ground $1s(A_1)$ and excited $1s(E)$ donor states which are coupled by interaction with a ~ 2.92 THz intervalley transverse acoustic g-phonon:

$$\hbar\omega_S = \hbar\omega_{PUMP} - \Delta E \qquad (1)$$

$$\Delta E = E_{1s(E)} - E_{1s(A1)} \approx \hbar\omega_{g-TA} \qquad (2)$$

This resonant impurity-phonon interaction serves as outcoming resonance and increases the efficiency of the Raman scattering process. By tuning the pump laser frequency, the Stokes laser frequency can be varied from 4.6 to 5.8 THz (150 - 190 μm).

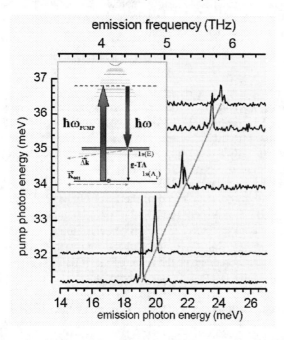

emission frequency (THz)

pump photon energy (meV)

emission photon energy (meV)

FIGURE 2. Emission spectra of the Raman-type silicon laser. By tuning the pump light photon energy, the silicon laser emission is linearly tuned over the 4.6 - 5.8 THz frequency range. On the inset: schematic of the silicon Raman laser. The light scattering is mediated by all-intracenter processes. Electrons, bound to the ground donor state, $1s(A_1)$, are photoexcited by the pump light into a virtual state (dashed line) and then decay to the excited $1s(E)$ donor state with an emission of a Stokes-shifted light. Further fast relaxation of the bound electron into the ground state occur due to resonant interaction of $1s(E)$ and $1s(A_1)$ donor states with the intervalley transverse acoustic g-phonon (g-TA).

This result may lead the way for the development of effective lasers for far- and mid-infrared wavelengths based on scattering mediated by particular impurity states, which are resonantly coupled with principal phonons of the semiconductor host lattice.

ACKNOWLEDGMENTS

This work was partly supported by the Investitionsbank Berlin, Deutsche Forschungs-gemeinschaft, and the Russian Foundation for Basic Research (joint grant 436 RUS 113/206/0 (R) and 03-02-04010, and RFBR grants 05-02-16734, 05-02-16762). We gratefully acknowledge the support by the Stichting voor Fundamenteel Onderzoek der Materie (FOM) in providing the required beam time on FELIX and highly appreciate the skilful assistance by the FELIX staff.

REFERENCES

1. S. G. Pavlov, R. Kh. Zhukavin, E. E. Orlova, V. N. Shastin, A. V. Kirsanov, H.-W. Hübers, K. Auen, and H. Riemann, *Phys. Rev. Lett.* **22**, 5220-5223 (2000).
2. H.-W. Hübers, S. G. Pavlov, and V. N. Shastin, *Semicond. Sci. Technol.*.**20**, S211-S221 (2005).
3. for a comprehensive review see: L. Pavesi, S. Gaponenko, and L. Dal Negro, *Towards the first silicon laser*, NATO Science Series, Kluwer Academic, Dordrecht, 2003.
4. H. Rong, A. Liu, R. Jones, O. Cohen, D. Hak, R. Nicolaescu, A. Fang, and M. Paniccia, *Nature* **433**, 292-294 (2005).
5. S. G. Pavlov, H.-W. Hübers, J. N. Hovenier, T. O. Klaassen, D. A. Carder, P. J. Phillips, B. Redlich, H. Riemann, R. Kh. Zhukavin, and V. N. Shastin, *Phys. Rev. Lett.* **96**, 037404 (2006).

Quantum-cascade lasers operating at low electric field strengths

L. Schrottke, M. Giehler, R. Hey and H. T. Grahn

Paul-Drude-Institut für Festkörperelektronik, Hausvogteiplatz 5–7, 10117 Berlin, Germany

Abstract. The gain coefficient of several GaAs/(Al,Ga)As quantum-cascade lasers (QCLs) has been calculated as a function of transition energy and electric field strength using the actual layer thicknesses and Al content obtained from x-ray diffraction. The operation field strength of the QCLs is determined by comparing the calculated gain characteristics with the experimental values of the lasing energy. The analysis of the operating field strengths and the threshold current densities indicates larger internal losses for higher operating field strengths. A QCL designed for operation at 30 kV/cm exhibits a rather low threshold current density at low temperatures, which is attributed to reduced leakage currents.

Keywords: Quantum-Cascade Lasers
PACS: 42.55.Px, 73.63.Hs, 78.67.Pt

The application of quantum-cascade lasers (QCLs), which are promising light sources in the wavelength range from mid-infrared (MIR) [1] to THz radiation [2], poses still a challenge insofar as the threshold current densities, in particular for MIR GaAs/(Al,Ga)As QCLs, are quite large. In order to lower the threshold current densities of QCLs, there have been several attempts to modify the subband structure of the devices. After the demonstration of the first GaAs/Al$_{0.33}$Ga$_{0.67}$As QCLs by Sirtori *et al.* [3], significant progress has been achieved by Page *et al.* [4] using Al$_{0.45}$Ga$_{0.55}$As barriers. Lasers with higher barriers exhibit smaller threshold current densities as well as higher maximum operating temperatures, which is in part attributed to a reduction of the leakage currents. So far, the highest operating temperatures for GaAs/(Al,Ga)As QCLs have been achieved by Pflügl *et al.* [5] using the so-called bound-to-continuum design. Since we calculate a rather small value of the gain coefficient for this design, we conjecture that the lower operating field strength F_{op} is probably one reason for smaller leakage currents, which can lead to improved lasing properties. Therefore, we have carried out a systematic study of the internal losses as a function of the operating field strength for a series of GaAs/(Al,Ga)As QCLs with various designs for the mid-infrared spectral region including a new design operating at 30 kV/cm with improved gain values.

While a detailed experimental investigation of the individual processes in QCLs is already challenging because of their complex structure, it is very difficult to experimentally obtain an accurate value of the internal operating field strength. For this analysis, we calculate the gain of the respective structures as a function of the transition energies and the electric field strength for a large number of values for energy and field strength

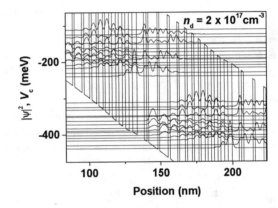

FIGURE 1. Conduction band profile and wave functions for sample D at 30 kV/cm.

in the framework of the self-consistent solution of the Schrödinger and Poisson equations using a transport model on the basis of a system of scattering-rate equations [6]. Using the actual lasing energies, we estimate F_{op} from these characteristics.

We analyzed GaAs/Al$_x$Ga$_{1-x}$As QCLs following the designs by Page *et al.* [4] (sample A), Indjin *et al.* [7] (sample B), and Pflügl *et al.* [5] (sample C, corresponding to sample S1 of Ref. [5]). In addition, we also investigated a series of 6 additional samples, which are based on the design of sample A, but show some minor deviations from the nominal layer structure. Sample D is a QCL designed to operate at 30 kV/cm but with larger gain than sample C. For this sample, we used the following layer thicknesses in nm starting with the injection barrier (bold: barrier, underlined: doped) **4.9**, 1.8, **1.4**, 6.5, **1.5**, 5.9, **1.5**, 5.0, **1.5**, 3.9, **1.5**, 3.3, **1.5**, 3.2, **1.5**, 2.8, **2.0**, 2.6, **2.0**, <u>2.4</u>, **2.0**, <u>2.5</u>, **2.5**, 2.9 with $x = 0.4$ and a nom-

CP893, *Physics of Semiconductors, 28th International Conference*
edited by W. Jantsch and F. Schäffler
© 2007 American Institute of Physics 978-0-7354-0397-0/07/$23.00

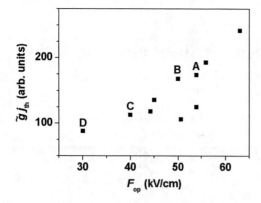

FIGURE 2. Product of calculated values of $\tilde{g}$ and measured values of j_{th} as a function of operating field strength.

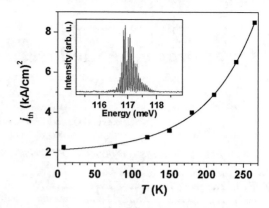

FIGURE 3. j_{th} vs. T for sample D. The solid line is a guide to the eye. The inset shows a lasing spectrum at 7 K.

inal sheet doping density $n_{2D} = 1.9 \times 10^{11}$ cm^{-2} per period (cf. Fig. 1). The samples were grown by molecular-beam epitaxy on GaAs(100) substrates. The actual layer thicknesses for the cascade structure and the actual Al content x of the barriers, which we use for the calculations, were obtained from a comparison of the experimental (002) and (004) x-ray diffraction curves, respectively, with simulations. Additional information can be found in Ref. [6].

Assuming the same resonator properties for all samples, the product of the measured threshold current density j_{th} and the calculated gain coefficient $\tilde{g}$ is expected to be the same for all samples. However, there is a clear increase of the value for $\tilde{g}j_{th}$ with increasing F_{op} as shown in Fig. 2. We conclude that the losses increase with increasing field strength. Since the optical (external) losses are assumed to be independent of the field strength, this result implies that the internal losses significantly increase with increasing field strength between 30 and 60 kV/cm. These losses can be due to leakage currents which result from scattering of electrons into quasi-continuum states above the barrier. This process becomes more probable as the field strength increases. The quasi-continuum states do not contribute to the calculated current in our model, since only subbands below the barrier band edge are taken into account.

Figure 3 shows the temperature (T) dependence of the threshold current density and a typical lasing spectrum for sample D. The lasing parameters of sample D, which operates at $F_{op} = 30$ kV/cm, but exhibits a larger $\tilde{g}$ compared to sample C, confirm this conclusion. The value for j_{th} of 2.2 kA/cm^2 at low temperatures is the best value of the complete set of samples investigated under comparable conditions, although the maximum operating temperature of this QCL is below 270 K. The light-current characteristics (not shown here) exhibits a maximum close to 9 kA/cm^2 for all temperatures. For this value of the current density, the current-voltage curve exhibits a rever-

sal point which is most significant at low temperatures. These features are attributed to the misalignment of the injector and upper laser level for higher field strengths, which can be observed only in sample D due to its rather low doping density. Furthermore, an optimization of the doping density is expected to improve the lasing properties of such low-field QCLs, in particular the maximum operating temperature.

ACKNOWLEDGMENTS

The authors would like to thank M. Höricke, H. Kostial, and E. Wiebicke for sample preparation.

REFERENCES

1. J. Faist, F. Capasso, D. L. Sivco, C. Sirtori, A. L. Hutchinson, and A. Y. Cho, *Science* **264**, 553–556 (1994).
2. R. Köhler, A. Tredicucci, F. Beltram, H. E. Beere, E. H. Linfield, A. G. Davies, D. A. Ritchie, R. C. Iotti, and F. Rossi, *Nature (London)* **417**, 156–159 (2002).
3. C. Sirtori, P. Kruck, S. Barbieri, P. Collot, J. Nagle, M. Beck, J. Faist, and U. Oesterle, *Appl. Phys. Lett.* **73**, 3486–3488 (1998).
4. H. Page, C. Becker, A. Robertson, G. Glastre, V. Ortiz, and C. Sirtori, *Appl. Phys. Lett.* **78**, 3529–3531 (2001).
5. C. Pflügl, W. Schrenk, S. Anders, G. Strasser, C. Becker, C. Sirtori, Y. Bonetti, and A. Muller, *Appl. Phys. Lett.* **83**, 4698–4700 (2003).
6. L. Schrottke, M. Giehler, R. Hey, and H. T. Grahn, *J. Appl. Phys.*, submitted (2006).
7. D. Indjin, A. Mirčetić, P. Harrison, R. W. Kelsall, Z. Ikonić, V. D. Jovanović, V. Milanović, M. Giehler, R. Hey, and H. T. Grahn, "GaAs/Al$_{0.45}$Ga$_{0.55}$As Double Phonon Resonance Quantum Cascade Lasers" in *27th Conference on the Physics of Semiconductors*, edited by Jose Menendez and Chris G. van der Walle, AIP Conference Proceedings 772, American Institute of Physics, New York, 2005, pp. 1565–1566.

Electron-photon Coupling in Opto-electronic Quantum Devices: from Electroluminescence to Lasing

Rita C. Iotti*, Salvatore Savasta† and Fausto Rossi*

*Dipartimento di Fisica, Politecnico di Torino, Corso Duca degli Abruzzi 24, 10129 Torino, Italy
†Dipartimento di Fisica della Materia e Tecnologie Fisiche Avanzate, Università di Messina, Salita Sperone 31, 98166 Messina, Italy

Abstract. A microscopic treatment of the charge-carrier and photon dynamics in semiconductor-based opto-electronic quantum devices is proposed. In particular, two coupled Boltzmann-like equations for the carrier-photon system are derived and then sampled by means of a weighted Monte Carlo technique. Preliminary results for the lasing build-up in state-of-the-art quantum-cascade lasers confirm the effectiveness of the proposed strategy.

Keywords: optoelectronic quantum devices, Monte Carlo simulations
PACS: 85.35.Be, 85.60.Bt, 73.63.-b

The modeling of semiconductor-based opto-electronic quantum devices poses several challenges related to the proper description of the charge-carrier (electron, hole) and photon dynamics in an active region/resonator-waveguide heterostructure. This is not trivial, especially for complex device designs like, e.g., quantum cascade lasers (QCLs) [1]. Indeed, the various theoretical approaches proposed till now, ranging from rate-equation schemes to more sophisticated kinetic pictures, generally provide a focus on the bare electron system, leaving its coupling with the optical cavity at a subsequent phenomenological stage. To provide a better insight into the physics involved, in this contribution we generalize our former microscopic approach for the electron dynamics [2], to include its coupling with the cavity mode.

The dynamical evolution of the coupled carrier and photon systems in semiconductor-based quantum devices may be described at various levels of accuracy [3]. Within the Fermi's golden rule approximation, the cavity feedback on the electronic dynamics is treated as an additional contribution in the Boltzmann transport equation [4]. In particular, for the case of a single-mode optical cavity, the latter has the form:

$$\frac{\mathrm{d}}{\mathrm{d}t} f_{v\mathbf{k}}\bigg|_{\text{light}} = \sum_{v'\mathbf{k}'} \left[P^{\text{light}}_{v\mathbf{k},v'\mathbf{k}'} f_{v'\mathbf{k}'} - P^{\text{light}}_{v'\mathbf{k}',v\mathbf{k}} f_{v\mathbf{k}} \right] . \quad (1)$$

In the probabilities $P^{\text{light}}_{v\mathbf{k},v'\mathbf{k}'}$ appearing in Eq. (1) the following two terms, corresponding to absorption and emission processes, may be identified

$$P^{\text{light}}_{v\mathbf{k},v'\mathbf{k}'} = P^{\text{abs}}_{v\mathbf{k},v'\mathbf{k}'} + P^{\text{em}}_{v\mathbf{k},v'\mathbf{k}'}, \quad (2)$$

with

$$P^{\text{abs}}_{v\mathbf{k},v'\mathbf{k}'} = g_{v\mathbf{k},v'\mathbf{k}'} \mathcal{N} (1 - f_{v\mathbf{k}}) \quad (3)$$

and

$$P^{\text{em}}_{v\mathbf{k},v'\mathbf{k}'} = g_{v\mathbf{k},v'\mathbf{k}'} (\mathcal{N} + 1)(1 - f_{v\mathbf{k}}), \quad (4)$$

here, $\mathcal{N}$ is the photon population of the mode and $g_{v\mathbf{k},v'\mathbf{k}'}$ is the carrier-photon coupling term. The latter is defined as follows

$$g_{v\mathbf{k},v'\mathbf{k}'} = \frac{2\pi}{\hbar} \left[\frac{e\hbar}{m} \right]^2 \frac{|p|^2}{\varepsilon_0 V} \frac{1}{\pi} \frac{\gamma}{\hbar(\gamma^2 + \delta^2)} \frac{1}{\hbar\omega}, \quad (5)$$

where e and m are the electron charge and mass, respectively, V is the cavity volume, p the momentum matrix element, ω the mode frequency, γ the spontaneous emission rate and δ the frequency detuning.

The Boltzmann transport equation for the electron subsystem, with the additional contribution in Eq. (1), goes together with the following photon counterpart:

$$\frac{\mathrm{d}}{\mathrm{d}t} \mathcal{N} = (A - \Gamma)\mathcal{N} + B \quad (6)$$

where

$$A = \sum_{v\mathbf{k},v'\mathbf{k}'} g_{v\mathbf{k},v'\mathbf{k}'} (f_{v\mathbf{k}} - f_{v'\mathbf{k}'}), \quad (7)$$

$$B = \sum_{v\mathbf{k},v'\mathbf{k}'} g_{v\mathbf{k},v'\mathbf{k}'} f_{v\mathbf{k}}, \quad (8)$$

and the $\Gamma\mathcal{N}$ term accounts for loss processes. In state-of-the-art QCLs, the latter are mainly due to quality of the mirrors and to free-carrier absorption in the doped semiconductor regions and in the metallic contact layers [1].

Due to their Boltzmann-like structure, the coupled equations (1) and (6) can be sampled by means of a Monte Carlo (MC) technique and therefore implemented in state-of-the-art simulation tools [2, 5]. However, this implementation is not so straightforward since the carrier

CP893, *Physics of Semiconductors, 28th International Conference*
edited by W. Jantsch and F. Schäffler
© 2007 American Institute of Physics 978-0-7354-0397-0/07/$23.00

and photon dynamics are characterized by extremely different timescales. Indeed, while the electronic ensemble reorganizes itself within picoseconds, the build-up of the photon population in an 'empty' device might take several hundreds of picoseconds. The proper control of statistical fluctuations, which are unavoidable when dealing with rare events, becomes then a crucial part of the simulation. These considerations suggest that the best strategy to evaluate the evolution of the coupled electron-photon system is by means of a so-called weighted MC simulation [6].

The weighted MC technique for the simulation of electron transport in semiconductor devices derives from the general formulation of the MC method [7], the latter being a powerful stochastic numerical technique for the sampling of integro-differential equations. Within this context, the 'natural' probabilities occurring in our transport equations may be adjusted, or weighted, to optimize the simulation efficiency and reduce the statistical fluctuations. This is the essence of a weighted MC approach and allows to guide the carriers to sample particular phase-space regions. In this way better information on phenomena related to the fine details of the distribution function may be obtained; a larger fraction of computer time is in fact devoted to investigate the features of main interest. The traditional MC technique is a special case of the weighted scheme, in which the arbitrary probabilities assigned to the various processes coincide with the natural ones.

In the spirit of the weighted MC scheme, the carrier-photon scattering probabilities in Eq. (1), $P^{\text{light}}_{v\mathbf{k},v'\mathbf{k}'}$, can be artificially enhanced to effectively control the statistical fluctuations. This artefact can then be compensated by a renormalization of the carrier and photon counters, so that the steady-state results do not depend on the weighting factor. Due to the rare-event nature of the problem, the transient dynamics may show significant variations, especially when simulating the photon build-up in an initially empty cavity. This is evident from Fig. 1 which refers to the prototypical GaAs-based QCL design of Ref. [8]. Here the simulated photon populations are reported as a function of time for the initial condition of 10 photons in the cavity at time $t = 0$ ns, and for two different sequences of (pseudo)random numbers (full and dotted lines) [5]. Such instability is a mathematical feature of the photon equation (6) and not an anomaly of the weighting procedure.

To reduce computing resources, without seriously affecting the most relevant physical aspects, the simulations of Fig. 1 have been performed in the presence of only carrier-phonon scattering in the electron dynamics [beyond, of course, the carrier-light term in Eq. (1)]. The relevant cavity parameters in equations (1) and (6) are taken from reference [8], while the spontaneous emission

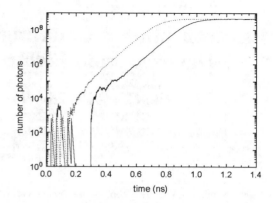

FIGURE 1. Microscopic Monte Carlo simulations of the lasing build-up in the device of Ref. [8]. The initial transients show the typical oscillations of a rare-event problem (see text).

linewidth is adjusted to reproduce the emitted power of the operating device. Such a free parameter (varying in the range 9-12 meV, in extremely good agreement with the experimental findings [8]) includes the contributions of all intrinsic (carrier-carrier, carrier-phonon, etc.) as well as extrinsic (carrier-impurity, interface roughness, etc.) scattering mechanisms and is therefore strongly device dependent.

Analogously to the present case, the MC simulation of other semiconductor-based devices, such as quantum-well infrared photodetectors, would also greatly benefit from a weighting strategy. Indeed, these system are the prototypical candidates for an alternative steady-state weighted MC scheme that we have recently proposed [9].

REFERENCES

1. C. Gmachl, F. Capasso, D. L. Sivco, and A. Y. Cho, *Rep. Prog. Phys.* **64**, 1533–1601 (2001).
2. R. C. Iotti, and F. Rossi, *Phys. Rev. Lett.* **87**, 146603 (2001).
3. See, e.g., *Microscopic theory of semiconductors: Quantum kinetics, confinement and laser*, edited by S. W. Koch, World Scientific, Singapore, 1996.
4. M. Sargent III, M. O. Scully, and W. E. Lamb, *Laser Physics*, Addison Wesley, London, 1974.
5. R. C. Iotti, and F. Rossi, *Rep. Prog. Phys.* **68**, 2533–2571 (2005).
6. F. Rossi, P. Poli, and C. Jacoboni, *Semicond. Sci. Technol.* **7**, 1017–1035 (1992).
7. See, e.g., M. H. Kalos and P. A. Whitlock, *Monte Carlo methods*, Wiley, New York, 1986.
8. C. Sirtori, P. Kruck, S. Barbieri, P. Collot, J. Nagle, M. Beck, J. Faist, and U. Oesterle, *Appl. Phys. Lett.* **73**, 3486–3488 (1998).
9. S. Portolan, R. C. Iotti and F. Rossi, *Monte Carlo Methods Appl.* **10**, 531–539 (2004).

Room-temperature operation of mid-infrared surface-plasmon quantum cascade lasers

M. Bahriz[1], V. Moreau[1], J. Palomo[1], A.B. Krysa[3], D. Austin[2], J.W. Cockburn[2], J.S. Roberts[3], L.R. Wilson[2], F. Julien[1], R. Colombelli[1]

[1]Institut d'Electronique Fondamentale- UMR8622 CNRS, Université Paris Sud, 91405 Orsay - France.
[2]Department of Physics and Astronomy, University of Sheffield, Sheffield S3 7RH, UK
[3]EPSRC National Centre for III-V Technologies, Department of Electronic & Electrical Engineering, University of Sheffield, Sheffield, S1 3JD, UK

Abstract. We report the pulsed, room-temperature operation of an InGaAs/AlInAs quantum cascade laser at an operating wavelength of ≈ 7.5 μm in which the optical mode is a surface-plasmon polariton excitation. The use of a silver-based electrical contact with reduced optical losses at the laser emission wavelength allows for a reduction of the laser threshold current by a factor of two relative to samples with a gold-based contact layer.

Keywords: semiconductor lasers, mid-infrared, surface-plasmons
PACS: 42.55.Px, 73.20.Mf, 07.57.Hm, 42.72.Ai

INTRODUCTION

Surface-plasmon polaritons are mixed electromagnetic modes that originate from the coupling between the electromagnetic field and plasmonic excitations, typically in metallic thin films [1]. The recent intensive study of surface-plasmon related effects [2] is essentially motivated by their ability to confine light down to sub-wavelength dimensions. This characteristic makes a surface-plasmon approach desirable for light/signal transmission applications in which metallo-dielectric structures are used to fabricate integrated optical devices, with structural elements smaller than the wavelength. To date, surface-plasmon excitations have been generated by optical means. However, their intrinsic *non-radiative* nature complicates the task. A room-temperature, all-electrical generator of surface-plasmons would be therefore an advance in the field. The most direct way to obtain emission and, even better, stimulated emission of surface plasmons is to couple the surface-bound electromagnetic mode with a material that exhibits optical gain [3].

Surface-plasmons are already successfully used in the THz range as a guiding solution for THz quantum cascade (QC) lasers. The surface-plasmon damping along the propagation direction can be approximated with the following formula [1,4]:

$$\alpha \approx \frac{4 \cdot \pi}{\lambda} \cdot \frac{n_m \cdot n_d^3}{k_m^3}$$

where k_m and n_m are the imaginary and real part of the metal index of refraction, n_d is the real part of the semiconductor index of refraction, λ is the wavelength. The $1/k^3\lambda$ dependence of the propagation losses makes this a low-loss waveguiding solution in the THz range of the electromagnetic spectrum. However these devices do not work at room-temperature. Surface-plasmons have also been used for waveguiding at shorter wavelengths ($\lambda\approx$8-11μm) [4,5], but pulsed, room-temperature operation has not been achieved yet. We show that by carefully choosing the metal surface-plasmon guiding layer (silver in this case), and by combining it with high performance semiconductor material, it is possible to obtain pulsed room-temperature operation of surface-plasmon QC lasers at shorter wavelengths ($\lambda\approx$7.5 μm).

FABRICATION AND CHARACTERIZATIONS

The laser structure (MR2230) described here was grown by metal organic vapour phase epitaxy (MOVPE) using an $In_{0.53}Ga_{0.47}As$/ $Al_{0.48}In_{0.52}As$ lattice matched to a highly-doped InP substrate. Details of the growth process can be found in [6]. The active regions used are based on a standard 2-phonon-resonance

CP893, *Physics of Semiconductors, 28th International Conference*
edited by W. Jantsch and F. Schäffler

design (see Ref. [7]), with the lasing transition designed to emit at 7.5 μm. Fifty active-region/injector stages were grown, preceded by a 500-nm-thick InGaAs layer doped to $n = 5 \times 10^{16}$ cm^{-3} and followed by contact facilitating layers.

A silver-based contact layer was used for the surface-plasmon waveguide because of the desirable refractive index properties of this metal. From equation 1, it can be seen that in order to achieve low waveguide losses for a particular wavelength it is important to minimize the value of n_m/k_m^3. Table I summarizes the n_m and k_m values for gold (Au), palladium (Pd) and silver (Ag). The low value of n_m/k_m^3 for silver relative to the other metals suggests that an improvement in device performance can be obtained by using a silver-based surface-plasmon waveguide.

The wafer was processed into a range of laser ridge widths, following the procedure in Ref. [8]. The sample was cleaved into 2 parts before the top-contact metal evaporation. On one half a simple Ti/Au contact (3/300 nm) was deposited, while on the other half a Ti/Ag/Ni/Au contact (3/150/10/250 nm) was used instead. Typical laser emission spectra for the Ag-based sample are reported in Fig. 1 (top panel). The laser emission wavelength at 78K is ≈ 7.5 μm, in agreement with the band-structure calculations. The spectra are typically multimode, but regular Fabry-Perot fringes do not usually appear. We suspect that this phenomenon originates from the refractive index dispersion of the metal.

The Au-based lasers operate up to a maximum temperature of 260 K. On the other hand, the Ag-based lasers operate up to 300K (Figure 1, bottom panel). The threshold current density at 78 K for the Au-based devices tested lies in the range (2.9±0.4) kA/cm^2, whilst for the Ag-based devices we measured

(1.5±0.2) kA/cm^2. The performance improvement depends solely on the reduced losses induced by the Ag-based contact, since all the other characteristics (semiconductor material, processing procedure, ridge dimensions, laser packaging) are identical for the two sets of devices.

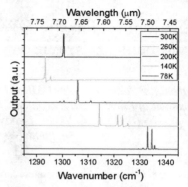

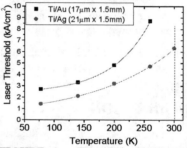

FIGURE 1. Top: Pulsed (50ns pulse width, 84 kHz repetition rate) emission spectra for a typical device with an Ag-based surface-plasmon waveguide. The spectral resolution was set to 0.125 cm^{-1}. Bottom: Threshold current densities as a function of operating temperatures for typical (Ti)/Au and (Ti)/Ag/Ni/Au devices. An improvement of approximately a factor of two in the current threshold has been obtained using Ag-based electrical contacts.

TABLE 1. Real and imaginary parts of the refractive index for different metals, for a QCL operating wavelength of λ~8μm. All values are from Ref [9]. It can be seen that surface plasmon waveguides utilizing silver are predicted to have lower losses than gold- or palladium based waveguides.

Metal	n_m	k_m	n_m/k_m^3
Gold (Au)	7.78	57	4.2×10^{-5}
Palladium (Pd)	3.13	36	6.7×10^{-5}
Silver (Ag)	3.35	57	1.8×10^{-5}

ACKNOWLEDGMENTS

We thank C. Sirtori, O. Painter, Y. Chassagneux, A. de Rossi, for useful discussions. This work was conducted as part of a EURYI scheme award. See www.esf.org/euryi. This work is supported by the UK Engineering and Physical Sciences Research Council.

REFERENCES

1. P. Yeh, "Optical Waves in Layered Media", John Wiley & Sons, 2005.

2. J. B. Pendry, L. Martín-Moreno, F. J. Garcia-Vidal, Science **305**, 847 (2004).

3. J. Seidel, S. Grafström, and L. Eng, Phys. Rev. Lett. **94**, 177401 (2005).

4. C. Sirtori et al., Opt. Lett. **23**, 1366 (1998).

5. R. Colombelli et al., Science **302**, 1374 (2003).

6. A.B. Krysa, et al., J. Cryst. Growth, **272**, 682 (2004).

7. R. P. Green, et al., Appl. Phys. Lett. **85**, 5529 (2004).

8. V. Moreau, et al., Electron. Lett. **41**, 1175 (2005).

9. E. S. Koteles and W. R. Datars, Solid State Comm. **19**, 221 (1976).

Optimization Of InP-Based Waveguides For High-Performance Mid-Infrared Quantum Cascade Lasers

Oana Malis[1*], Deborah L. Sivco[1], Jianxin Chen[1], Liming Zhang[2], A. Michael Sergent[1], Zhijun Liu[3], and Claire Gmachl[3]

[1]Bell Laboratories, Lucent Technologies, 600 Mountain Ave., Murray Hill, NJ, 07974, USA
[2]Bell Laboratories, Lucent Technologies, 791 Holmdel-Keyport Rd., Holmdel, NJ, 07733, USA
[3]Dept. of Electrical Engineering and PRISM, Princeton Univ., Princeton, NJ, USA 08544
*Email: malis@lucent.com

Abstract. Using a combination of semiconductor overgrowth, epi-side down mounting, and high-reflectance coating of the back facet, continuous-wave operation up to 320 K of a quantum cascade laser emitting at 8 μm was achieved. In pulsed mode at 300 K the devices exhibit threshold current densities of 1.8 kA/cm^2, peak output powers of 260 mW, and maximum slope efficiencies of 346 mW/A. In cw mode at 300 K the threshold current density was measured to be 2.5-kA/cm^2, the slope efficiency was 52 mW/A, and the output power was 20 mW.

Keywords: quantum cascade lasers, molecular beam epitaxy
PACS: 42.55.Px, 81.05.Ea, 81.10.J

The maximum output power and operating temperature of mid-infrared quantum cascade lasers (QCLs) is determined to a large extent by the optical and thermal properties of the waveguides. To achieve room-temperature, continuous-wave operation of QCLs, we focused on improving the InP-based waveguides. Due to its low refractive index, InP is the material of choice for both transversal and lateral optical confinement. Moreover, the high thermal conductivity of InP facilitates the extraction of heat from the active region. QCL structures with InP top claddings were grown by solid-source molecular beam epitaxy (MBE). To minimize the optical losses, the doping of each waveguide layer was carefully optimized. Deep-etched ridge-waveguides were defined employing either selective wet etching or dry etching. Using a combination of semiconductor overgrowth, epitaxial-side down mounting, Au electroplating, and high-reflectance coating of the back facet, continuous-wave (cw) operation up to 320 K of a QCL emitting at 8 μm was achieved. The detailed structure of the active region/injector section of the laser was presented elsewhere [1-2]. Figure 1 shows a deep-etched ridge-waveguide QCL device with an 8-μm thick electroplated Au top-contact. In pulsed mode at 300 K the devices exhibit threshold current densities of 1.8 kA/cm^2, peak output powers of 260 mW, and maximum slope efficiencies of 346 mW/A. In cw mode at 300 K the threshold current density was measured to be 2.5 kA/cm^2, and the slope efficiency was 52 mW/A. Figure 2 summarizes the performance of a 4.25 mm long, 15 μm wide device in cw mode. An output power of 20 mW in cw mode was achieved at 300 K. The devices operate in cw mode up to 320 K, which is the maximum temperature in our experimental setup. The temperature dependence of the threshold current is detailed in Fig. 3. A characteristic temperature T_0 of 126 K and 100 K was estimated for the pulsed, and cw mode, respectively. Using the dependence of the threshold current on cavity length, the waveguide losses were also estimated and found to be more than twice as high as calculated theoretically based on material free carrier absorption (13 cm^{-1} as opposed to 6 cm^{-1}). The exact origin of these losses in not completely understood at this point, but they are likely due to resonant and non-resonant carrier absorption in the laser active region as well as to waveguide scattering losses.

We also investigated the effect of InP lateral confinement on the room-temperature performance of QCLs. Buried heterostructures were fabricated by growing semi-insulating InP on the sides of the ridges with metal-organic chemical-vapor deposition. For wide ridges (>10 μm wide) mounted epitaxial-side down, the effect of the InP lateral confinement on the optical and thermal properties of the devices is small.

CP893, *Physics of Semiconductors, 28th International Conference*
edited by W. Jantsch and F. Schäffler

As a consequence the lasers have similar performance to the devices without buried heterostructures, as illustrated in Fig. 4. The most significant impact of the buried heterostructures was on the reliability of the devices, by reducing breakdown during high voltage, high current operation. We expect the effect of InP lateral confinement on narrow devices (<5 μm wide) to be significantly stronger, and we are currently in the process of examining this effect.

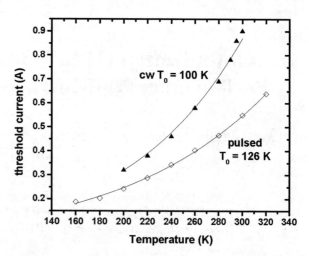

FIGURE 3. Temperature dependence of the threshold current in pulsed (open diamonds) and cw (filled triangles) mode for a 3-mm long, 10-μm-wide laser mounted epi-side down with a thick Au electroplated top contact and HR coating on the back facet. The characteristic temperatures T_0 were estimated in each case by fitting the experimental data with the functional form $J_{th}=J_0\times exp(T/T_0)$ (fit shown in continuous lines).

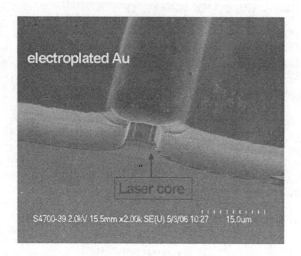

FIGURE 1. Deep-etched ridge-waveguide QCL device with thick electroplated Au top contact.

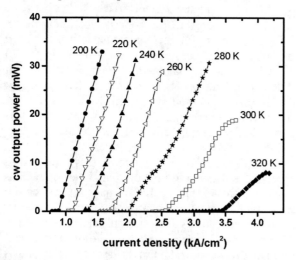

FIGURE 2. Light output power as a function of injection current density in cw mode for a 4.25 mm long, 15-μm-wide laser mounted epi-side down with a thick Au electroplated top contact and HR coating on the back facet.

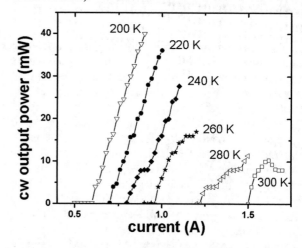

FIGURE 4. Deep-etched ridge-waveguide QCL device with thick electroplated Au top contact. Light output power as a function of injection current density in cw mode for a 3 mm long, 10-μm-wide laser with MOCVD-grown InP side-claddings, a thick Au electroplated top contact and HR coating on the back facet. The device was mounted epitaxial-side down.

REFERENCES

1. Z. Liu, D. Wasserman, S. S. Howard, A. J. Hoffman, C. F. Gmachl, X. Wang, T. Tanbun-Ek, L. Cheng, and F.-S. Choa, IEEE Photonics Tech. Lett. **18**, pp.1347-1349 (2006).
2. O. Malis et al., Proceedings of the IEEE conference on InP and related materials, 2006.

High-order THz-sideband generation in semiconductors

Ren-Bao Liu* and Bang-Fen Zhu†

*Department of Physics, The Chinese University of Hong Kong, Shatin, N.T., Hong Kong, China[1]
†Department of Physics, Tsinghua University, Beijing 100083, China

Abstract. The optical sideband generation in semiconductors under intense THz lasers presents flat wide-band spectra with the cutoff determined by the maximum energy-gain of electron-hole pairs in quantum trajectories under the THz field. The approximation based on the quantum trajectory picture agrees well with the numerical simulations.

Keywords: Terahertz, Sideband generation, Quantum trajectory
PACS: 78.20.Bh, 42.65.Ky, 78.20.Jq

INTRODUCTION

Semiconductors under intense THz lasers possess a wealth of physical effects such as the dynamical localization [1], dynamical Franz-Keldysh effect [2], and excitonic stabilization [3]. In this contribution, We will discuss the high-order sideband spectra of semiconductors under intense THz lasers, which resembles on several aspects the high-order harmonic generation by atoms under super-intense optical lasers [4]. The sideband spectra present flat wide-band plateaux, which can be well understood in the quantum trajectory theory developed in atomic physics to understand the plateau spectra of high harmonic generation [4]. The sideband generation by excitons, however, differs fundamentally from the harmonic generation in atomic systems, since the former starts from the creation of elementary excitations in solids and hence has tunable excitation energy while the latter involves atoms with fixed binding energy. Thus the THz-sideband spectroscopy is expected to provide more flexibility in studying the quantum trajectory, a central notion in many basic physics problems such as the quantum tunneling in macro-magnets. The high-order THz-sideband generation could also be useful in many electro-optical applications such as wide-band optical multiplexers, optical pulses with ultra-high repetition rate, and optical communication with THz bandwidth.

FORMALISM

The dynamics of electron-hole pairs excited by an optical field $\mathbf{E}(t)$ in semiconductors under an intense THz field [expressed by a vector potential $\mathbf{A}(t)$] can be described by the inhomogeneous Schrödinger equation

$$i\partial_t \psi = H(t)\psi + \mathbf{d} \cdot \mathbf{E}(t), \qquad (1)$$

with the Hamiltonian given (in the Rydberg unit system) by

$$H = [\mathbf{p} - \mathbf{A}(t)]^2 + E_g - 2/r, \qquad (2)$$

where $\mathbf{d}$ is the interband dipole matrix element in the semiconductor and E_g is the bandgap. The sideband generation is determined by the optical polarization $\mathbf{P}(t) = -\mathbf{d}^* \psi(0,t)$. By solving Eq. (1) numerically, the sideband generation spectrum can be readily calculated [3]. For an input optical field $\mathbf{E}(t) = \mathbf{E}_p(t)e^{-i\Omega t}$ and a THz field with angular frequency ω, the sideband intensity of the $2N$th order with output frequency $\Omega + 2N\omega$ is $I_{2N} \propto P_{2N}^2$ (the odd order sidebands are vanishing due to the inversion symmetry of the system), where

$$\mathbf{P}_{2N} = i \int \mathbf{d}^* \mathbf{d} \cdot \mathbf{E}_p(t-\tau)\theta(\tau)e^{iS(\mathbf{p},t,\tau)}dt\,d\tau\,d\mathbf{p}/(2\pi)^3 \quad (3)$$

with the action

$$S(\mathbf{p},t,\tau) \equiv -\int_{t-\tau}^{t} H(t'')dt'' + (\Omega - E_g)\tau + 2N\omega t, \quad (4)$$

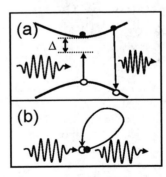

FIGURE 1. Schematics for the THz-sideband generation in semiconductors. (b) Schematic illustration of quantum trajectories in the THz-sideband generation.

[1] Electronic mail: rbliu@phy.cuhk.edu.hk

CP893, *Physics of Semiconductors, 28th International Conference*
edited by W. Jantsch and F. Schäffler
© 2007 American Institute of Physics 978-0-7354-0397-0/07/$23.00

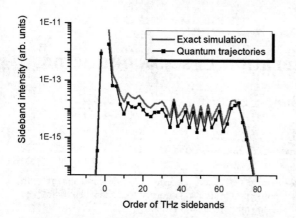

FIGURE 2. THz-sideband generation spectra in bulk GaAs driven by a THz field with $\omega = 5$ meV and $F = 35$ kV/cm, calculated with the exact numerical simulation and the quantum trajectory approximation, respectively. The input optical field has such frequency that $\Omega - E_g = -32$ meV.

giving the phase accumulation along an arbitrary path in the phase space characterized by the momentum $\mathbf{p}$, the delay time (τ) between the excitation and recombination of excitons, and the recombination time (t).

When the THz driving field is strong, the motion amplitude of the electron-hole pairs is much larger than the wavepacket diffusion (the quantum fluctuation), so the quantum dynamics can be well approximated as trajectories constrained by the classical kinetic equations plus the Gaussian quantum fluctuation, i.e., the action can be approximated as [4]

$$S(\mathbf{p},t,\tau) \approx S(\mathbf{p_0},t_0,\tau_0) + \frac{1}{2}\delta(\mathbf{p},t,\tau) \cdot \partial^2_{\mathbf{p},t,\tau}S \cdot \delta(\mathbf{p},t,\tau).$$

For simplicity, we will neglect the Coulomb interaction between the electron and the hole, which is a well-justified approximation when the energy-gain from the THz field is much larger than the exciton binding energy. Thus the trajectory parameters can be easily determined by the saddle-point equations [4]

$$\partial_\tau S = 0 \;\Rightarrow\; [\mathbf{p} - \mathbf{A}(t-\tau)]^2 = \Omega - E_g \equiv -\Delta, \tag{5}$$

$$\partial_t S = 0 \;\Rightarrow\; [\mathbf{p} - \mathbf{A}(t)]^2 - [\mathbf{p} - \mathbf{A}(t-\tau)]^2 = 2N\omega, \tag{6}$$

$$\partial_\mathbf{p} S = 0 \;\Rightarrow\; \mathbf{p}\tau - \int_{t-\tau}^{t}\mathbf{A}(t')dt' = 2\int_{t-\tau}^{t}\dot{\mathbf{r}}(t')dt' = 0, \tag{7}$$

which correspond respectively to the energy conservation at excitation, the energy conservation at sideband generation, and the condition that the electron and the hole should be at the same position at the recombination time, as schematically illustrated in Fig. 1. Such trajectories are quoted as "quantum" since in general no classical solution may exist which requires $\mathbf{p}$, t, and τ be real numbers. Let $A(t) = -(F/\omega)\sin(\omega t)$, it can be easily seen that the energy-gain from the THz field by the

electron-hole pair in the quantum trajectories is bounded by $E_{max} \approx 3.2U_p + \Delta$ [4] (where the ponderomotive energy $U_p \equiv F^2\omega^{-2}/2$), and hence the sideband generation will be cut off at $2N\omega \approx E_{max}$, similar to the cutoff effect in the high-order harmonic generation [4].

RESULTS

Figure 2 presents a typical example of THz-sideband generation spectra in semiconductors. For the parameter used, the ponderomotive energy U_p is about 98 meV, much larger than the THz laser frequency ($\omega = 5$ meV) and the exciton binding energy ($\sim$4 meV) in GaAs, so the sideband generation is well described by the quantum trajectories, as can be seen from the good agreement between the trajectory approximation and the exact numerical simulation. The spectrum presents a plateau as wide as close to 70 times the fundamental frequency. The cut-off is well consistent with the calculation of the maximum energy gain $E_{max} \approx 68\omega$. Such a flat wide-band sideband spectrum is of potential application in optical pulses with ultra-high repetition rate. Since the exciton as an elementary excitation can be excited by optical pulses at selected time and frequency, the quantum trajectories can be controlled with much more flexibility than in atomic physics, which may lead to further physical insight and to novel electro-optical applications.

ACKNOWLEDGMENTS

This work was partially supported by the Hong Kong RGC Direct Grant 2060284.

REFERENCES

1. A. A. Ignatov and Y. A. Romanov, Phys. Status Solidii B **73**, 327 (1976); D. H. Dunlap and V. M. Kenkre, Phys. Rev. B **34**, 3625 (1986).
2. A. P. Jauho and K. Johnsen, Phys. Rev. Lett. **76**, 4576 (1996).
3. R. B. Liu and B. F. Zhu, Phys. Rev. B **66**, 033106 (2002).
4. M. Lewenstein, Ph. Balcou, M. Yu. Ivanov, A. L'Huillier, and P. B. Corkum, Phys. Rev. A **49**, 2117 (1994).

"Continuous" Focal-Plane Array
for Detection of Terahertz Radiation

Aleksei Artamkin[1], Andrei Nikorici[2], Valery Shklover[3], Ludmila Ryabova[1], and Dmitry Khokhlov[1]

[1]*Moscow State University, Leninskie Gory 1, 119992 Moscow, Russia*
[2]*Institute of Applied Physics, Academiei str. 5, MD-2028 Kishinev, Moldova*
[3]*Swiss Federal Institute of Technology, Wolfgang Pauli Str. 10, CH-8093 Zürich, Switzerland*

Abstract. It is shown that local long-lived non-equilibrium states are generated in $Pb_{1-x}Sn_xTe(In)$ alloys at low temperatures under the action of local Terahertz excitation. This result opens a possibility for construction of a "continuous" focal-plane array for detection of terahertz radiation. The ideas for readout of information from this array are discussed.

Keywords: Terahertz, Radiation, Detector, Focal-Plane Array.
PACS: 07.57.Kp; 85.60.Gz

INTRODUCTION

Existence of the persistent photoconductivity effect induced by Terahertz radiation in $Pb_{1-x}Sn_xTe(In)$ alloys at low temperatures is due to existence of a barrier between the states with localized and free electron [1]. Previously these states have been mainly investigated using spatially homogeneous excitation of a sample. However some experiments show that the local long-lived excited states may be formed under the action of strong electric field [2]. The easiest way for generation of this kind of states is local illumination of a sample.

We have investigated local non-equilibrium states generated by Terahertz radiation in $Pb_{1-x}Sn_xTe(In)$ alloys at low temperatures.

EXPERIMENTAL DETAILS

The samples under investigation were $Pb_{1-x}Sn_xTe(In)$ single crystals. The tin content $x = 0.25$ was chosen in order to provide pinning of the Fermi level within the gap [3], so the sample was in a semiinsulating state at low temperatures.

The experiment geometry is shown in the insert in the Fig.1. The conductivity σ was measured between the contact couples 1,2,3... simultaneously. The region between the couple 1 contacts (shaded in the insert in the Fig.1) was illuminated through the hole in a needle using a thermal source of Terahertz radiation [3] with characteristic temperature $10\ K < T^* < 50\ K$. The measurements were performed using vacuum metallic chamber cooled by liquid helium. This construction shields completely the background radiation.

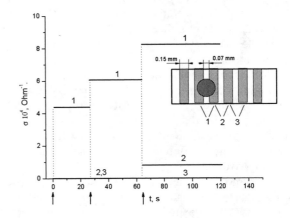

FIGURE 1. Conductivity σ of different sample regions under the action of Terahertz radiation. Arrows indicate moments when short radiation pulses affect the sample. The experiment geometry is shown in the insert. Figures correspond to the numbers of contact couples. The illuminated region of the sample is shaded. The characteristic sizes are shown in the insert.

CP893, *Physics of Semiconductors, 28th International Conference*
edited by W. Jantsch and F. Schäffler
© 2007 American Institute of Physics 978-0-7354-0397-0/07/$23.00

The typical experimental curves are shown in the Fig.1. Radiation pulses of about 0.3 s duration illuminated the sample at the moments shown by arrows. One can clearly see that after the first two pulses photoconductivity occurs only within the illuminated region. When the radiation pulse length (or T*) increases, the photoexcitation slightly spreads out to the adjacent region 2.

When the radiation is switched off, the conductivity of all regions 1,2,3... slowly relaxes. The recombination rate of excited electrons always exceeds the diffusion rate independently of the sample temperature.

The characteristic time of excitation propagation is at least more than 10^4 s at T = 4.2 K. The spatial characteristic scale is at least less than ~ 100 μm which is comparable by the order of magnitude to the wavelength of Terahertz radiation used for excitation. The physical picture of the processes involved is the following. Photoexcited free electrons cannot diffuse far away from the region of generation due to electrostatic attraction to photoionized impurity centers. On the other hand these electrons cannot recombine because of the existence of a barrier between the local and extended states.

READOUT TECHNIQUES

One can see that distribution of radiation doze over sample surface reflects in distribution of concentration of long-lived free electrons. In other words, it is possible to construct a focal plane "continuous" array, where the signal is internally integrated in every effective element.

The readout technique is a special problem. There are several ideas on how to do it. The first one is contact readout, when two mutually perpendicular sets of contacts isolated in the knots are deposited on a sample. The second way is a non-contact readout by electron beam. Both of these methods have considerable disadvantages.

The third way seems to be the most promising. Let us consider a thin slice of $Pb_{1-x}Sn_xTe(In)$ with a semitransparent electrode deposited on one side (Fig.2). The investigated radiation flux illuminates the sample from the left-hand side in the Fig.2. A buffer insulating fluoride layer is deposited on another side of the sample plate followed by a thin layer of a semiconductor with relatively wide gap, and a second semitransparent electrode. If the sample is illuminated by a short-wavelength laser from the right-hand side (Fig.2), it is possible to form a local highly conductive region in the wide-gap semiconductor.

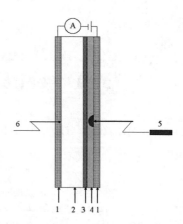

FIGURE 2. Readout of information from a "contineous" focal-plane array. 1 - semitransparent electrodes, 2 - active $Pb_{1-x}Sn_xTe(In)$ layer, 3 - fluoride buffer layer, 4 – wide-gap semiconductor layer, 5 - short-wavelength laser, 6 - incident radiation flux.

If bias is applied between the electrodes, the current is defined by the $Pb_{1-x}Sn_xTe(In)$ sample conductivity in the region of the laser spot. If the recombination rate in the wide-gap semiconductor is high enough, it is easy to reconstruct the conductivity distribution over the $Pb_{1-x}Sn_xTe(In)$ sample simply by scanning the laser beam over the structure surface and by measuring the respective current.

SUMMARY

We have demonstrated experimentally the possibility for construction of a "continuous" focal-plane array for detection of Terahertz radiation based on $Pb_{1-x}Sn_xTe(In)$. The idea for information readout is presented.

ACKNOWLEDGMENTS

The research described in this paper was supported in part by the grants ## 04-02-16497, 05-02-16657, 06-02-90867 of the Russian Foundation for the Basic Research, and by the grant # IB7320-110921/1 of the Swiss National Science Foundation.

REFERENCES

1. B.A. Volkov, L.I. Ryabova, and D.R. Khokhlov, *Physics-Uspekhi* **45**, 819 (2002).
2. B.A. Akimov, N.B. Brandt, and V.N. Nikiforov, *Sov. Phys. Solid State* **26**, 973 (1984)].

Phase Coherent Photorefractive Effect in ZnSe Quantum Wells Using Ultrashort Pulses

S. Tripathy, P. Bajracharya, H. P. Wagner

Department of Physics, University of Cincinnati, Cincinnati, Ohio 45221-0011 U.S.A.

Abstract. We report on an exciton resonant phase coherent photorefractive effect in ZnMgSe/ZnSe single quantum wells using 30 fs light pulses. The experiments are performed in a four-wave-mixing configuration using two or three pulses. The PCP effect is attributed to the formation of an electron grating within the QW that is caused by the interference of excitons in the ZnMgSe barrier.

Keywords: Photorefractive effect, excitons, coherence.
PACS: 78.67.De, 42.50.Md, 71.55.Gs, 71.35.-y

INTRODUCTION

Present photorefractive multiple quantum well (QW) devices reveal high sensitivity and fast response [1] but they require externally applied electric fields and do not use the coherence of excitons to conserve the phase information of incident light fields. In this paper we report on a phase coherent photorefractive (PCP) effect that is capable of preserving this information. The observation of PCP using ultrashort laser pulses (~10 fs) has potential for optical coherence imaging (OCI) with depth resolution of several μm.

EXPERIMENTAL DETAILS

The investigated ZnSe single quantum well (QW) was pseudomorphically grown on (001) oriented GaAs substrate by molecular beam epitaxy. The sample consists of a 10 nm wide ZnSe QW sandwiched between two 30 nm $Zn_{0.9}Mg_{0.1}Se$ barriers, and a 20 nm thick ZnSe buffer layer between the barrier and the GaAs substrate. A description of the sample preparation is given in [2]. A frequency doubled mode locked Ti-sapphire laser providing 30 fs pulses at a repetition rate of 80 MHz was used for the optical excitation. Two- and three-beam four-wave mixing (FWM) experiments involving linearly or circularly polarized pulses k_1, k_2 and k_3 have been performed in a back scattering geometry with the sample mounted in a Helium flow cryostat. A more detailed description of the experimental setup is given elsewhere [3, 4].

EXPERIMENTAL RESULTS

Recently we reported on an all-optical PCP effect in a $ZnSe/Zn_{0.94}Mg_{0.06}$ Se single QW using 90 fs laser pulses that do not overlap in time [3, 4]. The center energy of the pulses with ~25 meV bandwidth was resonantly tuned to the exciton transition energy. The observed PCP effect is attributed to the formation of a long living electron grating that is generated in various steps: First, electrons are optically excited in the GaAs substrate and captured in the ZnSe QW. Subsequently an exciton grating is generated by the interference of coherent excitons. Finally, the QW electrons are redistributed by the exciton grating into regions of low exciton density due to Coulomb interaction and Pauli blocking. After the exciton lifetime (~100 ps) the exciton density grating vanishes by recombination, while the electron grating that is stabilized by localized holes at the ZnSe/GaAs interface accumulates over many pulse cycles. Three-beam as well as two-beam experiments with significantly reduced repetition rate of subsequent pulse pairs reveal a grating lifetime longer than 10 μs [5]. The electron grating supplies longitudinal space charge fields between the QW and localized interface charges leading to a spectral diffraction efficiency of $\eta \approx 3 \cdot 10^{-4}$ [3]. The PCP signal is observable at total incident light intensities as low as 100 μWcm^{-2} [5]. Due to the coherent generation process the PCP signal exhibits an exponential decay as a function of the delay between pulses that is equal to the exciton dephasing rate and it

CP893, *Physics of Semiconductors, 28th International Conference*
edited by W. Jantsch and F. Schäffler
© 2007 American Institute of Physics 978-0-7354-0397-0/07/$23.00

shows a pronounced suppression at the temporal overlap of incident pulses.

More recent experiments demonstrate significant modifications of the PCP signal when spectrally broad 30 fs pulses of ~80 meV bandwidth are used. Figure 1 shows the spectrally resolved diffracted signals close to temporal pulse overlap for collinear polarized pulses with pulse center energy of 2.79 eV (top) and 2.84 eV (bottom). These experiments were performed at 35 K. The total intensity of pulses $\mathbf{k}_1$ and $\mathbf{k}_2$ was ~2.0 MW/cm^2. Due to the large spectral width of the pulses various heavy-hole (11h, 12h, 13h) as well as light-hole excitons (11l, 12l) are excited. The transitions were identified by comparison with calculated exciton energies. Transition $X_{barrier}$ indicates ZnMgSe barrier excitons that are excited at pulse energy 2.84 eV, XX indicates the 11h exciton-to-biexciton transition.

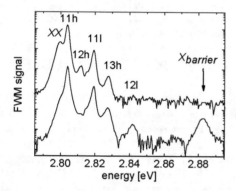

FIGURE 1. Two-beam FWM spectra at pulse energy 2.79 eV (top) and 2.84 eV (bottom) recorded at 35 K near pulse overlap ($\tau_{12} \approx 0$). The spectra are offset for better visibility.

Figure 2 (top) shows the trace of the 11h diffracted signal as a function of pulse delay τ_{12} at pulse energy 2.79 eV. The PCP signal is strongly reduced beyond pulse overlap. The diffracted signal is dominated by $\chi^{(3)}$ FWM processes where the slope for negative delay times ($\mathbf{k}_2$ arrives first) is two times higher than for positive delay. The slope for positive delay is $2\gamma_2$ with $\gamma_2 = 0.7$ ps^{-1} being the 11h exciton dephasing rate. The oscillations in the FWM trace correspond to quantum beats between different exciton transitions. The strong reduction of the PCP effect using 30 fs pulses is attributed to the generation of a roughly four times higher electron-hole (*eh*)-pair density compared to the exciton grating density. This high background of free carriers prevents an effective redistribution of electrons in the QW by the exciton grating. Three-beam FWM experiments [5] demonstrate that the signal at pulse overlap is still dominated by the PCP effect. In this case the excitation density in the GaAs substrate is spatially modulated which leads to an accumulating electron grating in the QW.

Figure 2 (bottom) shows the 11h signal trace at pulse energy 2.84 eV. In this case a symmetric PCP signal is observable. The signal slope is significantly lower than the 11h dephasing rate $2\gamma_2$. It corresponds to dephasing rate $2\gamma_2'$ of ZnMgSe barrier excitons (γ_2' = 5 ps^{-1}). The fast oscillations in this slope are interferences between 11h and $X_{barrier}$ excitons that have an energy separation of ~80 meV. Hence the electron grating generation process is explained as follows: Excited electrons moving from the GaAs substrate toward the QW are efficiently redistributed by the $X_{barrier}$ exciton grating without disturbance of *eh*-pairs in the QW. The electron grating is stabilized by localized holes at the ZnSe/GaAs interface and is subsequently captured by the QW. Two- and three-beam experiments [5] reveal a diffraction efficiency that is similar to the PCP effect described in [3]. For positive delay times greater than 500 fs again $\chi^{(3)}$ FWM processes become dominant, showing a pronounced beating and a signal slope of $2\gamma_2$.

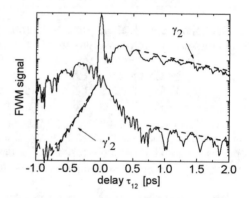

FIGURE 2. FWM traces at the 11h exciton transition at pulse energy 2.79 eV (top) and 2.84 eV (bottom) recorded at 35 K. The spectra are offset for better visibility.

ACKNOWLEDGMENTS

This work is supported by the National Science Foundation (DMR 0305076).

REFERENCES

1. D. D. Nolte, *J. Appl. Phys.* **85**, 6259 (1999).
2. M Wörz, E. Griebl, Th. Reisinger, B. Flierl, D. Haserer, T. Semmler, T. Frey, W. Gebhardt, *Phys. Stat. Sol. B* **202**, 805 (1997).
3. H. P. Wagner, S. Tripathy, H.-P. Tranitz, W. Langbein, *Phys. Rev. Lett.* **94**, 147402 (2005).
4. H. P. Wagner, S. Tripathy, P. Bajracharya, H.-P. Tranitz, *Phys. Rev. B* **73**, 085318 (2006).
5. P. Bajracharya , S. Tripathy, A. Kabir, H. P. Wagner, to be published.

Optical Ionization Of Amino Acids Using Amino-acid/Semiconductor Junctions

Masato Oda[1,2], Takashi Nakayama[2], Takahisa Ohno[1]

1. Computational Materials Science Center, National Institute for Materials Science, 1-2-1 Sengen, Tsukuba, Ibaraki 305-0047, Japan
2. Department of physics, Chiba University, 1-33 Yayoi, Inage, Chiba 263-8522, Japan

Abstract. Electronic structure and optical properties of amino acids on Si substrate are investigated using density functional calculations. It is shown that when phenylalanine, one of twenty bio amino acids, is adsorbed on Si substrate, the optical excitation probability from the HOMO of phenylalanine to the conduction bands of Si is generated. This result indicates that one can control the positive ionization of phenylalanine by optical excitations.

Keywords: Bio-device, Protein, Amino acids, Ab-initio calculation, Photo ionization
PACS: 85.30.De, 87.83.+a

INTRODUCTION

One of targets in nano-bio science is the artificial control of biomaterial functions[1]. In this work, we focus on the proteins, which work as effective catalysts of almost all chemical reactions in living bodies. These functions emerge when amino acids inside the protein are ionized. In our previous work [2], we studied electronic structures of amino-acid/Si junctions and proposed new types of bio-devices that control the protein functions by applying the gate voltage and injecting carriers from semiconductors. The purpose of this study is to theoretically investigate another ionization method to switch on the protein functions; *i.e.*, the possibility of optical ionization of amino acids on semiconductor surfaces.

METHODS

The amino-acid/semiconductor junctions are simulated using 4ML 2x2 Si(111) repeated-slab model. Figure 1(a) shows the top view of the unit cell of this surface. We assume that a single amino acid is covalently bonded to one of dangling bonds of surface Si as shown in Fig.1(b). The other dangling bonds on Si surface are terminated by hydrogen atoms. Electronic structures and dielectric functions of these systems are calculated by using ab-initio density functional theory in a local density approximation (LDA) and linear response theory. Wave functions are expanded in plane waves with a cutoff energy of

10.24Ry. By comparing the Hartree-Fock calculations, we found that this cutoff energy is slightly small but enough to qualitatively describe electronic structures of organic molecules. To compensate the band-gap underestimation in LDA, we employ a scissors operator recipe by adding 0.668eV to energies of conduction bands.

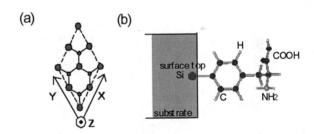

FIGURE 1. Schematic views of the model unsed in this work. (a) Top view of Si(111) surface and direction of unit vectors. (b) phenylalanine/Si(111) junctions.

RESULTS AND DISCUSSIONS

Figure 2 shows calculated band structure of phenylalanine/Si joint system. Both the highest valence and the lowest conduction bands originate from the Si substrate. Molecule-originated electronic states have little dispersion along the surface. We can see that the highest occupied molecular orbital (HOMO) of phenylalanine is located at about 1eV below the valence band top, while the lowest

CP893, *Physics of Semiconductors, 28th International Conference*
edited by W. Jantsch and F. Schäffler
© 2007 American Institute of Physics 978-0-7354-0397-0/07/$23.00

unoccupied molecular state is not present within the energy range in Fig.2.

Then, we calculate the dielectric functions of amino-acids/Si joint systems. To clarify what change occurs in optical properties by the production of junction, we show in Fig.3 the differential spectrum responding to the imaginary part of molecular dielectric function for the case of phenylalanine/Si. This spectrum is obtained as a difference of dielectric function between a plain Si substrate and a joint system and corresponds to the surface photo absorption spectrum in experiments. For comparison, the corresponding spectrum of an isolated phenylalanine molecule is displayed as a dashed line, which is calculated by using the same size and geometry of the unit cell. It is clearly seen that the junction produces a new absorption channel, *i.e.*, a large and broad absorption region from 4 to 5 eV. By analyzing the wave functions, we found that this absorption is caused by the optical excitations of electrons from the localized HOMO states of phenylalanine to the extended conduction-band states of Si substrate, similar to the photoelectric effect where the electron is excited into vacuum. Such transitions become possible because the hybridization of electronic states occurs between amino acid and Si. Similar results are obtained for other kinds of amino acids (not shown here).

Finally, we comment on how to separate the above-mentioned excitation to realize the efficient ionization.

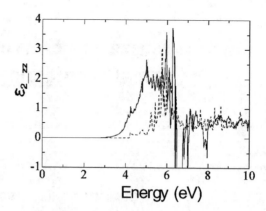

FIGURE 3. Dielectric functions (zz polarization) of phenylalanine. Solid line: differential spectrum of phenyl-alanine/Si joint system, dashed line: isolated phenylalanine.

The absorption around 4 eV in Fig.3 is apparently embedded in the absorption Si substrate. However, if we use other semiconductor substrates such as GaN having lower valence-band-top energy than that of amino-acid HOMO states, the absorption is expected in band gaps of semiconductors and one can positively ionize amino acids selectively.

SUMMARY

The possibility of optical ionization of amino acids on semiconductor surfaces was studied using ab-initio LDA calculations. We found that when amino acids are bounded to the Si (111) surface, the optical transitions from HOMOs of amino acids to conduction bands of Si are generated due to the electronic-state hybridization at the amino-acid/Si junction. This new excitation channel might enable the selective ionization of amino acids and the switch of protein functions.

ACKNOWLEDGMENTS

This work was supported by the Ministry of Education, Culture, Sports, Sciences and Technology, Japan, CREST-JST, and the 21COE program. We also thank the Super Computer Centers, ISSP, University of Tokyo and Chiba Universiy for the use of facilities.

REFERENCES

1. E. R. Goldman, E. D. Blighan, H. Mattoussi, M. K. Kuno, J. M. Mauro, P. T. Tran, and G. P. Anderson : J. Am. Chem. Soc. 124 6347 (2002)
2. M. Oda and T. Nakayama : Appl. Surf. Sci **244** (2005) 627

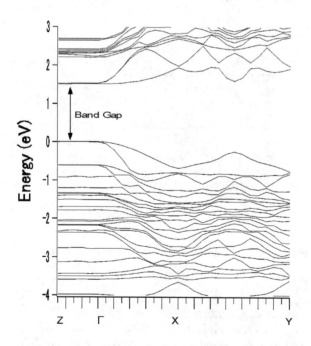

FIGURE 2. Caluculated band structure of phenylalanine/ Si(111) junction system. ΓX and ΓY correspond to the directions along the Si surface as shown in Fig.1(a). .

Power-optimized single-mode slot waveguides

Paul Müllner and Rainer Hainberger

ARC Seibersdorf research GmbH, Nano-System-Technologies, Donau-City Str. 1, 1220 Vienna, Austria

Abstract. The influence of the geometric parameters of slot waveguides on the optical power confinement in the low-index slot region and the modal characteristic is numerically studied. A design map for power-optimized silicon-on-insulator slot waveguides with single-mode behavior at a wavelength of 1550 nm is provided.

Keywords: optical waveguide, silicon photonics, slot waveguide, finite element method
PACS: 42.79.Gn, 02.70.Dc

INTRODUCTION

In slot waveguides the guided light is strongly confined in a narrow low-index gap between two high-index photonic wires [1, 2, 3]. This enables the realization of new silicon photonic devices in which low-index active optical materials can be efficiently utilized. In this work, we numerically investigate the potential for further improvement of silicon-on-insulator (SOI) slot waveguides.

SIMULATION RESULTS

We employ a full-vectorial finite element method (FEM) eigenmode analysis to study the characteristics of slot waveguides at a wavelength of 1550 nm. As can be seen in Fig. 1, the combination of two silicon wires separated by a silica gap results in a strongly coupled system, where the modes of the single waveguides cannot be treated independently of each other. The quasi-TM polarized fundamental modes of the two high-index wires can couple either symmetric or antisymmetric. In both cases, the optical power is mainly confined in the high index region. In contrast, the optical power of the symmetric coupled quasi-TE polarized fundamental mode is concentrated in the vertical slot region. The antisymmetric coupled quasi-TE polarized fundamental mode occurs only for sufficiently large slot thicknesses S, which are out of scope of this study.

First, the dependence of the optical power confinement in the slot region of the symmetric coupled fundamental quasi-TE mode on the geometry parameters is investigated. Fig. 2 shows the percentage of the total optical power confined in the slot region as function of the waveguide thickness D and the slot thickness S for a waveguide height of $B = 600$ nm. The confined optical power depends critically on D, whereas the influence of S is much less and can therefore be omitted. For higher waveguides the amount of optical power guided in the slot re-

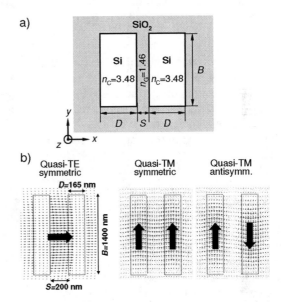

a)

b)

FIGURE 1. a) Cross section of a vertical slot waveguide and b) electric field distribution of the fundamental modes at λ=1550 nm.

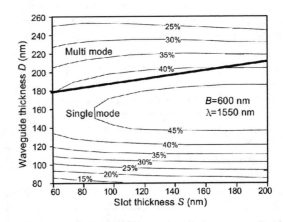

FIGURE 2. Percentage of the total optical power confined in the slot region and the single-mode condition (dark line) for an SOI slot waveguide with B=600 nm at λ=1550 nm.

CP893, *Physics of Semiconductors, 28th International Conference*
edited by W. Jantsch and F. Schäffler
© 2007 American Institute of Physics 978-0-7354-0397-0/07/$23.00

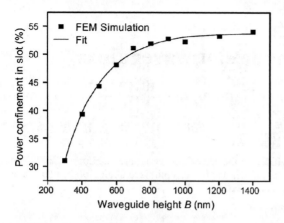

FIGURE 3. Dependence of the maximum achievable optical power confinement in the slot region of an SOI slot waveguide on the waveguide height at $\lambda = 1550$ nm.

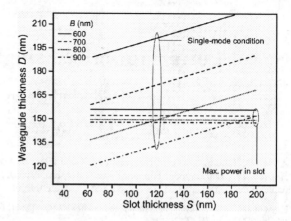

FIGURE 4. Design rule for SOI slot waveguides with maximum optical power confinement (horizontal lines) in the slot region and single-mode behavior (sloped lines) at $\lambda = 1550$ nm.

gion can be increased to more than 54%, as can be seen in Fig. 3, which plots the maximum achievable optical power confinement in the slot as a function of the waveguide height. As the waveguide height increases the optimum waveguide thickness at which the maximum optical power is confined in the slot region shifts to smaller values.

At the same time, with increasing waveguide height multi-mode behavior becomes an issue. For $B = 600$ nm the region of interest with high power confinement is located in the single-mode domain, *i.e.*, where the second vertical symmetric quasi-TE mode is not supported. For waveguide geometries with larger heights B, however, the single-mode condition of the symmetric quasi-TE mode shifts to smaller values of waveguide thickness D. In contrast to the optical power confinement in the slot region, the single-mode condition shows a nearly linear interdependence between the slot thickness S and the waveguide thickness D with a slope that is independent of the waveguide height B. This makes the slot thickness a suitable parameter for the design of slot waveguides with large power confinement and single-mode behavior.

Fig. 4 summarizes the results in a design rule for slot waveguides. The sloped lines show the single-mode behavior, which shifts to lower values of D with increasing height B. This means that for waveguides with larger height B the waveguide thickness D has to be reduced to ensure single-mode behavior for a fixed slot thickness S. The horizontal lines represent the optimum waveguide thickness D at which the maximum optical power is confined in the slot region for a given height B. In order to demonstrate the use of Fig. 4 let us consider a slot waveguide with a height B of 800 nm. According to Fig. 3 this structure confines about 52% optical power in the slot. The optimized waveguide thickness D and the slot thickness S are determined with the help of Fig. 4. Maximum

optical power confinement in the slot region is achieved with a waveguide thickness D of 150 nm, while the slot thickness S must be larger than approximately 120 nm to ensure single-mode behavior. This design rule can be directly applied to optically active materials that have a refractive index similar to SiO_2.

CONCLUSION

The results show that slot waveguides with height-to-width ratios of up to 9.5:1 allow maximizing the optical power confinement in the slot region up to 54%. From a technological point of view the realization of such power optimized single-mode slot waveguides requires a horizontal multilayer structure [4]. Employing a horizontal instead of a vertical slot structure used so far significantly relaxes the requirements with respect to feature size in the lithographic process. Moreover, scattering losses are kept to a minimum. Therefore, horizontal slot waveguides represent a highly attractive platform for the realization of active silicon photonic devices.

REFERENCES

1. V. Almeida, Q. Xu, R. Panepucci, C. Barrios, and M. Lipson, "Light guiding in low index materials using high-index-contrast waveguides," Materials Research Society 2003 Fall Meeting Proceedings, Symposium W, Vol. 797, *Engineered Porosity for Microphotonics and Plasmonics*, Boston, 2003, W6.10.
2. V. Almeida, Q. Xu, C. Barrios, and M. Lipson, *Optics Letters*, **29**, 1209–1211 (2004).
3. Q. Xu, A. R. Vilson, R. Panepucci, and M. Lipson, *Optics Letters*, **29**, 1626–1628 (2004).
4. C. Barrios and M. Lipson, *Optics Express*, **13**, 10 092– 10 101 (2005).

Extraordinary Optoconductance in In-GaAs and In-InSb Metal-Semiconductor Hybrid Structures

K. A. Wieland,[1] Yun Wang,[1] S. A. Solin,[1] A. M. Girgis,[2] and L. R. Ram Mohan[2]

[1]Washington University in St. Louis, One Brookings Drive, St. Louis MO, 63130 USA
[2]Worcester Polytechnic Institute, 100 Institute Road, Worcester MA, 01609 USA

Abstract. Metal-semiconductor hybrid sensors have been shown to enhancing optical signal levels relative to that of the bare semiconductor through a process labeled extraordinary optoconductance. An EOC of 480% at 30K in GaAs has been demonstrated but this drops to − 15% at 300K. Because of the increased differential mobility in intrinsic InSb, a room temperature EOC of order 50% has now been achieved as reported here.

Keywords: photoconductance, optical sensor
PACS: 72.20.Jv, 72.40.+W, 72.80.Ey

INTRODUCTION

It was recently realized that extraordinary magnetoresistance (EMR)[1] was but one example of a general class of geometry driven "EXX" phenomena (E =extraordinary, XX = perturbing effect). This enhancement is associated with the properties of macroscopic and nanoscopic metal-semiconductor hybrid structures (MSHs) of the type depicted schematically in inset (a) of Fig 1. The second such effect, extraordinary piezoconductance (EPC),[2] was also demonstrated. Here we report new experimental results observed with an InSb:In MSH on a third EXX effect, extraordinary optoconductance (EOC).[3,4]

GaAs-In MSHs have an observed maximum EOC of order 500% at 30K where

$$EOC\% = \frac{(V_{ws} - V_{ns})}{V_{ns}} \times 100\% \qquad (1)$$

and V_{ns} (V_{ws}) is the output voltage of the bare (shunted) sample. Most noteworthy, a linear position sensitivity of 137mV/mm was observed[3] making the EOC competitive with conventional lateral photovoltaic effect (LPE)[5] position sensitive detectors. The position and temperature dependence of the EOC has been quantitatively accounted for with a 1-adjustable-parameter drift-diffusion model[6] using the finite element method.[7]

The desirability of extending EOC performance to room temperature is obvious. Accordingly we report here the observation of EOC ~ 50% with an InSb-In MSH.

EXPERIMENTAL SETUP

Two material EOC systems have been studied: In-GaAs and In-InSb. The MSHs consisted of degenerately doped GaAs:Si (n_c=1.25x10^{18} cm^{-3}) or intrinsic InSb:Te (n_c=4x10^{14} cm^{-3}) of macroscopic dimensions (2mm x 10mm x 0.4mm) configured in the 4-lead van der Pauw plate structure[1,8] along with corresponding In-shunted MSHs. The semiconductor regions of these samples were illuminated with focused Ar laser (λ=476.5nm) radiation and the signal (voltage) generated was studied as a function of the position (x,y) of the laser spot. As previously noted,[4] because the hybrid and bare samples have different resistances and both respond linearly to current, the voltage bias was removed to study the photogenerated carriers.

DISCUSSION

The photovoltage generated by the laser beam is due to the Dember effect.[9] The skin depth is such that the physics is treated two dimensionally. The majority and minority carriers have different mean free paths ℓ (lifetimes τ) due to their mobilities μ, mass m^*, and carrier concentration n, where

$$\ell = v_F \tau = \frac{\hbar}{m^*} k_F \frac{\mu m^*}{e} = \hbar\sqrt{2\pi nt}\frac{\mu}{e} \qquad (2)$$

and t is the sample thickness. Thus, the majority carriers diffuse away leaving a net concentration of

CP893, *Physics of Semiconductors, 28th International Conference*
edited by W. Jantsch and F. Schäffler
© 2007 American Institute of Physics 978-0-7354-0397-0/07/$23.00

minority carriers as can be deduced from Eq. (2). As the beam traverses the sample in the x dimension this charge imbalance follows, resulting in the voltage pattern seen in Fig. 1. In the y direction the voltage decreases monotonically to near zero at the shunt. Because the shunt affects the carrier dynamics, the resulting x scan has a higher peak (trough) and also a lower baseline.

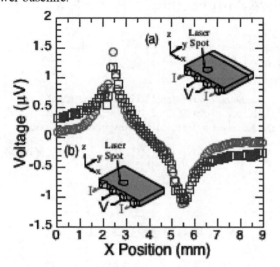

FIGURE 1. Room temperature positional voltage dependence of the hybrid (a) ○, and bare sample (b) □, of InSb-In for Y=0.1mm. The power density of the incident laser beam on the sample is 6.3×10^4 W/cm^2.

The corresponding EOC (x,y) plots for InSb-In in Fig. 2 show a maximum room temperature EOC of 49% for $(x,y) = (2.1$mm, 0.1mm$)$. This is the highest room temperature reported EOC to date and is indicative of the importance of mobility and carrier concentration.

SUMMARY AND CONCLUDING REMARKS

The EOC position dependence is incorporated through the Dember effect[9] wherein the model parameter that determines the electron-hole pair generation rate is found to vary linearly with laser power density while the EOC, in the range of parameters studied, is found to be independent of both power density and bias current.[4] Because the InSb studied here was intrinsic, a further order of magnitude increase should be possible by controlling the doping. This expectation together with the current result reported here portend the possible use of EOC devices in a number of applications.

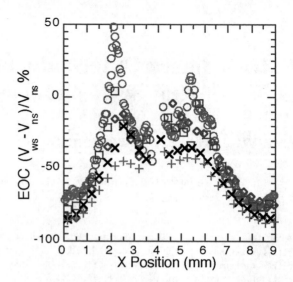

FIGURE 2. The room temperature positional voltage dependence of EOC in InSb-In. The symbols correspond to Y=0.1 mm, ○; 0.3 mm, □; 0.5 mm, ◇;0.7 mm, ✕; and 0.9 mm, +. The power density of the incident laser beam on the sample is 6.3×10^4 W/cm^2.

ACKNOWLEDGMENTS

We thank Y. Shao for useful discussions. This work is supported by the US NSF under grant ECS-0329347 & by the US NIH under grant 1U54CA11934201. LRR thanks Washington U. in St. Louis for the Harrison Fellowship which supported his collaborative visit during part of which this work was carried out.

REFERENCES

1. S. A. Solin, D. R. Hines, T. Thio and J. Heremans, Science **289**, 1530 (2000).
2. A. C. H. Rowe, D. R. Hines and S. A. Solin, Appl. Phys. Lett. **83**, 1160 (2003).
3. K. Wieland, Yun Wang, L. R. Ram-Mohan, S. A. Solin, and A. M. Girgis, Appl. Phys. Lett., **88** 52105 (2006);
4. K.A. Wieland, Yun Wang, S. A. Solin, A. M. Girgis, and L. R. Ram-Mohan, Phys. Rev. B, **73** 155305 (2006).
5. J. Henry and J. Livingstone, IEEE Sensors J. **3**, 519 (2003); J. T. Wallmark, Proc. IRE **45**, 474 (1957).
6. S.L. Chuang, *Physics of Optoelectronic Devices* (Wiley, NY, 1995); J.P. McKelvey, Solid State and Semiconductor Physics (Harper & Row, NY, 1966).
7. L. R. Ram-Mohan, *Finite Element and Boundary Element Applications in Quantum Mechanics*, (Oxford University Press, Oxford, UK, 2002).
8. T. Zhou, D. R. Hines, and S. A. Solin, Appl. Phys. Lett. **78**, 667 (2001).
9. H. Dember, Phys. Z. **32**, 544 (1931).

Extraordinary Electroconductance in In-GaAs Metal-Semiconductor Hybrid Structures

Yun Wang, K.A. Wieland, and S.A. Solin[*]

*Washington University in St. Louis, Center for Materials Innovation,
Department of Physics, St. Louis, Missouri 63130 USA
* E-mail:solin@wuphys.wustl.edu*

Abstract. In-GaAs metal-semiconductor hybrids (MSHs) are found to exhibit enhanced room-temperature electroconductance in the presence of an external electric field. The lowering effect of the Schottky barrier that forms at the MS interface plays a key role in the extraordinary electroconductance (EEC) effects. At room temperature and a field 12kV/cm, we obtained EEC~ 20% without bias voltage.

Keywords: EEC, Schottky barrier
PACS: 73.40.-c, 73.40.Ns

INTRODUCTION

Following the demonstration of extraordinary magnetoresistance (EMR)[i] in MSHs, it has been realized that EMR is but one example of a general class of EXX phenomena that can be geometrically enhanced by the judicious choice of sample geometry. Two other EXX phenomena reported recently are extraordinary piezoconductance, (EPC)[ii] and extraordinary optoconductance, (EOC).[iii] Here we report a fourth/new EXX phenomenon, extraordinary electroconductance, (EEC).[iv]

SAMPLE DESIGN

The active sensing area of the EEC sensor is the metal-semiconductor interface. In order to maximize the sensitivity, a layered configuration is adopted. The MSHs consists of moderately doped GaAs:Si ($n=2\times10^{16}$ cm^{-3}) configured in the 4-lead van der Pauw plate structure with an In shunt deposited on top of the GaAs. The microscopic EEC sensors are depicted below.

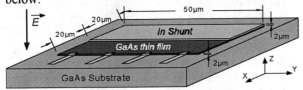

FIGURE 1. A schematic diagram of a microscopic EEC sensor. The dimensions are specified on the diagram.

In this study, the samples employed had typical macroscopic dimensions of 10mm•2mm•400μm.

CURRENT RESULTS

At room temperature, thermionic emission dominates the current transport, where electrons in the semiconductor cross over the potential barrier into the metal. When the bias voltage V>3kT/q (78mV), the current depends on V exponentially.[v]

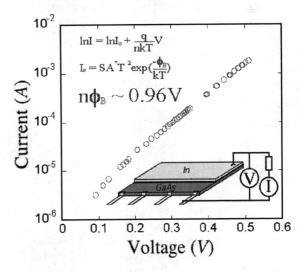

$$\ln I = \ln I_o + \frac{q}{nkT}V$$

$$I_o = SA^*T^2 \exp\left(\frac{-\phi_B}{kT}\right)$$

$$n\phi_B \sim 0.96V$$

FIGURE 2. The Schottky barrier I-V semilog plot. The inset shows the experimental setup. The effective barrier height is about 1eV.

CP893, *Physics of Semiconductors, 28th International Conference*
edited by W. Jantsch and F. Schäffler
© 2007 American Institute of Physics 978-0-7354-0397-0/07/$23.00

$$I = SA^*T^2 \exp(\frac{-\phi_B}{kT})[\exp(\frac{qV}{nkT} - 1)] \quad (1)$$

Here A^* is effective Richardson constant, and ϕ_B is the Schottky barrier height.

The Schottky interface of the In-GaAs is very sensitive to the external electric field. Under the constant background current, the voltage drop across the barrier increases exponentially as the external E field increases. However, for MSHs prepared with an ohmic interface and for bare GaAs, the E field response is essentially zero as can be seen from Fig. 3.

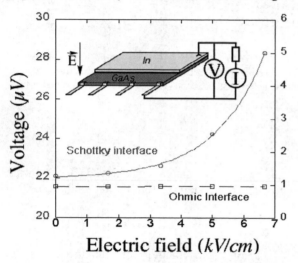

FIGURE 3. The E field effects on the diode setup. The inset shows the experimental setup. The bias current is 10nA for the Schottky hybrids and 1μA for ohmic hybrids.

When the metal and semiconductor have an intimate contact, positive charges accumulate on the surface of the semiconductor. If an electric field is applied perpendicular to the interface, the induced image force lowers the potential barrier for charge carrier emission. The Schottky barrier lowering, $\Delta\phi$, can be expressed as

$$\Delta\phi = \sqrt{\frac{qE}{4\pi\varepsilon_s}} \quad (2)$$

where ε_s is the permittivity of the semiconductor. For E=10kV/cm, $\Delta\phi$~11mV. Although the barrier lowering is small comparing to the Schottky barrier height (usually in the range of 0.4V to 0.8V), it has a profound effect on the electron transport.

The upper left inset of Fig.4 shows that the sample conductance increases exponentially with external E field from 0 to 12kv/cm. We define the EEC effect to be the percentage change of the sample conductance with and without field,

$$EEC = \frac{G_{With\ field} - G_{No\ field}}{G_{No\ field}} \times 100\% \quad (3)$$

At room temperature and a field of 12kV/cm, the EEC effect obtained is 20% without any bias voltage. For bare GaAs and In-GaAs ohmic interface hybrids, the EEC effect is basically zero.

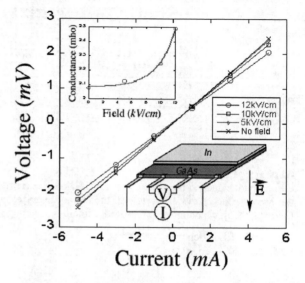

FIGURE 4. The EEC effect. An Electric field is applied perpendicular to the interface. The upper left inset shows the field-dependent conductance. The lower right inset shows the experimental setup. The inverse of the slope of the plot is the sample conductance.

ACKNOWLEDGMENTS

We thank Y. Shao for useful discussions. This work is supported by the US NSF under grant ECS-0329347 & the US NIH under grant 1U54CA11934201.

REFERENCES

i. S. A. Solin, D. R. Hines, T. Thio and J. Heremans, Science **289**, 1530 (2000).
ii. A. C. H. Rowe, D. R. Hines and S. A. Solin, Appl. Phys. Lett. **83**, 1160 (2003).
iii. K. A. Wieland, Yun Wang, L. R. Ram-Mohan, S. A. Solin, and A. M. Girgis, Appl. Phys. Lett., **88** 52105 (2006); K. A. Wieland, Yun Wang, S. A. Solin, A. M. Girgis, and L. R. Ram-Mohan, Phys. Rev. B, **73** 155305 (2006).
iv. Yun Wang, K.A. Wieland, and S. A. Solin, to be published.
v. S. M. Sze, *Physics of Semiconductor Devices* (Wiley-Interscience, NY, 1981).

Ultimate Control of the Thermal Shift of a Tilted Cavity Laser Wavelength

M. B. Lifshits[*,†], V. A. Shchukin[†,*], N. N. Ledentsov[†,*] and D. Bimberg[†]

[*]A. F. Ioffe Physical Technical Institute, 194021 St.-Petersburg, Russia
[†]Institut für Festkörperphysik, Technische Universität Berlin, D-10623 Berlin, Germany

Abstract.
We report the possibility to realize complete thermal stabilization of the lasing wavelength λ_{opt} in an all-epitaxial tilted cavity semiconductor laser, wherein the lasing wavelength is governed by the maximum resonance transparency of a lossy waveguide. When the positive temperature coefficient of the refractive index dn/dT is a non-linear function of the alloy composition, which is the case in most semiconductor alloys, there exists the possibility to achieve ultimate control of the resonance transparency wavelength. The thermal shift $d\lambda_{opt}/dT$ can be positive, zero, or negative. An absolute thermal stabilization of the lasing wavelength is unique as compared to any conventional type of lasers.

Keywords: Tilted Cavity Laser, wavelength stabilization
PACS: 78.20.Bh, 42.70.Qs, 85.60.-q, 42.60.By

Wavelength-stabilized high-power semiconductor lasers are highly needed for pumping of solid state lasers and optical fiber amplifiers as the emitted laser light must be at resonance with a rather narrow atomic transition. Application of high-power lasers for the frequency conversion also requires thermal stabilization, as the conversion efficiency of non-linear crystals often shows a resonance behavior. Conventional approaches include using a distributed feedback (DFB) lasers or fiber grating which enormously increases the costs with respect to standard all-epitaxial edge-emitting lasers.

A newly proposed concept of a Tilted Cavity Laser (TCL) [1] combines the advantages of edge-emitting lasers (high power operation) and VCSELs (wavelength-selective operation). A TCL operates in a high-order optical mode, the mode angle of which is intermediate between that for a typical edge-emitter and that for a surface emitter. A TCL operating in the edge-emitting geometry typically contains a cavity, wherein an active medium is placed, and a multilayer interference reflector (MIR). The cavity and the MIR are constructed such that the resonance features of the two elements meet at only one mode angle and only one, optimum, wavelength [2]. The wavelength of an optical mode confined by a cavity as a function of the mode angle follows a first dispersion law, and the reflectivity maximum of the MIR stopband follows a second dispersion law. The two functions coincide at one angle ϑ_{opt} and one wavelength λ_{opt}. If $\lambda = \lambda_{opt}$, the light in the optical mode confined by the cavity is strongly reflected by the MIR, and the mode has a low leakage loss to the substrate and/or contacts. If λ is far from λ_{opt}, the light in the optical mode is only weakly reflected by the MIR, and the mode has

a high leakage loss. This enables wavelength-selective lasing at λ_{opt}. The shift of the lasing wavelength upon temperature variations is governed by the temperature dependence of the refractive indices of the constituent materials and is generally slower than that in conventional edge-emitting lasers where it is governed by the shift of the gain spectrum. First experimental studies of TCLs based on GaAs/GaAlAs multilayer waveguides and using (Ga)InAs quantum dots [2] or GaInAs quantum wells [3] as an active medium have demonstrated a thermal shift of the lasing wavelength 2 to 3 times slower that that in conventional edge-emitters.

In the present paper we show that the possibilities to control the thermal shift of the resonance wavelength can be substantially extended. We demonstrate that, in planar multilayer structures, where the refractive index of every single layer increases upon temperature, the resonance wavelength can, surprisingly, exhibit both a red shift for some realizations of the structure and a blue shift for the others. In particular and most important, the absolute thermal stabilization of the lasing wavelength of a semiconductor laser can be realized which is unique as compared to any conventional type of lasers.

A model TCL laser structure emitting close to 980 nm consists of a thick substrate, a MIR, and a cavity comprising an active medium. The MIR consists of 8 and a half periods, each of which is formed of 4 layers ($295nm Ga_{0.4}Al_{0.6}As$ / $698nm Ga_{0.8}Al_{0.2}As$ / $295nm Ga_{0.4}Al_{0.6}As$ / $712nm Ga_{0.8}Al_{0.2}As$). The cavity contains a control element which we first take as 2000 nm of homogeneous $Ga_{0.54}Al_{0.46}As$, 25 nm of $Ga_{0.3}Al_{0.7}As$, a central part of 95 nm GaAs including two GaInAs quantum wells, and a 1665 nm-thick

CP893, *Physics of Semiconductors, 28th International Conference*
edited by W. Jantsch and F. Schäffler
© 2007 American Institute of Physics 978-0-7354-0397-0/07/$23.00

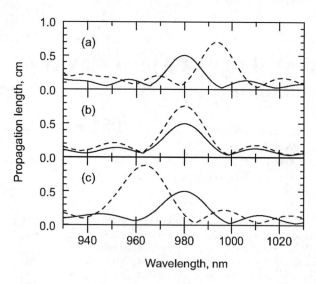

FIGURE 1. Propagation length of the optical mode in the tilted cavity waveguide versus wavelength of light. (a) Red shift of the resonance wavelength. (b) Absolute thermal stabilization of the resonance wavelength. (c) Blue shift of the resonance wavelength. Solid lines: 300 K. Dashed lines: 400 K

$Ga_{0.3}Al_{0.7}As$ cladding layer.

The thermal shift of the lasing wavelength of a TCL is in contrast to that in VCSELs. Whereas $d\lambda_{opt}/dT$ in VCSELs is governed basically by the shift of the average refractive index of the cavity and mirrors and is always positive, the thermal shift of a TCL wavelength is determined by the thermal shift of the matching point of a cavity and a MIR and can be manipulated by choosing an appropriate control element. We use one comprising alternating thin layers of GaAs and $Ga_{1-x}Al_xAs$. As long as the thickness of each layer is significantly smaller than the wavelength in the crystal, the control element may be considered as a single layer with a certain averaged refractive index. The key point is that the refractive index temperature coefficient dn/dT of $Ga_{1-x}Al_xAs$ in the spectral region near 980 nm is a *strongly non-linear function of the alloy composition*. Therefore we can construct several realizations of the control elements provided that the averaged refractive index n_{av} is the same at room temperature, and dn_{av}/dT is highly different. This allows us to control the thermal shift of λ_{opt} while all other waveguide parameters are almost stable.

The mode analysis of the lossy waveguide has been carried out by the perfectly matched layer method [4], and a complex effective refractive index of the optical mode, $n_{eff} = n'_{eff} + in''_{eff}$ has been obtained. The resonance wavelength is the one corresponding to the minimum leakage loss $\alpha = 4\pi n''_{eff}/\lambda$, or the the maximum propagation length of the optical mode, α^{-1} which realizes the maximum transparency of the waveguide. Figure 1 illustrates a temperature-induced change of the spectral dependence of the propagation length for three realizations of the control element. Each is a periodic structure, a period containing 3 nm of GaAs and a layer of GaAlAs of corresponding thickness and Al content to keep the averaged refractive index the same at room temperature. The larger the volume fraction of GaAs is in the control element, the larger is the averaged index at an elevated temperature. The thermal shift of λ_{opt} changes from a positive value $+0.138$nm/K (Fig 1(a)) for the homogeneous $Ga_{0.54}Al_{0.46}As$ alloy to a negative value -0.163nm/K (Fig. 1(c)) for the control element consisting of alternating $3nmGaAs/4nmGa_{0.19}Al_{0.81}As$. The $3nmGaAs/4nmGa_{0.38}Al_{0.62}As$ control element realizes the absolute thermal stabilization ($+0.001$nm/K) (Fig. 1(b)).

Thus, the multilayer control element indeed operates allowing the control of the thermal shift of the lasing wavelength and the absolute temperature stabilization of λ_{opt} can be achieved in tilted cavity waveguide geometry.

To conclude, we have demonstrated a unique concept enabling to control the thermal shift of the lasing wavelength of a semiconductor laser in all-epitaxial design based on the Tilted Cavity concept. Even if the refractive indices of all constituent layers increase upon temperature, the lasing wavelength governed by the resonance transparency wavelength of a leaky waveguide can exhibit either a red shift or a blue shift, which can be chosen by proper constructing an optical composite control element consisting of sub-wavelength insertions of different materials. An absolute thermal stabilization of the lasing wavelength can be achieved, which is unique as compared to any conventional type of lasers, including distributed feedback or surface emitting lasers, and can lead to a breakthrough, e.g., towards uncooled low cost dense wavelength division multiplexing systems.

We acknowledge support by the SANDiE Network of Excellence of the European Commission, contract number NMP4-CT-2004-500101 and by the Russian Foundation for Basic Research.

REFERENCES

1. N.N. Ledentsov *et al.*, *Opt. Eng.* **41**, 3193 (2002).
2. N.N. Ledentsov *et al.*, *Semicond. Sci. Technol.* **19**, 1183 (2004).
3. V.A. Shchukin *et al.*, In: *Nanomodeling*, ed. by A. Lakhtakia and S.A. Maksimenko, *Proc. SPIE* **5509**, 61 (2004), SPIE, Belingham, WA.
4. W.P. Huang *et al.*, *IEEE Photon. Techol. Lett.* **8**, 652 (1996).

Novel Nanoelectronic Device Applications Based on the Nonlinearity of Three-Terminal Ballistic Junctions

Jie Sun[a], D. Wallin[a], P. Brusheim[a], I. Maximov[a], Z. G. Wang[b] and H. Q. Xu[a]

[a]Division of Solid State Physics, Lund University, P. O. Box 118, S-221 00 Lund, Sweden
[b]Key Laboratory of Semiconductor Materials Science, Institute of Semiconductors, Chinese Academy of Sciences, Beijing 100083, China

Abstract. Nanometer-scale electron devices containing three-terminal ballistic junctions are fabricated by electron-beam lithography on InP/InGaAs two-dimensional electron gas materials. Based on the intrinsic nonlinearity of the devices, frequency mixer, phase detector and RS flip-flop memory functioning at room temperature are successfully achieved. The devices have simple structure layout and small size, and are expected to function at high speed.

Keywords: Three-terminal ballistic junctions, frequency mixer, phase detector, RS flip-flop memory
PACS: 73.63.-b

INTRODUCTION

It is theoretically predicted[1] and experimentally verified[2] that three-terminal ballistic junctions (TBJs) show novel nonlinear electrical properties due to the ballistic nature of electron transport in the devices. This new phenomenon will contribute not only to the fundamental physics, but also to nanoelectronic circuit applications. In this paper, we present our results of TBJ-based devices working as frequency mixer, phase detector and RS flip-flop memory (also known as latch) at room temperature. The results show that TBJs serve as possible building blocks in the future analog and digital nanoelectronics.

DEVICE PERFORMANCES

Frequency Mixer and Phase Detector

Our devices were fabricated by electron-beam lithography on standard InP/InGaAs two-dimensional electron gas materials.[3] The inset of Fig. 1(c) shows an atomic force microscopy (AFM) image of a fabricated TBJ device (a T-branch) and the measurement circuit setup for operating as a frequency mixer and a phase detector. The distance between the left and right quantum point contacts is 170 nm. It is comparable to the room temperature mean free path of 150 nm in the materials and therefore the electron transport in the device can be approximately regarded as a ballistic procedure. We apply two AC signals (9 Hz and 10 Hz)

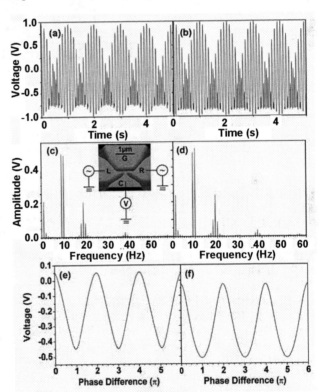

FIGURE 1. (a) and (b): Frequency mixer output from the central branch in time domain. (c) and (d): The same output in frequency domain. The inset shows an AFM image of the device. (e) and (f): Phase detector DC output from the central branch. The left panels show the measured data, while the right panels show the extracted results from the static properties of the device.

CP893, *Physics of Semiconductors, 28th International Conference*
edited by W. Jantsch and F. Schäffler
© 2007 American Institute of Physics 978-0-7354-0397-0/07/$23.00

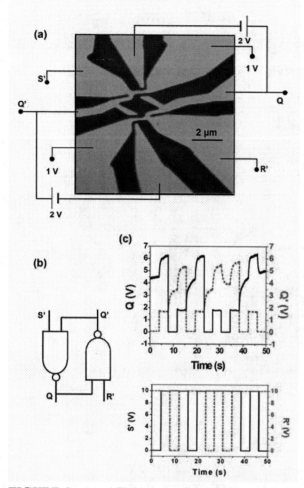

FIGURE 2. (a): AFM image of the TBJ-based latch device and measurement circuit setup. (b): An equivalent circuit demonstrating the functionality of the latch. (c): Experimental logic input and output of the device. The solid lines are for the input S' and output Q, while the dashed lines are for R' and Q'.

with the amplitude of 1 V to the left and right branches and measure the output from the central branch with an oscilloscope. The outputs recorded in time and frequency domains are shown in Figs. 1(a) and 1(c). Figures 1(b) and 1(d) show the corresponding curves derived from the static properties of the device, which are consistent with the experimental data. The signals at 0, 1 (10-9), 19 (10+9) Hz are detected indicating a good frequency mixing behavior. Subsequently, we apply AC signals of $V_L=V\sin(2\pi 10000t+\varphi_{0L})$ and $V_R=V\sin(2\pi 10000.2t+\varphi_{0R})$ as the two inputs and measure the phase difference at the central lead. If we treat the two signals as they have the same frequency, the phase difference $\Delta\varphi$ is thus a slow time-dependent function with a period of 5s. The middle branch DC output V_C of a phase detector is known to be related to $\Delta\varphi$. We plot in Figs. 1(e) and 1(f) the experimental and extracted data of the relationship between V_C (DC) and

$\Delta\varphi$. Again, they are in agreement with each other. Note that it is found that the mixer and phase detector behavior persists up to MHz in this study. However, due to the impedance mismatch the high frequency output of mixer can not be well recorded with our currently available measurement setup. However this can not influence the DC output measurement. Therefore, at the MHz regime the phase detector DC data show almost no decay compared to the extracted ones from the static properties of the device.

RS Flip-Flop Memory

It is known that the TBJ itself is a logic AND gate. If coupled with a quantum point contact through an in-plane gate, it can be operated as a NAND gate.[4] Two NANDs coupling to each other can form an RS flip-flop device, as is shown in the equivalent circuit given in Fig. 2 (b). A fabricated TBJ-based RS flip-flop device is shown in Fig. 2 (a), where two TBJs are capacitively coupled to each other through their central branches. However, in our design the quantum point contacts can only be pinched off if the gate voltages are less than 0 V. Therefore, we introduce two DC power supplies to shift the gate voltage by 2 V. The channels are thus controlled by the two additional gates, as can be seen in Fig. 1(a). Figure 3(c) shows the input and output signals of an as-prepared device. The logic 1 is defined to be 10 V for S' and R', and 3-7 V for Q and Q'. The logic 0 is defined to be 0 V for S' and R', and 0-1 V for Q and Q'. It is seen that switching of Q and Q' to the lower logic states is fast due to the ballistic nature of electron transport. Switching of Q and Q' to the higher logic states is, however, slow, because of the large capacitance of the two outer power supplies. The problem could be solved by further optimization of the design.

CONCLUSIONS

In summary, we have made frequency mixer, phase detector and RS flip-flop devices using TBJs. The experimental data suggest TBJ can be used as building blocks in nanoelectronic circuits.

REFERENCES

1. H. Q. Xu, *Appl. Phys. Lett.* **78**, 2064-2066 (2001).
2. I. Shorubalko, H. Q. Xu, I. Maximov, P. Omling, L. Samuelson, and W. Seifert, *Appl. Phys. Lett.* **79**, 1384-1386 (2001).
3. D. Wallin and H. Q. Xu, *Appl. Phys. Lett.* **86**, 253510 (2005).
4. H. Q. Xu, I. Shorubalko, D. Wallin, I. Maximov, P. Omling, L. Samuelson, and W. Seifert, *IEEE Electron Device Lett.* **25**, 164-166 (2004).

CHAPTER 14

NEW MATERIALS, CONCEPTS, AND TECHNIQUES

Magnetotransport of Two-dimensional Electrons at *In-situ* Cleaved InAs Surfaces

Toshimitsu Mochizuki, Yukihide Tsuji, Masayuki Hio and Tohru Okamoto

Department of Physics, University of Tokyo
Hongo 7-3-1 Bunkyo-ku, Tokyo, Japan

Abstract. Low-temperature magnetotransport measurements have been performed on adsorbate-induced electron systems formed at *in situ* cleaved surfaces of *p*-type InAs. The Ag-coverage dependence of the surface electron density strongly suggests that adsorbed Ag atoms act as surface donors whose energy level lies above the conduction band minimum. The observation of integer quantum Hall effect demonstrates the perfect two dimensionality of the surface electron system. We have extended the study to various adsorbates and found peculiar transport phenomena, such as the strong positive magnetoresistance of Fe-induced surface electrons in the in-plane magnetic field configuration.

Keywords: Indium arsenide, III-V semiconductors, cleaved surface, magnetotransport, two-dimensional electron systems, quantum Hall effect, in-plane magnetic field
PACS: 71.55.Eq, 72.10.Fk, 73.25.+I, 73.43.-f

INTRODUCTION

At the surfaces of InAs, conduction electrons can be induced by submonolayer deposition of other materials. Research on electrons at semiconductor surfaces has great future potential because of the variety of adsorbates and the application of scanning probe microscopy techniques. Most of the previous photoelectron spectroscopy and scanning tunneling spectroscopy measurements have been done on n-type InAs crystals where electrical contact to two-dimensional (2D) like surface electrons was made through the substrate [1-6]. In order to investigate 2D transport properties, however, the surface electrons should be separated from 3D carriers in the substrate. In this work, we have successfully performed the first low-temperature (T = 1.5 K) magnetotransport measurements on adsorbate-induced electron systems (ESs) formed at in situ cleaved surfaces of p-type InAs.

RESULTS AND DISCUSSION

Ag-induced 2DESs

The Hall measurement enabled us to determine the surface electron density as a function of the coverage of Ag [7].

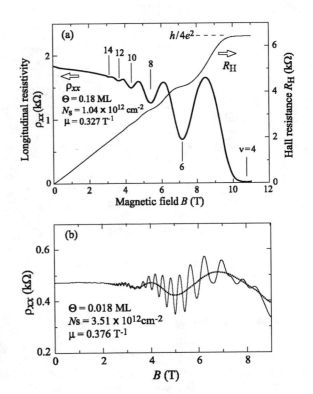

FIGURE 1. (a) Longitudinal resistivity ρ_{xx} (left axis) and Hall resistance R_H (right axis) for Ag coverage Θ = 0.18 ML. (b) Beating patterns in Shubnikov-de Haas (SdH) oscillation for Θ = 0.018 ML.

CP893, *Physics of Semiconductors, 28th International Conference*
edited by W. Jantsch and F. Schäffler
© 2007 American Institute of Physics 978-0-7354-0397-0/07/$23.00

The obtained result strongly supports a simple model based on a surface donor level lying above the conduction-band minimum. In a high magnetic field (~11 T), we found the quantized Hall resistance and zero longitudinal resistivity for $\nu = 4$ as shown in Fig. 1 (a). The observation of the integer quantum Hall effect demonstrates the perfect two dimensionality of the surface ES. We also observed the Rashba effect due to the strong asymmetry of the confining potential well as shown in Fig. 1 (b).

Fe-induced 2DESs

Strong positive magnetoresistance was observed in the in-plane magnetic field configuration (Fig. 2). The resistivity increases by a factor of 2 when B reaches 9 T. While the in-plane magnetic field dependence should be attributed to the spin effect, the Pauli paramagnetism of 2D electrons causes the spin polarization less than 1 % even at 9 T. We consider that exchange interactions between localized moments of adsorbed Fe atoms and 2D electrons play an essential role.

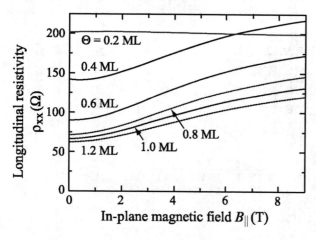

FIGURE 2. Longitudinal resistivity of Fe induced 2DESs. Large positive magnetoresistance is observed for $\Theta \geq 0.4$ ML.

Other adsorbate-induced 2DESs

We extended the study to various adsorbates. (a) The quantum Hall effect is also observed for Ge-induced 2DESs. (b) The positive magnetoresistance due to the suppression of weak antilocalization is observed in the weak perpendicular magnetic field region. The magnetoresistance curve for an Au-induced 2DES is different from that for a Ge-induced 2DES as shown in Fig. 3. This is associated with the spin-orbit scattering of an Au atom. (c) The Hall measurements were also performed for cleaved surfaces of p-InSb with adsorption of Ag or Cs. Clear

Shubnikov-de Haas oscillations are observed (not shown here).

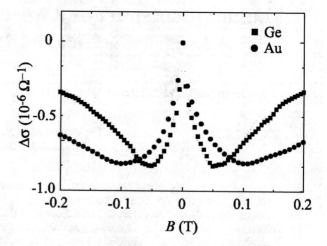

FIGURE 3. Magnetoconductivity of Ge and Au induced 2DESs in the weak perpendicular magnetic field. Electron densities are $1.0 \times 10^{12} \mathrm{cm^{-2}}$ for these two systems.

ACKNOWLEDGMENTS

The authors thank N. Kayukawa and S. Masuda for their experimental contributions and T. Inaoka for useful discussions. This work was partly supported by Sumitomo Foundation, Grant-in-Aid for Scientific Research (B) (No. 18340080), Grant-in-Aid for Scientific Research on Priority Area "Physics of new quantum phases in superclean materials" (No. 18043008) and Grant-in-Aid for JSPS Fellows from MEXT, Japan.

REFERENCES

1. H. U. Baier, L. Koenders, and W. Mönch, *Solid State Commun.* **58**, 327-331 (1986).
2. V. Y. Aristov, I. L. Bolotin, and S. G. Gelakhova, *Surf. Sci.* **251**, 453-456 (1991).
3. V. Y. Aristov, G. Le Lay, L. T. Vinh, K. Hricovini, and J. E. Bonnet, *Phys. Rev. Lett.* **47**, 2138-2145 (1993).
4. V. Y. Aristov, G. Le. Lay, L. T. Vinh. K. Hricovini, and J. E. Bonnet, J. Osvald, and O. Olsson, *Europhys. Lett.* **26**, 359-364 (1994).
5. M. Morgenstern, M. Getzlaff, D. Haude. R. L. Johnson, and R. Wiesendanger, *Phys. Rev. B* **61**, 13805-13812 (2000).
6. M. Getzlaff, M. Morgenstern, C. Meyer, R. Brochier, R. L. Johnson, and R. Wiesendanger, *Phys. Rev. B* **63**, 205305 (2001).
7. Y. Tsuji, T. Mochizuki, and T. Okamoto, *Appl. Phys. Lett.* **87**, 062103 (2005).

Synthesis and Optical Properties of Multiband III-V Semiconductor Alloys

K. M. Yu[1], W. Walukiewicz[1], R. Farshchi,[1,2] O. D. Dubon[1,2], J.W. Ager III[1], I. D. Sharp[1,2], and E. E. Haller[1,2]

[1.] *Materials Sciences Division, Lawrence Berkeley National Laboratory, Berkeley, California 94720*
[2.] *Department of Materials Science & Engineering, University of California, Berkeley, California 94720*

Abstract. Quaternary $GaN_xAs_{1-y}P_y$ alloys have been synthesized using N ion implantation into $GaAs_{1-y}P_y$ (y=0-0.4) epilayers followed by pulsed laser melting (II-PLM). We observed strong optical transitions from the valence band to both the lower (E_-) and upper (E_+) conduction subbands that arise from the N induced splitting of the conduction band (E_M) of the $GaAs_{1-y}P_y$ host. As predicted by the band anticrossing model, $GaN_xAs_{1-x-y}P_y$ with y>0.3 is a three band semiconductor alloy with potential applications for high-efficiency intermediate band solar cells.

Keywords: multiband semiconductors, intermediate band solar cells, pulsed laser melting, GaAsP
PACS: *71.20.Nr; 78.66.Fd; 61.72.Vv; 89.30.Cc*

INTRODUCTION

Highly mismatched alloys (HMAs) are compound semiconductors in which small fractions (<10%) of electronegative (metallic) atoms are replaced by metallic (electronegative) atoms [1,2]. Applying the concept of band anticrossing (BAC) [1,3], we have demonstrated that $Zn_{1-x}Mn_xO_yTe_{1-y}$ is a multiband semiconductor due to the anticrossing interaction between the O level E_O located ~0.2 eV below the conduction band edge and the extended conduction band states in $Zn_{1-y}Mn_yTe$ alloys. [4]. This material can be made so that its absorption edges fall within the solar energy spectrum, making it well suited for the proposed high efficiency intermediate band solar cells (IBSCs) concepts [5]. Analysis of the conduction band offsets indicates that in III-V semiconductors, the criterion for a multiband semiconductor can be met for N substituting on the anion sublattice in $GaAs_{1-y}P_y$ with y> 0.3. Here, we report the synthesis and optical properties of $GaN_xAs_{1-x-y}P_y$ layers with y ranging from 0 to 0.4 using ion implantation followed by pulsed laser melting (II-PLM).

EXPERIMENTAL PROCEDURE

Sequential N^+ implantation in ~0.5 μm thick $GaAs_{1-y}P_y$ (y=0-0.38) epitaxial films was used to create a ~0.2 μm thick layer with a uniform N atomic concentration of ~4.4×10^{20} cm^{-3} (2 mole percent). The implanted structures were subjected to single pulse laser melting (PLM) in air using a KrF excimer laser (λ=248 nm, FWHM~18 ns) with photon fluence of 0.4J/cm^2 at the sample. The rapid melting and solidification (on the order of 10^{-7} s) prevents secondary phase formation even when the equilibrium solubility limit has been exceeded by orders of magnitude [6]. We found that 0.4 J/cm^2 laser pulses followed by rapid thermal annealing at 950°C for 150 sec were the optimum conditions for the synthesis of GaN_xAs_{1-x} [7]. The band gaps of the films were measured using photomodulated reflectance (PR) at room temperature.

RESULTS AND CONCLUSION

Fig. 1 shows a series of PR spectra from $GaAs_{1-y}P_y$ samples with 0≤y≤0.38 after II-PLM. The positions of the energy gap, E_M of as-grown $GaAs_{1-y}P_y$ and the N level E_N are indicated in the figure. The PR spectrum from the N^+-implanted GaAs sample after PLM and RTA exhibit a strong, well-resolved transition from the valence band maximum to the lower subband E_- at ~1.23 eV. This location of E_- corresponds to ~1% of substitutional N incorporated in the GaAs lattice [7].

Two well resolved optical transitions E_- and E_+, are observed for $GaAs_{1-y}P_y$ samples (with 0.1<y>0.4) after II-PLM. These transitions are distinctly different from E_M of the corresponding unimplanted materials. In

CP893, *Physics of Semiconductors, 28th International Conference*
edited by W. Jantsch and F. Schäffler
© 2007 American Institute of Physics 978-0-7354-0397-0/07/$23.00

GaAs and in As-rich GaAs$_{1-y}$P$_y$ the E. transition is much stronger than E$_+$ transition. The relative strength of the E$_+$ transitions increases with increasing P content and becomes stronger than E. for y>0.25. This behavior can be explained by the BAC model, taking into account the much weaker dipole optical coupling of the valence band to E$_N$ compared with the coupling between the valence band and E$_M$. Fig. 2 shows that the energy values of the E. transitions follow E$_M$ (E$_N$) at low (high) P contents; on the other hand E$_+$ transitions mostly follow E$_N$ (E$_M$) at low (high) y. The character of the wavefunctions and thus also the strength of the optical transitions depend on the location of the E. and E$_+$ states relative to E$_N$ and E$_M$.

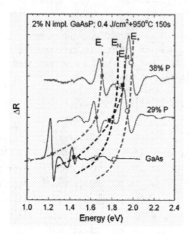

FIGURE 1. PR spectra from 2% N implanted GaAs$_{1-y}$P$_y$ (y=0 to 0.4) PLM at 0.4 J/cm^2 followed by 950°C 150s RTA.

Fig. 2 shows the experimental data together with the BAC calculated values of E$_+$ and E. transitions assuming a N concentration of 0.3, 1 and 2% in the GaN$_x$As$_{1-x-y}$P$_y$ layers [1]. Comparison between the calculated and measured E$_+$ and E. values shows that for GaAs$_{1-y}$P$_y$ layers with y≤0.12 ~1% of N is incorporated in the film. For GaAs$_{1-y}$P$_y$ layers with y>0.12, the incorporated N concentration is smaller (x~0.003), and corresponds to an activation efficiency of only 15% of the implanted N. This may be due to the high density of the misfit dislocations in GaAs$_{1-y}$P$_y$ epitaxial layers coming from the large lattice mismatch with the GaAs substrate (>0.4% for y>0.12). These dislocations may act as a sink for the preferential segregation of N during the PLM and RTA processing steps.

The GaN$_x$As$_{1-x-y}$P$_y$ with y>0.3 is a multiple band gap system analogous to the ZnOTe system [4]. Although only small fraction of N (x=0.003) is incorporated in GaAs$_{1-y}$P$_y$ layers with y > 0.2 using the present II-PLM conditions, strong and distinctive optical transitions are indeed observed. As illustrated by the BAC calculation shown in Fig. 2, for a

GaN$_x$As$_{1-y}$P$_y$ multiband semiconductor with y = 0.4 and an x=0.02 a N derived narrow band of extended states E. is separated from the upper subband E$_+$ by about 0.8 eV. A theoretical maximum efficiency of between 55% and 60% for IBSCs fabricated using this alloy can be expected [5].

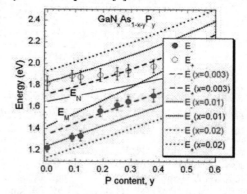

FIGURE 2. Measured values of the E. and E$_+$ transitions in GaNAsP (symbols) are shown with the Γ point conduction band minimum for the GaAs$_{1-y}$P$_y$ substrate and the N level E$_N$. BAC calculated values of the E. and E$_+$ transitions for x=0.003, 0.01 and 0.02 are also shown.

In conclusion we have synthesized GaN$_x$As$_{1-y}$P$_y$ with y=0 to 0.4 using the II-PLM technique. With an implanted N concentration of 2%, the N concentration incorporated in the As sublattice amounts to about 1% and 0.3% for films with y≤0.12 and y>0.12, respectively. GaN$_x$As$_{1-y}$P$_y$ alloys with y>0.3 have a three band structure making them suitable for testing the theoretical predictions of the highly-efficient intermediate band solar cell concept.

ACKNOWLEDGMENTS

This work was supported by the Director's Innovation Initiative Program, National Reconnaissance Office and the Director, Office of Science, Office of Basic Energy Sciences, Division of Materials Sciences and Engineering, of the U. S. Department of Energy under Contract No. DE-AC02-05CH11231.

REFERENCES

1. W. Walukiewicz *et al.*, *Phys. Rev. Lett.* **85**, 1552 (2000).
2. see for example, Semiconductor Science and Technology **17**, 2002, Special Issue: III-N-V Semiconductor Alloys.
3. W. Shan *et al.*, *Phys. Rev. Lett.* **82**, 1221(1999).
4. K. M. Yu *et al.*, *Phys. Rev. Lett.* **91**, 246203 (2003).
5. A. Luque, A. Marti., Phys. Rev. Lett., **78**, 5014 (1997).
6. C. W. White *et al.*, J. Appl. Phys. 51 738 (1980).
7. K. M. Yu *et al.*, J. Appl. Phys. **94**, 1043 (2003).

Optical Band Gap and Bonding Character of Li_3GaN_2

K. Kuriyama*, T. Ishikawa*, and K. Kushida[†]

*College of Engineering and Research Center of Ion Beam Technology, Hosei University, Koganei, Tokyo 184-8584, Japan
[†]Dept. of Arts and Sciences, Osaka Kyoiku University, Kashiwara, Osaka 582-8582, Japan

Abstract. The structure of Li_3GaN_2 (a = 9.605 Å), like Li_3AlN_2 (a = 9.427 Å), is closely related to the antifluorite type. The band gap of Li_3GaN_2 is found to be 4.15 eV by the optical absorbance and photoacoustic spectroscopy methods. This value is close to that (E_g = 4.40 eV) of Li_3AlN_2 rather than that (~3.27 eV) of zinc-blende GaN. This means that the bonding character of the Li_3AlN_2 type structure is essentially attributed to the six ionic Li-N bonds in eightfold coordinated N with two Ga and six Li nearest neighbors. The remaining two covalent bonds of Ga-N (Al-N) only modify slightly the band gap value. Indeed, the Ga-N (Al-N) bond distance is about 9 % (13 %) smaller than that of the Li-N bond, reflecting a difference in energy gap between Li_3GaN_2 and Li_3AlN_2.

Keywords: Nitride compounds, Wide gap semiconductors, Bonding character, Photoacoustic spectroscopy
PACS: 71.20.Nr; 78.40.-q; 78.20.Hp

INTRODUCTION

Li_3GaN_2 is an interesting material for the GaN single crystal growth [1]. The structure of Li_3GaN_2 is closely related to the antifluorite type [2]. Recently, the band gap nature [3] of Li_3AlN_2 (a = 9.427 Å) [viewed as the assemblage of eight hypothetical zinc-blende-like AlN sublattice $(Li_{0.5}Al_{0.5}N)^-$ filled with He-like Li^+ interstitials at the empty tetrahedral sites next to the anions] has been studied according to the *interstitial insertion rule* of Wood *et al.*[4]. The band gap of Li_3AlN_2 was found to be direct with its energy 4.40 eV, suggesting that when Li^+ ions are in its interstitial sites, the X conduction band of the Brillouin zone is shifted to higher energies more than the other bands, as predicted by the interstitial insertion rule. However, the band gap is much smaller than that (5.34 eV [5]) of the zinc-blende AlN. In the present study, the band gap of Li_3GaN_2 is determined by the optical absorbance and photoacoustic spectroscopy methods to clarify the bonding nature of Li_3AlN_2 type crystals. A 1/8 sublattice of Li_3GaN_2 is shown in Fig. 1[3]. Ga and Li are coordinated with four N atoms, respectively, but N is eightfold coordinated with two Ga and six Li nearest neighbors. The Ga-N bond lenghth is about 9 % smaller than that of the Li-N bond [2]. In each sublattice, 50 % of Ga atoms in zinc-blende GaN are substituted with Li, leading to a hypothetical zincblende GaN-like $(Li_{0.5}Ga_{0.5}N)^-$ lattice filled with

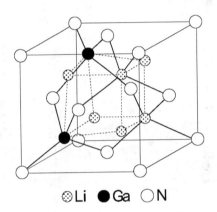

⊚Li ●Ga ○N

FIGURE 1. A 1/8 sublattice of Li_3GaN_2

He-like Li^+ at the empty tetrahedral sites next to N. Accordingly, Li_3GaN_2 consisting of the eight sublattices leads to a new type of filled tetrahedral semiconductor.

RESULTS AND DISCUSSION

Li_3GaN_2 is synthesized by direct reaction between Li_3N and Ga with the molar ratio Li_3N : Ga of ~2.3 : 1. The reaction is performed at 800 °C for 12 h under a nitrogen atmosphere of 700 Torr. Any contamination from the growth system such as Ta crucibles was not

CP893, *Physics of Semiconductors, 28th International Conference*
edited by W. Jantsch and F. Schäffler

detected. The details of the crystal growth will be reported elsewhere. According to the factor group analysis for Li_3GaN_2 (space group: *Ia3*), eight Raman peaks (199, 336, 372, 410, 432, 495, 554, and 574 cm^{-1}) were observed.

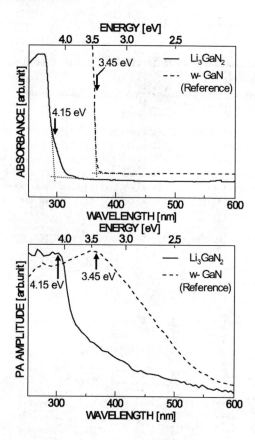

FIGURE 2. Absorbance (top) and photoacoustic (bottom) spectra of Li_3GaN_2 at room temperature.

Figure 2 shows a typical absorbance spectrum of Li_3GaN_2 together with that of a wurtzite GaN film as a reference sample, taken by a scanning spectrophotometer at room temperature. The absorbance curve showed an abrupt change at around 300 nm (4.15 eV), suggesting that the absorption edge of Li_3GaN_2 lies in ~ 4.1 eV. Photoacoustic (PA) spectrum of Li_3GaN_2 (solid line) was measured using a PA spectroscopy (PAS) to confirm the band gap value obtained by the optical absorbance. PAS is a useful tool for studying optical absorption of light scattering materials such as powders. Therefore, the samples for the PAS measurements were obtained by powdering the synthesized Li_3GaN_2. The PA signal of Li_3GaN_2 showed the saturation at ~ 300 nm (~ 4.15 eV), while the signal of powdered GaN (dashed line) with E_g = 3.45 eV as a reference sample saturated at ~ 360 nm (3.45 eV). Therefore, PAS data supports the result of the absorbance measurements.

The band gap of Li_3GaN_2 is close to that of Li_3AlN_2 rather than that (~3.27 eV [6]) of zinc-blende GaN. This means that the bonding character of the Li_3AlN_2 type structure is essentially attributed to the six ionic Li-N bonds in eightfold coordinated N. The remaining two covalent bonds of Ga-N (Al-N) only modify slightly the band gap value. Indeed, the Ga-N (Al-N) bond distance [2] is about 9 % (13 %) smaller than that of the Li-N bond, reflecting a difference in the orbital overlap of wave-functions between Ga (Al) and N. This would cause a slight difference in energy gap between Li_3GaN_2 and Li_3AlN_2.

CONCLUSION

The band gap of Li_3GaN_2 was found to be 4.15 eV by the optical absorbance and photoacoustic spectroscopy methods. This value is close to that (E_g = 4.40 eV) of Li_3AlN_2 rather than that (~3.27 eV) of zinc-blende GaN. This means that the bonding character of the Li_3AlN_2 type structure is essentially attributed to the six ionic Li-N bonds in eightfold coordinated N with two Ga and six Li nearest neighbors. The remaining two covalent bonds of Ga-N (Al-N) only modify slightly the band gap value, reflecting a difference in covalent bond length between Ga-N and Al-N bonds in Li_3AlN_2 type structure.

ACKNOWLEDGMENTS

The present work was supported in part by a Grant-in-Aid for Scientific Research on Basic Areas from the Japanese Ministry of Education, Culture, Sports, Science and Technology (No.17656007), and also supported by a Yazaki Memorial Foundation for Science and Technology.

REFERENCES

1. Y. Song, W. Wang, W. Yuan, X. Wu, and X. Chen, J. Cryst. Growth, **247**, 275 (2003).
2. R. Juza and F. Hund, Z. Anorg. Chem. **257**, 13 (1948).
3. K. Kushida, Y. Kaneko, and K. Kuriyama, Phys. Rev. B **70**, 233303 (2004); in *Proceedings of the ICPS27, Flagstaff, 2004*, AIP Conference Proceedings, **772**, 289 (2005).
4. D. M. Wood, A. Zunger and R. de Grood, Phys. Rev. **B31**, 2570 (1985).
5. M. P. Thompson, G. W. Auner, T. S. Zheleva, K. A. Jones, S. J. Simko, J. N. Hilfiker, J. Appl. Phys. **89**, 3331 (2001).
6. J. Menniger, U. Jahn, O. Brandt, H. Yang, and K. Ploog, Phys. Rev. B **53**, 1881 (1996).

Atomic force microscopy observation of the Jahn-Teller instability in spinel LiMn$_2$O$_4$ embedded in silicon substrates

K. Kuriyama*, A. Onoue*, Y. Yuasa* and K. Kushida[†]

*College of Engineering and Research Center of Ion Beam Technology, Hosei University, Koganei, Tokyo 184-8584, Japan
[†]Dept. of Arts and Sciences, Osaka Kyoiku University, Kashiwara, Osaka 582-8582, Japan

Abstract. Surface morphology of 3.5×3.5 μm^2 area of spinel LiMn$_2$O$_4$ embedded in Si substrates, a typical cathode material for Li ion secondary batteries, is studied using an atomic force microscopy (AFM) with a conductive probe. Under the negative bias voltage to attract Li$^+$ ions, electric current abruptly increases at 5.5 V, indicating Li$^+$ ion movement toward the surface. Increase in current accordingly, part of scale-shaped grains covering the whole surface expand and flatten, suggesting that the Jahn-Teller phase transition was induced by the repulsive interaction between the Mn-e$_g$ and O-2p electrons in Li accumulated layer.

Keywords: Atomic force microscopy, Jahn Teller instability, Li secondary batteries, On-chip batteries
PACS: 68.37.Ps; 68.35.Rh; 68.55.Jk

INTRODUCTION

Mounting all solid state Li secondary microbatteries on microelectromechanical systems (MEMS) is a new concept of an electric power supply. In previous studies, we demonstrated a *hundred-micron-sized* all-solid-state secondary battery with a spinel LiMn$_2$O$_4$ cathode embedded into Si substrates [1] and realized a 5×5 μm^2 battery area of the embedded battery using an atomic force microscopy (AFM) with a conductive probe [2]. Spinel LiMn$_2$O$_4$ is a typical cathode material for Li secondary batteries [1-3]. In the case that Li$^+$ ions are inserted into the empty octahedral sites in spinel LiMn$_2$O$_4$, LiMn$_2$O$_4$ shows Jahn-Teller phase transition from cubic spinel to tetragonal structures [4]. Since the phase transition causes the volume expansion by 6 % [4], a visible change of the surface morphology is expected. In the present study, we report a surface morphology change of spinel-LiMn$_2$O$_4$ under the negative bias voltage using an AFM with a conductive probe. We suggest that an abrupt increase in current due to the Li$^+$ ion diffusion correlates with the Jahn-Teller phase transition inducing the morphology change.

RESULTS AND DISCUSSION

In order to move Li$^+$ ions toward the surface, a negative bias voltage (0 to 12 V) was applied to a Pt/Ir coated conductive probe. Spinel LiMn$_2$O$_4$ layer was prepared by a *sol-gel spin-coating* method on a polycrystalline silicon layer (~300 Ω) embedded into a Si substrate as shown in Fig. 1 (top) [1,2]. The AFM images of 3.5×3.5 μm^2 LiMn$_2$O$_4$ surface indicated by the black square in Fig. 1 (top) were taken while measuring the electric current collected by the conductive probe. The electric current has its peak at around 6.5 V as shown in Fig. 1(bottom), indicating Li$^+$ ionic conduction resulting from the movement of Li$^+$ ions extracted from the tetrahedral sites toward the surface. The number of the involved Li$^+$ ions is estimated to be 5.1×10^{11} ions [5]. Near the surface, the moving Li$^+$ ions can be inserted into the empty octahedral sites (xLi$^+$ + LiMn$_2$O$_4$ + xe$^-$ → Li$_{1+x}$Mn$_2$O$_4$, x = 0 to 1.2) [4], which introduces electron injection from the conductive probe to neutralize the excess positive charge due to Li$^+$. The injected electrons would be incorporated in anti-bonding Mn-e$_g$ orbitals, resulting in the repulsive interaction between Mn-e$_g$ and O-2p electrons of MnO$_6$ clusters in LiMn$_2$O$_4$. Jahn-Teller instability due to the repulsive interaction causes the phase transition from the cubic spinel to the tetragonal structures to relax the repulsion [4].

Figure 2 (1), (2), and (3) show a typical AFM image of LiMn$_2$O$_4$ surface at 0 V, the surface roughness, and the variation in area of grains, as referred to A~E, respectively. The surface morphology of the area consists of scale-shaped grains of 0.2 ~ 1.0

CP893, *Physics of Semiconductors, 28th International Conference*
edited by W. Jantsch and F. Schäffler

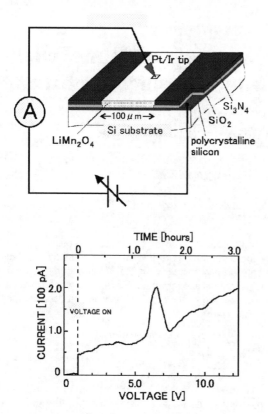

FIGURE 1. Schematic of the measurement system (top). Voltage dependence of electric current through the $LiMn_2O_4$ surface (bottom).

μm in diameter. The surface roughness of each grain can be quantitatively identified by the root-mean-squared roughness (R_{ms}). The R_{ms} of the grains gradually decreased above around 3.5 V and the grains remarkably flattened around 7.5 V. Furthermore, the area of the grains B and D abruptly increased at around 6.0 V. Whereas, the neighboring grain C showed a decrease in area at around 6.0 V. The expansion and /or shrinkage of the grains occurred above 6.0 V, corresponding to the peak of the electric current resulting from the Li^+ ion movement toward the surface. Therefore, the morphology change is correlated with the Jahn-Teller phase transition of spinel $LiMn_2O_4$. The mechanism of the morphology change will be reported in details elsewhere.

CONCLUSION

The dynamic change of the surface morphology in $3.5 \times 3.5 \mu$ m^2 area of spinel $LiMn_2O_4$ was studied under negative voltages by AFM. The present study suggests the Jahn-Teller phase transition induced by the repulsive interaction between the $Mn-e_g$ and $O-2p$ electrons in Li accumulated layer near the surface.

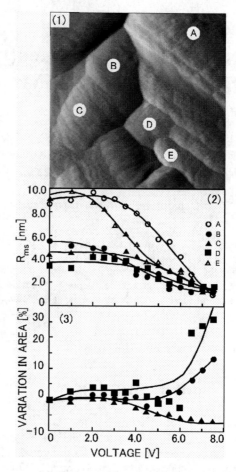

FIGURE 2. (1) AFM image taken at the bias voltage of 1 V. (2) root-mean-squared roughness (R_{ms}) of the grains A~E and (3) variation in area of the grains B, C and D.

ACKNOWLEDGMENTS

The present work was supported in part by a Grant-in-Aid for Scientific Research on Basic Areas from the Japanese Ministry of Education, Culture, Sports, Science and Technology (No.17656007 and No.15360014), and also supported by a Yazaki Memorial Foundation for Science and Technology.

REFERENCES

1. K. Kushida, K. Kuriyama, and T. Nozaki, Appl. Phys. Lett. **81**, 5066 (2002).
2. K. Kushida and K. Kuriyama, Appl. Phys. Lett. **84**, 3456 (2004).
3. F. K. Shokoohi, J. M. Tarascon, and B. J. Wilkens, Appl. Phys. Lett. **59**, 1260 (1991).
4. M. M. Thackeray, W. I. F. David, P. G. Bruce, and J. B. Goodenough, Mat. Res. Bull., **18**, 461 (1983).
5. The number of moved Li^+ ions (N_{Li}) was estimated from the integration of the peak current in Fig.1 (bottom).

Optical Properties of Cylindrite

Chris Sturm*, Rüdiger Schmidt-Grund*, Ronny Kaden†, Holger von Wenckstern*, Bernd Rheinländer*, Klaus Bente† and Marius Grundmann*

*Institut für Experimentelle Physik II, Universität Leipzig, Linnéstr. 5, D-04103 Leipzig, Germany
†Institut für Mineralogie, Kristallographie und Materialwissenschaft, Universität Leipzig, Scharnhorststr. 20, D-04275 Leipzig, Germany

Abstract. We have studied the optical constants of cylindrite in the spectral range of $(1.0 - 3.5)\,\mathrm{eV}$ by spectroscopic ellipsometry and in the range of $(1.8 - 3.2)\,\mathrm{eV}$ by microreflection. The dielectric function was obtained by using a layer model and model dielectric functions. The obtained dielectric function of cylindrite shows similar behaviour as dielectric functions typical for semiconductors.

Keywords: cylindrite, optical constants, ellipsometry, dielectric function
PACS: 71.20.Ps, 78.20.-e, 78.20.Ci, 78.40.Fy, 81.05.Hd

INTRODUCTION

Cylindrite ($FeSn_4Pb_3Sn_2S_{14}$) is a sulfosalt with a metallic lustre. The triclinic crystal structure is formed of two incommensurate alternating layers, a pseudo-tetragonal slab and a pseudo-hexagonal slab [1]. The lattice constants of the slabs are shown in Table 1.

TABLE 1. The lattice constants of the two slabs of cylindrite [1].

	pseudo-tetragonal	pseudo-hexagonal
a (nm)	1.173	1.171
b (nm)	0.579	0.367
c (nm)	0.581	0.632

In contrast to the majority of known materials cylindrite naturally occurs as lamellae and cylinders. Therefore, it could be an interesting material for self-assembled micro- and nanostructures. In this work we report about the determination of the optical properties in the visible spectral range, which are not known very well.

EXPERIMENTAL DETAILS AND DATA ANALYSIS

The samples were synthesized by chemical vapour transport (CVT) in silica tubes with iodine as transport agent. From the preparation we got two different sample types. The first one are lamella-type samples with a size of about $2 \times 3\,\mathrm{mm}^2$. The surface of this type is characterized by formations of steps, that means borders between areas with different height. The crystallographic axes b and c of this sample type are perpendicular and the a-axis is parallel to the surface normal. The second

type are the cylinder-type samples. We have investigated cylindrically shaped samples with diameters in the range of $4\,\mu m$ up to $12\,\mu m$. The crystallographic c-axis was found to be parallel to the symmetry axis, the a-axis parallel to the surface normal, and the b-axis tangentially oriented to the surface of the cylinder. Particle Induced X-ray Emission (PIXE) measurements showed different chemical compositions of the two sample types. The cylinder-type samples contain 21% up to 34% more lead and 10% to 20% less tin than the lamella-type samples.

To determine the optical constants we used ellipsometry in the spectral range of $(1.0 - 3.5)\,\mathrm{eV}$ and microreflection in the spectral range of $(1.8 - 3.2)\,\mathrm{eV}$, respectively. The reflected light in the microreflection measurements was detected by a CCD camera. These studies were used for an initial sample characterisation. The small sample size made it necessary to use confocal spatially-resolved technique in the microreflection. The resulting diameter of the spot size was about $5\,\mu m$. This made it possible to measure both sample types. In the ellipsometry the beam was focussed and the diameter of the spot size was about $200\,\mu m$. So it was possible to measure the lamella-type samples.

The ellipsometry determines the change of the polarisation of a light beam after reflection (or transmission) on a sample surface, described by the ratio of the p- and s-polarized complex reflection coefficients (r_p and r_s):

$$\frac{r_p}{r_s} = e^{i\Delta} \tan \Psi. \qquad (1)$$

To analyze the spectrum it is necessary to use a layer model. The unknown dielectric function (DF) of cylindrite will be described by a model dielectric function

(MDF), which contains the band-to-band transitions of the types E_0, E_1, $E_1 + \Delta_1$, and E_2 of semiconductors, using an approach suggested by Adachi [2]. A pole function was used accounting for the contribution from transitions above the experimental spectral range.

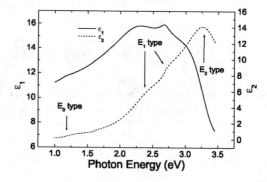

FIGURE 3. The dielectric function of cylindrite.

RESULTS AND DISCUSSION

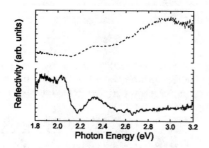

FIGURE 1. A typical reflectivity spectrum of a lamella-type sample (solid line) and a cylinder-type sample (dashed line).

Spectra of the microreflection are shown in Fig. 1. It can be seen that the spectra of the two sample types are different to each other. We attribute this behaviour to the different chemical composition of the two sample types. Because of the triclinic crystal structure one would expect cylindrite behaves optically anisotropic. In our experiments, the anisotropy was found to be negligible. One reason for this fact could be a non perfect crystal structure. Therefore, standard ellipsometry was used [3]. The ellipsometry Ψ- and Δ-spectra of a lamella-type sample are shown in Fig. 2 along with the best model calculated spectra. Structures due to multiple reflection interferences are observable at photon energies up to 1.5 eV. The beginning absorption at about 1.1 eV causes the damping of the amplitudes of the multiple reflection interferences with increasing photon energy until they vanish at approximately 1.7 eV. The DF of the lamella-

type cylindrite, calculated from the best model, is shown in Fig. 3. The spectral position of the band-to-band transitions are indicated by arrows. The comparison of the determined DF with those of semiconductors shows, that these are similar to each other. The parameter E_0 of the MDF representing the band gap energy of semiconductors was found to be 1.15 eV. The MDF involves contributions which are also used to describe band-structure critical points of semiconductors. The spectral arrangement of these critical points in the DF of cylindrite is the same as for semiconductors. In addition, Hall-effect measurement on natural cylindrite samples shows that the values of the carrier density and electron mobility are in the data ranges of semiconductors. All these findings permits us to conclude that cylindrite is a semiconductor.

ACKNOWLEDGMENTS

The authors thank S. Werner, Ch. Meinecke and F. Menzel for determining the chemical composition using PIXE.
This work was funded by the DFG in the framework of FOR522 (project No. Rh 28/4-2).

REFERENCES

1. E. Makovicky, *N. Jb. Miner. Monatsh. 6* p. 235 (1974).
2. S. Adachi, *Properties of Group-IV, III-V and II-VI Semiconductors*, John Wiley and Sons Ltd, 2005, ISBN 0470090324.
3. M. Schubert, *Phys. Rev. B* **53**, 4265 (1996).

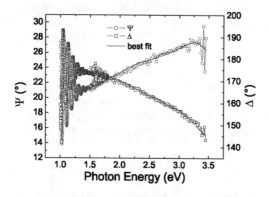

FIGURE 2. Measured and fitted Ψ and Δ spectra of cylindrite for an angle of incidence of 60°.

Superionic Conduction
in Hydrogen-Bonded Dielectric Materials

Hiroshi Kamimura, Seiichiro Ikehata, Yasumitsu Matsuo and Yukihiko Yoshida

Department of Applied Physics, Tokyo University of Science, 1-3 Kagurazaka, Shinjuku-ku, Tokyo 162-8601, Japan

Abstract. Based on the mechanism of the proton-induced superionic conduction in hydrogen-bonded $M_3H(XO_4)_2$ [M=K,Rb, X=S,Se] materials developed by Ito and Kamimura [1], the frequency-dependent dielectric function $\varepsilon_2(\omega)$ is derived, and theoretical and experimental features of $\varepsilon_2(\omega)$ at the giga- to tera-hertz region are discussed.

Keywords: <superprotonic conduction, dielectric function, van Hove singularity, terahertz>
PACS: <66.10.Ed, 66.30.Dn, 66.90.+r, 78.20.Bh, 78.20Ci>

INTRODUCTION

Hydrogen-bonded materials, whose nature is closely related to the behavior of protons in hydrogen-bonds, have recently aroused keen interests among semiconductor researchers. In this context we have been working on the superionic conduction in $M_3H(XO_4)_2$ [M=K,Rb, X=S,Se] type dielectric crystals. These materials exhibit a ferroelastic phase transition at high temperature such as 400K, and an anomalously large increase of electrical conductivity has been observed near the phase transition temperature T_c. Further, above T_c the ionic conductivity is very high so that the paraelastic phase is called the superionic phase. The mechanism of superionic conduction above T_c has been clarified by Ito and Kamimura [1] (see also Kamimura et al.[2]) as follows: Two kinds of ionic states, $H_2XO_4^{(+e)}$ and $XO_4^{(-e)}$, are thermally formed as excited states in the superionic phase. These excited states move coherently as the result of successive proton tunneling among the hydrogen bonds. This quantum-mechanical nature of ionic conduction gives rise to a unique feature of the density of states. Ito and Kamimura [1] calculated the density of states (DOS) for the two kinds of excited states. Their calculated results of DOS are shown in Figs. 1(a) and 1(b), respectively, for $H_2XO_4^{(+e)}$ and $XO_4^{(-e)}$ states . These curves show the feature of a twin-peak structure, reflecting the characteristics of the Bethe lattice. This means that the coherent motion of $H_2XO_4^{(+e)}$ and $XO_4^{(-e)}$ excited states exhibit a one-dimensional feature although the itineration of these excited states occurs over a two-dimensional layer in these materials. The widths of DOS in Figs. 1(a) and 1(b) correspond to $4 \times \sqrt{2}\Gamma$ and $4 \times \sqrt{2}\Gamma'$, where Γ and Γ' are the transfer interactions of the $H_2XO_4^{(+e)}$ and $XO_4^{(-e)}$ excited states, respectively. The values of these transfer interactions are of the order of 10^{-4} eV. Ito and

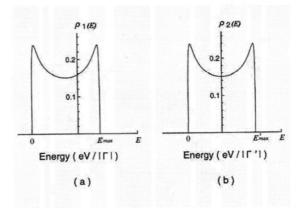

FIGURE 1. a) Density of states for the itinerant motion of $H_2XO_4^{+e}$ excited state $\rho_1(E)$. b) Density of states for the XO_4^{-e} state $\rho_2(E)$. Energy E is measured from the left edge. Here $E_{max}=4 \times \sqrt{2}\Gamma$ in (a) and $4 \times \sqrt{2}\Gamma'$ in (b).

Kamimura also calculated the ionic mobility by using the Kubo formula [3]. The calculated mobility is very high of the order of 10^{-4} to 10^{-2} S/cm just above T_c, consistent with experimental results [2].

The theoretical treatment by Ito and Kamimura have been made for a static electric field (frequency $\omega = 0$). On the other hand, Yoshida et al.[4] recently measured the frequency dependent dielectric function up to the terahertz region. In this context it is necessary to extend the theory by Ito and Kamimura for the zero-frequency [1] to the regime of the frequency-dependent dielectric function. In this paper, thus, the frequency-dependent dielectric function for the proton-induced superionic conduction in a zero-dimensional hydrogen-bonded network system is derived, and a result is compared with experimental results by Yoshida et al.[4].

CP893, *Physics of Semiconductors, 28th International Conference*
edited by W. Jantsch and F. Schäffler

FREQUENCY-DEPENDENT DIELECTRIC FUNCTION $\varepsilon_2(\omega)$ AND ITS EXPERIMENTAL RESULT IN THE TERA-HERTZ REGION

In this section we derive the frequency-dependent conductivity $\sigma(\omega)$ for the superionic phase in $M_3H(XO_4)_2$, with use of the Kubo formula [3] following Mott [5]. We suppose that an alternating electric field $F = F_0 \exp(i\omega t)$ is applied along the a-axis (we take x-axis) in $M_3H(XO_4)_2$ sample. Then the excited states $H_2XO_4^{(+e)}$ and $XO_4^{(-e)}$ which occupy the lowest-energy states with energy E at the left edges in their densities of states (DOS) ρ_1 and ρ_2 in Figs. 1(a) and 1(b), respectively, make a transition to any of the states with energy $E + \hbar\omega$ within DOS ρ_1 and ρ_2 by interactions with a photon field. Then the transition probability of the excited states $H_2XO_4^{(+e)}$ and $XO_4^{(-e)}$ from a state with energy E to a state with energy $E + \hbar\omega$ is given by

$$P = \frac{1}{4}e^2 F^2 (2\pi/\hbar)| < E + \hbar\omega|x|E > |^2 \rho_i(E + \hbar\omega),$$

with $i = 1$ or 2. (1)

The transition matrix element by the interaction of a proton with a photon field is defined as

$$< E'|x|E >= \int \psi_{E'}^* x \psi_E d^3x. \tag{2}$$

The functions ψ_E represents the wave function of the excited state $H_2XO_4^{(+e)}$ or $XO_4^{(-e)}$ at the energy E and $E + \hbar\omega$. Here we denote

$$< E + \hbar\omega|x|E >= (\hbar/M\omega)Q_{E+\hbar\omega,E} \tag{3}$$

where M is the proton mass and

$$Q_{E',E} = \int \psi_{E'}^* (\partial/\partial x) \psi_E d^3x. \tag{4}$$

Thus we obtain the formula for the frequency-dependent dielectric function $\varepsilon_2(\omega)$ as follows;

$$\varepsilon_2(\omega) = 4\pi\sigma(\omega)/\omega = \frac{8\pi^2 e^2 \hbar^3}{\omega m^2} \cdot \tag{5}$$

$$\int \frac{\{f(E) - f(E + \hbar\omega)\}|Q|_{av}^2 \rho_i(E)\rho_i(E + \hbar\omega)}{\hbar\omega} dE.$$

Here we introduce a joint density of states for the transition of $H_2XO_4^{(+e)}$ or $XO_4^{(-e)}$ from E to $E + \hbar\omega$ as follows;

$$\bar{\rho}_i(\omega) = \rho_i(E)\rho_i(E + \hbar\omega), i = 1 \text{ or } 2 \tag{6}$$

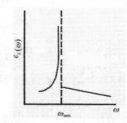

FIGURE 2. Schematic dependence of the imaginary part of the dielectric constant $\varepsilon_2(\omega)$ on frequency near a Van Hove singularity ω_{max}.

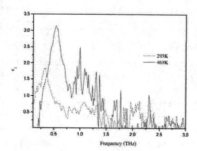

FIGURE 3. Frequency dependence of $\varepsilon_2(\omega)$ observed in the tera-heltz region.

Since DOS in Figs. 1(a) and 1(b), $\rho_1(E)$ and $\rho_2(E)$, show van-Hove singularities at both edges, the joint density of states $\bar{\rho}_i(E)$ in eq.(6) with i = 1 and 2 also show the saddle point singularity near the highest energy. Thus, corresponding to the van-Hove singularity in $\rho_i(E)$ at $E = E_{max}$, $\varepsilon_2(\omega)$ in eq.(5) has also a van-Hove singularity at ω_{max} defined by $\omega_{max} = E_{max}/\hbar$, as shown in Fig. 2. Since $E_{max} = 4 \times \sqrt{2}\Gamma$ or $4 \times \sqrt{2}\Gamma'$, and Γ and Γ' are of the order of 10^{-4} eV, we expect that a peak in $\varepsilon_2(\omega)$ will appear in a frequency region of 100 giga-hertz to several tera-hertz. Theoretical result shown in Fig. 2 is compared with experimental data shown in Fig. 3, where we measured $\varepsilon_2(\omega)$ for $Rb_3H(SeO_4)_2$ with $T_c = 449K$ in the tera-heltz region for T = 293K and 463K. As one sees in Fig. 3, a strong peak in $\varepsilon_2(\omega)$ appears in a region around 1 terahertz for 463K, and this may be considered as corresponding to a peak in Fig.2

REFERENCES

1. Y. Ito and H. Kamimura, *J. Phy. Soc. Jpn.* **67** (1998) 1999.
2. H. Kamimura, Y. Matuso, S. Ikehata, T. Ito, M. Komukae, and T. Osaka, *Phys. Stat. Solidi* (b) **241** (2004) 61.
3. R. Kubo, *J. Phys. Sco. Jpn.* **12** (1957) 570.

4. Y. Yoshida, J. Hatori, Y. Matsuo, S. Ikehata, H. Kamimura T. Kondo, K. Hirakawa, Phys.Rev.Lett. (to be submitted)
5. Sir Nevill Mott, Conduction in Non-Crystalline Materials (Oxford University Press,Oxford, 1987)

Large nitrogen composition of GaNSb grown by RF-MBE

Kouichi Akahane, Naokatsu Yamamoto, Shin-ichiro Gozu, Akio Ueta, and
Masahiro Tsuchiya

National Institute of Information and Communications Technology (NICT)
4-2-1 Nukui-Kitamachi, Koganei, Tokyo 184-8795, Japan

Abstract. GaNSb films were grown using molecular beam epitaxy with a nitrogen radio frequency plasma source. GaNSb films with up to 1% nitrogen composition were obtained by changing the growth temperature. The GaNSb absorption edge which is longer than that of GaSb, was confirmed at about 0.53 eV using a Fourier transform infrared spectrometer in the sample grown at 450°C.

Keywords: dilute nitride, GaSb, GaNSb, molecular beam epitaxy
PACS: 78.66.-w , 78.66.Fd, 77.84.Bw

INTRODUCTION

Dilute-nitride compound semiconductors, such as GaNAs and GaInNAs, have recently attracted much attention because including a small concentration of nitrogen results in a large modification of the band structure of GaAs and InGaAs. For example, large band-gap bowing occurred when nitrogen was included in GaAs and InGaAs so that long-wavelength emission, especially emissions at wavelengths of 1.3 and 1.55 μm, which are suitable for fiber-optic communication systems, was obtained using a GaAs substrate[1]. Although band-gap bowing has been reported in (In)GaAs, there has been little research on GaNSb[2]. GaNSb material systems have a potential for being useful in fabrication of fiber-optic communication devices and in mid-infrared applications, such as gas sensing devices[3-4]. In this work, we report the growth of GaNSb by using molecular beam epitaxy (MBE).

EXPERIMENTAL

All samples were fabricated on n-type GaAs(001) substrates. Each substrate was thermally cleaned by maintaining the temperature at 610°C in the MBE growth chamber. After cleaning, a 5-nm-thick AlSb and a 500-nm-thick GaSb buffer layer were grown at 500°C. Finally, a 500-nm-thick GaN_xSb_{1-x} layer was grown at 1.0 ML/s. Nitrogen plasma was supplied by a radio frequency (RF) plasma source. We changed the growth conditions, such as substrate temperature,

RF- plasma power, and nitrogen flow rate. The samples were characterized by X-ray diffraction (XRD) to determine their nitrogen composition. Atomic force microscope (AFM) measurements were performed to evaluate surface morphology of the samples. An absorption spectrum was measured using a Fourier transform infrared (FTIR) spectrometer to determine the band edge of GaNSb at room temperature.

RESULTS AND DISCUSSION

The results of a ω-2θ scan from XRD indicated a GaSb (004) diffraction peak at 30.35°. The GaNSb(004) diffraction peak appeared in the higher angle region as an additional peak or shoulder. The

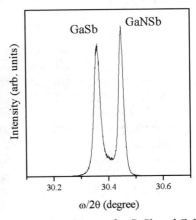

FIGURE 1. XRD ω-2θ scan for GaSb and GaNSb (004).

CP893, *Physics of Semiconductors, 28th International Conference*
edited by W. Jantsch and F. Schäffler
© 2007 American Institute of Physics 978-0-7354-0397-0/07/$23.00

result of XRD measurement of a GaNSb film grown at 450°C using a nitrogen plasma power of 450 W and a flow rate of 0.08 sccm is shown in Fig. 1. A nitrogen composition of 1.0% was estimated from this result. The band gap energy of this sample was about 0.5 eV, which is smaller than that of GaSb (0.726 eV)[2].

The dependence of nitrogen composition and surface roughness of the GaNSb films on substrate temperature are shown in Fig. 2. A nitrogen plasma power of 450 W and a flow rate of 0.08 sccm were used in these cases. The nitrogen composition strongly depends on the substrate temperature. When the substrate temperature was decreased the nitrogen composition increased. The surface roughness of the sample grown at 450°C evaluated by AFM was 1.78 nm, which is sufficiently low to fabricate optical devices. The nitrogen composition of the sample grown at 450°C is higher than that reported elsewhere[2] because we used a low nitrogen back pressure, which might enhance nitrogen incorporation into the GaSb films. Low nitrogen back pressure means that the mean free pass of reactive nitrogen is large.

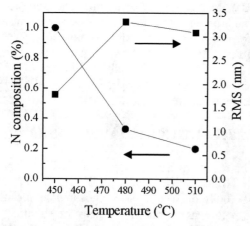

FIGURE 2. Substrate temperature dependence of nitrogen composition (circle) and surface roughness (square).

The absorption spectrum is shown in Fig. 3. The solid line and dotted line indicate the results of GaNSb film grown at 450°C and the reference sample in which only GaSb was grown. In each case, an increase in absorption was observed at about 0.72 eV, which is attributed to GaSb band-edge absorption. In the spectrum of the GaNSb sample, additional absorption was observed at lower energies, which is attributed to GaNSb band-edge absorption. The estimated absorption band edge is 0.53 eV. The band gap energy of GaNSb estimated from FTIR is slightly larger than that calculated from the nitrogen composition, which was obtained by XRD measurement. The reason is that this might be the effect of strain in the GaNSb film on the XRD measurements. In addition, more detailed

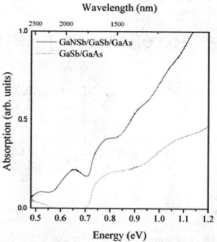

FIGURE 3. Absorption spectra for GaNSb (solid line) and GaSb (dotted line).

theoretical calculations are needed to determine the characteristics of dilute nitride-antimonide compound semiconductors. However, absorption at wavelengths greater than 2 μm was observed in this sample, which is useful to fabricate various optical devices operating at longer wavelengths.

SUMMARY

GaNSb films were grown by molecular beam epitaxy. A nitrogen composition of about 1% was confirmed by XRD measurements in the sample grown at 450°C. The nitrogen composition of the GaNSb strongly depends on the growth temperature. The 0.53 eV absorption band edge was observed by using FTIR measurements in the sample grown at 450°C.

ACKNOWLEDGMENTS

We would like to thank Masataka Higashiwaki and Toshiaki Matsui at NICT for their help in making the XRD measurements and thank Fumihiko Tomita, Toshikazu Itabe, and Masayuki Izutsu of NICT for their encouragement.

REFERENCES

1. M. Kondow, K. Uomi, A. Niwa, T. Kitatani, S. Watahiki, and Y. Yazawa *Jpn. J. Appl. Phys.* **35** 1273-1275 (1996)
2. L. Buckle, B. R. Bennett, S. Jollands, T. D. Veal, N. R. Wilson, B. N. Murdin, C. F. McConville, and T. Ashley *J. Cryst. Growth* **278** 188-192 (2005)
3. M. Grau, C. Lin, O. Dier, C. Lauer, and M. -C. Amann *Appl. Phys. Lett.* **87**, 241104 (2005)
4. P. Werle and A. Popov *Appl. Opt.* **38** 1494-1501 (1999)

Determination of the U term by a density-density correlation function in the LDA+U Hamiltonian

M. Takahashi[*,†], K. Kusakabe[*] and N. Suzuki[*]

[*]Graduate School of Engineering Science, Osaka University, 1-3 Machikaneyama-cho, Toyonaka, Osaka, 560-8531, Japan
[†]Toshiba Corporation Semiconductor Company, 8 Shinsugita-cho, Isogo-ku, Yokohama, 235-8522, Japan.

Abstract. We have developed the fluctuation reference method to determine the LDA+U Hamiltonian by a multi-reference density functional theory, in which the Hubbard term is determined so that the density fluctuation on a relevant localized orbital is adjusted to the true value given by the Coulomb system. To test the validity of the method, we investigated various extra approximations to solve the LDA+U Hamiltonian in the fitting procedure. Using the Hartree-Fock mean-field approximation, the fluctuation, *i.e.* a local density-density correlation function, is fixed at a value of the weak-correlation limit, while it is stuck to 0 of the strong-correlation limit when the Dudarev form of LDA+U is selected. To fit the value of the Coulomb correlation, we are required at least to utilize the LDA++ approach for magnetic impurity problems. A simple example of the hydrogen molecule shows that the multi-reference calculation gives the self-consistent solution from the weak coupling regime to the strong coupling regime, in which the value of U continuously changes as a function of a parameter of the system.

Keywords: Kondo problem, density functional theory, LDA+U
PACS: 31.15.Ew, 71.15.Mb, 71.10.-w, 71.10.Fd

INTRODUCTION

Methods for theoretical analysis of materials are developing but some of them are approaching a stage satisfying requirements for materials design by computational simulations of N electron systems. As for the magnetic effects appearing in magnetic impurities and magnetic semiconductors, we have to consider short-range electron-correlation effects explicitly in the simulation on one hand. On the other hand, the first-principles calculation, which enables self-consistent determination of electron charge density, is demanded for the prediction of stability of materials. Inclusion of the correlation effects directly in the density-functional theory with the local density approximation (DFT-LDA) has been attempted by the LDA+U approaches[1, 2] and the methods have partly filled the gap between the DFT calculation and the study of electron models with effective interaction terms. Recently, we have proposed an approach to determine the LDA+U-type effective Hamiltonian by the first-principles manner[3]. The method is based on a uniqueness theorem on the effective many-body interaction term, *i.e.* the U term.[4, 5] By demanding the extended Kohn-Sham scheme to reproduce density fluctuation defined on a localized orbital, the U term is uniquely determined. We call this technique the fluctuation reference method. In the practical application, we need to introduce extra apploximation to solve the effective Hamiltonian. In this study, we compare known methods to handle the LDA+U-type model and investigate their characteristics for the full first-principles calculations of the magnetic impurity problems.

FLUCTUATION REFERENCE

For the determination of the U term in the fluctuation reference method, we need 1) a reference system for which precise estimation of density fluctuation on a relevant orbital $\langle \underline{n_i^2} \rangle$ is possible, and 2) a self-consistent calculation to determine $\langle \underline{n_i^2} \rangle$ for the effective model and 3) to fit it to the reference by adjusting U. Here, using $\overline{n}_{i,\sigma} = \langle \Psi | n_{i,\sigma} | \Psi \rangle$, $\langle \underline{n_i^2} \rangle$ is defined to be

$$\langle \underline{n_i^2} \rangle = \langle (n_{i,\uparrow} + n_{i,\downarrow} - \overline{n}_{i\uparrow} - \overline{n}_{i\downarrow})^2 \rangle, \quad (1)$$

and the reduced exchange-correlation energy functional is given as,

$$\langle \Psi | V_{red} | \Psi \rangle = \frac{U}{2} \langle \underline{n_i^2} \rangle$$
$$= U \left\{ \langle n_{i,\uparrow} n_{i,\downarrow} \rangle + \frac{1}{2} (\overline{n}_{i\uparrow} + \overline{n}_{i\downarrow})(1 - \overline{n}_{i\uparrow} - \overline{n}_{i\downarrow}) \right\} \quad (2)$$

For the case of magnetic impurity, we may introduce a set of localized orbitals. Extension of the positive definite fluctuation is possible satisfying symmetry requirements.

Let us consider a magnetic impurity with a half-filled localized orbital. In the step 2), if we utilize a mean-field approximation with a single reference description, the fluctuation is fixed at 0.5 of the metallic value. While it is stuck to 0 of the correlation limit, when the Dudarev form is selected.[2] This is because the Dudarev functional is

CP893, *Physics of Semiconductors, 28th International Conference*
edited by W. Jantsch and F. Schäffler
© 2007 American Institute of Physics 978-0-7354-0397-0/07/$23.00

constructed to keep integer occupation of each localized orbital with a specified spin to have the Ising configuration for the anti-ferromagnetic substances. Thus these approaches are inappropriate for the realization of our fluctuation reference method. To have a U-dependent fluctuation, we are inevitably required to introduce the multi-reference description.

In our multi-reference DFT approach, the self-consistent calculation is possible by applying the next procedure. The Kohn-Sham equation included in the extended Kohn-Sham scheme[5] is possible to be solved for a multi-reference state, if occupation of each reference state, *i.e.* a set of coefficients of the multi Slater determinant, is known. The many-body effective Hamiltonian is solved by applying a diagonalization technique among the numerical diagonalization, the numerical renormalization group method, the quantum Monte-Carlo method and perturbative approximations for the simplified many-body system. This procedure determines the coefficients. Fixing the occupation, the Kohn-Sham equation is self-consistently solved. After finding the renewed localized orbital and effective single-body Hamiltonian, we know the value of U. Here, an important point is that the extended Kohn-Sham equation is guaranteed to be the first-principles method irrespective of the value of U. Thus, the determination of U is realized after solving the Kohn-Sham part by fixing occupation of reference states. An application of the method to a Hydrogen molecule (Fig.1) has revealed the next two facts. A self-consistent solution of the multi-reference calculation exists for any combination of $(a, \langle \underline{n}_i^2 \rangle)$. Since the value of U as a function of $(a, \langle \underline{n}_i^2 \rangle)$ is continuous, the determination of U is possible. These results indicate that $\langle \underline{n}_i^2 \rangle$ is actually fitted by changing U. The obtained U value does not exceed about $U \simeq 10[\text{eV}]$ due to reduction in the transfer term, even if the system is in the Heitler-London regime for for $a \geq 3$. Here a is the interatomic distance. In our MR-DFT, $U \simeq 0.7[\text{eV}]$ appears even for the equilibrium molecular structure, since $\langle \underline{n}_i^2 \rangle < 0.5$ and there is finite Coulomb correlation.

CONCLUSION

With utilizing the conventional LDA+U approximation, in which the mean-field approximation is introduced, the density-density correlation loses dependence on U. In the LDA++ approximation, if the local correlation is estimated by the numerical renormalization group method or by an equivalently precise method, it is recovered. Thus, a method to treat the multi-reference description is inevitable to determine U in the fluctuation reference method.

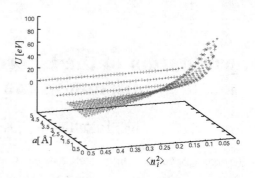

FIGURE 1. The value of U of a H_2 molecule determined by the multi-reference DFT calculation. By fitting $\langle \underline{n}_i^2 \rangle$ as a function of the inter-atomic distance a to the value of a reference calculation, U is determined.

ACKNOWLEDGMENTS

This work is partly supported by the Grand-in-Aid for the scientific research (No. 15GS0213 and No. 17064006) and the 21st COE Program by the Japan Society for Promotion of Science.

REFERENCES

1. V.I. Anisimov and J. Zaanen and O.K. Andersen, Phys. Rev. B **44**, 943 (1991).
2. S.L. Dudarev and G.A. Botton and S.Y. Savrasov and C.J. Humphreys and A.P. Sutton, Phys. Rev. B **57**, 1505 (1998).
3. K. Kusakabe and M. Takahashi and N. Suzuki, Physica B **378-380**, 271 (2006).
4. K. Kusakabe, cond-mat/0505703 (2005).
5. K. Kusakabe, J. Phys. Soc. Jpn **70**, 2038 (2001).

Hard X-ray photoelectron spectroscopy on ultra shallow plasma-doped silicon layers

M. Kobata[1*], E. Ikenaga[1], J. J. Kim[1], M.Yabashi[1] K. Kobayashi[1]
D. Miwa[2], Y. Nishino[2], K. Tamasaku[2], T. Ishikawa[2]
C. G. Jin[3] Y. Sasaki[3], K. Okashita[3], H. Tamura[3], H. Ito[3], B. Mizuno[3], T. Okumura[4]

[1]JASRI/SPring-8 , Kouto 1-1-1, Mikazuki-cho, Sayo-gun, Hyogo 679-5198, Japan
[2]RIKEN/SPring-8 Kouto 1-1-1, Mikazuki-cho, Sayo-gun, Hyogo 679-5198, Japan
[3]Ultimate Junction Technologies Inc. 3-1-1, Yagumonakamachi, Moriguchi Kadomai, Osaka, 570-8501, Japan
[4]Matsushita Electric Industrial Co., Ltd., 3-1-1, Yagumonakamachi, Moriguchi Kadoma, Osaka, 570-8501, Japan

Abstract. Recently, we have shown that hard X-ray photoemission spectroscopy (HX-PES) using undulator X-rays at SPring-8 is quite feasible with both high resolution and high throughput. Here we report an application of HX-PES to the characterization of electronic and chemical states of ultra shallow plasma doped samples. We found that the shift in chemical binding energy by impurity activation can be measured with high accuracy. The binding energy of Si 1s changes according to the shift in Fermi level as the carrier concentration varies. Thus, the active carrier concentration of ultra-shallow junction region can be measured by non-destructive HX-PES with high accuracy.

Keywords: hard X-ray photoelectron spectroscopy, ultra shallow junction, plasma doping
PACS: 79.60.-i, 78.40.Fy

1. Introduction

As a result of continuous demand for the downsizing of the device structure in MOS transistors, the formation of ultra-shallow junctions (USJ) with low resistivity is required in order to minimize the short channel effects and maximize the drive current. Typical targets for 45nm technology nodes include junction depths (Xj) of less than 10nm and sheet resistance (Rs) of less than 1kΩ [1]. Shallow junctions are formed conventionally using low energy ion implantation, however an alternative method is urgently required due to the low throughput and difficulty in controlling the range of doping less than 10 nm for boron impurities. Junction depths of 10nm or less can be achieved by plasma doping (PD) followed by rapid non-equilibrium annealing processes [2]. This novel method can provide the perfect solution for the productivity problem as it can achieve high throughput with ultra-low energy.

We have investigated ultra shallow PD samples on chemical binding states using HX-PES at BL47XU, SPring-8. HX-PES is a very effective tool for investigating the electronic structure and chemical states of bulk materials, nanoscale buried layers and their interfaces. This is because the contribution to the surface region is negligible due to the large probing depth compared to conventional photoemission spectroscopy. The detection depth of HX-PES for the Si 1s core electron is ideally matched to the ultra shallow doped region of within ~10 nm from the surface to characterize the chemical bonding states and monitor the Fermi level shift due to carrier activation [3].

2. Experimental

An n-type 8-inch Si wafer (10Ωcm) was introduced into the PD chamber, in which a helicon wave plasma of helium for pre-amorphization or B_2H_6 (diluted by He) for PD was generated and irradiated onto the Si wafer with an external DC bias potential. The doped wafers were annealed by the spike RTA, flash lamp annealing (FLA), All Solid-State Laser Annealing (ASLA). The Rs was measured by four point probe. The annealing conditions of samples are summarized in Table 1.

Table 1.The annealing conditions of samples		
Method	Annealing conditions	
ASLA	Laser energy 1500mJ/cm²	Rs 428(Ω/sq.)
FLA	Temperature 1626K	Rs 330(Ω/sq.)
Spike-RTA	Temperature 1348K	Rs 373(Ω/sq.)

HX-PES experiments were performed at an undulator beam line, BL47XU, of SPring-8 with the excitation energy of 7.94 keV. Total energy resolution was estimated to be 170~300meV at RT, depending on the lens parameters of the electron analyzer, by the Fermi energy (E_F) of Au plates.

CP893, *Physics of Semiconductors, 28th International Conference*
edited by W. Jantsch and F. Schäffler

3. Results and discussion

Fig.1 showed Si 1s spectra of ultra shallow PD samples before and after three different annealing processes (spike RTA, FLA, ASLA) compared with that of n-Si substrate. After PD, the electron density of the n-Si substrate decreased to that of the intrinsic Si level due to defect-induced carrier traps. The Si1s spectra shifted to the low binding energy side by increase of hole density after annealing. In addition, after both spike RTA and FLA, the PD samples showed excellent single chemical states with high carrier activation. The ASLA spectrum is resolved into two components as showed in Fig.2. Take-off angle dependence measurements of Si1s spectra in the ASLA sample resolved that lower binding energy components is originated from the layer near the surface, where the higher binding energy component from the layer behind.

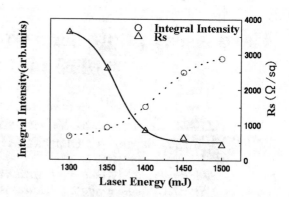

FIGURE 3.Integral intensity of layer near the surface component and Rs dependence on the laser energy in ASLA sample.

Fig.3 showed Integral intensity of layer near the surface component and the Rs dependence on the laser energy in the ASLA sample. With increasing integral intensity of component of layer near the surface, the Rs decrease. In other words, the carrier concentration increases in layer near surface. From comparison of shift of binding energy of Si1s spectra, the carrier concentration of the ASLA sample is higher than that of other annealing processes after anneal.

In summary, HX-PES successfully monitored the Fermi level shift and differences of chemical binding states, which depend on the doping and the annealing processes, with high accuracy. We would like to remark that this method is extremely useful for the optimizing of semiconductor doping process and thermal activation process for 45 nm technology node and beyond.

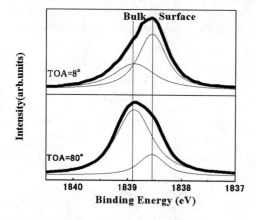

FIGURE 1.Si 1s spectra of ultra shallow PD samples before and after three different annealing processes (spike-RTA, FLA, ASLA) compared with that of n-Si substrate. These spectra are normalized to peak intensity.

4. Acknowledgments

This work was partially supported by through a Grant-in-Aid for Scientific Research (A) (No.15206006) and also partially supported by a Nanotechnology Support Project of The Ministry of Education, Culture, Sports, Science and Technology

5. References

1. A. Hori and B. Mizuno, Tech. Dig. of IEDM, (1999) p.641.
2. C.G. Jin, et al., International Workshop on Junction Technology (2004), 102.
3. K. Kobayashi, et al., Appl. Phys. Lett. 83 (2003) 1005

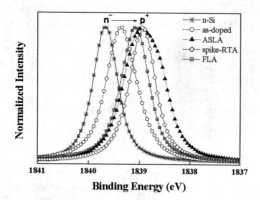

FIGURE 2.Take-off angle dependence measurements of Si1s spectra in the ASLA sample. The hair-line indicates curve fits using Voigt functions.

Simulation of Guided-Wave Photonic Devices with Variational Mode-Matching

N. Finger, C. Pacher and W. Boxleitner

ARC Seibersdorf research GmbH (ARC-sr), Donau-City-Str. 1, 1220 Vienna, Austria,
`mailto:norman.finger@arcs.ac.at`, `http://www.smart-systems.at`

Abstract. We present an efficient method — the variational mode-matching (VMM) method — which preserves the advantages of mode-matching techniques while increasing the numerical robustness significantly and providing the capability of local refinement. This makes it very attractive for the simulation of ultra-high-index-contrast waveguide structures as is proved by applying it to different grating-based guided-wave devices.

Keywords: Mode-matching, waveguide, grating coupler, radiation loss, surface emission, Bragg reflector, simulation
PACS: 42.79.-e, 42.82.-m, 42.82.Bq, 85.60.-q, 85.60.Bt

THEORETICAL FRAMEWORK

The in-depth simulation of complex guided-wave opto-electronic and photonic devices comprising ultra-high-index-contrast materials such as metal/dielectric waveguide structures in TM-polarization or couplers employing deeply etched surface gratings requires rigorous numerical methods. Among these are mode-matching (MM) techniques [1, 2] which must be combined with perfectly-matched layers (PMLs) [3] to mimic an open system permitting an accurate description of radiation effects. However, in the presence of PMLs instabilities can emerge in the determination of a proper set of local eigenmodes. In addition, MM shows only slow convergence as the number of modes is increased. The variational mode-matching (VMM) method elaborated in the following overcomes these drawbacks.

With the 2D-assumption $\partial_y = 0$ Maxwell's equations for media characterized by the dielectric tensor $\underline{\varepsilon} = \mathrm{diag}(\varepsilon_{xx}, \varepsilon_{yy}, \varepsilon_{zz})(x,z)$ come as

$$\left\{ \partial_x \hat{a} \partial_x + \partial_z \hat{b} \partial_z + k_0^2 \hat{c} \right\} \phi(x,z) = 0, \tag{1}$$

where $\phi = E_y, \hat{a} = \hat{b} = 1, \hat{c} = \varepsilon_{yy}$ for TE- and $\phi = H_y, \hat{a} = \frac{1}{\varepsilon_{zz}}, \hat{b} = \frac{1}{\varepsilon_{xx}}, \hat{c} = 1$ for TM-polarization, respectively; $k_0 = \frac{2\pi}{\lambda_0}$ with the vacuum wavelength λ_0. In the z-direction the simulation domain is terminated by either electric or magnetic walls which are covered with PMLs using the complex variable-stretching technique [3].

To solve the field equations (1) for a layered system in each layer l ($x_{l-1} \leq x \leq x_l$) the ansatz

$$\phi^{(l)}(x,z) = \tag{2}$$
$$\sum_{j,\rho=1}^{N} \varphi_j(z) C_{j\rho}^{(l)} \left\{ A_\rho^{(l)} e^{i\beta_\rho^{(l)}(x-x_{l-1})} + B_\rho^{(l)} e^{-i\beta_\rho^{(l)}(x-x_l)} \right\}$$

is made. The shape functions $\varphi_j(z)$ must satisfy the outer boundary conditions but they can be chosen rather freely offering the possibility of local refinement in z-regions where rapid variations of the optical field are expected. Especially in metal/dielectric waveguide structures in TM-polarization where surface-plasmon-like modes occur the utilization of well-adapted shape functions improves the convergence and accuracy tremendously in comparison to conventional MM techniques. For TE-polarization VMM is superior to MM as well.

The modal constants $\{\beta_\rho^{(l)}, C_{j\rho}^{(l)}\}$ are solutions of a linear $N \times N$ eigenproblem which is obtained from applying a Galerkin scheme to (1). To determine the A- and B-coefficients in (2) the continuity of ϕ and $\hat{a}\partial_x\phi$ across the x-interfaces is enforced in a weak sense. This yields (inverse) scattering matrices of the form

$$\begin{bmatrix} \mathbf{t}_l \vec{A}^{(l)} \\ \mathbf{t}_{l+1} \vec{B}^{(l+1)} \end{bmatrix} = \begin{bmatrix} \mathbf{R}_{l,l+1} & \mathbf{T}_{l,l+1} \\ \mathbf{T}_{l+1,l} & \mathbf{R}_{l+1,l} \end{bmatrix} \cdot \begin{bmatrix} \vec{B}^{(l)} \\ \vec{A}^{(l+1)} \end{bmatrix} \tag{3}$$

where $\mathbf{t}_l = \mathrm{diag}(e^{i\beta_\rho^{(l)}(x_l - x_{l-1})})$ which are used to model the multilayer system in a numerically stable way.

RESULTS

The first two devices (labeled I and II) having been investigated are air/SiN/SiO waveguide structures with rectangular-shaped surface-relief gratings designed for an operation at $\lambda_0 \approx 1.5\,\mu m$. The SiN-core is $0.5\,\mu m$ thick, and the grating depth is $h = 0.125\,\mu m$.

Device I is an in-coupler comprising 50 grating periods with pitch $p = 0.85\,\mu m$. 40 periods are illuminated by a plane wave with the angle of incidence θ. In Fig. 1 the calculated power transfer efficiencies from the incident wave into the $\mathrm{TE}_0/\mathrm{TM}_0$ waveguide mode are com-

CP893, *Physics of Semiconductors, 28th International Conference*
edited by W. Jantsch and F. Schäffler

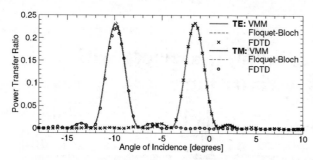

FIGURE 1. Calculated power transfer efficiencies for the grating in-coupler (device I, $\lambda_0 = 1.5\,\mu$m).

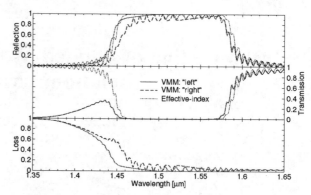

FIGURE 2. Reflection-, transmission-, and loss-spectra for device II excited from the left and the right.

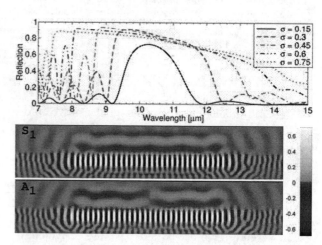

FIGURE 3. Reflectivities of the DBR for different relative air-slot widths for device III; optical field of two laser modes.

pared for different approaches: VMM, a Floquet-Bloch (FB) model based on [4], and FDTD (FullWAVE™ by RSoft Design Group). The agreement concerning the line-shapes, the peak-positions and -heights is excellent though different modelings of the exciting field have been used: in FB and FDTD the exciting *field* is directly prescribed whereas in VMM a *source-current* of the form $j_{\mathrm{exc}}(x,z;\theta) = j_0(x;\theta)e^{ik_0 \sin\theta x}\delta(z-z_S)$ is applied. Regarding the computational effort VMM is significantly more efficient than FDTD: the execution times for a single θ-point are ≈ 4s (VMM) and ≈ 1h (FDTD).

Device II is a broad-band reflector designed for operation in TE-polarization employing a chirped grating with 200 periods where the pitch varies from $p = 0.44\,\mu$m (Bragg wavelength: $\lambda_B \approx 1.47\,\mu$m, bulk-wave onset: $\lambda_b \approx 1.38\,\mu$m) to $p = 0.47\,\mu$m ($\lambda_B \approx 1.555\,\mu$m, $\lambda_b \approx 1.465\,\mu$m) in a cosine-shaped manner. In Fig. 2 the reflection- (R), transmission- (T) and loss-spectra (L) for excitation from the left (short-period side) and the right are shown. Due to the presence of radiation damping R and L depend on the excitation direction — only T is the same in both cases. The ripples inside the stopband are due to parasitic reflections and scattering losses originating from a mismatch of the optical field across the interface between the homogeneous waveguide- and grating region. These effects are missing in a simple 1D effective-index model that has to ignore radiation. The VMM model contains ≈ 100k unknowns and occupies 500 MB RAM. The runtime for each λ_0-point is 40s on a computer with a 2.4 GHz CPU.

Device III is a short-cavity surface-emitting quantum-cascade laser based on a waveguide structure with a metalized surface-grating [5]. Deeply etched 1st-order distributed Bragg reflectors (DBRs) with 8 periods are used for the optical feedback. Figure 3 indicates that scattering losses in the DBRs limit device performance: the breakaway of the long-wavelength stop-band edge stems from antiguiding effects in the air-slots. Therefore, DBRs with small relative air-slot widths of $\sigma = 0.3$ are employed. The active section of the device comprises 30 periods of the surface-emitting waveguide-grating struc-

ture with pitch $p = 3\,\mu$m. Gain g modifies the permittivity in the active region: $\varepsilon_{zz} \mapsto \varepsilon_{zz} - i\frac{n_{\mathrm{act}}\lambda_0}{\pi}g$. The laser oscillations are computed from the transmission condition $(T_{l\to r}(\lambda_0,g))^{-1} = 0$ using a non-linear root-solver. The lowest-threshold modes (mode no.: $\lambda_0\,[\mu$m], $g\,[$cm$^{-1}]$) are found to be: (A_{-1}: 9.292, 64.5), (S_{-1}: 9.429, 52.6), (A_0: 9.574, 40.4), (S_1: 9.724, 60.3), (A_1: 9.880, 63.1), (S_2: 10.042, 67.3). In Fig. 3 the optical field of the modes S_1 (symmetric) and A_1 (antisymmetric) are shown.

REFERENCES

1. A. S. Sudbo, *Pure and Appl. Optics* **2**, 211–233 (1993).
2. O. P. Franza, and W. C. Chew, *IEEE Trans. Microwave Theory Techn.* **44**, 87–92 (1996).
3. F. L. Teixeira, and W. C. Chew, *IEEE Microwave Guided Wave Lett.* **8**, 223–225 (1998).
4. N. Finger, and E. Gornik, *IEEE J. Quantum Electron.* **35**, 832–843 (1999).
5. N. Finger, W. Schrenk, and E. Gornik, *IEEE J. Quantum Electron.* **36**, 780–786 (2000).

High Precision Alignment in Multi-Layer NanoImprint Lithography

M. Mühlberger[1], W. Schwinger[1], M. Gmainer[1], R. Schöftner[1], T. Glinsner[2], Ch. Hasenfuß[3], K. Hingerl[3], H. Schmidt[4], E.-B. Kley[4]

[1] Profactor GmbH, Im Stadtgut A2, 4407 Steyr, Austria
[2] EV Group, DI Erich Thallner Straße 1, 4782 St. Forian/Inn, Austria
[3] CD Laboratory of Surface Optics, Altenbergerstr. 69, 4040 Linz, Austria
[4] Friedrich-Schiller-Universität, Institute of Applied Physics, Max-Wien Platz 1,07743 Jena, Germany

Abstract. Nanoimprint lithography (NIL) is a cost efficient technique for the mass production of nanostructures. We demonstrate alignment accuracies in the range of 100 nm and below in UV nanoimprint lithography (UV-NIL) using a simple optical technique. The advantages of this technique are the relative simplicity of the marker-design and the whole setup combined with the possibility of an upgrade of existing equipment and still ultra-high precision alignment capabilities.

Keywords: nanoimprint lithography, UV-NIL, alignment, Moiré.
PACS: 81.16.Nd, 42.70.Qs

INTRODUCTION

Our goal is to use nanoimprint lithography to fabricate several layers of a photonic crystal in woodpile structure on top of each other. The period d of the structure designed for a wavelength of 1.5μm is around 600nm. Essential is the precise alignment of the subsequent layers. In order to achieve a photonic bandgap the 3rd layer has to be aligned to the 1st with a precision of better than $d/4$.

ALIGNMENT IN UV-NIL

In the UV-NIL process a nanostructured stamp is brought into contact with a UV-curable polymer under well controlled conditions. UV hardening of the polymer and removal of the stamp transfers the pattern into the polymer for possible further processing. The stamp is usually structured by e-beam lithography and reactive ion etching. UV-NIL therefore allows the rapid production of nanoscale structures in a fast and parallel process.

We work with an EVG®620 nanoimprinter using a 10x flat objective video optics setup and a motorized alignment stage with a minimal step width of 100nm. The experiments have been performed using SiO_2 stamps and glass substrates. The stamps with a size of 25x25 mm² typically contain structures with 400 nm depth and 200 nm width.

Alignment Marker Design

Our alignment markers consist of standard alignment crosses, Vernier structures and several Moiré patterns and are designed for a multi-step alignment procedure. At first the standard cross structures are used for coarse alignment then the Vernier patterns are employed. This is done to overcome the ambiguity of the linear Moiré structures. Finally high precision alignment is achieved using the Moiré structures. Furthermore also unambiguous circular Moiré patterns are included on the stamp in contrast to other works [1]. By choosing the alignment markers of two subsequent layers in such a way that the period of the patterns p_1 and p_2 differs only by a small amount, a Moiré pattern is created by overlaying the two layers, with a period $p_{total} = p_1 \cdot p_2/(p_1-p_2)$, which is moved by a distance of $d = \Delta \cdot (p_{total}/p_2)$ with $p_{total}/p_2 > 1$, when Δ is the actual displacement between the two layers during alignment.

The use of Moiré patterns for alignment has been mentioned already in the 1960s and 1970s (e.g. [2][3]). Such patterns are used by the group of Prof. Chou in Princeton for hot embossing and is also implemented in the technology of Molecular Imprints, Inc. [4] and

CP893, *Physics of Semiconductors, 28th International Conference*
edited by W. Jantsch and F. Schäffler
© 2007 American Institute of Physics 978-0-7354-0397-0/07/$23.00

in UV-NIL [5], however the presented method is used for the first time for sub 100nm alignment in UV-NIL.

Alignment Procedure

At first an imprint e.g. on a microscope slide is made, which is then covered by a layer of 10nm Al. This is done to obtain a refractive index contrast for the second imprint. When covered with the second resist layer the first one would otherwise be invisible.

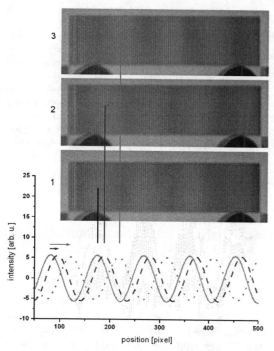

FIGURE 1. Movement of the Moiré patterns during alignment. In the graph a sinusoidal fit to the grayscale data of the images above is show.

For simplicity and to test the alignment process the second imprint is then made just on top of this structure without any further processing. Alignment is performed by observing the Moiré patterns closely during the whole sequence of contact steps. Figure 1 shows a series of video images taken during the alignment and in the graph the evaluation using grey-scale image processing is sketched. It can be seen that the movement of the Moiré patterns can be followed nicely. A shift of 5 pixels, which can be well detected, corresponds in our case to approximately 110nm actual displacement.

Results

The result of an alignment experiment is shown in figure 2 on the right. Both layers can be seen in this optical microscope image. Evaluating the Vernier

patterns for the alignment marker an alignment accuracy in x- and y-direction of certainly better than 100nm can be estimated. The circular appearance of the circular Moiré patterns is an indication of excellent alignment. Results in this range can be achieved routinely, with various marker designs. The imprint process has to be controlled precisely and alignment has to be performed at all stages of imprinting.

CONCLUSIONS

Alignment accuracies around 50nm (below 100nm routinely) have been achieved on an EVG®620 nanoimprinter during UV-NIL. To our knowledge the achieved alignment accuracy is the best so far implemented with this process.

The advantages of the implemented Moiré technique are the relative simplicity of the design and the whole setup combined with the possibility of an unproblematic upgrade of existing equipment while still providing ultra-high precision alignment capabilities.

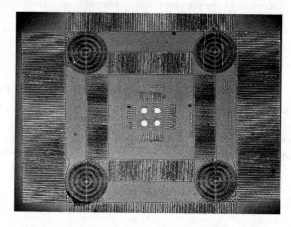

FIGURE 2. Optical microscope image of both aligned imprints on top of each other.

ACKNOWLEDGMENTS

The authors acknowledge research funding from the European Community's 6th Framework Programme (COOP-CT-2004-512667 3DNanoPrint www.3Dnanoprint.org).

REFERENCES

1. W. Moreno et al., www.princeton.edu/~pccm/outreach/reuarchive/REU2002 'PresentationsPDF/MORENO.pdf (2002)
2. L.O. Vargardy er al., Applied Optics (1964)
3. M.C. King, D.H. Berry, Applied Optics (1972)
4. Molecular Imprints Press Release (November 2004)
5. A. Fuchs et al., NNT ´04

Experimental Investigation on Carrier Dynamics at the Thermal Breakdown

S. Reggiani[1], E. Gnani[1], M. Rudan[1], G. Baccarani[1], S. Bychikhin[2], J. Kuzmik[2],
D. Pogany[2], E. Gornik[2], M. Denison[3], N. Jensen[3], G. Groos[4], M. Stecher[3]

[1] "E. De Castro" Advanced Research Center on Electronic Systems and Department of Electronics, Viale Risorgimento, 2, University of Bologna, I-40136, Bologna, Italy. [2] Institute for Solid State Electronics, Vienna University of Technology, Vienna, Austria. [3] Infineon Technologies AG, München, Germany. [4] University of the Federal Armed Forces Munich, Neubiberg, Germany.

Abstract. A theoretical and experimental investigation on the electron impact ionization in silicon has been carried out in a temperature range up to about 1000 K. The proposed impact-ionization model amply extends the range of simulation tools up to temperatures which are important to predict the failure threshold of ESD-protection and power devices. Different protection diodes are investigated with electro-thermal simulation and transient interferometric thermal-mapping experiments in a new complementary approach. The prediction capability of the simulation tool is validated up to the thermal failure of the p-n junction. The temperature distribution and its dynamics during the application of high-current pulses are studied by comparing the calculated and experimental optical phase shifts: a quantitative agreement both in temporal evolution and thermal distribution is obtained up to temperatures of the order of 1000 K.

Keywords: Electrostatic discharge (ESD), electrothermal effects, impact ionization, nonequilibrium Auger effect, semiconductor device modeling, thermal mapping, thermo-optic effects.
PACS: 79.20.Ap, 79.20.Fv

INTRODUCTION

Device simulation has proved to be a powerful tool for technology development. Electrostatic discharge (ESD) phenomena, however, have been somewhat elusive in the past, due to the complex physical mechanisms involved in current filamentation and second breakdown. The availability of electro-thermal simulators has improved our understanding of device self-heating under high current conditions [1]. However, built-in models are in general not suitable for the simulation of ESD events characterized by high currents, high local temperatures and very fast and energetic pulses: physical effects like avalanche breakdown, snapback, second breakdown and thermal runaway do in fact require physical models experimentally verified up to temperatures of the order of 1000 K.

As a consequence, the design of ESD devices turns out to be a difficult task, even more so because minor changes in the device structure can cause considerable shifts in the parameters which are relevant for the high-current response of protection structures, namely: the breakdown voltage, the trigger current and voltage, the holding voltage, etc.

IMPACT-IONIZATION MODEL AND ELECTROTHERMAL SIMULATIONS

An experimental investigation on high-temperature electron impact-ionization in silicon has been carried out with the aim of improving the qualitative and quantitative understanding of carrier transport under electrostatic discharge (ESD) conditions. The analysis of the interplay of doping profiles, self-heating and carrier generation due to impact-ionization has been carried out by using the electro-thermal model within DESSIS-ISE [2]. The physically-based model for the impact-ionization coefficient by [3], especially suited for the simulation of devices up to very high operating temperatures, has been incorporated. Such a model has theoretically been confirmed and experimentally verified up to 800 K. It provides accurate predictions of physical effects like avalanche breakdown, snapback, second breakdown and thermal runaway,

CP893, *Physics of Semiconductors, 28th International Conference*
edited by W. Jantsch and F. Schäffler

with local self-heating reaching temperatures higher than 1000 K.

The compact model has an innovative aspect with respect to standard approaches, in that the contribution of the non-equilibrium Auger generation is accounted for. From a microscopic standpoint, Auger generation and impact ionization are the same process but with different energy sources: the Auger generation is a thermally-activated, quasi-equilibrium process. As a consequence, in the low-field regime, the distribution function behaves as in the equilibrium case: if the temperature increases, the tail of the distribution function and the electron mean energy increase as well. Thus, the Auger generation becomes higher at high T. The impact coefficient extracted at 623 K is reported in Fig. 1 vs. the inverse electric field: the new model is compared with three different models available in the literature (and implemented in [2]). Most of the local-field models available at date are based on the same phenomenological approach [4]. If the electric field is very sharply peaked over a distance comparable with the carrier mean free path, the impact process has to be described by a non-local approach within a hydrodynamic transport model [5].

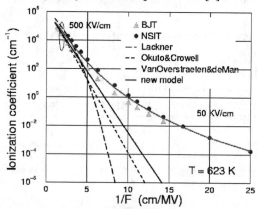

FIGURE 1. Electron impact coefficient vs. inverse electric field at 623 K. Symbols refer to two different devices, a standard BJT and a static-induction transistor (SIT). Three models based on Cynoweth's law are shown for comparison with the new model.

EXPERIMENTAL VALIDATION

The new model has been successfully validated with the Transient Interferometric Mapping (TIM) experiments on a number of different protection diodes. The TIM technique [6] has previously been used to verify the existence of hot spots in ESD protection devices predicted by device simulation. Special test devices were designed and manufactured using Infineon's SPT5 technology: three different diodes are investigated with electro-thermal simulation and transient interferometric thermal-mapping

experiments in a new complementary approach [7]. The local temperature within the device has been monitored during the application of large voltage and current pulses by using the thermal-mapping setup. The device simulation tool, based on the new impact-ionization model has successfully been validated with experiments on a number of different devices up to the thermal failure. The temperature distribution and its dynamics during the application of high-current pulses have been studied by comparing the calculated and experimental optical phase shifts: a quantitative agreement both in temporal evolution and space distribution of temperature has been obtained up to 1100 K. In Fig. 2, the phase shift calculated at the end of 100-ns current pulses for different stress levels is compared with experiments carried out with the TIM setup.

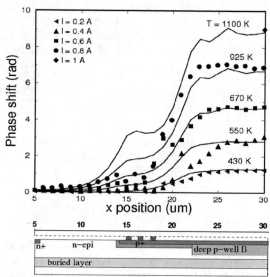

FIGURE 2. Phase-shift distribution along the cross section of a diode. The phase shift is measured at the end of the pulse (t = 100 ns) for different current levels. Solid lines: simulation; symbols: experiments. Bottom: schematic device cross section.

ACKNOWLEDGMENTS

This work has been supported by the European Commission through the IST 2000 30033 Project (DEMAND).

REFERENCES

1. A. Amerasekera, et al., *IEEE TED* **40**, 1836 (1993).
2. ISE AG. ISE-TCAD release 8.5. 2002.
3. S. Reggiani et al., *IEEE Trans. on ED* **52**, 2290 (2005).
4. W. Maes et al., Solid-St. Electr. **33**, 705 (1990).
5. W. Quade et al., Solid-St. Electr. **36**, 1493 (1993).
6. D. Pogany et al., *IEEE EDL.***23**, 606-608 (2002).
7. S. Reggiani et al., *IEEE EDL* **26**, 916-918 (2005).

Optical Modulation Spectroscopy Based On Real-Space Electron Transfer In Semiconductor Selective–Doped Heterostructures

Oleg A. Ryabushkin[*¶], Ekaterina I. Lonskaya[¶]

[¶]Institute of Radio Engineering and Electronics of Russian Academy of Sciences, pl. Vvedenskogo 1, 141190 Fryazino, Moscow oblast, Russia
[*]Moscow Institute of Physics and Technology (State University), Dolgoprydnyi, Moscow oblast, 141700 Russia

Abstract. New techniques of optical modulation spectroscopy are proposed for reliable registration of real–space electron transfer effect in semiconductor selectively doped heterostructures. In these methods, free charge carriers are heated by an electric current, RF or microwave electric fields, directed laterally to heterostructure layers. The heated electrons from high conductivity regions of a structure migrate across the sample layers and can reach sample regions with low conductivity. Such electrons transfer results in modifications of both built–in (transverse) electric field and excitonic states that, in turn, cause the probe light reflectance to vary in energy range near the fundamental absorption edge.

Keywords: real–space electron transfer, MODFET, GaAs/AlGaAs heterostructure, photoreflectance.
PACS: 73.40.Kp, 73.50.Lw, 78.40.Fy, 78.66.Fd

The heating of free charge carriers by external electric field in semiconductor selective-doped heterostructures results in changing their both electrical and optical properties. Under the action of electric field of several kV/cm applied along the heterostructure layers, the heated electrons can migrate from high electron mobility layers to adjacent low mobility layers. This real-space electron transfer (RST) was first proposed as a phenomenon to obtain negative differential resistance (NDR) in layered structures and then was employed for some practical device applications [1]. RST effect is characterized by spatial modification of charge carriers' concentration and thus leads to changing built-in (transverse) electric fields in heterostructure layers. Typically, the experimental evidence of RST is associated with the N-shaped NDR region observed in lateral I–V characteristics. However, I–V curves measurements can't in principle provide information on amount of the electrons transferred from one layer to another layer [1] and besides can't record a weak heating of electrons and a possible spatial redistribution of electrons in this case.

We first proposed new techniques of modulated light reflectance (MR) based on RST – contactless radio-frequency MR (RMR) and microwave MR (MMR), and current MR (CMR) [2, 3]. In RMR and MMR methods, the electrons are heated by using a radio-frequency or microwave alternating electric field directed along the heterostructure layers. In CMR, ac needs to be passed through ohmic contacts also along the structure layers. The heated electrons are spatially redistributed in the transverse to layers direction resulting in modification of built-in electric fields. For registration of MR spectra, the sample is illuminated with probe light of constant intensity with the photon energy around the bandgap energies of heterostructure layers [2]. The change of built-in fields due to spatial redistribution of the heated electrons causes the probe light reflectance to vary. The relative change of the intensity of the reflected probe light is measured at frequency of an applied field or a current by lock-in technique and allows to recover a MR spectrum. The spatial redistribution of hot electrons also results in changes of the excitonic states which are known to be very sensitive to variations in electronic concentration that, in turn, contributes to MR spectra forming [2,3].

The developed techniques were applied for investigation of the effect induced by electrons heating on a band diagram and electron energy states in MBE–grown GaAs/AlGaAs selectively doped heterostructures. Such type of selectively doped heterostructures is characterized by a high conductivity region (a channel) formed at the AlGaAs/GaAs interface. The measured spectra demonstrated that for each heterostructure and different applied lateral electric fields RST exhibited its own features. In case of strong heating (for the

CP893, *Physics of Semiconductors, 28th International Conference*
edited by W. Jantsch and F. Schäffler
© 2007 American Institute of Physics 978-0-7354-0397-0/07/$23.00

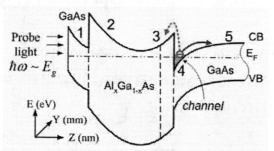

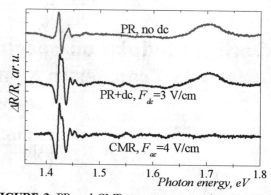

FIGURE 1. Band diagram of active part of GaAs/AlGaAs selectively doped heterostructure under study. CB here is the bottom of conduction band, VB – the top of valence band, E_F – Fermi level.

FIGURE 3. PR and CMR spectra measured at 291 K. The pointed values of lateral electric field applied to the sample correspond to the electric current density of ~ 2 kA/cm^2.

lateral fields of 100 V/cm and up), hot electrons from GaAs channel can overcome the GaAs/AlGaAs conduction band discontinuity and migrate in AlGaAs layer (dotted arrow in fig.1). Under the low applied fields (5–30 V/cm), the weakly heated electrons can't overcome the potential barrier in conduction band and transfer in depth of GaAs buffer layer leading to a modification of excitonic states (solid arrow, fig.1).

As an example, let us consider RST in case of rather low applied electric field. The band diagram of a typical GaAs/Al$_x$Ga$_{1-x}$As selective-doped structure ($x \approx 0.2$) is shown in fig.1. This heterostructure consisted of a 100 Å undoped GaAs cap layer (1 in fig.1), a 600 Å n-AlGaAs ($N_D \approx 7 \cdot 10^{17}$ cm^{-3}) – 2, a 100 Å AlGaAs spacer layer – 3, ~2 μm undoped GaAs buffer layer – 4–5, GaAs/AlGaAs technological superlattice layers grown on semi-insulating GaAs substrate.

The central part of the experimental setup for CMR spectra measurement is schematically shown in fig.2. In CMR experiments, ac (square pulse) with frequency of 1 kHz was passed along the sample layers (at Y axis, fig.1,2). Besides CMR spectra, both traditional photoreflectance (PR) spectra and PR spectra in the conditions of a lateral dc flow (PR+dc) were measured, more experimental details can be found in [2,5]. The electrons' heating with dc passing was controlled

by photoluminescence spectra measurements.

The PR, PR+dc and CMR spectra measured at room temperature are shown in fig. 3. The lineshape of traditional PR spectrum (without dc) is typical for such structures [4]. The PR spectrum modification with dc flow along the sample layers (at Y axis, fig.1,2) corresponds to variations of the built–in transverse electric fields (at Z axis, fig.1) and excitonic states in GaAs layers. Both physical and mathematical models were developed for calculations of PR+dc spectra [5]. We found that applying to the sample lateral electric field of ~10 V/cm, the built–in transverse fields in GaAs channel region 4 reduced by 25% at room temperature [4–5]. For CMR spectra measurements, only ac used. The CMR spectral features' lineshape in GaAs band gap energy region 1.35–1.5 eV is similar to PR+dc one. No CMR signals were observed in energy range 1.5–1.8 eV near the AlGaAs band gap energy. Hence, it's clearly seen from these spectra that the weakly heated electrons from GaAs channel 4 can't overcome the AlGaAs/GaAs heterojunction barrier and transfer mainly into the depth of GaAs buffer layer 5 (fig.1).

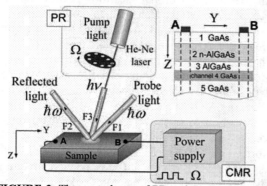

FIGURE 2. The central part of PR and CMR spectra measurements. F1, F2, F3 – optical fibers with diameter of 300 μm. In insert: arrangement of ohmic contacts (A and B) and sample layers.

ACKNOWLEDGMENTS

E.I. Lonskaya gratefully acknowledges the Organizing Committee of ICPS–28 and the Russian Foundation of Basic Research (grant 06-02-26972) for financial support of participation in ICPS–28.

REFERENCES

1. Z. Gribnikov, K. Hess, G. Kosinovsky, *J. Appl. Phys.* **77**, 1337–1373 (1995).
2. O. A. Ryabushkin, E. I. Lonskaya, A. E. Sotnikov, M. A. Chernikov, *Phys. Stat. Sol. (a)* **202**, 1282–1291 (2005).
3. O. A. Ryabushkin and V. A. Sablikov, *JETP Letters* **67**, 233–238 (1998).
4. E. I. Lonskaya and O. A. Ryabushkin, *JETP Letters* **82**, 664–668 (2005).
5. E. I. Lonskaya and O. A. Ryabushkin, to be published in *Phys. Stat. Sol. (a)* (2006).

Ferromagnetic and Infrared Properties of Ni-Filled Self-Organized Mesoporous Silicon

K. Rumpf[1], P. Granitzer[1], M. Hofmayer[1], P. Pölt[2], A. Reichmann[2], H. Krenn[1]

[1] Institute of Physics, Karl-Franzens-University, Universitaetsplatz 5, 8010 Graz, Austria
[2] Institute for Electron Microscopy, Technical University of Technology, Steyrergasse 17, 8010 Graz, Austria

Abstract. An electrochemically formed mesoporous silicon (PS) template of oriented pores perpendicular to the surface with a high aspect ratio up to 1000 is filled with Ni in a galvanic deposition process. Various characterization methods like AES and EDXS prove the Ni filling over the entire pore length. The incorporated metallic Ni consists of particles with spherical, ellipsoidal and elongated shape. The mutual distribution of the Ni precipitations and the overall gradient of the Ni-filling within the porous layer can be varied over the full pore length from the surface region to the pore tips by different deposition parameters. The Ni/PS-composite is investigated magnetically and optically. Optical investigations in the mid IR indicate that this metal/Si nanocomposite shows IR-absorption specific to features of the Ni/Si-interface.

Keywords: Mesoorous Silicon, ferromagnetic composite, Ni nanostructures, electrodeposition
PACS: 75.30.Gw; 75.75.+a; 78.55.Mb; 61.43.Gt;

INTRODUCTION

Silicon and silicon based materials are of great interest not only for basic research but also for technological as well as industrial applications. Nanostructured magnetic materials used in magnetic storage technology as well as spintronic devices are of great interest. In this field self-assembled arrangements are preferred because of low-costs and less time consuming preparation compared with lithographically fabricated structures. Most popular are porous alumina structures with a hexagonal pore-arrangement [1] offering pores between 18 nm and 180 nm in diameter [2]. We present a Si based nanosystem of self-organized oriented mesopores with rather homogeneous distribution of pore diameters. This porous silicon template is filled with a ferromagnetic metal in a galvanic deposition process. The magnetic properties of the system can be varied by accurate control of the deposition parameters.

PREPARATION AND EXPERIMENTS

The PS-matrix results from an anodization process of Si using an aqueous HF-solution as electrolyte. By varying the electrochemical parameters the pore diameter as well as the pitch of the arrangement can be tuned in a small regime (pore diameter between 30 nm and 100 nm). The pore diameter increases with

increasing current density. If the current density reaches the critical value which is between 150 mA/cm^2 and 200 mA/cm^2 electropolishing of the surface occurs. The interpore spacing increases with decreasing current density (j). Beneath a certain j (< 50 mA/cm^2) the pores grow in a dendritic manner as usual in the mesoporous regime (pore diameter: 10 – 25 nm).

The achieved Si-based template is filled with Ni during galvanic metal-deposition. As electrolyte a Ni-chlorine (NiCl$_2$) and boric acid (H$_3$BO$_3$) solution is used [3]. The incorporation of Ni into the channels depends on deposition parameters like current density and pulse duration of the deposition current [4]. The precipitations consist of spheroidal, ellipsoidal and elongated Ni-structures up to wires. The structural characterization of the samples is carried out by SEM (figure1), AES [5] and EDXS (figure 1).

Magnetic measurements are performed by SQUID-magnetometry and the optical properties are investigated by FTIR-spectroscopy.

Magnetic and Infrared Properties of the PS/Ni-Nanocomposite

Magnetization measurements have been carried out in a temperature range between 4.2 K and 300 K. The magnetization curves show FM behavior and substantial vertical anisotropy $H_{C\perp} \sim 2 \cdot H_{C\parallel}$ from the different directions of the applied magnetic field with

CP893, *Physics of Semiconductors, 28th International Conference*
edited by W. Jantsch and F. Schäffler

respect to the sample surface. The coercivities vary for different Ni-fillings as shown in figure 2, e.g. $H_{C\perp}$ between 280 Oe and 40 Oe. The saturation magnetization varies because of the different content of metallic Ni.

Considering the hystereses loops at various temperatures H_C decreases with increasing temperature and so does the squareness. $H_{C\perp}$ (4.2 K) = 330 Oe and $H_{C\perp}$ (250 K) = 140 Oe. The squareness decreases from 36% to 16%.

Optical investigations have been performed in the mid IR-range. Considering the bare PS-sample interference fringes due to multiple reflections within the porous layer can be used to determine the length of the pores (refractive index of PS ~ 2.7 at a porosity of 40%) which agree well with SEM-images. The transmission spectra of Ni-filled PS-specimens show a broad absorption peak at a wavenumber of about 3500 cm^{-1} which can be attributed either to some NiO$_x$-species [6] or Schottky barrier absorption across the interface between Ni and Si (figure 3). The barrier energies of a flat Ni/Si interface [7] are not too far from the measured ones.

 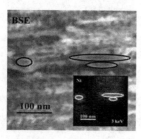

a)   b)

Figure 1a: SEM-image of the cleaved edge of a PS-sample showing oriented pores. A sharp termination between PS-layer and c-Si is noticed. In the inset an EDX-map of the Ni-distribution within PS is shown.

Figure 1b: BSE-micrograph shows 3 individual Ni-particles. The inset demonstrates that Ni is concentrated in the marked areas.

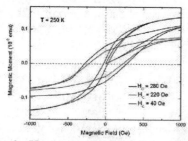

Figure 2: Hystereses loops measured along easy axis direction $H_\perp$ showing different H_C for various Ni-filling parameters, respective for different distributions of the incorporated Ni-structures. Ni: blue curve: 3.8·10^{-6} cm^3, red curve: 2.8·10^{-6} cm^3, black curve: 1.9·10^{-6} cm^3.

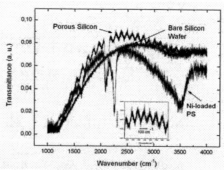

Figure 3: FTIR-spectra of bare Si, PS and a Ni/PS-sample. The absorption peaks of PS are due to Si-H vibration modes at a wavenumber around 2100 cm^{-1}. The Ni-filled sample exhibits a broad absorption peak at a wavenumber of about 3500 cm^{-1} due to NiO$_x$ [6] or Schottky barrier absorption as well as O-Si-H modes at ~ 2200 cm^{-1}.

CONCLUSION

In summary oriented growth of Ni-nanowires cancels the normally expected dipolar in-plane anisotropy of a coalescent layer. Substantial vertical anisotropy occurs, with an increase of coercivity from 20 Oe up to 280 Oe. Its origin is a stress-induced magnetoelastic interaction between the Ni-wires and the PS-matrix. Schottky barrier absorption across the Ni/NiSi/Si-interfaces in the below Si-band-gap spectral range proves the true existence of an oriented ferromagnet/semiconductor hybrid system with residual IR-transmission via the supporting PS-skeleton.

ACKNOWLEDGMENTS

We thank the Austrian FWF-fund for his grant under project P18593 and acknowledge the support by the Austrian MNA nano-network.

REFERENCES

1. H. Masuda, K. Fukuda, *Science* **268**, 63 (1995).
2. M. Vazquez, M. Hernandez-Velez, K. Pirota, A. Asenjo, D. Navas, J. Velazquez, P. Vargas, C. Ramos, *Eur. Phys. J. B* **40**, 489-497 (2004).
3. P. Granitzer, K. Rumpf, H. Krenn, *Mat. Res. Soc. Symp. Proc.* **876E**, R8.9 (2005).
4. P. Granitzer, K. Rumpf, P. Pölt, A. Reichmann, H. Krenn, *Mat. Res. Soc. Symp. Proc.* **872**, J13.13 (2005).
5. P. Granitzer, K. Rumpf, S. Surnev, H. Krenn, *JMMM* **290-291**, 735 (2005).
6. X. Liu, C. M. Chun, I. A. Aksay, W. H. Shih, *Ind. Eng. Chem. Res.* **39**, 684 (2000).
7. S. M. Sze, Physics of semiconductor devices, 2nd edition, Wiley (1981).

Optically Detected Extended X-Ray Absorption Fine Structure Study of InGaN/GaN Single Quantum Wells

N. Rigopoulos[a], B. Hamilton[a], G. J. Davies[a], B. M. Towlson[a], N. R. J. Poolton[b], P. Dawson[c], D. M. Graham[c*], M. J. Kappers[d], C. J. Humphreys[d], and S. Carlson[e]

[a]School of Electrical and Electronic Engineering, The University of Manchester, Manchester M60 1QD, UK
[b]Synchrotron Radiation Department, Daresbury Laboratory, Daresbury, Warrington WA4 4AD, UK
[c]School of Physics and Astronomy, The University of Manchester, Manchester M60 1QD, UK
[d]Dept. of Materials Science and Metallurgy, University of Cambridge, Pembroke Street, Cambridge CB2 3QZ, UK
[e]MAX-lab, Lund University, P.O. Box 118, SE- 221 00 Lund, Sweden

Abstract. We have investigated the local atomic environment of the Ga atoms in an $In_xGa_{1-x}N$ single quantum well structure using Optically Detected Extended X-ray Absorption Fine Structure (OD-EXAFS). A comparison of the OD-EXAFS data with a theoretical model shows the technique to be site selective for this particular structure and reveals that the quantum well emission originates from regions with x=0.15.

Keywords: EXAFS, InGaN, Quantum Well,
PACS: 78.55.Cr, 78.67.De, 61.10.Ht

INTRODUCTION

The nature of the carrier localization is of fundamental importance for understanding the behavior of devices that incorporate InGaN/GaN quantum wells. However, the nature of the localizing sites is still a matter for debate, with the prime candidates being fluctuations in the quantum well width and/or fluctuations in the local chemical composition [1].

Extended X-ray Absorption Fine Structure (EXAFS) is a technique that provides information on the local atomic coordination environment of the X-ray absorbing atom [2], and has its origin in the scattering of the wave function of the outgoing photoelectron by atoms in the nearest coordination shells. This perturbation produces a damped oscillation in the absorption spectrum above the primary absorption edge. By comparing theory with experiment analysis of this fine structure enables information on the local chemical coordination of the absorbing atom to be extracted.

Any physical process that is directly related to the X-ray absorption event, such as X-ray fluorescence, can reflect the absorption coefficient, and in this work we have used light emission from an $In_xGa_{1-x}N/GaN$ single quantum well (SQW) to detect the Ga K-shell X-ray absorption. When X-ray excited photoluminescence (X-PL) is used to detect EXAFS it is referred to as optically detected EXAFS (OD-EXAFS). Specially, OD-EXAFS has the potential to provide a link between the emission process and the associated local chemical environment [3].

We report here OD-EXAFS measurements on an InGaN SQW and demonstrate that site selectivity can be achieved by monitoring the recombination from the SQW.

RESULTS AND DISCUSSION

The details of the growth, microstructural and optical techniques used to study the samples have been described elsewhere [1]. Of particular note is that the InGaN quantum well is 7.5 nm below the GaN free surface. The X-ray absorption measurements were carried out on beamline I811 at the MAX-lab synchrotron source at the University of Lund, Sweden.

The X-PL spectrum measured at a temperature of 10 K is shown in Fig. 1. At the Ga K-edge the X-ray photons excite electron/hole pairs throughout the whole structure, including the GaN buffer layer. The spectrum in Fig. 1 shows emission from the SQW

---

* Corresponding author e-mail: Darren.Graham@manchester.ac.uk

CP893, *Physics of Semiconductors, 28th International Conference*
edited by W. Jantsch and F. Schäffler
© 2007 American Institute of Physics 978-0-7354-0397-0/07/$23.00

(2.684 eV), the GaN exciton (3.474 eV), donor-acceptor-pair recombination in the GaN (consisting of a zero phonon line at 3.282 eV and a series of LO phonon replicas) and the so-called yellow luminescence band (2.207 eV).

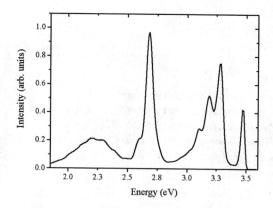

FIGURE 1. X-PL spectrum obtained at T=10 K. The excitation energy was 30 eV above the Ga K-edge.

For the OD-EXAFS experiment the Ga K-edge spectra were measured by detecting on each of the different emission bands. In Fig. 2 are shown the Fourier filtered data and fits, obtained from the detection of the SQW and GaN exciton emissions.

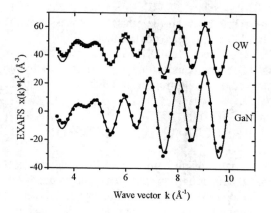

FIGURE 2. Fourier filtered (range 1-3.8 Å) OD-EXAFS data for the SQW and GaN exciton emission bands. The fits are shown by the solid lines and the raw data by the dots.

For the case of the GaN exciton emission, the EXAFS fit using a pure GaN model is good over the full k-range. The same choice of fitting parameters does not explain the low k-vector data for the SQW emission. To achieve the fit for the SQW data the fitting parameters were changed by incorporating In atoms into the split second metallic shell. It was found that by choosing the number of In atoms to be

equivalent to an average In fraction of 0.15 a good fit was obtained.

A critical point to emerge from the experimental data is that the OD-EXAFS yields information that is *specific* to the quantum well. We explain the specificity as follows. Firstly, the carriers excited in the GaN barriers could have an extremely short diffusion length, so only a very few are captured by the quantum well. If this was the case we might expect to see not only strong emission from the SQW but also emission from the GaN when an excitation photon energy of 3.815 eV is used. Note that 90 % of light of this photon energy is absorbed within the first 180 nm of GaN. In fact, all we see (*spectrum not shown*) associated with the bulk GaN is very weak excitonic emission. This suggests either that the carriers excited in the GaN are captured by the quantum well, which would negate the site selectivity of the OD-EXAFS experiment, or they are annihilated by a non radiative mechanism. A possible route for the latter is that we note [4] that the SQW is located in the surface depletion field. So that any carriers that are optically excited in the GaN would be swept apart and fail to be captured by the quantum well or recombine radiatively in the GaN. Thus we propose that the SQW emission is caused principally by carriers that are excited in the quantum well. It should be stressed at this point that the arguments presented above apply to the case of UV excitation. The particular aspect of this argument that applies to our interpretation of the X-ray data is the general conclusion that excitation of carriers in the GaN barriers is only a very small contribution to the carrier density in the quantum well and hence the emission from the quantum well.

Unlike the UV excitation case, the X-ray absorption cross-section for the quantum well is not dramatically reduced by the internal electric field. The quantum well and barrier absorption coefficients are equal to within a few percent, since both are determined by the K-shell interactions. So for the specific case of InGaN quantum wells, the carrier generation rate from direct excitation of the quantum well is relatively much stronger for X-PL than for optical inter sub band excitation. Thus we propose that this coupled with the arguments presented above on the lack of carrier migration to the quantum well is the basis for the site selectivity of OD-EXAFS.

REFERENCES

1. D. M. Graham *et al.*, *J. Appl. Phys.* **97**, 103508 (2005).
2. V. L. Aksenov *et al.*, *Phys. Part. Nucl.* **32**, 675 (2001).
3. N. R. J. Poolton *et al.*, *Phys. Stat. Sol.* (b) **241**, 3656 (2004).
4. O. Mayrock *et al.*, *Phys. Rev. B* **62**, 16870 (2000).

A

Abermann, S., 293
Abram, R. A., 1159
Abramof, E., 1233
Abrosimov, N. V., 231
Abstreiter, G., 695
Acbas, G., 1217
Adams, A. R., 837
Adell, M., 113
Aers, G. C., 789
Agafonov, O. B., 1369
Ager III, J. W., 191, 213, 231, 343, 1477
Ahlswede, E., 675
Ahmed, S. S., 847, 849
Ahn, D., 261, 359, 807
Ahopelto, J., 579, 599, 1241
Aichele, T., 1097
Aikawa, H., 855
Airey, R., 551, 651
Aitchison, J. S., 1165
Aizin, G. R., 501
Akabori, M., 1271, 1373
Akahane, J., 973
Akahane, K., 69, 973, 975, 1145, 1487
Akanuma, Y., 107, 117
Akasaka, T., 361, 373
Akazaki, T., 389, 1291
Akçakir, Y., 1051
Akera, H., 665, 667
Akimoto, R., 449, 467
Akinaga, H., 1193, 1335
Akinci, Ö., 171
Akis, R., 41, 715, 1115
Akiyama, H., 85, 475, 861, 863
Akiyama, T., 55
Aku-Leh, C., 1195, 1295
Alekseev, P. S., 1259
Alekseyev, L., 1425
Aleksiejunas, R., 295, 461
Alén, B., 909
Aleshkin, V. Y., 219
Alfaro-Martínez, A., 95
Alghoraibi, I., 889
Allison, G., 591
Alonso, M. I., 377
Alonso-Gutiérrez, P., 185
Alperovich, V. L., 13
Al Salman, A., 971
Alves, H. W. Leite, 311, 321
Amaha, S., 853
Amand, T., 1309, 1319, 1345
Amann, A., 543

Amo, A., 1139, 1153, 1327
Anappara, A. A., 523
Anderson, T., 111
Ando, H., 451, 1245
Ando, T., 621, 707, 1017, 1029, 1033, 1035, 1305
André, L., 917
André, R., 1139, 1185
Andreev, A. D., 933
Andreev, B. A., 219
Andrews, A. M., 51, 485, 505, 511
Andrianov, A. V., 209, 509
Andronikov, D. A., 405
Angelova, T. I., 865
Ankiewicz, A. O., 63
Anni, M., 1069
Antonov, A. V., 219
Antonova, I. V., 785
Aoki, K., 127, 327, 1377
Aoki, N., 365, 713, 715, 1039
Aoyagi, Y., 1013
Apetrii, G., 695
Arahara, K., 1181
Arai, K., 1099
Arai, Y., 435
Arakawa, Y., 101, 1129
Araki, K., 361
Arapov, Y. G., 631, 647
Arciszewska, M., 1231
Arenholz, E., 1177
Arens, C., 1071
Armani, N., 31
Armstrong, A., 223
Arsenault, A. C., 1051
Artamkin, A., 141, 1457
Artemyev, M. V., 1071
Asada, Y., 1029
Aseev, A. L., 739
Ashkenov, N., 271
Ashkinadze, B. M., 415, 1123
Ashley, T., 729, 1111
Aslam, F., 1065
Ašmontas, S., 1419
Attolini, G., 29
Aubry, E., 979, 1323
Austerer, M., 505
Austin, D. A., 507, 1451
Austing, D. G., 655, 789
Averkiev, N. S., 247, 555, 1329
Axt, V. M., 989, 1005
Azevedo, D. L., 1027
Azize, M., 1379

B

Babarada, F., 3
Babiński, A., 905
Baccarani, G., 737, 1497
Bacher, G., 417, 1355
Bachmann, M., 611
Baczewski, L. T., 103
Badalyan, S., 629
Badcock, T. J., 909, 951
Bădescu, Ş. C., 1085
Bagaev, V. S., 175, 931, 937
Bagraev, N. T., 693, 1283
Bahir, G., 525
Bahriz, M., 507, 1451
Baidus, N. V., 1257
Bais, G., 31, 59, 155, 157
Bajoni, D., 1143
Bajracharya, P., 419, 1459
Bakarov, A. K., 911
Bakin, A., 277
Balanov, A., 543
Balderas-Navarro, R. E., 11
Balili, R. B., 397
Ballarini, D., 1139, 1153
Baltz, R. v., 1321
Ban, S. L., 273
Bang, K., 803
Baranov, A. N., 523, 743
Baranovskii, S., 1275
Baranowski, J. M., 905
Barate, D., 523
Barbara, P., 1049
Bardoux, R., 941
Bardyszewski, W., 1191
Barisien, T., 351
Barrena, E., 377
Barthold, P., 815
Bartlett, C. J., 729, 1111
Bastard, G., 489, 497, 963, 1073, 1423
Bastiaansen, C. W., 1163
Bauer, G., 0, 39, 97, 1135, 1317, 1411
Baumann, E., 335, 481
Baumgartner, A., 759
Bawendi, M. G., 1067
Bayer, M., 1303, 1361
Beaudoin, G., 71
Bechstedt, F., 1249
Becker, C. R., 491
Becker, P., 231
Becla, P., 235
Beeman, J. W., 191, 1177
Beere, H., 691, 741
Beggs, D. M., 1159
Behan, A. J., 1189
Beirne, G. J., 875, 1001

Bekeny, C., 289
Belas, E., 299
Bel'kov, V. V., 1255, 1311
Bell, D., 35
Bell, G. R., 101
Bellet-Amalric, E., 335, 423, 481, 525, 1173
Belton, C., 355
Beltram, F., 615, 691
Benedict, K. A., 395
Benndorf, G., 271, 409
Benson, O., 1097
Bente, K., 1483
Benyoucef, M., 761
Benz, A., 51, 511
Berezovska, N. I., 27
Berger, C., 619
Bergman, J. P., 381
Bernardot, F., 437, 979, 1323
Bernhard, C., 33
Bertagnolli, E., 93, 293
Berti, M., 155
Bertolotti, J., 1051
Bertru, N., 889
Besombes, L., 91
Betbeder-Matibet, O., 1349
Beyoucef, M., 1149
Bharagava, R. N., 1053
Bianchetti, R., 709
Biasiol, G., 49, 463, 523
Bichler, M., 797, 827
Biehne, G., 301
Biermann, K., 473
Biesemans, S., 1397
Bimberg, D., 779, 919, 957, 1381, 1413, 1469
Binks, D. J., 1065
Bird, J. P., 365, 713
Birner, S., 981, 1003
Bischoff, L., 93
Bisognin, G., 155
Blamire, M. G., 1281
Blažej, J., 1429
Bleibaum, O., 1267
Bloch, J., 411, 1119, 1143
Block, M., 77
Blythe, H. J., 1189
Böberl, M., 1135
Bock, C., 363
Bockowski, M., 1201
Boeuf, F., 1379
Bogaart, E. W., 949
Bogusławski, P., 337
Bokor, J., 1093
Bominaar-Silkens, I., 683
Bonapasta, A. Amore, 233, 237, 239
Bondarenko, O. V., 509

Grundmann, M., 63, 271, 301, 325, 409, 611,
   1057, 1137, 1187, 1483
Gružinskis, V., 1419
Grydlik, M., 1411
Grynberg, M., 251, 1379
Grzegory, I., 113, 303, 1201, 1409
Gubański, A., 235
Gudina, S. V., 647
Guérineau, N., 469
Guhl, H., 15
Gühne, T., 1137
Guillet, T., 941
Guillot, F., 335, 423, 481, 483, 525
Guimarães, P. S. S., 487, 757
Guldner, Y., 985
Gulyaev, D. V., 421
Gulyaev, M. B., 785
Gumienny, Z., 813
Guo, F. Z., 49
Gupta, J. A., 789
Gurevich, A. S., 1329
Gusev, A. V., 231
Gusev, G. M., 549, 563, 627, 633, 677
Gustavsson, S., 751
Gutowski, J., 277, 289, 1147
Guzenko, V. A., 1271
Guziewicz, M., 813
Guzmán, A., 425
Gvozdić, D. M., 1371

H

Ha, S. H., 273
Hackbarth, T., 717
Haendel, K., 1369
Haidar, R., 469
Hainberger, R., 1463
Haller, E. E., 191, 213, 231, 343, 1177, 1477
Halm, S., 1355
Halsall, M., 427
Hamada, T., 1393
Hamal, K., 1429
Hamanaka, Y., 1011
Hamazaki, J., 477
Hameau, S., 503
Hamilton, A. R., 681, 687, 699
Hamilton, B., 1503
Hammerschmidt, T., 73
Han, I., 825
Han, K., 1207
Hanna, S., 479
Hansel, S., 131
Hansen, W., 573, 689, 763, 833
Harada, N., 161
Harada, Y., 265, 1245

Harako, S., 159, 1427
Harbord, E., 1289
Harke, B., 793
Harley, R. T., 1297, 1301
Harris, J. J., 561
Harrison, N. M., 89
Harrison, P., 427, 1419, 1441
Hartmann, J. M., 537, 559
Hartmann, L., 1187
Harus, G. I., 631, 647
Hasegawa, A., 167
Hasenfu, C., 1495
Hashimoto, K., 319
Hashimoto, S., 265
Hashimoto, T., 81
Hashimoto, Y., 475, 669
Haskell, B., 315, 341
Hatano, T., 853
Hatori, N., 837
Hatou, T., 207
Häu, M., 367
Haug, J., 1369
Haug, R. J., 793, 809, 815
Hauschild, R., 163
Haverkort, J. E. M., 949
Hawecker, J. H., 1133
Hawrylak, P., 655
Hayashi, T., 753
Hayne, M., 779, 947, 951
He, H., 539, 1203, 1253
He, H. T., 285
Healy, S. B., 1431
Heimbrodt, W., 267, 1179, 1275
Hein, G., 491
Heiss, W., 1135
Heitmann, D., 1127
Heitsch, S., 409
Heitzinger, C., 847, 849
Heliotis, G., 355
Helm, M., 243, 473, 485
Hemmi, M., 713
Henini, M., 521, 651, 759, 1297, 1301
Henneberger, F., 1355
Henriques, A. B., 1233
Heremans, J. J., 1287
Hermannstädter, C., 875
Hernández-Calderón, I., 95, 99, 229
Herrera-Perez, J. L., 177
Hess, O., 969
Hetterich, J., 1285
Hetterich, M., 1133, 1285
Heun, S., 49
Hey, R., 533, 651, 1273, 1351, 1447
Heyman, J. N., 35
Heyn, C., 689, 763, 1127
Heyn, Ch., 573

Lugli, P., 1327
Lugstein, A., 93
Luisier, M., 711
Luo, H., 1307
Luo, X. D., 45
Lupaca-Schomber, J., 1133, 1285
Lupu, A., 525
Łusakowska, E., 103, 113, 337
Łusakowski, J., 1379
L'vova, T. V., 83
Lyon, S., 1317
Lyon, S. A., 1093
Lyublinskaya, O. G., 83, 1359

M

Ma, T., 1205
Maan, J., 683
MacDonald, A. H., 773
Maehashi, K., 1031
Maejima, K., 1039
Maemoto, T., 577, 1391
Maeng, I., 935, 1043
Magnus, F., 1281
Magnus, W., 733
Mahajan, S. V., 1055
Mahapatra, S., 65
Mahne, N., 59
Mailly, D., 651, 663
Maingault, L., 91, 917
Maire, N., 815
Majewski, J. A., 345, 1277, 1337
Majkusiak, B., 1379
Makino, T., 43, 467
Makita, Y., 1061
Malakooti, R., 1051
Malevannyy, S. V., 703
Malinauskas, T., 295
Malis, O., 1453
Malissa, H., 1317
Malyarenko, A. M., 693
Mandl, B., 97
Mangum, J., 111
Manna, L., 1063, 1069
Mano, T., 109
Marcadet, X., 1435
Marcet, S., 1171
Marchi, A., 737
Marent, A., 1381
Marie, X., 1309, 1319, 1345
Mariette, H., 91, 403, 917, 1171, 1173
Maršík, P., 33
Mariucci, L., 31
Markelz, A., 1307
Marko, I. P., 837

Marques, A. E. B., 17
Marques, M., 257, 1227, 1249
Martelli, F., 31, 59, 155, 157
Mårtensson, T., 97
Martín, M. D., 1153
Martin, R. W., 953
Martinez, A., 913
Martinez, G., 619
Martínez-Cantón, A. E., 229
Martini, S., 17
Martín, M. D., 1139, 1151
Maruta, Y., 529
Maryško, M., 1219
Masago, A., 9
Masia, F., 31, 157, 313, 327
Maslov, A. Y., 883
Massé, N. F., 837
Masselink, W. T., 329
Masu, H., 775
Masumoto, Y., 961, 1325
Matěj, Z., 1219
Matsubayashi, D., 805
Matsuda, K., 173
Matsuishi, K., 1061
Matsukawa, K., 225
Matsumoto, K., 1031
Matsumoto, T., 323, 327
Matsunami, J., 1353
Matsuo, Y., 1485
Matsushita, D., 1403
Mattei, G., 241
Mattioli, G., 233
Maude, D. K., 137, 551, 625, 651, 655
Maurer, A., 1215
Maximov, I., 1471
Maximov, M. V., 987, 1413
Mayorov, A. S., 595
McAleese, C., 347
McCann, E., 617
McFarlane, J., 1091
Mchedlidze, T., 227
Mehta, A., 1053
Meier, L., 1365
Meisels, R., 1157, 1161
Melet, R., 351, 913
Melnik, R. N. V., 393
Mendach, S., 1149
Mendes Filho, J., 1027
Mendez, E. E., 533
Mendoza-Alvarez, J. G., 177, 943
Mentes, T. O., 49
Merlin, R., 1175
Messina, G., 1023
Metzner, C., 243
Meyer, K., 331
Meziani, Y., 137

Michel, C., 1275
Michler, P., 875, 1001
Michon, A., 71
Micolich, A. P., 681, 699
Migliori, A., 1051
Miguel-Sánchez, J., 425
Mikhailova, M. P., 547
Mikhalyov, G. Y., 817
Mikhrin, S. S., 1413
Mikhrin, V. S., 787
Milekhin, A. G., 911
Milone, C., 1023
Minami, F., 109, 167, 453, 921, 977
Minami, K., 57
Minkov, G., 705
Mino, H., 449, 467
Minor, A. M., 191
Miotkowski, I., 211
Miranda, R. P., 939
Miriametro, A., 313
Mirlin, D. N., 1183
Mironenko, K., 1321
Mironov, O. A., 557
Mishra, U. K., 223
Misiewicz, J., 431, 671, 1303
Mita, Y., 125
Mitsumori, Y., 1099
Mityagin, Y., 589
Mityagin, Y. A., 143
Miura, M., 605
Miwa, D., 1491
Miwa, H., 137
Miyakoshi, K., 389
Miyashita, S., 527, 529
Miyata, Y., 451
Miyoshi, Y., 1281
Mizerov, A. M., 269
Mizuki, J., 75
Mizuno, B., 1491
Mlinar, V., 721
Mochizuki, T., 1475
Moehl, S., 917
Mofor, A. C., 277
Mohamed, M. B., 971
Moiseev, K. D., 547
Moldaschl, T., 955
Molenkamp, L. W., 65
Molinari, E., 877, 959
Molitor, F., 623
Momida, H., 215
Monemar, B., 269, 341
Monroy, E., 309, 335, 423, 481, 483, 525, 1173
Moon, P., 391
Moreau, S., 583
Moreau, V., 507, 1451

Morello, G., 1069
Morhain, C., 1171
Morimoto, T., 713, 715, 1039
Morino, M., 643
Morón, M. C., 185
Morris, R., 395
Morris, R. D., 1339, 1343
Mortensen, N., 821
Mortimer, I. B., 1009, 1047
Moshchalkov, V. V., 779, 947, 951
Mourokh, L., 799
Mowbray, D. J., 909, 951
Mühlberger, M., 1495
Muljarov, E. A., 915
Müller, T., 955, 1113
Müllner, P., 1463
Munzar, D., 33
Muraki, K., 681
Muraoka, K., 1403
Murayama, A., 465, 1169, 1299
Muro, K., 449, 1181, 1293
Murray, R., 355, 1289
Murzin, V. N., 589
Mustre, J., 99
Muto, D., 137
Myronov, M., 557

N

Na, J. H., 981, 1003
Nabanja, S., 35
Nabavi, E., 951
Naber, W., 755
Nabetani, Y., 327
Nachtwei, G., 491, 493, 649
Nagai, Y., 665
Naito, R., 713
Nakajima, M., 467
Nakamura, A., 107, 117, 1011, 1235
Nakamura, J., 5, 775
Nakamura, K., 55, 245
Nakamura, S., 315, 341
Nakanishi, T., 841
Nakasaki, Y., 1403
Nakata, H., 207
Nakayama, T., 25, 169, 217, 997, 1461
Nakazato, H., 1109
Nakazato, T., 867
Nanishi, Y., 137
Napolitani, E., 155
Narimanov, E. E., 1425
Nash, G. R., 1111
Nastaushev, Y. V., 739
Natori, A., 5, 775
Natsume, Y., 845

Oto, K., 449, 569, 571, 661, 1181
Otsuka, T., 855
Ozin, G. A., 1051, 1165

P

Pacher, C., 1493
Pacherová, O., 1219
Pachinger, D., 87
Pacuski, W., 339, 1171
Pagès, O., 197
Pagnossin, I. R., 677
Pal, B., 961, 1325
Palankovski, V., 1399
Palczewska, M., 1201
Pallavi, S. Rao, 1067
Palomo, J., 507, 1451
Panevin, V. Y., 479, 509
Pang, Q., 45, 1073
Panin, G., 743
Pantelides, S. T., 119
Papagelis, K., 1045
Parashkov, R., 353, 369
Parfeniev, R. V., 139
Park, B., 121
Park, C. M., 981, 1003
Park, H. J., 111
Park, J., 887, 995
Park, K., 601
Park, S., 261, 391, 607
Park, Y., 807
Park, Y. S., 981, 1003
Pascher, H., 1135, 1223
Pascual-Winter, M. F., 965, 1131
Paskova, T., 341
Paspalakis, E., 471
Pasquarello, A., 7, 195, 307
Passow, T., 1133, 1285
Pasternak, I., 337
Patanè, A., 759
Patriarche, G., 71, 983
Paulsson, M., 727
Pavlov, S. G., 1445
Payette, C., 789
Pedersen, J., 821
Peeters, F. M., 721, 851
Pellegrini, S., 987
Pellegrini, V., 615, 959
Pelosi, C., 29, 145
Peng, L., 701
Pepper, M., 531, 699, 723
Pereira, Jr., J. M., 721
Perel, V. I., 1259
Perestoronin, A. V., 143
Perez, F., 1195, 1295

Pérez-Willard, F., 1133
Perlin, P., 1409
Permogorov, S., 1321
Peronne, E., 1131
Perovic, D. D., 1165
Perrin, B., 965, 1131
Perrin, M., 411
Peter, E., 1143
Petroff, P. M., 1091
Petrov, P. V., 247
Petrov, S., 1051
Pettinari, G., 31, 157
Pfannkuche, D., 799
Pfeffer, P., 541
Pfeiffer, L. N., 85, 397, 415, 615, 745, 861, 863, 959, 1123
Pham, D. V., 363
Phillips, P. J., 963, 1445
Piazza, V., 691
Piccin, M., 31, 59, 155, 157
Pickett, N., 1065
Piersa, M., 1201
Pierz, K., 815
Pillwein, G., 599
Pinczuk, A., 959
Piot, B. A., 651
Piotrowska, A., 337
Pires, M. P., 443, 487, 757, 943
Piron, R., 889
Piskorska, E., 79
Pistone, A., 1023
Płaczek-Popko, E., 235, 813
Platero, G., 637, 773
Platonov, A. V., 403, 1329
Ploog, K. H., 429, 527, 651, 1209, 1273, 1351
Podgornyh, S. M., 631, 647
Pogany, D., 1497
Pohl, H.-J., 231
Pohl, U. W., 919
Polimeni, A., 31, 155, 157, 313, 327
Polischuk, O. V., 501
Pölt, P., 1237, 1501
Pongratz, P., 93
Ponomarev, I. V., 871, 873
Poolton, N. R. J., 1503
Popov, V. V., 501
Popovici, N., 1199
Porowski, S., 113, 303, 1409
Portal, J. C., 537, 549, 559, 627, 677
Porteanu, H.-E., 179, 183
Portnoi, M. E., 703, 1021
Posilovic, K., 1413
Postels, B., 289
Postnikov, A. V., 197

T

Tyryshkin, A. M., 1093, 1317

U

Ubyivovk, E. V., 403
Uda, T., 215
Ueda, A., 839
Ueda, N., 451
Uematsu, M., 193
Ueta, A., 69, 1145, 1487
Ujihara, T., 117
Ulloa, S., 645
Umeno, A., 361, 373
Umezu, I., 43, 895, 1433
Ungersboeck, E., 1389
Ünlü, H., 171
Unterrainer, K., 51, 443, 511, 515, 955, 1423, 1435
Unuma, T., 475, 495
Urban, A., 163
Urbaszek, B., 1319, 1345
Ursaki, V. V., 279
Uryu, S., 1033, 1035
Usami, M., 215
Ushiyama, T., 1335
Usikova, A. A., 83
Uskova, E. A., 631, 647, 1257
Usman, M., 847, 849
Ustinov, V. M., 479, 957, 987, 1381, 1413
Usuki, T., 107

V

Vaccaro, P. O., 965
Vagov, A., 989
Valušis, G., 427, 1419
van der Drift, E., 1163
van der Heijden, R., 1163
van der Heijden, R. W., 1163
van der Poel, M., 1121
van der Wiel, W. G., 755
van der Zwan, G., 971
Van Dorpe, P., 1289
Vandyshev, E. N., 1059
van Genuchten, H. C. M., 213
van Lippen, T., 903
van Mourik, F., 971
Van Roy, W., 1287, 1289
Vardi, A., 525
Vasanelli, A., 489, 497
Vasi'ev, A. P., 1381
Vasile, G., 491, 649
Vasil'ev, A. P., 1413
Vasilev, A. P., 787

Vasilevskiy, M. I., 795, 939, 1257
Vasilopoulos, P., 721, 823, 1367
Vasilyev, Y. B., 491, 493
Vasko, F. T., 201
Vasson, A., 269
Vekris, E. W., 1165
Verbin, S. Y., 1325
Verna, A., 241
Vieira, G. S., 487, 757
Villas-Boas, J. M., 443, 943
Viña, L., 1139, 1151, 1153, 1327
Vinokur, V. M., 557
Vinter, B., 497
Vitanov, S., 1399
Vladimirova, M., 1185, 1347
Voisin, P., 1319, 1341, 1345
Voliotis, V., 351, 913
Vollenweider, K., 1113
Volodin, V. A., 817
von Freymann, G., 1051
von Klitzing, K., 675
Von Ortenberg, M., 131
Von Wenckstern, H., 1483
Vorobjev, L. E., 479, 509
Vorona, I. P., 227, 383
Voronina, T. I., 547
Vörös, Z., 397
Voss, T., 277, 289

W

Waag, A., 277, 289
Wachsmuth, S., 1267
Wada, K., 19
Wada, N., 927
Wada, O., 249, 1245
Wade, A., 497
Wagenhuber, K., 439
Wagner, H. P., 357, 419, 1459
Wakabayashi, K., 735, 1269
Wallin, D., 1471
Walukiewicz, W., 213, 343, 1477
Wang, D., 1175
Wang, J., 291, 539, 1073, 1203, 1253, 1431
Wang, J. N., 45, 285
Wang, L., 875
Wang, N., 45
Wang, S., 1307
Wang, T., 23
Wang, X., 383, 519, 701, 1367
Wang, Y., 291, 291, 539, 1203, 1465, 1467
Wang, Z. G., 1471
Wanke, M. C., 243
Warburton, R. J., 1091
Warde, E., 525

Warming, T., 957
Wasik, D., 1201
Wasilewski, Z. R., 551, 583, 651, 905
Wasserman, D., 519
Watanabe, S., 9
Watson, I. M., 355
Watson, I. W., 953
Weber, A., 301
Weber, B., 687
Weber, W., 1311
Wegscheider, W., 439, 793, 797, 827, 1113, 1215, 1255
Weinstein, B. A., 181
Weis, J., 675
Weiss, D., 1255
Welsch, H., 1127
Wen, X. G., 45
Wenckstern, H. v., 301
Wenin, M., 1079
Wenus, J., 369
Werner, P., 739
West, K. W., 85, 397, 615, 745, 861, 863, 959
Whall, T. E., 557
White, H. W., 1421
Whittaker, D. M., 1083
Wiater, M., 813
Wieck, A. D., 431, 719, 725, 777, 1303
Wieczorek, W., 957
Wieland, K. A., 1465, 1467
Wiersig, J., 1125
Wiersma, D. S., 1051
Wieser, U., 717, 719
Wietler, T. F., 67
Wilamowski, Z., 1313, 1317
Wilhelm, F., 1173
Willatzen, M., 393, 767
Wille, U., 1279
Williams, D. P., 933
Williams, E. D., 371
Wilson, L. R., 507, 963, 1451
Wiltshire, J. G., 1047
Winkler, R., 1369
Winnerl, S., 473, 485
Winter, A., 1223
Wiren, Z. Q., 1197
Wirtz, L., 623
Wischmeier, L., 277, 289
Witte, G., 363
Wodziński, D., 635
Woggon, U., 1071
Wójcik, M., 1231
Wójs, A., 431, 635, 671
Wojtowicz, T., 65, 103, 813, 1181, 1223, 1361
Wöll, C., 363
Wolos, A., 1201, 1313

Wolter, J. H., 683, 903
Wolverson, D., 403
Wong, K. S., 305, 367
Wraback, M., 315, 333, 513
Wróbel, J., 103
Wrobel, J. M., 235
Wu, J., 455
Wu, L., 367
Wu, Y., 23
Wu, Z., 1437
Wysmolek, A., 1201

X

Xie, M. H., 53
Xu, H., 1471
Xu, Q., 191, 1187
Xu, X. H., 1189

Y

Yabashi, M., 1491
Yabumoto, K., 165
Yagara, A., 571
Yaguchi, Y., 1039
Yajima, C., 435
Yakimov, A. I., 811, 817
Yakovlev, D. R., 1303, 1361
Yakovlev, Y. P., 547
Yakunin, M. V., 631, 647
Yamada, S., 1271, 1373
Yamagiwa, M., 109, 921
Yamaguchi, D. M., 343
Yamaguchi, H., 529
Yamaguchi, M., 61, 281, 389
Yamaguchi, S., 323, 1387
Yamaguchi, T., 79, 1013
Yamakawa, I., 107, 117
Yamamoto, A., 137, 323, 475, 1387
Yamamoto, M., 747, 1265
Yamamoto, N., 69, 973, 975, 1145, 1487
Yamamoto, T., 215
Yamasaki, T., 215
Yamauchi, J., 1405
Yamazaki, J., 1387
Yang, A., 231
Yang, C., 609, 1203, 1253
Yang, C. L., 285
Yang, S., 1073
Yang, S. H., 45
Yang, T., 1129
Yannouleas, C., 783
Yano, M., 319
Yanovitskaya, Z. S., 785

Z